New Progress in

MATHEMATICS

Series Consultants

Adrienne Aiken
Mathematics Consultant
Galveston-Houston Diocese
Houston, Texas

Pat Echols
Instructional Officer
Klein School District
Spring, Texas

Claire M. Fanning
Teacher of Gifted Children
Ridley School District
Folsom, Pennsylvania

Sr. Helen Lucille Habig
Assistant Superintendent
Archdiocese of Cincinnati,
Cincinnati, Ohio

Rowland Hughes
Professor of Mathematics
Education
Fordham University
New York, New York

Sr. Ellenore Mary Jordan
Mathematics Coordinator
Archdiocese of Hartford
Hartford, Connecticut

Jeanne Joseph
Teacher
Robbinsdale School District
Minneapolis, Minnesota

Mary E. Lester
Director of Mathematics
Dallas Independent School
District
Dallas, Texas

Teresa Meyer
Teacher
Diocese of Louisville
Louisville, Kentucky

Jane L. Stone
Computer Consultant
Houston, Texas

Sr. Margaret Zimmermann
Associate Superintendent
Diocese of Orange
Orange, California

Rose Anita McDonnell

Dyanne B. Dandridge
Patrice Marie Miklos
Anne Veronica Burrows

with
Elinor R. Ford

SADLIER • OXFORD

Table of Contents

Home Office: 11 Park Place, New York, NY 10007
ISBN: 0-87105-363-2
123456789/98765

Florence Mulvaney, Edward Williams, *Executive Editors*
Julius Bronstein, *Creative Group, Inc., Designer*
Kao & Kao Associates, *Art Direction and Photo Editing*

Illustrators
  Bob Gleason, Bob Dowe, Ray Keane,
  April Blair Stewart, Lisa Harteker

Photo Credits
Mary Ellen Donnelly-Ridder, *Director of Photo Research*

The photographs reproduced on the pages listed
are from the following sources:
Diane J. Ali 35, 207.
Comstock: Michael Stuckey 11, 164; Mike and Carol
Werner 135.
D.P.I.: Ballard 111.
F.P.G.: J. Gajda 185; Richard Laird 237.
Index Stone International: Index stock 85.
Monkmeyer: Les Mahon 281; Hugh Rogers 259.
Omni: John Lei 325; Jack Parsons 299.
Woodfin Camp: Patrick Ward 59.

PROBLEM-SOLVING STEPS

To solve a problem, read the problem very carefully to find out:

- What facts are given
- What facts are hidden
- What facts are missing
- The exact question or questions that are being asked

2
NAME
List and label
the facts and question.

3
THINK
Outline what to do.

4
COMPUTE
Do it.

1
IMAGINE
Create a picture
in your mind.

5
CHECK
Check it.

The five problem-solving steps are:

1 **IMAGINE**—Create a picture in your mind.

2 **NAME**—List and label the facts and questions.

3 **THINK**—Outline what to do.

4 **COMPUTE**—Do it!

5 **CHECK**—Check it!

IMAGINE

Create a picture in your mind.

Read the problem. Create a picture in your mind, making believe you are there in the problem. This will help you think about:
- what the problem is asking
- what facts you will need to answer the questions
- how you will solve the problem

After reading the problem, draw and label a picture of what you imagine the problem is all about.

NAME

List and label.

Facts: List and label all the facts you can find in the problem. Look for "hidden facts." These are words that hide more information.

> Jim rides his bicycle 4 miles a day. How far does he ride in a week?

> **FACT:** 4 miles a day
> **HIDDEN FACT:** 7 days = 1 week
> The word "week" hid this fact.

Questions: Write the question or questions that the problem is asking.

THINK

Choose and outline a plan.

Think about how to solve the problem by:

- Looking at the picture you drew.

- Remembering what you did when you solved similar problems. (Pages 8 to 10 and every unit in this book show you how to solve different kinds of problems.)

- Then choosing a plan for solving the problem, such as:
  - Use simpler numbers.
  - Draw a picture.
  - Make a table.
  - Guess and check.

COMPUTE

Do it!

Do the computations.

CHECK

Check it!

Check your computations.

Ask yourself: Does my answer make sense?

Problem Solving: "Finding Patterns" Strategy

Problem: Cheryl wants to solve this mystery
           number pattern. Can you help her?

           1, 6, 5, 10, 9, _?_, 13, _?_, _?_, 22, 21, . . .

 1 IMAGINE   As you copy over the pattern
                   for yourself, you notice that
                   the numbers get larger, get
                   smaller, and get larger.

2 NAME   *Facts:*   8 numbers given
                            3 missing numbers

               Question: What numbers are missing?

3 THINK   Look at the numbers.
               The numbers get larger, get smaller,
               and get larger again.
                   Can I keep adding? (No.)
                   Can I keep subtracting? (No.)
                   Can I add, subtract, add, subtract,
                   and so on? (Try it.)

4 COMPUTE   1 + _?_ = 6   (5)
                    6 − _?_ = 5   (1)   The pattern looks like:
                    5 + _?_ = 10   (5)   Add 5, subtract 1.
                   10 − _?_ = 9   (1)

               Try this pattern with the rest of the numbers.

                    9 + 5 = 14 ———→ 14 − 1 = 13
                   13 + 5 = 18 ———→ 18 − 1 = 17

               The missing numbers are: 14, 18, and 17.

5 CHECK   Check your computations.

8

Problem Solving: "Guess and Check" Strategy

Problem: A pencil and an eraser cost $1.00. The pencil costs 40¢ more than the eraser. What does the eraser cost?

1 IMAGINE   Draw and label a picture of the problem.

2 NAME

Facts: $1.00 pencil and eraser
$ .40 more for the pencil than for the eraser

Question: What does the eraser cost?

3 THINK   Make a guess. Then check it.

Make a table to keep track.

Eraser	Pencil	Both	Check
10¢	50¢	60¢	Less than $1.00
20¢	60¢	?	?
30¢	70¢	?	?

4 COMPUTE

The eraser guess plus 40¢ more

10¢ + 40¢ = 50¢
20¢ + 40¢ = 60¢
30¢ + 40¢ = 70¢

The cost together

10¢ + 50¢ = 60¢
20¢ + 60¢ = 80¢
30¢ + 70¢ = $1.00

The eraser costs 30¢. The pencil costs 70¢.

5 CHECK   Check: Are any of the totals $1.00? Yes.

$$30¢ + 70¢ = $1.00$$

Is the pencil 40¢ more than the eraser? Yes.

(70¢ − 40¢ = 30¢) The answer checks.

9

Problem Solving: "Hidden Facts" Strategy

Problem: Chris wants to use 4 crepe paper streamers to decorate the table. Each streamer is 2 yards long. Each package of crepe paper is marked "25 feet." Is one package enough?

1 IMAGINE

You want to measure 4 crepe paper streamers in yards.

2 NAME

Facts: 4 streamers
            2 yards each streamer
            25 feet in one package

Question: Does one package contain enough crepe paper?

3 THINK

Is there a "hidden fact" in the problem? (Yes.)

3 feet in 1 yard

To change the 2 yards to feet, multiply: $2 \times 3 = \underline{\ ?\ }$ ft in one streamer

To find the number of feet needed for 4 streamers, multiply:

$4 \times \underline{\ ?\ }$ ft in 1 streamer $= \underline{\ ?\ }$ ft for 4 streamers

4 COMPUTE

$2 \times 3 = 6$ ft for one streamer
$4 \times 6 = 24$ ft for four streamers
Ask: Is 24 ft $<$ 25 ft? Yes
One package of crepe paper is enough.

5 CHECK

Do the problem another way.

4×2 yd for 1 streamer $= 8$ yd for 4 streamers
8×3 ft $= 24$ ft in 8 yd
24 ft $<$ 25 ft   The answer checks.

10

1

Addition and Subtraction Facts

In this unit you will:

- Use addition facts through 18
- Use subtraction facts through 18
- Find families of facts
- Add two or more addends
- Find missing addends
- Look for number patterns
- Solve problems by making a table

Do you remember?

Addition and subtraction are opposites.

$$3 + 2 = 5$$

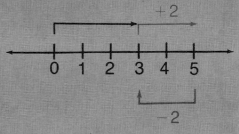

$$5 - 2 = 3$$

11

1-1 Addition Facts Through 10

How many pigs are there in all?

Add.

$$4 \longleftarrow \textbf{addend}$$
$$\underline{+2} \longleftarrow \textbf{addend}$$
$$6 \longleftarrow \textbf{sum}$$

$4 + 2 = 6 \longleftarrow$ **sum**

4 plus two equals 6.

There are 6 pigs in all.

Add.

1. $\begin{array}{r} 2 \\ +1 \\ \hline \end{array}$ ★ ★
★

2. $\begin{array}{r} 3 \\ +4 \\ \hline \end{array}$ ★ ★ ★
★ ★ ★ ★

3. $\begin{array}{r} 5 \\ +0 \\ \hline \end{array}$ ★ ★ ★ ★ ★

4. $\begin{array}{r} 1 \\ +2 \\ \hline \end{array}$

5. $\begin{array}{r} 5 \\ +3 \\ \hline \end{array}$

6. $\begin{array}{r} 4 \\ +5 \\ \hline \end{array}$

7. $\begin{array}{r} 3 \\ +3 \\ \hline \end{array}$

8. $\begin{array}{r} 2 \\ +7 \\ \hline \end{array}$

9. $\begin{array}{r} 2 \\ +4 \\ \hline \end{array}$

10. $\begin{array}{r} 3 \\ +6 \\ \hline \end{array}$

11. $\begin{array}{r} 0 \\ +7 \\ \hline \end{array}$

12. $\begin{array}{r} 2 \\ +6 \\ \hline \end{array}$

13. $\begin{array}{r} 6 \\ +1 \\ \hline \end{array}$

14. $\begin{array}{r} 0 \\ +9 \\ \hline \end{array}$

15. $\begin{array}{r} 5 \\ +2 \\ \hline \end{array}$

16. $\begin{array}{r} 7 \\ +3 \\ \hline \end{array}$

17. $\begin{array}{r} 4 \\ +3 \\ \hline \end{array}$

18. $\begin{array}{r} 6 \\ +4 \\ \hline \end{array}$

19. $\begin{array}{r} 9 \\ +1 \\ \hline \end{array}$

20. $\begin{array}{r} 3 \\ +0 \\ \hline \end{array}$

21. $\begin{array}{r} 1 \\ +7 \\ \hline \end{array}$

22. $\begin{array}{r} 8 \\ +2 \\ \hline \end{array}$

23. $\begin{array}{r} 0 \\ +6 \\ \hline \end{array}$

24. $\begin{array}{r} 1 \\ +8 \\ \hline \end{array}$

25. $\begin{array}{r} 3 \\ +1 \\ \hline \end{array}$

26. $\begin{array}{r} 5 \\ +5 \\ \hline \end{array}$

27. $\begin{array}{r} 4 \\ +6 \\ \hline \end{array}$

Find the sum.

28. 4 + 1	**29.** 3 + 7	**30.** 1 + 9	**31.** 2
32. 7 + 2	**33.** 3 + 5	**34.** 5 + 5	**35.** 5 + 4
36. 1 + 5	**37.** 3 + 2	**38.** 4 + 3	**39.** 0 + 1
40. 3 + 3	**41.** 1 + 1	**42.** 4 + 4	**43.** 8 + 1
44. 2 + 5	**45.** 6 + 3	**46.** 0 + 5	**47.** 0 + 0

Solve.

48. What is the sum of 3 and 4?

49. What is the sum of 6 and 2?

50. What number is 3 more than 7?

51. What number is 8 more than 2?

52. 4 added to itself gives what number?

53. 6 added to 0 gives what number?

Solve.

54. 7 birds are in a tree.
3 more birds join them.
How many birds are in the tree?

55. 3 birds find worms to eat.
2 more birds find worms.
How many birds find worms?

56. 5 birds fly in the air.
4 more fly in the air.
How many birds are flying?

57. 3 birds sit on a fence.
6 more birds join them.
How many birds are on
the fence?

Addition Facts Through 18

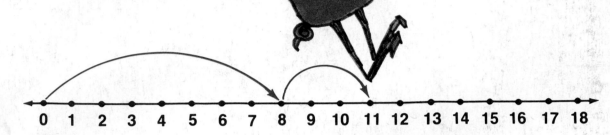

How far did
the pig jump?

$$8 + 3 = 11$$

The pig jumped 11 spaces in all.

Add. Use the number line if you want.

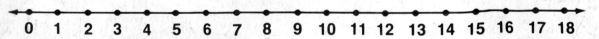

1. 7 + 4   2. 4 + 6   3. 5 + 8   4. 2 + 9

5. 6 + 9   6. 8 + 3   7. 9 + 5   8. 7 + 5

9. 8 + 7   10. 4 + 9   11. 9 + 7   12. 8 + 8

Find the sum.

13.	7 +8	14.	3 +7	15.	6 +5	16.	9 +4	17.	4 +8	18.	6 +6

19.	9 +3	20.	8 +9	21.	4 +7	22.	8 +6	23.	7 +9	24.	5 +6

Add.

25. 5 +7   **26.** 6 +7   **27.** 3 +8   **28.** 9 +6   **29.** 7 +6   **30.** 8 +2

31. 9 +2   **32.** 8 +5   **33.** 8 +4   **34.** 6 +8   **35.** 7 +7   **36.** 9 +8

37. 3 +9   **38.** 9 +7   **39.** 5 +9   **40.** 9 +9   **41.** 6 +9   **42.** 1 +9

Solve.

43. What is the sum of 4 and 7?

44. What number is 8 more than 9?

45. 8 plus 6 is what number?

46. 7 children buy milk.
6 more children buy milk. How many children now have milk?

47. 5 children each buy a cone.
6 children each buy a pop. How many cones and pops are sold?

Add.

48. 10 + 2   **49.** 3 + 13   **50.** 12 + 6

51. 11 + 5   **52.** 15 + 3   **53.** 4 + 12

54. 16 + 1   **55.** 11 + 7   **56.** 8 + 10

1-3 Order in Addition

The order of the addends can be changed without changing the sum.

$$2 + 5 = 7 \text{ and } 5 + 2 = 7$$

Use the addition table to find the sum of 2 plus 5 and 5 plus 2.

$2 + 5 = \underline{\ ?\ }$

Find 2 along the side.
Find 5 along the top.
Trace across from 2 and down from 5 to meet at 7.

$2 + 5 = 7$

$5 + 2 = \underline{\ ?\ }$

Now find 5 along the side.
Find 2 along the top.
Trace across from 5 and down from 2 to meet at 7.

$5 + 2 = 7$

Addition Table

+	0	1	2	3	4	5	6	7	8	9
0	0	1	2	3	4	5	6	7	8	9
1	1	2	3	4	5	6	7	8	9	10
2	2	3	4	5	6	7	8	9	10	11
3	3	4	5	6	7	8	9	10	11	12
4	4	5	6	7	8	9	10	11	12	13
5	5	6	7	8	9	10	11	12	13	14
6	6	7	8	9	10	11	12	13	14	15
7	7	8	9	10	11	12	13	14	15	16
8	8	9	10	11	12	13	14	15	16	17
9	9	10	11	12	13	14	15	16	17	18

Find the sum. Use the Addition Table.

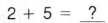

1. $\begin{array}{r} 4 \\ +3 \end{array}$ $\begin{array}{r} 3 \\ +4 \end{array}$
2. $\begin{array}{r} 2 \\ +7 \end{array}$ $\begin{array}{r} 7 \\ +2 \end{array}$
3. $\begin{array}{r} 9 \\ +5 \end{array}$ $\begin{array}{r} 5 \\ +9 \end{array}$
4. $\begin{array}{r} 6 \\ +7 \end{array}$ $\begin{array}{r} 7 \\ +6 \end{array}$

5. $\begin{array}{r} 8 \\ +1 \end{array}$ $\begin{array}{r} 1 \\ +8 \end{array}$
6. $\begin{array}{r} 9 \\ +0 \end{array}$ $\begin{array}{r} 0 \\ +9 \end{array}$
7. $\begin{array}{r} 7 \\ +4 \end{array}$ $\begin{array}{r} 4 \\ +7 \end{array}$
8. $\begin{array}{r} 9 \\ +8 \end{array}$ $\begin{array}{r} 8 \\ +9 \end{array}$

16

Add.

9. 9 +3	**10.** 0 +3	**11.** 4 +6	**12.** 1 +9	**13.** 8 +1	**14.** 6 +3
15. 7 +3	**16.** 8 +2	**17.** 3 +6	**18.** 3 +7	**19.** 5 +6	**20.** 1 +4
21. 5 +2	**22.** 7 +5	**23.** 8 +5	**24.** 4 +0	**25.** 2 +4	**26.** 7 +8
27. 5 +7	**28.** 8 +6	**29.** 7 +1	**30.** 8 +7	**31.** 6 +8	**32.** 2 +9

Find the sum.

33. 9 + 0	**34.** 8 + 7	**35.** 5 + 8	**36.** 8 + 5
37. 6 + 5	**38.** 3 + 9	**39.** 7 + 8	**40.** 5 + 6
41. 0 + 7	**42.** 3 + 8	**43.** 9 + 4	**44.** 7 + 6
45. 8 + 4	**46.** 9 + 8	**47.** 6 + 8	**48.** 8 + 0

Solve.

49. On one side of the barn there were 3 horses and 2 horses. On the other side of the barn there were 2 horses and 3 horses. How many horses were on each side of the barn? Why?

50. Look at the Addition Table. Find 0. Draw a diagonal line from 0 through 18. What kind of numbers does the diagonal cross? What kind of numbers are on either side of the diagonal?

17

1-4 Subtraction Facts Through 10

How many raccoons are left?

To find how many are left, subtract:

$$7$$
$$-3$$
$$\overline{4}\longleftarrow\textbf{difference.}$$

There are 4 raccoons left.

$$7 - 3 = 4 \longleftarrow \textbf{difference}$$

7 minus 3 equals 4

Find the difference.

1. $\begin{array}{r}3\\-1\\\hline\end{array}$ 	2. $\begin{array}{r}4\\-3\\\hline\end{array}$ 	3. $\begin{array}{r}2\\-0\\\hline\end{array}$	

4. $\begin{array}{r}6\\-3\\\hline\end{array}$ 5. $\begin{array}{r}10\\-4\\\hline\end{array}$ 6. $\begin{array}{r}3\\-2\\\hline\end{array}$ 7. $\begin{array}{r}8\\-4\\\hline\end{array}$ 8. $\begin{array}{r}6\\-5\\\hline\end{array}$ 9. $\begin{array}{r}9\\-4\\\hline\end{array}$

10. $\begin{array}{r}9\\-6\\\hline\end{array}$ 11. $\begin{array}{r}8\\-6\\\hline\end{array}$ 12. $\begin{array}{r}7\\-7\\\hline\end{array}$ 13. $\begin{array}{r}8\\-3\\\hline\end{array}$ 14. $\begin{array}{r}9\\-8\\\hline\end{array}$ 15. $\begin{array}{r}10\\-5\\\hline\end{array}$

16. $\begin{array}{r}4\\-0\\\hline\end{array}$ 17. $\begin{array}{r}7\\-1\\\hline\end{array}$ 18. $\begin{array}{r}5\\-3\\\hline\end{array}$ 19. $\begin{array}{r}8\\-7\\\hline\end{array}$ 20. $\begin{array}{r}10\\-2\\\hline\end{array}$ 21. $\begin{array}{r}7\\-6\\\hline\end{array}$

22. $\begin{array}{r}3\\-3\\\hline\end{array}$ 23. $\begin{array}{r}10\\-3\\\hline\end{array}$ 24. $\begin{array}{r}8\\-1\\\hline\end{array}$ 25. $\begin{array}{r}9\\-7\\\hline\end{array}$ 26. $\begin{array}{r}7\\-5\\\hline\end{array}$ 27. $\begin{array}{r}8\\-8\\\hline\end{array}$

Find the difference.

28. 9 − 5   **29.** 6 − 4   **30.** 9 − 1   **31.** 4 − 2

32. 5 − 2   **33.** 9 − 3   **34.** 10 − 8   **35.** 5 − 5

36. 7 − 4   **37.** 10 − 7   **38.** 4 − 4   **39.** 9 − 2

40. 8 − 5   **41.** 7 − 2   **42.** 6 − 1   **43.** 10 − 6

44. 10 − 1   **45.** 8 − 0   **46.** 1 − 1   **47.** 9 − 9

Solve.

48. What number is 2 less than 7?   **49.** 2 minus 1 is what number?

50. 3 minus 0 is what number?   **51.** What number is 3 less than 9?

52. 5 minus 4 is what number?   **53.** 8 minus 7 is what number?

54. What number is 6 less than 6?   **55.** What number is 0 less than 5?

Solve.

56. 9 dominos are standing up.
4 dominos fall over.
How many are left standing?

57. Cindy has 6¢.
She lost 2¢.
How much money is left?

58. 8 children are on bicycles
in the park. 7 ride away.
How many children are left?

Challenge!   **59.** Follow the path to the end. Watch the signs.

7 − 3 = →   ? − 2 = →   ? − 9 = 0

? + 1 = ↑   ? + 6 = ↑

19

Subtraction Facts Through 18

Where will the raccoon land?

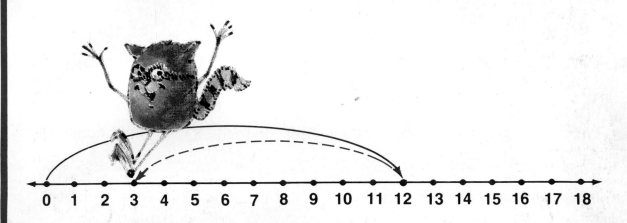

$$12 - 9 = 3$$

The raccoon landed on the 3.

Subtract. Use the number line if you want.

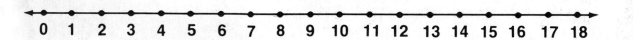

1. 12 − 8	**2.** 12 − 6	**3.** 11 − 2	**4.** 12 − 3
5. 18 − 9	**6.** 10 − 1	**7.** 14 − 8	**8.** 14 − 7
9. 12 − 5	**10.** 16 − 7	**11.** 15 − 6	**12.** 10 − 3
13. 15 − 9	**14.** 10 − 9	**15.** 12 − 4	**16.** 14 − 6
17. 13 − 7	**18.** 16 − 9	**19.** 15 − 8	**20.** 11 − 7
21. 17 − 8	**22.** 15 − 7	**23.** 16 − 8	**24.** 14 − 5
25. 11 − 6	**26.** 13 − 4	**27.** 14 − 9	**28.** 11 − 9

Find the difference.

29.	30.	31.	32.	33.	34.
14 −6	16 −8	11 −3	10 −4	12 −5	11 −8

35.	36.	37.	38.	39.	40.
15 −8	13 −6	18 −9	12 −6	15 −7	11 −9

41.	42.	43.	44.	45.	46.
13 −5	12 −7	13 −8	17 −9	13 −9	14 −7

47.	48.	49.	50.	51.	52.
11 −5	16 −7	15 −6	14 −9	11 −4	16 −9

Solve.

53. 10 children each have a balloon. 2 balloons broke. How many balloons are left?

54. John has 15¢. He paid 8¢ for juice. How much money does John have left?

55. Stephanie's sticker book has 17 pages. She filled 8 pages with stickers. How many pages are left to fill?

56. Jack has 5¢ more than Willy. Jack has 12¢. How much money does Willy have?

Challenge!	**Subtract.**		
	57. 15 − 3	58. 16 − 5	59. 14 − 2
	60. 17 − 1	61. 13 − 2	62. 18 − 8
	63. 17 − 6	64. 12 − 1	65. 16 − 4

Families of Facts

Addition and subtraction facts that use the same numbers are a **family of facts**.

2 Addition Facts

   6
+4
10

   4
+6
10

2 Subtraction Facts

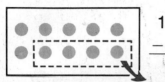   10
−4
6

   10
−6
4

Write two other facts to complete each family of facts.

1. 9   2
   +2   +9
   11   11

2. 3   5
   +5   +3
    8   8

3. 14   14
   −8   −6
    6   8

4. 13   13
   −6   −7
    7   6

5.   7   16
    +9   −9
    16   7

6. 11   8
   −3   +3
    8   11

Write four facts to show each family of facts.

7. 12, 8, 4

8. 10, 7, 3

9. 17, 9, 8

10. 15, 9, 6

11. 13, 8, 5

12. 11, 7, 4

13. 11, 6, 5

14. 14, 9, 5

15. 12, 7, 5

16. 15, 8, 7

17. 13, 9, 4

18. 12, 9, 3

Each family of facts has:

two addition sentences   and   two subtraction sentences.

$$7 + 5 = 12$$
$$5 + 7 = 12$$

$$12 - 5 = 7$$
$$12 - 7 = 5$$

Complete. Then write two more sentences for each family.

19. $2 + 8 = 10$
    $8 + 2 = \underline{?}$

20. $9 + 3 = 12$
    $3 + 9 = \underline{?}$

21. $11 - 6 = \underline{?}$
    $11 - 5 = \underline{?}$

22. $12 - 4 = \underline{?}$
    $12 - 8 = \underline{?}$

23. $8 + 5 = \underline{?}$
    $5 + 8 = \underline{?}$

24. $7 + 8 = \underline{?}$
    $15 - 8 = \underline{?}$

25. $13 - 4 = \underline{?}$
    $13 - 9 = \underline{?}$

26. $1 + 9 = 10$
    $10 - 9 = \underline{?}$

27. $9 + 6 = 15$
    $15 - 6 = \underline{?}$

28. $15 - 9 = \underline{?}$
    $15 - 6 = \underline{?}$

29. $9 + 7 = \underline{?}$
    $16 - 7 = \underline{?}$

30. $8 + 4 = \underline{?}$
    $4 + 8 = \underline{?}$

31. $10 - 4 = \underline{?}$
    $10 - 6 = \underline{?}$

32. $15 - 7 = \underline{?}$
    $15 - 8 = \underline{?}$

33. $8 + 6 = \underline{?}$
    $14 - 6 = \underline{?}$

34. $5 + 6 = \underline{?}$
    $\underline{?} - 6 = 5$

35. $3 + 7 = \underline{?}$
    $\underline{?} - 7 = 3$

36. $\underline{?} + 8 = 11$
    $11 - 8 = \underline{?}$

CHALLENGE

Write a question for each.

37. 8 children play soccer.
    5 children sit on the bench.

38. 13 children are on the
    soccer team. 7 of them are girls.

23

More Than Two Addends

Beth and Joe keep score for basketball. The blue team made 2, 3, and 6 baskets. Beth added down and Joe added up. How many baskets did the blue team make in all?

| Add down. | or | Add up. |

Remember:
You can add in any order.

The blue team made 11 baskets in all.

Find the sum.

1.	2.	3.	4.	5.	6.
5	5	3	6	2	7
1	2	5	3	6	0
+4	+9	+3	+1	+7	+4

7.	8.	9.	10.	11.	12.
4	2	2	7	1	6
3	2	4	2	5	2
1	5	4	3	6	0
+5	+1	+3	+4	+3	+2

To make addition easier:

Add Doubles

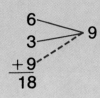

$$\begin{array}{r} 4 \\ 3 \\ +4 \\ \hline 11 \end{array}$$ 8

$$\begin{array}{r} 6 \\ 3 \\ +9 \\ \hline 18 \end{array}$$ 9

Add Tens

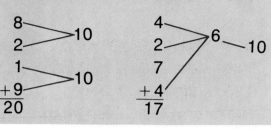

$$\begin{array}{r} 8 \\ 2 \\ 1 \\ +9 \\ \hline 20 \end{array}$$ 10 10

$$\begin{array}{r} 4 \\ 2 \\ 7 \\ +4 \\ \hline 17 \end{array}$$ 6 10

Add.

13.	**14.**	**15.**	**16.**	**17.**	**18.**
5	4	9	2	5	4
9	2	8	4	0	6
+4	+4	+1	2	5	3
			+4	+6	+3

Parentheses are also used to group addends.
Complete. (The first two are done.)

19. $2 + 5 + 7 =$ ___?___
$(2 + 5) + 7 =$ ___?___
$7 + 7 = 14$

20. $3 + 4 + 6 =$ ___?___
$3 + (4 + 6) =$ ___?___
$3 + 10 = 13$

21. $6 + 2 + 2 =$ ___?___
$6 + (2 + 2) =$ ___?___

22. $9 + 8 + 1 =$ ___?___
$9 + (8 + 1) =$ ___?___

23. $3 + 5 + 6 + 2 =$ ___?___
$(3 + 5) + (6 + 2) =$ ___?___

24. $2 + 3 + 5 + 5 =$ ___?___
$(2 + 3) + (5 + 5) =$ ___?___

Solve.

25. The red team made 6 baskets in the first half of the game. The blue team made 7 baskets. In the second half, the reds made 5 and the blues made 4. How many baskets were made in the game?

Missing Addends

7 children are at Steffi's birthday party. 10 children were invited. How many are still to come?

Think : 7 plus what number
        equals 10?

$7 + \underline{\ ?\ } = 10$

$7 + \ \ 3\ \ = 10$

3 children are still to come.

Find the missing addend.

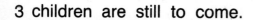

1. $3 + \underline{\ ?\ } = 7$ 2. $9 + \underline{\ ?\ } = 10$ 3. $2 + \underline{\ ?\ } = 5$

4. $\underline{\ ?\ } + 4 = 9$ 5. $\underline{\ ?\ } + 3 = 6$ 6. $5 + \underline{\ ?\ } = 7$

7. $4 + \underline{\ ?\ } = 12$ 8. $\underline{\ ?\ } + 9 = 15$ 9. $7 + \underline{\ ?\ } = 12$

10. $9 + \underline{\ ?\ } = 11$ 11. $3 + \underline{\ ?\ } = 10$ 12. $\underline{\ ?\ } + 9 = 9$

Solve.

13. What number plus 5 equals 11?

14. What number plus 3 equals 10?

15. What number and 7 is 16?

16. What number and 9 is 18?

17. What number added to 3 equals 12?

18. What number added to 8 equals 14?

19. What number and 7 is 7?

20. What number and 5 is 5?

Number Patterns

Look for a pattern. Write the next example.
Write the answers. (The first two are done.)

1.	0	0	0	0	0	2.	14	14	14	14	14
	+1	+2	+3	+4	+5		−5	−6	−7	−8	−9
	1	2	3	4	5		9	8	7	6	5

3.	9	9	9	9	?	4.	17	17	17	17	?
	+5	+6	+7	+8	+?		−4	−5	−6	−7	−?

5.	6	6	6	6	?	6.	16	16	16	16	?
	+4	+5	+6	+7	+?		−3	−4	−5	−6	−?

7.	2	2	2	2	?	8.	13	13	13	13	?
	+4	+3	+2	+1	+?		−4	−3	−2	−1	−?

Look for a pattern. Write the next number.
(The first two are done.)

9. 17, 20, 23, 26, <u>29</u>
  └₊₃┘└₊₃┘└₊₃┘└₊₃┘

10. 18, 22, 21, 25, 24, 28, <u>27</u>
  └₊₄┘└₋₁┘└₊₄┘└₋₁┘└₊₄┘└₋₁┘

11. 3, 4, 5, 6, <u>?</u>

12. 3, 6, 9, 12, <u>?</u>

13. 20, 16, 12, 8, <u>?</u>

14. 24, 18, 12, 6, <u>?</u>

15. 21, 18, 15, 12, <u>?</u>

16. 7, 12, 17, 22, <u>?</u>

17. 3, 6, 4, 7, 5, 8, <u>?</u>

18. 4, 8, 5, 9, 6, 10, <u>?</u>

19. 6, 4, 7, 5, 8, 6, <u>?</u>

20. 9, 5, 7, 3, 5, 1, <u>?</u>

21. 7, 9, 8, 10, 9, 11, <u>?</u>

22. 17, 10, 13, 6, 9, 2, <u>?</u>

1-10 Addition and Subtraction Practice

Add or subtract quickly. (Watch for + or −.)

1. $\begin{array}{r} 3 \\ +2 \\ \hline \end{array}$	2. $\begin{array}{r} 4 \\ +7 \\ \hline \end{array}$	3. $\begin{array}{r} 5 \\ +0 \\ \hline \end{array}$	4. $\begin{array}{r} 8 \\ +6 \\ \hline \end{array}$	5. $\begin{array}{r} 7 \\ +1 \\ \hline \end{array}$	6. $\begin{array}{r} 5 \\ +8 \\ \hline \end{array}$
7. $\begin{array}{r} 7 \\ +5 \\ \hline \end{array}$	8. $\begin{array}{r} 3 \\ +6 \\ \hline \end{array}$	9. $\begin{array}{r} 9 \\ +7 \\ \hline \end{array}$	10. $\begin{array}{r} 0 \\ +9 \\ \hline \end{array}$	11. $\begin{array}{r} 6 \\ +8 \\ \hline \end{array}$	12. $\begin{array}{r} 9 \\ +9 \\ \hline \end{array}$
13. $\begin{array}{r} 15 \\ -7 \\ \hline \end{array}$	14. $\begin{array}{r} 10 \\ -8 \\ \hline \end{array}$	15. $\begin{array}{r} 14 \\ -6 \\ \hline \end{array}$	16. $\begin{array}{r} 11 \\ -8 \\ \hline \end{array}$	17. $\begin{array}{r} 6 \\ -4 \\ \hline \end{array}$	18. $\begin{array}{r} 13 \\ -5 \\ \hline \end{array}$
19. $\begin{array}{r} 14 \\ -9 \\ \hline \end{array}$	20. $\begin{array}{r} 17 \\ -9 \\ \hline \end{array}$	21. $\begin{array}{r} 8 \\ -2 \\ \hline \end{array}$	22. $\begin{array}{r} 16 \\ -9 \\ \hline \end{array}$	23. $\begin{array}{r} 12 \\ -7 \\ \hline \end{array}$	24. $\begin{array}{r} 14 \\ -8 \\ \hline \end{array}$
25. $\begin{array}{r} 18 \\ -9 \\ \hline \end{array}$	26. $\begin{array}{r} 7 \\ -2 \\ \hline \end{array}$	27. $\begin{array}{r} 16 \\ -7 \\ \hline \end{array}$	28. $\begin{array}{r} 11 \\ -4 \\ \hline \end{array}$	29. $\begin{array}{r} 17 \\ -8 \\ \hline \end{array}$	30. $\begin{array}{r} 15 \\ -9 \\ \hline \end{array}$
31. $\begin{array}{r} 14 \\ -5 \\ \hline \end{array}$	32. $\begin{array}{r} 9 \\ -5 \\ \hline \end{array}$	33. $\begin{array}{r} 12 \\ -4 \\ \hline \end{array}$	34. $\begin{array}{r} 13 \\ -4 \\ \hline \end{array}$	35. $\begin{array}{r} 13 \\ -6 \\ \hline \end{array}$	36. $\begin{array}{r} 11 \\ -5 \\ \hline \end{array}$
37. $\begin{array}{r} 8 \\ +8 \\ \hline \end{array}$	38. $\begin{array}{r} 5 \\ +9 \\ \hline \end{array}$	39. $\begin{array}{r} 6 \\ +5 \\ \hline \end{array}$	40. $\begin{array}{r} 6 \\ +9 \\ \hline \end{array}$	41. $\begin{array}{r} 0 \\ +8 \\ \hline \end{array}$	42. $\begin{array}{r} 5 \\ +5 \\ \hline \end{array}$
43. $\begin{array}{r} 7 \\ +9 \\ \hline \end{array}$	44. $\begin{array}{r} 8 \\ +7 \\ \hline \end{array}$	45. $\begin{array}{r} 7 \\ +6 \\ \hline \end{array}$	46. $\begin{array}{r} 1 \\ +9 \\ \hline \end{array}$	47. $\begin{array}{r} 4 \\ +9 \\ \hline \end{array}$	48. $\begin{array}{r} 9 \\ +8 \\ \hline \end{array}$

Write each example whose sum or difference is in the box.

49.

| **12** | 8
+5 | 7
+5 | 9
−3 | 12
−0 | 6
+6 | 12
−6 |

50.

| **9** | 12
− 3 | 13
−5 | 5
+4 | 17
−9 | 9
−0 | 9
+0 |

51.

| **13** | 9
+4 | 8
−5 | 7
+6 | 9
+5 | 10
−3 | 13
+0 |

Add or subtract. (Watch the signs!)

52. 5 + 8   **53.** 7 + 3   **54.** 2 + 7   **55.** 9 + 4

56. 11 − 3   **57.** 13 − 6   **58.** 14 − 7   **59.** 10 − 1

60. 9 + 9   **61.** 11 − 7   **62.** 6 + 4   **63.** 7 + 0

64. 12 − 5   **65.** 17 − 8   **66.** 8 + 8   **67.** 0 + 9

Solve

68. 6 blue jays are in a tree. 7 yellow finches join them. How many birds are in the tree?

69. 13 birds are in a tree. Then 9 birds fly away. How many birds are left?

70. 8 birds are in a tree. 7 birds join them. Then 9 birds fly away. How many are left?

Problem Solving: Make a Table

Problem: A milk deliverer left 3 containers of milk at the first house. At the second house she left one more. At the third house she left two more than at the first house, and so on. How many containers of milk did she leave at the seventh house?

House	Number of Containers
1	3
2	$(3 + 1) = 4$
3	$(3 + 2) = 5$
4	
5	
6	
7	

1 IMAGINE

Make a table that shows what is happening in the problem.

2 NAME

Facts: 3   1st house

3 + 1   2nd house

3 + 2   3rd house

Question: How many containers are left at the 7th house?

3 THINK

Complete the table.
Remember, at each succeeding house *one more* container is left.

4 COMPUTE

$(3 + 3) = 6$ 4th house

$(3 + 4) = 7$ 5th house   9 containers are left

$(3 + 5) = 8$ 6th house   at the 7th house

$(3 + 6) = 9$ 7th house

5 CHECK

Is there one more container at each house?
Look at your completed table to check.

9 is 1 more than 8,

8 is 1 more than 7, and so on.

Solve by making a table.

1. Craig shakes hands with every second person who comes into the room. If 15 people come into the room, how many hands does Craig shake?

People	Write "Yes" If Craig Shakes Their Hand.
1	
2	Yes
3	
4	Yes
5	
6	Yes
7	
8	
9	
10	
11	
12	
13	
14	
15	
Total Number of "Yes" Tallies	

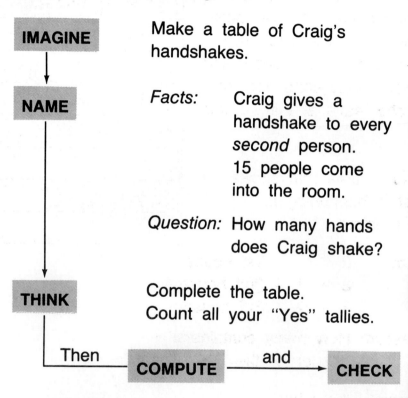

IMAGINE → Make a table of Craig's handshakes.

NAME → *Facts:* Craig gives a handshake to every *second* person. 15 people come into the room.

Question: How many hands does Craig shake?

THINK → Complete the table. Count all your "Yes" tallies.

Then **COMPUTE** and **CHECK**

2. If Craig shakes hands with every third person who enters the room, how many hands does he shake?

3. If Craig shakes the hand of every fifth person who enters the room, and 25 people come in the room, how many hands does Craig shake?

4. The milk deliverer (from page 30) left 5 containers at the first house. How many did she leave at the seventh house?

More Practice

Find the sum.

1. 1 +5	**2.** 7 +2	**3.** 3 +3	**4.** 9 +5	**5.** 0 +7	**6.** 9 +8

7. 2 + 4 **8.** 5 + 5 **9.** 6 + 8 **10.** 7 + 8

Find the difference.

11. 8 −1	**12.** 4 −4	**13.** 7 −3	**14.** 12 −4	**15.** 9 −8	**16.** 8 −0

17. 12 − 6 **18.** 8 − 6 **19.** 14 − 5 **20.** 11 − 5

Add or subtract. (Watch the signs!)

21. 6 −2	**22.** 5 +4	**23.** 8 −8	**24.** 13 −5	**25.** 7 +7	**26.** 0 +6

27. 3 + 9 + 6 **28.** 2 + 8 + 7 **29.** 4 + 5 + 6

Write four facts to show each family of facts.

30. 10, 7, 3   **31.** 12, 4, 8

Find the missing addend.

32. 7 + ? = 16 **33.** ? + 6 = 14

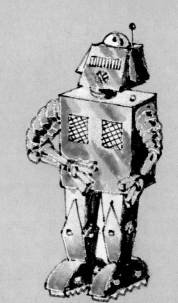

Solve.

34. Steve has 3 robots and Mike has 3. How many robots do they have together?

35. Cindy found 11 shells, but 9 were broken. How many shells were not broken?

32

(See *Still More Practice*, p.355.)

Math-e-Magic

NUMBER PUZZLES

A Martian landed on earth. It took a path and found something that all earth people want. What did the Martian find?

Solve each example and then use the code.

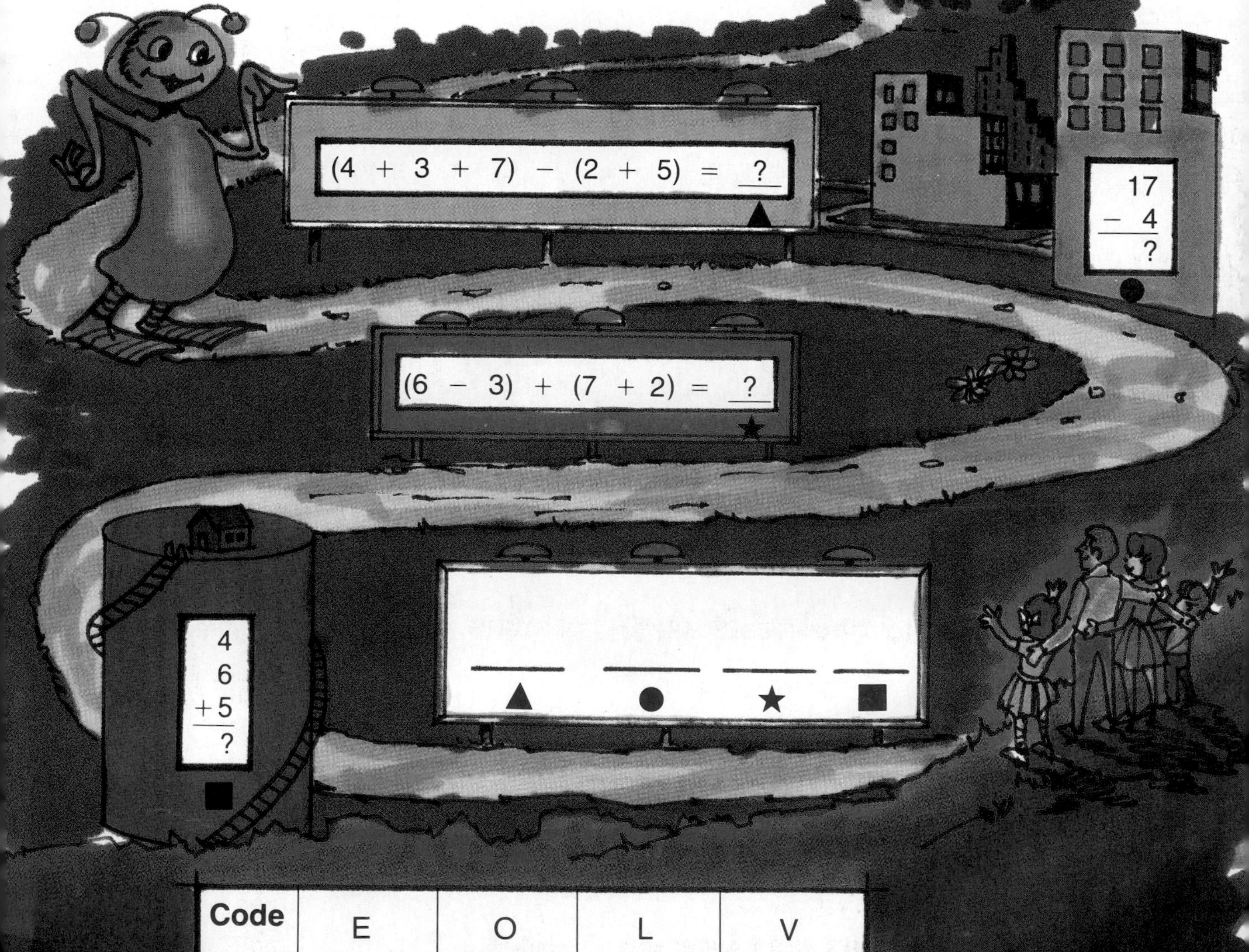

$$(4 + 3 + 7) - (2 + 5) = \underline{}\ \blacktriangle$$

$$\begin{array}{r} 17 \\ -\ 4 \\ \hline ? \end{array}$$

$$(6 - 3) + (7 + 2) = \underline{}\ \bigstar$$

$$\begin{array}{r} 4 \\ 6 \\ +5 \\ \hline ? \end{array}\ \blacksquare$$

$$\underline{}\ \ \underline{}\ \ \underline{}\ \ \underline{}$$
$$\blacktriangle \qquad \bullet \qquad \bigstar \qquad \blacksquare$$

Code	E	O	L	V
	15	13	7	12

33

Check Your Mastery

Find the sum.

See pp. 12-17, 24-25

1.	3	**2.**	0	**3.**	5	**4.**	9	**5.**	6	**6.**	8
	+5		+9		+6		+8		+7		+7

7. $9 + 8$ **8.** $8 + 9$ **9.** $7 + 7 + 3$ **10.** $4 + 9 + 2$

Find the difference.

See pp. 18-21

11.	7	**12.**	10	**13.**	6	**14.**	18	**15.**	16	**16.**	11
	−4		−0		−4		−9		−7		−5

Write four facts to show each family of facts.

See pp. 22, 23

17. 11, 7, 4   **18.** 10, 8, 2   **19.** 14, 9, 5

Find the missing addend.

See p. 26

20. $5 + \underline{?} = 11$ **21.** $3 + \underline{?} = 12$ **22.** $\underline{?} + 4 = 10$

Solve.

See pp. 14-15, 20-21, 26

23. What number do you add to 6 to get 12?

24. What number added to 9 equals 16?

25. Jamie had 11 raisins and ate 3. How many raisins were left?

Numeration

2

In this unit you will:

- Read and write numbers through 999
- Order and compare numbers
- Round numbers to the nearest tens and hundreds
- Count by 2's, 3's, 5's, and 10's
- Identify even and odd numbers
- Read and write numbers through 999,999
- Compare larger numbers
- Read and write ordinal numbers
- Write Roman numerals through twenty
- Solve problems by using data from a table.

Do you remember?

1 ten	= 10
2 tens	= 20
1 ten 3 ones	= 13
2 tens 7 ones	= 27

Tens and Ones

To write **numbers** use
these ten **digits**.

0, 1, 2, 3, 4, 5, 6, 7, 8, 9

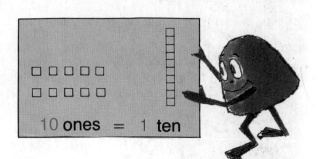

10 ones = 1 ten

The **value** of the digit depends
on its **place** in a number.

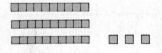

3 ones

Tens	Ones
	3

Standard Form	Word Name
3 ——→	three

3 tens 0 ones

Tens	Ones
3	0

Standard Form	Word Name
30 ——→	thirty

3 tens 3 ones

Tens	Ones
3	3

Standard Form	Word Name
33 ——→	thirty-three

Write the number in standard form.

1. 2 tens 5 ones   **2.** 6 tens 3 ones   **3.**   5 ones

4. 4 tens 7 ones   **5.** 1 ten 9 ones   **6.**   8 tens

7. 1 ten 1 one   **8.** 5 tens 5 ones   **9.** 9 tens 9 ones

Complete.

10. 17 = _?_ ten _?_ ones   **11.** 74 = _?_ tens _?_ ones

12. 40 = _?_ tens _?_ ones   **13.** 9 = _?_ tens _?_ ones

Read the number.

14. 10　　15. 41　　16. 23　　17. 16　　18. 21

19. 66　　20. 26　　21. 75　　22. 80　　23. 99

Write the number.

24. twenty-six　　25. eleven　　26. forty-five

27. thirty　　28. seventy-seven　　29. ninety

In what place is the underlined digit? What is its value?

30. 1<u>7</u>　　31. <u>7</u>1　　32. 4<u>6</u>　　33. <u>6</u>4　　34. <u>6</u>0

35. <u>8</u>　　36. <u>8</u>3　　37. <u>1</u>8　　38. <u>4</u>1　　39. <u>4</u>

40. <u>9</u>0　　41. <u>9</u>　　42. <u>1</u>9　　43. <u>9</u>3　　44. <u>9</u>9

What does the digit 5 mean in each number.

45. 58　　46. 15　　47. 5　　48. 95　　49. 50

Challenge!

Use the newspaper at the right.
Write the number and the word
name for each:
(The first one is done.)

50. the cost of the skateboard
($22; twenty-two dollars)

51. the page number

52. the number of letters in the title

53. the cost of the bike

54. the cost of the guitar

55. the cost of the doll

The Planet

Page 18

Bike　$99.

Skate Board　$22.

Guitar　$58.

Doll　$8.

Hundreds

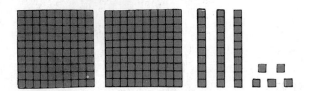

10 tens = 1 hundred
10 tens = 100

2 hundreds   3 tens   5 ones = 235

200   +   30   +   5   = 235

Expanded Form   **Standard Form**

Read 235 as: two hundred thirty-five.

Study these.

Hundreds	Tens	Ones
5	6	7
7	3	1
8	0	4
9	2	0

$500 + 60 + 7 = 567$
$700 + 30 + 1 = 731$
$800 + 0 + 4 = 804$
$900 + 20 + 0 = 920$

Write the number in standard form.

1.

2.

3.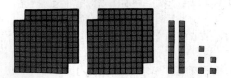

4.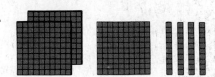

Complete.

5. 576 = __?__ hundreds __?__ tens __?__ ones

6. 412 = __?__ hundreds __?__ ten __?__ ones

7. 890 = __?__ hundreds __?__ tens __?__ ones

8. 605 = __?__ hundreds __?__ tens __?__ ones

9. 500 = __?__ hundreds __?__ tens __?__ ones

Write the number.

10. 300 + 50 + 2

11. 200 + 40 + 8

12. 600 + 10 + 1

13. 700 + 70 + 7

14. 500 + 60 + 3

15. 100 + 50 + 5

16. 400 + 0 + 4

17. 800 + 70 + 0

18. 900 + 0 + 0

In what place is the underlined digit? What is its value?

19. 6_7_1

20. 85_7_

21. _7_91

22. 80_7_

23. _7_5

24. 96_4_

25. _4_05

26. 4_8_

27. 74_1_

28. _4_

29. 8_8_8

30. 8_0_8

31. _8_00

32. 8_8_

33. _8_0

Write the word name for each.

	Hundreds	Tens	Ones
34.	6	5	4
36.	1	2	9
38.	1	1	0
40.	8	7	0

	Hundreds	Tens	Ones
35.	3	7	8
37.	4	1	6
39.	9	0	2
41.	6	0	0

CHALLENGE

42. 462 is how much greater than 362?

43. 875 is how much less than 975?

44. Write a number 300 greater than 651.

45. Write a number 400 less than 869.

Comparing and Ordering Numbers

You can compare numbers by using a number line.

Compare: 299 _?_ 312

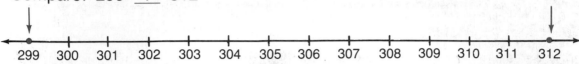

299 300 301 302 303 304 305 306 307 308 309 310 311 312

Think: 299 comes *before* 312.
299 is *less than* 312.

So, 299 < 312

You can also compare numbers by using the place value of their digits.

Compare: 299 _?_ 312

H	T	O
2	9	9
3	1	2

Look at the digits with the greatest place value.
2 < 3
So, 299 < 312

Study these.

Compare: 305 _?_ 310

H	T	O
3	0	5
3	1	0

3 = 3
0 < 1

So, 305 < 310

Compare: 305 _?_ 301

H	T	O
3	0	5
3	0	1

3 = 3
0 = 0
5 > 1

So, 305 > 301

Compare. Write < or > .

1. 24 _?_ 57

2. 36 _?_ 18

3. 75 _?_ 78

4. 458 _?_ 325

5. 651 _?_ 615

6. 876 _?_ 872

Compare. Write < or >.

7. 58 _?_ 51   **8.** 11 _?_ 17   **9.** 88 _?_ 78

10. 572 _?_ 872   **11.** 212 _?_ 112   **12.** 752 _?_ 782

13. 431 _?_ 438   **14.** 970 _?_ 979   **15.** 857 _?_ 854

Comparing Money

1 dollar = 100¢	1 dime = 10¢	1 penny = 1¢

You can make a place value chart for money
and compare money as you do other numbers.

Compare: $4.75 _?_ $3.84

Dollars	Dimes	Cents
4	7	5
3	8	4

Look at the dollars.
     4 > 3
So, $4.75 > $3.84

Compare: $6.25 _?_ $6.70

Dollars	Dimes	Cents
6	2	5
6	7	0

Dollars are the same.
Look at the dimes.
     2 < 7
So, $6.25 < $6.70

Compare. Write < or >.

16. $2.45 _?_ $5.75   **17.** $8.64 _?_ $4.64   **18.** $3.50 _?_ $2.75

19. $4.65 _?_ $4.55   **20.** $.69 _?_ $.65   **21.** $7.35 _?_ $7.15

22. $9.99 _?_ $9.90   **23.** $5.53 _?_ $5.58   **24.** $2.79 _?_ $2.75

Challenge!

Arrange in order from least to greatest.

25. 18, 65, 37, 72, 9   **26.** 86, 325, 117, 70, 268

27. 456, 487, 442, 451, 459   **28.** 775, 771, 779, 770, 778

Rounding Numbers

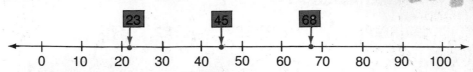

Round numbers to tell **about** how many.

Round to the nearest ten.

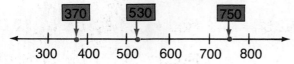

23 is *nearer to* 20 than 30.

Round 23 *down* to 20.

45 is *halfway* between 40 and 50.

Round 45 *up* to 50.

68 is nearer to 70 than 60.

Round 68 *up* to 70.

Round to the nearest hundred.

> Less than halfway round down
> Halfway or more round up

370 is nearer to 400 than 300.

Round 370 *up* to 400.

750 is halfway between 700 and 800.

Round 750 *up* to 800.

530 is nearer to 500 than 600.

Round 530 *down* to 500

Name the tens each is between. (The first is done.)

1. 80 < 86 < 90   2. ? < 54 < ?

3. ? < 68 < ?   4. ? < 25 < ?

Round to the nearest ten.

5. 86   6. 54   7. 68   8. 25   9. 11

10. 45   11. 58   12. 71   13. 82   14. 85

Name the hundreds each is between. (The first one is done.)

15. 400 < 486 < 500

16. ? < 392 < ?

17. ? < 738 < ?

18. ? < 550 < ?

Round to the nearest hundred.

19. 486   20. 392   21. 738   22. 550   23. 110

24. 671   25. 543   26. 859   27. 247   28. 752

Rounding Money

Round to the nearest dollar.

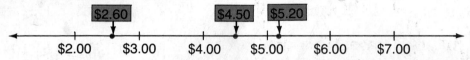

$2.60 is nearer to $3.00 than $2.00.   Round $2.60 *up* to $3.00.

$4.50 is halfway between   Round $4.50 *up* to $5.00
   $4.00 and $5.00.

$5.20 is nearer to $5.00 than $6.00.   Round $5.20 *down* to $5.00.

Name the dollars each is between. (The first one is done.)

29. $4.00 < $4.65 < $5.00

30. ? < $3.18 < ?

31. ? < $7.50 < ?

32. ? < $6.75 < ?

Round to the nearest dollar.

33. $4.65   34. $3.18   35. $7.50   36. $6.75   37. $5.15

38. $8.55   39. $2.45   40. $1.80   41. $4.50   42. $3.49

Challenge!

Round to the nearest ten. (The first one is done.)

43. 225   230   44. 649   45. 325   46. 817   47. 478

43

Skip Counting

Count by twos.

Start at zero. Count by twos to 20.

0, 2, 4, 6, 8, 10, 12, 14, 16, 18, 20

These are called **even numbers**.
Even numbers end with the digits 0, 2, 4, 6, or 8.

Start at one. Count by twos to 21.

1, 3, 5, 7, 9, 11, 13, 15, 17, 19, 21

These are called **odd numbers**.
Odd numbers end with the digits 1, 3, 5, 7, or 9.

Count by threes to 30.

0, 3, 6, 9, 12, 15, 18, 21, 24 , 27, 30

Count by fives to 50.

0, 5, 10, 15, 20, 25, 30, 35, 40, 45, 50

Count by tens to 100.

0, 10, 20, 30, 40, 50, 60, 70, 80, 90, 100

Count by twos. Tell if the numbers are even or odd.

1. Start at 12.
   End at 26.

2. Start at 21.
   End at 35.

3. Start at 15.
   End at 25.

3. Start at 110.
   End at 120.

4. Start at 105.
   End at 115.

5. Start at 122.
   End at 130.

Count by threes.

7. Start at 33.
End at 48.

8. Start at 40.
End at 52.

9. Start at 50.
End at 65.

Count by fives.

10. Start at 15.
End at 40.

11. Start at 35.
End at 65.

12. Start at 110.
End at 140.

13. Start at 5¢.
End at 25¢.

14. Start at 30¢.
End at 55¢.

15. Start at $1.05.
End at $1.30.

Count by tens.

16. Start at 40.
End at 80.

17. Start at 100.
End at 150.

18. Start at 120.
End at 160.

19. Start at 20¢.
End at 70¢.

20. Start at 50¢.
End at $1.00.

21. Start at $1.10.
End at $1.50.

Write the missing numbers.

22. 2, 4, 6, _?_, 10, 12, 14, _?_

23. 15, 20, 25, _?_, _?_, 40, _?_, 50

24. 21, 24, 27, _?_, _?_, 36, _?_, 42

25. 70, 80, _?_, 100, _?_, 120, 130, _?_

26. $.30, $.35, _?_, $.45, $.50, _?_, _?_

27. $1.20, $1.30, _?_, $1.50, _?_, _?_, $1.80

28. $.40, _?_, $.50, _?_, _?_, _?_, $.70

29. Name the odd numbers starting at 73 and ending at 83.

30. Name the even numbers starting at 46 and ending at 60.

Thousands

10 hundreds = 1 thousand
10 hundreds = 1000

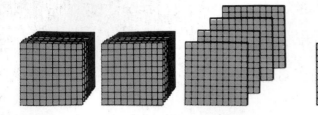

2 thousands 4 hundreds 1 ten 6 ones = 2416
2000 + 400 + 10 + 6 = 2416

Expanded Form   **Standard Form**

Read 2416 as: two thousand four hundred sixteen.

Study these.

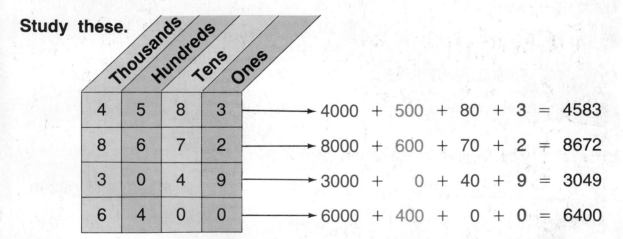

Thousands	Hundreds	Tens	Ones
4	5	8	3
8	6	7	2
3	0	4	9
6	4	0	0

4000 + 500 + 80 + 3 = 4583
8000 + 600 + 70 + 2 = 8672
3000 + 0 + 40 + 9 = 3049
6000 + 400 + 0 + 0 = 6400

Write the number in standard form.

1.

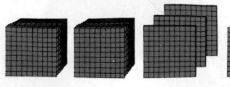

2.

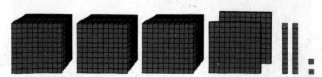

Write the number.

3. 4 thousands 8 hundreds 6 tens 4 ones

4. 2 thousands 3 hundreds 5 tens 6 ones

5. 9 thousands 0 hundreds 7 tens 7 ones

6. 5 thousands 5 hundreds 0 tens 0 ones

Complete.

7. 7216 = ? thousands ? hundreds ? ten ? ones

8. 5594 = ? thousands ? hundreds ? tens ? ones

9. 6020 = ? thousands ? hundreds ? tens ? ones

10. 3401 = ? thousands ? hundreds ? tens ? one

Write the number.

11. 8000 + 400 + 20 + 6   12. 3000 + 900 + 70 + 8

13. 7000 + 800 + 0 + 3   14. 9000 + 0 + 40 + 0

15. six thousands 7 hundreds   16. eight thousands

In what place is the underlined digit? What is its value?

17. 14<u>9</u>   18. <u>9</u>582   19. 561<u>9</u>   20. 9<u>9</u>45   21. 90<u>9</u>0

22. 4<u>1</u>82   23. 111<u>1</u>   24. 8<u>1</u>81   25. <u>1</u>818   26. 10<u>1</u>0

27. 511<u>5</u>   28. 1<u>5</u>15   29. <u>5</u>005   30. 50<u>5</u>0   31. 555<u>5</u>

CHALLENGE

32. What is the largest 4-digit number that can be written?

33. What is the smallest 4-digit number that can be written if zero is *not* one of the digits?

Comparing and Ordering Larger Numbers

Grace counted 2187 eggs and Oscar counted 1576 eggs. Who counted more eggs?

Compare: 2187 ? 1576

Th	H	T	O
2	1	8	7
1	5	7	6

Look at the digits with the greatest place value.

$2 > 1$

So, $2187 > 1576$

Study these.

Compare: 3465 ? 3781

Th	H	T	O
3	4	6	5
3	7	8	1

The digits in the thousands place are the same. Look at the hundreds place.

$4 < 7$

So, $3465 < 3781$

Compare: 5484 ? 5475

Th	H	T	O
5	4	8	4
5	4	7	5

The digits in both the thousands and the hundreds places are the same. Look at the tens place.

$8 > 7$

So, $5484 > 5475$

Compare. Write $<$ or $>$.

1. 7000 ? 9000

2. 8128 ? 6134

3. 7654 ? 7489

4. 5062 ? 5042

5. 9090 ? 9080

6. 6666 ? 6676

Compare. Write < or >.

7. 2176 _?_ 2542   **8.** 3721 _?_ 3700   **9.** 5280 _?_ 5290

10. 1728 _?_ 950   **11.** 5300 _?_ 5320   **12.** 8617 _?_ 8671

13. 3030 _?_ 3040   **14.** 7836 _?_ 7936   **15.** 9909 _?_ 9990

Least to Greatest

Write in order from least to greatest.

3976, 5189, 3689

Compare thousands	⟶	Compare hundreds

Compare thousands	Compare hundreds
5189	3976
3976	3689
3689	9 > 6
5 > 3	3976 > 3689

5189 is greatest

In order from least to greatest: 3689,   3976,   5189

Write in order from least to greatest.

16. 2492, 5050, 1492, 3000, 4444

17. 6500, 7900, 6770, 8000, 6125

18. 4495, 4152, 4017, 4681, 4318

19. 7652, 7615, 7687, 7605, 7631

Solve. Use the chart at the right.

20. Which grade collected the most cans?

21. Did grade 1 or grade 3 collect *more* cans?

22. Did grade 2 or grade 5 collect *fewer* cans?

Lincoln School	
Grade	Number of Cans Collected
1	1740
2	2083
3	2155
4	1900
5	3400
6	1016

49

Ten Thousands and Hundred Thousands

At one football game there were 61,876 people. At five games there were 346,423 people.

To show these numbers, we extend the place-value chart.

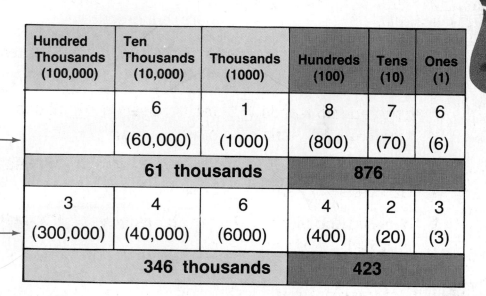

Hundred Thousands (100,000)	Ten Thousands (10,000)	Thousands (1000)	Hundreds (100)	Tens (10)	Ones (1)
	6 (60,000)	1 (1000)	8 (800)	7 (70)	6 (6)
61 thousands			876		
3 (300,000)	4 (40,000)	6 (6000)	4 (400)	2 (20)	3 (3)
346 thousands			423		

Expanded Form   **Standard Form**

60,000 + 1000 + 800 + 70 + 6 = 61,876

300,000 + 40,000 + 6000 + 400 + 20 + 3 = 346,423

Read 61,876 as: sixty-one thousand, eight hundred seventy-six

Read 346,423 as: three hundred forty-six thousand, four hundred twenty-three

Complete.

1. 40,000 = _?_ thousands
2. 80,000 = _?_ thousands
3. 35,000 = _?_ thousands
4. 57,000 = _?_ thousands
5. 200,000 = _?_ thousands
6. 700,000 = _?_ thousands
7. 550,000 = _?_ thousands
8. 926,000 = _?_ thousands

Complete.

9. 82,346 = _?_ ten thousands _?_ thousands _?_ hundreds _?_ tens _?_ ones

10. 10,430 = _?_ ten thousand _?_ thousands _?_ hundreds _?_ tens _?_ ones

11. 375,482 = _?_ hundred thousands _?_ ten thousands _?_ thousands _?_ hundreds _?_ tens _?_ ones

12. 498,576 = _?_ hundred thousands _?_ ten thousands _?_ thousands _?_ hundreds _?_ tens _?_ ones

13. 601,038 = _?_ hundred thousands _?_ ten thousands _?_ thousand _?_ hundreds _?_ tens _?_ ones

Write the number in standard form.

14. 2 ten thousands
15. 7 hundred thousands
16. 20,000 + 7000 + 40 + 3
17. 600,000 + 80,000 + 4000 + 90 + 1
18. seven hundred forty-two thousand, nine hundred twenty-five

In what place is the underlined digit? What is its value?

19. _4_7,896
20. _3_16,000
21. 88_1_,720
22. _5_73,128

2-9 Ordinal Numbers

JULY						
S	M	T	W	Th	F	S
	1	2	3	4	5	6
7	8	9	10	11	12	13
14	15	16	17	18	19	20
21	22	23	24	25	26	27
28	29	30	31			

Beth is having her birthday party on the second Saturday in July. What day of the month is her party?

Look at the calendar.

Count to the second Saturday.

Beth's party is on the thirteenth, or July 13th.

Numbers that show order are called **ordinal numbers**.

13th is an ordinal number.

The eighth day is a Monday.

8th is an ordinal number.

The last day of July is the thirty-first. 31st is an ordinal number.

Copy and complete. (The first two are done.)

1. first   1st
2. second   2nd
3. third   ?
4. fourth   ?
5. ?   5th
6. sixth   ?
7. seventh   ?
8. eighth   ?
9. ?   9th
10. tenth   ?
11. ?   11th
12. twelfth   ?
13. thirteenth   ?
14. ?   14th
15. ?   15th
16. sixteenth   ?
17. seventeenth   ?
18. ?   18th
19. nineteenth   ?
20. twentieth   ?
21. ?   21st

Write the ordinal number for each winner.
(The first one is done.)

22. Alan (second)
23. Susan
24. Jamal
25. Joe
26. Dennis
27. Willie
28. Lara
29. Sandy
30. Bud
31. Betty

Sports Day Winners	
1. Joe	6. Bud
2. Alan	7. Betty
3. Willie	8. Lara
4. Jamal	9. Dennis
5. Susan	10. Sandy

Copy and complete.

32. __?__ is the 5th month.
33. August is the __?__ month.
34. __?__ is the twelfth month.
35. __?__ is the first month.
36. March is the __?__ month.
37. June is the __?__ month.

Calculator Activity

Use a calculator to solve.

38. Add the numbers for the dates of all the Mondays.

39. Subtract the date of the first Tuesday from the date of the last Tuesday.

40. Add the dates of all the Fridays together.

Problem Solving: Using Data from a Table

Problem: The third graders in five schools in the district had a contest to see which third graders read the most pages during the summer. The **bar graph** shows the result of the contest. Which school won?

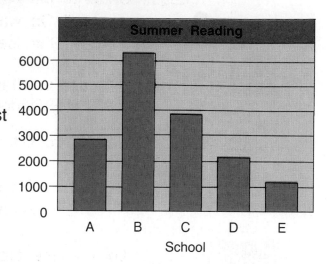

1 IMAGINE

You have to name the winning school.

2 NAME

Facts: Are shown on the bar graph.

Question: Which school won?

3 THINK

Use the data from the graph to complete this chart. Remember to round your answer to the nearest thousand.

School A	School B	School C	School D	School E
3000	6000	4000	2000	1000

4 COMPUTE

Write the numbers in order from least to greatest.
1000, 2000, 3000, 4000, 6000
The winner is School B.

5 CHECK

Look at the bar graph.
Which bar is longest?   School B.
The answer checks.

Use the data from the table to solve.

1. **Problem:** Margo's family made a weekly budget. On what did her family spend the most? On what did her family spend the least?

Item	Amount Spent Each Week
Food	$300
Travel	$180
Rent	$400
Fun	$ 75
Light	$ 50
Allowances	$ 15

IMAGINE

You are in charge of the family budget.

NAME

Facts: Are listed in the table.

Questions: On what did Margo's family spend the most? the least?

THINK

Look at the table. Arrange the amounts in order from least to greatest.

Then → **COMPARE** — and → **CHECK**

2. Did Margo's family spend more for travel or for light?

3. Did Margo's family spend less for food or for fun?

Make a survey of the television programs your classmates watch on Fridays. Use this table to help you make your survey.

Each tally mark stands for 1 student.
$\cancel{||||}$ = 5 students

Answer these questions.

4. What program is watched the most?

5. What program is watched the least?

Names of TV Programs	Number Who Watch
Black Beauty	$\cancel{||||}$

More Practice

Write the number in standard form.

1. 6 tens 5 ones

2. 4 hundreds 8 tens 1 one

3. 10,000 + 7000 + 10

4. 5 ten thousands

5. 7 hundred thousands

6. 6 thousands 2 tens

7. 6000 + 0 + 80 + 1

8. 800,000 + 60,000 + 4000 + 50 + 3

Compare. Use < or > .

9. 23 _?_ 29

10. 37 _?_ 44

11. 354 _?_ 763

12. 1352 _?_ 2943

13. 652 _?_ 682

14. 7628 _?_ 7630

In what place is the underlined digit? What is its value?

15. 3<u>6</u>5

16. 46,<u>7</u>18

17. 8<u>9</u>73

18. <u>6</u>56,756

19. <u>8</u>1,925

Round to the nearest ten.

20. 72

21. 28

22. 85

23. 55

Round to the nearest hundred.

24. 754

25. 747

26. 434

27. 385

Round to the nearest dollar.

28. $4.16

29. $9.75

30. $6.45

31. $8.50

Solve.

32. Name the odd numbers between 9 and 20.

33. Name the even numbers between 6 and 15.

34. What is the tenth letter of the alphabet?

35. What is the third letter of your teacher's last name?

(See *Still More Practice*, p. 356.)

Math-e-Magic

ROMAN NUMERALS

The ancient Romans used a different system for writing numbers. Here are the first twenty numbers written in Roman numerals.

1 = I	6 = VI	11 = XI		16 = XVI	
2 = II	7 = VII	12 = XII	10 plus 1, 2, 3, 4, 5	17 = XVII	10 plus 6, 7, 8, 9, 10
3 = III	8 = VIII	13 = XIII		18 = XVIII	
4 = IV (5-1)	9 = IX (10-1)	14 = XIV		19 = XIX	
5 = V	10 = X	15 = XV		20 = XX	

1. What 3 letters are repeated in the chart? For what number does each stand?

2. Write 2 numbers from the chart for which you must subtract.

Write the following in Roman numerals.

3. 8   **4.** 3   **5.** 4   **6.** 12   **7.** 9

8. 17   **9.** 19   **10.** 18   **11.** 14   **12.** 20

13. your age

14. the number of letters in your family name

15. the number of letters in the name of your school

16. the number of letters in the name of your state

17. Make a calendar for this month.

18. Change all the dates to Roman numerals. (Hint: 30 = XXX)

57

Check Your Mastery

Write the number in standard form.

See pp. 36-39, 46-47, 50-51

1. 30 + 7
2. 5 hundreds 7 ones
3. 3 thousands 8 tens
4. 7 ten thousands 6 thousands

Compare. Write < or >.

See pp. 40-41, 48-49

5. 40 _?_ 50
6. 400 _?_ 325
7. 3721 _?_ 2423

Round to the nearest ten.

See pp. 42-43

8. 25
9. 57
10. 12

Round to the nearest hundred.

See pp. 42-43

11. 117
12. 547
13. 877

Round to the nearest dollar.

See pp. 42-43

14. $8.25
15. $5.50
16. $7.60

In what place is the underlined digit?

See pp. 36-39, 46-47, 50-51

17. 778,465
18. 65,743
19. 41,424
20. 78,625

Write the missing numbers.

See pp. 44-45

21. 23, 25, _?_, 29, _?_
22. 110, _?_, 120, _?_, 130

23. Write the number for:
six hundred seventy-five thousand, four hundred eight.

See pp. 50-51

24. What is the seventh letter of the alphabet?

See pp. 52-53

25. Name the numbers between 8 and 17.

See pp. 44-45

3

Addition

In this unit you will:

- Regroup ones, tens, and hundreds
- Add two-, three-, and four-digit numbers with regrouping
- Learn shortcuts for mental math
- Add money
- Estimate sums
- Estimate money sums
- Use a calculator
- Solve problems by using simpler numbers

Do you remember?

10 ones	=	1 ten
10 tens	=	1 hundred
10 hundreds	=	1 thousand

So

13 ones	=	1 ten 3 ones
13 tens	=	1 hundred 3 tens
13 hundreds	=	1 thousand 3 hundreds

3-1 Adding: No Regrouping

Add: 365 + 504 = ?

Add the ones. → Add the tens. → Add the hundreds.

H	T	O
3	6	5
+5	0	4
		9

H	T	O
3	6	5
+5	0	4
	6	9

H	T	O
3	6	5
+5	0	4
8	6	9

365 + 504 = 869

Add.

1.
T	O
3	3
+4	4

2.
T	O
6	5
+1	1

3.
T	O
2	6
+5	3

4.
H	T	O
4	7	3
+2	1	6

5.
H	T	O
8	0	3
+1	9	1

6. 84
   +15

7. 91
   + 7

8. 30
   +52

9. 47
   +31

10. 82
    +15

11. 8
   +60

12. 30
    +60

13. 351
    +547

14. 82
    +417

15. 666
    + 31

16. 861
    +137

17. 752
    +146

18. 900
    + 51

19. 279
    +600

20. 500
    +300

21. 753
    +106

22. 615
    +304

23. 824
    +173

24. 564
    +302

25. 956
    + 33

60

3-2 Regrouping Ones

Jackson has 9 pennies in one pocket
and 7 pennies in another.
He wants to change his money for
dimes and pennies.

How many dimes can Jackson get?

How many pennies can he get?

10 pennies = 1 dime

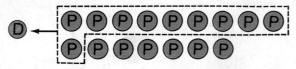

Think: 16 pennies = 10 pennies and 6 pennies
= 1 dime 6 pennies

Jackson can get 1 dime and 6 pennies.

Regroup ones to make tens. (The first two are done.)

1. 14 ones = _1_ ten _4_ ones

2. 1 ten 19 ones =
   _2_ tens _9_ ones

3. 1 ten 12 ones =
   _?_ tens _?_ ones

4. 2 tens 10 ones =
   _?_ tens _?_ ones

5. 4 tens 16 ones =
   _?_ tens _?_ ones

6. 3 tens 19 ones =
   _?_ tens _?_ ones

7. 2 tens 18 ones =
   _?_ tens _?_ ones

8. 6 tens 13 ones =
   _?_ tens _?_ ones

9. 5 tens 14 ones =
   _?_ tens _?_ ones

10. 1 ten 11 ones =
    _?_ tens _?_ one

61

3-3 Adding: Regrouping Once

Allison built a robot with 35 blocks.
Scott used 17 blocks to build his robot.
How many blocks did they use in all?

To find how many blocks,
add: 35 + 17 = ___?___

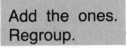
Add the ones.
Regroup. → 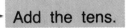 Add the tens.

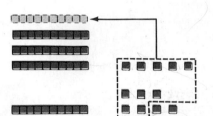

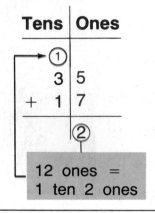

Tens	Ones
①	
3	5
+ 1	7
	②

12 ones =
1 ten 2 ones

Tens	Ones
1	
3	5
+ 1	7
5	2

Allison and Scott used
52 blocks in all.

Study these.

Tens	Ones
①	
2	3
+ 4	9
7	②

12 ones =
1 ten 2 ones

Tens	Ones
①	
3	6
+ 2	8
6	④

14 ones =
1 ten 4 ones

Tens	Ones
①	
5	1
+ 2	9
8	⓪

10 ones =
1 ten 0 ones

Complete.

1.
```
  1
  2 5
+ 5 9
  ? 4
```

2.
```
  1
  1 7
+ 2 4
  ? 1
```

3.
```
  1
  4 7
+   8
  ? ?
```

4.
```
  ?
  4 5
+ 3 7
  ? 2
```

5.
```
  ?
  6 1
+ 1 9
  ? 0
```

6.
```
  ?
  2 8
+ 4 2
  ? ?
```

Add. Regroup where needed.

7.	54	8.	38	9.	58	10.	33	11.	38	12.	78
	+26		+29		+31		+ 9		+24		+18

13.	87	14.	24	15.	34	16.	45	17.	23	18.	62
	+ 8		+66		+49		+19		+37		+24

19.	55	20.	29	21.	34	22.	26	23.	47	24.	59
	+28		+24		+ 8		+59		+32		+ 9

Line up and add.

25. 58 + 25		26. 35 + 42		27. 38 + 6	
28. 29 + 25		29. 69 + 27		30. 77 + 18	
31. 20 + 59		32. 19 + 3		33. 36 + 6	
34. 25 + 46		35. 47 + 33		36. 35 + 48	
37. 67 + 19		38. 45 + 45		39. 86 + 5	

Solve.

40. Scott added 25 blocks to his robot. His first robot had only 17 blocks. How many blocks did he use in all?

41. Andy built a rocket ship with 45 blocks. He used 39 blocks to build another one. How many blocks did he use in all?

42. Juanita built a moon home with 63 red blocks and 28 blue blocks. How many blocks did she use in all?

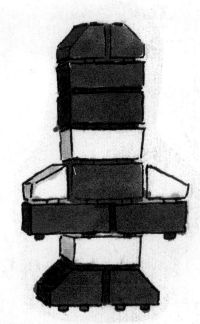

63

Regrouping Tens

Regroup: 2 hundreds 12 tens = _?_ hundreds _?_ tens

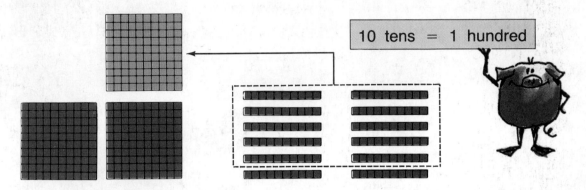

10 tens = 1 hundred

2 hundreds 12 tens = _3_ hundreds _2_ tens

Study these.

16 tens = 10 tens + 6 tens
      = 1 hundred 6 tens

20 tens = 10 tens + 10 tens
      = 1 hundred + 1 hundred
      = 2 hundreds

Regroup tens to make hundreds.

1. 18 tens =
   _?_ hundred _?_ tens

2. 14 tens =
   _?_ hundred _?_ tens

3. 13 tens =
   _?_ hundred _?_ tens

4. 16 tens =
   _?_ hundred _?_ tens

5. 7 hundreds 11 tens =
   _?_ hundreds _?_ ten

6. 4 hundreds 10 tens =
   _?_ hundreds _?_ tens

7. 6 hundreds 19 tens =
   _?_ hundreds _?_ tens

8. 3 hundreds 20 tens =
   _?_ hundreds _?_ tens

3-5 Adding: Regrouping Tens

Add: 58 + 71 = ?

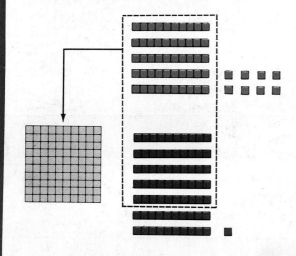

Add the ones. →	Add the tens. Regroup.

H	T	O
	5	8
+	7	1
		9

H	T	O
	5	8
+	7	1
①	②	9

12 tens =
1 hundred 2 tens

Complete.

1.

H	T	O
	6	4
+	7	3
1	3	?

2.

H	T	O
	5	1
+	9	6
1	?	?

3.

H	T	O
	8	4
+	7	5
?	5	?

4.

H	T	O
	9	0
+	8	7
?	?	?

Add.

5. 43 +72

6. 86 +50

7. 72 +71

8. 32 +97

9. 27 +81

10. 63 +95

11. 84 +84

12. 16 +83

13. 96 +21

14. 35 +84

15. 55 +71

16. 90 +46

17. 61 +88

18. 76 +92

19. 82 +45

20. 55 +32

21. 91 +63

22. 63 +84

Adding: Regrouping Twice

Mary has been saving pennies. She has 58 pennies in one bank and 74 pennies in another. How many pennies does she have in all?

To find how many pennies, add: 58 + 74 = __?__

Add the ones. Regroup. →	Add the tens. Regroup.		10 ones = 1 ten

10 ones = 1 ten
10 tens = 1 hundred

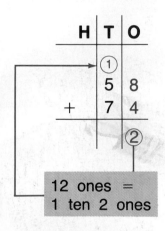

```
  H | T | O
      ①
      5   8
  +   7   4
          ②
```

12 ones = 1 ten 2 ones

```
  H | T | O
      1
      5   8
  +   7   4
  ① ③   2
```

13 tens = 1 hundred 3 tens

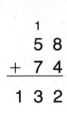

```
      1
      5 8
  +   7 4
  1 3 2
```

Mary has 132 pennies in all.

Complete.

	1.	2.	3.	4.	5.	6.
	1	1	1	1	?	?
	6 7	4 9	8 1	4 8	8 6	4 7
	+ 5 8	+ 7 5	+ 9 9	+ 5 2	+ 7 8	+ 8 3
	? ? 5	? ? 4	? ? 0	? 0 ?	? ? 4	? ? 0

	7.	8.	9.	10.	11.	12.
	65	56	83	76	99	49
	+99	+84	+67	+67	+86	+97

Find the sum.

| 13. | 69 +48 | 14. | 39 +61 | 15. | 43 +97 | 16. | 58 +39 | 17. | 75 +29 | 18. | 86 +17 |

| 19. | 39 +82 | 20. | 54 +64 | 21. | 79 +99 | 22. | 76 +45 | 23. | 27 +57 | 24. | 99 +33 |

| 25. | 63 +89 | 26. | 86 +87 | 27. | 67 +56 | 28. | 47 +62 | 29. | 82 +98 | 30. | 89 +98 |

Line up and add.

31. 16 + 99

32. 28 + 77

33. 43 + 88

34. 66 + 55

35. 44 + 86

36. 96 + 7

Solve.

37. Beth has 49 puffy stickers. She collected 79 more. How many stickers does Beth have in all?

38. Sarah picked 68 strawberries on Monday and 98 strawberries the next day. How many strawberries did she pick in all?

39. Jorge weighs 87 pounds and his friend Manny weighs 73 pounds. How many pounds do they weigh together?

··· CHALLENGE ··· ·

40. Karen and Clara want to collect 185 stamps. Karen has 87 and Clara has 95. Do they have enough stamps?

Adding Three-Digit Numbers: Regrouping Once

Ms. Brown is a mail carrier. She has 248 first class letters and 171 airmail letters. How many letters does she have in all?

To find how many letters, add: 248 + 171 = __?__

Add the ones.	Add the tens. Regroup.	Add the hundreds.

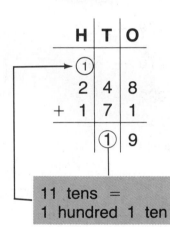

H	T	O
	2	4	8
+	1	7	1
			9

H	T	O
①		
2	4	8
+ 1	7	1
①	9

11 tens = 1 hundred 1 ten

H	T	O
1		
2	4	8
+ 1	7	1
4	1	9

Ms. Brown has 419 letters in all.

Complete.

1.
```
  1
  4 5 2
 +3 9 2
  ? 4 4
```

2.
```
    1
  2 6 5
 +3 1 8
  ? 8 ?
```

3.
```
  1
  1 8 7
 +1 6 2
  3 ? ?
```

4.
```
    1
  2 4 6
 +5 4 4
  ? ? 0
```

5.
```
    ?
  1 7 1
 +2 9 8
  ? ? 9
```

6.
```
  264
 +127
```

7.
```
  305
 +405
```

8.
```
  491
 +333
```

9.
```
  270
 +459
```

10.
```
  909
 + 56
```

Add and check. (The first one is done.)

11.
```
  1
  391  | Add        391  ↑ Check:
+ 464  ↓ down.     + 464  | add up.
  855               855
```

12.
```
  126
+ 126
```

13.
```
  246
+ 183
```

14.
```
  184
+ 725
```

15.
```
  192
+  42
```

16.
```
  526
+ 208
```

17.
```
  136
+  83
```

18.
```
  909
+  31
```

19.
```
  417
+ 319
```

20.
```
  293
+ 386
```

21.
```
  735
+  56
```

22.
```
  625
+   9
```

23.
```
  372
+ 255
```

Line up and add.

24. 677 + 151

25. 408 + 129

26. 281 + 181

27. 526 + 318

28. 776 + 52

29. 293 + 635

30. 117 + 192

31. 682 + 222

32. 24 + 566

33. 7 + 486

34. 82 + 470

35. 101 + 809

Solve.

36. At the post office Mr. Rossi bought 123 first class stamps and 95 airmail stamps. How many stamps did he buy?

37. Iyo has 578 stamps in one stamp album and 219 stamps in another album. How many stamps are in his collection?

38. Karen bought 91 stamps from Ms. Brown. Ms. Jett bought 126 stamps from her. How many stamps did Ms. Brown sell?

3-8 Adding Three-Digit Numbers: Regrouping More Than Once

Mr. Furey sold 657 morning newspapers and 267 evening newspapers. How many papers did he sell in all?

To find how many papers,
add: 657 + 267 = __?__

Add the ones. Regroup.	→	Add the tens. Regroup.	→	Add the hundreds.

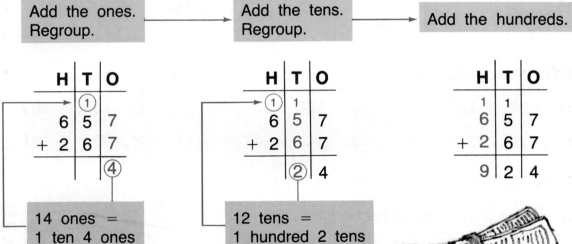

H	T	O
	①	
6	5	7
+ 2	6	7
		④

14 ones = 1 ten 4 ones

H	T	O
①	1	
6	5	7
+ 2	6	7
	②	4

12 tens = 1 hundred 2 tens

H	T	O
1	1	
6	5	7
+ 2	6	7
9	2	4

Mr. Furey sold 924 newspapers in all.

Complete.

1.
```
  1 1
  7 5 9
+ 1 8 9
  ? 4 8
```

2.
```
  1 1
  8 7 3
+   6 8
  ? 4 1
```

3.
```
  1 1
  4 2 7
+ 3 9 6
  ? 2 ?
```

4.
```
  1 1
  3 5 4
+ 4 5 6
  ? ? 0
```

5.
```
  ? 1
  6 2 9
+ 2 8 9
  ? 1 ?
```

6.
```
  ? ?
  5 2 4
+ 3 8 7
  ? ? 1
```

7.
```
  ? ?
  4 2 9
+ 2 9 5
  ? ? 4
```

8.
```
  ? ?
  3 2 4
+ 5 7 7
  ? 0 ?
```

9.
```
  ? ?
  6 0 5
+ 1 9 7
  8 ? ?
```

10.
```
  ? ?
  8 0 9
+   9 9
  9 ? ?
```

70

Find the sum.

11.	328 +295	12.	672 +285	13.	384 +357	14.	857 + 99	15.	386 +479
16.	753 +177	17.	419 +245	18.	178 + 12	19.	191 +609	20.	377 +333
21.	298 +518	22.	75 +546	23.	193 +755	24.	638 +293	25.	196 +106
26.	429 +496	27.	176 +327	28.	328 +183	29.	179 +209	30.	421 +189

Add and check.

31. 388 + 226   32. 686 + 224   33. 438 + 369

34. 884 + 47   35. 461 + 479   36. 729 + 181

Solve.

37. Mr. Furey sold 576 sports magazines in May and 325 in June. How many magazines did he sell in all?

38. The morning paper has 163 ads. The evening paper has 147. How many ads are there in all?

39. Ms. Gold ordered 183 papers for the sixth grade classes and 127 more for the fifth grade. How many newspapers did she order?

40. There are 497 history books and 47 science books in the school library. How many science or history books are there in all?

3-9 Mental Math

Study how to do these sums in your head.

Think: **Sums of ten**

```
  1
  1 8
  2 1        8 + 2 = 10
 +3 2        10 + 1 = 11
  ___
  7 1        11 = 1 ten 1 one
```

Think: **Addition facts and adding tens**

8 + 5 = 13 ⟶ So, 18 + 5 = 23 ⟶ 28 + 5 = 33 ⟶ 38 + 5 = 43

9 + 7 = 16 ⟶ So, 19 + 7 = 26 ⟶ 29 + 7 = 36 ⟶ 39 + 7 = 46

Think: **Changing the order and the grouping of the addends does not change the sum.**

```
37 + 4 = (30 + 7) + 4        26 + 45 = (20 + 6) + (40 + 5)
       = 30 + (7 + 4)                = (20 + 40) + (6 + 5)
       = 30 +     11                 =     60      +    11
       = 41                          = 71
```

Add mentally.

1.	2.	3.	4.	5.	6.
17	25	44	20	19	36
32	13	16	18	28	42
+23	+15	+14	+22	+21	+14

7. 19 + 9   8. 29 + 9   9. 39 + 9   10. 49 + 9

11. 5 + 56   12. 5 + 66   13. 5 + 76   14. 5 + 86

72

Regrouping Hundreds

Regroup: 1 thousand 13 hundreds = _?_ thousands _?_ hundreds

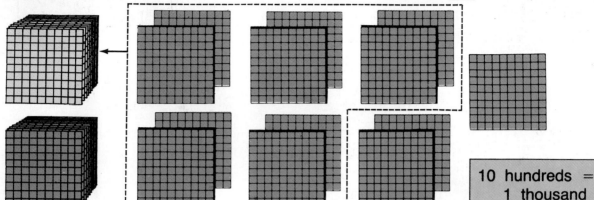

10 hundreds =
1 thousand

1 thousand 13 hundreds = _2_ thousands _3_ hundreds

Study these.

16 hundreds = 10 hundreds + 6 hundreds
       = 1 thousand 6 hundreds

20 hundreds = 10 hundreds + 10 hundreds
       = 1 thousand + 1 thousand
       = 2 thousands

Regroup hundreds to make more thousands.

1. 17 hundreds =
   _?_ thousand _?_ hundreds

2. 11 hundreds =
   _?_ thousand _?_ hundred

3. 14 hundreds =
   _?_ thousand _?_ hundreds

4. 18 hundreds =
   _?_ thousand _?_ hundreds

5. 2 thousands 13 hundreds =
   _?_ thousands _?_ hundreds

6. 7 thousands 15 hundreds =
   _?_ thousands _?_ hundreds

7. 6 thousands 26 hundreds =
   _?_ thousands _?_ hundreds

8. 4 thousands 44 hundreds =
   _?_ thousands _?_ hundreds

| 3-11 | **Three Addends With Regrouping** |

Jo's math book has 315 pages, her science book has 420 pages, and her reading book has 275 pages. How many pages are there in Jo's three books?

To find **how many pages in all,** add: **315 + 420 + 275 = ?**

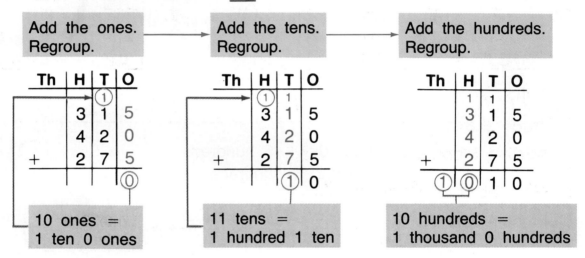

Add the ones. Regroup.

Th	H	T	O
	3	①	5
	4	2	0
+	2	7	5
			⓪

10 ones = 1 ten 0 ones

Add the tens. Regroup.

Th	H	T	O
	①	1	
	3	1	5
	4	2	0
+	2	7	5
		①	0

11 tens = 1 hundred 1 ten

Add the hundreds. Regroup.

Th	H	T	O
	1	1	
	3	1	5
	4	2	0
+	2	7	5
①	⓪	1	0

10 hundreds = 1 thousand 0 hundreds

There are 1010 pages in Jo's books.

Complete.

1.
```
  1
  3 7
  8 1
+ 2 9
1 ? 7
```

2.
```
1 1
1 2 5
  3 4
+   9 2
2 5 ?
```

3.
```
  1 ?
  2 5 0
    4 7
+ 1 9 9
  ? ? 6
```

4.
```
? ?
4 3 0
3 0 6
+ 1 6 9
? 0 ?
```

5.
```
      ?
  2 6 6
  6 8 0
+ 4 0 1
1 ? ? ?
```

Line up and add.

6. 26 + 17 + 38   7. 350 + 229 + 406   8. 77 + 325 + 9

74

Add and check.

9.
```
   182
   142
 + 125
```

10.
```
   416
   377
 + 186
```

11.
```
   335
   115
 + 206
```

12.
```
   933
   233
 + 155
```

13.
```
   284
   800
 + 491
```

14.
```
   143
   287
 + 651
```

15.
```
   134
   718
 +  79
```

16.
```
   325
   275
 + 350
```

17.
```
   213
   904
 + 492
```

18.
```
   175
    48
 + 200
```

19.
```
    82
   763
 + 385
```

20.
```
   530
   607
 +  73
```

21.
```
   415
   514
 + 145
```

22.
```
   385
   327
 + 358
```

23.
```
   463
   538
 +   7
```

Adding Money.

Add: $3.79 + $4.45 = ?

| Line up the dollars and cents. | → | Add as usual. | → | Write $ and . in the sum. |

```
   $ 3.7 9
   +  4.4 5
```

```
      1 1
   $ 3.7 9
   +  4.4 5
   ─────────
      8 2 4
```

```
      1 1
   $ 3.7 9
   +  4.4 5
   ─────────
   $ 8.2 4
```

Find the sum.

24.
```
  $1.54
 +  2.45
```

25.
```
  $3.62
 +  4.15
```

26.
```
  $4.60
 +  1.05
```

27.
```
  $8.07
 +   .12
```

28.
```
  $4.17
 +  5.34
```

29.
```
  $8.14
 +  1.87
```

30.
```
  $3.75
 +  6.56
```

31.
```
  $5.25
 +  6.75
```

32.
```
  $6.18
 +  4.25
```

33.
```
  $3.83
 +  9.78
```

3-12 Adding Four-Digit Numbers

A plant recycled 5928 tires one week and 2197 the next week. How many tires were recycled in all?

To find **how many tires,**
add: 5928 + 2197 = __?__

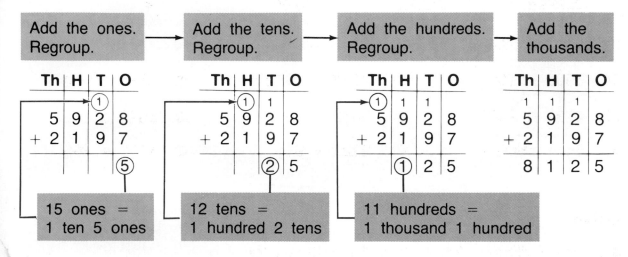

Add the ones. Regroup.	Add the tens. Regroup.	Add the hundreds. Regroup.	Add the thousands.
Th H T O ① 5 9 2 8 + 2 1 9 7 ⑤	Th H T O ① 1 5 9 2 8 + 2 1 9 7 ② 5	Th H T O ① 1 1 5 9 2 8 + 2 1 9 7 ① 2 5	Th H T O 1 1 1 5 9 2 8 + 2 1 9 7 8 1 2 5
15 ones = 1 ten 5 ones	12 tens = 1 hundred 2 tens	11 hundreds = 1 thousand 1 hundred	

8125 tires were recycled in all.

Add.

1.	2935 +4508	2.	4853 +3649	3.	8147 + 269	4.	1007 +6397	5.	3333 +1777
6.	6551 +2709	7.	1173 +5416	8.	848 +8152	9.	2126 +3929	10.	5555 +2555
11.	3784 +5247	12.	4062 +2076	13.	1647 +1843	14.	2399 + 606	15.	3784 +5247

Find the sum.

16.	5783 +1811	17.	4623 + 899	18.	7053 +1008	19.	4716 + 604	20.	7777 +1223
21.	6040 +2382	22.	3086 + 90	23.	519 +4986	24.	6081 +2019	25.	8080 +1030
26.	6379 +2669	27.	4056 +4157	28.	295 +5786	29.	6049 + 92	30.	8999 + 111

31. 2633 + 199   32. 87 + 1604   33. 401 + 3195

34. 5999 + 19   35. 4651 + 2123   36. 6153 + 1087

37. 4731 + 2422   38. 3452 + 1830   39. 5672 + 3333

40. 66 + 6666   41. 2222 + 99   42. 1111 + 899

Solve.

43. The Skillman School had 1074 labels for playground equipment. Another 2308 labels were donated. How many labels were there in all?

44. To assemble the equipment, 3148 3-inch bolts and 4616 5-inch bolts were used. How many bolts were used in all?

45. 3784 tires were collected for recycling in April and 4730 in May. How many tires were collected in all?

3-13 Estimating Sums

On Monday 44 students bought the hot lunch. The next day 28 students bought the hot lunch. *About* how many hot lunches were sold?

To find *about* how many, estimate the sum: 44 + 28 = ?

To estimate the sum:

Round the numbers.
Then add the rounded numbers.

Round to nearest ten.		Add.

$$\begin{array}{r} 4\,4 \\ +\ 2\,8 \end{array} \longrightarrow \begin{array}{r} 4\,0 \\ 3\,0 \end{array} \qquad \begin{array}{r} 4\,0 \\ +\ 3\,0 \\ \hline 7\,0 \end{array} \longleftarrow \text{Estimated sum}$$

About 70 hot lunches were sold.

Estimate each sum. First round each number to tens. Then add the rounded numbers.

1. 24
   +13

2. 42
   +49

3. 73
   +16

4. 58
   +34

5. 87
   +29

6. 38
   +21

7. 87
   +21

8. 74
   +11

9. 14
   +19

10. 25
    +29

11. 56
    +32

12. 75
    +17

13. 66
    +11

14. 48
    +29

15. 81
    +13

Estimate each sum. First round each number to hundreds. Then add. (The first one is done.)

16. $569 \longrightarrow 600$
    $\underline{+166} \longrightarrow \underline{+200}$
    $\qquad\qquad\quad 800$

17. 485
    $\underline{+179}$

18. 711
    $\underline{+210}$

19. 822
    $\underline{+113}$

20. 244
    $\underline{+716}$

21. 687
    $\underline{+245}$

22. 509
    $\underline{+419}$

23. 133
    $\underline{+288}$

24. 155
    $\underline{+772}$

Estimating Sums of Money

You can also estimate sums of money.

Estimate these sums:

$27 + $21 = \underline{\ ?\ }$

Round to nearest ten dollars. $\longrightarrow$ Add.

$\quad\ 27 \longrightarrow $30 \qquad 30
$+\ \ 21 \longrightarrow $20 \qquad \underline{+20}$
$\qquad\qquad\qquad\qquad\quad 50
$\qquad\qquad\qquad\qquad\quad \uparrow$
$\qquad\qquad\qquad$ Estimated sum

$4.99 + $1.19 = \underline{\ ?\ }$

Round to nearest dollar. $\longrightarrow$ Add.

$4.99 \longrightarrow $5 \qquad\quad 5
$+1.19 \longrightarrow $1 \qquad\quad \underline{+\ 1}$
$\qquad\qquad\qquad\qquad\quad 6
$\qquad\qquad\qquad\qquad\quad \uparrow$
$\qquad\qquad\qquad$ Estimated sum

Solve.

25. Mr. Robb bought a radio for $36 and some records for $12. *About* how much did he spend?

26. Peg bought a plant for $3.55 and a plant stand for $6.89. *About* how much did she spend?

3-14 Problem Solving: Use a Simpler Number

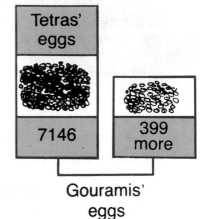

Tetras' eggs

7146

399 more

Gouramis' eggs

Problem: In one year all the neon tetras in Cathy's Creature Haven laid 7146 eggs. The gouramis laid 399 more eggs than the tetras. How many eggs did the gouramis lay?

1 IMAGINE

Draw and label a picture.

2 NAME

Facts: 7146 tetras' eggs
              399 more eggs, gouramis

Question: How many eggs did the gouramis lay?

3 THINK

Use simpler numbers like 6 and 2. Use 6 for 7146 and 2 for 399. Reread the problem using the simpler numbers.
Now think:
    If the tetras laid 6 eggs and the gouramis laid 2 more, how many eggs did the gouramis lay? 8
How did you get your answer?
    6 + 2 = number of gouramis' eggs
Now use the numbers given in the problem.
    7146 + 399 = __?__

4 COMPUTE

$$\begin{array}{r} {\scriptstyle 1\ 1} \\ 7\,1\,4\,6 \\ +\ \ \ 3\,9\,9 \\ \hline 7\,5\,4\,5 \end{array}$$ The gouramis laid 7545 eggs.

5 CHECK

Is 7545 greater than 7146? Yes. Your answer makes sense.

Solve by using simpler numbers like 6 and 2.

1. The Aquarium's fish tank has 4784 blue stones and 3945 red stones. How many stones are in the tank?

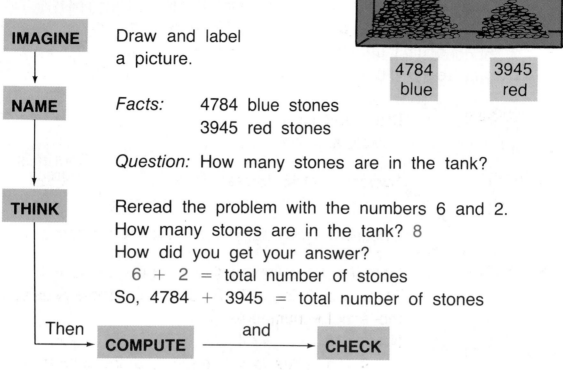

4784 blue

3945 red

IMAGINE — Draw and label a picture.

NAME — *Facts:* 4784 blue stones
3945 red stones

Question: How many stones are in the tank?

THINK — Reread the problem with the numbers 6 and 2.
How many stones are in the tank? 8
How did you get your answer?
  6 + 2 = total number of stones
So, 4784 + 3945 = total number of stones

Then **COMPUTE** and **CHECK**

2. At Hill School 8453 students have goldfish. Another 1396 have tropical fish. How many students have pet fish?

3. The pet store has 419 gouramis and 739 neon tetras. How many fish are there?

4. A shipment of 5144 cans of tuna fish and 6288 cans of codfish were delivered. How many cans were delivered?

5. One football player weighs 210 pounds. Another weighs 195 pounds. A third weighs 230 pounds. What do the three players weigh altogether?

More Practice

Complete.

1. 5 tens 11 ones =
    ? tens ? one

2. 3 tens 23 ones =
    ? tens ? ones

3. 19 tens =
    ? hundred ? tens

4. 30 tens =
    ? hundreds ? tens

5. 1 hundred 12 tens =
    ? hundreds ? tens

6. 4 hundreds 21 tens =
    ? hundreds ? ten

7. 11 hundreds =
    ? thousand ? hundred

8. 21 hundreds =
    ? thousands ? hundred

9. 2 thousands 13 hundreds =
    ? thousands ? hundreds

10. 1 thousand 15 hundreds =
    ? thousands ? hundreds

Add.

11. 28
    + 7

12. 43
    +28

13. 38
    +26

14. 46
    +69

15. 69
    +79

16. 254
    +661

17. 126
    + 59

18. 684
    +197

19. 304
     223
    +516

20. 295
     902
    + 89

21. $4.08
    + 7.92

22. $5.04
    + 9.68

23. 3053
    +1980

24. 1757
    +5648

25. 207
    +3899

Solve. Check by estimation.

26. At the orchard, Hani picked 88 apples, 106 peaches, and 71 pears. How many pieces of fruit did Hani pick?

27. Jerry stacked the fruit stand with 214 apples, 306 peaches, and 80 pears. How many pieces of fruit did he use?

(See *Still More Practice*, p. 357.)

Math-e-Magic

USING A CALCULATOR.
Look for these keys on your calculator.

ON	
OFF	→ A solar calculator does not have ON or OFF.
C	Clear. Start over.
+	Add.
−	Subtract.
=	Answer

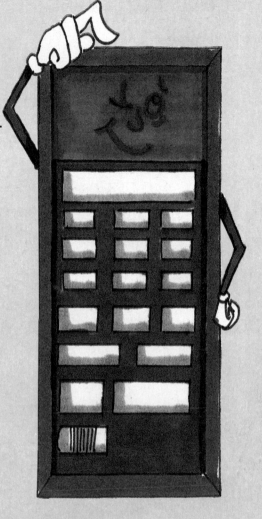

Add: 371 + 185 + 505 = __?__

Check your answer on your calculator.

Enter the numbers like this:

- Press the ON key.

- Press the C key to clear the calculator.

- Press the numbers 3, 7, 1.

- Press + to add.

- Press the numbers 1, 8, 5.

- Press + to add.

- Press the numbers 5, 0, 5.

- Press = for the sum. ←

Does your answer check?

- Press the C key to clear for another example.

Why could you enter + and get the same answer?

Find each sum on your calculator.

1.	4375	2.	5005	3.	9999	4.	3033	5.	9999
	9378		6179		8888		7777		999
	+4444		+3040		+7777		+6006		+ 99

Check Your Mastery

Complete.

See pp. 61, 64, 73

1a. 4 tens 16 ones =
    _?_ tens _?_ ones

1b. 8 tens 19 ones =
    _?_ tens _?_ ones

2a. 1 hundred 11 tens =
    _?_ hundreds _?_ ten

2b. 3 hundreds 15 tens =
    _?_ hundreds _?_ tens

3a. 13 hundreds =
    _?_ thousand _?_ hundreds

3b. 20 hundreds =
    _?_ thousands _?_ hundreds

4a. 3 thousands 18 hundreds =
    _?_ thousands _?_ hundreds

4b. 5 thousands 12 hundreds =
    _?_ thousands _?_ hundreds

Find the sum.

See pp. 62-63, 65, 66-71, 74-77

5.	6.	7.	8.	9.
78	57	62	46	19
+14	+82	+19	+69	+88

10.	11.	12.	13.	14.
162	284	661	425	216
+284	+547	+ 70	509	35
			+364	+755

15.	16.	17.	18.	19.
$5.56	$7.83	3691	2095	4527
+ 3.74	+ 9.98	+ 662	+6909	+ 398

Solve. Check by estimation.

See pp. 78-81

20. The zookeeper fed 317 animals one day. She fed 407 animals the next. How many animals did she feed in all?

84

4

Subtraction

In this unit you will:

- Regroup tens, hundreds, and thousands
- Subtract two-, three-, and four-digit numbers with regrouping
- Subtract money
- Check subtraction by addition
- Estimate differences
- Estimate money differences
- Read data from a map
- Solve problems by choosing addition or subtraction

Do you remember?

$$1 \text{ ten} = 10 \text{ ones}$$
$$1 \text{ hundred} = 10 \text{ tens}$$
$$1 \text{ thousand} = 10 \text{ hundreds}$$

So

$$4 \text{ tens} = \begin{array}{l} 3 \text{ tens} \\ 10 \text{ ones} \end{array}$$
$$4 \text{ hundreds} = \begin{array}{l} 3 \text{ hundreds} \\ 10 \text{ tens} \end{array}$$
$$4 \text{ thousands} = \begin{array}{l} 3 \text{ thousands} \\ 10 \text{ hundreds} \end{array}$$

4-1 Subtracting: No Regrouping

Warren had 39 strawberries. He ate 11 at lunch. How many strawberries does he have left?

To find how many are left, subtract: 39 − 11 = ?

Subtract the ones.	→	Subtract the tens.

Tens	Ones
3	9
− 1	1
	8

Tens	Ones
3	9
− 1	1
2	8

```
  3 9
− 1 1
  2 8
```

Warren has 28 strawberries left.

Subtract.

	T O		T O		T O		T O		T O		T O
1.	7 8 −2 6	**2.**	4 9 − 7	**3.**	9 7 −2 7	**4.**	5 6 −3 4	**5.**	8 7 − 4	**6.**	6 3 −1 0

7.	35 − 4	**8.**	37 −21	**9.**	84 −32	**10.**	29 − 6	**11.**	78 −52	**12.**	52 − 2
13.	68 −25	**14.**	98 −91	**15.**	89 −43	**16.**	99 −45	**17.**	57 −23	**18.**	68 −57

86

Subtracting Three-Digit Numbers

Subtract: 379 − 167 = ___?___

Subtract the ones.	→	Subtract the tens.	→	Subtract the hundreds.

H	T	O
3	7	**9**
− 1	6	**7**
		2

H	T	O
3	**7**	9
− 1	**6**	7
	1	2

H	T	O
3	7	9
− 1	6	7
2	1	2

379 − 167 = 212

Subtract.

19.
H	T	O
7	4	6
−	1	5

20.
H	T	O
8	7	4
−3	2	3

21.
H	T	O
5	8	6
−3	4	3

22.
H	T	O
9	5	8
−	2	6

23. 595
− 164

24. 475
− 304

25. 864
− 62

26. 296
− 240

27. 968
− 255

28. 263
− 42

29. 917
− 512

30. 257
− 43

31. 999
− 909

32. 551
− 51

Line up and subtract.

33. 38 − 17

34. 46 − 5

35. 87 − 30

36. 335 − 124

37. 675 − 55

38. 988 − 203

Solve.

39. There were 435 people at the concert in the park. When it was over, 224 people left. How many people remained?

Regrouping Tens to Ones

Regroup 1 ten as 10 ones.

Regroup: 1 ten 9 ones = _?_ ones

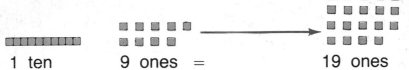

1 ten   9 ones =   19 ones

Study these.

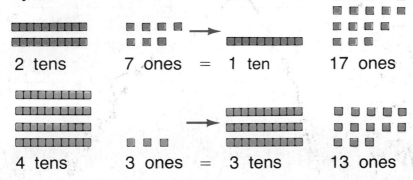

2 tens   7 ones = 1 ten   17 ones

4 tens   3 ones = 3 tens   13 ones

Complete. Regroup 1 ten as 10 ones. (The first one is done.)

1. 5 tens 3 ones =
   _4_ tens _13_ ones

2. 9 tens 4 ones =
   _?_ tens _?_ ones

3. 6 tens 5 ones =
   _?_ tens _?_ ones

4. 3 tens 2 ones =
   _?_ tens _?_ ones

5. 4 tens 9 ones =
   _?_ tens _?_ ones

6. 2 tens 7 ones =
   _?_ tens _?_ ones

7. 8 tens 8 ones =
   _?_ tens _?_ ones

8. 4 tens 0 ones =
   _?_ tens _?_ ones

9. 6 tens 0 ones =
   _?_ tens _?_ ones

10. 9 tens 9 ones =
   _?_ tens _?_ ones

11. 5 tens 5 ones =
   _?_ tens _?_ ones

12. 7 tens 0 ones =
   _?_ tens _?_ ones

4-3 Subtracting Two-Digit Numbers: Regrouping Once

Subtract: 53 − 24 = __?__

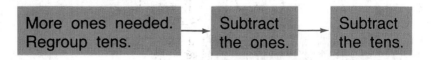

More ones needed. Regroup tens. → Subtract the ones. → Subtract the tens.

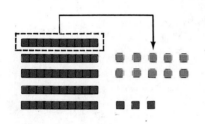

Tens	Ones
4	13
5̶	3̶
− 2	4

5 tens 3 ones = 4 tens 13 ones

Tens	Ones
4	13
5̶	3̶
− 2	4
	9

Tens	Ones
4	13
5̶	3̶
− 2	4
2	9

53 − 24 = 29

Subtract. Regroup where needed.

| 1. | 61 −23 | 2. | 42 −25 | 3. | 93 −49 | 4. | 55 −36 | 5. | 43 −20 | 6. | 83 −27 |

| 7. | 72 −43 | 8. | 69 −52 | 9. | 21 − 8 | 10. | 30 − 9 | 11. | 94 −57 | 12. | 42 −19 |

| 13. | 48 −29 | 14. | 56 −37 | 15. | 62 −58 | 16. | 97 −69 | 17. | 89 −25 | 18. | 90 −81 |

| 19. | 65 − 8 | 20. | 83 − 5 | 21. | 34 −29 | 22. | 48 −13 | 23. | 71 −26 | 24. | 92 −46 |

Regrouping Hundreds to Tens

Regroup: 2 hundreds 3 tens = __?__ hundred __?__ tens

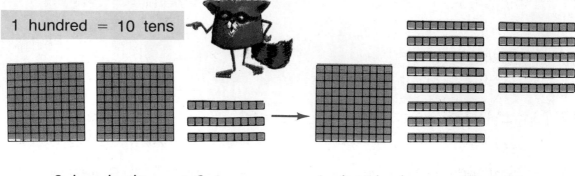

1 hundred = 10 tens

2 hundreds   3 tens   =   _1_ hundred   _13_ tens

Study these.

8 hundreds	5 hundreds 6 tens
= 7 hundreds + 1 hundred	= 4 hundreds + 1 hundred + 6 tens
= 7 hundreds + 10 tens	= 4 hundreds + 10 tens + 6 tens
= 7 hundreds 10 tens	= 4 hundreds + 16 tens
	= 4 hundreds 16 tens

Complete. Regroup 1 hundred as 10 tens. (The first one is done.)

1. 7 hundreds 7 tens =
   _6_ hundreds _17_ tens

2. 5 hundreds 1 ten =
   __?__ hundreds __?__ tens

3. 4 hundreds 8 tens =
   __?__ hundreds __?__ tens

4. 6 hundreds 6 tens =
   __?__ hundreds __?__ tens

5. 2 hundreds 8 tens =
   __?__ hundred __?__ tens

6. 3 hundreds 0 tens =
   __?__ hundreds __?__ tens

7. 8 hundreds 9 tens =
   __?__ hundreds __?__ tens

8. 9 hundreds 9 tens =
   __?__ hundreds __?__ tens

Regroup 1 hundred to make more tens.

9. 4 hundreds 1 ten =
   _?_ hundreds _?_ tens

10. 6 hundreds 8 tens =
    _?_ hundreds _?_ tens

11. 2 hundreds 4 tens =
    _?_ hundred _?_ tens

12. 5 hundreds 7 tens =
    _?_ hundreds _?_ tens

13. 9 hundreds 6 tens =
    _?_ hundreds _?_ tens

14. 7 hundreds 1 ten =
    _?_ hundreds _?_ tens

15. 8 hundreds 3 tens =
    _?_ hundreds _?_ tens

16. 3 hundreds 2 tens =
    _?_ hundreds _?_ tens

17. 5 hundreds 5 tens =
    _?_ hundreds _?_ tens

18. 9 hundreds 9 tens =
    _?_ hundreds _?_ tens

19. 1 hundred 3 tens =
    _?_ hundreds _?_ tens

20. 6 hundreds 0 tens =
    _?_ hundreds _?_ tens

··· CHALLENGE ···

Regroup 2 hundreds to make more tens. (The first one is done.)

21. 6 hundreds 0 tens =
    _5_ hundreds _10_ tens
    _4_ hundreds _20_ tens

22. 5 hundreds 1 ten
    _?_ hundreds _?_ tens
    _?_ hundreds _?_ tens

23. 2 hundreds 8 tens =
    _?_ hundred _?_ tens
    _?_ hundreds _?_ tens

24. 3 hundreds 9 tens =
    _?_ hundreds _?_ tens
    _?_ hundreds _?_ tens

25. 4 hundreds 0 tens =
    _?_ hundreds _?_ tens
    _?_ hundreds _?_ tens

Subtracting Three-Digit Numbers: Regrouping Once

A jumbo jet can seat 426 passengers. A smaller jet holds 165. How many more people can fly in the jumbo jet than in the smaller jet?

To find how many more people, subtract: 426 − 165 = __?__

Subtract the ones.	More tens needed. Regroup hundreds. Subtract the tens.	Subtract the hundreds.

H	T	O
4	2	**6**
− 1	6	**5**
		1

H	T	O
	³	¹²
4̶	2̶	6
− 1	6	5
	6	1

4 hundreds 2 tens =
3 hundreds 12 tens

H	T	O
	³	¹²
4̶	2̶	6
− 1	6	5
2	6	1

261 more people can fly in the jumbo jet.

Complete.

1.
```
  ? 11
  8̶ 1̶ 9
 −1 7 5
  ? ? 4
```

2.
```
  6 ?
  7̶ 5̶ 7
 − 2 8 3
  ? 7 ?
```

3.
```
    ? 12
  2 9̶ 2̶
 − 1 2 7
  ? 6 ?
```

4.
```
  ? ?
  4̶ 5̶ 8
 −  9 7
  ? 6 ?
```

5.
```
    ? ?
  5 8̶ 1̶
 − 3 2 9
  2 ? ?
```

6.
```
  464
 −391
```

7.
```
  858
 −149
```

8.
```
  759
 −376
```

9.
```
  680
 −217
```

10.
```
  909
 −222
```

Subtract.

11. 446
    −256

12. 186
    − 78

13. 839
    −449

14. 214
    −122

15. 928
    −709

16. 692
    −288

17. 555
    −473

18. 139
    − 69

19. 319
    −175

20. 659
    −289

21. 774
    − 26

22. 302
    −161

23. 293
    −125

24. 678
    −484

25. 912
    −107

Line up and subtract.

26. 377 − 108

27. 109 − 65

28. 752 − 647

29. 555 − 464

30. 888 − 607

31. 879 − 93

Solve.

32. When a jumbo jet landed at Busy Airport, 292 of its 465 passengers got off the plane. How many people did not get off?

33. During one week, 337 small jets and 94 jumbo jets took off from Busy Airport. How many more smaller jets took off than jumbo jets?

Calculator Activity

Use a calculator to complete these number sentences, using only 565, 371, 253, 166.

34. __?__ − __?__ = 118

35. __?__ − __?__ = 194

36. __?__ − __?__ = 205

93

Subtracting Three-Digit Numbers Regrouping Twice

A polar bear weighs 624 pounds and a black bear weighs 446 pounds. How many more pounds does the polar bear weigh?

To find how many more pounds, subtract: 624 − 446 = ?

More ones needed. Regroup tens. Subtract the ones.	More tens needed. Regroup hundreds. Subtract the tens.	Subtract the hundreds.

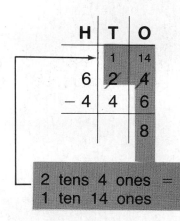

	H	T	O
		1	14
	6	2̸	4̸
−	4	4	6
			8

2 tens 4 ones = 1 ten 14 ones

	H	T	O
	5	11	14
	6̸	2̸	4̸
−	4	4	6
		7	8

6 hundreds 1 ten = 5 hundreds 11 tens

	H	T	O
	5	11	14
	6̸	2̸	4̸
−	4	4	6
	1	7	8

The polar bear weighs 178 pounds more than the black bear.

Complete.

1.
```
        15
    3  5  13
    4̸ 6̸ 3̸
  − 1  6  5
    ?  ?  8
```

2.
```
        16
    8  6̸ 15
    9̸ 7̸ 5̸
  − 3  9  8
    ?  ?  ?
```

3.
```
        13
    5  3̸  ?
    6̸ 4̸ 0̸
  − 2  8  2
    ?  ?  ?
```

4.
```
     ?  ?
    2̸ ? ?
  − 1  0  7
    ?  ?  4
```

5.
```
        ?
     ?  ?  ?
    4̸ 5̸ 8̸
  −    8  9
    ?  ?  ?
```

Find the difference. Use a calculator to check your answers.

6. 587
  −468
	7. 260
	  − 75
		8. 317
		  − 99
			9. 523
			  −237
				10. 781
				  −372

11. 324
  −165
	12. 864
	  −375
		13. 457
		  −236
			14. 636
			  −478
				15. 743
				  −686

16. 536
  −187
	17. 473
	  −294
		18. 660
		  −351
			19. 423
			  −234
				20. 715
				  −236

Subtracting Money

Subtract: $8.53 − $2.65 = __?__

Line up the dollars and cents.	→	Subtract as usual.	→	Write $ and . in the difference.

$$\begin{array}{r} \$\ 8.5\ 3 \\ -\ \ 2.6\ 5 \\ \hline \end{array}$$

$$\begin{array}{r} {\scriptstyle 14} \\ {\scriptstyle 7\ \ 4\ \ 13} \\ \$\ 8.5\ 3 \\ -\ \ 2.6\ 5 \\ \hline 5\ 8\ 8 \end{array}$$

$$\begin{array}{r} {\scriptstyle 14} \\ {\scriptstyle 7\ \ 4\ \ 13} \\ \$\ 8.5\ 3 \\ -\ \ 2.6\ 5 \\ \hline \$\ 5.8\ 8 \end{array}$$

Find the difference.

21. $5.65
  − 1.27
	22. $9.90
	  − 6.72
		23. $8.09
		  − 7.85
			24. $6.94
			  − 2.27
				25. $4.59
				  − 1.87

26. $9.36
  − 2.49
	27. $7.47
	  − 1.79
		28. $6.40
		  − 3.37
			29. $8.15
			  − 3.94
				30. $5.62
				  − 4.74

Subtracting Three-Digit Numbers: Regrouping With Zeros

A music store has 400 cassette tapes on sale. During the sale, 258 tapes were sold. How many tapes were not sold?

More ones needed. More tens needed. Regroup hundreds.	→	Regroup tens.	→	Subtract.

More ones needed. More tens needed. Regroup hundreds.

```
   H   T   O
   3  10
   4/  0/  0
 - 2   5   8
```

4 hundreds =
3 hundreds 10 tens

Regroup tens.

```
       9
   3  10  10
   4/  0/  0/
 - 2   5   8
```

10 tens =
9 tens 10 ones

Subtract.

```
       9
   3  10  10
   4/  0/  0/
 - 2   5   8
   1   4   2
```

There were 142 cassette tapes left after the sale.

Complete. (The first one is done.)

```
            9
        5  10  10
1.  $ 6/ . 0/  0/
   -   4 . 2 8
    $ 1 . 7 2
```

```
        9
    4  10  10
2.  5/  0/  0/
  - 3   1  5
    ?   ?  5
```

```
        9
    1  10  10
3.  2/  0/  0/
  - 1   8  2
    ?   ?
```

```
            ?
        ?  10  ?
4.  $ 8/ . 0/  1/
   -   2 . 2 2
    $ ? . ? ?
```

Subtract.

5.	6.	7.	8.	9.
800 −273	400 −186	900 −367	500 −485	100 − 27

10.	11.	12.	13.	14.
603 −248	880 −191	208 − 67	902 −895	330 − 28

15.	16.	17.	18.	19.
$6.00 − 3.33	$4.03 − 3.43	$7.07 − 1.09	$3.00 − 1.06	$8.00 − 5.75

Line up and subtract.

20. 900 − 52   **21.** 307 − 103   **22.** 610 − 512

23. 107 − 98   **24.** 800 − 107   **25.** 627 − 405

Solve.

26. In October, 207 radios were sold at the music store. In December, 500 radios were sold. How many more radios were sold in December?

27. There are 168 hours in a week. The music store is open for 77 hours each week. How many hours of each week is the store closed?

28. For the sale, the music store ordered 300 Read and Listen Books. 198 were sold during the sale. How many books were not sold?

4-8 Checking Subtraction

To check subtraction, add the number that was subtracted to the difference.

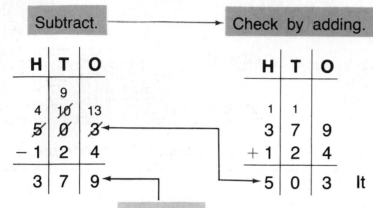

Subtract. ⟶ Check by adding.

H	T	O
	9	
4	1̶0̶	13
5̶	0̶	3̶
− 1	2	4
3	7	9

difference

H	T	O
1	1	
3	7	9
+ 1	2	4
5	0	3

It checks.

Subtract and check.

1. 543 −438	**2.** 619 −127	**3.** 305 −217	**4.** 800 −526	**5.** 498 −199

6. 472 −194	**7.** 452 −381	**8.** 978 −364	**9.** $8.04 − 2.76	**10.** $5.10 − 1.92

Check each answer.
If it is wrong, find the correct answer.

11. 772 −274 502	**12.** 810 −583 233	**13.** 258 −167 81	**14.** 946 −582 364	**15.** 500 −498 2

16. 607 −482 125	**17.** 234 − 83 262	**18.** $4.01 − 3.31 $ .70	**19.** $1.78 − 1.29 $ .51	**20.** $6.66 − 5.73 $1.93

98

Regrouping Thousands to Hundreds

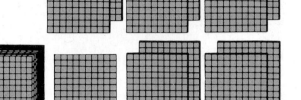

1 thousand =
10 hundreds

Regroup: 2 thousands 1 hundred =
_?_ thousand _?_ hundreds

2 thousands 1 hundred   =   1 thousand 11 hundreds

Study these.

4 thousands = 3 thousands + 1 thousand
= 3 thousands + 10 hundreds
= 3 thousands 10 hundreds

6 thousands 3 hundreds = 5 thousands + 1 thousand + 3 hundreds
= 5 thousands + 10 hundreds + 3 hundreds
= 5 thousands 13 hundreds

Complete. Regroup 1 thousand as 10 hundreds.

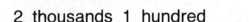

1. 5 thousands 8 hundreds = _?_ thousands _?_ hundreds

2. 8 thousands 2 hundreds = _?_ thousands _?_ hundreds

3. 3 thousands 9 hundreds = _?_ thousands _?_ hundreds

4. 7 thousands 6 hundreds = _?_ thousands _?_ hundreds

5. 9 thousands 0 hundreds = _?_ thousands _?_ hundreds

6. 1 thousand 9 hundreds = _?_ thousands _?_ hundreds

7. 6 thousands 6 hundreds = _?_ thousands _?_ hundreds

8. 2 thousands 0 hundreds = _?_ thousands _?_ hundreds

4-10 Subtracting Four-Digit Numbers

The Lodi Hardware Store has 8010 brass tacks and 6983 stainless steel tacks. How many more brass tacks are in stock?

To find how many more brass tacks, subtract: 8010 − 6983 = ?

| Regroup tens. Subtract ones. | → | Regroup thousands. Regroup hundreds. Subtract tens. | → | Subtract hundreds. | → | Subtract thousands. |

Th	H	T	O
		0	10
8	0	1̸	0̸
− 6	9	8	3
			7

1 ten =
0 tens 10 ones

Th	H	T	O
	9	10	
7	10	0̸	10
8̸	0̸	1̸	0̸
− 6	9	8	3
		2	7

8 thousands =
7 thousands 10 hundreds =
7 thousands 9 hundreds 10 tens

Th	H	T	O
	9	10	
7	10	0̸	10
8̸	0̸	1̸	0̸
− 6	9	8	3
	0	2	7

Th	H	T	O
	9	10	
7	10	0̸	10
8̸	0̸	1̸	0̸
− 6	9	8	3
1	0	2	7

There are 1027 more brass tacks in stock.

Subtract.

1.	2.	3.	4.	5.
6050	2573	9561	5386	7006
−4967	−1259	−4715	− 997	−1543

100

Find the difference.

6.	5190	7.	2222	8.	3014	9.	7159	10.	5483
	−4738		− 68		− 314		−6037		−2007

11.	8616	12.	4318	13.	1700	14.	7008	15.	4040
	−1208		−3318		−1507		−5009		− 594

Subtract and check. (The first one is done.)

16.	4600	2193	17.	3535	18.	8784	19.	9001
	−2407	+2407		− 416		−1935		−4090
	2193	4600						

20.	$74.19	21.	$60.87	22.	$74.93	23.	$90.00	24.	$60.06
	− .27		− 54.89		− 63.82		− 57.03		− 46.77

Solve.

25. The hardware store had 1300 gallons of paint in stock. In May, 863 gallons were sold. How many gallons were left?

26. There are 2540 centimeters of tape on a roll of masking tape. Plastic tape has 1270 centimeters on each roll. How much more masking tape is on a roll?

27. In two flights, the space shuttle Quest I traveled 353,672 kilometers. On its first trip it traveled 157,350 kilometers. How many kilometers was the second trip?

28. It is 432,017 kilometers to the far side of the moon. It is 428,173 kilometers to the near side. What is the difference?

CHALLENGE

4-11 Estimating Differences

A restaurant served 65 spinach salads and 34 tossed salads. About how many more spinach salads were served than tossed salads?

To find *about* how many more, estimate the difference: 65 − 34 = _?_ .

To estimate the difference:

Round the numbers.
Then subtract.

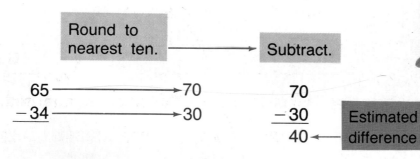

Round to nearest ten. → Subtract.

$$65 \longrightarrow 70 \qquad 70$$
$$-34 \longrightarrow 30 \qquad -30$$
$$ 40 \leftarrow \text{Estimated difference}$$

About 40 more spinach salads were served.

Estimate each difference. First round each number to the nearest ten. Then subtract.

1. 78 − 56	**2.** 21 − 12	**3.** 64 − 48	**4.** 55 − 16	**5.** 94 − 35	**6.** 88 − 66
7. 67 − 47	**8.** 39 − 12	**9.** 71 − 16	**10.** 88 − 63	**11.** 45 − 9	**12.** 75 − 24
13. 85 − 41	**14.** 52 − 14	**15.** 76 − 24	**16.** 58 − 19	**17.** 93 − 37	**18.** 66 − 64

Estimating With Larger Numbers

Study these examples.

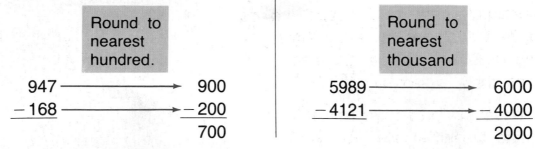

Round to nearest hundred.		Round to nearest thousand	
947 ⟶	900	5989 ⟶	6000
−168 ⟶	−200	−4121 ⟶	−4000
	700		2000

You can also estimate differences with money.

Round to nearest ten dollars.		Round to nearest dollar.	
$76 ⟶	$80	$9.89 ⟶	$10
− 23	− 20	− 6.23 ⟶	− 6
	$60		$ 4

Estimate each difference. First round to the nearest hundred.

19.	674	20.	803	21.	941	22.	736	23.	457
	−211		−587		−639		−284		−176

Estimate each difference. First round to the nearest thousand.

24.	8346	25.	5432	26.	8888	27.	5718	28.	1863
	−6794		−2345		−4444		−2662		− 893

Solve.

29. A restaurant began Monday morning with 427 eggs. By 11 A.M., 135 eggs were left. *About* how many eggs were served?

30. Rosa wants to buy a record that costs $8.79. She has $5.36. *About* how much more money does she need?

4-12 Problem Solving: Add or Subtract?

Addition: Join or put together sets or groups of objects.
How many in all?
How many altogether?

Subtraction: Separate or take away from a set or group of objects.
How many are left?
Compare.
How many more are there?

Problem: There are 43 boys and 29 girls in the pool. How many children are swimming in all?

```
bbbbb   ggggg
bbbbb   ggggg
bbbbb   ggggg
bbbbb   ggggg
bbbbb   ggggg
bbbbb   gggg
bbbbb   ‿‿‿
bbbbb   29 girls
bbb
‿‿‿
43 boys
```

1 IMAGINE
Draw and label a picture of the problem.

2 NAME
Facts: 43 boys
           29 girls

Question: How many children are there in all?

3 THINK
Look at the picture.
What are you doing? Joining 2 groups.
What do you do, add or subtract? Add.

4 COMPUTE
$$\begin{array}{r} {}^{1}\;\; \\ 43 \\ +29 \\ \hline 72 \end{array}$$
There were 72 children in the pool in all.

5 CHECK
Look at the picture and count all the children.

Solve by addition or subtraction.

1. How many more boys than girls are in the pool?

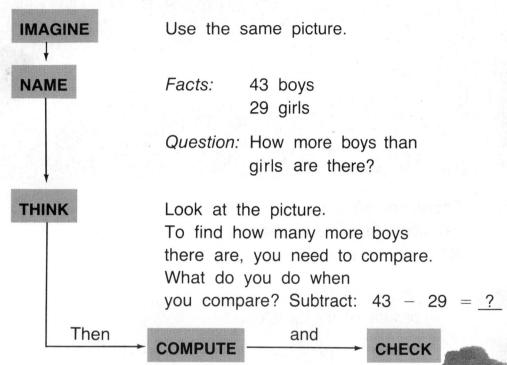

IMAGINE   Use the same picture.

NAME   *Facts:*   43 boys
29 girls

Question: How more boys than
girls are there?

THINK   Look at the picture.
To find how many more boys
there are, you need to compare.
What do you do when
you compare? Subtract: $43 - 29 = $ _?_

Then   ➜   **COMPUTE**   and   ➜   **CHECK**

2. Allie must read 173 pages to be in the Bookworm Club. She has already read 96 pages. How many more pages must she read?

3. At a toll gate, 114 tolls are collected in the morning on the first day and 198 tolls in the afternoon. How many tolls are collected in all?

4. A sea horse measures 13 cm. A catfish measures 71 cm. How much longer is the catfish?

5. The Mazzoni's drive 621 miles on vacation. They drive 319 miles. How far do they still have to drive?

More Practice

Complete. (The first one is done.)

1. 3 tens 5 ones =
   <u>2</u> tens <u>15</u> ones

2. 8 tens 1 one =
   <u>?</u> tens <u>?</u> ones

3. 2 hundreds 4 tens =
   <u>?</u> hundred <u>?</u> tens

4. 5 hundreds 4 tens =
   <u>?</u> hundreds <u>?</u> tens

5. 4 hundreds 0 tens =
   <u>?</u> hundreds <u>?</u> tens

6. 1 hundred 2 tens =
   <u>?</u> hundreds <u>?</u> tens

7. 6 thousands =
   <u>?</u> thousands <u>?</u> hundreds

8. 2 thousands =
   <u>?</u> thousands <u>?</u> hundreds

9. 7 thousands 3 hundreds =
   <u>?</u> thousands <u>?</u> hundreds

10. 9 thousands 0 hundreds =
    <u>?</u> thousands <u>?</u> hundreds

Find the difference.

11.	12.	13.	14.	15.
43 −16	76 −29	418 −372	742 −592	652 −343

16.	17.	18.	19.	20.
913 −865	500 −485	531 −218	$4.48 − 1.69	$7.07 − 4.99

Subtract and check.

21.	22.	23.	24.	25.
8341 −2858	6007 −4030	7000 −2425	$70.46 − 24.79	$51.05 − 13.48

Solve. Check by estimating the difference.

26. A gas station had 283 customers on Monday. In the morning 154 people bought gas. How many people bought gas in the afternoon?

(See *Still More Practice*, p. 358.)

Math-e-Magic

READING A MAP

A flock of Canadian geese are traveling to
Bird Beach from Webfoot. Use a calculator
to help Gus plan their trip.

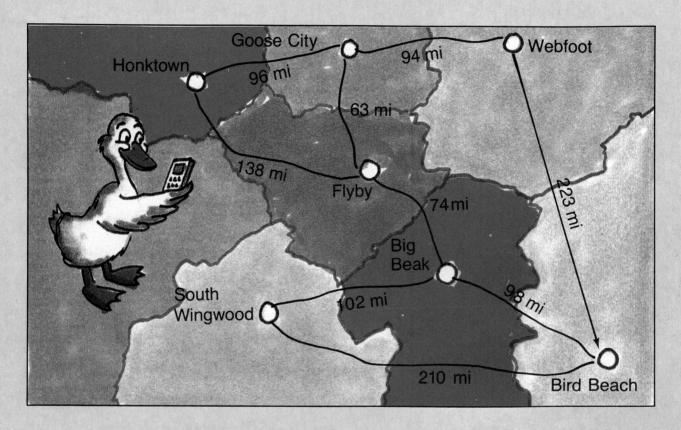

1. The geese want to sightsee in *only* three cities
   before they get to Bird Beach. What cities
   should they visit and how far will they travel?

2. If the flock visits every city on the map, how
   far will they fly?

3. How many miles less would it be to fly
   directly to Bird Beach

Check Your Mastery

Complete.

See pp. 88, 90-91, 99

1a. 2 tens 8 ones =
  ? ten ? ones

1b. 6 tens 5 ones =
  ? tens ? ones

2a. 1 hundred 1 ten =
  ? hundreds ? tens

2b. 9 hundreds 4 tens =
  ? hundreds ? tens

3a. 7 hundreds 2 tens =
  ? hundreds ? tens

3b. 3 hundreds 0 tens =
  ? hundreds ? tens

4a. 1 thousand 0 hundreds =
  ? thousands ? hundreds

4b. 7 thousand 1 hundred =
  ? thousands ? hundreds

Subtract and check.

See pp 86-87, 89, 92-98, 100-101

5.	**6.**	**7.**	**8.**	**9.**
98	43	74	91	86
−46	−15	−66	−36	−27

10.	**11.**	**12.**	**13.**	**14.**
925	876	857	$6.12	$7.03
−302	−419	−377	− 2.35	− 2.97

15.	**16.**	**17.**	**18.**	**19.**
2158	6154	5005	$40.41	$63.02
− 789	−4327	−2168	− 19.50	− 34.77

Estimate the difference.

See pp. 102-103

20.	**21.**	**22.**	**23.**	**24.**
73	557	$8.99	6709	8499
−26	−252	− 6.47	−3442	−1811

Solve.

See pp. 104-105

25. Of 1307 tickets sold for the circus, 476 were adult tickets. How many children's tickets were sold?

Cumulative Test I

Find the sum.

| 1. | 6
 +4 | 2. | 8
 +7 | 3. | 65
 +11 | 4. | 13
 +46 | 5. | 39
 +73 |

| 6. | 123
 +321 | 7. | 857
 +725 | 8. | 427
 +352 | 9. | 353
 +209 | 10. | 651
 +149 |

Find the difference.

| 11. | 8
 −5 | 12. | 17
 − 8 | 13. | 14
 − 6 | 14. | 29
 −13 | 15. | 73
 −16 |

| 16. | 129
 −108 | 17. | 453
 −224 | 18. | 725
 −382 | 19. | 698
 −499 | 20. | 800
 −547 |

Find the sum.

| 21. | 5
 1
 4
 +3 | 22. | 4
 2
 3
 +4 | 23. | 5
 6
 3
 +1 | 24. | 6
 2
 0
 +5 | 25. | 7
 4
 2
 +6 |

Compare. Write <, =, or >.

26. 43 ? 49   27. 47 ? 54   28. 254 ? 782

29. 1752 ? 2925   30. 351 ? 351   31. 9628 ? 7930

Round to the nearest ten.

32. 85   33. 43   34. 12   35. 39

Round to the nearest hundred.

36. 456   37. 841   38. 327   39. 438

Round to the nearest dollar.

40. $7.26   41. $8.75   42. $2.54   43. $9.50

Write the standard number.

44. forty-five = __?__

45. 3000 + 700 + 80 + 9 = __?__

46. 900 + 30 + 6 = __?__

47. 4 hundreds 2 tens 5 ones = __?__

48. two hundred thousands = __?__

49. 4 thousands 6 tens = __?__

Find the missing number.

50. 85, 86, __?__

51. __?__, 4583, 4584

52. 7514, 7516, __?__

53. __?__, 650, 652

54. 3756, 3759, __?__

55. 9623, __?__, 9629

56. __?__, 792, 796

57. 2835, 2840, __?__

58. 8972, 8982, __?__

Write.

59. the odd numbers between 19 and 30.
__?__, __?__, __?__, __?__, __?__

60. the ninth letter of the alphabet.

61. the even numbers between 4 and 13.
__?__, __?__, __?__, __?__

62. the third letter in your first name.

Find the sum.

63.
366
580
+401

64.
325
77
+291

65.
126
217
+ 38

66.
415
514
+145

67.
143
651
+287

Solve.

68. Jaime had 329 baseball cards. He gave away 131 cards. How many cards does he have left?

69. Lance wants to buy a puzzle for $2.50, a ball for $1.99, and a pack of football cards for $.47. About how much money will Lance spend?

70. The Adams School has 272 students. The Williams School has 318 students. How many students are in the two schools?

71. There were 545 people at the fireworks display. When it was over, 224 people left. How many remained?

72. Steve has 578 shells in his collection. His sister Joan has 349. How many more shells does Steve have than Joan?

73. Josie has 59 raisins, Rico has 63, and Julio has 65. How many raisins do they have in all?

74. Julio picked 129 strawberries on Thursday and 96 more on Friday. How many strawberries did he pick in the two days?

75. Dolly made 374 stuffed animals for the gift shop. If 248 of them were sold, about how many stuffed animals still remained to be sold?

5

Time and Money

1 balloon costs $1.50.

In this unit you will:

- Tell time by the hour, half hour, and quarter hour
- Use both A.M. and P.M. time
- Read minutes before and after the hour
- Read a calendar
- Use money from a penny to ten dollars
- Make change
- Add and subtract money
- Estimate with dollars and cents
- Solve problems in which not enough information is given

Do you remember?

3 o'clock

A clock has two hands. The long hand tells the minutes. The short hand tells the hour. Every hour has 60 minutes.

Hour, Half Hour, and Quarter Hour

The short hand tells the hour. The long hand tells how many minutes.

There are 60 minutes in an hour.

    It is two o'clock.

2:00

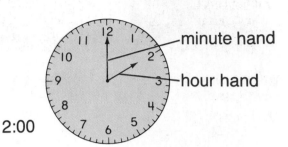

There are 30 minutes in a half hour.

    It is two thirty.

2:30

There are 15 minutes in a quarter hour.

    It is two fifteen.

2:15

It is a quarter to three
or
two forty-five.

2:45

Read the time.

1.

2.

3.

4.

5.

6.

Digital clocks show time this way.

Write the time as it shows on a digital clock. (The first one is done.)

7.

11 : 00

8.

? : ?

9.

? : ?

10.

? : ?

Draw the time on a clock face. Show both hands.

11.

12.

13.

14.

A.M. and P.M.

A.M. means the time after 12:00 midnight and before 12:00 noon.

P.M. means the time after 12:00 noon and before 12:00 midnight.

Solve.

15. Mrs. Watkins started packing for the family vacation at 3:00 P.M.. She finished at 6:00 P.M.. How long did it take her?

Challenge!

16. Mr. Watkins is two hours away from Highway 75. It is 11:30 A.M. now. What time will he reach the highway?

Minutes

It takes five minutes for the minute hand to move from one number to the next.
It is 5 minutes after 10.

or

It is 5 minutes past 10.

10:05

It is 24 minutes before 11.

or

It is 36 minutes after 10.

10:36

Write the time. (The first one is done.)

1.

<u>15</u> minutes after <u>12</u>
<u>45</u> minutes before <u>1</u>

2.

<u>?</u> minutes after <u>?</u>
<u>?</u> minutes before <u>?</u>

3.

<u>?</u> minutes after <u>?</u>
<u>?</u> minutes before <u>?</u>

4.

<u>?</u> minutes after <u>?</u>
<u>?</u> minutes before <u>?</u>

5.

<u>?</u> minutes after <u>?</u>
<u>?</u> minutes before <u>?</u>

6.

<u>?</u> minutes after <u>?</u>
<u>?</u> minutes before <u>?</u>

Write the time another way. (The first one is done.)

7. 25 minutes before 9
<u>8</u> : <u>35</u>

8. 53 minutes past 2
<u>?</u> : <u>?</u>

9. 3 minutes after 3
<u>?</u> : <u>?</u>

10. 1 minute before 10
<u>?</u> : <u>?</u>

11. 40 minutes past 5
<u>?</u> : <u>?</u>

12. 37 minutes after 7
<u>?</u> : <u>?</u>

13. 12 minutes before 1
<u>?</u> : <u>?</u>

14. 22 minutes before 8
<u>?</u> : <u>?</u>

Draw the time on a clock face. Show both hands.

15. 1:30   **16.** 4:10   **17.** 6:53   **18.** 5:16

19. 3:41   **20.** 8:27   **21.** 11:59   **22.** 12:32

How long does it take to go from:

23. Orlando to Rockford?

24. Rockford to Maywood?

25. Maywood to Bay City?

26. Orlando to Maywood?

27. Rockford to Bay City?

28. Orlando to Bay City?

TIMETABLE	
City	Arrives
Orlando	9:45
Rockford	10:55
Maywood	11:35
Bay City	12:00

5-3 Calendar

This is a calendar for November in the year 2000.

NOVEMBER						
S	M	T	W	Th	F	S
			1	2	3	4
5	6	7	8	9	10	11
12	13	14	15	16	17	18
19	20	21	22	23	24	25
26	27	28	29	30		

 Election day   Thanksgiving day

There are 12 months in a year.
There are usually 365 days in a year.
In a **leap year** there are 366 days.
February then has 29 days.

Look at the dates and days of the week.

There are ? days in November.
There are ? full weeks.

The first Thursday is what day?
Look under Th. See the 2.

Complete.

1. Each year has ____ months.

2. Usually every year has ____ days.

3. Leap year has ____ days.

4. Every week has ____ days.

5. Name the weekdays that begin with "T."

Complete the rhyme about the months of the year.

6. 30 days has September,
   April, June and ____?____
   All the rest have 31
   Except February that has ?
   Except in leap year that has 29.

116

Use your November 2000 calendar to answer each question.

8. Give the day of the week for:
   a. November 21   **b.** November 12th   **c.** November sixth

   d. Election day   **e.** the first day of Nov.   **f.** the last day of Nov.

9. Which Sunday of the month is November 26?

10. Give the date in November for:
   a. the first Saturday   **b.** the last Saturday

   c. the 5th Wednesday   **d.** the last day

   e. the 4th Monday   **f.** the 3rd Tuesday

   g. the 4th day of the   **h.** the day before
   3rd week   Thanksgiving

11. What day of the week is December 1, 2000?

Solve.

12. Which month of every year is the:
   a. third?   **b.** seventh?   **c.** twelfth?

13. Which months have 30 days?

14. Which months have 31 days?

15. Which month has the fewest number of days?

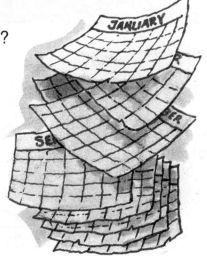

Money Less Than $1.00

| 1¢ | 5¢ | 10¢ | 25¢ | 50¢ |
| $.01 | $.05 | $.10 | $.25 | $.50 |

Complete the chart. Show how much money. (The first two are done.)

	Coin	Value	Use ¢	Use $ and .
1.	penny	1 cent	1¢	$.01
2.	nickel	5 cents	5¢	$.05
3.	dime	10 cents	?	?
4.	quarter	25 cents	?	?
5.	half dollar	50 cents	?	?

Use ¢ to show how much money.
Then use $ and . .

6.

7.

118

Complete. (The first one is done.)

8.   <u>5</u> pennies

9.   <u>?</u> pennies or
 <u>?</u> nickels

10.    <u>?</u> pennies or
 <u>?</u> nickels

11.    <u>?</u> pennies or
 <u>?</u> dimes

Here is George's dime bank.
His record book is below.

Write the number of dimes he put in each day. (The first one is done.)

	Day	Earnings from Paper Route	Number of Dimes
12.	Sunday	$3.20	32
13.	Monday	$ .80	?
14.	Tuesday	$2.00	?
15.	Wednesday	$3.50	?
16.	Thursday	$1.10	?
17.	Friday	$2.20	?
18.	Saturday	$ .70	?

5-5 Money Less Than $10.00

1 silver dollar = 100 pennies

1 one-dollar bill = 100 pennies
1 five-dollar bill = 500 pennies

Donna has 1 dollar, 4 nickels, and 8 pennies. Does she have enough money to buy the felt marker?

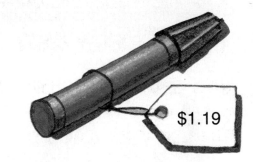

Count Donna's money. $1.28
Look at the price tag. $1.19
Compare the two amounts.
        $1.19 < $1.28

$1.19

Donna has enough money.

Solve.

1. Jo saved her money to buy the model truck. She has 2 dollars, 1 half dollar, 5 dimes, and 5 nickels. Can Jo buy the truck?

FUEL $3.18

$4.98

2. Eric wants to buy the toy elephant for his sister. He has 4 dollars, 2 half dollars, 1 quarter, and 8 dimes. Can Eric buy the toy?

Solve.

3. Peter has a silver dollar and 4 dimes. Does he need more money to buy the calendar?

$1.50

4. Florence has a five-dollar bill from her grandmother. She also saved a dollar to buy a record. Does she have enough money to buy the record?

$4.60

Write how much money. Use $ and . .

5. 1 five-dollar bill, 2 nickels, 2 pennies

6. 4 nickels, 3 dimes, 1 penny

7. 2 half dollars, 3 quarters

8. 1 dollar, 2 half dollars, 3 dimes

9. 3 dollars, 1 half dollar, 3 nickels

Which is more money?

10. **a.** 12 pennies   or   **b.** $.15

11. **a.** 5 nickels, 2 pennies   or   **b.** $.25

12. **a.** 1 dollar, 2 quarters   or   **b.** $1.30

13. **a.** 2 dollars, 1 dime   or   **b.** $2.15

14. **a.** 3 half dollars   or   **b.** $2.00

15. **a.** 1 dollar, 4 quarters   or   **b.** $1.85

16. **a.** 2 quarters, 2 dimes   or   **b.** $.75

121

5-6 Adding Money

A cent sign or a dollar sign and a decimal point are used when adding money.

The ¢ is often used for small amounts.
5¢   3¢   10¢

The $ and . are used for all amounts.
$.15 $4.39 $27.80

To add money:

- Line up the money signs.
- Add.
- Write the money signs in the sum.

```
            1  1              1
  1 1 ¢     $ 5 . 6 9       $ . 3 9
+ 2 2 ¢    +  2 . 9 5      +  . 2 6
  3 3 ¢     $ 8 . 6 4       $ . 6 5
```

Find the sum.

1.	2.	3.	4.	5.
25¢ +40¢	33¢ +58¢	16¢ + 5¢	27¢ +39¢	45¢ +38¢

6.	7.	8.	9.	10.
$7.50 + 1.25	$4.25 + .61	$1.05 + 2.10	$2.00 + 4.19	$3.62 + 2.17

11.	12.	13.	14.	15.
$3.16 + .52	$2.76 + .17	$1.85 + 3.06	$4.19 + 2.34	$1.02 + 1.28

16.	17.	18.	19.	20.
$.75 + .16	$.46 + .34	$1.63 + 2.88	$4.55 + 1.55	$2.64 + 3.79

Add.

21.	22.	23.	24.	25.
$24.86	$30.46	$17.75	$ 5.19	$27.58
+ 19.37	+ 49.68	+ 9.87	+ 14.81	+ 36.49

Solve.

26. Rose needs a baseball hat and a glove. The hat costs $2.68 and the glove costs $9.50. How much money does Rose need?

27. Mark and his brother go shopping. They have $10.00. Do they have enough money to buy a baseball shirt for $3.50, baseball pants for $4.50, and baseball socks for $1.50?

28. The club spent $19.00 for sandwiches, $13.20 for apple juice, $7.75 for fruit, and $5.30 for cupcakes. How much money did the club spend in all?

29. How much does this outfit cost?

 $3.25   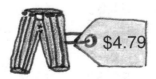 $4.79    $2.70    $9.98

5-7 Subtracting Money

To subtract money:

- Line up the money signs.
- Then subtract.
- Write the money signs in the difference.

```
              13                9
           6  ⁶⃥ 16          4  1⁶⃥ 10
  2 7¢    $ . 9 9    $ 7 . 4̸ 6̸    $ 5̸ . 0̸ 0̸
 -1 7¢    - . 2 6    - 2 . 5 9    - 1 . 5 9
  1 0¢    $ . 7 3    $ 4 . 8 7    $ 3 . 4 1
```

Find the difference.

1. 65¢ − 22¢	**2.** 87¢ − 45¢	**3.** 98¢ − 19¢	**4.** 86¢ − 79¢	**5.** 62¢ − 34¢
6. $8.05 − 8.04	**7.** $3.49 − 1.08	**8.** $2.70 − .29	**9.** $5.25 − 1.65	**10.** $7.06 − 2.37
11. $4.11 − 2.20	**12.** $36.63 − 17.54	**13.** $24.73 − 18.80		

Solve.

14. Jessica has a dollar bill and 2 quarters. She buys a jump rope for $1.37. What is her change?

15. Andy has 2 half dollars and 4 quarters. He buys a ball for $1.79. What is his change?

SNACK MENU

Popcorn	80¢	Milk	25¢
Juice	55¢	Hamburgers	$1.75
Pretzels	45¢	Cheeseburgers	$1.85
Apples	25¢		

Solve.

16. How much less than popcorn do pretzels cost?

17. A pretzel costs how much more than an apple?

18. Juice costs how much more than milk?

19. Gil buys juice and an apple. What is his change from a dollar?

20. Sue buys a hamburger, milk, and popcorn. What is her change from $5.00?

CHALLENGE

Solve.

21. If you had 3 quarters, what could you buy and still have 30¢ left?

125

Counting Change

John buys a notebook for $3.67.
He gives the cashier $5.00. How
much change will John get?

To find John's change,
count the difference between
$3.67 and $5.00.

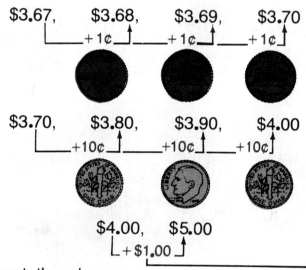

$3.67, $3.68, $3.69, $3.70
└──+1¢─┘────+1¢─┘────+1¢─┘

$3.70, $3.80, $3.90, $4.00
└──+10¢─┘────+10¢─┘────+10¢─┘

$4.00, $5.00
└─+$1.00─┘

Count the change:
$.03 + $.30 + $1.00 = $1.33

Now find the change by subtracting:
$5.00 − $3.67 = $1.33

John got $1.33 change.

Solve.

1. Give another way John can get $1.33
   change:
   a. use only coins.   **b.** use no dimes.

Choose the correct change.

2. Cal buys glue for $.79. He gives the cashier 2 half dollars.

a.   or b.

3. Sheila pays $1.58 for a ribbon. She gives the cashier 1 dollar and 3 quarters.

a.   or b.

4. Mark pays $1.74 for a notebook. He gives the cashier $2.00.

a.  or b.

Draw the change.

5. Sally buys a pencil. She gives the cashier 2 quarters.

6. Don buys a pencil too. He gives the cashier 5 dimes.

7. Marvin gives the cashier a five-dollar bill for the yo-yo.

8. Kim buys the doll. She gives the cashier 2 five-dollar bills.

Rounding Money

Jim wants to buy a pencil and a pen. He has 90¢. Does he have enough money?

Jim uses a money line to help him shop.

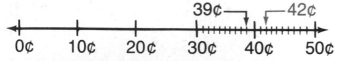

The pencil costs 39¢.
39¢ is closer to 40¢ than to 30¢.
Round 39¢ to 40¢.

The pen costs 42¢.
42¢ is closer to 40¢ than to 50¢.
Round 42¢ to 40¢.

Add: 40¢ + 40¢ = 80¢

Jim should have enough money to buy both the pencil and the pen.

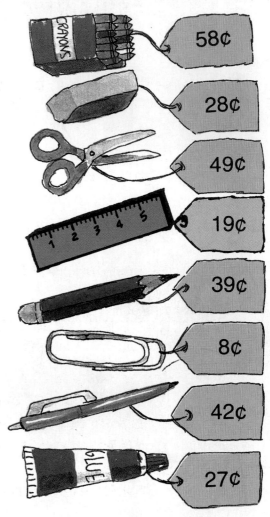

Does Jim have enough money to buy: (Hint: Use a money line.)

1. crayons and scissors?

2. a pen and a clip?

3. a ruler and an eraser?

4. glue and scissors?

5. 2 pencils and a ruler?

6. crayons and glue?

7. glue and a pen?

8. a pencil and an eraser?

9. a ruler and scissors?

10. 2 pens and a clip?

Estimating Dollars and Cents

Mother went to the store with $10.00. She wants to buy a box of cereal for $1.18, a chicken for $5.94, and soap powder for $2.88. Does she have enough money?

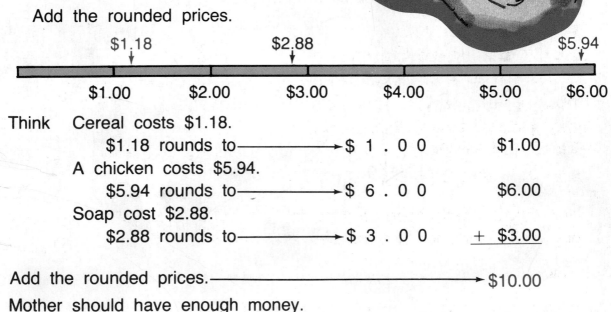

Round each price to the nearest dollar.

Add the rounded prices.

	$1.18		$2.88			$5.94
$1.00	$2.00	$3.00	$4.00	$5.00	$6.00

Think   Cereal costs $1.18.

$1.18 rounds to ⟶ $ 1 . 0 0 $1.00

A chicken costs $5.94.

$5.94 rounds to ⟶ $ 6 . 0 0 $6.00

Soap cost $2.88.

$2.88 rounds to ⟶ $ 3 . 0 0   + $3.00

Add the rounded prices. ⟶ $10.00

Mother should have enough money.

Estimate each total cost.

1.	$4.27	2.	$2.39	3.	$3.25	4.	$1.98	5.	$7.55
	+ 3.19		+ 1.78		+ 2.56		+ 4.49		+ 1.47

6.	$6.63	7.	$4.73	8.	$4.11	9.	$2.75	10.	$5.25
	+ 3.54		+ 1.80		+ 2.20		+ 5.29		+ 1.65

5-11 Problem Solving: Missing Information

Problem: Parking costs 25¢ an hour. Tom parked his car at 9:00 A.M. How many quarters did he need for the parking meter?

1 IMAGINE

Draw and label a picture of what Tom is doing.

2 NAME

Facts: 25¢ an hour to park
9:00 A.M., parked car

Question: How many quarters did Tom need?

3 THINK

Look at the picture. Can you find the number of quarters?

No, you do not know how long Tom was parked.
Information is missing.

Make up a time, like 11:00 A.M., when Tom came back to his car.

From 9:00 A.M. to 11:00 A.M. is _?_ hours?

4 COMPUTE

There are two hours between 9:00 A.M. and 11:00 A.M.
Tom needs 2 quarters.

5 CHECK

Look at the clock. Count the hours between 9:00 A.M. and 11:00 A.M.
There are 2 hours. The answer checks.

Find the missing information.

Make it up and then solve the problem.

1. Denise wants to buy a notebook for $2.00 and a ballpoint pen. She has $2.70. Can Denise buy both the notebook and the pen?

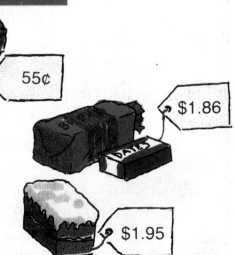

IMAGINE

Draw and label a picture of the problem.

↓

NAME

Facts: $2.00 cost of notebook.
$2.70 money Denise has.

Question: Does Denise have enough money to buy both the notebook and the pen?

↓

THINK

Look at the picture.
What information is missing?
The cost of the pen is missing.
Make it up: $1.00
Find the total cost of the notebook and the pen:
$2.00 + $1.00 = ?
Ask: Is $2.70 enough money?

Then → **COMPUTE** and → **CHECK**

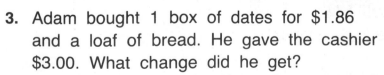

2. Tasha bought a gingerbread cookie and juice. She spent 55¢. How much change did she receive?

3. Adam bought 1 box of dates for $1.86 and a loaf of bread. He gave the cashier $3.00. What change did he get?

4. A 2-pound carrot cake costs $1.95. The 3-pound carrot cake costs more. How much more does the 3-lb cake cost?

More Practice

Write the time.

1.

__?__ minutes after __?__

2.

__?__ minutes after __?__

3.

__?__ minutes before __?__

Write the time another way.

4. 20 minutes before 10

   __?__ : __?__

5. 42 minutes past 5

   __?__ : __?__

6. 33 minutes after 9

   __?__ : __?__

7. 2 minutes before 1

   __?__ : __?__

Write how much money. Use $ and ..

8. 1 half dollar, 2 quarters, 3 dimes, 1 penny

9. 2 dimes, 1 quarter, 4 nickels, 3 pennies

10. 1 five-dollar bill, 1 nickel

Solve.

11. Kim pays $1.53 for ribbon. What is her change from $2.00?

12. A toy robot costs $4.29. What is the change from $10.00?

Estimate each total cost.

13.   47¢
     +21¢

14.   15¢
     +38¢

15. $1.76
    + 2.35

16. $2.98
    + 1.49

132

(See *Still More Practice*, p. 359.)

Math-e-Magic

MAKING CHANGE

Draw and complete the chart.

1. In how many ways can you make change for a quarter?

2. Which way uses the least number of coins?

3. Which way uses the greatest number of coins?

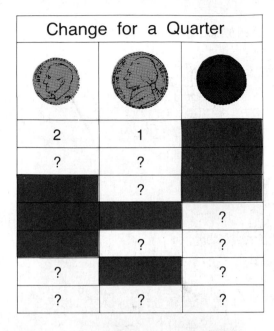

Change for a Quarter		
(dime)	(nickel)	●
2	1	■
?	?	■
■	?	■
■	■	?
■	?	?
?	■	?
?	?	?

Change for a Half Dollar			
(quarter)	(dime)	(nickel)	●
?	■	■	■
?	?	?	■
■	?	?	?
?	■	?	■
?	?	?	?
■	■	■	?

Now draw and complete this chart.

4. In how many ways does the chart show how to make change for a half dollar?

5. Which way uses the least number of coins?

6. Which way uses the greatest number of coins?

7. Think of 2 other ways to make change for a half dollar.

Check Your Mastery

Write the time.

See pp. 112-115

1.

__?__ : __?__

2.

__?__ : __?__

3.

__?__ : __?__

4.

__?__ : __?__

Write A.M. or P.M.

See p. 113

5. Mike leaves school at 3 _?_.

6. Sara eats breakfast at 8 _?_.

Write how much money. Use $ and .

See pp. 118-121

7. 1 half dollar, 3 quarters, 2 dimes

8. 1 dollar, 1 dime, 1 penny

9. 3 half dollars, 1 nickel, 4 pennies

Add.

See pp. 122-123

10.	**11.**	**12.**	**13.**	**14.**
22¢	45¢	$1.50	$1.98	$2.73
+19¢	+38¢	+ 2.49	+ .49	+ 1.07

Subtract.

See pp. 124-125

15.	**16.**	**17.**	**18.**	**19.**
47¢	70¢	$3.54	$4.33	$2.16
−19¢	−34¢	− 1.22	− 1.27	− .47

Solve.

See pp. 126-127

20. Julie has $6.00 to buy milk for $1.98 and bread for $1.19. What is her change?

6

Multiplication Facts Through 9 × 5

In this unit you will:

- Understand the operation of multiplication
- Multiply 0, 1, 2, 3, 4 and 5
- Learn about order in multiplication
- Find missing factors
- Find number patterns
- Solve problems by drawing pictures

Do you remember?

2 sets or groups of three is the same as 2 threes.
2 threes = 6

3 sets or groups of four is the same as 3 fours.
3 fours = 12

6-1 Understanding Multiplication

Biki has 5 bunches of bananas.
There are 2 bananas in each bunch.
How many bananas are there in all?

To find how many bananas in all,
you can add:

$$2 + 2 + 2 + 2 + 2 = 10$$
$$5 \text{ twos} = 10$$

You can also **multiply** since there
is the same number in each group:

$$5 \text{ twos} = 10$$
$$5 \times 2 = 10$$

Read: **"Five times two equals ten."**

There are 10 bananas in all.

Complete. (The first one is done.)

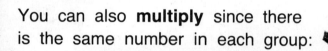

1.

$$2 + 2 + 2 = \underline{6}$$
$$3 \text{ twos} = \underline{6}$$
$$3 \times 2 = \underline{6}$$

2.

$$4 + 4 = \underline{?}$$
$$2 \text{ fours} = \underline{?}$$
$$2 \times 4 = \underline{?}$$

3.

$$3 + 3 + 3 + 3 = \underline{?}$$
$$4 \text{ threes} = \underline{?}$$
$$4 \times 3 = \underline{?}$$

136

$$5 + 5 + 5 + 5 = 20$$
$$4 \quad \text{fives} \quad = 20$$
$$4 \quad \times \quad 5 = 20$$

number ↑ number in ↑ ↑ number
of groups ⌐ each group ⌐ ⌐ in all

Complete. (The first one is done.)

4.

4 twos = <u>8</u>
4 × 2 = <u>8</u>

5.

3 fives = <u>?</u>
3 × 5 = <u>?</u>

6.

2 threes = <u>?</u>
2 × 3 = <u>?</u>

7.

5 fours = <u>?</u>
5 × 4 = <u>?</u>

8.

3 fours = <u>?</u>
3 × 4 = <u>?</u>

9.

5 threes = <u>?</u>
5 × 3 = <u>?</u>

Draw dots or circles to show each. (The first one is done.)

10. 2 fours ⠿ ⠿

11. 3 twos

12. 3 + 3 + 3

13. 5 threes

14. 5 × 2

15. 6 × 3

16. 6 + 6

17. 6 × 2

18. 2 sixes

137

6-2 Another Way to Show Multiplication

There are 3 muffins in each package. How many muffins are there in all?

Multiply to find the number of muffins in all.

Multiplication can be written two ways:

$$2 \times 3 = 6$$

number of groups   number in each group   number in all

or

3 ← number in each group
× 2 ← number of groups
6 ← number in all

Read both: **"Two times three equals six."**

There are 6 muffins in all.

Multiply. (The first one is done.)

1.

$$\begin{array}{r} 2 \\ \times 4 \\ \hline 8 \end{array}$$

2.

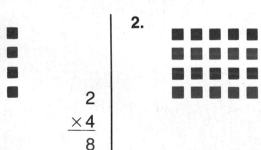

$$\begin{array}{r} 5 \\ \times 4 \\ \hline \end{array}$$

3.

$$\begin{array}{r} 4 \\ \times 3 \\ \hline \end{array}$$

4.

$$\begin{array}{r} 2 \\ \times 5 \\ \hline \end{array}$$

5.

$$\begin{array}{r} 5 \\ \times 6 \\ \hline \end{array}$$

6.

$$\begin{array}{r} 4 \\ \times 6 \\ \hline \end{array}$$

Write each another way. (The first one is done.)

7. $9 \times 3 = 27$
$\begin{array}{r} 3 \\ \times 9 \\ \hline 27 \end{array}$
   8. $7 \times 2 = 14$ **9.** $2 \times 5 = 10$ **10.** $3 \times 6 = 12$

11. $\begin{array}{r} 3 \\ \times 2 \\ \hline 6 \end{array}$
12. $\begin{array}{r} 3 \\ \times 6 \\ \hline 18 \end{array}$
13. $\begin{array}{r} 2 \\ \times 6 \\ \hline 12 \end{array}$
14. $\begin{array}{r} 3 \\ \times 7 \\ \hline 21 \end{array}$
15. $\begin{array}{r} 5 \\ \times 4 \\ \hline 20 \end{array}$
16. $\begin{array}{r} 2 \\ \times 8 \\ \hline 16 \end{array}$

Draw dots or circles to show each. (The first one is done.)

17. $3 \times 2 = 6$ :: ::   **18.** $4 \times 3 = 12$ **19.** $5 \times 2 = 10$ **20.** $2 \times 4 = 8$

21. $\begin{array}{r} 2 \\ \times 4 \\ \hline 8 \end{array}$
22. $\begin{array}{r} 3 \\ \times 5 \\ \hline 15 \end{array}$
23. $\begin{array}{r} 2 \\ \times 6 \\ \hline 12 \end{array}$
24. $\begin{array}{r} 3 \\ \times 1 \\ \hline 3 \end{array}$

25. $\begin{array}{r} 2 \\ \times 1 \\ \hline 2 \end{array}$
26. $\begin{array}{r} 4 \\ \times 1 \\ \hline 4 \end{array}$

Calculator Activity

Go from "Start" to "Finish."

139

Multiplying Twos

How many ice cubes are there in all?

To find how many ice cubes in all,
multiply: 4 × 2 = ___?___

4 × 2 = 8   or   2 ← **factor**
                     × 4 ← **factor**

factor   **factor**   **product**   8 ← **product**

There are 8 ice cubes in all.

Complete. (The first one is done.)

1.	**2.**	**3.**
3 twos = 6 3 × 2 = 6	___?___ twos = 10 5 × 2 = ___?___	___?___ twos = 14 7 × 2 = ___?___
4.	**5.**	**6.**
___?___ twos = 8 4 × 2 = ___?___	___?___ twos = 16 8 × 2 = ___?___	___?___ twos = 4 2 × 2 = ___?___

140

Find the product.

7.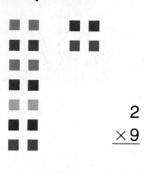
$$\begin{array}{r} 2 \\ \times 9 \\ \hline \end{array}$$

8.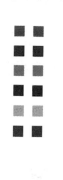
$$\begin{array}{r} 2 \\ \times 6 \\ \hline \end{array}$$

9.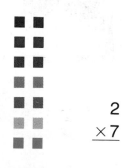
$$\begin{array}{r} 2 \\ \times 7 \\ \hline \end{array}$$

Multiply.

10. 3×2 **11.** 5×2 **12.** 9×2 **13.** 7×2

14. 1×2 **15.** 4×2 **16.** 6×2 **17.** 3×2

18. $\begin{array}{r} 2 \\ \times 4 \\ \hline \end{array}$ **19.** $\begin{array}{r} 2 \\ \times 6 \\ \hline \end{array}$ **20.** $\begin{array}{r} 2 \\ \times 8 \\ \hline \end{array}$ **21.** $\begin{array}{r} 2 \\ \times 2 \\ \hline \end{array}$ **22.** $\begin{array}{r} 2 \\ \times 1 \\ \hline \end{array}$ **23.** $\begin{array}{r} 2 \\ \times 9 \\ \hline \end{array}$

Complete the table. (The first one is done.)

24.

1×2	2×2	3×2	4×2	5×2	6×2	7×2	8×2	9×2
2	?	?	?	?	?	?	?	?

Solve.

25. Mark made 8 groups of 2 blocks each. How many blocks did he use?

26. Susan made 6 groups of 2 blocks each. How many blocks did she use?

27. Carlos made 9 groups of 2 blocks each. How many blocks did he use?

28. Who used the most blocks, Mark or Susan or Carlos?

6-4 Multiplying Threes

How many golf balls are there in all?

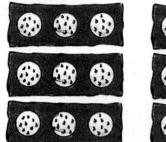 

To find how many golf balls in all,
multiply, 6 × 3 = __?__

$$6 \times 3 = 18 \quad \text{or} \quad \begin{array}{r} 3 \\ \times 6 \\ \hline 18 \end{array}$$

There are 18 golf balls in all.

Complete. (The first one is done.)

1.  4 threes = 12 4 × 3 = __12__	2. __?__ threes = 6 2 × 3 = __?__	3. __?__ threes = 15 5 × 3 = __?__
4.  __?__ threes = 18 6 × 3 = __?__	5. __?__ threes = 27 9 × 3 = __?__	6. 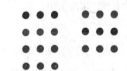 __?__ threes = 21 7 × 3 = __?__

142

Multiply.

7.
∙ ∙ ∙
∙ ∙ ∙

$$\begin{array}{r} 3 \\ \times 2 \\ \hline \end{array}$$

8.
∙ ∙ ∙
∙ ∙ ∙
∙ ∙ ∙
∙ ∙ ∙

$$\begin{array}{r} 3 \\ \times 4 \\ \hline \end{array}$$

9.
∙ ∙ ∙
∙ ∙ ∙
∙ ∙ ∙
∙ ∙ ∙
∙ ∙ ∙
∙ ∙ ∙

$$\begin{array}{r} 3 \\ \times 6 \\ \hline \end{array}$$

10.
∙ ∙ ∙ ∙ ∙ ∙
∙ ∙ ∙ ∙ ∙ ∙
∙ ∙ ∙
∙ ∙ ∙
∙ ∙ ∙

$$\begin{array}{r} 3 \\ \times 8 \\ \hline \end{array}$$

11.
∙ ∙ ∙
∙ ∙ ∙
∙ ∙ ∙
∙ ∙ ∙
∙ ∙ ∙

$$\begin{array}{r} 3 \\ \times 5 \\ \hline \end{array}$$

12.
∙ ∙ ∙
∙ ∙ ∙
∙ ∙ ∙

$$\begin{array}{r} 3 \\ \times 3 \\ \hline \end{array}$$

Find the product.

13. 2×3 **14.** 5×3 **15.** 7×3 **16.** 6×3

17. $\begin{array}{r} 3 \\ \times 4 \\ \hline \end{array}$ **18.** $\begin{array}{r} 3 \\ \times 9 \\ \hline \end{array}$ **19.** $\begin{array}{r} 3 \\ \times 8 \\ \hline \end{array}$ **20.** $\begin{array}{r} 3 \\ \times 3 \\ \hline \end{array}$ **21.** $\begin{array}{r} 3 \\ \times 1 \\ \hline \end{array}$ **22.** $\begin{array}{r} 3 \\ \times 7 \\ \hline \end{array}$

Complete the table. (The first one is done.)

23.

1×3	2×3	3×3	4×3	5×3	6×3	7×3	8×3	9×3
3	?	?	?	?	?	?	?	?

Solve.

24. Cary sold 7 packages of golf balls. There are 3 balls in each package. How many golf balls did Cary sell in all?

25. Tom gave his mother 4 packages of golf balls. Each package has 3 balls in it. How many golf balls did Tom give his mother?

Practice Multiplying Twos and Threes

Multiply.

1.

$$\begin{array}{r} 2 \\ \times 3 \\ \hline \end{array}$$

2.

$$\begin{array}{r} 3 \\ \times 4 \\ \hline \end{array}$$

3.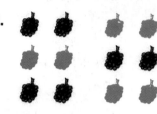

$$\begin{array}{r} 2 \\ \times 6 \\ \hline \end{array}$$

4.

$$\begin{array}{r} 3 \\ \times 3 \\ \hline \end{array}$$

5.

$$\begin{array}{r} 2 \\ \times 4 \\ \hline \end{array}$$

6.

$$\begin{array}{r} 3 \\ \times 5 \\ \hline \end{array}$$

7.

$$\begin{array}{r} 2 \\ \times 5 \\ \hline \end{array}$$

8.

$$\begin{array}{r} 3 \\ \times 6 \\ \hline \end{array}$$

9.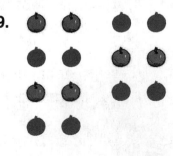

$$\begin{array}{r} 2 \\ \times 7 \\ \hline \end{array}$$

Multiply quickly.

10. 3 × 2   **11.** 4 × 3   **12.** 6 × 2   **13.** 5 × 3

14. 8 × 2   **15.** 4 × 2   **16.** 6 × 3   **17.** 7 × 2

18. 8 × 3   **19.** 5 × 2   **20.** 1 × 3   **21.** 8 × 2

Find the product.

22. 2 ×9	**23.** 3 ×2	**24.** 3 ×7	**25.** 2 ×2	**26.** 3 ×3	**27.** 3 ×6
28. 2 ×5	**29.** 3 ×5	**30.** 2 ×7	**31.** 3 ×9	**32.** 2 ×6	**33.** 2 ×1
34. 2 ×4	**35.** 3 ×8	**36.** 2 ×3	**37.** 3 ×4	**38.** 2 ×8	**39.** 3 ×1

Solve.

40. 7 girls each buy 2 pears. How many pears did the girls buy in all?

41. There are 3 bananas in each bunch. How many bananas are there in 6 bunches?

42. 4 boys each buy 3 apples. How many apples did they buy in all?

43. Mary buys 2 peaches every day. How many peaches will she buy in 8 days?

44. There are 3 oranges in a package. How many oranges are in 8 packages?

6-6 Multiplying Fours

How many sticks of butter are there in all?

To find how many sticks of butter in all, multiply: $3 \times 4 = \underline{\ ?\ }$

$$3 \times 4 = 12 \quad \text{or} \quad \begin{array}{r} 4 \\ \times 3 \\ \hline 12 \end{array}$$

There are 12 sticks of butter in all.

Complete. (The first one is done.)

1. ▲ ▲ ▲ ▲ ▲ ▲ ▲ ▲ 2 fours = 8 $2 \times 4 = \underline{8}$	**2.** ▲ ▲ ▲ ▲ $\underline{\ ?\ }$ fours = 4 $1 \times 4 = \underline{\ ?\ }$	**3.** ▲ ▲ ▲ ▲ ▲ ▲ ▲ ▲ ▲ ▲ ▲ ▲ $\underline{\ ?\ }$ fours = 12 $3 \times 4 = \underline{\ ?\ }$
4. ▲ ▲ ▲ ▲ ▲ ▲ ▲ ▲ ▲ ▲ ▲ ▲ ▲ ▲ ▲ ▲ ▲ ▲ ▲ ▲ $\underline{\ ?\ }$ fours = 20 $5 \times 4 = \underline{\ ?\ }$	**5.** ▲ ▲ ▲ ▲ ▲ ▲ ▲ ▲ ▲ ▲ ▲ ▲ ▲ ▲ ▲ ▲ ▲ ▲ ▲ ▲ ▲ ▲ ▲ ▲ $\underline{\ ?\ }$ fours = 24 $6 \times 4 = \underline{\ ?\ }$	**6.** ▲ ▲ ▲ ▲ ▲ ▲ ▲ ▲ ▲ ▲ ▲ ▲ ▲ ▲ ▲ ▲ $\underline{\ ?\ }$ fours = 16 $4 \times 4 = \underline{\ ?\ }$

146

Multiply.

7.

▲ ▲ ▲ ▲ ▲ ▲ ▲ ▲
▲ ▲ ▲ ▲ ▲ ▲ ▲ ▲
▲ ▲ ▲ ▲ ▲ ▲ ▲ ▲
▲ ▲ ▲ ▲

$$\begin{array}{r} 4 \\ \times 7 \\ \hline \end{array}$$

8.

▲ ▲ ▲ ▲ ▲ ▲ ▲ ▲
▲ ▲ ▲ ▲ ▲ ▲ ▲ ▲
▲ ▲ ▲ ▲ ▲ ▲ ▲ ▲
▲ ▲ ▲ ▲ ▲ ▲ ▲ ▲
▲ ▲ ▲ ▲

$$\begin{array}{r} 4 \\ \times 9 \\ \hline \end{array}$$

9.

▲ ▲ ▲ ▲ ▲ ▲ ▲ ▲
▲ ▲ ▲ ▲ ▲ ▲ ▲ ▲
▲ ▲ ▲ ▲ ▲ ▲ ▲ ▲
▲ ▲ ▲ ▲ ▲ ▲ ▲ ▲

$$\begin{array}{r} 4 \\ \times 8 \\ \hline \end{array}$$

Find the product.

10. 2×4 **11.** 5×4 **12.** 7×4 **13.** 6×4

14. $\begin{array}{r} 4 \\ \times 3 \\ \hline \end{array}$ **15.** $\begin{array}{r} 4 \\ \times 8 \\ \hline \end{array}$ **16.** $\begin{array}{r} 4 \\ \times 9 \\ \hline \end{array}$ **17.** $\begin{array}{r} 4 \\ \times 6 \\ \hline \end{array}$ **18.** $\begin{array}{r} 4 \\ \times 1 \\ \hline \end{array}$ **19.** $\begin{array}{r} 4 \\ \times 4 \\ \hline \end{array}$

Complete the table. (The first one is done.)

20.

1×4	2×4	3×4	4×4	5×4	6×4	7×4	8×4	9×4
4	?	?	?	?	?	?	?	?

Solve.

21. There are 9 packages of butter with 4 sticks in each package. How many sticks are there in all?

22. Carrie uses 3 packages of butter with 4 sticks in each package. How many sticks are there in all?

23. Jack uses 3 packages of butter. Mark uses 4 times as many packages. How many packages does Mark use?

147

6-7 Multiplying Fives

How many flowers are there in all?

To find how many flowers in all,
multiply: $6 \times 5 = \underline{?}$

$$6 \times 5 = 30 \quad \text{or} \quad \begin{array}{r} 5 \\ \times 6 \\ \hline 30 \end{array}$$

There are 30 flowers in all.

Complete.

1.

3 fives = 15
$3 \times 5 = \underline{?}$

2.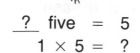

$\underline{?}$ five = 5
$1 \times 5 = \underline{?}$

3.

$\underline{?}$ fives = 10
$2 \times 5 = \underline{?}$

4.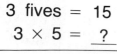

$\underline{?}$ fives = 25
$5 \times 5 = \underline{?}$

5.

$\underline{?}$ fives = 20
$4 \times 5 = \underline{?}$

6.

$\underline{?}$ fives = 30
$6 \times 5 = \underline{?}$

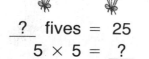

148

Multiply.

7. ✳✳✳✳✳
✳✳✳✳✳
✳✳✳✳✳
✳✳✳✳✳
✳✳✳✳✳
✳✳✳✳✳
✳✳✳✳✳
✳✳✳✳✳   5
        ×8

8. ✳✳✳✳✳
✳✳✳✳✳
✳✳✳✳✳
✳✳✳✳✳
✳✳✳✳✳
✳✳✳✳✳   5
        ×7

9. ✳✳✳✳✳
✳✳✳✳✳
✳✳✳✳✳
✳✳✳✳✳
✳✳✳✳✳
✳✳✳✳✳
✳✳✳✳✳   5
✳✳✳✳✳ ×9

Find the product.

10. 3×5 11. 6×5 12. 5×5 13. 8×5

14.	15.	16.	17.	18.	19.
5	5	5	5	5	5
×4	×7	×5	×1	×9	×2

Complete the table. (The first one is done.)

20.

1×5	2×5	3×5	4×5	5×5	6×5	7×5	8×5	9×5
5	?	?	?	?	?	?	?	?

Solve.

21. Robert buys 5 bunches of flowers. Each bunch has 5 flowers in it. How many flowers are there in all?

22. Marie put 5 flowers in each of 6 vases. How many flowers did she use?

Challenge   23. Mrs. Martin got 2 bunches of flowers from each of 3 children. There are 5 flowers in each bunch. How many flowers did she get in all?

6-8 Practice Multiplying Fours and Fives

Multiply.

1. ★ ★ ★ ★
   ★ ★ ★ ★

   $$\begin{array}{r} 4 \\ \times 2 \\ \hline \end{array}$$

2. ★ ★ ★ ★ ★
   ★ ★ ★ ★ ★
   ★ ★ ★ ★ ★

   $$\begin{array}{r} 5 \\ \times 3 \\ \hline \end{array}$$

3. ★ ★ ★ ★
   ★ ★ ★ ★
   ★ ★ ★ ★
   ★ ★ ★ ★
   ★ ★ ★ ★

   $$\begin{array}{r} 4 \\ \times 5 \\ \hline \end{array}$$

4. ★ ★ ★ ★ ★
   ★ ★ ★ ★ ★
   ★ ★ ★ ★ ★
   ★ ★ ★ ★ ★
   ★ ★ ★ ★ ★
   ★ ★ ★ ★ ★

   $$\begin{array}{r} 5 \\ \times 6 \\ \hline \end{array}$$

5. ★ ★ ★ ★
   ★ ★ ★ ★
   ★ ★ ★ ★
   ★ ★ ★ ★
   ★ ★ ★ ★
   ★ ★ ★ ★
   ★ ★ ★ ★
   ★ ★ ★ ★
   ★ ★ ★ ★

   $$\begin{array}{r} 4 \\ \times 9 \\ \hline \end{array}$$

6. ★ ★ ★ ★ ★
   ★ ★ ★ ★ ★
   ★ ★ ★ ★ ★
   ★ ★ ★ ★

   $$\begin{array}{r} 5 \\ \times 4 \\ \hline \end{array}$$

Find the product.

7. ★ ★ ★ ★
   ★ ★ ★ ★
   ★ ★ ★ ★
   ★ ★ ★ ★
   ★ ★ ★ ★
   ★ ★ ★ ★
   ★ ★ ★ ★
   ★ ★ ★ ★

   $$\begin{array}{r} 4 \\ \times 8 \\ \hline \end{array}$$

8. ★ ★ ★ ★ ★
   ★ ★ ★ ★ ★
   ★ ★ ★ ★ ★
   ★ ★ ★ ★ ★
   ★ ★ ★ ★ ★
   ★ ★ ★ ★ ★
   ★ ★ ★ ★ ★

   $$\begin{array}{r} 5 \\ \times 7 \\ \hline \end{array}$$

9. ★ ★ ★ ★
   ★ ★ ★ ★
   ★ ★ ★ ★
   ★ ★ ★ ★
   ★ ★ ★ ★
   ★ ★ ★ ★

   $$\begin{array}{r} 4 \\ \times 6 \\ \hline \end{array}$$

150

Multiply quickly.

10. 3×4 **11.** 4×5 **12.** 7×4

13. 8×5 **14.** 2×5 **15.** 9×4

16. 7×5 **17.** 4×4 **18.** 9×5

19. 8×4 **20.** 5×5 **21.** 1×4

22. $\begin{array}{r} 4 \\ \times 2 \\ \hline \end{array}$ **23.** $\begin{array}{r} 5 \\ \times 9 \\ \hline \end{array}$ **24.** $\begin{array}{r} 4 \\ \times 1 \\ \hline \end{array}$ **25.** $\begin{array}{r} 4 \\ \times 6 \\ \hline \end{array}$ **26.** $\begin{array}{r} 5 \\ \times 3 \\ \hline \end{array}$ **27.** $\begin{array}{r} 4 \\ \times 4 \\ \hline \end{array}$

28. $\begin{array}{r} 4 \\ \times 8 \\ \hline \end{array}$ **29.** $\begin{array}{r} 5 \\ \times 6 \\ \hline \end{array}$ **30.** $\begin{array}{r} 5 \\ \times 2 \\ \hline \end{array}$ **31.** $\begin{array}{r} 4 \\ \times 5 \\ \hline \end{array}$ **32.** $\begin{array}{r} 5 \\ \times 5 \\ \hline \end{array}$ **33.** $\begin{array}{r} 5 \\ \times 7 \\ \hline \end{array}$

34. $\begin{array}{r} 4 \\ \times 7 \\ \hline \end{array}$ **35.** $\begin{array}{r} 5 \\ \times 4 \\ \hline \end{array}$ **36.** $\begin{array}{r} 5 \\ \times 1 \\ \hline \end{array}$ **37.** $\begin{array}{r} 4 \\ \times 3 \\ \hline \end{array}$ **38.** $\begin{array}{r} 5 \\ \times 8 \\ \hline \end{array}$ **39.** $\begin{array}{r} 4 \\ \times 9 \\ \hline \end{array}$

Solve.

40. There are 9 bags with 4 marbles in each bag. How many marbles are there in all?

41. Bob has 4 friends. He gives each friend 5 baseball cards. How many baseball cards did Bob give in all?

42. Lisa has 9 stacks of baseball cards. There are 5 cards in each stack. How many baseball cards does Lisa have in all?

43. Joel put 4 marbles in each of 7 bags. How many marbles did he use in all?

Zero and One As Factors

Each letter has 1 stamp on it.
There are 2 letters.
How many stamps are there in all?

To find how many stamps in all,   1
multiply: $2 \times 1 = 2$ or ⟶ $\underline{\times 2}$
                                            2

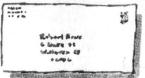

The product of any number and 1 is the number.

Each of these letters has 0 stamps.
There are 2 letters.
How many stamps are there in all?

To find how many stamps in all,   0
multiply: $2 \times 0 = 0$ or ⟶ $\underline{\times 2}$
                                            0

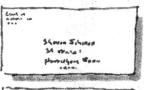

The product of any number and 0 is 0.

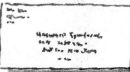

Multiply.

1. 3×1 **2.** 4×0 **3.** 6×1 **4.** 7×0

5.   1   **6.**   0   **7.**   1   **8.**   0   **9.**   1
      $\underline{\times 4}$ $\underline{\times 5}$ $\underline{\times 6}$ $\underline{\times 8}$ $\underline{\times 9}$

...CHALLENGE...

Solve.

10. Draw 5 large rectangles to represent letters.
Draw 1 small rectangle on each large
rectangle to represent stamps. What
multiplication sentence does this show?

Addition and Subtraction Practice

Add or subtract. (Watch the signs.)

1. 234
   +545

2. 641
   −230

3. 423
   −115

4. 536
   +318

5. 948
   −376

6. 335
   +189

7. 2663
   +4728

8. 6574
   −2978

9. 4098
   +1927

10. 8406
   −3217

11. $.89
   − .53

12. $.47
   + .39

13. $7.70
   + .15

14. $9.16
   − .78

15. $5.55
   − 2.22

16. $4.68
   + 1.90

17. $8.37
   − 1.98

18. $2.79
   + 3.51

19. $1.23
   + .65

20. $4.42
   − 1.16

Solve.

21. Trish practiced her piano lesson for 30 minutes. If she started at 1:15 P.M., when did she finish?

22. Mark's family traveled 296 miles in one day and 135 miles the next day. How many miles did they travel altogether?

23. Sue put 75 pictures in her photo album. It holds 144 pictures. How many more pictures can Sue put in her album?

24. Jeff bought gifts for his friends. The gifts cost $2.49, $3.29, and $2.98. What was the total cost of the 3 gifts?

153

Order in Multiplication

How many bees?

4 threes = 12

$4 \times 3 = 12$ or $\begin{array}{r} 3 \\ \times 4 \\ \hline 12 \end{array}$

factor factor product

There are 12 bees.

3 fours = 12

$3 \times 4 = 12$ or $\begin{array}{r} 4 \\ \times 3 \\ \hline 12 \end{array}$

factor factor product

There are 12 bees.

The order of the factors does not change the product.

Find the product.

1. $8 \times 2 = 16$
   $2 \times 8 = \underline{?}$

2. $6 \times 5 = 30$
   $5 \times 6 = \underline{?}$

3. $7 \times 3 = 21$
   $3 \times 7 = \underline{?}$

4. $6 \times 4 = 24$
   $4 \times 6 = \underline{?}$

5. $1 \times 2 = 2$
   $2 \times 1 = \underline{?}$

6. $9 \times 2 = 18$
   $2 \times 9 = \underline{?}$

7. $8 \times 4 = 32$
   $4 \times 8 = \underline{?}$

8. $9 \times 5 = 45$
   $5 \times 9 = \underline{?}$

9. $3 \times 2 = \underline{?}$
   $2 \times 3 = \underline{?}$

10. $9 \times 4 = \underline{?}$
    $4 \times 9 = \underline{?}$

11. $6 \times 3 = \underline{?}$
    $3 \times 6 = \underline{?}$

12. $8 \times 3 = \underline{?}$
    $3 \times 8 = \underline{?}$

13. $7 \times 5 = \underline{?}$
    $5 \times 7 = \underline{?}$

14. $5 \times 4 = \underline{?}$
    $4 \times 5 = \underline{?}$

15. $6 \times 2 = \underline{?}$
    $2 \times 6 = \underline{?}$

16. $9 \times 3 = \underline{?}$
    $3 \times 9 = \underline{?}$

Multiply.

17. 5   3
     ×3   ×5

18.   4   2
       ×2   ×4

19.   0   4
       ×4   ×0

20. 2   7
     ×7   ×2

21. 5   8
     ×8   ×5

22. 3   1
     ×1   ×3

23. 0   8
     ×8   ×0

24. 4   6
     ×6   ×4

25. 5   9
     ×9   ×5

Complete.

26. $3 \times 2 = \underline{?} \times 3$

27. $1 \times 2 = \underline{?} \times 1$

28. $3 \times 5 = \underline{?} \times 3$

29. $2 \times 5 = \underline{?} \times 2$

30. $7 \times 4 = \underline{?} \times 7$

31. $6 \times 0 = \underline{?} \times 6$

Draw dots or circles to show:

32. $5 \times 2 = 2 \times 5$

33. $4 \times 2 = 2 \times 4$

34. $5 \times 4 = 4 \times 5$

35. $4 \times 3 = 3 \times 4$

36. $7 \times 3 = 3 \times 7$

37. $6 \times 5 = 5 \times 6$

Solve.

38. Joan put 6 stamps on each of 3 pages in her stamp album. How many stamps did she put in altogether?

39. Mark put 8 stamps on each of 2 pages in his stamp album. How many stamps did he put in altogether?

40. A red photo album has 5 pages with 4 pictures on each page. A blue photo album has 4 pages with 5 pictures on each page. How many pictures are there in each album?

6-12 Missing Factors

Daffy has 6 kites.
She put them in groups
of 2 kites each.
How many groups are there?

To find the number of groups, think:
  What number times 2 equals 6?

$$\underline{?} \times 2 = 6$$

Factor   Factor   Product

$$3 \times 2 = 6$$

3 is the missing factor.

Daffy has 3 groups of 2 kites each.

?	×	2	=	6
Number of groups		Number in each group		Number in all

Complete. Find the missing factor.

1.

$$\underline{?} \times 2 = 8$$

2.

$$\underline{?} \times 5 = 15$$

3.

$$\underline{?} \times 3 = 6$$

Find the missing factor.

4. $\underline{\ ?\ } \times 2 = 12$ 5. $\underline{\ ?\ } \times 3 = 15$ 6. $\underline{\ ?\ } \times 5 = 20$ 7. $\underline{\ ?\ } \times 4 = 12$

8. $2 \times \underline{\ ?\ } = 10$ 9. $4 \times \underline{\ ?\ } = 8$ 10. $3 \times \underline{\ ?\ } = 9$ 11. $4 \times \underline{\ ?\ } = 4$

12. $\underline{\ ?\ } \times 3 = 18$ 13. $5 \times \underline{\ ?\ } = 25$ 14. $8 \times \underline{\ ?\ } = 16$ 15. $\underline{\ ?\ } \times 4 = 24$

Find each product.

16. $\begin{array}{r} 4 \\ \times 9 \\ \hline \end{array}$ 17. $\begin{array}{r} 2 \\ \times 8 \\ \hline \end{array}$ 18. $\begin{array}{r} 3 \\ \times 9 \\ \hline \end{array}$ 19. $\begin{array}{r} 4 \\ \times 7 \\ \hline \end{array}$ 20. $\begin{array}{r} 3 \\ \times 6 \\ \hline \end{array}$ 21. $\begin{array}{r} 5 \\ \times 5 \\ \hline \end{array}$

22. $\begin{array}{r} 3 \\ \times 4 \\ \hline \end{array}$ 23. $\begin{array}{r} 2 \\ \times 7 \\ \hline \end{array}$ 24. $\begin{array}{r} 3 \\ \times 8 \\ \hline \end{array}$ 25. $\begin{array}{r} 5 \\ \times 6 \\ \hline \end{array}$ 26. $\begin{array}{r} 0 \\ \times 3 \\ \hline \end{array}$ 27. $\begin{array}{r} 2 \\ \times 5 \\ \hline \end{array}$

28. $\begin{array}{r} 3 \\ \times 7 \\ \hline \end{array}$ 29. $\begin{array}{r} 5 \\ \times 9 \\ \hline \end{array}$ 30. $\begin{array}{r} 2 \\ \times 6 \\ \hline \end{array}$ 31. $\begin{array}{r} 4 \\ \times 8 \\ \hline \end{array}$ 32. $\begin{array}{r} 4 \\ \times 5 \\ \hline \end{array}$ 33. $\begin{array}{r} 5 \\ \times 8 \\ \hline \end{array}$

Complete.

34.

factor	factor	product
7	?	21
?	5	30
1	?	2
7	?	35
?	4	32
7	?	14
?	4	16
1	?	5

35.

factor	factor	product
3	?	3
?	4	20
7	?	28
?	5	45
?	2	0
9	?	18
?	3	24
?	5	40

6-13 Problem Solving: Draw a Picture

Addition: Use when joining sets or groups with an unequal *or* equal number of objects in them.	**Multiplication:** Use when joining sets or groups with *only* an equal number of objects in them.

Problem: Each box of crayons holds 5 crayons. Tony buys 8 boxes. How many crayons does Tony have?

5 in each box

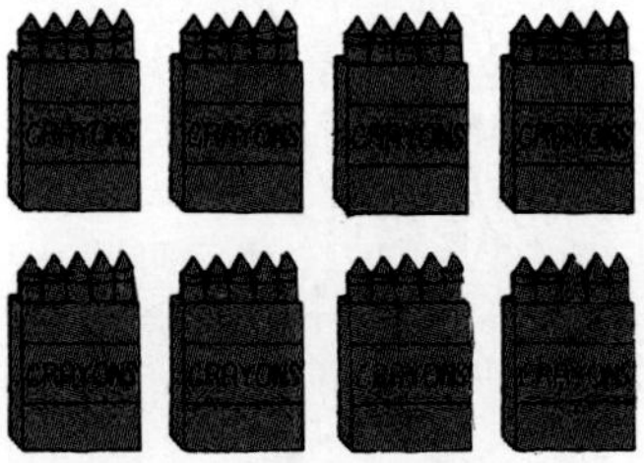

8 boxes

1 IMAGINE
Draw and label a picture of Tony's crayons

2 NAME
Facts: 5 crayons in *each* box
8 boxes

Question: How many crayons are there in all?

3 THINK
Look at the picture.
Each box has the *same* number of crayons, so multiply to find how many in all.

$$8 \quad \times \quad 5 \quad = \quad ?$$

Number of boxes	Number in *each* box	Number in all

4 COMPUTE
$8 \times 5 = 40$
Tony has 40 crayons.

5 CHECK
Look at the picture. Add the crayons.
$5 + 5 + 5 + 5 + 5 + 5 + 5 + 5 = 40$
The answer checks.

Solve. Draw a picture. Choose addition or multiplication.

1. Juanita filled her notebook with 175 sheets of paper. Later she added 125 sheets. How many sheets are in her notebook in all?

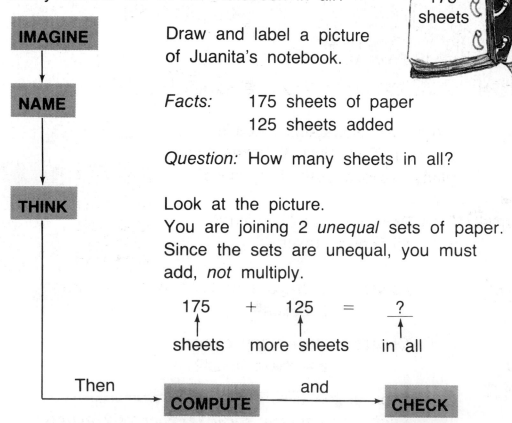

IMAGINE

Draw and label a picture of Juanita's notebook.

NAME

Facts: 175 sheets of paper
125 sheets added

Question: How many sheets in all?

THINK

Look at the picture.
You are joining 2 *unequal* sets of paper.
Since the sets are unequal, you must add, *not* multiply.

175 + 125 = ?
↑ ↑ ↑
sheets more sheets in all

Then → **COMPUTE** and → **CHECK**

2. Sandy bought 4 packages of pens with 3 pens in each package. How many pens did Sandy buy?

3. Cathy bought a pencil sharpener for 50¢ and an eraser for 35¢. How much money did she spend in all?

4. Tom's pencil case holds 7 pencils. Julie's case holds 2 times as many. How many pencils does Julie's case hold?

More Practice

Multiply.

1. 3×2 2. 4×3 3. 3×5 4. 6×4

5. 6×3 6. 7×4 7. 6×5 8. 1×3

9. 5×0 10. 9×2 11. 3×4 12. 5×3

13. $\begin{array}{r} 5 \\ \times 2 \\ \hline \end{array}$ 14. $\begin{array}{r} 3 \\ \times 9 \\ \hline \end{array}$ 15. $\begin{array}{r} 0 \\ \times 2 \\ \hline \end{array}$ 16. $\begin{array}{r} 2 \\ \times 6 \\ \hline \end{array}$ 17. $\begin{array}{r} 5 \\ \times 9 \\ \hline \end{array}$ 18. $\begin{array}{r} 5 \\ \times 5 \\ \hline \end{array}$

19. $\begin{array}{r} 2 \\ \times 8 \\ \hline \end{array}$ 20. $\begin{array}{r} 5 \\ \times 4 \\ \hline \end{array}$ 21. $\begin{array}{r} 2 \\ \times 5 \\ \hline \end{array}$ 22. $\begin{array}{r} 1 \\ \times 2 \\ \hline \end{array}$ 23. $\begin{array}{r} 5 \\ \times 7 \\ \hline \end{array}$ 24. $\begin{array}{r} 4 \\ \times 4 \\ \hline \end{array}$

25. $\begin{array}{r} 4 \\ \times 9 \\ \hline \end{array}$ 26. $\begin{array}{r} 3 \\ \times 7 \\ \hline \end{array}$ 27. $\begin{array}{r} 5 \\ \times 8 \\ \hline \end{array}$ 28. $\begin{array}{r} 2 \\ \times 7 \\ \hline \end{array}$ 29. $\begin{array}{r} 0 \\ \times 6 \\ \hline \end{array}$ 30. $\begin{array}{r} 3 \\ \times 8 \\ \hline \end{array}$

Complete.

31. $2 \times 4 = \underline{?} \times 2$ 32. $9 \times 0 = \underline{?} \times 9$ 33. $\underline{?} \times 6 = 6 \times 3$

Find the missing factor.

34. $\underline{?} \times 3 = 21$ 35. $\underline{?} \times 5 = 5$ 36. $4 \times \underline{?} = 8$ 37. $\underline{?} \times 4 = 0$

Solve.

38. 8 children have 4 books each. How many books do the children have in all?

39. Brenda read 3 stories. Kim read 3 times as many stories. How many stories did Kim read in all?

(See *Still More Practice,* p. 360.)

Math-e-Magic

NUMBER PATTERNS

Study the pattern.

A.   0
       1   ●
    +2   ● ●
       3

C.   2   ● ●
       3   ● ● ●
    +4   ● ● ● ●
       9

B.   1   ●
       2   ● ●
    +3   ● ● ●
       6

D.   3   ● ● ●
       4   ● ● ● ●
    +5   ● ● ● ● ●
       12

Use the pattern to complete each sentence.

1.   0 + 1 + 2 = _?_

2.   1 + 2 + 3 = _?_

3.   2 + 3 + 4 = _?_

4.   3 + 4 + 5 = _?_

5.   4 + _?_ + _?_ = _?_

6.   5 + _?_ + _?_ = _?_

7.   _?_ + _?_ + _?_ = _?_

8.   _?_ + _?_ + _?_ = _?_

9.   _?_ + _?_ + _?_ = _?_

10.   _?_ + _?_ + _?_ = _?_

(Read each sum. What did you discover?)

Something Extra
Find the pattern. Complete each sentence.

11.   1 + 3 = _2_ × _2_

12.   1 + 3 + 5 = _3_ × _3_

13.   1 + 3 + 5 + 7 = _?_ × _?_

14.   1 + _?_ + _?_ + _?_ + _?_ = _?_ × _?_

15.   _?_ + _?_ + _?_ + _?_ + _?_ + _?_ = _?_ × _?_

Check Your Mastery

Complete.

See pp. 136-137

1.

▲ ▲ ▲ ▲ ▲
▲ ▲ ▲ ▲ ▲
▲ ▲ ▲ ▲ ▲

3 fives = _?_

3 × 5 = _?_

2.

▲ ▲ ▲
▲ ▲ ▲
▲ ▲ ▲
▲ ▲ ▲

4 threes = _?_

4 × 3 = _?_

Multiply.

See pp. 138-152

3. 4 × 2   **4.** 8 × 4   **5.** 6 × 3   **6.** 9 × 5

7. 1 × 4   **8.** 9 × 2   **9.** 7 × 10   **10.** 5 × 4

11. 2	**12.** 3	**13.** 4	**14.** 1	**15.** 5	**16.** 3
×6	×9	×4	×5	×7	×0

Complete.

See pp. 154-155

17. 6 × 5 = _?_ × 6   **18.** 3 × 2 = _?_ × 3   **19.** 5 × 0 = _?_ × 5

Find the missing factors.

See pp. 156-157

20. _?_ × 5 = 20   **21.** 8 × _?_ = 16   **22.** _?_ × 3 = 9   **23.** 1 × _?_ = 2

Solve.

See pp. 146-147, 148-149, 158-159

24. There are 5 books on each of 7 tables in the library. How many books are there in all?

25. There are 8 rows of desks in a classroom. Each row has 4 desks. How many desks are there in all?

162

7

Division Facts

In this unit you will:

- Learn two meanings of division
- Relate multiplication and division by finding missing factors
- Divide by 1, 2, 3, 4, and 5
- Find fact families
- Solve problems by choosing the right operation

Do you remember?

Multiplication joins equal sets or groups of objects

$3 + 3 + 3 + 3 + 3 = 15$

$5 \text{ threes} = 15$

$5 \times 3 = 15$

Meaning of Division

Karen has 12 flowers. She puts 3 flowers in a vase. How many vases does she need?

To find how many vases:

| Subtract threes | **or** | Divide by three. OR
Find how many groups of three |

$$12 \begin{array}{c} \\ -\ 3 \\ \hline 9 \end{array} \quad 9 \begin{array}{c} \\ -\ 3 \\ \hline 6 \end{array} \quad 6 \begin{array}{c} \\ -\ 3 \\ \hline 3 \end{array} \quad 3 \begin{array}{c} \\ -\ 3 \\ \hline 0 \end{array}$$

$$12 \div 3 = 4$$

in all   in each   vases or
vase   groups of flowers

Think: 4 threes subtracted from 12

Think: 12 divided by 3 is 4
or
12 divided into groups of 3
is 4 groups.

There are 4 vases.

Find how many groups. (The first one is done.)

1. 12 wheels in all.

  6 groups of 2 wheels.

2. 24 wheels in all.

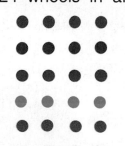

  ? groups of 4 wheels.

3. 18 wheels in all.

  ? groups of 6 wheels.

Two Meanings of Division

Divide to find:

1. How many groups?   or   **2. How many in each group?**

15 flowers in all   15 flowers in all
 3 flowers in a group   5 groups of flowers
 ? groups of flowers   ? in each group

5 groups of flowers   3 in each group

Complete the division.

4. 8 wheels in all.

4 in each group.
8 ÷ 4 = _?_ groups

5. 12 wheels in all.

2 in each group.
12 ÷ 2 = _?_ groups

6. 10 wheels in all.

2 in each group.
10 ÷ 2 = _?_ groups

Calculator Activity

Follow these instructions.

7. Press: 14 − 2 − 2 − 2 − 2 − 2 − 2 − 2 =

How many twos were subtracted?

8. Press: 14 ÷ 2 =

What have you discovered?

165

7-2 **Relating Multiplication and Division**

Ms. Lopez has 24 lemons in all. There are 3 lemons in each bag. How many bags are there?

To find how many bags, divide: 24 ÷ 3 = _?_

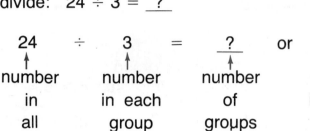

$$\begin{array}{ccccc} 24 & \div & 3 & = & \underline{\quad?\quad} \\ \uparrow & & \uparrow & & \uparrow \\ \text{number} & & \text{number} & & \text{number} \\ \text{in} & & \text{in each} & & \text{of} \\ \text{all} & & \text{group} & & \text{groups} \end{array}$$

or

$$\begin{array}{c} \quad?\longleftarrow \text{number of groups} \\ 3\,\overline{)\,2\,4} \longleftarrow \text{number} \\ \uparrow \qquad\qquad \text{in all} \\ \text{number} \\ \text{in each} \\ \text{group} \end{array}$$

Every division fact has a related multiplication fact.

$$\begin{array}{ccccccccccc} 24 & \div & 3 & = & \underline{\quad?\quad} & \text{is the same as} & \underline{\quad?\quad} & \times & 3 & = & 24 \\ \uparrow & & \uparrow & & \uparrow & & \uparrow & & \uparrow & & \uparrow \\ \text{number} & & \text{number} & & \text{number} & & \text{number} & & \text{number} & & \text{number} \\ \text{in} & & \text{in each} & & \text{of} & & \text{of} & & \text{in each} & & \text{in} \\ \text{all} & & \text{group} & & \text{groups} & & \text{groups} & & \text{group} & & \text{all} \end{array}$$

Think: 24 ÷ 3 = _?_ ⟶ _?_ × 3 = 24 ⟶ 8 × 3 = 24

There are 8 bags.

Write a related multiplication fact for each.

1.

12 ÷ 4 = __3__

2.

$$3\,\overline{)\,6}^{\,2}$$

3.

$$5\,\overline{)\,1\,5}^{\,3}$$

Write a related division fact for each.

4.

$5 \times 2 = 10$

5.

$5 \times 4 = 20$

6.

$4 \times 4 = 16$

Complete.

7. $4 \times 2 = \underline{\ ?\ }$

$8 \div 2 = \underline{\ ?\ }$

8. $6 \times 3 = \underline{\ ?\ }$

$18 \div 3 = \underline{\ ?\ }$

9. $6 \times 4 = \underline{\ ?\ }$

$24 \div 4 = \underline{\ ?\ }$

10. $4 \times 5 = \underline{\ ?\ }$

$20 \div 5 = \underline{\ ?\ }$

11. $8 \times 2 = \underline{\ ?\ }$

$16 \div 2 = \underline{\ ?\ }$

12. $7 \times 5 = \underline{\ ?\ }$

$35 \div 5 = \underline{\ ?\ }$

13. $9 \times 3 = \underline{\ ?\ }$

$27 \div 3 = \underline{\ ?\ }$

14. $4 \times 8 = \underline{\ ?\ }$

$32 \div 8 = \underline{\ ?\ }$

15.
$$\begin{array}{c} 3 \\ \underline{\times 4} \\ ? \end{array} \qquad 3\overline{)12}$$

16.
$$\begin{array}{c} 2 \\ \underline{\times 7} \\ ? \end{array} \qquad 2\overline{)14}$$

17.
$$\begin{array}{c} 4 \\ \underline{\times 8} \\ ? \end{array} \qquad 4\overline{)32}$$

18.
$$\begin{array}{c} 5 \\ \underline{\times 9} \\ ? \end{array} \qquad 5\overline{)45}$$

Solve.

19. Four apples weigh about a pound. There are 24 apples. About how many pounds are there?

20. There are 15 squash in all. Each carton holds 3 squash. How many cartons are there?

167

Dividing by Two

There are 10 toy cars. Two cars fit in each box. How many boxes are there?

To find how many boxes there are, divide:

$$10 \div 2 = \underline{?} \quad \text{or} \quad 2\overline{)10}$$

$\uparrow$ number in all $\qquad \uparrow$ number in each group $\qquad \uparrow$ number of groups

Think: $10 \div 2 = \underline{?} \longrightarrow \underline{?} \times 2 = 10 \longrightarrow 5 \times 2 = 10$

So, $10 \div 2 = 5$ or $2\overline{)1\,0}$.

The answer in division is called the quotient.

There are 5 boxes.

Find how many groups of two.

1.

$6 \div 2 = \underline{?}$

2.

$8 \div 2 = \underline{?}$

3.

$4 \div 2 = \underline{?}$

4.

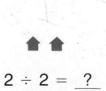

$2 \div 2 = \underline{?}$

5.

$16 \div 2 = \underline{?}$

6.

$10 \div 2 = \underline{?}$

Find how many in each group.

7.

14 ÷ 2 = _?_

8.

12 ÷ 2 = _?_

9.

18 ÷ 2 = _?_

Find each quotient.

10. 8 ÷ 2 = _?_   **11.** 10 ÷ 2 = _?_   **12.** 16 ÷ 2 = _?_   **13.** 18 ÷ 2 = _?_

14. 2)4   **15.** 2)12   **16.** 2)14   **17.** 2)10   **18.** 2)16

Complete the table.

19.

2 ÷ 2	4 ÷ 2	6 ÷ 2	8 ÷ 2	10 ÷ 2	12 ÷ 2	14 ÷ 2	16 ÷ 2	18 ÷ 2
1	?	?	?	?	?	?	?	?

Solve.

20. There are 8 cars in all. There are 2 parking garages. How many cars are there in each garage?

21. The garage has a parking section for every 2 cars. How many sections are there for 16 cars?

22. Michael drove his car 14 kilometers in all. Each day he drove 2 kilometers. How many days did he drive his car?

7-4 Dividing by Three

There are 3 bars of soap in each package. There are 15 bars of soap in all. How many packages are there?

To find how many packages there are, divide:

$$15 \div 3 = \underset{\uparrow}{?} \quad \text{or} \quad 3\overline{)15}$$

15	÷	3	=	?	or	3)15

number in all   number in each group   number of groups

Think: $15 \div 3 = \underline{?} \longrightarrow \underline{?} \times 3 = 15 \longrightarrow 5 \times 3 = 15$

So, $15 \div 3 = 5$ or $3\overline{)15}^{\,5}$.

There are 5 packages.

Find how many groups of three.

1.
✳ ✳ ✳
✳ ✳ ✳

$6 \div 3 = \underline{\ ?\ }$

2.
✳ ✳ ✳
✳ ✳ ✳
✳ ✳ ✳
✳ ✳ ✳

$12 \div 3 = \underline{\ ?\ }$

3.
✳ ✳ ✳
✳ ✳ ✳
✳ ✳ ✳

$9 \div 3 = \underline{\ ?\ }$

4.
✳ ✳ ✳
✳ ✳ ✳
✳ ✳ ✳
✳ ✳ ✳
✳ ✳ ✳

$15 \div 3 = \underline{\ ?\ }$

5.
✳ ✳ ✳

$3 \div 3 = \underline{\ ?\ }$

6.
✳ ✳ ✳ ✳ ✳ ✳
✳ ✳ ✳ ✳ ✳ ✳
✳ ✳ ✳
✳ ✳ ✳

$18 \div 3 = \underline{\ ?\ }$

170

Find how many in each group.

7.

∗∗∗∗∗∗∗∗∗
∗∗∗∗∗∗∗∗∗
∗∗∗∗∗∗∗∗∗

27 ÷ 3 = _?_

8.

∗∗∗∗∗∗∗∗
∗∗∗∗∗∗∗∗
∗∗∗∗∗∗∗∗

24 ÷ 3 = _?_

9.

∗∗∗∗∗∗∗
∗∗∗∗∗∗∗
∗∗∗∗∗∗∗

21 ÷ 3 = _?_

Find each quotient.

10. 9 ÷ 3 **11.** 15 ÷ 3 **12.** 24 ÷ 3 **13.** 21 ÷ 3 **14.** 27 ÷ 3

15. 18 ÷ 3 **16.** 12 ÷ 3 **17.** 3 ÷ 3 **18.** 8 ÷ 2 **19.** 6 ÷ 3

20. 3)‾9 **21.** 3)‾15 **22.** 3)‾21 **23.** 3)‾24 **24.** 3)‾18

25. 3)‾6 **26.** 3)‾12 **27.** 2)‾18 **28.** 3)‾3 **29.** 3)‾27

Complete the table.

30.

3÷3	6÷3	9÷3	12÷3	15÷3	18÷3	21÷3	24÷3	27÷3
1	?	?	?	?	?	?	?	?

Solve.

31. There are 12 bars of soap. 3 children divide the soap into equal groups. How many bars does each child receive?

32. Each bar weighs 3 ounces. All the bars of soap together weigh 18 ounces. How many bars of soap are there?

Practice Dividing by Two and Three

Complete.

1. How many in each group?

   ▲ ▲ ▲ ▲
   ▲ ▲ ▲ ▲

   8 ÷ 2 = _?_ in each group.

2. How many in each group?

   ▲ ▲ ▲ ▲ ▲
   ▲ ▲ ▲ ▲ ▲

   10 ÷ 2 = _?_

3. How many groups?

   ▲ ▲ ▲ ▲
   ▲ ▲ ▲ ▲
   ▲ ▲ ▲ ▲

   12 ÷ _?_ = 4

4. How many groups?

   ▲ ▲ ▲

   ▲ ▲ ▲

   6 ÷ _?_ = 3

Divide.

5. 4 ÷ 2   6. 9 ÷ 3   7. 10 ÷ 2   8. 18 ÷ 3   9. 6 ÷ 3

10. 14 ÷ 2   11. 24 ÷ 3   12. 18 ÷ 2   13. 12 ÷ 2   14. 27 ÷ 3

15. 2)6̄   16. 3)1̄2̄   17. 2)8̄

18. 2)1̄2̄   19. 3)1̄5̄   20. 2)1̄6̄

21. 2)1̄8̄   22. 3)2̄1̄   23. 3)2̄7̄

Solve. Use the numbers 18 and 3.

24. Write a problem that asks how many in each group.

25. Write a problem that asks how many groups.

172

Multiplication Practice

Find each product.

1. 3×2 2. 4×0 3. 4×3 4. 5×1 5. 6×7

6. 8×2 7. 6×5 8. 9×4 9. 7×2 10. 4×4

11. $\begin{array}{r} 5 \\ \times 2 \\ \hline \end{array}$ 12. $\begin{array}{r} 4 \\ \times 6 \\ \hline \end{array}$ 13. $\begin{array}{r} 5 \\ \times 7 \\ \hline \end{array}$ 14. $\begin{array}{r} 2 \\ \times 9 \\ \hline \end{array}$ 15. $\begin{array}{r} 3 \\ \times 8 \\ \hline \end{array}$ 16. $\begin{array}{r} 3 \\ \times 7 \\ \hline \end{array}$

17. $\begin{array}{r} 2 \\ \times 2 \\ \hline \end{array}$ 18. $\begin{array}{r} 1 \\ \times 3 \\ \hline \end{array}$ 19. $\begin{array}{r} 4 \\ \times 8 \\ \hline \end{array}$ 20. $\begin{array}{r} 1 \\ \times 2 \\ \hline \end{array}$ 21. $\begin{array}{r} 0 \\ \times 5 \\ \hline \end{array}$ 22. $\begin{array}{r} 5 \\ \times 3 \\ \hline \end{array}$

23. $\begin{array}{r} 5 \\ \times 9 \\ \hline \end{array}$ 24. $\begin{array}{r} 3 \\ \times 6 \\ \hline \end{array}$ 25. $\begin{array}{r} 0 \\ \times 2 \\ \hline \end{array}$ 26. $\begin{array}{r} 4 \\ \times 2 \\ \hline \end{array}$ 27. $\begin{array}{r} 5 \\ \times 5 \\ \hline \end{array}$ 28. $\begin{array}{r} 4 \\ \times 9 \\ \hline \end{array}$

Find the missing factor.

29. $\underline{\ ?\ } \times 2 = 8$ 30. $\underline{\ ?\ } \times 4 = 4$ 31. $\underline{\ ?\ } \times 5 = 20$

32. $\underline{\ ?\ } \times 3 = 27$ 33. $2 \times \underline{\ ?\ } = 6$ 34. $3 \times \underline{\ ?\ } = 15$

35. $3 \times \underline{\ ?\ } = 12$ 36. $5 \times \underline{\ ?\ } = 20$ 37. $\underline{\ ?\ } \times 4 = 36$

38. $\begin{array}{r} ? \\ \times 8 \\ \hline 40 \end{array}$ 39. $\begin{array}{r} ? \\ \times 3 \\ \hline 0 \end{array}$ 40. $\begin{array}{r} 2 \\ \times ? \\ \hline 12 \end{array}$ 41. $\begin{array}{r} 4 \\ \times ? \\ \hline 28 \end{array}$ 42. $\begin{array}{r} ? \\ \times 4 \\ \hline 16 \end{array}$ 43. $\begin{array}{r} ? \\ \times 3 \\ \hline 9 \end{array}$

Change the order of the factors and multiply.

44. 2×3 45. 4×2 46. 5×4 47. 5×3 48. 3×4

Solve.

49. Three boxes of greeting cards are packed in a carton. Laura sells 12 cartons to her friends. How many boxes of greeting cards did Laura sell?

7-7 Dividing by Four

There are 24 stamps in all. There are 4 stamps in each row. How many rows of stamps are there?

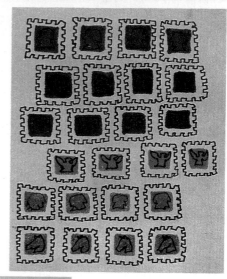

To find how many rows there are, divide:

$24 \div 4 = \underline{}$ or $4\overline{)24}$

Think: $24 \div 4 = \underline{} \longrightarrow \underline{} \times 4 = 24 \longrightarrow 6 \times 4 = 24$

There are 6 rows of stamps.

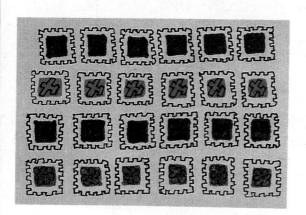

The 24 stamps are divided into 4 equal rows. How many stamps are there in each row?

To find how many stamps there are in each row, divide:

$24 \div 4 = \underline{}$ or $4\overline{)24}$

Think: $4 \times \underline{} = 24 \longrightarrow 4 \times 6 = 24$

There are 6 stamps in each row.

Find how many groups of four.

1.
✳ ✳ ✳ ✳
✳ ✳ ✳ ✳

$8 \div 4 = \underline{}$

2.
✳ ✳ ✳ ✳
✳ ✳ ✳ ✳
✳ ✳ ✳ ✳

$12 \div 4 = \underline{}$

3.
✳ ✳ ✳ ✳
✳ ✳ ✳ ✳
✳ ✳ ✳ ✳
✳ ✳ ✳ ✳

$16 \div 4 = \underline{}$

4. ＊＊＊＊

$4 \div 4 =$ ___?___

5. ＊＊＊＊ ＊＊＊＊
＊＊＊＊ ＊＊＊＊
＊＊＊＊ ＊＊＊＊

$24 \div 4 =$ ___?___

6. ＊＊＊＊ ＊＊＊＊
＊＊＊＊ ＊＊＊＊
＊＊＊＊

$20 \div 4 =$ ___?___

Find how many in each group.

7. $24 \div 4 =$ ___?___

8. $28 \div 4 =$ ___?___

9. $32 \div 4 =$ ___?___

Find the quotient.

10. $8 \div 4$

11. $12 \div 4$

12. $4 \div 4$

13. $20 \div 4$

14. $24 \div 4$

15. $12 \div 3$

16. $28 \div 4$

17. $32 \div 4$

18. $36 \div 4$

19. $16 \div 4$

20. $4\overline{)8}$

21. $4\overline{)20}$

22. $4\overline{)4}$

23. $4\overline{)28}$

24. $4\overline{)32}$

25. $4\overline{)12}$

26. $2\overline{)18}$

27. $4\overline{)24}$

28. $4\overline{)16}$

29. $4\overline{)36}$

Complete the table.

30.

$4 \div 4$	$8 \div 4$	$12 \div 4$	$16 \div 4$	$20 \div 4$	$24 \div 4$	$28 \div 4$	$32 \div 4$	$36 \div 4$
1	?	?	?	?	?	?	?	?

Use dots and circles to show each division fact.

31. 32 in all
8 in each group
4 groups

32. 36 in all
4 in each group
9 groups

33. 20 in all
5 in each group
4 groups

34. $4\overline{)20}$

35. $4\overline{)36}$

36. $4\overline{)28}$

7-8 Dividing by Five

There are 20 curtain rings.
There are 5 curtain rings on each
rod. How many rods are there?

To find how many rods there
are, divide:

20	÷	5	=	?	or 5)20
↑		↑		↑	
number		number		number	
in		in each		of	
all		group		groups	

Think: $20 ÷ 5 = ?$ ⟶ $? × 5 = 20$ ⟶ $4 × 5 = 20$

So, $20 ÷ 5 = 4$ or   5)2 0 with 4 above

There are 4 rods.

Find how many groups of five.

1. ♥♥♥♥♥ ♥♥♥♥♥	2. ♥♥♥♥♥ ♥♥♥♥♥ ♥♥♥♥♥	3. ♥♥♥♥♥ ♥♥♥♥♥ ♥♥♥♥♥ ♥♥♥♥♥ ♥♥♥♥♥
$10 ÷ 5 = \underline{?}$	$15 ÷ 5 = \underline{?}$	$25 ÷ 5 = \underline{?}$

♥♥♥♥♥	5. ♥♥♥♥♥ ♥♥♥♥♥ ♥♥♥♥♥ ♥♥♥♥♥ ♥♥♥♥♥ ♥♥♥♥♥	6. ♥♥♥♥♥ ♥♥♥♥♥ ♥♥♥♥♥ ♥♥♥♥♥ ♥♥♥♥♥ ♥♥♥♥♥ ♥♥♥♥♥ ♥♥♥♥♥
 $5 ÷ 5 = \underline{?}$	 $30 ÷ 5 = \underline{?}$	 $40 ÷ 5 = \underline{?}$

176

Find how many are in each group.

7. 30 ÷ 5 = _?_   **8.** 40 ÷ 5 = _?_   **9.** 45 ÷ 5 = _?_

Divide.

10. 10 ÷ 5   **11.** 20 ÷ 5   **12.** 15 ÷ 5   **13.** 25 ÷ 5

14. 35 ÷ 5   **15.** 5 ÷ 5   **16.** 30 ÷ 5   **17.** 40 ÷ 5

18. 5)15   **19.** 5)5   **20.** 4)24   **21.** 5)20   **22.** 5)45

23. 5)10   **24.** 5)25   **25.** 5)35   **26.** 5)30   **27.** 5)40

Complete the table.

28.

5 ÷ 5	10 ÷ 5	15 ÷ 5	20 ÷ 5	25 ÷ 5	30 ÷ 5	35 ÷ 5	40 ÷ 5	45 ÷ 5
1	?	?	?	?	?	?	?	?

Solve.

29. 35 divided by 5 equals what number?

30. Find the quotient when 15 is divided by 5.

31. The Video Tape Mart receives 35 new video tapes. Five video tapes can be stored on each shelf. How many shelves are needed?

32. Mr. Burns has 45 rings. He puts 5 rings in each box. How many boxes does he need?

One as a Divisor and Quotient

There are 3 bees. Each bee lands on
1 flower. How many flowers are there?

To find the number of flowers,
divide:

$$3 \div 1 = 3 \quad \text{or} \quad 1\overline{)3}^{\,3}$$

Think: Any number divided by 1 is
the number.

There are 3 flowers.

There are 3 bees. The 3 bees land on
a flower. How many flowers are there?

To find the number of flowers,
divide:

$$3 \div 3 = 1 \quad \text{or} \quad 3\overline{)3}^{\,1}$$

Think: Any number divided by itself is 1.

There is 1 flower.

Find the quotient.

1. $2 \div 2$ 2. $4 \div 1$ 3. $5 \div 5$ 4. $2 \div 1$

5. $4 \div 4$ 6. $3 \div 3$ 7. $5 \div 1$ 8. $3 \div 1$

9. $1\overline{)2}$ 10. $3\overline{)3}$ 11. $1\overline{)4}$ 12. $5\overline{)5}$ 13. $1\overline{)5}$

14. $4\overline{)4}$ 15. $2\overline{)2}$ 16. $1\overline{)3}$ 17. $1\overline{)2}$ 18. $3\overline{)3}$

7-10 Division Practice

Complete.

1.

   8 shirts.
   2 shirts in each box.
   There are __?__ boxes.

2.

   6 hats.
   3 boxes.
   There are __?__ in each box.

3. 10 ties.
   5 ties in each box.
   There are __?__ boxes.

4. 12 pairs of socks.
   4 boxes.
   There are __?__ in each box.

Find the quotient.

5. 4 ÷ 2   6. 12 ÷ 4   7. 6 ÷ 2   8. 20 ÷ 5   9. 14 ÷ 2

10. 18 ÷ 3   11. 24 ÷ 4   12. 25 ÷ 5   13. 3 ÷ 1   14. 35 ÷ 5

15. 24 ÷ 3   16. 36 ÷ 4   17. 5 ÷ 1   18. 18 ÷ 2   19. 3 ÷ 3

20. 2)10   21. 4)28   22. 5)30   23. 3)24   24. 4)4

25. 2)18   26. 3)21   27. 4)40   28. 1)4   29. 4)36

30. 2)16   31. 3)27   32. 4)32   33. 5)5   34. 4)16

35. 3)9   36. 2)12   37. 5)45   38. 1)5   39. 3)3

Solve.

40. There are 15 sweaters. Mr. Williams puts
    3 sweaters in each box. How many boxes?

41. Make up a division problem. Use the
    numbers 12 and 4.

Problem Solving: Choose the Operation

Multiplication	Division
Join equal groups	**Separate into equal groups**
How many in all?	How many equal groups?
OR	OR
How many altogether?	How many in each group?

Problem: There are 24 triangles on the chalkboard.
Each row has 4 triangles. How many rows of triangles are there?

24 triangles
4 in a row

1 IMAGINE Draw and label a picture of the triangles.

2 NAME *Facts:* 24 triangles in all
4 triangles in each row

Question: How many rows are there?

3 THINK Look at the picture.
What are you looking for?
You are looking for the number of rows.
You are looking for the number of equal groups.
Divide: 24 ÷ 4 = ___?___

4 COMPUTE
$$4\overline{)24} = 6$$
There are 6 rows of triangles.

5 CHECK 6 × 4 = 24
Or, count the number of rows.

Solve.

1. Every 2 students share a paint easel. There are 8 paint easels. How many students are in the art class?

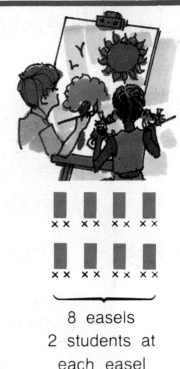

IMAGINE	Draw and label a picture.

Facts: 8 easels
2 students, each easel.

NAME	

Question: How many students are in the class?

THINK	

Are you looking for how many students in all? Yes.
Multiply: $8 \times 2 = \underline{\ ?\ }$

8 easels
2 students at
each easel

Then → **COMPUTE** and → **CHECK**

2. It takes 3 minutes for Ms. Young to grade a paper. There are 9 papers. How many minutes does it take her to grade all the papers?

3. Twenty-five students are playing a math game. The students are separated into 5 equal teams. How many students are on each team?

4. Five horses are in each corral. There are 4 corrals. How many horses are there in all?

5. There are 35 students in a class. There are the same number of students in each of 5 rows. How many students are in each row?

6. Ms. Hawley has 28 papers to pass out to her students. There are 4 rows of students. How many students are in each row?

More Practice

Divide.

1. $4 \div 2$ 2. $6 \div 3$ 3. $12 \div 4$ 4. $10 \div 5$ 5. $16 \div 2$

6. $8 \div 4$ 7. $18 \div 2$ 8. $15 \div 3$ 9. $20 \div 4$ 10. $30 \div 5$

11. $2\overline{)6}$ 12. $3\overline{)21}$ 13. $4\overline{)16}$ 14. $5\overline{)40}$ 15. $3\overline{)3}$

16. $3\overline{)18}$ 17. $5\overline{)35}$ 18. $2\overline{)12}$ 19. $4\overline{)36}$ 20. $5\overline{)45}$

21. $2\overline{)14}$ 22. $1\overline{)2}$ 23. $3\overline{)24}$ 24. $4\overline{)32}$ 25. $5\overline{)5}$

Complete.

26. $4 \times 2 = \underline{\ ?\ }$ 27. $3 \times 3 = \underline{\ ?\ }$ 28. $7 \times 4 = \underline{\ ?\ }$

     $8 \div 2 = \underline{\ ?\ }$ $9 \div 3 = \underline{\ ?\ }$ $28 \div 4 = \underline{\ ?\ }$

29. $9 \times 3 = \underline{\ ?\ }$ 30. $5 \times 1 = \underline{\ ?\ }$ 31. $5 \times 5 = \underline{\ ?\ }$

     $27 \div 3 = \underline{\ ?\ }$ $5 \div 1 = \underline{\ ?\ }$ $25 \div 5 = \underline{\ ?\ }$

32. $\begin{array}{r} 2 \\ \times 5 \end{array}$ $2\overline{)10}$ 33. $\begin{array}{r} 4 \\ \times 6 \end{array}$ $4\overline{)24}$ 34. $\begin{array}{r} 1 \\ \times 3 \end{array}$ $1\overline{)3}$ 35. $\begin{array}{r} 5 \\ \times 5 \end{array}$ $5\overline{)25}$

Solve.

36. Mrs. Wright picked 32 pounds of peaches in 4 hours. How many pounds did she pick each hour?

37. Frank picked 3 quarts of strawberries in an hour. How many quarts did he pick in 7 hours?

38. There are 4 bananas on each branch. How many bananas are there on 7 branches?

(See *Still More Practice*, pp. 361.)

Math-e-Magic

FACT FAMILIES

Study these examples.

number of groups		number in each group		number in all		number in each group		number of groups		number in all
↓		↓		↓		↓		↓		↓
2	×	5	=	10		5	×	2	=	10
10	÷	5	=	2		10	÷	2	=	5
↑		↑		↑		↑		↑		↑
number in all		number in each group		number of groups		number in all		number of groups		number in each group

These examples form a **fact family** for multiplication and division. A fact family contains all the same numbers for multiplication and division.

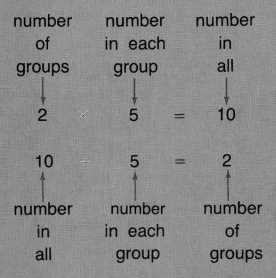

Now look at this example.

$3 \times 3 = 9$
$9 \div 3 = 3$

> You can only write one multiplication fact and one division fact for 3, 3, and 9.

Write the fact family for each set of drawings.

1. ★ ★ ★ ★   ★ ★ ★
   ★ ★ ★ ★   ★ ★ ★
   ★ ★ ★ ★   ★ ★ ★
                ★ ★ ★

2. ★ ★   ★ ★ ★
   ★ ★   ★ ★ ★
   ★ ★

3. ★ ★ ★ ★ ★   ★ ★ ★ ★
   ★ ★ ★ ★ ★   ★ ★ ★ ★
   ★ ★ ★ ★ ★   ★ ★ ★ ★
   ★ ★ ★ ★ ★   ★ ★ ★ ★
                ★ ★ ★ ★

Write the fact family for these numbers.

4. 2, 7, and 14   5. 3, 7, and 21   6. 3, 8, and 24

183

Check Your Mastery

Divide.

See pp. 164-165, 168-172, 174-179

1. $6 \div 3$
2. $12 \div 4$
3. $8 \div 2$
4. $10 \div 5$

5. $15 \div 5$
6. $18 \div 3$
7. $24 \div 4$
8. $18 \div 2$

9. $2\overline{)4}$
10. $3\overline{)21}$
11. $4\overline{)16}$
12. $5\overline{)20}$
13. $4\overline{)36}$

14. $2\overline{)16}$
15. $3\overline{)27}$
16. $5\overline{)30}$
17. $4\overline{)28}$
18. $5\overline{)45}$

19. $3\overline{)24}$
20. $4\overline{)32}$
21. $5\overline{)25}$
22. $3\overline{)3}$
23. $5\overline{)35}$

Complete.

See pp. 166-167

24. $3 \times 2 = \underline{\ ?\ }$
    $6 \div 2 = \underline{\ ?\ }$

25. $5 \times 3 = \underline{\ ?\ }$
    $15 \div 3 = \underline{\ ?\ }$

26. $8 \times 5 = \underline{\ ?\ }$
    $40 \div 5 = \underline{\ ?\ }$

27. $1 \times 2 = \underline{\ ?\ }$
    $2 \div 2 = \underline{\ ?\ }$

28. $4 \times 3 = \underline{\ ?\ }$
    $12 \div 3 = \underline{\ ?\ }$

29. $6 \times 4 = \underline{\ ?\ }$
    $24 \div 4 = \underline{\ ?\ }$

30. $\begin{array}{r} 2 \\ \times 7 \\ \hline \end{array}$ $\quad 2\overline{)14}$

31. $\begin{array}{r} 3 \\ \times 3 \\ \hline \end{array}$ $\quad 3\overline{)9}$

32. $\begin{array}{r} 3 \\ \times 4 \\ \hline \end{array}$ $\quad 3\overline{)12}$

33. $\begin{array}{r} 4 \\ \times 5 \\ \hline \end{array}$ $\quad 4\overline{)20}$

Solve.

See pp. 168-169, 176-177, 180-181

34. Juan has 18 marbles in two pockets. How many marbles are there in each pocket?

35. Cindy has 5 piles of baseball cards. She has 45 baseball cards in all. How many baseball cards are in each pile?

8

Measurement

In this unit you will:

- Choose the most reasonable metric and customary unit for length or distance, capacity, and weight
- Measure to the nearest inch, half inch, and quarter inch
- Use the liquid measure of cup, pint, quart, gallon, and liter
- Measure weights using ounce, pound, gram, and kilogram
- Measure lengths to the nearest centimeter and meter
- Read a thermometer and record temperatures in degrees Celsius, and in degrees Fahrenheit
- Solve problems using number sentences

Do you remember?

paper clip = 1 unit

about 3 paper clips long

185

8-1 Inch, Foot, Yard, Mile

Small objects are measured by the **inch**.
The width of this quarter is *about* 1 inch (in.).

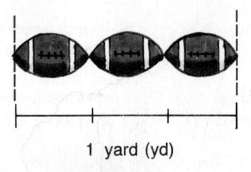

Some measures are not exact.
These measures are given to the
nearest unit.

Longer objects are measured by the
foot or **yard**.

Two dollar bills put end to end
are *about* 1 foot long.

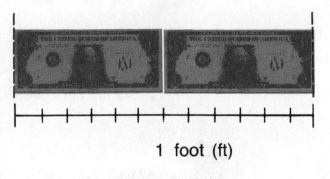

These 3 footballs are
about 1 yard.

1 foot (ft)

1 yard (yd)

1 ft = 12 in.

1 yd = 3 ft

Very long lengths are measured by miles.

The distance from New York to
Cape Cod is *about* 260 miles (mi).

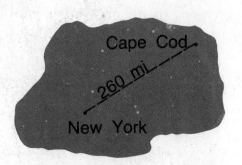

1 mi = 5280 ft

Write what unit you use to measure:

1. the width of this book.

2. the height an airplane flies.

3. your height.

4. the width of a calculator.

5. the length of a truck.

6. the length of a river.

Choose the reasonable answer.

7. The distance a car can travel in one hour.
   a. 55 yd   **b.** 55 mi   **c.** 55 in.   **d.** 55 ft

8. The height of a basketball player.
   a. 7 ft   **b.** 7 yd   **c.** 7 mi   **d.** 7 in.

9. The length of a football field.
   a. 100 in.   **b.** 100 ft   **c.** 100 yd   **d.** 100 mi

10. The length of your pencil.
    a. 6 in.   **b.** 6 mi   **c.** 6 yd   **d.** 6 ft

Use your tape measure or ruler to measure to the nearest foot:

11. the height of your desk.

12. the length of the work table.

13. from your shoulder to the floor.

Use your tape measure to measure to the nearest yard:

14. the length of the chalkboard.

15. the length of the bulletin board.

16. the length of a jump rope.

17. the length of your home.

Inch, Half Inch, Quarter Inch

Length can be measured on a ruler with **inches**, **half inches**, and **quarter inches**.

Look at these markings on a ruler.

inch	longest lines marked 1, 2, 3, 4, 5, and 6
half inch	next longest lines halfway between the inches.
quarter inch	halfway between the inch and the half inch

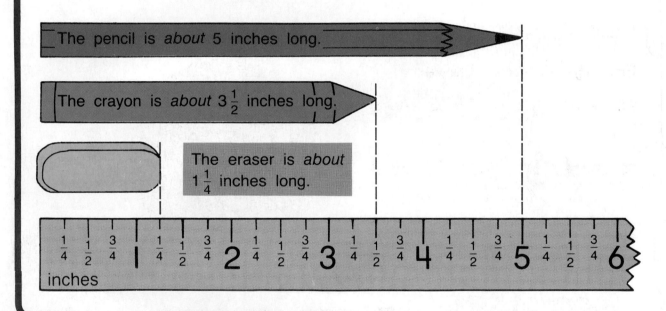

The pencil is *about* 5 inches long.

The crayon is *about* $3\frac{1}{2}$ inches long.

The eraser is *about* $1\frac{1}{4}$ inches long.

Use your ruler to measure each to the nearest inch.

1.

2.

3.

4.

Measure the length to the nearest half inch.

5. your pen

6. your thumb

7. your schoolbag

8. your foot

Measure the length to the nearest quarter inch.

9. a pair of scissors

10. the top of your desk

11. an art brush

12. a spiral notebook

Draw a line for each length.

13. 3 in.

14. 7 in.

15. 12 in.

16. $6\frac{1}{2}$ in.

17. $9\frac{1}{2}$ in.

18. $10\frac{1}{4}$ in.

19. $4\frac{1}{2}$ in.

20. $3\frac{3}{4}$ in.

Find the distance between:

21. A and C

22. C and B

23. A and B

24. A and D

25. C and D

26. B and D

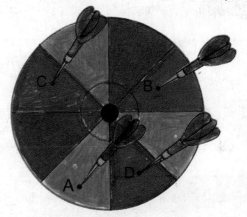

Draw the following letters. Use a ruler.

27. From a starting point, draw down 2 in. Then draw to the right 1 in. What letter did you draw?

28. From a starting point, draw a line 2 in. to the left. From there, draw a line 3 in. down. Then draw a line 2 in. to the right followed by a line $1\frac{1}{2}$ in. up. Now draw another 2 in. to the left. What number did you draw?

189

Cup, Pint, Quart, Gallon

The **cup**, **pint**, **quart**, and **gallon** are units used to measure amounts of liquids.

1 cup (c)

1 pint (pt)

1 pt = 2 c

1 quart (qt)

1 qt = 2 pt

1 gallon (gal)

1 gal = 4 qt

Which unit would you use to measure:

1. the amount of milk in a glass?

2. the amount of water in a bathtub?

3. the amount of water in a large vase?

4. the amount of juice in a small container?

5. the amount of milk for baking?

6. the amount of lemonade in a large pitcher?

Complete.

7. If 1 pt = 2 c, then

    a. 2 pt = _?_ c   **b.** 3 pt = _?_ c   **c.** 8 pt = _?_ c

8. If 1 qt = 2 pt, then

    a. 2 qt = _?_ pt   **b.** 3 qt = _?_ pt   **c.** 6 qt = _?_ pt

9. If 1 qt = 4 c, then

    a. 2 qt = _?_ c   **b.** 3 qt = _?_ c   **c.** 4 qt = _?_ c

10. If 1 gal = 4 qt, then

    a. 3 gal = _?_ qt   **b.** 4 gal = _?_ qt   **c.** 5 gal = _?_ qt

11. If 1 gal = 8 pt, then

    a. 3 gal = _?_ pt   **b.** 5 gal = _?_ pt   **c.** 2 gal = _?_ pt

12. If 1 gal = 16 c, then

    a. 2 gal = _?_ c   **b.** 4 gal = _?_ c   **c.** 5 gal = _?_ c

Write "cup (c)", "pint (pt)", "quart (qt)", or "gallon (gal)" for each.

13.

14.

15.

16.

8-4　Ounce, Pound

Ounces (oz) : a unit used to measure the weight of small things.

Pounds (lb) : a unit used to measure the weight of larger things.

1 pound = 16 ounces

1 lb = 16 oz

A box of soap is *about* 1 pound.

An apple is *about* 5 oz.

The bologna weighs 15 oz.

A dog is *about* 50 pounds.

Study this table.

ounces	16	32	48	64	80	96	112
pounds	1	2	3	4	5	6	7

Compare. Write <, =, or >. (Use the chart above.)

1. 16 oz _?_ 1 lb

2. 64 oz _?_ 4 lb

3. 2 lb _?_ 30 oz

4. 7 lb _?_ 90 oz

5. 8 oz _?_ 1 lb

6. 80 oz _?_ 3 lb

7. 3 lb _?_ 50 oz

8. 15 oz _?_ 1 lb

9. 32 oz _?_ 2 lb

10. 4 lb _?_ 48 oz

11. 4 lb _?_ 40 oz

12. 96 oz _?_ 6 lb

Practice:
Customary Measures

cup	half inch	quarter inch	pound	pint

quart	gallon	ounce	inch

Write the unit of measure you would use to measure each. Choose from the above.

1.

2.

3.

4. your height

5. your weight

6. width of your hand

7. Cut out pictures to show the measures you did not use.

Compare. Write < , =, or > .

8. 10 oz __?__ 2 lb

9. $6\frac{1}{2}$ in. __?__ $8\frac{1}{4}$ in.

10. 4 qt __?__ 1 gal

11. 3 c __?__ 1 pt

Challenge!

12. Draw your foot. Then measure each part to the nearest inch, half inch, or quarter inch.

Centimeter

Length can be measured using small units.

This crayon is about 3 paper clips long.

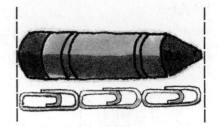

This stack of 8 dimes is *about* 1 cm high. 1 cm

A dollar bill is *about* 15 cm long.

15 cm

The distance from this bird's beak to its tail is *about* 4 cm.

4 cm

Measure each to the nearest centimeter.

1.

?

2.

?

Measure the distance each needs to finish the race.
(Use a centimeter ruler.)

START   FINISH

5. _____?_ cm

6. _____?_ cm

7. _____?_ cm

8. _____?_ cm

9. _____?_ cm

10. _____?_ cm

11. _____?_ cm

Find the distance between:

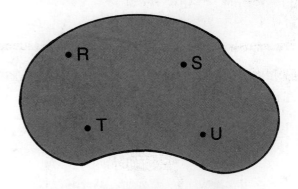

12. R and T   13. S and T

14. R and S   15. R and U

16. T and U   17. S and U

Draw a line for each length.

18. 7 cm   19. 16 cm   20. 9 cm   21. 11 cm

22. 20 cm   23. 3 cm   24. 19 cm   25. 25 cm

8-7 Meter and Kilometer

The centimeter (cm) is a unit used to measure the lengths of small objects.

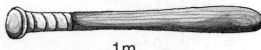

1m

The length of a baseball bat is *about* 1 meter.

Meter (m): a unit used to measure longer lengths.

1 meter = 100 centimeters

| 1 m = 100 cm |

Very long distances can be measured with **kilometers** (km).

1 kilometer = 1000 meters

| 1 km = 1000 m |

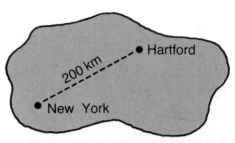

200 km — Hartford — New York

The distance from New York to Hartford is *about* 200 kilometers.

Write what unit you use to measure:

1. the height of the doorway.

2. the distance from Los Angeles to Chicago.

3. the height of a cup.

4. the distance from home to school.

5. the height an airplane flies.

Use your metric tape measure or ruler to measure each to the nearest meter.

6. the width of the doorway   7. the length of the room

8. the width of the chalkboard   9. the width of the room

Choose the reasonable answer.

10.

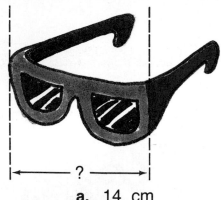

?

a. 14 cm
b. 14 m
c. 14 km

11.

?

a. 200 cm
b. 200 km
c. 200 m

12. the width of a penny

a. 2 cm **b.** 2 m **c.** 2 km

13. the thickness of a slice of bread

a. 1 km **b.** 1 m **c.** 1 cm

14. the height an airplane flies

a. 8 cm **b.** 8 km **c.** 8 m

Solve.

15. James worked at the drugstore after school. He delivered medicine to Mrs. Smith and to Mr. Lowery and then returned to the drugstore. How far did he go?

16. James went to Mr. Kent and to Mr. Lowery and then returned to the drugstore. How far did he go?

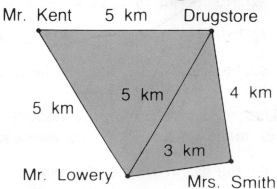

Mr. Kent — 5 km — Drugstore

5 km

5 km

4 km

3 km

Mr. Lowery

Mrs. Smith

8-8 Liter

The **liter** is a unit for measuring amounts of liquid.

1 liter

4 liters

50 liters

A liter of liquid will fill about 4 glasses.

Write "*more than a liter*" **or** "*less than a liter.*"

1.

2.

3.

4.

5.

6.

198

8-9 Gram and Kilogram

The **gram** (g) is a unit for measuring the weight of small objects.

A feather weighs about 2 g.

Grams are used to weigh small things like hot dogs, feathers, and rolls.

Kilograms (kg) are used to weigh larger things like bags of potatoes.

1 kilogram = 1000 grams

1 kg = 1000 g

A bag of potatoes weighs about 2 kg.

Write what unit (g, kg) you use to measure:

1.

2.

3.

Compare. Write <, =, or >.

4. 1 kg _?_ 900 g   **5.** 440 g _?_ 4 kg   **6.** 2000 g _?_ 2 kg

Choose the sensible answer.

7. the weight of a loaf of bread.
   a. 700 g   **b.** 7000 g   **c.** 70 g

8. the weight of a large dog.
   a. 25 kg   **b.** 250 kg   **c.** 2500 kg

199

8-10 Fahrenheit Thermometer

A thermometer is used to measure temperature.

The unit for measuring temperature is the degree **Fahrenheit**. It is written as °F.

Normal body temperature is between 98°F and 99°F. It is 98.6°F.

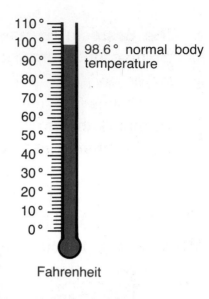

110°
100° — 98.6° normal body temperature
90°
80°
70°
60°
50°
40°
30°
20°
10°
0°

Fahrenheit

Read and write the temperature.

1.

60°
50°
40°
30°
20°
10°
0°

water freezes ?

2.

220°
210°
200°
190°
180°
170°

water boils ?

3.

80°
70°
60°
50°
40°
30°
20°

average room temperature ?

4.

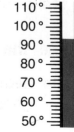

110°
100°
90°
80°
70°
60°
50°

hot summer day ?

200

8-11 Celsius Thermometer

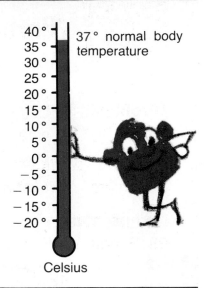

40° 35° 30° 25° 20° 15° 10° 5° 0° −5° −10° −15° −20°

37° normal body temperature

Celsius

The degree **Celsius** is another unit for measuring temperature. It is written as °C.

Normal body temperature is 37°C on the Celsius thermometer.

Read and write the temperature.

1.

5° 0° −5° −10° −15° −20°

water freezes ?

2.

105° 100° 95° 90° 85° 80° 75° 70°

water boils ?

3.

0° −5° −10° −15° −20°

cold day ?

4.

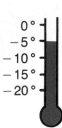

30° 25° 20° 15° 10° 5° 0°

hot day ?

5. the temperature outside today ?

Choose the sensible answer.

6. the best temperature to eat a popsicle.
  a. 35°C   **b.** 10°C   **c.** 90°C

7. playing outside in Chicago in January.
  a. 3°C   **b.** 23°C   **c.** 33°C

201

Problem Solving: Writing Number Sentences

Problem: Cliff weighs his best friends. Mark weighed 57 pounds. Don weighed 63 pounds, and Rita weighed 54 pounds. What is their total weight?

1 IMAGINE

Cliff weighs 3 friends.

2 NAME

Facts: 57 lb Mark
63 lb Don
54 lb Rita

Question: What is their total weight?

3 THINK

Write a number sentence for the total weight.

$$\text{Total weight} = \text{Mark's weight} + \text{Don's weight} + \text{Rita's weight}$$

$$\text{Total weight} = 57 \text{ lb} + 63 \text{ lb} + 54 \text{ lb}$$

4 COMPUTE

Total weight = 57 + 63 + 54
Total weight = 174

The total weight is 174 pounds.

5 CHECK

Subtract the weights from 174 pounds.

$$
\begin{array}{r} 174 \\ -\ 57 \\ \hline 117 \end{array}
\longrightarrow
\begin{array}{r} 117 \\ -\ 63 \\ \hline 54 \end{array}
\longrightarrow
\begin{array}{r} 54 \\ -\ 54 \\ \hline 0 \end{array}
$$

0 is the difference. The answer checks.

Write a number sentence and solve.

1. There are 23 quarts of water in the fish tank. Seven students each remove a quart. How many quarts are now in the fish tank?

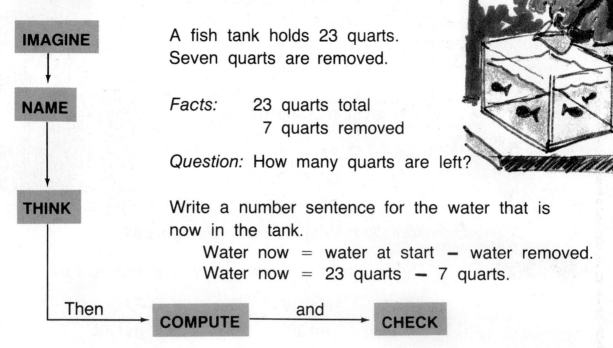

IMAGINE

A fish tank holds 23 quarts. Seven quarts are removed.

NAME

Facts: 23 quarts total
            7 quarts removed

Question: How many quarts are left?

THINK

Write a number sentence for the water that is now in the tank.

Water now = water at start − water removed.
Water now = 23 quarts − 7 quarts.

Then → **COMPUTE** — and → **CHECK**

2. The flasks on the science table each hold 1 liter. There are 5 flasks. How much liquid do the flasks hold?

3. Four boxes of computer paper weigh 36 kg. How much does each box weigh?

4. It was 52°F when the class started on a field trip to the ocean. It warmed up 7 degrees by the time they got there. What was the temperature at the ocean?

5. Enid made 28 birthday cards. She sold 12 of them. How many were not sold?

More Practice

Choose the reasonable answer.

1. A car travels __?__ per hour.
   - **a.** 55 in.
   - **b.** 55 ft
   - **c.** 55 yd
   - **d.** 55 mi

2. The length of a parking lot.
   - **a.** 200 mi
   - **b.** 20 in.
   - **c.** 200 yd
   - **d.** 20 ft

3. The length of a piece of paper.
   - **a.** 11 in.
   - **b.** 11 ft
   - **c.** 11 yd
   - **d.** 11 mi

Measure each to the nearest half inch.

4.

5.

Complete.

6. If 1 pt = 2 c, then 4 pt = __?__ c

7. If 1 gal = 4 qt, then 6 gal = __?__ qt

8. If 1 qt = 2 pt, then 5 qt = __?__ pt

Compare. Write <, =, or >.

9. 12 oz __?__ 1 lb   10. 4 lb __?__ 60 oz   11. 32 oz __?__ 2 lb

Choose the reasonable answer.

12. Chris baked bread at __?__ °F.
    - **a.** 350
    - **b.** 212
    - **c.** 100
    - **d.** 50

13. The water is warm enough for swimming in at __?__ °C.
    - **a.** 15
    - **b.** 20
    - **c.** 40
    - **d.** 80

14. It may snow when the temperature is __?__ °C.
    - **a.** 5
    - **b.** 15
    - **c.** −5
    - **d.** 32

204

(See *Still More Practice*, p. 362.)

Math-e-Magic

LOGICAL REASONING

A rabbit, a pig, and a dog ran the 100-meter dash at a track meet.

Use these clues to complete the table. Write "yes" when the fact is true. Write "no" when the fact is false.

1. The rabbit, wearing number 341, did *not* win.

2. The pig, wearing number 247, did *not* come in third.

3. The pig ran the race 2 seconds slower than the animal wearing number 100.

Runner	Place		
	1st	2nd	3rd
Rabbit	no		
Pig		yes	no
Dog			

In what order did they finish the race? (Hint: The pig finished second. Why?)

Check Your Mastery

Choose the reasonable answer.

See pp. 192

1. The weight of an adult
   a. 15 oz   **b.** 150 oz   **c.** 15 lb   **d.** 150 lb

2. The weight of a dollar bill
   a. 2 oz   **b.** 20 oz   **c.** 2 lb   **d.** 20 lb

3. The weight of a car
   a. 1000 oz   **b.** 3000 lb   **c.** 300 oz   **d.** 300 lb

Compare. Write <, =, or >.

See pp. 186-187

4. 6 in. _?_ 60 ft   5. 10 yd _?_ 90 ft   6. 7 ft _?_ 84 in.

Complete.

See pp. 186-187, 190-191

7. If 1 gal = 4 qt, then 2 gal = _?_ qt

8. If 1 qt = 4 c, then 3 qt = _?_ c

9. If 1 yd = 3 ft, then 3 yd = _?_ ft

Which metric unit — cm, m, or km— should be used to measure each?

See pp. 194-197

10. the length of a gasoline truck

11. the width of a stamp

12. the length of a baseball bat

13. the width of an envelope

Solve.

See pp. 190-191, 200

14. When Joan awoke it was 37°F. Later it was 49°F. How much warmer was it?

15. Lynn used 4 quarts of water. Sandra used 9 pints of water. Who used more water?

206

Cumulative Test II

Complete.

1. 4 ×3	**2.** 5 ×1	**3.** 4 ×4	**4.** 2 ×6	**5.** 5 ×3	**6.** 3 ×6
7. 0 ×7	**8.** 4 ×5	**9.** 0 ×3	**10.** 2 ×2	**11.** 2 ×4	**12.** 3 ×9
13. 5 ×8	**14.** 4 ×9	**15.** 5 ×5	**16.** 4 ×7	**17.** 5 ×7	**18.** 4 ×8

Add or subtract.

19. $7.37 − 2.98	**20.** $2.79 + 4.50	**21.** $4.68 + 3.90	**22.** $9.60 − 6.25	**23.** $4.69 + 3.50

Estimate the sum or difference.

24. $4.54 − 1.23	**25.** $7.42 + 2.31	**26.** $9.14 − 5.22	**27.** $1.82 + 6.95	**28.** $9.16 − 4.78

Complete.

29. $8 \times \underline{\ ?\ } = 40$ **30.** $\underline{\ ?\ } \times 3 = 24$ **31.** $7 \times \underline{\ ?\ } = 21$

32. $6 \times \underline{\ ?\ } = 12$ **33.** $5 \times \underline{\ ?\ } = 15$ **34.** $\underline{\ ?\ } \times 4 = 36$

35. $9 \div 3 = \underline{\ ?\ }$ **36.** $24 \div 4 = \underline{\ ?\ }$ **37.** $15 \div 5 = \underline{\ ?\ }$

38. $18 \div 2 = \underline{\ ?\ }$ **39.** $32 \div 4 = \underline{\ ?\ }$ **40.** $28 \div 4 = \underline{\ ?\ }$

41. $3\overline{)21}$ **42.** $4\overline{)12}$ **43.** $3\overline{)15}$ **44.** $4\overline{)36}$ **45.** $2\overline{)10}$

46. $5\overline{)30}$ **47.** $4\overline{)20}$ **48.** $5\overline{)25}$ **49.** $3\overline{)27}$ **50.** $4\overline{)16}$

Tell time another way.

51. 3 minutes before 2 = $\underline{\ ?\ }$: $\underline{\ ?\ }$

52. 53 minutes past 7 = $\underline{\ ?\ }$: $\underline{\ ?\ }$

53. 46 minutes after 5 = $\underline{\ ?\ }$: $\underline{\ ?\ }$

Write how much money. Use . and $.

54. 1 half dollar, 3 quarters, 2 dimes, 1 nickel = $\underline{\ ?\ }$

55. 3 dollars, 1 quarter, 7 nickels, 4 pennies = ?

56. 1 five-dollar bill, 1 dime, 9 pennies = ?

Write A.M. or P.M.

57. Carol eats breakfast at 7:30 ? .

58. Mr. Ryan leaves school at 4:00 ? .

59. Rico plays baseball at 6:15 ? .

Complete.

60. If 1 quart = 2 pints, then 8 qt = ? pt.

61. If 16 ounces = 1 pound, then 48 oz = ? lb.

62. If 1000 meters = 1 kilometer, then 5 km = ? m.

63. If 100 centimeters = 1 meter, then 300 cm = ? m.

64. If 12 inches = 1 foot, then 36 in. = ? ft.

65. If 1 gallon = 4 quarts, then 4 gal = ? qt.

Solve.

66. Lucia bought a book for $3.25 and a pencil for $.79. How much money did she spend?

67. Norman drives his truck 9 kilometers to work each day. How many kilometers does he drive in 5 days?

68. Stan has $5.00 to buy milk for $1.89 and a bag of noodles for $1.29. How much change will he receive?

69. Mrs. Washington has 15 winter blankets for the family. In the spring she packs them away in 3 boxes. How many blankets does she pack into each box?

70. There are 16 pens to be divided equally among 8 children. How many pens will each child receive?

71. Larry weighs 47 pounds, Jeff weighs 52 pounds, and Norman weighs 58 pounds. What is the boys' total weight?

72. If 20 tomatoes are packaged into 5 boxes, how many tomatoes will go into each box?

73. Sharon planted 4 tulip plants in each row of her flower bed. If there are 3 rows, how many tulip plants are in her flower bed?

74. Fran can pick 6 pints of blueberries in an hour. How many pints could she pick in 4 hours?

75. There are 28 cornstalks in the garden. If there are 4 cornstalks in each row, how many rows are there?

9

More Multiplication and Division Facts

In this unit you will:

- Multiply 6, 7, 8, and 9
- Multiply three numbers
- Divide by 6, 7, 8, and 9
- Study 0 in division
- Find number patterns
- Multiply and divide using the number line
- Find extra information when solving problems

Do you remember?

Multiplication and division are opposites.

$5 \times 6 = 30$ ⟶ product
$30 \div 6 = 5$ ⟶ quotient

These multiplication and division facts form a fact family.

(5, 6, 30) Family

$$5 \times 6 = 30$$
$$6 \times 5 = 30$$
$$30 \div 6 = 5$$
$$30 \div 5 = 6$$

9-1 Multiplication Review

Tom put 2 shells in each of 5 pails.
How many shells are there in all?
Multiply: $5 \times 2 = \underline{?}$

You can **multiply** to find the number in all if
each group has the *same* number in it.

5	×	2	=	10	or	2 ← factors
groups		in each		in all		$\times\ 5$ ←
		group				10 ← product

Tom put 10 shells in all in the pails.

Multiply.

1. $\begin{array}{r} 3 \\ \times 2 \\ \hline \end{array}$
2. $\begin{array}{r} 2 \\ \times 4 \\ \hline \end{array}$
3. $\begin{array}{r} 4 \\ \times 4 \\ \hline \end{array}$
4. $\begin{array}{r} 3 \\ \times 7 \\ \hline \end{array}$
5. $\begin{array}{r} 2 \\ \times 2 \\ \hline \end{array}$
6. $\begin{array}{r} 5 \\ \times 0 \\ \hline \end{array}$

7. $\begin{array}{r} 2 \\ \times 5 \\ \hline \end{array}$
8. $\begin{array}{r} 3 \\ \times 8 \\ \hline \end{array}$
9. $\begin{array}{r} 5 \\ \times 4 \\ \hline \end{array}$
10. $\begin{array}{r} 5 \\ \times 8 \\ \hline \end{array}$
11. $\begin{array}{r} 1 \\ \times 5 \\ \hline \end{array}$
12. $\begin{array}{r} 0 \\ \times 4 \\ \hline \end{array}$

13. $\begin{array}{r} 3 \\ \times 5 \\ \hline \end{array}$
14. $\begin{array}{r} 1 \\ \times 2 \\ \hline \end{array}$
15. $\begin{array}{r} 4 \\ \times 8 \\ \hline \end{array}$
16. $\begin{array}{r} 2 \\ \times 9 \\ \hline \end{array}$
17. $\begin{array}{r} 1 \\ \times 4 \\ \hline \end{array}$
18. $\begin{array}{r} 3 \\ \times 1 \\ \hline \end{array}$

19. $\begin{array}{r} 5 \\ \times 7 \\ \hline \end{array}$
20. $\begin{array}{r} 3 \\ \times 9 \\ \hline \end{array}$
21. $\begin{array}{r} 4 \\ \times 6 \\ \hline \end{array}$
22. $\begin{array}{r} 3 \\ \times 5 \\ \hline \end{array}$
23. $\begin{array}{r} 5 \\ \times 9 \\ \hline \end{array}$
24. $\begin{array}{r} 5 \\ \times 1 \\ \hline \end{array}$

Solve.

25. Sal bought 3 packages of 4 shells. How
    many shells did Sal buy?

26. Rita collects 5 shells on each of 8 days.
    How many shells does Rita collect in all?

210

9-2 Multiplying Sixes

The store clerk counted 7 packages of fruit juice. Each package has 6 cans of juice. How many cans of juice did the store clerk count?

To find the number of cans, multiply: $7 \times 6 = \underline{\ ?\ }$

$7 \times 6 = 42$

There are 42 cans of fruit juice.

Think: 7 sets of 6 cans
or 7 sixes
or 7×6

Find the product.

1.

0×6	1×6	2×6	3×6	4×6	5×6	6×6	7×6	8×6	9×6
0	6	?	?	?	?	?	?	?	?

Multiply.

2. 6
   ×2

3. 4
   ×6

4. 6
   ×5

5. 3
   ×6

6. 6
   ×7

7. 6
   ×9

8. 1
   ×6

9. 6
   ×8

10. 5
   ×6

11. 0
   ×6

12. 6
   ×6

13. 6
   ×4

14. 2
   ×6

15. 3
   ×5

16. 5
   ×8

17. 4
   ×7

18. 5
   ×9

19. 4
   ×9

Multiplying Sevens

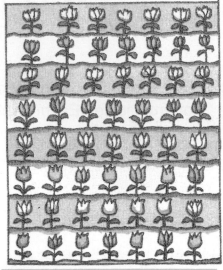

Mr. Olson is planting tulips. He plants 8 rows with 7 tulips in each row. How many tulips is Mr. Olson planting in all?

To find the number of tulips, multiply: $8 \times 7 = \underline{\ ?\ }$

$$8 \times 7 = 56$$

There are 56 tulips.

Think: 8 sets of 7 tulips
or 8 sevens
or 8×7

Write each multiplication fact.

1.

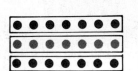

$3 \times 7 = \underline{\ ?\ }$

2.

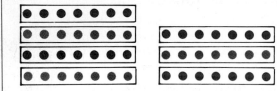

$7 \times 7 = \underline{\ ?\ }$

3.

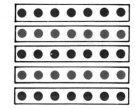

$\underline{\ ?\ } \times 7 = \underline{\ ?\ }$

4.

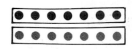

$\underline{\ ?\ } \times \underline{\ ?\ } = \underline{\ ?\ }$

5.

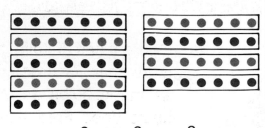

$\underline{\ ?\ } \times \underline{\ ?\ } = \underline{\ ?\ }$

6.

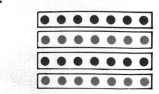

$\underline{\ ?\ } \times \underline{\ ?\ } = \underline{\ ?\ }$

Draw dots and circles to show each multiplication fact.

7.	8.	9.	10.
7 $\times 2$	7 $\times 3$	7 $\times 4$	7 $\times 5$

Find the product.

11.

0×7	1×7	2×7	3×7	4×7	5×7	6×7	7×7	8×7	9×7
0	7	?	?	?	?	?	?	?	?

Multiply.

12.	13.	14.	15.	16.	17.
7 $\times 2$	7 $\times 3$	7 $\times 4$	7 $\times 5$	7 $\times 1$	7 $\times 8$

18.	19.	20.	21.	22.	23.
7 $\times 6$	7 $\times 7$	6 $\times 7$	9 $\times 7$	7 $\times 0$	4 $\times 7$

Solve.

24. Mr. Olson plants 7 rows each day for 9 days. How many rows does he plant in all?

25. Betty collects 7 shells. Carol collects 3 times as many shells. How many shells does Carol have in all?

···· CHALLENGE ····

26. George has 5 tulip bulbs. Wally has 2 more than George. Fred has 7 times as many bulbs as Wally. How many bulbs does Fred have in all?

9-4 Multiplying Eights

The postal worker puts a letter in each post office box. There are 9 rows of 8 boxes. How many boxes are there in all?

To find the number of boxes, multiply: $9 \times 8 = $ _?_

$9 \times 8 = 72$

There are 72 boxes in all.

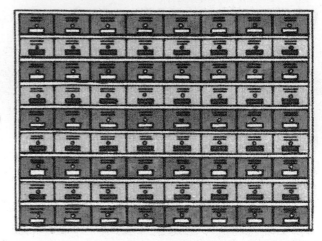

Think: 9 sets of 8 boxes
or 9 eights
or 9×8

Write each multiplication fact.

1.

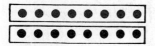

$2 \times 8 = $ _?_

2.

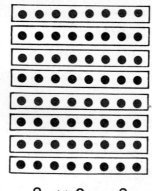

_?_ $\times 8 = $ _?_

3.

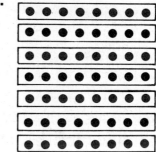

$7 \times $ _?_ $ = $ _?_

4.

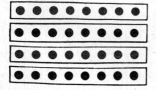

_?_ $\times$ _?_ $ = $ _?_

5.

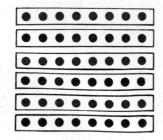

_?_ $\times$ _?_ $ = $ _?_

6.

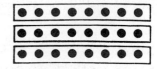

_?_ $\times$ _?_ $ = $ _?_

Find the product.

7.

0×8	1×8	2×8	3×8	4×8	5×8	6×8	7×8	8×8	9×8
0	8	?	?	?	?	?	?	?	?

Multiply.

8. 8 ×2	9. 8 ×3	10. 8 ×4	11. 8 ×5	12. 8 ×6
13. 8 ×9	14. 7 ×8	15. 8 ×8	16. 8 ×0	17. 8 ×1
18. 0 ×8	19. 8 ×7	20. 6 ×8	21. 4 ×8	22. 5 ×8

Solve.

23. Sue has 6 pages in her stamp book. Each page has 8 stamps. How many stamps does Sue have in all?

24. Lee buys 8 stamps on Monday. Friday, he buys 4 times as many stamps. How many stamps does Lee buy on Friday?

25. Rich gets 8¢ change from the postal clerk. Tim gets 7 times as much change. How much change does Tim get?

26. Lucy bought 6 packages of 8 shells. Mary bought 7 packages of 8 shells. Who bought more shells?

9-5 Multiplying Nines

There are 3 baskets with 9 apples in each. How many apples are there in all?

To find the number of apples, multiply: $3 \times 9 = \underline{?}$

$3 \times 9 = 27$

Think: 3 sets of 9 apples
or 3 nines or 3×9

Write each multiplication fact.

1.

$9 \times 9 = \underline{?}$

2.

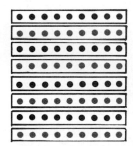

$\underline{?} \times 9 = \underline{?}$

3.

$7 \times \underline{?} = \underline{?}$

4.

$\underline{?} \times \underline{?} = \underline{?}$

5.

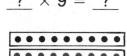

$\underline{?} \times \underline{?} = \underline{?}$

6.

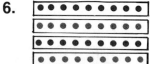

$\underline{?} \times \underline{?} = \underline{?}$

Show each multiplication fact.

7.   9
    $\times 3$

8.   9
    $\times 5$

9.   9
    $\times 7$

10.   9
    $\times 6$

11.   9
    $\times 2$

12.   9
    $\times 4$

13.   9
    $\times 9$

14.   9
    $\times 8$

216

Find the product.

15.	0 × 9	1 × 9	2 × 9	3 × 9	4 × 9	5 × 9	6 × 9	7 × 9	8 × 9	9 × 9
	0	9	?	?	?	?	?	?	?	?

Multiply.

16. $\begin{array}{r} 9 \\ \times 2 \\ \hline \end{array}$　17. $\begin{array}{r} 9 \\ \times 5 \\ \hline \end{array}$　18. $\begin{array}{r} 9 \\ \times 3 \\ \hline \end{array}$　19. $\begin{array}{r} 9 \\ \times 6 \\ \hline \end{array}$　20. $\begin{array}{r} 9 \\ \times 8 \\ \hline \end{array}$　21. $\begin{array}{r} 9 \\ \times 4 \\ \hline \end{array}$

22. $\begin{array}{r} 9 \\ \times 7 \\ \hline \end{array}$　23. $\begin{array}{r} 9 \\ \times 1 \\ \hline \end{array}$　24. $\begin{array}{r} 9 \\ \times 9 \\ \hline \end{array}$　25. $\begin{array}{r} 9 \\ \times 0 \\ \hline \end{array}$　26. $\begin{array}{r} 6 \\ \times 0 \\ \hline \end{array}$　27. $\begin{array}{r} 8 \\ \times 9 \\ \hline \end{array}$

28. $\begin{array}{r} 7 \\ \times 9 \\ \hline \end{array}$　29. $\begin{array}{r} 5 \\ \times 9 \\ \hline \end{array}$　30. $\begin{array}{r} 1 \\ \times 9 \\ \hline \end{array}$　31. $\begin{array}{r} 4 \\ \times 9 \\ \hline \end{array}$　32. $\begin{array}{r} 6 \\ \times 9 \\ \hline \end{array}$　33. $\begin{array}{r} 2 \\ \times 9 \\ \hline \end{array}$

Find the product.

34. 8 × 9　　　　35. 9 × 8　　　　36. 9 × 0

37. 9 × 6　　　　38. 6 × 9　　　　39. 0 × 9

40. 9 × 9　　　　41. 8 × 8　　　　42. 7 × 7

Solve.

43. Kathy buys a basket of 9 apples each week for 6 weeks. How many apples does she buy in all?

CHALLENGE

Name a multiplication fact whose product is:

44. a multiple of ten

45. one more than a multiple of ten

Multiplying Three Numbers

Each day Mrs. Kelly buys 2 packages of rolls. There are 4 rolls in each package. How many rolls in all does she buy in 2 days?

To find how many rolls in all,
multiply: $2 \times 4 \times 2 = $ <u>?</u>

To multiply three numbers:

- Group the *first* two factors using these symbols: ( ).

  $(2 \times 4) \times 2 = $ <u>?</u>

- Multiply these numbers first.

  $8 \times 2 = $ <u>?</u>

- Complete the multiplication.

  $8 \times 2 = 16$

   OR

- Group the *last* two factors using these symbols: ( ).

  $2 \times 4 \times 2 = $ <u>?</u>
  $2 \times (4 \times 2) = $ <u>?</u>

- Follow the steps above.

  $2 \times \quad 8 \quad = $ <u>?</u>
  $2 \times \quad 8 \quad = 16$

When you multiply, you can change the grouping and get the same product.

Multiply. (Use the grouping shown.)

1. $(2 \times 3) \times 2 = $ <u>?</u>
   $6 \times 2 = $ <u>?</u>

2. $(3 \times 2) \times 4 = $ <u>?</u>
   $6 \times 4 = $ <u>?</u>

3. $(4 \times 2) \times 5 = $ <u>?</u>
   $8 \times 5 = $ <u>?</u>

4. $(3 \times 2) \times 6 = $ <u>?</u>
   <u>?</u> $\times 6 = $ <u>?</u>

5. $(1 \times 4) \times 5 = $ <u>?</u>
   <u>?</u> $\times 5 = $ <u>?</u>

6. $(2 \times 4) \times 8 = $ <u>?</u>
   <u>?</u> $\times 8 = $ <u>?</u>

7. $2 \times (3 \times 2) = $ <u>?</u>
   $2 \times $ <u>?</u> $= $ <u>?</u>

8. $9 \times (1 \times 6) = $ <u>?</u>
   $9 \times $ <u>?</u> $= $ <u>?</u>

9. $3 \times (3 \times 3) = $ <u>?</u>
   $3 \times $ <u>?</u> $= $ <u>?</u>

Find the product. (Use the grouping shown.)

10. $2 \times (3 \times 3) =$ ___?___
     $2 \times$ ___?___ $=$ ___?___

11. $(2 \times 2) \times 4 =$ ___?___
     ___?___ $\times 4 =$ ___?___

12. $9 \times (1 \times 8) =$ ___?___
     $9 \times$ ___?___ $=$ ___?___

13. $(2 \times 4) \times 3 =$ ___?___
     ___?___ $\times$ ___?___ $=$ ___?___

14. $4 \times (3 \times 3) =$ ___?___
     ___?___ $\times$ ___?___ $=$ ___?___

15. $5 \times (1 \times 2) =$ ___?___
     ___?___ $\times$ ___?___ $=$ ___?___

Find the product. (Use any grouping you want.)

16. $3 \times 2 \times 2 =$ ___?___

17. $6 \times 3 \times 2 =$ ___?___

18. $2 \times 4 \times 5 =$ ___?___

19. $6 \times 1 \times 9 =$ ___?___

20. $6 \times 8 \times 0 =$ ___?___

21. $3 \times 3 \times 5 =$ ___?___

Solve.

22. Muffins are packed in 2 rows of 3 muffins each. How many muffins are there in 3 packages?

23. There are 8 rows of 2 ice cubes in each tray. How many ice cubes are there in 2 trays?

24. A carton of eggs has 2 rows of 3 eggs each. How many eggs are there in 4 cartons?

25. A layer of blocks has 5 rows with 3 blocks in each row. How many blocks are there in 3 layers?

Calculator Activity

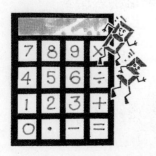

Multiply.

26. $3 \times 1 \times 9 =$ ___?___

27. $3 \times 1 \times 3 =$ ___?___

28. $1 \times 9 \times 3 =$ ___?___

29. $1 \times 3 \times 3 =$ ___?___

30. $2 \times 4 \times 4 =$ ___?___

31. $4 \times 4 \times 2 =$ ___?___

32. $2 \times 2 \times 0 =$ ___?___

33. $2 \times 0 \times 2 =$ ___?___

9-7 Division Review

Dorothy has 18 records. She puts 3 records in each pile. How many piles of records are there?

To find out how many sets of 3 records make 18, divide:

$$18 \div 3 = \underline{\ ?\ } \quad \text{or} \quad 3\overline{)18}$$

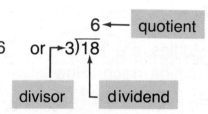

$\underline{\ ?\ }$ piles of 3 records is 18 records

Division is the opposite of multiplication.

Think:
$$18 \div 3 = \underline{\ ?\ }$$
$$\underline{\ ?\ } \times 3 = 18$$
$$6 \times 3 = 18 \longrightarrow 18 \div 3 = 6 \quad \text{or} \quad 3\overline{)18}$$

6 ← quotient

divisor   dividend

There are 6 piles of 3 records.

Divide.

1. $2\overline{)6}$ 2. $3\overline{)12}$ 3. $4\overline{)8}$ 4. $5\overline{)15}$ 5. $2\overline{)18}$

6. $3\overline{)18}$ 7. $4\overline{)20}$ 8. $5\overline{)10}$ 9. $3\overline{)21}$ 10. $2\overline{)2}$

11. $4\overline{)24}$ 12. $5\overline{)30}$ 13. $2\overline{)16}$ 14. $3\overline{)24}$ 15. $4\overline{)16}$

16. $5\overline{)35}$ 17. $3\overline{)9}$ 18. $2\overline{)14}$ 19. $4\overline{)28}$ 20. $5\overline{)5}$

21. $2\overline{)12}$ 22. $3\overline{)27}$ 23. $4\overline{)32}$ 24. $5\overline{)40}$ 25. $4\overline{)4}$

26. $3\overline{)15}$ 27. $4\overline{)36}$ 28. $2\overline{)10}$ 29. $3\overline{)3}$ 30. $5\overline{)45}$

Complete. Find the number pattern.
(Hint: Remember the division facts.)

31. 16, 8, _?_ , 2   **32.** 27, _?_ , 3, 1   **33.** 32, 8, _?_

34. 25, 5, _?_   **35.** 12, 6, _?_   **36.** 18, 6, _?_

Solve.

37. Nancy has a record case holding 32 records. She divides the case into 4 sections. How many records will each section hold?

38. Peter wrapped 45 records in packages. Each package held 5 records. How many packages did Peter wrap?

39. Fran joins a record club. She must buy 2 records a month and 16 records in all. How many months will it take Fran to buy the records?

40. One side of a record album plays for 45 minutes. Each song is 5 minutes long. How many songs are on one side?

Calculator Activity

Compute.

41. $9 \times 7 \div 3 =$ _?_   **42.** $6 \times 5 \div 2 =$ _?_

43. $8 \div 2 \times 4 =$ _?_   **44.** $45 \div 5 \times 3 =$ _?_

45. $8 \times 6 \div 4 =$ _?_   **46.** $36 \div 4 \times 0 =$ _?_

Dividing by Six

The janitor has 42 keys. How many groups of 6 keys does the janitor have?

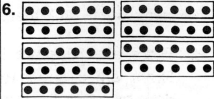

To find how many groups there are, divide:

$$42 \div 6 = \underline{\ ?\ } \quad \text{or} \quad 6\overline{)42}$$

Think: $42 \div 6 = \underline{\ ?\ }$

$\underline{\ ?\ } \times 6 = 42$

$7 \times 6 = 42$

So, $42 \div 6 = 7$ or $6\overline{)42}^{\,7}$

There are 7 groups of 6 keys.

Write the division fact for each.

1.
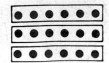

$36 \div 6 = \underline{\ ?\ }$

2.
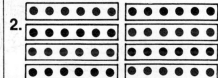

$48 \div 6 = \underline{\ ?\ }$

3.
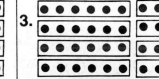

$54 \div 6 = \underline{\ ?\ }$

4.
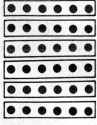

$18 \div \underline{\ ?\ } = \underline{\ ?\ }$

5.
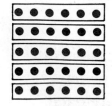

$\underline{\ ?\ } \div 6 = \underline{\ ?\ }$

6.

$\underline{\ ?\ } \div \underline{\ ?\ } = \underline{\ ?\ }$

Draw dots or circles to show each division fact.

7. $12 \div 6$.　　　8. $18 \div 6$.　　　9. $6\overline{)24}$　　　10. $6\overline{)30}$

Find the quotient.

11.

$6 \div 6$	$12 \div 6$	$18 \div 6$	$24 \div 6$	$30 \div 6$	$36 \div 6$	$42 \div 6$	$48 \div 6$	$54 \div 6$
1	?	?	?	?	?	?	?	?

Divide.

12. $6\overline{)12}$　　13. $3\overline{)24}$　　14. $6\overline{)18}$　　15. $6\overline{)30}$　　16. $6\overline{)42}$

17. $6\overline{)48}$　　18. $6\overline{)6}$　　19. $6\overline{)36}$　　20. $6\overline{)54}$　　21. $5\overline{)30}$

Solve.

22. The janitor has 24 keys in all. How many keys does she have on each of 6 key rings?

23. The janitor buys 48 rolls of paper towels. There are 6 rolls in each package. How many packages of paper towels does she buy?

24. It takes the janitor 42 minutes to sweep the floors in 6 rooms. How many minutes does it take to sweep each room?

25. There are 54 apartments in all. There are 6 apartments on each floor. How many floors are there?

26. There are 36 seats in the classroom. There are 6 equal rows of seats. How many seats are there in each row?

223

9-9 Dividing by Seven

There are 56 golf balls.
How many groups of 7 balls?

To find how many groups there are, divide:

$$56 \div 7 = \underline{} \quad \text{or} \quad 7\overline{)56}$$

Think: $56 \div 7 = \underline{}$

$\underline{} \times 7 = 56$

$8 \times 7 = 56$

So, $56 \div 7 = 8 \quad \text{or} \quad 7\overline{)56}^{\,8}$

There are 8 groups of 7 balls.

Write the division fact for each.

1.

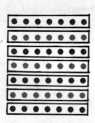

$49 \div 7 = \underline{}$

2.

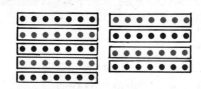

$63 \div 7 = \underline{}$

3.

$35 \div 7 = \underline{}$

4.

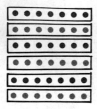

$42 \div \underline{} = \underline{}$

5.

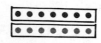

$\underline{} \div 7 = \underline{}$

6.

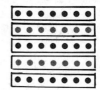

$\underline{} \div 7 = \underline{}$

224

Complete.

7. $14 \div 7 = \underline{\quad?\quad}$
$\underline{\quad?\quad} \times 7 = 14$

8. $21 \div 7 = \underline{\quad?\quad}$
$\underline{\quad?\quad} \times 7 = 21$

9. $28 \div 7 = \underline{\quad?\quad}$
$\underline{\quad?\quad} \times 7 = 28$

10. $7 \div 7 = \underline{\quad?\quad}$
$\underline{\quad?\quad} \times 7 = 7$

11. $35 \div 7 = \underline{\quad?\quad}$
$\underline{\quad?\quad} \times 7 = 35$

12. $42 \div 7 = \underline{\quad?\quad}$
$\underline{\quad?\quad} \times 7 = 42$

13. $49 \div 7 = \underline{\quad?\quad}$
$\underline{\quad?\quad} \times 7 = 49$

14. $63 \div 7 = \underline{\quad?\quad}$
$\underline{\quad?\quad} \times 7 = 63$

Divide.

15. $7\overline{)21}$ **16.** $7\overline{)56}$ **17.** $7\overline{)49}$ **18.** $7\overline{)63}$ **19.** $7\overline{)42}$

Find the quotient.

20.

$7 \div 7$	$14 \div 7$	$21 \div 7$	$28 \div 7$	$35 \div 7$	$42 \div 7$	$49 \div 7$	$56 \div 7$	$63 \div 7$
1	?	?	?	?	?	?	?	?

Solve.

21. The golf pro has 63 golf clubs. He puts 7 clubs into each golf bag. How many golf bags are there?

22. Todd finds 42 golf balls near the woods at the golf course. He puts an equal number of balls into 7 baskets. How many golf balls are in each basket?

23. The golf instructor divides 35 balls equally between 7 students. How many balls does each student get?

Dividing by Eight

The store clerk received 72 pens.
How many groups of 8 pens were there?

To find how many groups,

divide: $72 \div 8 = \underline{\ ?\ }$ or $8\overline{)72}$

Think: $72 \div 8 = \underline{\ ?\ }$

$\underline{\ ?\ } \times 8 = 72$

$9 \times 8 = 72$

So, $72 \div 8 = 9$ or $8\overline{)72}\ ^9$

There are 9 groups of 8 pens.

Write each division fact.

1.
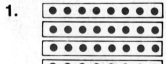

$64 \div 8 = \underline{\ ?\ }$

2.

$56 \div 8 = \underline{\ ?\ }$

3.
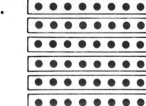

$48 \div 8 = \underline{\ ?\ }$

4.
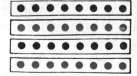

$32 \div \underline{\ ?\ } = \underline{\ ?\ }$

5.

$\underline{\ ?\ } \div 8 = \underline{\ ?\ }$

6.
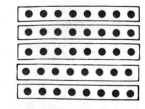

$\underline{\ ?\ } \div \underline{\ ?\ } = \underline{\ ?\ }$

Complete.

7. $16 \div 8 = \underline{?}$
   $\underline{?} \times 8 = 16$

8. $24 \div 8 = \underline{?}$
   $\underline{?} \times 8 = 24$

9. $32 \div 8 = \underline{?}$
   $\underline{?} \times 8 = 32$

10. $8 \div 8 = \underline{?}$
    $\underline{?} \times 8 = 8$

11. $40 \div 8 = \underline{?}$
    $\underline{?} \times 8 = 40$

12. $48 \div 8 = \underline{?}$
    $\underline{?} \times 8 = 48$

13. $56 \div 8 = \underline{?}$
    $\underline{?} \times 8 = 56$

14. $64 \div 8 = \underline{?}$
    $\underline{?} \times 8 = 64$

Divide.

15. $8)\overline{32}$ 16. $8)\overline{40}$ 17. $8)\overline{72}$ 18. $8)\overline{48}$ 19. $8)\overline{56}$

Find the quotient.

20.

$8 \div 8$	$16 \div 8$	$24 \div 8$	$32 \div 8$	$40 \div 8$	$48 \div 8$	$56 \div 8$	$64 \div 8$	$72 \div 8$
1	?	?	?	?	?	?	?	?

Solve.

21. There are 48 pairs of scissors. The store clerk puts 8 pairs in each box. How many boxes of scissors are there?

22. Lisa buys 8 pencils for 72¢. How much does one pencil cost?

23. The office uses 24 pencils in 8 weeks. How many are used in one week?

24. Sheila works 32 hours each week. She works 8 hours each day. How many days does she work each week?

Dividing by Nine

There are 54 Ping-Pong balls. How many groups of 9 balls are there?

To find how many groups, divide:

$$54 \div 9 = \underline{\ ?\ } \quad \text{or} \quad 9\overline{)54}$$

Think: $54 \div 9 = \underline{\ ?\ }$
$$\underline{\ ?\ } \times 9 = 54$$
$$6 \times 9 = 54$$

So, $54 \div 9 = 6 \quad \text{or} \quad 9\overline{)54}^{\,6}$

There are 6 groups of 9 balls.

Write the division fact for each.

1.
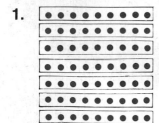

$$63 \div 9 = \underline{\ ?\ }$$

2.
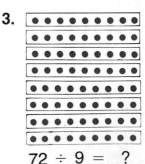

$$36 \div 9 = \underline{\ ?\ }$$

3.

$$72 \div 9 = \underline{\ ?\ }$$

4.
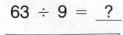

$$\underline{\ ?\ } \div 9 = \underline{\ ?\ }$$

5.
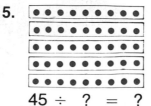

$$45 \div \underline{\ ?\ } = \underline{\ ?\ }$$

6.

$$\underline{\ ?\ } \div \underline{\ ?\ } = \underline{\ ?\ }$$

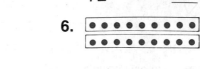

Complete.

7. $18 \div 9 = \underline{\ ?\ }$
    $\underline{\ ?\ } \times 9 = 18$

8. $27 \div 9 = \underline{\ ?\ }$
    $\underline{\ ?\ } \times 9 = 27$

9. $36 \div 9 = \underline{\ ?\ }$
    $\underline{\ ?\ } \times 9 = 36$

10. $45 \div 9 = \underline{\ ?\ }$
    $\underline{\ ?\ } \times 9 = 45$

11. $9 \div 9 = \underline{\ ?\ }$
    $\underline{\ ?\ } \times 9 = 9$

12. $63 \div 9 = \underline{\ ?\ }$
    $\underline{\ ?\ } \times 9 = 63$

13. $72 \div 9 = \underline{\ ?\ }$
    $\underline{\ ?\ } \times 9 = 72$

14. $81 \div 9 = \underline{\ ?\ }$
    $\underline{\ ?\ } \times 9 = 81$

Divide.

15. $9\overline{)45}$ 16. $9\overline{)54}$ 17. $9\overline{)63}$ 18. $9\overline{)81}$ 19. $9\overline{)72}$

Find the quotient.

20.

$9 \div 9$	$18 \div 9$	$27 \div 9$	$36 \div 9$	$45 \div 9$	$54 \div 9$	$63 \div 9$	$72 \div 9$	$81 \div 9$
1	?	?	?	?	?	?	?	?

Solve.

21. There are 81 Ping-Pong balls. 9 teams get an equal number of balls. How many balls does each team get?

22. If the product is 48 and one factor is 6, what is the other factor? What is the related division fact?

23. 72 new players are picked for Little League. They are to be divided equally among 9 teams. How many new players does each team get?

229

Zero in Division

Robert had 8 fishbowls.
He had no fish.
How many fish were in each bowl?

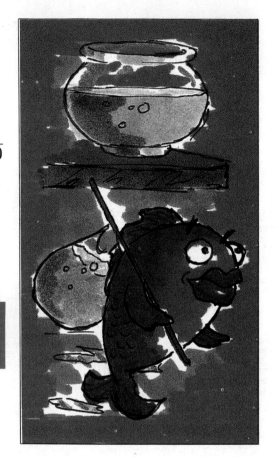

To find how many fish in each bowl,
divide: $0 \div 8 = \underline{\ ?\ }$ or $8\overline{)0}$

number in all	number of groups	number in each group

Think: $\underline{\ ?\ } \times 8 = 0 \longrightarrow 0 \times 8 = 0$

$0 \div 8 = 0$ or $8\overline{)\overset{0}{0}}$

Zero divided by any number is zero.

There are 0 fish in each bowl.

Remember:
Never divide by zero.

Divide.

1. $7\overline{)0}$ 2. $7\overline{)7}$ 3. $1\overline{)7}$ 4. $9\overline{)0}$ 5. $1\overline{)9}$

6. $8\overline{)64}$ 7. $6\overline{)48}$ 8. $7\overline{)63}$ 9. $9\overline{)54}$ 10. $6\overline{)42}$

11. $7\overline{)35}$ 12. $8\overline{)0}$ 13. $9\overline{)81}$ 14. $7\overline{)56}$ 15. $8\overline{)64}$

16. $0 \div 6$ 17. $8 \div 8$ 18. $7 \div 1$ 19. $0 \div 9$ 20. $42 \div 7$

9-13 Number Patterns

Compute. Then write the next example.

1. $\begin{array}{r}9\\\times6\end{array}$ $\begin{array}{r}9\\\times7\end{array}$ $\begin{array}{r}9\\\times8\end{array}$ $\begin{array}{r}?\\\times?\end{array}$ 2. $\begin{array}{r}7\\\times9\end{array}$ $\begin{array}{r}7\\\times8\end{array}$ $\begin{array}{r}7\\\times7\end{array}$ $\begin{array}{r}?\\\times?\end{array}$

3. $8\overline{)72}$ $8\overline{)64}$ $8\overline{)56}$ $?\overline{)?}$ 4. $7\overline{)35}$ $7\overline{)42}$ $7\overline{)49}$ $?\overline{)?}$

5. $6\overline{)36}$ $6\overline{)42}$ $6\overline{)48}$ $?\overline{)?}$ 6. $9\overline{)72}$ $9\overline{)63}$ $9\overline{)54}$ $?\overline{)?}$

Find the pattern. Write the next number.

7. 18, 24, 30, 36, __?__   8. 45, 40, 35, 30, __?__

9. 1, 2, 4, 8, __?__   10. 8, 12, 16, __?__

11. 1, 7, 13, 19, __?__   12. 28, 21, 14, 7, __?__

13. 4, 8, 16, __?__   14. 1, 3, 9, __?__

15. 54, 48, 42, __?__   16. 72, 64, 56, __?__

Solve.

17. Wednesday is May 2. What are the dates of the next four Wednesdays?

18. Thursday is August 31. What are the dates of the four Thursdays before August 31?

19. A jar is filled with 24 cookies. Carlos takes half of them. Wanda takes half of what is left. Fred then takes half of what Wanda left. How many cookies remain in the jar?

231

Problem Solving: Too Much Information

Problem: The library has 54 chairs. The library is open from 8 A.M. until 8 P.M. Each table has 6 chairs. How many tables are in the library?

1 IMAGINE

Draw and label a picture of the problem.

2 NAME

Facts: 54 chairs
6 chairs to a table
8 A.M.— 8 P.M. hours open

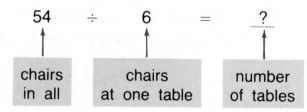
6 chairs to a table
(54 chairs)

Question: How many tables are there in the library?

3 THINK

Look at your drawing.
This information is needed:

$$54 \div 6 = \ ?$$

| chairs in all | chairs at one table | number of tables |

What information is not needed?

8 A.M.— 8 P.M., hours open

4 COMPUTE

$54 \div 6 = 9$
There are 9 tables in the library.

5 CHECK

Check your answer by multiplication.

$9 \times 6 = 54$

The answer checks.

Find the extra information.
Then solve.

1. Each of the 9 tables in the library has 7 books and 8 magazines on it. How many books are on the tables?

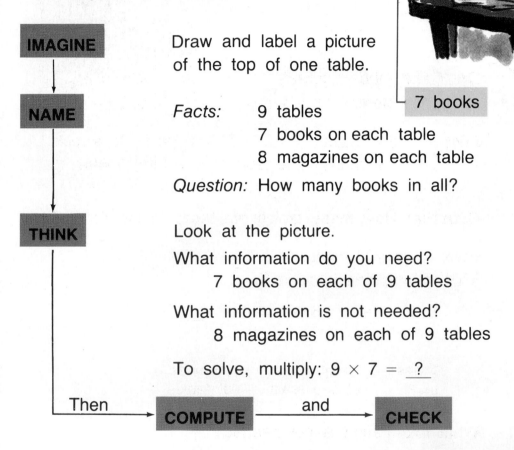

7 books   8 magazines

IMAGINE

Draw and label a picture of the top of one table.

NAME

Facts: 9 tables
7 books on each table
8 magazines on each table

Question: How many books in all?

THINK

Look at the picture.

What information do you need?
7 books on each of 9 tables

What information is not needed?
8 magazines on each of 9 tables

To solve, multiply: $9 \times 7 = \underline{\ ?\ }$

Then → **COMPUTE** — and → **CHECK**

2. Mr. Phillips works in the library 35 hours in 5 days. He reads 3 hours a day. How many hours does Mr. Phillips work each day?

3. There are 8 groups of 9 students visiting the library. A teacher stays with each group. How many students are visiting the library?

More Practice

Multiply.

1. 2 × 6   **2.** 3 × 7   **3.** 4 × 8   **4.** 5 × 9   **5.** 1 × 7

6. 7 ×2   **7.** 6 ×8   **8.** 9 ×7   **9.** 6 ×6   **10.** 8 ×9   **11.** 9 ×9

12. 3 ×8   **13.** 4 ×9   **14.** 9 ×6   **15.** 8 ×7   **16.** 1 ×9   **17.** 8 ×8

18. 4 ×3   **19.** 6 ×5   **20.** 7 ×9   **21.** 0 ×7   **22.** 9 ×4   **23.** 7 ×6

Find each product.

24. 2 × 3 × 3 = _?_   **25.** 6 × 1 × 0 = _?_

26. 7 × 1 × 6 = _?_   **27.** 3 × 3 × 3 = _?_

28. 4 × 2 × 3 = _?_   **29.** 3 × 2 × 3 = _?_

Divide.

30. 18 ÷ 6   **31.** 28 ÷ 7   **32.** 40 ÷ 8   **33.** 54 ÷ 9

34. 8)‾16   **35.** 6)‾24   **36.** 8)‾72   **37.** 9)‾27   **38.** 7)‾63

39. 9)‾18   **40.** 7)‾42   **41.** 8)‾8   **42.** 9)‾81   **43.** 8)‾64

Solve.

44. There are 36 birds. There are 9 bird feeders. How many equal groups of birds can feed at each feeder?

45. 6 boys went fishing. Each boy caught 9 fish. How many fish did they catch in all?

234

(See *Still More Practice*, pp. 363.)

Math-e-Magic

NUMBER LINES FOR MULTIPLICATION AND DIVISION

Study the number lines.

The number line shows multiplication:

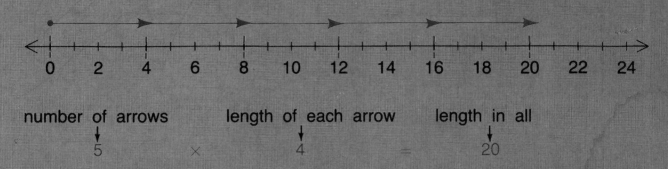

number of arrows   length of each arrow   length in all

        5   ×   4   =   20

The number line shows division:

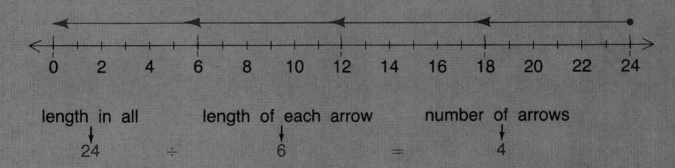

length in all   length of each arrow   number of arrows

     24   ÷   6   =   4

Use a number line to show each multiplication and division fact.

1. 5×4 2. 3×7 3. 2×8

4. 6×5 5. 9×2 6. 4×3

7. $6 \div 2$ 8. $9 \div 3$ 9. $16 \div 4$

10. $5\overline{)10}$ 11. $6\overline{)12}$ 12. $8\overline{)24}$

Check Your Mastery

Multiply.

See pp. 210-217

1. 7×9
2. 7×7
3. 6×8
4. 9×9

5. $\begin{array}{r} 8 \\ \times 7 \\ \hline \end{array}$
6. $\begin{array}{r} 8 \\ \times 8 \\ \hline \end{array}$
7. $\begin{array}{r} 6 \\ \times 7 \\ \hline \end{array}$
8. $\begin{array}{r} 7 \\ \times 9 \\ \hline \end{array}$
9. $\begin{array}{r} 8 \\ \times 9 \\ \hline \end{array}$
10. $\begin{array}{r} 9 \\ \times 6 \\ \hline \end{array}$

11. $\begin{array}{r} 6 \\ \times 4 \\ \hline \end{array}$
12. $\begin{array}{r} 7 \\ \times 6 \\ \hline \end{array}$
13. $\begin{array}{r} 8 \\ \times 4 \\ \hline \end{array}$
14. $\begin{array}{r} 9 \\ \times 0 \\ \hline \end{array}$
15. $\begin{array}{r} 1 \\ \times 8 \\ \hline \end{array}$
16. $\begin{array}{r} 6 \\ \times 8 \\ \hline \end{array}$

Find the product.

See pp. 218-219

17. $2 \times 3 \times 2 =$?
18. $7 \times 4 \times 0 =$?
19. $6 \times 1 \times 8 =$?
20. $2 \times 2 \times 2 =$?
21. $6 \times (2 \times 3) =$?
22. $(3 \times 3) \times 4 =$?

Divide.

See pp. 220-229

23. $7\overline{)28}$
24. $6\overline{)54}$
25. $8\overline{)56}$
26. $7\overline{)42}$
27. $9\overline{)45}$

28. $8\overline{)48}$
29. $6\overline{)36}$
30. $9\overline{)81}$
31. $7\overline{)63}$
32. $9\overline{)9}$

Solve.

See pp. 224-229

33. Our class has 27 volleyball players. There are 9 players for each team. How many teams are there?

34. 63 crayons are packed in 7 boxes. Each box has an equal number of crayons. How many crayons are in each box?

35. A package of stamps costs $8. Rose spent $48 for stamps. How many packages of stamps did she buy?

10

Multiplication

In this unit you will:

- Multiply 10's and 100's
- Multiply two- and three-digit numbers without regrouping
- Multiply two- and three-digit numbers with regrouping
- Multiply with money
- Estimate products
- Solve problems using estimation

Do you remember?

$$7 \times 3 = 21$$

factor   factor   product

$$
\begin{array}{r}
3 \leftarrow \text{factor} \\
\times 7 \leftarrow \text{factor} \\
\hline
21 \leftarrow \text{product}
\end{array}
$$

10-1 Patterns in Multiplying

Look at the pattern:

$$\begin{array}{r} 2 \\ \times 3 \\ \hline 6 \end{array}$$

3 times 2 ones is 6 ones.

$$\begin{array}{r} 2\,0 \\ \times\ 3 \\ \hline 6\,0 \end{array}$$

3 times 2 tens is 6 tens.

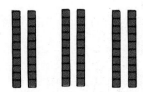

$$\begin{array}{r} 2\,0\,0 \\ \times\ \ 3 \\ \hline 6\,0\,0 \end{array}$$

3 times 2 hundreds is 6 hundreds.

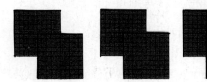

Multiply.

1.

$$\begin{array}{r} 4 \\ \times 2 \\ \hline \end{array}$$

2.

$$\begin{array}{r} 40 \\ \times\ 2 \\ \hline \end{array}$$

3.

$$\begin{array}{r} 400 \\ \times\ \ 2 \\ \hline \end{array}$$

4.
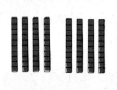

$$\begin{array}{r} 3 \\ \times 3 \\ \hline \end{array}$$

5.
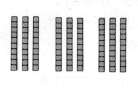

$$\begin{array}{r} 30 \\ \times\ 3 \\ \hline \end{array}$$

6.
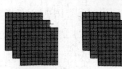

$$\begin{array}{r} 300 \\ \times\ \ 3 \\ \hline \end{array}$$

Find the product.

7. $3 \times 1 = \underline{?}$
   $3 \times 10 = \underline{?}$
   $3 \times 100 = \underline{?}$

8. $5 \times 1 = \underline{?}$
   $5 \times 10 = \underline{?}$
   $5 \times 100 = \underline{?}$

9. $2 \times 2 = \underline{?}$
   $2 \times 20 = \underline{?}$
   $2 \times 200 = \underline{?}$

10. $2 \times 3 = \underline{?}$
    $2 \times 30 = \underline{?}$
    $2 \times 300 = \underline{?}$

11. $7 \times 1 = \underline{?}$
    $7 \times 10 = \underline{?}$
    $7 \times 100 = \underline{?}$

12. $4 \times 1 = \underline{?}$
    $4 \times 10 = \underline{?}$
    $4 \times 100 = \underline{?}$

Multiply.

13. $\begin{array}{r} 5 \\ \times 7 \\ \hline \end{array}$

14. $\begin{array}{r} 50 \\ \times 7 \\ \hline \end{array}$

15. $\begin{array}{r} 1 \\ \times 6 \\ \hline \end{array}$

16. $\begin{array}{r} 10 \\ \times 6 \\ \hline \end{array}$

17. $\begin{array}{r} 100 \\ \times 6 \\ \hline \end{array}$

18. $\begin{array}{r} 1 \\ \times 8 \\ \hline \end{array}$

19. $\begin{array}{r} 10 \\ \times 8 \\ \hline \end{array}$

20. $\begin{array}{r} 100 \\ \times 8 \\ \hline \end{array}$

21. $\begin{array}{r} 4 \\ \times 4 \\ \hline \end{array}$

22. $\begin{array}{r} 40 \\ \times 4 \\ \hline \end{array}$

23. $\begin{array}{r} 6 \\ \times 6 \\ \hline \end{array}$

24. $\begin{array}{r} 60 \\ \times 6 \\ \hline \end{array}$

25. $\begin{array}{r} 1 \\ \times 9 \\ \hline \end{array}$

26. $\begin{array}{r} 10 \\ \times 9 \\ \hline \end{array}$

27. $\begin{array}{r} 100 \\ \times 9 \\ \hline \end{array}$

Solve.

28. Zeke has 3 boxes of colored chalk. Each box contains 20 pieces of chalk. How many pieces does Zeke have?

29. On Tuesday 300 people bought lunch at Pepe's Restaurant. If each person bought 2 tacos, how many tacos did Pepe sell?

30. Juan's family went fishing for 4 days. Each day they caught a total of 20 fish. How many fish did they catch?

31. Mr. Gray can clean a fish in 5 minutes. How long will it take him to clean 20 fish?

10-2 Multiplying Two Digits

There are 2 bird cages at the zoo.
Each cage holds 23 birds. How many
birds are there in all?

To find the number of birds in all,
multiply: $2 \times 23 =$ __?__

Multiply the ones by 2.	⟶	Multiply the tens by 2.

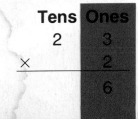

Tens	Ones
2	3
×	2
	6

2 × 3 ones = 6 ones
Write 6 in the ones place.

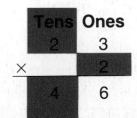

Tens	Ones
2	3
×	2
4	6

2 × 2 tens = 4 tens
Write 4 in the tens place.

There are 46 birds in all.

Complete.

1. 22 × 3		**2.** 32 × 2		**3.** 14 × 2		**4.** 10 × 7		**5.** 21 × 4	
6. 11 × 8		**7.** 40 × 2		**8.** 33 × 3		**9.** 10 × 9		**10.** 12 × 3	
11. 20 × 4		**12.** 24 × 2		**13.** 11 × 6		**14.** 20 × 3		**15.** 23 × 2	

240

Multiply.

16. 42 × 2	**17.** 11 × 5	**18.** 12 × 4	**19.** 23 × 3	**20.** 34 × 2
21. 13 × 3	**22.** 31 × 2	**23.** 10 × 5	**24.** 41 × 2	**25.** 21 × 3
26. 22 × 4	**27.** 13 × 2	**28.** 43 × 2	**29.** 30 × 3	**30.** 44 × 2

Find the product.

31. 3×31 **32.** 2×33 **33.** 4×20 **34.** 2×12

35. 2×24 **36.** 3×30 **37.** 4×22 **38.** 9×11

Solve.

39. Terry's soccer team played 11 games. Terry scored 2 goals in each game. How many goals did Terry score in all?

40. A store had 22 shoe boxes on a shelf. There were 2 shoes in each box. How many shoes were there?

41. Theresa has 14 pairs of colored shoe laces in a drawer. How many laces does she have in all?

... CHALLENGE ...

42. Jamal had 12 pairs of white socks and 10 pairs of colored socks. How many socks did he have in all?

10-3 Multiplying Two Digits with Regrouping

Jack has 3 sets of problems.
Each set has 16 examples. How
many examples are there in all?

To find the number of examples,
multiply: 3 × 16 = __?__

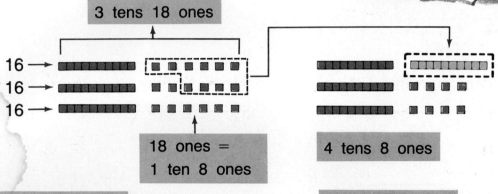

3 tens 18 ones

16 →
16 →
16 →

18 ones =
1 ten 8 ones

4 tens 8 ones

Multiply the ones. Regroup.

```
    1
    1 6
 ×    3
      8
```

18 ones = 1 ten 8 ones

Multiply the tens.

```
    1
    1 6
 ×    3
    4 8
```

3 × 1 ten = 3 tens
3 tens + 1 ten = 4 tens

Complete.

1. 25 × 3	**2.** 16 × 4	**3.** 14 × 5	**4.** 27 × 2	**5.** 12 × 8
6. 13 × 7	**7.** 24 × 3	**8.** 14 × 6	**9.** 28 × 2	**10.** 19 × 4

Multiply.

11.	12.	13.	14.	15.
15 × 5	18 × 4	35 × 2	13 × 6	29 × 2

16.	17.	18.	19.	20.
19 × 3	38 × 2	17 × 5	47 × 2	12 × 7

21.	22.	23.	24.	25.
17 × 4	26 × 3	13 × 5	37 × 2	24 × 4

Find the product.

26. 3×18 27. 2×45 28. 4×23 29. 4×14

30. 4×19 31. 4×15 32. 2×39 33. 3×28

34. 4×15 35. 3×27 36. 5×18 37. 2×49

Solve.

38. The pet store has 15 cages for kittens. There are 3 kittens in each cage. How many kittens are there?

39. Theresa had 3 different colors of balloons. She gave away 18 of each color. How many balloons did she give away.

40. There are 36 tour guides at the museum. Each guide leads 2 tours a day. How many tours are there each day?

41. In a group of 16 tourists, each bought 5 postcards. How many postcards were purchased?

10-4 More Multiplying Two Digits with Regrouping

Each bus holds 32 people. There are 4 buses. How many people are there in all?

To find the number of people, multiply: $4 \times 32 = $ __?__

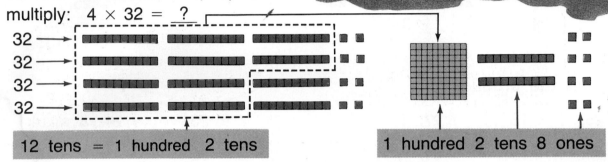

32 →
32 →
32 →
32 →

12 tens = 1 hundred 2 tens

1 hundred 2 tens 8 ones

| **Multiply the ones by 4.** | → | **Multiply the tens by 4.** |

```
  3 2
×   4
    8
```
4 × 2 ones = 8 ones

There are 128 people.

```
  3 2
×   4
1 2 8
```
4 × 3 tens = 12 tens
12 tens = 1 hundred 2 tens

```
  3 2
×   4
1 2 8
```

Multiply.

1. 41
   × 3

2. 52
   × 4

3. 40
   × 7

4. 63
   × 3

5. 54
   × 2

6. 21
   × 6

7. 31
   × 5

8. 62
   × 3

9. 71
   × 8

10. 51
    × 4

Regrouping Tens and Ones

Multiply: $3 \times 45 = \underline{\ ?\ }$

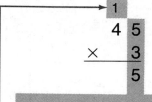

Multiply the ones by 3. Regroup.	→	Multiply the tens by 3. Then add the 1 ten.

$$\begin{array}{r} {}^{1}\ \ \\ 4\,5 \\ \times\ \ \ 3 \\ \hline 5 \end{array}$$

3×5 ones = 15 ones
15 ones = 1 ten 5 ones

$$\begin{array}{r} {}^{1}\ \ \\ 4\,5 \\ \times\ \ \ 3 \\ \hline 1\,3\,5 \end{array}\qquad \begin{array}{r} {}^{1}\ \\ 45 \\ \times\ 3 \\ \hline 135 \end{array}$$

3×4 tens = 12 tens
12 tens + 1 ten = 13 tens
13 tens = 1 hundred 3 tens

Multiply.

11. $\begin{array}{r}47\\ \times\ 5\\ \hline\end{array}$	12. $\begin{array}{r}23\\ \times\ 9\\ \hline\end{array}$	13. $\begin{array}{r}74\\ \times\ 8\\ \hline\end{array}$	14. $\begin{array}{r}37\\ \times\ 6\\ \hline\end{array}$	15. $\begin{array}{r}64\\ \times\ 7\\ \hline\end{array}$
16. $\begin{array}{r}23\\ \times\ 9\\ \hline\end{array}$	17. $\begin{array}{r}37\\ \times\ 4\\ \hline\end{array}$	18. $\begin{array}{r}75\\ \times\ 3\\ \hline\end{array}$	19. $\begin{array}{r}78\\ \times\ 2\\ \hline\end{array}$	20. $\begin{array}{r}94\\ \times\ 5\\ \hline\end{array}$
21. $\begin{array}{r}27\\ \times\ 3\\ \hline\end{array}$	22. $\begin{array}{r}42\\ \times\ 7\\ \hline\end{array}$	23. $\begin{array}{r}33\\ \times\ 8\\ \hline\end{array}$	24. $\begin{array}{r}25\\ \times\ 6\\ \hline\end{array}$	25. $\begin{array}{r}86\\ \times\ 4\\ \hline\end{array}$

Solve.

26. If an inchworm can crawl 74 inches in one hour, how far can it crawl in 5 hours?

27. Rita collects shells for 5 days. Each day she collects 18 shells. How many shells does she collect in all?

28. Paul has 3 packages of fruit juice. Each package has 36 cans. How many cans of juice does he have in all?

Practice

Find the missing factors.

1. _?_ × 3 = 24   2. _?_ × 8 = 32   3. _?_ × 5 = 35   4. _?_ × 9 = 63

5. _?_ × 6 = 48   6. _?_ × 6 = 54   7. _?_ × 8 = 56   8. _?_ × 4 = 16

9. _?_ × 9 = 54   10. _?_ × 7 = 49   11. _?_ × 7 = 35   12. _?_ × 9 = 36

13. _?_ × 5 = 25   14. _?_ × 9 = 81   15. _?_ × 8 = 48   16. _?_ × 6 = 42

Find the quotient.

17. 4)‾20‾   18. 7)‾21‾   19. 6)‾36‾   20. 3)‾27‾   21. 5)‾45‾

22. 9)‾72‾   23. 2)‾18‾   24. 7)‾35‾   25. 6)‾48‾   26. 8)‾64‾

27. 5)‾40‾   28. 7)‾28‾   29. 8)‾32‾   30. 9)‾63‾   31. 4)‾24‾

Compute. Watch for + or −.

32.	33.	34.	35.	36.
3924	6597	286	4853	7185
+ 2895	− 5734	+ 4755	− 2964	+ 935

37.	38.	39.	40.	41.
$23.65	$90.40	$62.50	$40.00	$ 2.77
+ 22.90	− 37.25	+ 1.79	− 11.55	+ 9.75

42.	43.	44.	45.	46.
$31.82	$35.98	$ 3.48	$83.46	$75.32
+ 16.45	− 36.01	+ 21.62	− 47.95	+ 9.18

Compare. Write <, =, or >.

47. 9 km _?_ 9 m   48. 3 cm _?_ 3 m

49. 8 in. _?_ 8 ft   50. 5 mi _?_ 5 yd

51. 3 c _?_ 3 gal   52. 16 lb _?_ 16 oz

Multiplying Three Digits

Peter and Terrell collect bird pictures. Peter has 212. Terrell has 3 times as many. How many does Terrell have?

To find the number of pictures Terrell has, multiply: $3 \times 212 = $ _?_

Multiply the ones.	→	Multiply the tens.	→	Multiply the hundreds.

```
    2 1 2                2 1 2                2 1 2
  ×     3              ×     3              ×     3
        6                3 6                6 3 6
```

3×2 ones = 6 ones	3×1 ten = 3 tens	3×2 hundreds = 6 hundreds

Terrell has 636 bird pictures.

Complete.

1. 422
    × 2

2. 132
    × 3

3. 102
    × 4

4. 343
    × 2

5. 122
    × 4

6. 401
    × 2

7. 111
    × 5

8. 231
    × 3

9. 144
    × 2

10. 320
    × 2

11. 110
    × 6

12. 121
    × 4

13. 101
    × 7

14. 431
    × 2

15. 332
    × 3

16. 202
    × 3

17. 123
    × 2

18. 333
    × 3

19. 111
    × 2

20. 444
    × 2

Multiplying Three Digits With Regrouping

The Daily Parking Garage holds 124 cars. It was filled for 4 days. How many cars were parked there?

To find how many cars were parked, multiply: 4 × 124 = ___?___

Multiply the ones. Regroup.	Multiply the tens. Add the regrouped ten.	Multiply the hundreds.

```
    1                 1                 1
  1 2 4             1 2 4             1 2 4
×     4           ×     4           ×     4
      6               9 6             4 9 6
```

4 × 4 ones = 16 ones 16 ones = 1 ten 6 ones	4 × 2 tens = 8 tens 8 tens + 1 ten = 9 tens	4 × 1 hundred = 4 hundreds

There were 496 cars parked.

Complete.

1. 238 × 2	2. 112 × 5	3. 102 × 8	4. 218 × 4	5. 325 × 3
6. 105 × 7	7. 127 × 2	8. 107 × 9	9. 437 × 2	10. 102 × 6
11. 214 × 4	12. 115 × 6	13. 104 × 8	14. 227 × 3	15. 117 × 5

Regrouping tens

Multiply: $3 \times 162 = $?

Multiply the ones.

$$\begin{array}{r} 1\ 6\ 2 \\ \times\qquad 3 \\ \hline 6 \end{array}$$

Multiply the tens.
Regroup.

$$\begin{array}{r} \overset{1}{} \\ 1\ 6\ 2 \\ \times\qquad 3 \\ \hline 8\ 6 \end{array}$$

Multiply the hundreds.
Add the regrouped hundreds.

$$\begin{array}{r} \overset{1}{} \\ 1\ 6\ 2 \\ \times\qquad 3 \\ \hline 4\ 8\ 6 \end{array}$$

3 × 6 tens = 18 tens
18 tens = 1 hundred 8 tens

3 × 1 hundred = 3 hundreds
3 hundreds + 1 hundred =
4 hundreds

Find the product.

16. 281 × 3	**17.** 162 × 4	**18.** 140 × 7	**19.** 382 × 2	**20.** 121 × 5
21. 242 × 3	**22.** 131 × 6	**23.** 192 × 4	**24.** 253 × 3	**25.** 121 × 8
26. 182 × 4	**27.** 121 × 5	**28.** 150 × 6	**29.** 142 × 3	**30.** 493 × 2

Solve.

31. If the Wiley twins each have 254 shells, how many shells do they have in all?

32. Mr. Wiley sailed 162 km along the coast each day. How far did he sail in 3 days?

249

10-8 More Multiplying Three Digits with Regrouping

A bag of raisins has 164 raisins in it. How many raisins are in 3 bags?

To find the number of raisins, multiply: $3 \times 164 =$ ___?___

Multiply the ones. Regroup.	→	Multiply the tens. Add the regrouped ten. Regroup again.	→	Multiply the hundreds. Add the regrouped hundred.

```
    1
  1 6 4
×     3
      2
```
3 × 4 ones =
12 ones =
1 ten 2 ones

```
  1 1
  1 6 4
×     3
    9 2
```
3 × 6 tens = 18 tens
18 tens + 1 ten =
19 tens =
1 hundred 9 tens

```
  1 1
  1 6 4
×     3
  4 9 2
```
3 × 1 hundred = 3 hundreds
3 hundreds + 1 hundred =
4 hundreds

There are 492 raisins in all.

Multiply.

1. 246
   × 4

2. 358
   × 2

3. 143
   × 7

4. 137
   × 3

5. 157
   × 4

6. 477
   × 2

7. 138
   × 7

8. 149
   × 6

9. 118
   × 8

10. 126
    × 5

11. 113
    × 4

12. 132
    × 5

13. 294
    × 3

14. 129
    × 7

15. 123
    × 6

250

1044

Multiply.

16.	355 × 2	17.	247 × 4	18.	153 × 5	19.	499 × 2	20.	122 × 6

21.	248 × 3	22.	128 × 7	23.	224 × 4	24.	113 × 8	25.	131 × 5

26.	135 × 7	27.	158 × 6	28.	172 × 5	29.	386 × 2	30.	243 × 4

Find the product.

31.	235 × 4	32.	141 × 7	33.	239 × 3	34.	106 × 8	35.	303 × 2

36.	256 × 3	37.	264 × 4	38.	117 × 8	39.	137 × 6	40.	105 × 5

Solve.

41. If light bulbs are packed 2 in a box, how many are in 128 boxes?

42. Michael Todd planted 6 rows of tomato plants. He put 120 plants in each row. How many did he plant in all?

43. The Shop-Here Store has 6 cases of pencils. Each case contains 144 pencils. How many are there in all?

44. An airplane travels at a rate of 475 miles an hour. How far does it go in 2 hours?

45. If 285 students each sold 3 tickets to a school play, how many tickets were sold?

Multiplying Money

Julie bought 3 gift cards at $.75 each.
How much did Julie spend?

To find how much Julie spent,
multiply: 3 × $.75 = ? .

Think of

$$\begin{array}{r} \$.75 \\ \times\ \ \ 3 \\ \hline \end{array}$$ as $$\begin{array}{r} 75\cent \\ \times\ \ \ 3 \\ \hline 225\cent \end{array}$$ as $$\begin{array}{r} \$.75 \\ \times\ \ \ 3 \\ \hline \$\,2.25 \end{array}$$

$225\cent \longrightarrow \$2.25$

225¢ ⟶ $2.25

Multiply.

1. $$\begin{array}{r} \$.22 \\ \times\ \ \ 3 \\ \hline \end{array}$$

2. $$\begin{array}{r} \$.37 \\ \times\ \ \ 2 \\ \hline \end{array}$$

3. $$\begin{array}{r} \$.19 \\ \times\ \ \ 4 \\ \hline \end{array}$$

4. $$\begin{array}{r} \$.72 \\ \times\ \ \ 5 \\ \hline \end{array}$$

5. $$\begin{array}{r} \$.65 \\ \times\ \ \ 6 \\ \hline \end{array}$$

6. $$\begin{array}{r} \$.90 \\ \times\ \ \ 5 \\ \hline \end{array}$$

7. $$\begin{array}{r} \$.48 \\ \times\ \ \ 7 \\ \hline \end{array}$$

8. $$\begin{array}{r} \$.91 \\ \times\ \ \ 8 \\ \hline \end{array}$$

9. $$\begin{array}{r} \$.36 \\ \times\ \ \ 9 \\ \hline \end{array}$$

10. $$\begin{array}{r} \$.55 \\ \times\ \ \ 6 \\ \hline \end{array}$$

11. $$\begin{array}{r} \$.29 \\ \times\ \ \ 8 \\ \hline \end{array}$$

12. $$\begin{array}{r} \$.99 \\ \times\ \ \ 9 \\ \hline \end{array}$$

13. $$\begin{array}{r} \$.25 \\ \times\ \ \ 8 \\ \hline \end{array}$$

14. $$\begin{array}{r} \$.49 \\ \times\ \ \ 7 \\ \hline \end{array}$$

15. $$\begin{array}{r} \$.40 \\ \times\ \ \ 6 \\ \hline \end{array}$$

16. $$\begin{array}{r} \$.23 \\ \times\ \ \ 5 \\ \hline \end{array}$$

Compare. Write <, =, or >.

17. $.19 × 6 ? 7 × $.18

18. 3 × $.57 ? 6 × $.28

10-10 Estimating Products

Today 6 buses arrived at the park. There were 48 people on each bus. About how many people were there in all?

To estimate a product, round the greater number to the nearest ten and multiply.

$$
\begin{array}{r} 4\,8 \\ \times\ 6 \end{array}
\longrightarrow \text{rounds to} \longrightarrow
\begin{array}{r} 5\,0 \\ \times\ 6 \\ \hline 3\,0\,0 \end{array}
$$

There were about 300 people in all.

Study this example.

Estimate: $4 \times 34 = \underline{?}$

$$
\begin{array}{r} 3\,4 \\ \times\ 4 \end{array}
\longrightarrow \text{rounds to} \longrightarrow
\begin{array}{r} 3\,0 \\ \times\ 4 \\ \hline 1\,2\,0 \end{array}
$$

120 is the estimate.

Estimate the product.

1. $\begin{array}{r} 62 \\ \times\ 4 \\ \hline \end{array}$
2. $\begin{array}{r} 67 \\ \times\ 4 \\ \hline \end{array}$
3. $\begin{array}{r} 37 \\ \times\ 3 \\ \hline \end{array}$
4. $\begin{array}{r} 43 \\ \times\ 5 \\ \hline \end{array}$
5. $\begin{array}{r} 56 \\ \times\ 4 \\ \hline \end{array}$

6. $\begin{array}{r} 76 \\ \times\ 3 \\ \hline \end{array}$
7. $\begin{array}{r} 29 \\ \times\ 2 \\ \hline \end{array}$
8. $\begin{array}{r} 78 \\ \times\ 4 \\ \hline \end{array}$
9. $\begin{array}{r} 47 \\ \times\ 8 \\ \hline \end{array}$
10. $\begin{array}{r} 52 \\ \times\ 5 \\ \hline \end{array}$

11. $\begin{array}{r} 31 \\ \times\ 6 \\ \hline \end{array}$
12. $\begin{array}{r} 64 \\ \times\ 5 \\ \hline \end{array}$
13. $\begin{array}{r} 13 \\ \times\ 9 \\ \hline \end{array}$
14. $\begin{array}{r} 72 \\ \times\ 4 \\ \hline \end{array}$
15. $\begin{array}{r} 43 \\ \times\ 7 \\ \hline \end{array}$

16. $\begin{array}{r} 29 \\ \times\ 7 \\ \hline \end{array}$
17. $\begin{array}{r} 45 \\ \times\ 8 \\ \hline \end{array}$
18. $\begin{array}{r} 36 \\ \times\ 5 \\ \hline \end{array}$
19. $\begin{array}{r} 41 \\ \times\ 9 \\ \hline \end{array}$
20. $\begin{array}{r} 54 \\ \times\ 6 \\ \hline \end{array}$

10-11 Problem Solving: Estimating the Answer

Problem: There are 28 children in Mr. Eldridge's third grade class. Each child has 2 workbooks. About how many workbooks does the class have? Is 40 a reasonable answer?

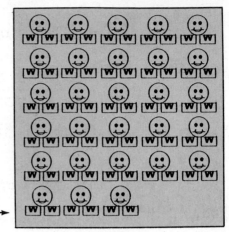

1 IMAGINE

28 children with
  2 workbooks each

2 NAME

Facts: 28 students
             2 workbooks each

Question: Is 40 a reasonable number of workbooks for the class?

3 THINK

To find how many workbooks the class has, multiply: $2 \times 28 = $ __?__

Ask: $2 \times 28 \overset{?}{=} 40$

Estimate to decide if the answer is reasonable.

4 COMPUTE

$$
\begin{array}{cc}
 & \text{rounds to} \\
28 \longrightarrow & 30 \\
\underline{\times\ 2} & \underline{\times\ 2} \\
 & 60
\end{array}
$$

40 is not reasonable because it is not close to the estimate, 60.

5 CHECK

$$
\begin{array}{r}
28 \\
\underline{\times\ 2} \\
56
\end{array}
$$

40 is not reasonable because it is not close to 56.

Decide if the given answer is reasonable. If it is not, give a reasonable answer.

1. Susan, Donna and Lilly went to the State Fair. Each ticket costs $11. About how much did they pay? Is $35 a reasonable answer?

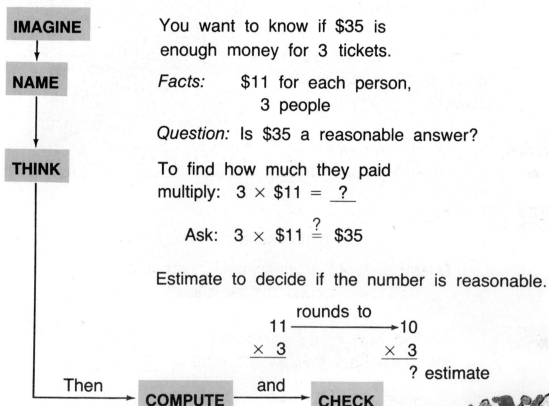

IMAGINE

You want to know if $35 is enough money for 3 tickets.

NAME

Facts: $11 for each person, 3 people

Question: Is $35 a reasonable answer?

THINK

To find how much they paid multiply: 3 × $11 = ?

Ask: 3 × $11 $\overset{?}{=}$ $35

Estimate to decide if the number is reasonable.

$$\begin{array}{ccc}
 & \text{rounds to} & \\
11 & \longrightarrow & 10 \\
\times\ 3 & & \times\ 3 \\
 & & \text{? estimate}
\end{array}$$

Then   COMPUTE   and   CHECK

2. There are 42 balloons in a box. About how many balloons are there in 5 boxes? Is 250 a reasonable answer?

3. Each of Karla's rose bushes had 39 flowers last summer. She had 6 rose bushes. About how many roses did she have? Is 240 a reasonable answer?

4. Each of three buses can carry 55 passengers. Estimate if the 3 buses can carry 160 passengers.

More Practice

Find the pattern. Multiply.

1. $6 \times 1 = \underline{?}$
   $6 \times 10 = \underline{?}$
   $6 \times 100 = \underline{?}$

2. $3 \times 2 = \underline{?}$
   $3 \times 20 = \underline{?}$
   $3 \times 200 = \underline{?}$

3. $4 \times 1 = \underline{?}$
   $4 \times 10 = \underline{?}$
   $4 \times 100 = \underline{?}$

Multiply.

4. $\begin{array}{r} 21 \\ \times 4 \\ \hline \end{array}$
5. $\begin{array}{r} 12 \\ \times 5 \\ \hline \end{array}$
6. $\begin{array}{r} 26 \\ \times 2 \\ \hline \end{array}$
7. $\begin{array}{r} 16 \\ \times 6 \\ \hline \end{array}$
8. $\begin{array}{r} 61 \\ \times 3 \\ \hline \end{array}$
9. $\begin{array}{r} 35 \\ \times 7 \\ \hline \end{array}$

10. $\begin{array}{r} 85 \\ \times 4 \\ \hline \end{array}$
11. $\begin{array}{r} 92 \\ \times 8 \\ \hline \end{array}$
12. $\begin{array}{r} 312 \\ \times 3 \\ \hline \end{array}$
13. $\begin{array}{r} 191 \\ \times 4 \\ \hline \end{array}$
14. $\begin{array}{r} 167 \\ \times 5 \\ \hline \end{array}$
15. $\begin{array}{r} 135 \\ \times 7 \\ \hline \end{array}$

Find the product.

16. 4×10
17. 3×22
18. 5×27
19. 6×41

20. 7×94
21. 4×212
22. 3×319
23. 2×465

24. 3×244
25. 5×320
26. 7×124
27. 9×106

Solve.

28. Joshua has 279 rocks in his collection. Todd has 3 times that many. How many does Todd have?

29. Tickets to the Strand Movie Theater cost $2.25. How much would it cost for 4 people to go to a movie?

30. Popcorn costs $.89 a box. How much would it cost for 6 friends to each buy a box?

(See *Still More Practice*, p.364.)

Math-e-Magic

NUMBER TABLES

1. Fill in the missing numbers to complete
   the addition table.

+	?	3	?	7
1	2	?	6	?
?	?	6	?	10
5	6	?	10	?
?	?	10	?	14

2. Fill in the missing numbers to complete
   the multiplication table.

×	2	?	?	8
2	4	8	?	?
4	?	?	24	32
?	?	?	36	?
?	?	32	?	64

3. Make an addition table using other numbers.
4. Make a multiplication table using other numbers.
   See how quickly your friends can complete them.

Check Your Mastery.

Find the pattern. Multiply.

See pp. 238-239

1. $8 \times 1 = $?
   $8 \times 10 = $?
   $8 \times 100 = $?

2. $4 \times 2 = $?
   $4 \times 20 = $?
   $4 \times 200 = $?

3. $3 \times 3 = $?
   $3 \times 30 = $?
   $3 \times 300 = $?

Multiply.

See pp. 240-245

4.   11
   $\times\ 7$

5.   46
   $\times\ 2$

6.   52
   $\times\ 3$

7.   17
   $\times\ 4$

8.   86
   $\times\ 7$

Find the product.

See pp. 240-247

9. $2 \times 33 = $?   **10.** $4 \times 51 = $?   **11.** $6 \times 82 = $?   **12.** $3 \times 213 = $?

Multiply.

See pp. 247-251

13.   121
   $\times\ 4$

14.   128
   $\times\ 3$

15.   182
   $\times\ 2$

16.   157
   $\times\ 5$

17.   309
   $\times\ 3$

Solve.

See pp. 252-255

18. Samuel buys 3 books for $1.75 each. How much must he pay?

19. Michelle can complete about 18 problems in a minute. About how many problems can she finish in 7 minutes?

20. There are 6 classes at Tyler school. Each class has 21 students. Estimate the total number of students.

Geometry

11

In this unit you will:

- Identify flat (plane) figures
- Study congruent figures and similar figures
- Identify solid shapes
- Find lines of symmetry in various figures
- Find perimeter, area, and volume
- Estimate perimeter
- Make solid shapes
- Solve problems by using drawings

Do you remember?

Open curve   Closed curve

Line segments

11-1 Flat Figures

Some flat figures (or plane figures) have special names.

circle
(0 sides)

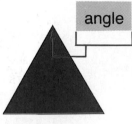
angle

triangle
(3 sides)

right angle

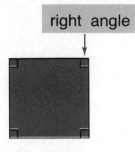

square
(4 sides)

rectangle
(4 sides)

The square and the rectangle have 4 sides.
The 4 sides of the square are the same length.
A square is also a rectangle.

Name the shape of each. Then find how many right angles there are in Figures 2 and 3.

1.

2.

3.

4.

5.

6.

7.

8.

Polygons

Flat figures with straight sides are called polygons.
Polygons also have special names.

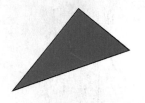  

triangle   quadrilateral   pentagon   hexagon

**Cut four 6-in. strips and four 4-in. strips
from drinking straws.**
From these 8 strips how many of these
figures can you form?

9. squares

10. triangles

11. quadrilaterals

12. pentagons

13. hexagons

14. octagons

Is each figure a polygon? Write "Yes" or "No."

15.    16.   17.    18.

**Name the type of polygon. Write the number of sides
each has.**

19.    20.    21.    22.

11-2 Congruent Figures

Congruent figures have the same size and same shape.

The rectangles are congruent figures.
The triangles are *not* congruent figures.
The circles are congruent figures.

Do the figures look congruent? Write "Yes" or "No."

1.
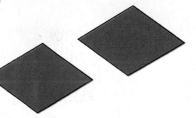

2.

3.

4.

5.
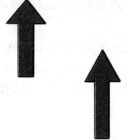

6.

Do the pairs look congruent? Write "Yes" or "No."

7.

8.

9.

10.

11.

12.

Find the 2 congruent shapes. Write their letters.

13. a. 　　**b.** 　　**c.** 　　**d.**

14. a. 　　**b.** 　　**c.**　　**d.**

... CHALLENGE ...

15. Look around the classroom. Find 4 pairs of shapes that are congruent. Make drawings of them for the bulletin board.

Similar Figures

Similar figures have the same shape.
They do not have to be the same size.

Do the figures look similar? Write "Yes" or "No."

1. 2. 3.

 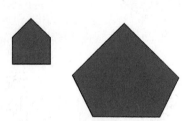 

4. 5. 6.

264

Do the pairs look similar? Write "Yes" or "No."

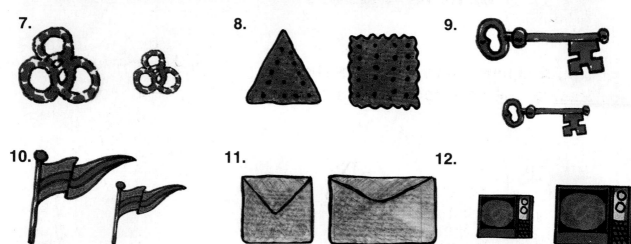

7.

8.

9.

10.

11.

12.

Find the 2 similar shapes. Write their letters.

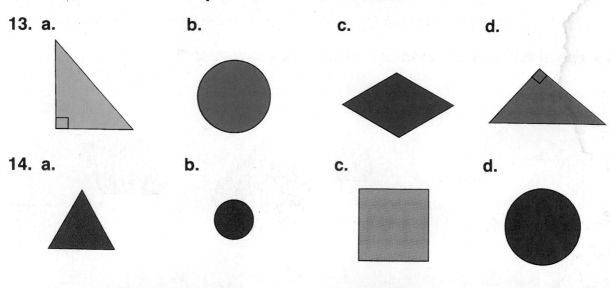

13. a.
    b.
    c.
    d.

14. a.
    b.
    c.
    d.

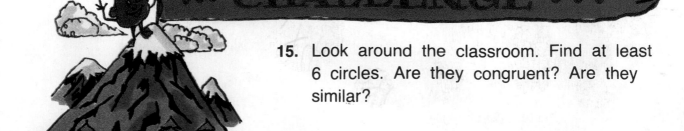

CHALLENGE

15. Look around the classroom. Find at least 6 circles. Are they congruent? Are they similar?

11-4 Solid Figures

Solid shapes are all around us. Some solid figures have special names.

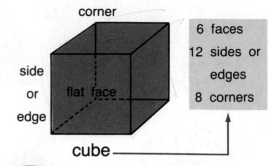

corner

side or edge

flat face

6 faces
12 sides or edges
8 corners

cube

   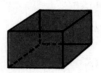

cylinder   sphere   pyramid   cone   rectangular prism

Find the 2 shapes that match. Write their letters.

1. a.    b.    c.    d.

2. a. 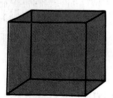   b.    c.   d.

3. a.   b.    c.   d.

266

Name each shape.

4.

5.

6.

7.

8.

9.

Cut out or draw a picture of each.

10. cereal box

11. can of peas

12. ice cream cone

13. baseball

14. toy block

15. milk carton

Complete the table.

	Solid Figure	Faces	Edges	Corners
16.	Cube	6	?	?
17.	Rectangular Prism	?	?	8
18.	Sphere	?	0	?

Each picture contains 2 solid shapes. Name them.

19.

20.

Symmetry

Each of these figures can be folded along the dotted line so that the two parts match.

The dotted line is a **line of symmetry**.

Some figures have two or more lines of symmetry.

Look at the dotted line. Is it a line of symmetry? Write "Yes" or "No."

1.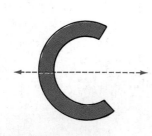

2.

3.

4.

5.

6.

7.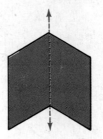

8.

Multiplication Practice

Multiply.

1. 32
    × 2

2. 12
    × 3

3. 23
    × 3

4. 21
    × 2

5. 11
    × 4

6. 25
    × 3

7. 36
    × 2

8. 15
    × 6

9. 19
    × 4

10. 48
    × 2

11. 64
    × 2

12. 52
    × 4

13. 31
    × 5

14. 21
    × 6

15. 51
    × 3

16. 38
    × 7

17. 24
    × 9

18. 77
    × 2

19. 38
    × 3

20. 27
    × 8

21. 421
    ×   2

22. 232
    ×   3

23. 116
    ×   6

24. 123
    ×   4

25. 108
    ×   5

26. 131
    ×   5

27. 291
    ×   2

28. 164
    ×   4

29. 149
    ×   6

30. 114
    ×   8

Solve.

31. The Toy World Store has 126 cartons of toy trucks. There are 4 trucks in each carton. How many trucks are there in all?

32. The Toy World Store sold 78 cartons of 4 trucks on Thursday. How many trucks did the store sell?

33. Each truck cost $8. Find the cost of 504 trucks.

34. The two factors are 97 and 8. Find the product.

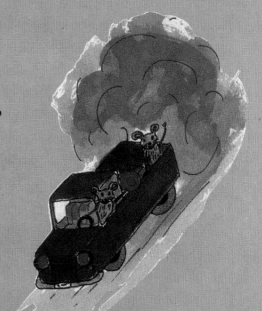

11-7 Perimeter

Mr. Valdez has a large yard. He measures the distance around the yard to find its **perimeter.** What is this distance?

To find the perimeter, add the lengths of the sides.

Perimeter = 30 + 25 + 30 + 25
Perimeter = 110 m

The distance around Mr. Valdez's yard is 110 m.

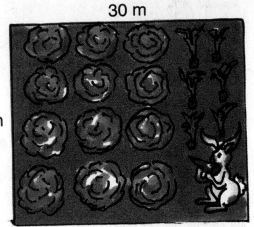

30 m

25 m   25 m

30 m

Find the perimeter.

1.

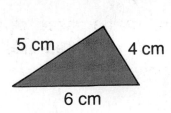

5 cm   4 cm

6 cm

2.

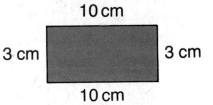

4 m

4 m   4 m

4 m

3.

10 cm

3 cm   3 cm

10 cm

4.

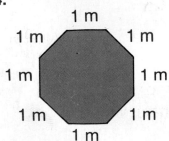

1 m

1 m   1 m

1 m   1 m

1 m   1 m

1 m

5.

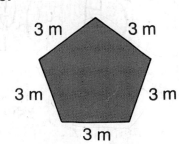

3 m   3 m

3 m   3 m

3 m

6.

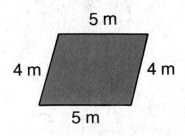

5 m

4 m   4 m

5 m

270

Use your metric ruler to find the perimeter.

7.

8.

9.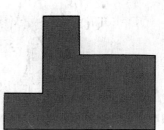

10.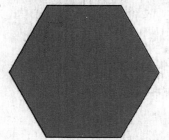

11.

12.

Solve.

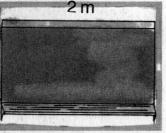

2 m

1 m

8 m

13. A chalkboard is 2 m long and 1m high. What is its perimeter?

14. A garden is in the shape of a polygon. Each side measures 8 m. Find the perimeter.

Calculator Activity

61 m

98 m

15. Estimate the perimeter of this soccer field. Check your estimate with a calculator.

11-8 Area

Susan has a new picture. One way to describe its size is to find its **area**. The area is the number of square units in the picture.

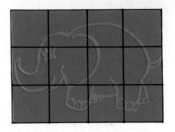

You can count the number of square units to find the area.

Use this square unit to find the area. ⟶ 1 square unit

The area of the picture is 12 square units.

Study these examples.

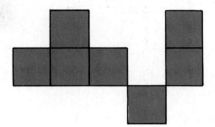

The area is 5 square units.   The area is 7 square units.

Write how many square units.

1.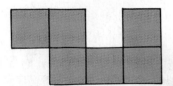

2.

3.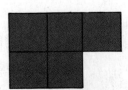

4.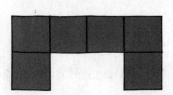

5.

6.

Find the area.

7.

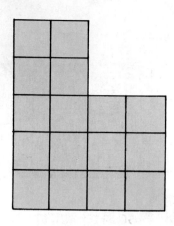

8.

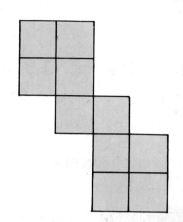

9.

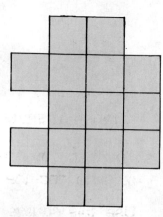

10.

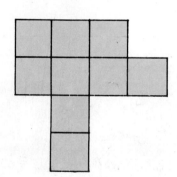

11.

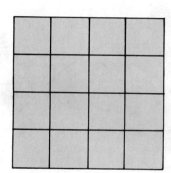

12.

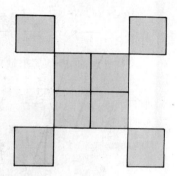

13.

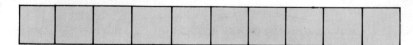

CHALLENGE

14. Tawny's bedroom measures 4 m by 5 m. How many square meters does it contain?

15. Susan has another picture in the shape of a square. Each side measures 2 ft. How many square feet does it contain?

273

Volume

Roberta filled a box with blocks. What is the volume of the box?

The **volume** of a solid shape is the **number of cubic units** in it.

Use this cubic unit to find volume. 1 cubic unit

Sometimes not all of the cubic units can be seen. Remember to count all of the cubic units in each layer.

The volume is 12 cubic units.

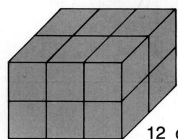 12 cubic units

How many cubic units are there?

1.

2.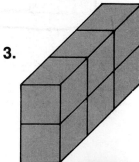

3.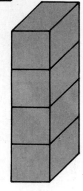

4.

5.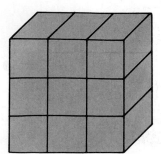

6.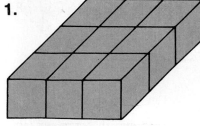

Find the volume.

7.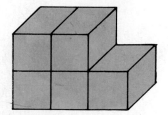

8.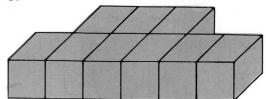

9.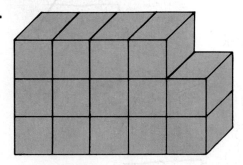

10.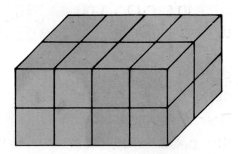

11.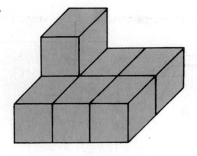

12.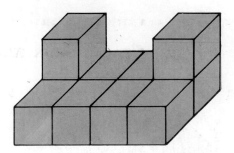

13.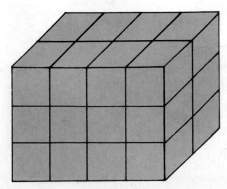

14.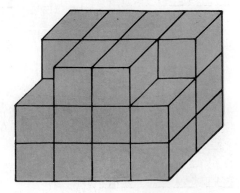

275

11-10 Problem Solving: Using Drawings

Problem: Omar made a patio in his backyard. The square blocks he used measured 1 square foot each. The area he covered measured 8 ft by 9 ft. How many blocks did he use?

1 IMAGINE

Draw and label a picture to show what Omar's garden looked like. Mark off square blocks in it.

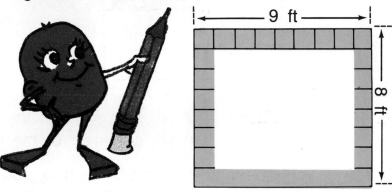

2 NAME

Facts: 8 ft ⎤
9 ft ⎦ the measures of the patio

Question: How many blocks did he use to make the patio?

3 THINK

Look at the diagram. Omar used 8 rows of 9 blocks each.

To find how many blocks he used, multiply: $8 \times 9 = $ _?_

4 COMPUTE

$8 \times 9 = 72$

5 CHECK

Look at the picture. Count the blocks. Is 72 the correct number of blocks?

Solve. Draw a picture for each problem.

1. Beth wants to put a fence around a rectangular garden next to her house. The sides of the rectangular garden measure 7 yd and 10 yd. The side of the house measures 10 yd. How much fencing does she need?

IMAGINE   Draw and label a picture to show the yard.

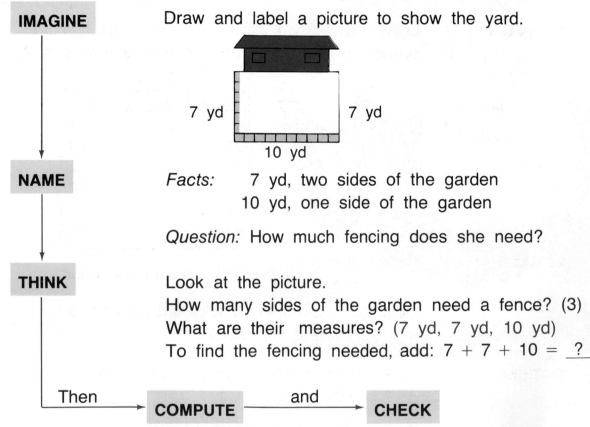

7 yd   7 yd

10 yd

NAME   *Facts:*   7 yd, two sides of the garden
                    10 yd, one side of the garden

Question: How much fencing does she need?

THINK   Look at the picture.
         How many sides of the garden need a fence? (3)
         What are their measures? (7 yd, 7 yd, 10 yd)
         To find the fencing needed, add: 7 + 7 + 10 = _?_

Then ──→ COMPUTE ── and ──→ CHECK

2. Draw square yards in Beth's garden in exercise 1. Find the number of square yards in Beth's garden.

3. Leila plans to make a flower garden 3 ft by 4 ft. She is going to plant different kinds of flowers in each square-foot section. How many kinds does she need?

More Practice

Name each.

1.

2.

3.

4.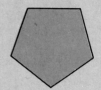

Do the figures look congruent? Write "Yes" or "No."

Do the figures look similar? Write "Yes" or "No."

5.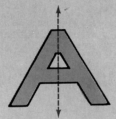

6.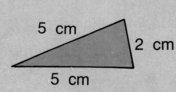

7.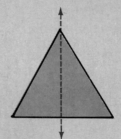

8.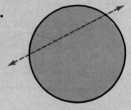

Find the dotted line. Is it a line of symmetry?

9.

10.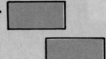

11.

Find the perimeter.

12.
4 m
2 m   2 m
4 m

13.
5 cm
2 cm
5 cm

14.
3 cm
3 cm   3 cm
3 cm   3 cm
3 cm

Find the area.

15.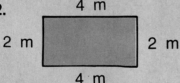

Find the volume.

16.

278

(See *Still More Practice*, p. 365.)

Math-e-Magic

MAKING SOLID SHAPES

Solid shapes can be made by folding flat shapes. Draw a flat shape like the one below. Use the lengths shown. Cut it out. Then fold it on the lines to make a cube.

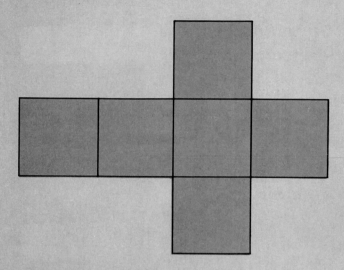

Cut pieces of paper in the shapes shown below. What solid shapes do they form?

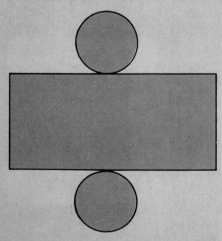

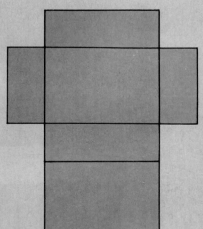

Try making some other solid shapes from flat shapes.

Label them and make a classroom display.

Check Your Mastery

Name each.

See pp. 260-261, 266-267

1.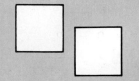

2.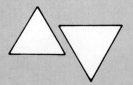

3.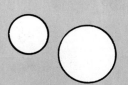

4.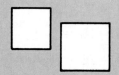

See pp. 262-263

Do the figures look congruent?
Write "Yes" or "No."

See pp. 264-265

Do the figures look similar?
Write "Yes" or "No."

5.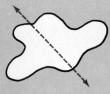

6.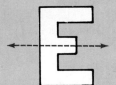

7.

8.

Look at the dotted line. Is it a line of symmetry?

See p. 268

9.

10.

11.

Find the perimeter.

See pp. 270-271

12.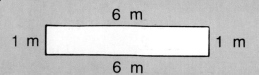

6 m

1 m   1 m

6 m

13.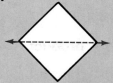

3 cm

3 cm   3 cm

3 cm

Find the area. See pp. 272-273

14.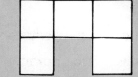

Find the volume. See pp. 274-275

15.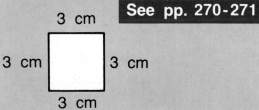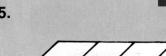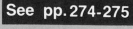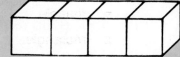

Cumulative Test III

Multiply.

1. 6
    ×9

2. 7
    ×6

3. 8
    ×8

4. 9
    ×7

5. 5
    ×8

6. 3
    ×9

7. 4
    ×8

8. 3
    ×7

9. 7
    ×7

10. 6
    ×6

11. 9
    ×2

12. 5
    ×4

13. 8
    ×7

14. 9
    ×8

15. $(3 \times 2) \times 4 =$ ___?___

16. $(8 \times 0) \times 6 =$ ___?___

17. $4 \times (6 \times 1) =$ ___?___

18. $(1 \times 9) \times 8 =$ ___?___

19. $4 \times (3 \times 3) \times 4 =$ ___?___

20. $5 \times (4 \times 2) =$ ___?___

Divide.

21. 9)81

22. 7)63

23. 6)48

24. 8)64

25. 9)20

26. 5)40

27. 3)27

28. 7)49

29. 8)45

30. 8)72

31. $18 \div 2 =$ ___?___

32. $63 \div 9 =$ ___?___

33. $72 \div 9 =$ ___?___

34. $25 \div 5 =$ ___?___

35. $48 \div 8 =$ ___?___

36. $32 \div 8 =$ ___?___

Find the missing factor.

37. ___?___ $\times 8 = 32$

38. $7 \times$ ___?___ $= 35$

39. ___?___ $\times 8 = 72$

40. $4 \times$ ___?___ $= 16$

41. ___?___ $\times 3 = 27$

42. ___?___ $\times 6 = 42$

Estimate the product.

43. 51
    × 6

44. 37
    × 8

45. 63
    × 7

46. 52
    × 5

47. 68
    × 4

Multiply.

48. 24
    × 2

49. 83
    × 3

50. 110
    × 6

51. 200
    × 2

52. 30
    × 8

53. 124
    × 3

54. 360
    × 2

55. 123
    × 5

56. $1.21
    × 8

57. $2.69
    × 5

Name each figure.

58.   a. triangle b. hexagon c. square d. pentagon

59.   a. rectangle b. circle c. triangle d. hexagon

60. a. pentagon b. hexagon c. square d. triangle

281

Choose the correct answer.

61. Find two similar figures.

a.   b.   c.   d.

62. Find two congruent figures.

a.   b.   c.   d.

63. Which figure shows symmetry?

a. b. c. d.

Find the perimeter.

64.

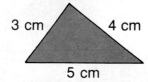

3 cm   4 cm

5 cm

65.

7 cm

4 cm

Find the area in square units.

66.

67.

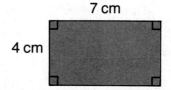

Solve.

68. Joe bought 2 cases of grapefruit juice. Each case contained 12 cans. How many cans of grapefruit juice did Joe buy?

69. Koyi's father worked 56 hours this week. If he worked 8 hours each day, how many days did he work this week?

70. Lil filled 9 pages of her photo album. Each page has 8 photos. How many photos does Lil have?

71. Pencils are selling at 12 cents each. James bought 8 of them. How much did James pay for the pencils?

72. Molly played a tape for 27 minutes. There are 9 musical pieces on the tape. About how long is each musical piece?

73. There are 54 baseball players. If each team has 9 players, how many teams can be formed?

74. The tennis coach divided 63 balls among 7 students. How many balls did each student receive?

75. 12 packages of raisins fill one carton. How many packages of raisins are there in 6 cartons?

282

12

Division

In this unit you will:

- Divide with remainders
- Divide with 1- and 2-digit quotients
- Divide with 1- and 2-digit quotients with remainders
- Estimate money quotients
- Solve two-step problems

Do you remember?

$$\text{Divisor} \quad 8\overline{)72}$$

9 ← Quotient
8)72 ← Dividend

Division has two meanings.

How many in each group?

18 balls ÷ 6 groups
= 3 in each group

How many groups?

18 balls ÷ groups of 3
= 6 groups

Division with Remainders

The Fun Zoo has 2 monkey swings. Three monkeys can swing on each swing. There are 8 monkeys. Can they all swing at once? How many are left?

2 swings are needed for 6 monkeys.

2 monkeys are left.

$8 \div 3 = 2$
remainder 2

Divide.

1.

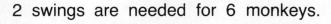

$9 \div 4 = 2$
remainder ?

2.

$10 \div 3 =$?
remainder ?

3.

$11 \div 5 =$?
remainder ?

Find the quotient and remainder.

4.

$11 \div 2 = \underline{}$
remainder $\underline{}$

5.

$7 \div 2 = \underline{}$
remainder $\underline{}$

6.

$13 \div 3 = \underline{}$
remainder $\underline{}$

7.

$17 \div 2 = \underline{}$
remainder $\underline{}$

8.

$13 \div 4 = \underline{}$
remainder $\underline{}$

9.

$15 \div 4 = \underline{}$
remainder $\underline{}$

Draw a picture to show each problem.

10. $12 \div 5 = 2$
remainder 2

11. $20 \div 6 = 3$
remainder 2

12. $10 \div 9 = 1$
remainder 1

Solve.

13. Mr. Coleman has 11 baby alligators to divide equally between 2 ponds. How many go in each pond? How many are left over?

285

1-Digit Quotients

Juan has 13 baseball cards to give to
4 friends. How many cards will each
friend get? How many will be left over?

To find the number of cards,
divide: 13 ÷ 4 = __?__

- Think: About how many 4's in 13?

$$3 \times 4 = 12 \quad \text{too small}$$

$$4 \times 4 = 16 \quad \text{too large}$$

13 is between
12 and 16. Try 3.

- Write 3 in the quotient above the 3 in 13.

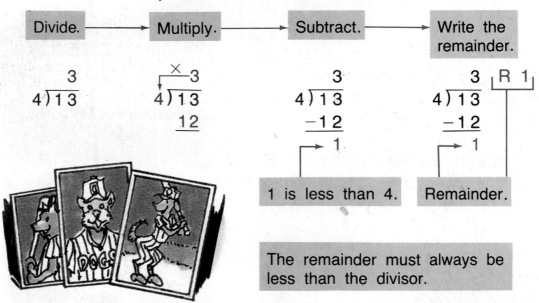

Divide.	Multiply.	Subtract.	Write the remainder.

```
   3             ×3            3            3 | R 1
4)13          4)13         4)13         4)13
              12           -12          -12
                             1            1
```

1 is less than 4.   Remainder.

The remainder must always be
less than the divisor.

Each friend gets 3 cards. One is left over.

Divide.

1. 2)17   2. 4)22   3. 5)33   4. 6)34   5. 7)24

Find the quotient and the remainder.

6. $2\overline{)15}$ 7. $3\overline{)14}$ 8. $5\overline{)32}$ 9. $6\overline{)56}$ 10. $4\overline{)38}$

11. $3\overline{)19}$ 12. $4\overline{)17}$ 13. $5\overline{)29}$ 14. $8\overline{)26}$ 15. $6\overline{)28}$

16. $9\overline{)30}$ 17. $5\overline{)28}$ 18. $4\overline{)25}$ 19. $6\overline{)19}$ 20. $5\overline{)23}$

21. $4\overline{)35}$ 22. $3\overline{)29}$ 23. $7\overline{)16}$ 24. $6\overline{)34}$ 25. $8\overline{)61}$

Divide.

26. $9 \div 5$ 27. $15 \div 6$ 28. $58 \div 7$ 29. $37 \div 4$

30. $19 \div 2$ 31. $18 \div 5$ 32. $41 \div 6$ 33. $89 \div 9$

34. $30 \div 7$ 35. $26 \div 4$ 36. $22 \div 3$ 37. $42 \div 8$

38. $52 \div 8$ 39. $45 \div 6$ 40. $75 \div 9$ 41. $51 \div 7$

Solve.

42. The circus has 43 fish to feed to 5 dancing bears. How many fish should each bear get? How many fish are left over?

43. 16 stickers are equally divided among 3 children. How many stickers does each child get? How many are left over?

Calculator Activity

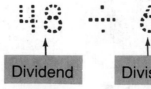

↑	↑	↑
Dividend	Divisor	Quotient

Divide. Use a calculator.

44. $42 \div 7 = \underline{\ ?\ }$ 45. $81 \div 9 = \underline{\ ?\ }$

46. $35 \div 7 = \underline{\ ?\ }$ 47. $63 \div 3 = \underline{\ ?\ }$

12-3 Division Practice

Divide.

1. $3\overline{)16}$ 2. $5\overline{)21}$ 3. $7\overline{)24}$ 4. $8\overline{)18}$ 5. $4\overline{)27}$

6. $3\overline{)28}$ 7. $4\overline{)31}$ 8. $6\overline{)38}$ 9. $5\overline{)27}$ 10. $8\overline{)50}$

11. $7\overline{)40}$ 12. $5\overline{)23}$ 13. $3\overline{)25}$ 14. $8\overline{)36}$ 15. $9\overline{)22}$

To check division, use multiplication.
Add any remainder.

$$\begin{array}{r} 4 \\ 5\overline{)20} \\ -20 \\ \hline 0 \end{array} \qquad \begin{array}{r} 5 \\ \times 4 \\ \hline 20 \end{array} \quad \text{Answer checks}$$

No Remainder

$$\begin{array}{r} 6 \;\; R3 \\ 4\overline{)27} \\ -24 \\ \hline 3 \end{array} \qquad \begin{array}{r} 4 \\ \times 6 \\ \hline 24 \\ +3 \\ \hline 27 \end{array} \quad \text{Answer checks}$$

Divide and check.

16. $5\overline{)14}$ 17. $3\overline{)26}$ 18. $7\overline{)20}$ 19. $4\overline{)39}$

20. $3\overline{)17}$ 21. $6\overline{)36}$ 22. $7\overline{)44}$ 23. $8\overline{)47}$

24. $9\overline{)65}$ 25. $5\overline{)42}$ 26. $5\overline{)49}$ 27. $6\overline{)54}$

28. $7\overline{)63}$ 29. $4\overline{)38}$ 30. $8\overline{)31}$ 31. $8\overline{)63}$

32. $9\overline{)69}$ 33. $7\overline{)67}$ 34. $9\overline{)72}$ 35. $6\overline{)46}$

Solve.

36. 43 students sit in 5 rows. How many sit
in each row? How many are left?

Practice

Find the product.

1.	12	2.	36	3.	44	4.	17	5.	96	6.	32
	× 8		× 3		× 4		× 3		× 6		× 7

7.	321	8.	238	9.	482	10.	157	11.	209	12.	107
	× 2		× 3		× 2		× 4		× 4		× 5

Estimate the answer. (Watch the signs!)

13. $11 + $19   **14.** $36 + $71   **15.** $51 − $39   **16.** $87 − $21

17. 3 × 63   **18.** 2 × 27   **19.** 9 × $3.70   **20.** 7 × $2.10

Find the perimeter.

21.

5 m / 2 m / 2 m / 5 m

22.
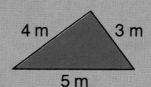
4 m / 3 m / 5 m

Find the area.

23.
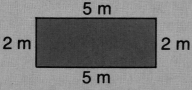

24.

Find the volume.

25.
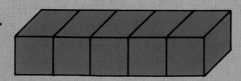

26.
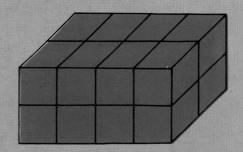

Solve.

27. The divisor is 9. The dividend is 53. Find the quotient and the remainder.

12-5 2-Digit Quotients

Mr. Bear packed 96 books. He put 4 books in a case. How many cases did he pack?

Divide: $96 \div 4 = $ __?__

To find the first digit in the quotient, think: __?__ tens $\times$ 4 = 9 tens

$2 \times 4 = 8$

$3 \times 4 = 12$

9 is between 8 and 12. Try 2.

Write 2 in the quotient above the 9 in 96.

Divide.	Multiply.	Subtract and compare.	Bring down.

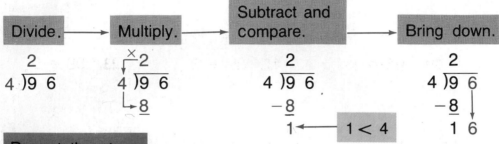

$$
\begin{array}{r} 2 \\ 4\overline{)9\ 6} \end{array}
\qquad
\begin{array}{r} \times\ 2 \\ 4\overline{)9\ 6} \\ 8 \end{array}
\qquad
\begin{array}{r} 2 \\ 4\overline{)9\ 6} \\ -8 \\ \hline 1 \end{array}
\qquad
\begin{array}{r} 2 \\ 4\overline{)9\ 6} \\ -8 \\ \hline 1\ 6 \end{array}
$$

$1 < 4$

Repeat the steps.

To find the second digit in the quotient, think: __?__ ones $\times$ 4 = 16 ones

$4 \times 4 = 16$ → Try 4.

Write 4 in the quotient above the 6 in 96.

Divide.	Multiply.	Subtract and compare.	Check.

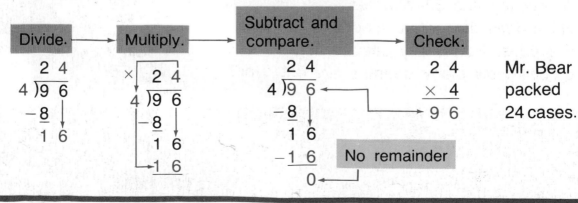

$$
\begin{array}{r} 2\ 4 \\ 4\overline{)9\ 6} \\ -8 \\ \hline 1\ 6 \end{array}
\qquad
\begin{array}{r} \times\ 2\ 4 \\ 4\overline{)9\ 6} \\ -8 \\ \hline 1\ 6 \\ 1\ 6 \end{array}
\qquad
\begin{array}{r} 2\ 4 \\ 4\overline{)9\ 6} \\ -8 \\ \hline 1\ 6 \\ -1\ 6 \\ \hline 0 \end{array}
\qquad
\begin{array}{r} 2\ 4 \\ \times\ 4 \\ \hline 9\ 6 \end{array}
$$

No remainder

Mr. Bear packed 24 cases.

Complete. (The first is done.)

1.
```
    1 6
  2)3 2
   -2 ↓
    1 2
   -1 2
```

2.
```
    1 ?
  3)3 9
   -3 ↓
      9
    -  ?
```

3.
```
    1 ?
  5)6 5
   -5 ↓
    ? 5
   -? ?
```

4.
```
    1 ?
  4)6 4
   -? ↓
    ? ?
   -? ?
```

Divide.

5. 2)26   6. 4)44   7. 3)72   8. 2)38   9. 4)76

10. 4)52   11. 6)84   12. 2)96   13. 6)78   14. 4)56

15. 6)96   16. 5)75   17. 7)84   18. 3)54   19. 7)91

Find the quotient.

20. 66 ÷ 3   21. 96 ÷ 8   22. 82 ÷ 2   23. 99 ÷ 9

Solve.

24. A store has 36 apples to put into 3 fruit baskets. How many apples go into each basket?

25. Sharon has 124 tiny dolls in her collection. She wants to put them on 4 shelves. How many go on each shelf?

26. A monkey has 52 peanuts in a bag. He divides the peanuts equally into 6 groups. How many peanuts are in each group? How many peanuts are left over?

Challenge!

27. A bus has 73 passengers. 6 passengers leave the bus at each of 12 stops. How many passengers are still on the bus?

291

2-Digit Quotients with Remainders

Mark has 47 stamps to divide equally among his 3 friends. How many stamps will each friend get? How many stamps will be left over?

To find the number of stamps, divide: 47 ÷ 3 = ___?___

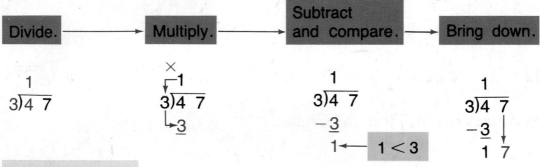

Divide.	Multiply.	Subtract and compare.	Bring down.

```
     1             ×-1            1              1
  3)4 7         3)4 7         3)4 7          3)4 7
                  -3           -3             -3
                                1    1 < 3     1 7
```

Repeat the steps.

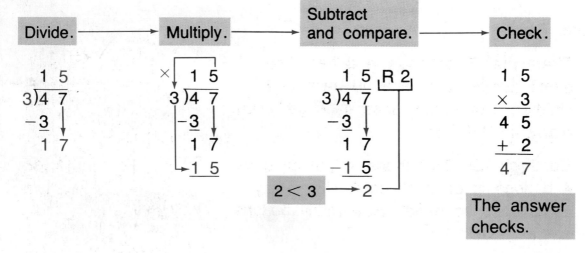

Divide.	Multiply.	Subtract and compare.	Check.

```
    1 5          × 1 5          1 5  R 2        1 5
  3)4 7        3)4 7         3)4 7           × 3
  -3           -3           -3               4 5
   1 7          1 7          1 7             + 2
                1 5         -1 5             4 7
                            2 < 3 → 2
```

The answer checks.

Mark gave each of his 3 friends 15 stamps.
He had 2 stamps left over.

Copy and complete.

1.
```
    1 4  R ?
  4)5 7
   -4 ↓
    1 7
   -? ?
     ?
```

2.
```
    1 ?  R ?
  3)4 6
   -3 ↓
    1 ?
   -? ?
     ?
```

3.
```
    1 ?  R ?
  5)5 9
   -? ↓
     9
   -?
     ?
```

4.
```
    ? ?  R ?
  3)7 0
   -? ↓
    ? 0
   -? ?
     ?
```

Divide and check.

5. 5)68   6. 2)93   7. 9)97   8. 4)63   9. 3)58

10. 3)82   11. 6)95   12. 5)81   13. 2)71   14. 7)92

15. 4)89   16. 3)40   17. 6)79   18. 7)83   19. 5)77

Find the quotient and the remainder.

20. 73 ÷ 7   21. 45 ÷ 2   22. 85 ÷ 4   23. 77 ÷ 3

24. 98 ÷ 3   25. 92 ÷ 8   26. 74 ÷ 5   27. 94 ÷ 4

Solve.

28. There are 75 balloons in a bag. The same number are given to each of 6 children. How many does each get? How many are left over?

29. Dominick has 97 buttons to put on cards. 4 buttons fit on each card. How many cards does he need? How many buttons are left over?

30. There are 38 nickels in all. Chris divides the nickels into 5 piles. How many piles of nickels can he make? How many nickels are left over?

293

Estimating Quotients

Records sell 4 for $15.76. Juanita has $5. Does she have enough money to buy 1 record?

To find out, estimate: $15.76 ÷ 4 = _?_

To estimate a quotient:

- Round to the
  nearest dollar. $15.76 ⟶ $16

- Divide mentally. $16 ÷ 4 = $4

Each record is about $4.
Juanita has enough money for 1 record.

Study these examples.

$12.23 ÷ 2 = _?_	$8.40 ÷ 8 = _?_	$5.75 ÷ 3 = _?_
Rounds to	Rounds to	Rounds to
$12.23 ⟶ $12	$8.40 ⟶ $8	$5.75 ⟶ $6
$12 ÷ 2 = $6	$8 ÷ 8 = $1	$6 ÷ 3 = $2

Round to the nearest dollar.

1. $4.60   2. $2.30   3. $1.75   4. $5.10   5. $1.25

6. $5.75   7. $1.05   8. $3.75   9. $2.75   10. $4.50

11. $10.10   12. $20.90   13. $17.60   14. $25.50   15. $30.10

16. $12.10   17. $17.99   18. $36.40   19. $48.60   20. $75.50

Estimate the quotient.

21. $4.60 ÷ 5   **22.** $2.30 ÷ 4   **23.** $1.75 ÷ 2   **24.** $5.10 ÷ 5

25. $12.10 ÷ 6   **26.** $17.99 ÷ 9   **27.** $6.40 ÷ 6   **28.** $6.60 ÷ 7

Estimate the quotient.

29. 4)$4.10   **30.** 2)$7.65   **31.** 3)$9.35   **32.** 5)$4.95   **33.** 3)$8.75

34. 6)$17.60   **35.** 9)$8.75   **36.** 7)$48.60   **37.** 8)$56.25   **38.** 9)$71.79

For Sale

3 for $11.58

1 for $15.97

3 for $27.27

3 for $26.59

4 for $35.50

1 for $19.88

Answer these questions by estimating.

39. How many sand pails can be bought with $5?

40. How many beach towels can be bought with $10?

41. With $20 how many floats can be bought? How many radios?

42. With $20 how many umbrellas can be bought? How many Ping-Pong sets?

43. Check your answers with a calculator.

295

12-8 Problem Solving: Two-Step Problems

Problem: Taeko has 23 decorated fans and Suki has 31. They divided them equally on 4 shelves at school. How many fit on each shelf?

4 shelves			
🪭	?	?	?
🪭	?	?	?
🪭	?	?	?
🪭	?	?	?

23 fans, Taeko
31 fans, Suki

1 IMAGINE

Draw and label a picture of the problem.

2 NAME

Facts: 23 fans, Taeko
31 fans, Suki
4 shelves

Question: How many fans fit on each shelf?

3 THINK

Look at the picture.
This is a two-step problem.
First, find the total number of fans by adding:
    23 + 31 = __?__

Then find the number of each shelf by dividing:

Total number   ÷ 4 =   Number on
    of fans   each shelf

4 COMPUTE

23 + 31 = 54 total number of fans

$$\begin{array}{r} 13 \text{ R2} \\ 4\overline{)54} \end{array}$$

13 fans fit on each shelf.
 2 fans are left over.

5 CHECK

Multiply: 13 × 4 = 52 ⟶ 52 + 2 = 54
The answer checks.

296

Solve these two-step problems.

1. Erasers cost 7¢ each. Lonnie bought 1 pencil for 10¢ and some erasers. He paid 94¢ in all. How many erasers did he buy?

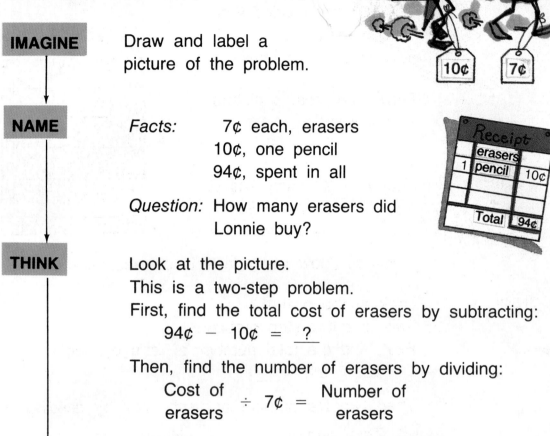

IMAGINE   Draw and label a picture of the problem.

NAME

Facts: 7¢ each, erasers
10¢, one pencil
94¢, spent in all

Question: How many erasers did Lonnie buy?

THINK

Look at the picture.
This is a two-step problem.
First, find the total cost of erasers by subtracting:
94¢ − 10¢ = ?

Then, find the number of erasers by dividing:

Cost of erasers ÷ 7¢ = Number of erasers

Then   **COMPUTE**   and   **CHECK**

2. Margo had $10. She spent $2 for a notebook. How many records could she buy if each record was $4?

3. Ellen read 5 books last month. The first 4 had 85 pages each. The last book had 95 pages. How many pages did she read?

4. Jay picked 4 kinds of flowers. He picked 12 of each kind. He divided them equally among 3 vases. How many flowers were put in each vase?

5. Make up a two-step problem.

More Practice

Divide.

1. 4)9
2. 5)17
3. 3)22
4. 7)30
5. 5)38

6. 6)66
7. 8)90
8. 8)96
9. 7)98
10. 9)75

Find the quotient and remainder.

11. 6)28
12. 9)42
13. 8)55
14. 7)68
15. 4)38

16. 3)45
17. 2)37
18. 4)51
19. 3)63
20. 2)19

21. 4)62
22. 5)67
23. 8)86
24. 7)93
25. 9)65

Divide.

26. 24 ÷ 5
27. 32 ÷ 9
28. 52 ÷ 5
29. 57 ÷ 3

30. 69 ÷ 4
31. 83 ÷ 3
32. 90 ÷ 8
33. 71 ÷ 7

Solve.

34. Mrs. Baker sold 8 bags of cookies. She sold 96 cookies in all. How many were in each bag if each had the same number?

35. Paint sets are on sale for 3 for $17.75. Joshua has $5. Estimate if he has enough money to buy 1 paint set.

36. Ruth has 73 stamps. 6 stamps fit on each page. How many pages can be filled? How many stamps are left over?

(See *Still More Practice*, p.366.)

Math-e-Magic

NUMBER GAMES

The Numerical Land of Oz

1.

2.

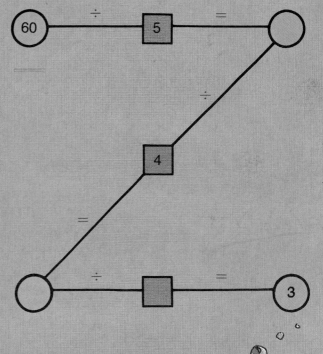

1. a. Find the missing numbers so that ◯ ÷ ▢ = 5

     Example: 20 ÷ 4 = 5

  b. Make your own circle so that ◯ ÷ ▢ = 6

2. a. Start with 60 and fill in the missing

     numbers to get to 3.

  b. Start with 80 and end with 2.

299

Check Your Mastery

Divide.

See pp. 284-288

1. $16 \div 5$ 2. $31 \div 6$ 3. $58 \div 9$ 4. $43 \div 7$

5. $75 \div 8$ 6. $62 \div 9$ 7. $37 \div 4$ 8. $41 \div 7$

Find the quotient.

See pp. 290-291

9. $3\overline{)33}$ 10. $2\overline{)28}$ 11. $6\overline{)78}$ 12. $5\overline{)70}$ 13. $7\overline{)84}$

Find the quotient and the remainder.

See pp. 292-293

14. $4\overline{)55}$ 15. $5\overline{)64}$ 16. $2\overline{)85}$ 17. $3\overline{)74}$ 18. $8\overline{)36}$

19. $6\overline{)73}$ 20. $5\overline{)99}$ 21. $7\overline{)89}$ 22. $7\overline{)93}$ 23. $6\overline{)57}$

Estimate the quotient.

See pp. 294-295

24. $\$3.97 \div 2$ 25. $\$7.75 \div 4$ 26. $\$14.17 \div 7$ 27. $\$62.75 \div 9$

Solve.

See pp. 284-293

28. Wendell had 75 pennies. He spent 5 of them each day. How many days did they last?

29. Frank has 62 snakes to divide equally into 8 pens. How many snakes go in each pen? How many are left over?

30. The librarian has 37 new books. He wants to place them equally on 5 shelves. How many books on each shelf? How many books left over?

13

Fractions and Decimals

In this unit you will:

- Find fractions as parts of a whole and parts of a set
- Find equivalent fractions
- Compare fractions
- Find part of a number
- Estimate fractional parts
- Study tenths and hundredths
- Study fractions and decimals larger than one
- Add and subtract decimals
- Solve problems by finding fractional parts

Do you remember?

3 equal parts

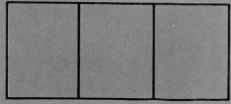

3 unequal parts

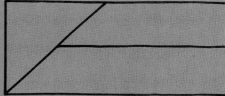

301

13-1 Fractions: Parts of a Whole

A fraction is a part of a whole.

Sue divided the circle into 4 equal parts. She cut out 1 of the parts.

Sue wrote this *fraction* to show the part she cut out.

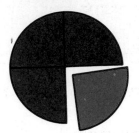

4 equal parts

Fraction: $\dfrac{1 \leftarrow \text{part cut out}}{4 \leftarrow \text{number of equal parts}}$

Read: one fourth

Study these examples.

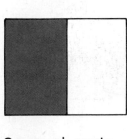

2 equal parts

Fraction: $\dfrac{1 \leftarrow \text{part shaded}}{2 \leftarrow \text{number of equal parts}}$

Read: one half

3 equal parts

Fraction: $\dfrac{2 \leftarrow \text{parts shaded}}{3 \leftarrow \text{number of equal parts}}$

Read: two thirds

5 equal parts

Fraction: $\dfrac{3 \leftarrow \text{parts shaded}}{5 \leftarrow \text{number of equal parts}}$

Read: three fifths

10 equal parts

Fraction: $\dfrac{10 \leftarrow \text{parts shaded}}{10 \leftarrow \text{number of equal parts}}$

Read: 10 tenths or 1 whole

302

halves	thirds	fourths	fifths	sixths	eighths	tenths

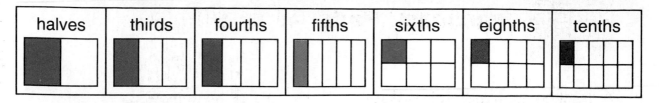

Write the fraction for the colored part.

1.

2.

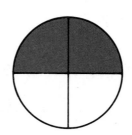

3.

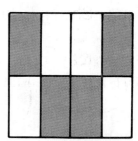

4.

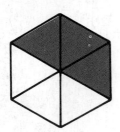

5.

6.

Write the fraction for the part not colored.

7.

8.

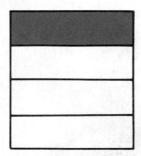

9.

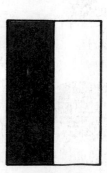

10.

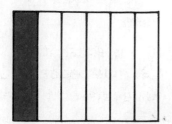

11.

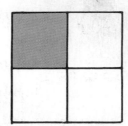

12.

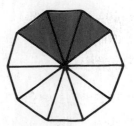

303

13-2 Fractions: Parts of a Set

Fractions measure parts of sets or groups of objects.

One bonnet is not colored.
There are 6 bonnets in all.
$\frac{1}{6}$ of the bonnets is not colored.

Three western hats are colored.
There are 9 western hats in all.
$\frac{3}{9}$ of the western hats are colored.

Write the fraction for the part that is not colored.

1.

2.

3.

4.

8 flowers

3 are white.

What part are white?

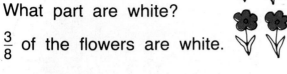

$\frac{3}{8}$ of the flowers are white.

$\frac{3}{8}$ ← white flowers ← flowers altogether

5. What part of the flowers are not white?

6. What part of the flowers are drooping?

DAYS OF THE WEEK						
SUNDAY	MONDAY	TUESDAY	WEDNESDAY	THURSDAY	FRIDAY	SATURDAY

These are the 7 days in the week.
Two days begin with the letter T.

What part of the week begins with the letter T?

$\frac{2}{7}$ ← days begin with T. ← days in the week

$\frac{2}{7}$ of the week begin with the letter T.

Write the fraction for each part.

7. What part is Monday?

8. What part begins with the letter S?

9. What part has 6 letters in its name?

10. What part has 8 letters in its name?

11. What part is a school day?

Challenge!

12. There are 12 months in a year. What part is July?

13. What part of a year begins with the letter J?

305

13-3 Equivalent Fractions

Equivalent fractions name the same amount.

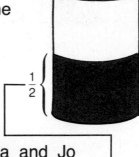

Linda filled a pitcher $\frac{1}{2}$ full.
Jo filled a pitcher $\frac{2}{4}$ full.

The picture shows that Linda and Jo filled the pitchers to the same level.

$$\frac{1}{2} = \frac{2}{4}$$

$\frac{1}{2}$ and $\frac{2}{4}$ are equivalent fractions.

Complete. Use the pictures.

1.

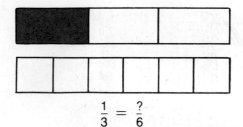

$$\frac{1}{3} = \frac{?}{6}$$

2.

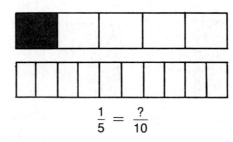

$$\frac{1}{5} = \frac{?}{10}$$

3.

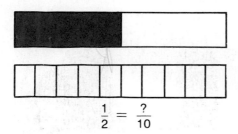

$$\frac{1}{2} = \frac{?}{10}$$

4.

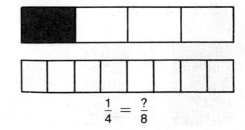

$$\frac{1}{4} = \frac{?}{8}$$

Complete. Use the pictures.

5.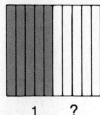

$$\frac{1}{2} = \frac{?}{10}$$

6.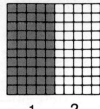

$$\frac{1}{2} = \frac{?}{100}$$

7.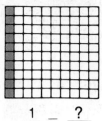

$$\frac{1}{10} = \frac{?}{100}$$

Complete.

8.

$$\frac{1}{4} = \frac{?}{8}$$

9.

$$\frac{2}{3} = \frac{?}{6}$$

10.

$$\frac{2}{5} = \frac{?}{10}$$

11.

$$\frac{2}{2} = ?$$

12.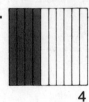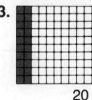

$$\frac{4}{10} = \frac{?}{5}$$

13.

$$\frac{20}{100} = \frac{?}{10}$$

Write "Yes" or ""No."

14.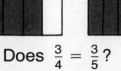

Does $\frac{3}{4} = \frac{3}{5}$?

15.

Does $\frac{1}{2} = \frac{2}{3}$?

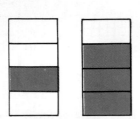

13-4 Comparing Fractions

Lydia planted $\frac{4}{8}$ of her garden.

John planted $\frac{3}{8}$ of his garden.

Who planted the greater part of the garden?

Lydia's garden   John's garden

$\frac{4}{8}$ is greater than $\frac{3}{8}$.

Write: $\frac{4}{8} > \frac{3}{8}$.

> is greater than

$\frac{3}{8}$ is less than $\frac{4}{8}$.

Write: $\frac{3}{8} < \frac{4}{8}$

< is less than

Compare. Write < or > to make each statement true.

1.

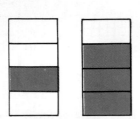

$\frac{1}{4}$ __?__ $\frac{3}{4}$

2.

$\frac{1}{5}$ __?__ $\frac{4}{5}$

3.

$\frac{3}{6}$ __?__ $\frac{4}{6}$

4.

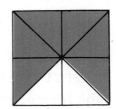

$\frac{7}{8}$ __?__ $\frac{6}{8}$

Compare. Write < or > to make each statement true.

5.
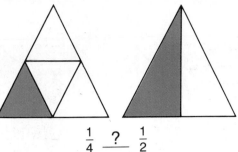

$$\frac{1}{4} \underline{\quad ? \quad} \frac{1}{2}$$

6.
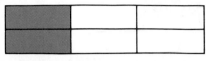

$$\frac{2}{6} \underline{\quad ? \quad} \frac{2}{12}$$

7.
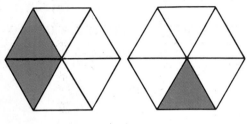

$$\frac{1}{3} \underline{\quad ? \quad} \frac{1}{6}$$

8.
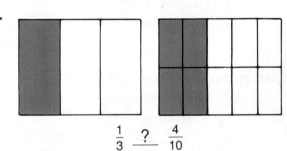

$$\frac{3}{4} \underline{\quad ? \quad} \frac{8}{10}$$

9.
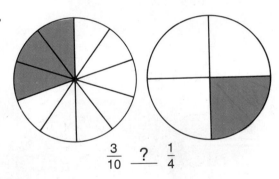

$$\frac{3}{10} \underline{\quad ? \quad} \frac{1}{4}$$

10.

$$\frac{1}{3} \underline{\quad ? \quad} \frac{4}{10}$$

Solve. (Hint: Draw a picture.)

11. Alice colored $\frac{3}{6}$ of a circle. Pat colored $\frac{5}{6}$ of a circle. Who colored the greater part of a circle?

12. Martha drank $\frac{3}{5}$ of a glass of milk. Florence drank $\frac{2}{5}$ of a glass of milk. Who drank more milk?

13. Mary ate $\frac{5}{8}$ of a box of crackers. Sam ate $\frac{4}{8}$ of a box of crackers. Who ate more crackers?

Finding Part of a Number

Fractions help us to find parts of a number.

Norman brought out 6 kites to fly. $\frac{1}{2}$ of the kites had tails.

How many kites had tails?

What is $\frac{1}{2}$ of 6?

To find $\frac{1}{2}$ of 6, divide:

Divide the kites into two equal groups.

6 kites are in 2 groups of 3.

So, $\frac{1}{2}$ of 6 = 3

$$6 \div 2 = 3 \qquad 2\overline{)6} = 3$$

$\frac{1}{2}$ of the 6 kites is 3 kites.

Study these examples.

$\frac{1}{5}$ of 15 = __?__

$15 \div 5 = 3$

$\frac{1}{4}$ of 20 = __?__

$20 \div 4 = 5$

Solve.

1.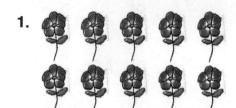

$\frac{1}{2}$ of 10 = __?__

2.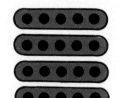

$\frac{1}{3}$ of 9 = __?__

Solve.

3.  $\frac{1}{5}$ of 5 = ___?___

4.  $\frac{1}{3}$ of 6 = ___?___

5. $\frac{1}{4}$ of 8 = ___?___

6. $\frac{1}{4}$ of 16 = ___?___

Complete.

7. $\frac{1}{3}$ of 6 = ___?___
6 ÷ 3 = ___?___

8. $\frac{1}{4}$ of 8 = ___?___
8 ÷ 4 = ___?___

9. $\frac{1}{2}$ of 4 = ___?___
4 ÷ 2 = ___?___

10. $\frac{1}{3}$ of 12 = ___?___
12 ÷ 3 = ___?___

11. $\frac{1}{4}$ of 16 = ___?___
16 ÷ 4 = ___?___

12. $\frac{1}{2}$ of 10 = ___?___
10 ÷ 2 = ___?___

Find part of the number.

13. $\frac{1}{3}$ of 12

14. $\frac{1}{2}$ of 8

15. $\frac{1}{3}$ of 15

16. $\frac{1}{2}$ of 20

17. $\frac{1}{4}$ of 32

18. $\frac{1}{3}$ of 27

19. $\frac{1}{4}$ of 20

20. $\frac{1}{5}$ of 25

21. $\frac{1}{10}$ of 40

22. $\frac{1}{7}$ of 21

23. $\frac{1}{5}$ of 45

24. $\frac{1}{6}$ of 18

Find the missing number.

25. $\frac{1}{2}$ of ___?___ = 5

26. $\frac{1}{3}$ of ___?___ = 6

27. $\frac{1}{4}$ of ___?___ = 7

28. $\frac{1}{5}$ of ___?___ = 7

29. $\frac{1}{6}$ of ___?___ = 6

30. $\frac{1}{10}$ of ___?___ = 2

CHALLENGE

13-6 Fractions Larger Than One

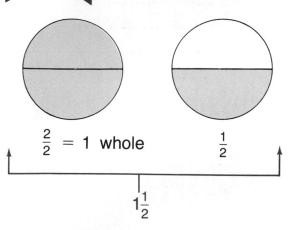

$\frac{2}{2}$ = 1 whole $\frac{1}{2}$

$1\frac{1}{2}$

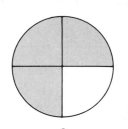

$\frac{4}{4}$ = 1 whole $\frac{3}{4}$

$1\frac{3}{4}$

$1\frac{1}{2}$ and $1\frac{3}{4}$ are called **mixed numbers.**

Write the mixed number.

1.

2.

3.

4.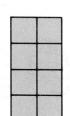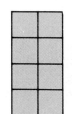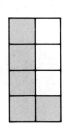

5.

312

Write the mixed number.

6.

7.

8.

9.

10.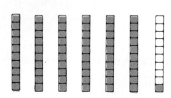

11.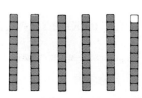

12.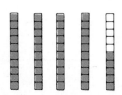

13.

Write the mixed number.

14.

15.

16.

17.

313

13-7 Fractions and Decimals

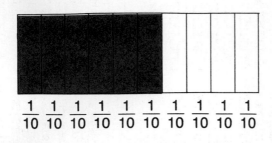

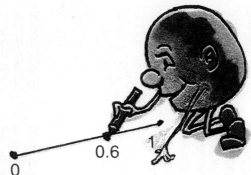

Six of the ten tenths are shaded.
Harry wrote a **decimal** and a **fraction**
to show this.

Fraction: $\frac{6}{10}$ Decimal: 0.6

The dot is the decimal point.

Read: six tenths   Read: six tenths

Decimals can be shown on the number line.

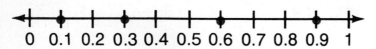

Study these examples shown on the number line.

$\frac{1}{10} = 0.1$ $\frac{3}{10} = 0.3$ $\frac{9}{10} = 0.9$

Write a fraction and a decimal for each.

1.

2.

3.

314

Write a decimal for the shaded part.

4.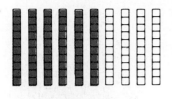

5.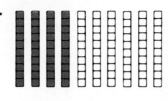

6.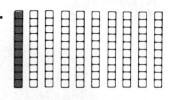

7.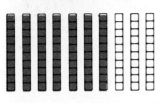

8.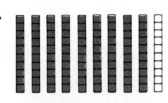

9.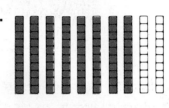

10.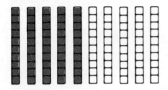

11.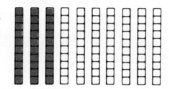

12.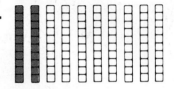

Read the word name for each.

13. 0.6   **14.** 0.8   **15.** 0.9   **16.** 0.5   **17.** 0.7

18. 10   **19.** 0.1   **20.** 40   **21.** 4   **22.** 0.4

Compare. Write <, =, or >.

23. 0.8 _?_ 0.9

24. 0.5 _?_ 0.7

25. 0.1 _?_ 0.5

26. $\frac{3}{10}$ _?_ 0.2

27. $\frac{7}{10}$ _?_ 0.7

28. 0.6 _?_ $\frac{4}{10}$

Solve.

29. Ken had nine tenths of his math correct. What part of his math was correct? Write the answer as a decimal.

315

Decimals Larger than 1

Chef Ray had these pies remaining.
How much pie is shown?

1 whole   1 whole   3 slices
out of 10

$2\frac{3}{10} = 2.3$

$2\frac{3}{10}$ pies are left, or 2.3 pies.

Read: two and three tenths.

Decimals larger than 1 can be shown on a number line.

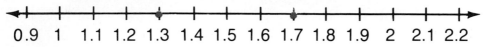

0.9 1 1.1 1.2 1.3 1.4 1.5 1.6 1.7 1.8 1.9 2 2.1 2.2

$1.3 < 1.7$

Study these.

$1\frac{4}{10} = 1.4$

$3\frac{1}{10} = 3.1$

Write a decimal for each.

1.

2.

Write a decimal for each.

3.

4.

Write a decimal for each.

5.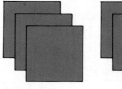

6.

7.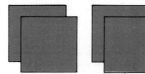

8.

Read each decimal.

9. 2.2   **10.** 3.4   **11.** 1.7   **12.** 4.2   **13.** 3.8

14. 1.4   **15.** 5.9   **16.** 5.6   **17.** 6.7   **18.** 4.3

Write as a decimal.

19. $3\frac{2}{10}$ **20.** $2\frac{3}{10}$ **21.** $1\frac{1}{10}$

22. $7\frac{2}{10}$ **23.** $1\frac{9}{10}$ **24.** $2\frac{7}{10}$

25. $5\frac{3}{10}$ **26.** $6\frac{4}{10}$ **27.** $4\frac{5}{10}$

Write "Yes" or "No". (Hint: draw pictures.)

28. Does $1\frac{4}{10}$ = 1.8?   **29.** Does $2\frac{5}{10}$ = 2.5?

30. Does $3\frac{5}{10}$ = 2.5?   **31.** Does $1\frac{1}{10}$ = 1.6?

32. Does $2\frac{2}{10}$ = 2.2?   **33.** Does $3\frac{3}{10}$ = 3.1?

13-9 Hundredths

There was a three-day math contest.
One hundred questions were asked.

Clare answered 75 out of 100 questions.

$\frac{75}{100} = 0.75$ Read: seventy-five hundredths

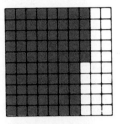

Bob answered 92 out of 100 questions.

$\frac{92}{100} = 0.92$ Read: ninety-two hundredths

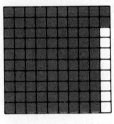

Frank answered 47 out of 100 questions.

$\frac{47}{100} = 0.47$ Read: forty-seven hundredths

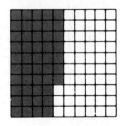

Read each decimal.

1. 0.25   **2.** 0.50   **3.** 0.75   **4.** 0.34   **5.** 0.56

6. 0.17   **7.** 0.08   **8.** 0.41   **9.** 0.12   **10.** 0.01

11. 0.87   **12.** 0.02   **13.** 0.35   **14.** 0.47   **15.** 0.94

318

Decimals Larger Than 1

1 whole   1 whole   1 whole $\frac{25}{100}$

This is a picture of: 3 and 0.25   or   3.25

Read: three and twenty-five hundredths

Write a decimal for the shaded parts.

16.

17.

18.

19.

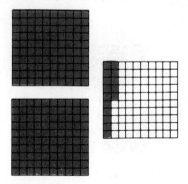

20.

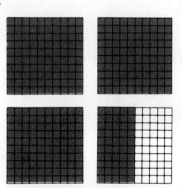

21.

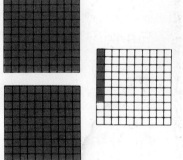

Compare. Write <, =, or >.

22. 0.46 ? 0.54

23. 0.50 ? $\frac{50}{100}$

24. 0.85 ? 0.48

25. 3.17 ? 2.71

26. 4.75 ? 5.25

27. 6.10 ? 8.10

28. 4.70 ? 4.07

29. 5.05 ? 5.50

30. 1.10 ? 1.01

319

13-10 Adding and Subtracting Decimals

Add and subtract decimals the same way you add and subtract whole numbers.

Add: 2.43 + 1.83 = __?__

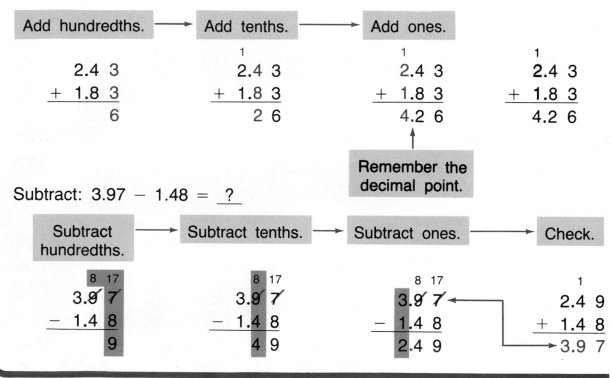

Add hundredths.	→	Add tenths.	→	Add ones.	

```
                          1              1            1
   2.4 3              2.4 3          2.4 3        2.4 3
 + 1.8 3            + 1.8 3        + 1.8 3      + 1.8 3
       6                2 6          4.2 6        4.2 6
                                      ↑
```

Remember the decimal point.

Subtract: 3.97 − 1.48 = __?__

Subtract hundredths.	→	Subtract tenths.	→	Subtract ones.	→	Check.

```
   8  17              8  17          8  17             1
  3.9 7              3.9 7          3.9 7           2.4 9
 − 1.4 8            − 1.4 8        − 1.4 8         + 1.4 8
       9                4 9          2.4 9           3.9 7
```

Find the sum.

1. 2.8
   +8.6

2. $6.75
   +4.23

3. 1.39
   +6.47

4. 1.49
   +9.20

5. 5.83
   +3.27

Find the difference.

6. 6.4
   −1.7

7. $7.35
   −2.69

8. 8.02
   −5.95

9. 9.26
   −8.56

10. 8.67
    −3.19

Add.

11.   3.9
       +2.3

12.   1.06
       +3.07

13.   2.5
       +2.2

14.   7.8
       +3.6

15.   7.3
       +3.5

16.   3.64
       +2.49

17.   4.55
       +2.75

18.   6.25
       +3.75

19.   7.51
       +5.10

20.   8.64
       +1.23

Subtract.

21.   8.0
       −4.3

22.   7.6
       −4.8

23.   6.0
       −4.7

24.   5.5
       −3.7

25.   5.9
       −4.2

26.   4.00
       −3.05

27.   4.55
       −2.78

28.   3.75
       −2.80

29.   9.43
       −7.76

30.   6.87
       −4.29

Find the sum.

31.   4.3
       2.6
      +8.8

32.   1.7
       6.2
      +3.1

33.   9.22
       6.84
      +1.73

34. $2.31
       4.79
      +8.27

35. $7.00
       3.95
      +2.19

Calculator Activity

36. Add 1.7, 2.3, 7.5, and 10.8. Then subtract 2.3.

37. Add 3.5, 2.6, 8.4 and 12.1. Then subtract 4.6.

38. Add 6.4, 1.0, 4.1, and 9.0. Then subtract 8.0.

39. Add 1.1, 2.2, 3.3, and 4.4. Then subtract 5.5.

Problem Solving: Finding Fractional Parts

Problem: Tammy made a dozen party baskets.
She put ribbons on $\frac{1}{3}$ of them.
How many baskets have ribbons?

1 IMAGINE   Draw and label a picture of the party baskets.

12 party baskets

2 NAME

Facts: 12 party baskets
$\frac{1}{3}$ with ribbons

Question: How many baskets have ribbons?

3 THINK   Look at the drawing.
It shows $\frac{1}{3}$ of 12 baskets have ribbons.

4 COMPUTE   Find $\frac{1}{3}$ of 12.

$\frac{1}{3}$ of 12 = __?__
12 ÷ 3 = 4

4 baskets have ribbons.

5 CHECK   Count the baskets with ribbons.
There are 4 baskets.
So, $\frac{4}{12}$ of the baskets have ribbons.
But, $\frac{4}{12} = \frac{1}{3}$. These are equivalent fractions.
The answer checks.

Solve.

1. Mrs. Murphy cut a watermelon into 8 equal pieces. Each child has one piece. They eat $\frac{1}{4}$ of the watermelon. How many children are there?

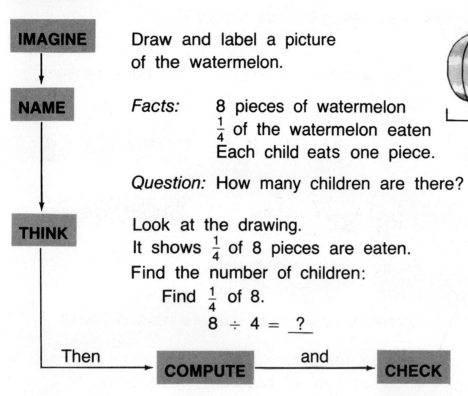

IMAGINE   Draw and label a picture of the watermelon.

NAME   *Facts:*   8 pieces of watermelon
                    $\frac{1}{4}$ of the watermelon eaten
                    Each child eats one piece.

           Question: How many children are there?

           $\frac{1}{4}$ $\frac{2}{4}$ $\frac{3}{4}$ $\frac{4}{4}$

THINK   Look at the drawing.
           It shows $\frac{1}{4}$ of 8 pieces are eaten.
           Find the number of children:
                Find $\frac{1}{4}$ of 8.
                $8 \div 4 = \underline{\ ?\ }$

      Then   ——→   **COMPUTE**   and   ——→   **CHECK**

2. What part of the watermelon was *not* eaten?

3. Matt bought 12 cans of juice. $\frac{1}{4}$ of the cans are orange juice. How many cans are orange juice?

4. One half of the bran muffins were gone when Jane came home. If there were 16 muffins to begin with, how many were left?

5. 33 children tried out for the soccer team. $\frac{1}{3}$ were picked. How many were picked?

More Practice

Write the fraction for the shaded areas.

1.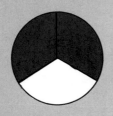

2.

3.

Write which part of the group is shaded.

4.

5.

6.

Write the equivalent fractions.

      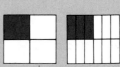

7. $\frac{1}{3} = \frac{?}{9}$

8. $\frac{1}{2} = \frac{?}{8}$

9. $\frac{3}{5} = \frac{?}{10}$

10. $\frac{1}{4} = \frac{?}{12}$

Complete.

11. $\frac{1}{2}$ of 10 = __?__

12. $\frac{1}{4}$ of 12 = __?__

13. $\frac{1}{3}$ of 9 = __?__

Add or subtract.

14.
$$\begin{array}{r} 4.3 \\ +2.5 \\ \hline \end{array}$$

15.
$$\begin{array}{r} 6.9 \\ -3.4 \\ \hline \end{array}$$

16.
$$\begin{array}{r} 7.32 \\ +2.59 \\ \hline \end{array}$$

17.
$$\begin{array}{r} 6.84 \\ -3.45 \\ \hline \end{array}$$

18.
$$\begin{array}{r} 4.83 \\ +5.27 \\ \hline \end{array}$$

324

(See *Still More Practice*, p. 367.)

Math-e-Magic

ESTIMATING WITH FRACTIONS

Estimate or compare different parts of
your body and height.

With a friend's help, cut a piece of
string equal to your height.

1. Cut one string in half.
    Can you find a part of your body that is
    about equal to the length of one of
    these pieces?
    > (Try: knee to foot; waist to foot.)
    > What did you find?

    These lengths are about $\frac{1}{2}$ of your height.
    Use your string to measure things in the
    classroom.
    > What did you find?

    These things measure about $\frac{1}{2}$ of your
    height.

2. Cut the piece of string you just used in
    half.
    Can you find a part of your body that is
    about equal to the new length of string?.
    > What did you find?

    These lengths are about $\frac{1}{4}$ of your height.
    Use your string to measure things in the
    classroom.
    > What did you find?

    These things measure about $\frac{1}{4}$ of your
    height.

Check Your Mastery

Write the fraction for the unshaded part.

See pp. 302-303

1.    **2.**    **3.**    **4.**

Write the equivalent fraction.

See pp. 306-307

5. $\frac{1}{4} = \frac{?}{8}$ **6.** $\frac{3}{9} = \frac{?}{3}$ **7.** $\frac{1}{5} = \frac{?}{15}$

Compare. Write <, =, or >.

See pp. 308-309, 314-319

8. $\frac{1}{3}$? $\frac{1}{6}$ **9.** 0.83 ? 0.95   **10.** 0.7 ? 0.4

11. 3.2 ? 3.7   **12.** 0.65 ? $\frac{65}{100}$ **13.** 5.25 ? 4.75

Add or subtract.

See pp. 320-321

14. 4.38
     + 2.71

15. 19.34
     − 7.25

16. 5.00
     − 1.25

17. 44.31
     + 7.39

18. 5.17
     − 3.74

Solve.

See pp. 320-321

19. Jim used 4.50 rolls of tape and Carl used 3.75 rolls. How many rolls were used?

20. Kathy drove 2.78 km. Janet drove 1.50 km. How much more did Kathy drive than Janet?

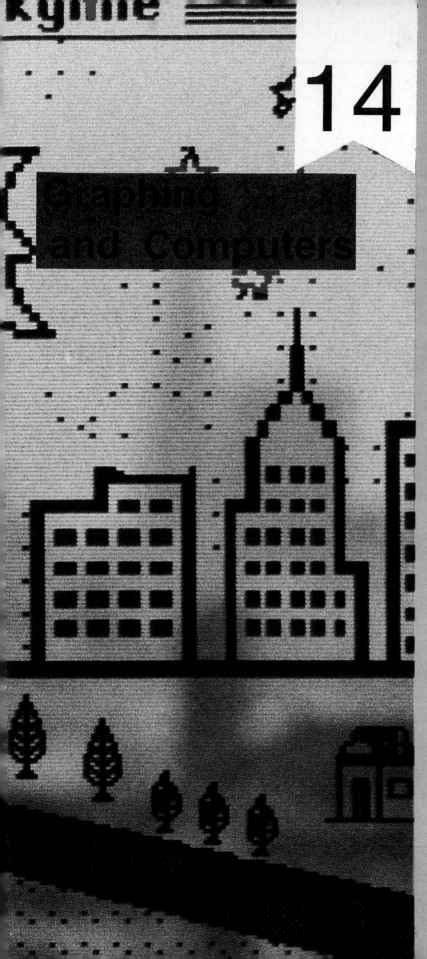

14

Graphing and Computers

In this unit you will:

- Read pictographs
- Read bar graphs
- Read and write number pairs on a grid
- Read circle graphs
- Solve problems using information from a table
- Use the RETURN and PRINT commands on a computer
- Use LOGO
- Enter programs
- Solve problems using flowcharts

Do you remember?

Each 🎂 = 2

🎂🎂 = 4

🎂🎂🎂 = 6

A **graph** shows information. Pictures are used to represent numbers in a **pictograph**.

This pictograph shows how many foreign stamps Stacy has collected.

Each ▨ symbol or picture is used to show 3 stamps.

Stacy's Stamp Collection	
Italy	▨ ▨ ▨
Ghana	▨ ▨ ▨ ▨
France	▨ ▨
Canada	▨ ▨ ▨ ▨ ▨
Brazil	▨ ▨ ▨ ▨
Key: Each ▨ = 3 stamps.	

There are 6 stamps from France.

Use the pictograph above to answer each question.
How many stamps does Stacy have from:

1. Canada?　　2. Ghana?　　3. Italy?　　4. Brazil?

From which country does Stacy have:

5. the least number of stamps?　　6. 9 stamps?

7. less than 7 stamps?　　8. 15 stamps?

9. How many more stamps are there from Canada than Italy?

This pictograph shows the number of birthdays in the third grade for four months.

Birthdays						
September	🎂	🎂	🎂			
October	🎂	🎂	🎂	🎂	🎂	🎂
November	🎂	🎂				
December	🎂	🎂	🎂	🎂		

Key: Each 🎂 = 2 birthdays.

Use the pictograph on the right to answer each question.

10. For how many birthdays does each cake stand?

11. How many birthdays are there in September?

12. Which month has the most birthdays?

13. Which month has the least number of birthdays?

14. How many children have birthdays in these four months?

15. How many more birthdays are in October than in December?

... CHALLENGE ...

16. There are 10 birthdays in January, 0 in February, and 2 in March. Draw a pictograph like the one above. Write the months on the graph and draw a cake for each birthday.

14-2 Bar Graphs

A **bar graph** can be used when you are reporting or comparing information.

This bar graph shows how many pencils of each color the school store sold in September.

- The shortest bar is for white pencils.

- White was the least popular color.

- 3 white pencils were sold.

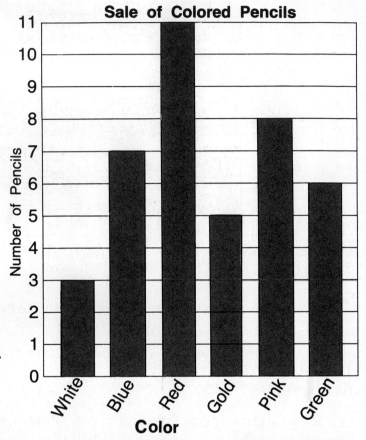

Sale of Colored Pencils

Number of Pencils / Color (White, Blue, Red, Gold, Pink, Green)

Use the bar graph above to answer each question.

1. How many blue pencils were sold?

2. How many more pink than white pencils were sold?

3. Were more gold pencils sold than green?

4. What color pencil was sold the most? How many were sold?

5. How many pencils were sold in all?

6. How many blue and pink pencils were sold in all?

The third graders took a survey of the kinds
of fruit in their lunch boxes.

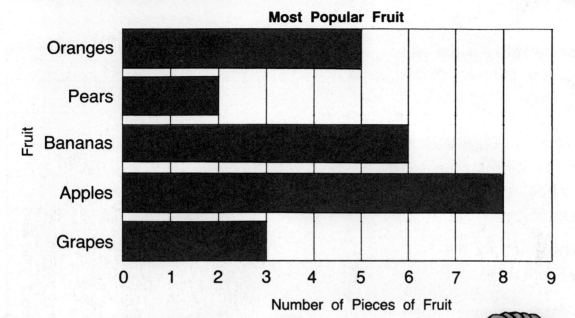

Most Popular Fruit

Fruit

| Oranges |
| Pears |
| Bananas |
| Apples |
| Grapes |

0 1 2 3 4 5 6 7 8 9

Number of Pieces of Fruit

Use the bar graph above to answer each question.

7. How many oranges does the graph show?

8. How many apples does the graph show?

9. How many more bananas are there than pears?

10. How many oranges and grapes are there in all?

11. What fruit is most popular?

12. What fruit is least popular?

13. The number of apples is how many
    times the number of pears?

CHALLENGE

14. Make a bar graph to display: 5 peaches;
    2 melons; and 7 cherries.

Number Pairs

Number pairs name the points on the graph.

Look at this graph.

What animal does the number pair (2, 3) locate?

To find the animal the number pair locates:

- Begin at Start.
- The **first number** tells you to move 2 spaces to the *right*.
- The **second number** tells you to move 3 spaces *up*.

The lion is located by the number pair (2, 3).

Where is the fox?

First move to the *right*.
Then move *up*.
The fox is 3 to the *right* and 0 *up*.
The fox is at (3, 0).

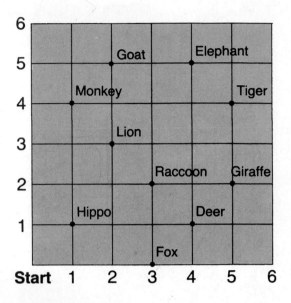

Use the graph to answer the questions. Begin at Start.

1. What animal has the number pair (4, 5)?

2. What animal is at (5, 2)?

Give the number pair for each animal.

3. deer

4. monkey

5. tiger

6. goat

7. hippo

8. raccoon

**Write the letter for each number pair.
Use the graph at the right.**

9. (1,2) 10. (4,4) 11. (3,3)

12. (2,1) 13. (1,5) 14. (4,1)

15. (2,3) 16. (3,2) 17. (4,5)

18. (4,0) 19. (1,6) 20. (5,5)

21. (5,3) 22. (0,1) 23. (6,0)

**Write the number pair for
each letter.**

24. G 25. I. 26. A

27. X 28. N 29. H

30. O 31. R 32. U

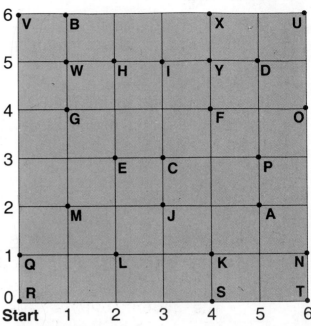

**Write the fruit for each number
pair. Use the graph at the
left to locate each.**

33. (1,5) 34. (2,3)

35. (1,1) 36. (3,6)

37. (3,0) 38. (1,2)

**Write the number pair for
each fruit.**

39. plum 40. banana.

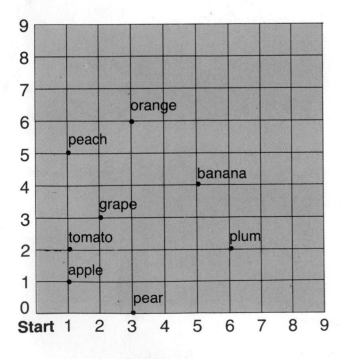

333

14-4 Circle Graphs

A **circle graph** shows information as parts of a circle.

The circle graph at the right shows the favorite sports of the students at Burnt Hill School.

What part of the students chose softball as their favorite sport?

To find the part of the students, write a fraction.

$\frac{1}{4}$ of the students chose softball as their favorite sport.

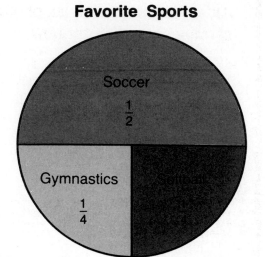

Favorite Sports

Soccer $\frac{1}{2}$

Gymnastics $\frac{1}{4}$

Softball $\frac{1}{4}$

Use the circle graph above to answer each question.

1. What part of the students chose gymnastics?

2. What part of the students chose soccer?

3. Did more students choose soccer than softball?

Use the circle graph on the right to answer each question.

4. What part of the students chose Hide and Seek?

5. What part of the students chose Tag?

6. What game was favored as much as Hide and Seek?

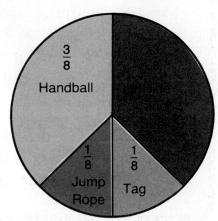

Favorite Games

$\frac{3}{8}$ Handball

$\frac{3}{8}$ Hide and Seek

$\frac{1}{8}$ Jump Rope

$\frac{1}{8}$ Tag

334

14-5 Permutation Fun

An arrangement of all or part of a set of things is a **permutation**.

You have a set of 4 geometric shapes: a circle, a triangle, a rectangle, and a square.

circle   triangle   square   rectangle

In how many ways can you arrange these 4 objects *in a line* so that the rectangle and triangle are *not* side by side?

The drawing above is a sample of one arrangement or permutation.

Complete.

1. Look at the picture. How many other arrangements of the 4 shapes are there? (Draw pictures or cut out the 4 shapes to help you find the answer.)

2. How many arrangements of a circle, a rectangle, and 2 squares are there if the squares are *not* side by side?

14-6 Problem-Solving: Using Information From a Table

Problem: The third grade made a survey to find the number of girls and boys in each grade at school. How many students are in the third and fourth grades?

Grade	Girls	Boys
1st	66	63
2nd	57	59
3rd	50	71
4th	68	67
5th	50	59
6th	55	61

1 IMAGINE

You have to read the results of the survey.

2 NAME

Facts: See the chart.

Question: How many students are in the third and fourth grades?

3 THINK

What part of the table has the information needed?

3rd	50	71
4th	68	67

Use this information to find the total:

| 3rd-grade girls | + | 3rd-grade boys | + | 4th-grade girls | + | 4th-grade boys | = | ? |

4 COMPUTE

```
  50   3rd-grade girls
  71   3rd-grade boys
  68   4th-grade girls
+ 67   4th-grade boys
 256   Students
```

There are 256 students in the third and fourth grades.

5 CHECK

Go back to the table. Estimate the sum.
$50 + 70 + 70 + 70 = 260$
260 is close to the exact answer of 256.

Solve. Use the table on page 336

1. Dora wanted to know if there were more girls or more boys in grades 1, 2, and 3 together.

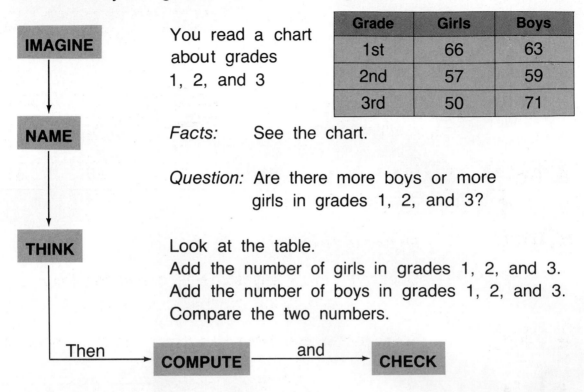

IMAGINE

You read a chart about grades 1, 2, and 3

Grade	Girls	Boys
1st	66	63
2nd	57	59
3rd	50	71

NAME

Facts: See the chart.

Question: Are there more boys or more girls in grades 1, 2, and 3?

THINK

Look at the table.
Add the number of girls in grades 1, 2, and 3.
Add the number of boys in grades 1, 2, and 3.
Compare the two numbers.

Then → **COMPUTE** and → **CHECK**

Solve. Use the table on page 336.

2. Which two grades have the same number of girls? of boys?

3. Which two grades have the same number of students in all?

4. Are there more boys or more girls in grades 1 through 6? How many more?

5. Make a chart for the number of boys and girls in grades 1, 2, and 3 in your school.

More Practice

Use this pictograph to answer each question.

1. Which is the least favorite day of the week?

2. How many more children like Thursday than Wednesday?

3. How many children like the most favorite day?

4. How many more children like Friday than Monday?

Favorite Day of the Week	
Monday	☺ ☺ ☺
Tuesday	☺
Wednesday	☺ ☺
Thursday	☺ ☺ ☺ ☺
Friday	☺ ☺ ☺ ☺ ☺ ☺

Each ☺ = 3 children.

Use the bar graph to answer each question.

5. How many children walk to school?

6. How many ride the bus?

7. How many ride their bicycle?

8. How do most children come to school?

9. How many more bicycle than come by car?

10. How many more children walk than come by car?

11. What vehicle is the least used?

12. How many children in all are included in this survey?

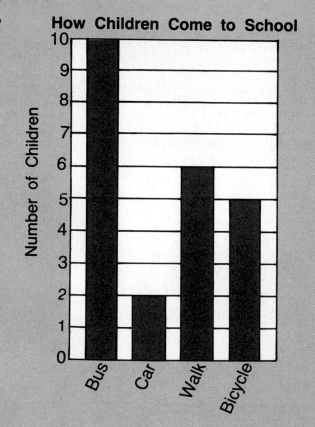

How Children Come to School

338

Check Your Mastery

See pp. 328-331, 334-335.

Use the pictograph to answer each question.

1. How many children wore blue socks?

2. How many more pink than brown socks were worn?

3. How many pairs were counted in all?

Numbers of Colored Socks

Brown	🧦🧦
White	🧦🧦🧦🧦🧦🧦🧦
Pink	🧦🧦🧦🧦
Blue	🧦🧦🧦🧦🧦
Yellow	🧦

Each 🧦 = 2 pairs worn.

Use the bar graph to answer each question.

4. How many points did Tim score?

5. Who scored the most points?

6. How many points did Steve and Jesse score together?

7. How many more points did Steve score than Beth?

Skating Contest Scores

Use the circle graph to answer each question.

8. What part of the students like dogs?

9. What part likes cats?

10. What part likes pets other than cats or dogs?

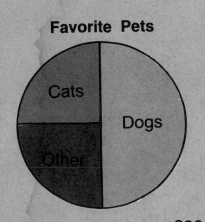

Favorite Pets

Cats

Dogs

Other

14-7 The PRINT Command

The computer keyboard is like the keyboard of a typewriter.

What you type on the keyboard is the **input**.

The instructions in the input are carried out by the computer.

The computer prints out the answer as **output** on the screen.

The PRINT command is used to print information on the screen.

Input ⟶ PRINT "CLOWN "

| Type on the keyboard. Press RETURN. |

CLOWN

| The computer will print whatever is in quotes. |

Output ⟶ CLOWN

| The output appears on the screen. |

Write the output that will be printed.

1. PRINT "MY NAME IS _____." RETURN

2. PRINT "I AM 8 YEARS OLD." RETURN

3. PRINT "COMPUTERS ARE FUN." RETURN

4. PRINT "1 + 3 + 5 = 9" RETURN

Compute

Input ⟶ PRINT 18 + 45   Type on the keyboard. Press RETURN.

18+45

The computer will compute the sum.

Output ⟶ 63   The output appears on the screen.

Solve. The asterisk (∗) tells the computer to multiply. The slash (/) tells it to divide. Press RETURN after each exercise.

5. PRINT 23 + 49

6. PRINT 298 − 47

7. PRINT 56/8

8. PRINT 27 + 31 + 93

9. PRINT 432/16

10. PRINT 5692 − 343

11. PRINT 729 ∗ 3217

12. PRINT 2 ∗ 3 ∗ 7

Write the output.

13. PRINT 9 ∗ 12 ∗ 7

14. PRINT "I LOVE TO SKI"

15. PRINT "5 + 6 + 3"

16. PRINT 5 + 6 + 3

Complete.

17. After each line of input, press the _?_ key.

18. To make the computer print just an answer, use the _?_ command.

19. To make the computer print what you have typed, use the PRINT command and _?_ marks.

14-8 Flowcharts

A list of step-by-step commands must
be given to the computer in correct order.

A **flowchart** helps you to plan these steps.
Look at the flowchart below.
Start at the left and follow the arrows.
Each box is an instruction.
Stop when you have followed all the steps.

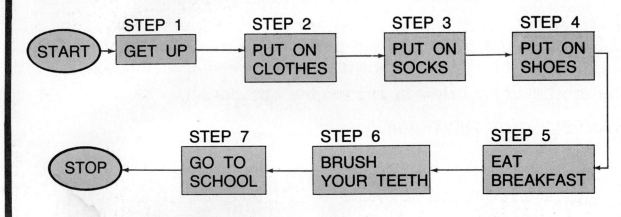

	STEP 1	STEP 2	STEP 3	STEP 4
START →	GET UP	PUT ON CLOTHES	PUT ON SOCKS	PUT ON SHOES

	STEP 7	STEP 6	STEP 5
STOP ←	GO TO SCHOOL	BRUSH YOUR TEETH	EAT BREAKFAST

Use the flowchart above to answer these questions.

1. Suppose you were going to eat breakfast
   in school. Which step would you leave out?

2. Suppose you wrote Step 4 before Step 3.
   How would that change the program?

3. Suppose you are asked to walk the dog
   before leaving for school. Where does that
   step best fit?

342

Use the flowchart below to answer the questions.

BUYING ICE CREAM

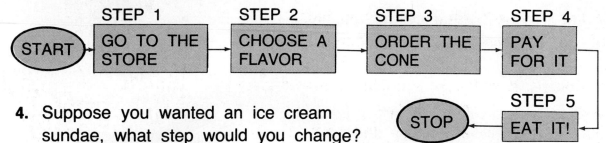

STEP 1	STEP 2	STEP 3	STEP 4
GO TO THE STORE	CHOOSE A FLAVOR	ORDER THE CONE	PAY FOR IT

STEP 5
EAT IT!
STOP

4. Suppose you wanted an ice cream sundae, what step would you change?

5. Suppose you wrote Step 3 before Step 2. How would that change the program?

6. If you left out Step 4 altogether, what would happen to your program?

Use the flowchart below to answer the questions.

PLANNING A BIRTHDAY PARTY

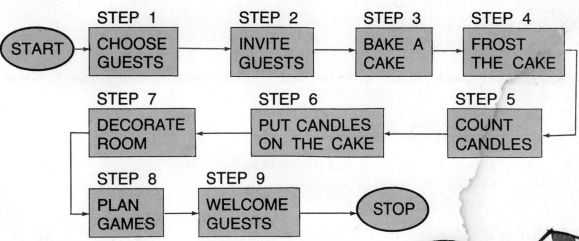

STEP 1	STEP 2	STEP 3	STEP 4
CHOOSE GUESTS	INVITE GUESTS	BAKE A CAKE	FROST THE CAKE

STEP 7	STEP 6	STEP 5
DECORATE ROOM	PUT CANDLES ON THE CAKE	COUNT CANDLES

STEP 8	STEP 9
PLAN GAMES	WELCOME GUESTS

STOP

7. If you left out Step 2 altogether, what would happen to your program?

8. What activity would you add to planning the birthday party? Where would that step best fit?

343

Programs

Computers do not think. A person called a programmer plans the commands given to the computer.

A list of step-by-step commands is a program.

Enter this program. Type the commands.

| The numbers tell the order of the steps. | 10 PRINT "HOW ARE YOU"
20 PRINT "ON THIS"
30 PRINT "SPRING DAY?" | Press RETURN after each line. |

When you enter a program, remember:
- The commands are numbered in order.
- The quotation marks make the computer print the numbers or words inside them.
- When you type RUN the computer will print the output.

Output

```
HOW ARE YOU
ON THIS
SPRING DAY?
```

Study this example.

```
10   PRINT "THE SUM OF"
20   PRINT "30 and 50 IS"
30   PRINT 30 + 50.
```

Output

```
THE SUM OF
30 AND 50
IS 80.
```

Copy these programs. Then type RUN.

1. 10   PRINT "EVERY CLOUD"
   20   PRINT "HAS A SILVER"
   30   PRINT "LINING."

2. 10   PRINT "35 DIVIDED BY"
   20   PRINT "5 EQUALS"
   30   PRINT 35/5.

Copy these programs. Then type RUN.

```
3.  10    PRINT "RUDOLPH ";
    20    PRINT "THE RED-NOSED REINDEER"
    30    PRINT "HAD A VERY SHINY NOSE."

4.  10    PRINT "THE SUM OF 30 AND 50 IS";
    20    PRINT 30 + 50.
```

Copy and complete. Then type RUN.

```
5.  10    PRINT "THERE WAS AN OLD WOMAN ";
    20    PRINT "WHO LIVED IN A   ?  ."
    30    PRINT "SHE HAD SO MANY   ?   ";
    40    PRINT "SHE DIDN'T KNOW ";
    50    PRINT "WHAT TO DO!"
```

```
6.  10    PRINT "ROSES ARE RED,"
    20     ?    "VIOLETS ARE BLUE,"
     ?    PRINT "SUGAR IS SWEET,"
    40    PRINT "AND SO ARE   ?  ."
```

```
7.  10    PRINT "RUB-A-DUB   ?  , ";
    20    PRINT "THREE   ?   IN A TUB."

8.  10    PRINT "THREE   ?     ?   ";
    20    PRINT "LOST   ?   MITTENS."

9.  10    PRINT "ONE, TWO, BUTTON ";
    20    PRINT "YOUR   ?  ."
    30    PRINT "  ?  , FOUR, CLOSE ";
    40    PRINT "THE   ?  ."
    50    PRINT "FIVE   ?  , PICK ";
    60    PRINT "  ?   STICKS."
    70    PRINT "  ?  ,   ?  , CLOSE ";
    80    PRINT "   GATE."
    90    PRINT "  ?  ,   ?  ,"
    100   PRINT "START   ?  ."
```

LOGO is a special computer language. It is used to tell a "turtle" how to draw shapes. The turtle moves FORWARD and BACK, and turns LEFT and RIGHT.

FORWARD 50 means: Move forward 50 turtle steps.
RIGHT 90   means: Turn right 90 degrees
                  or make a **right angle**.

LEFT 90   means: Turn left 90 degrees.
FORWARD 20 means: Move forward 20 turtle steps.

You can use the turtle to draw a rectangle.
Study the example below.

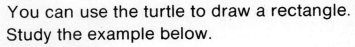

```
RECTANGLE

FORWARD 50
RIGHT 90
FORWARD 20
RIGHT 90
FORWARD 50
RIGHT 90
FORWARD 20
```

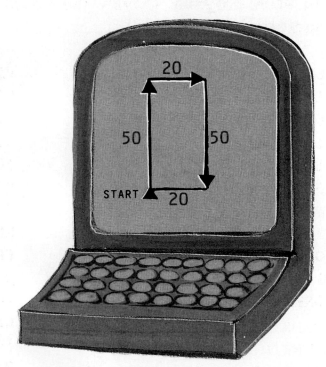

Complete.

1. **Use the turtle to draw**
   RECTANGLE

   FORWARD 30
   RIGHT 90
   FORWARD 60
   RIGHT 90
   FORWARD 30
   RIGHT 90
   FORWARD 60
   RIGHT 90

2. **Use the turtle to draw**
   SPIRAL.

   FORWARD 10
   RIGHT 90
   FORWARD 10
   RIGHT 90
   FORWARD 20
   RIGHT 90
   FORWARD 20
   RIGHT 90
   FORWARD 30

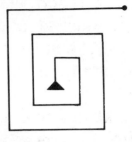

   Continue the program
   to complete the SPIRAL
   drawn at the right.

**Type in each program. Identify the southwestern
state indicated by each shape.**

3. FORWARD 32
   RIGHT 90
   FORWARD 14
   RIGHT 90
   FORWARD 8
   LEFT 90
   FORWARD 8
   RIGHT 90
   FORWARD 24
   RIGHT 90
   FORWARD 22

4. FORWARD 36
   RIGHT 90
   FORWARD 29
   RIGHT 90
   FORWARD 30
   RIGHT 90
   FORWARD 18
   LEFT 90
   FORWARD 3
   RIGHT 90
   FORWARD 8
   LEFT 90
   FORWARD 3
   RIGHT 90
   FORWARD 3

347

Cumulative Test IV

Divide.

1. $4\overline{)17}$ 2. $7\overline{)45}$ 3. $5\overline{)29}$ 4. $8\overline{)46}$ 5. $4\overline{)27}$

6. $8\overline{)75}$ 7. $9\overline{)38}$ 8. $6\overline{)31}$ 9. $7\overline{)22}$ 10. $8\overline{)68}$

11. $4\overline{)44}$ 12. $3\overline{)39}$ 13. $8\overline{)80}$ 14. $5\overline{)97}$ 15. $3\overline{)47}$

Estimate the quotient.

16. $18 \div 4 = \underline{\ ?\ }$ 17. $15 \div 2 = \underline{\ ?\ }$ 18. $24 \div 5 = \underline{\ ?\ }$

19. $41 \div 3 = \underline{\ ?\ }$ 20. $82 \div 5 = \underline{\ ?\ }$ 21. $78 \div 4 = \underline{\ ?\ }$

22. $96 \div 8 = \underline{\ ?\ }$ 23. $59 \div 5 = \underline{\ ?\ }$ 24. $97 \div 9 = \underline{\ ?\ }$

Write the equivalent fraction.

25. $\frac{1}{3} = \frac{?}{6}$ 26. $\frac{1}{2} = \frac{?}{8}$ 27. $\frac{1}{4} = \frac{?}{8}$

28. $\frac{1}{4} = \frac{?}{16}$ 29. $\frac{1}{5} = \frac{?}{10}$ 30. $\frac{1}{6} = \frac{?}{12}$

31. $\frac{3}{5} = \frac{?}{15}$ 32. $\frac{2}{3} = \frac{?}{12}$ 33. $\frac{3}{4} = \frac{?}{12}$

Write the fraction for the shaded part.

 34. $\underline{\ ?\ }$ 35. $\underline{\ ?\ }$ 36. $\underline{\ ?\ }$

 37. $\underline{\ ?\ }$ 38. $\underline{\ ?\ }$ 39. $\underline{\ ?\ }$

 40. $\underline{\ ?\ }$ 41. $\underline{\ ?\ }$ 42. $\underline{\ ?\ }$

Compare. Write <, =, or >.

43. $\frac{1}{4} \ \underline{\ ?\ } \ \frac{2}{4}$ 44. $\frac{5}{6} \ \underline{\ ?\ } \ \frac{4}{6}$ 45. $\frac{1}{2} \ \underline{\ ?\ } \ \frac{4}{8}$

Find the sum or the difference.

46. $\begin{array}{r} 0.3 \\ +0.4 \\ \hline \end{array}$ 47. $\begin{array}{r} 0.75 \\ +0.82 \\ \hline \end{array}$ 48. $\begin{array}{r} 8.43 \\ +6.76 \\ \hline \end{array}$ 49. $\begin{array}{r} 7.87 \\ -3.29 \\ \hline \end{array}$ 50. $\begin{array}{r} 4.55 \\ -2.87 \\ \hline \end{array}$

51. $\begin{array}{r} 7.25 \\ +4.75 \\ \hline \end{array}$ 52. $\begin{array}{r} 8.51 \\ -6.90 \\ \hline \end{array}$ 53. $\begin{array}{r} 8.64 \\ -2.28 \\ \hline \end{array}$ 54. $\begin{array}{r} 6.55 \\ +2.57 \\ \hline \end{array}$ 55. $\begin{array}{r} 4.64 \\ +2.49 \\ \hline \end{array}$

Use the pictograph to answer each question.

Sticker Collections	
Mary	◇ ◇ ◇ ◇
Sue	◇ ◇ ◇
Mike	◇ ◇ ◇ ◇
Tom	◇ ◇
Diana	◇ ◇ ◇ ◇ ◇
Key: Each ◇ = 4 stickers.	

How many stickers does each child have?

56. Mary _?_   **57.** Sue _?_   **58.** Mike _?_   **59.** Tom _?_   **60.** Diana _?_

61. Who has the most stickers?

62. Who has the fewest number of stickers?

63. How many more stickers does Mike have than Sue?

64. How many fewer stickers does Tom have than Diana?

65. How many stickers are there in all the collections?

Solve.

66. Simon planted an equal number of beanplants in 6 rows. He planted 84 beanplants in all. How many beanplants did he plant in each row?

68. Hiroshi walked 1.83 miles. Chad walked 2.14 miles. How much farther did Chad walk than Hiroshi?

70. A grocer has 48 pears to pack into 8 boxes. How many pears should he pack into each box?

72. Patrick has 126 minicars in his collection. He wants to put an equal number of them into 6 carriers. How many minicars will go into each carrier?

74. Mr. Jackson bought 15 cans of food. $\frac{1}{3}$ of them were cans of soup. How many cans of soup did he buy?

67. Bryan had 8 snaps on his jacket. 3 snaps fell off. What fraction of the snaps is still left on the jacket?

69. There are 16 books on a bookshelf. 4 of these are science books. What part of the group is science books?

71. There are 7 days in the week. How many days begin with the letter T? What fractional part of the week is that?

73. Carmen ate $\frac{3}{8}$ of a packet of almonds. Sean ate $\frac{5}{8}$ of a packet. Who ate more almonds?

75. Mrs. Chen has 86 seedlings to plant in her garden. 6 children will plant an equal number of them. How many seedlings will each child plant? How many seedlings will be left over?

349

More Computer Activities

To be used after Unit 1:

1. Solve these problems on your computer. Use the PRINT statement.

   a. $2 + 6$ **b.** $7 + 8$ **c.** $9 + 0$ **d.** $8 + 5$

   e. $9 + 4$ **f.** $0 + 5$ **g.** $1 + 7$ **h.** $8 + 9$

   i. $7 - 5$ **j.** $9 - 6$ **k.** $5 - 1$ **l.** $12 - 3$

2. Write the output. Use the computer to check your answers.

   a. PRINT "9 - 8"   **b.** PRINT "11 - 3 = 8"

   c. PRINT "4 + 3 + 2 = 9"   **d.** PRINT "18 - 9 = 9"

   e. PRINT "I LIKE THIS!"   **f.** PRINT "I'M GOOD AT IT."

To be used after Unit 3:

1. Solve these addition problems. Use the PRINT statement on your computer.

   a. $472 + 133$ **b.** $252 + 5384$ **c.** $367 + 129$

   d. $974 + 28 + 6$ **e.** $356 + 58 + 885$ **f.** $223 + 553 + 488$

   g. $2698 + 3179$ **h.** $1145 + 6873$ **i.** $5689 + 3045$

2. Solve these addition problems. Use the PRINT statement on your computer.

   a. $413 + 58 + 885$ **b.** $356 + 5384 + 194$ **c.** $223 + 129 + 298$

   d. $525 + 87 + 661$ **e.** $414 + 1000 + 101$ **f.** $333 + 199 + 777$

To be used after Unit 4:

Solve these subtraction problems. Use the PRINT statement on your computer. Check your answers.

   a. $16 - 3$ **b.** $48 - 28$ **c.** $583 - 244$

   d. $648 - 363$ **e.** $327 - 169$ **f.** $875 - 487$

   g. $9286 - 3179$ **h.** $6212 - 4105$ **i.** $6873 - 1943$

   j. $3850 - 2546$ **k.** $630 - 5697$ **l.** $1500 - 1269$

To be used after Unit 7:

1. Solve these problems. Use the PRINT statement on your computer. (Remember "*" means multiply and "/" means divide.)

   a. 6 × 2   **b.** 8 × 4   **c.** 2 × 0   **d.** 9 × 3
   e. 0 ÷ 3   **f.** 18 ÷ 2   **g.** 32 ÷ 4   **h.** 24 ÷ 1
   i. 5 × 7   **j.** 7 × 1   **k.** 30 ÷ 5   **l.** 45 ÷ 5

2. Give the output for each, then enter the PRINT statement to check.

   a. PRINT "24 / 6 = "   24 / 6   **b.** PRINT "6 x 3 = "   6 * 3
   c. PRINT "36 / 4 = "   36 / 4   **d.** PRINT "8 x 5 = "   8 * 5

To be used after Unit 9:

Solve these multiplication and division problems. Use the PRINT statement.

   a. 6 × 7   **b.** 7 × 4   **c.** 9 × 6   **d.** 8 × 5
   e. 48 ÷ 8   **f.** 8 ÷ 8   **g.** 56 ÷ 7   **h.** 0 ÷ 9

To be used after Unit 10:

Solve these multiplication problems. Use the PRINT statement.

   a. 2 × 13   **b.** 4 × 12   **c.** 5 × 13   **d.** 6 × 14
   e. 3 × 66   **f.** 7 × 23   **g.** 8 × 111   **h.** 2 × 432
   i. 2 × 193   **j.** 4 × 272   **k.** 5 × 217   **l.** 3 × 329

To be used after Unit 11:

Write out the steps and then make the LOGO turtle draw a rectangle with:

   a. a perimeter of 40 steps   **b.** an area of 40 square steps

To be used after Unit 12:

Write a PRINT statement to solve each problem. Check your answers.

   a. 84 ÷ 6   **b.** 69 ÷ 3   **c.** 75 ÷ 5   **d.** 96 ÷ 4

To be used after Unit 13:

Solve these money problems. Use the PRINT statement.

   a. $35.00 − $17.50   **b.** $1.26 + $1.90   **c.** $8.10 − $.79
   d. $9.20 + $5.50   **e.** $1.29 + $.36   **f.** $23.14 − $.89

MENTAL MATHEMATICS—By Topic

Set 1—COMPARING NUMBERS

Which number is greater?

1. 4 or 6	**2.** 34 or 39	**3.** 100 or 300	**4.** 9 or 6	**5.** 12 or 10
6. 90 or 60	**7.** 654 or 634	**8.** 35 or 53	**9.** 50 or 500	**10.** 52 or 520

Which number is less?

11. 9 or 3	**12.** 25 or 21	**13.** 300 or 500	**14.** 4 or 7	**15.** 59 or 61
16. 40 or 80	**17.** 357 or 337	**18.** 19 or 9	**19.** 84 or 48	**20.** 330 or 33

Set 2—PLACE VALUE OF NUMBERS

Which digit Is in the ones place?

1. 46	**2.** 87	**3.** 534	**4.** 302	**5.** 981

Which digit is in the tens place?

6. 492	**7.** 674	**8.** 902	**9.** 920	**10.** 1876

Which digit is in the hundreds place?

11. 893	**12.** 930	**13.** 450	**14.** 2306	**15.** 9027

Set 3—ROUNDING NUMBERS

Round to the nearest ten.

1. 52	**2.** 26	**3.** 89	**4.** 73	**5.** 48

Round to the nearest hundred.

6. 390	**7.** 410	**8.** 580	**9.** 880	**10.** 275

Round to the nearest dollar.

11. $2.99	**12.** $2.25	**13.** $4.78	**14.** $8.89	**15.** $6.88

Set 4—MISSING ADDENDS

1. $5 + \underline{\ ?\ } = 8$	**2.** $\underline{\ ?\ } + 6 = 9$	**3.** $3 + \underline{\ ?\ } = 8$	**4.** $\underline{\ ?\ } + 5 = 7$
5. $6 + \underline{\ ?\ } = 10$	**6.** $\underline{\ ?\ } + 4 = 11$	**7.** $5 + \underline{\ ?\ } = 11$	**8.** $\underline{\ ?\ } + 7 = 13$

352

Set 5—BASIC ADDITION FACTS

1. Add 2 to: 3, 8, 6, 4, 1, 0, 5, 7, 9, 2

2. Add 3 to: 1, 4, 6, 3, 7, 9, 0, 8, 2, 5

3. Add 4 to: 4, 1, 5, 9, 0, 3, 7, 2, 6, 8,

4. Add 5 to: 3, 1, 5, 8, 0, 7, 9, 6, 2, 4

5. Add 6 to: 1, 4, 6, 8, 0, 2, 7, 9, 3, 5

6. Add 7 to: 6, 3, 8, 4, 9, 2, 7, 5, 1, 0

7. Add 8 to: 0, 1, 3, 5, 7, 9, 4, 6, 2, 8

8. Add 9 to: 5, 0, 1, 2, 7, 4, 3, 6, 8, 9

Set 6—BASIC SUBTRACTION FACTS

1. Subtract 1 from: 1, 2, 4, 6, 8, 3, 5, 7, 9, 10

2. Subtract 2 from: 2, 3, 5, 7, 9, 4, 6, 8, 10, 11

3. Subtract 3 from: 3, 4, 6, 8, 10, 12, 5, 7, 9, 11

4. Subtract 4 from: 4, 5, 7, 9, 11, 13, 6, 8, 10, 12

5. Subtract 5 from: 5, 6, 8, 10, 12, 14, 7, 9, 11, 13

6. Subtract 6 from: 6, 7, 9, 11, 13, 15, 8, 10, 12, 14

7. Subtract 7 from: 7, 8, 10, 12, 14, 16, 9, 11, 13, 15

8. Subtract 8 from: 8, 9, 11, 13, 15, 17, 10, 12, 14, 16

9. Subtract 9 from: 9, 10, 12, 14, 16, 18, 11, 13, 15, 17

10. Subtract 10 from: 10, 11, 13, 15, 17, 19, 21, 23, 25, 27

Set 7—BASIC MULTIPLICATION FACTS

1. Multiply by 2: 3, 4, 5, 6, 1, 0, 7, 8, 9

2. Multiply by 3: 1, 4, 6, 2, 5, 0, 9, 8, 7

3. Multiply by 4: 1, 0, 5, 3, 6, 7, 9, 8, 2

4. Multiply by 5: 4, 2, 1, 0, 6, 9, 8, 7, 3

5. Multiply by 6: 3, 1, 2, 7, 4, 0, 9, 8, 5

6. Multiply by 7: 1, 0, 2, 9, 3, 8, 4, 6, 5

7. Multiply by 8: 5, 4, 3, 7, 9, 0, 1, 2, 6

8. Multiply by 9: 2, 8, 3, 7, 6, 1, 5, 4, 0

9. Multiply by 10: 5, 2, 3, 4, 6, 7, 8, 9, 1

Set 8—MISSING FACTORS

1.
$2 \times \underline{?} = 6$
$2 \times \underline{?} = 12$
$2 \times \underline{?} = 10$

2.
$3 \times \underline{?} = 9$
$3 \times \underline{?} = 15$
$3 \times \underline{?} = 6$

3.
$\underline{?} \times 4 = 8$
$\underline{?} \times 4 = 24$
$\underline{?} \times 4 = 36$

4.
$\underline{?} \times 5 = 10$
$\underline{?} \times 5 = 30$
$\underline{?} \times 5 = 25$

5.
$6 \times \underline{?} = 18$
$6 \times \underline{?} = 12$
$6 \times \underline{?} = 42$

6.
$\underline{?} \times 7 = 14$
$\underline{?} \times 7 = 28$
$\underline{?} \times 7 = 63$

7.
$\underline{?} \times 8 = 40$
$\underline{?} \times 8 = 16$
$\underline{?} \times 8 = 72$

8.
$9 \times \underline{?} = 9$
$9 \times \underline{?} = 27$
$9 \times \underline{?} = 54$

Set 9—BASIC DIVISION FACTS

1. Divide by 2: 4, 8, 12, 18, 10, 14, 16, 20, 22, 24

2. Divide by 3: 3, 6, 9, 12, 21, 24, 27, 15, 30, 33

3. Divide by 4: 4, 8, 16, 12, 36, 32, 20, 24, 28, 40

4. Divide by 5: 10, 20, 30, 40, 35, 25, 15, 5, 50, 55

5. Divide by 6: 6, 12, 24, 48, 54, 18, 30, 36, 42, 60

6. Divide by 7: 7, 21, 14, 63, 28, 49, 35, 28, 70, 77

7. Divide by 8: 24, 32, 40, 72, 16, 40, 8, 48, 56, 80

8. Divide by 9: 18, 9, 36, 45, 81, 72, 54, 45, 27, 90

Set 10—FRACTIONAL PARTS

1. $\frac{1}{2}$ of 8   2. $\frac{1}{2}$ of 12   3. $\frac{1}{2}$ of 4   4. $\frac{1}{2}$ of 10   5. $\frac{1}{2}$ of 16

6. $\frac{1}{4}$ of 12   7. $\frac{1}{4}$ of 32   8. $\frac{1}{4}$ of 8   9. $\frac{1}{4}$ of 36   10. $\frac{1}{4}$ of 20

Set 11—ADDITION PATTERNS

1. Add 2 to: 3, 13, 23, 33, 43, 53, 63, 73, 83, 93

2. Add 3 to: 6, 16, 26, 36, 46, 56, 66, 76, 46, 86

3. Add 4 to: 5, 15, 25, 35, 75, 85, 65, 95, 45, 55

4. Add 5 to: 9, 19, 89, 59, 79, 69, 49, 29, 39, 99

5. Add 6 to: 7, 17, 27, 77, 57, 37, 47, 67, 87, 97

6. Add 7 to: 8, 18, 28, 58, 88, 38, 48, 68. 78, 98

7. Add 8 to: 4, 24, 44, 54, 14, 84, 34, 64, 74, 94

8. Add 9 to: 2, 32, 42, 62, 12, 82, 72, 22, 52, 92

Set 12—SUBTRACTION PATTERNS

1. Subtract 2 from: 7, 17, 27, 37, 47, 57, 67, 77, 87, 97

2. Subtract 3 from: 8, 18, 28, 38, 48, 58, 68, 78, 88, 98

3. Subtract 4 from: 9, 19, 29, 39, 49, 59, 69, 79, 89, 99

4. Subtract 5 from: 11, 21, 31, 41, 51, 61, 71, 81, 91, 101

5. Subtract 6 from: 14, 24, 64, 54, 94, 84, 74, 34, 44, 104

6. Subtract 7 from: 13, 23, 63, 83, 93, 43, 73, 33, 53, 103

7. Subtract 8 from: 15, 25, 85, 75, 45, 35, 75, 55, 65, 105

8. Subtract 9 from: 16, 26, 76, 36, 96, 46, 56, 66, 86, 106

STILL MORE PRACTICE

Practice 1-1

1.   5
    +4

2.   4
    +5

3. 10
    − 7

4.   8
    −5

5. 3 + 5

6. 4 + 2

7. 7 + 2

8. 1 + 0

9. 10 − 4

10. 8 − 7

11. 9 − 5

12. 7 − 4

13. 5 + ? = 8

14. 8 − ? = 5

15. Complete the pattern.
    6, 8, 10, _?_, _?_
    3, 6, 4, 7, _?_, _?_

16. Gordon hit 2 home runs on Tuesday and 6 on Wednesday. How many more home runs did he hit on Wednesday than on Tuesday?

17. Rose has 3 gold barrettes and 4 silver barrettes. How many barrettes does she have altogether?

18. There are 3 boys and 3 girls on a team. How many children are on a team?

19. Ron completed 7 out of 10 math problems. How many did he have left to complete?

20. Tina walked 2 miles on Monday and 3 miles on Tuesday. How many miles did she walk in the two days?

Practice 1-2

1.   9
    +5

2. 13
   + 7

3. 15
   + 4

4. 18
   − 6

5. 14
   − 8

6. 12
   −10

7. 15 − 7

8. 14 − 8

9. 12 − 5

10. 16 − 2

11. 8 + 3 + 6

12. 9 + 4 + 2

13. 9 + 1 + 0

14. 3 + 6 + 5

15. 6 + 4 + 2

16. 5 + 1 + 7

17. 1 + 6 + 7

18. 3 + 5 + 7

Write a family of facts for each.

19. (4, 5, 9)

20. (9, 1, 10)

21. Find the sum of 9, 4, and 5.

22. What is the difference between 17 and 6?

23. Jose needs 13 stamps to complete his collection. If his father gives him 6 stamps, how many more stamps does he need?

24. Increase 5 by 7.

25. Treenia is 9 years old and her brother is 2 years younger. How old is her brother?

Practice 2-1

Write the number in standard form.

1. seventy
2. eighteen
3. 5 tens + 2 ones
4. 8 tens + 4 ones
5. 0 tens + 8 ones

What is the value of the underlined digit?

6. 4̲7
7. 6,4̲57

Compare. Write < or >.

8. 35 _?_ 38
9. 645 _?_ 298
10. 900 _?_ 776
11. 824 _?_ 850

Round to the nearest ten.

12. 39   13. 72   14. 17
15. 55   16. 48   17. 31

Round to the nearest hundred.

18. 773   19. 425   20. 656
21. How many tens are there in 75?
22. Which number is greater: 325 or 622?
13. Write the smallest 3-digit number with 2 in the tens place.
24. Write the largest 3-digit number with 5 in the hundreds place.
25. What does the digit 5 mean in 325? in 750? in 504?

Practice 2-2

Write the number.

1. 2 hundreds 6 tens 3 ones
2. 4 thousands 5 hundreds 0 tens 2 ones

3.
$$\begin{array}{r} 30 \\ +\ 5 \\ \hline \end{array}$$

4.
$$\begin{array}{r} 600 \\ 30 \\ +\ 2 \\ \hline \end{array}$$

5.
$$\begin{array}{r} 400 \\ 60 \\ +\ 8 \\ \hline \end{array}$$

6.
$$\begin{array}{r} 200 \\ 40 \\ +\ 3 \\ \hline \end{array}$$

Write "even," or "odd."

7. 62   8. 38   9. 35

Compare. Write < or >.

10. 9843 _?_ 9747
11. 8213 _?_ 8314
12. 3024 _?_ 2318
13. 1783 _?_ 2119

What is the value of the underlined digit?

14. 2̲3,874   15. 9̲82,563
16. 81,9̲26   17. 72̲,185

Complete.

18. 2, 4, 6, _?_, 10, _?_
19. 3, 6, _?_, 12, _?_
20. 20, 40, _?_, 80, _?_, 120
21. $0.10, $0.20, _?_, $0.40, _?_
22. $3.14, $3.20, _?_, $3.32, _?_
23. Write the next ordinal number after twenty-third.
24. Write the ordinal number before sixteenth.
25. Write the smallest 4-digit number with 2 in the tens place.

356

Practice 3-1

Complete.

1. 3 tens 11 ones = _?_ tens _?_ one

2. 5 hundreds 22 tens = 7 hundreds _?_ tens

3. 52 +17	**4.** 44 +25	**5.** 61 +24
6. 18 + 9	**7.** 14 +17	**8.** 32 +19
9. 421 +162	**10.** 604 +121	**11.** 153 + 46
12. $ .78 + .51	**13.** $3.08 + 2.59	**14.** $3.80 + 5.29

15. Estimate the sum of 49 and 52.

16. Bud has 62 baseball cards. Ella has 45 baseball cards. How many baseball cards do they have in all?

17. Peggy has 28 red beads and 7 blue beads. How many beads does she have in all?

18. Reggie read one book of 263 pages and another book of 284 pages. Find the total number of pages he read.

19. There were 346 large envelopes and 49 small envelopes in a box. How many envelopes were in the box?

20. Find the sum of 36 and 129.

Practice 3-2

1. 301 +197	**2.** 112 + 87	**3.** 347 +185
4. 216 375 +230	**5.** 302 193 + 45	**6.** 521 53 + 67
7. 34 94 +99	**8.** 562 308 + 161	**9.** 32 95 + 8
10. 3295 +2624	**11.** 3456 + 624	**12.** 4215 + 703
13. 3516 + 90	**14.** 327 + 4805	**15.** 7082 + 2181

16. The Reilly family went on vacation. They traveled 452 miles the first day and 189 miles the next day. How many miles did they travel in all?

17. A chef prepared 285 lunches and 145 dinners. How many meals did he prepare in all?

18. An airplane flew 368 miles to one destination and then 475 miles to another destination. How many miles did it travel in all?

19. There are 375 roses and 482 tulips in the greenhouse. How many roses and tulips are there in all?

20. Find the sum of 56, 238, and 110.

Practice 4-1

1. 48
   − 6

2. 97
   −34

3. 39
   −24

Regroup the tens to make more ones.

4. 4 tens 6 ones = 3 tens _____ ones

5. 3 tens 8 ones = 2 tens _____ ones

6. 17
   − 9

7. 15
   − 9

8. 44
   − 5

9. 33
   −18

10. 81
   −34

11. 40
   −12

Regroup the hundreds to make more tens.

12. 438 = 3 hundreds _?_ tens _?_ ones.

13. 654 = 5 hundreds _?_ tens _?_ ones.

14. 206
   −196

15. 608
   −378

16. 906
   −375

17. 452 − 27

18. 378 − 229

19. 895 − 239

20. 793 − 448

21. Ramon walked 33 km the first week and 22 km the second week. How many more kilometers did he walk the first week?

22. The boy scouts collected 3250 pounds of newspaper on Thursday and 1189 pounds on Friday. How many fewer pounds were collected on Friday than on Thursday?

23. Roger caught 38 small fish and 19 large fish. How many more small fish than large fish did he catch?

24. Jude's storybook has 208 pages. He has read 162 pages. How many more pages are left to read?

25. The school children are collecting bottle caps. They have collected 275 caps. How many more must they collect to win a prize for 450?

Practice 4-2

Subtract and check by addition.

1. 718
   −544

2. 896
   −678

3. 892
   −368

4. 900
   −684

5. 400
   −237

6. 5302
   −1179

7. 6248
   − 567

8. $8.80
   − 3.95

9. $6.14
   − .29

Estimate the difference.

10. 895 − 304

11. 723 − 578

12. 942 − 380

13. 607 − 395

14. 4461 − 1710

15. 4003 − 2006

16. A dairy farmer had 325 cows. 175 were brown cows. How many cows were not brown?

17. One school had 473 students. 294 students were boys. How many students were girls?

18. A living room set costs $800. Gina has saved $735. How much more does she need to buy the furniture?

19. Amy bought a book for $3.75. How much change did she receive from $5.00?

20. Liz baked 24 cookies. She ate 9 of them. How many cookies were left?

Practice 5-1

1. $0.30 + 0.55
2. $0.68 + 0.30
3. $4.75 + 1.62
4. $25.32 + 12.59

Round to the nearest dollar.

5. $1.98
6. $5.32
7. $4.51

Write as money. Use . and $.

8. 7 dimes 3 pennies
9. 6 dimes 2 nickels
10. 4 dollars 3 quarters 2 nickels
11. 5 dollars 5 dimes 1 penny

Estimate the cost.

12. $3.27
    + $2.98

13. $4.75
    + $1.20

Estimate the change.

14. $10.00 − $8.72
15. $5.00 − $2.68
16. Cal has 1 dollar, 4 dimes, and five pennies. How much money does Cal have?
17. Jean saved $5.25 last week and $1.35 this week. How much money has she saved in all?
18. Dave gave the clerk $3.50. He spent $3.10. How much change did he receive?
19. Alberto saved $4.38 to buy a pen set. The set costs $6.99. How much more money does he need?
20. Michele bought a T-shirt for $3.75. Estimate her change from a $10 bill.

Practice 5-2

Draw a dial clock showing each time.

1. 1:00
2. 5:30
3. 8:00

Write the digital time.

4. 40 min after 6
5. 15 min after 9
6. 10 min after 12
7. 10 min before 2

Write the date.

8. Christmas Day
9. Your birthday
10. New Year's Day
11. Independence Day
12. Name the sixth month.
13. Name the month after July.

14. How many days are there in each? June and July.
15. How long does it take the minute hand to go around the clock?
16. How long does it take the hour hand to go around the clock?
17. When the minute hand is on 5 and the hour hand is between 3 and 4, what time is it?
18. If it is 10:00 A.M. now, what time will it be 2 hours from now?
19. Katie left at 9:00 A.M. to go to the beach. The trip took 3 hours. What time did Katie arrive at the beach?
20. It takes Phil 20 minutes to walk from his home to the library. If he leaves home at 2:20 P.M., what time will he get to the library?

Practice 6-1

Write as a multiplication fact.

1. 4 sets of 2   **2.** 6 sets of 3

3. 6 sets of 4   **4.** 3 sets of 5

Write as factors and product.

5. $2 + 2 + 2 = 6$ **6.** $4 + 4 + 4 = 12$

Write the missing factor or product.

7. $3 \times \underline{\ ?\ } = 12$ **8.** $5 \times \underline{\ ?\ } = 20$

9. $4 \times \underline{\ ?\ } = 24$ **10.** $7 \times 2 = \underline{\ ?\ }$

11. $5 \times 3 = \underline{\ ?\ }$ **12.** $4 \times \underline{\ ?\ } = 16$

13. $4 \times 3 = \underline{\ ?\ }$ **14.** $2 \times 2 = \underline{\ ?\ }$

15. $6 \times \underline{\ ?\ } = 18$ **16.** $4 \times \underline{\ ?\ } = 16$

17. What is the product of 4 and 0?

18.
$$\begin{array}{r} 0 \\ \times\, 3 \\ \hline \end{array}$$

19.
$$\begin{array}{r} 1 \\ \times\, 5 \\ \hline \end{array}$$

Complete the pattern.

20. 5, 10, $\underline{\ ?\ }$, $\underline{\ ?\ }$, $\underline{\ ?\ }$, $\underline{\ ?\ }$, $\underline{\ ?\ }$

21. A teacher reads 2 stories each day. How many stories does she read in 4 days?

22. There are 4 boys playing in the snow. Each boy has a pair of gloves. How many gloves are there?

23. There are 3 rows of stamps. Each row has 4 stamps. How many stamps are there?

24. 5 children drew pictures. Each child drew 2 pictures. How many pictures were drawn?

25. What is the product of 5 and 2?

Practice 6-2

Write as factors and product.

1. $5 + 5 + 5 = 15$ **2.** $3 + 3 + 3 + 3 + 3 = 15$

Write the missing factor or product.

3. $7 \times \underline{\ ?\ } = 28$ **4.** $\underline{\ ?\ } \times 5 = 40$

5. $6 \times 3 = \underline{\ ?\ }$ **6.** $7 \times \underline{\ ?\ } = 21$

7. $4 \times 3 = \underline{\ ?\ }$ **8.** $\underline{\ ?\ } \times 4 = 32$

Write two facts for each multiplication family.

9. $(9, 5, 45)$ **10.** $(6, 4, 24)$

11. $(7, 2, 14)$ **12.** $(7, 3, 21)$

13. $(8, 5, 40)$ **14.** $(6, 3, 18)$

Complete the pattern.

15. 3, 6, 9, $\underline{\ ?\ }$, $\underline{\ ?\ }$, $\underline{\ ?\ }$, $\underline{\ ?\ }$

16. 4, 8, $\underline{\ ?\ }$, $\underline{\ ?\ }$, $\underline{\ ?\ }$, $\underline{\ ?\ }$

17. There are 5 children. Each child has 3 balloons. How many balloons are there in all?

18. Pepe worked 4 hours every day for 5 days. How many hours did he work in all?

19. There are 8 cars. Each car has 4 wheels. What is the total number of wheels on all 8 cars?

20. There are 4 bags of apples. 3 apples are in each group. How many apples are there?

Practice 7-1

Write the number of:

1. fives in ten.

2. fours in thirty-six.

3. fives in thirty-five.

4. twos in twelve.

5. $10 \div 2$
6. $18 \div 3$

7. $12 \div 2$
8. $25 \div 5$

9. $28 \div 4$
10. $15 \div 5$

Write 4 related multiplication and division facts for each family.

11. (4, 5, 20)
12. (3, 6, 18)

Complete.

13. $3 \times 2 = \underline{\ ?\ }$
14. $6 \div 2 = \underline{\ ?\ }$

15. $8 \times 4 = \underline{\ ?\ }$
16. $32 \div 4 = \underline{\ ?\ }$

17. $24 \div \underline{\ ?\ } = 6$
18. $6 \times \underline{\ ?\ } = 24$

19. $35 \div \underline{\ ?\ } = 7$
20. $7 \times \underline{\ ?\ } = 35$

21. There are 15 desks in 5 rows. How many desks are in each row?

22. 16 oranges were shared equally among 4 children. How many oranges did each child get?

23. There are 4 vases of roses and 20 roses in all. How many roses are in each vase?

24. Zelda has 15 seashells. How many groups of 3 seashells can she make?

25. Twelve plums were divided among six children. How many plums did each child receive?

Practice 7-2

Write the number of:

1. fours in sixteen.

2. twos in eighteen.

3. threes in twenty-seven.

4. fives in twenty.

5. $36 \div 4 = \underline{\ ?\ }$
6. $20 \div 4 = \underline{\ ?\ }$

7. $15 \div 5 = \underline{\ ?\ }$
8. $18 \div \underline{\ ?\ } = 2$

9. $21 \div \underline{\ ?\ } = 7$
10. $8 \div \underline{\ ?\ } = 4$

11. $24 \div 3 = \underline{\ ?\ }$
12. $24 \div 8 = \underline{\ ?\ }$

Write four related multiplication and division facts for each family.

13. (4, 3, 12)
14. (3, 4, 12)

15. (2, 5, 10)
16. (5, 3, 15)

17. $\begin{array}{r} 1 \\ \times 4 \\ \hline \end{array}$
18. $\begin{array}{r} 0 \\ \times 5 \\ \hline \end{array}$
19. $1\overline{)4}$
20. $5\overline{)0}$

21. What is the quotient of 24 divided by 4?

22. Donna and Dawn share 18¢. If they share equally, how much will each girl receive?

23. There are 12 pancakes. Each child will eat 4. How many children are there?

24. Ed, Raul, and Henry equally shared 15 coins. How many coins did each boy get?

25. Matilda bought 16 curtains. She needs 2 curtains for each window. How many windows are there?

Practice 8-1

Measure to the nearest inch.

1. a book   **2.** a pencil

3. a piece of chalk   **4.** your foot

Measure to the nearest foot:

5. the length of your leg

6. the width of your desk

Use a ruler to draw a line for each length.

7. 4 in.   **8.** $5\frac{1}{2}$ in.

9. $6\frac{1}{4}$ in.   **10.** $2\frac{3}{4}$ in.

UNIT 8

Complete.

11. 1 pt = _?_ c   **12.** 2 gal = _?_ qt

13. 4 qt = _?_ gal   **14.** 2 pt = _?_ c

15. 4 pt = _?_ qt   **16.** 3 qt = _?_ pt

17. How many quart containers will 3 gallons of milk fill?

18. Jason drank 2 pt of milk a day. How many pints did he drink in one week?

19. Yesterday the temperature was 95°F. Today it is 89°F. How much hotter was it yesterday?

20. The temperature was 68°F. It rose 12°F. What was the temperature after it rose?

Practice 8-2

Which unit, m or cm, should be used to measure each?

1. pen   **2.** truck

3. paper clip   **4.** flagpole

5. book   **6.** bridge

7. Which is lighter: 9 g or 9 kg?

8. Which is greater: 5L or 500L?

Give a temperature in degrees Celsius.

9. for a warm day

10. for boiling water

11. 200 cm = _?_ m **12.** 400 cm = _?_ m

13. 2000 m = _?_ km **14.** 5000 m = _?_ km

15. 3 m = _?_ cm   **16.** 6 m = _?_ cm

17. 4 km = _?_ m   **18.** 6 km = _?_ m

19. What is a metric unit for measuring liquids?

20. What is a metric unit for measuring length?

21. Measure the top of your desk in centimeters.

22. Which unit is smaller: gram or kilogram?

23. Carmen weighs 32 kilograms. Her sister weighs 25 kilograms. What is their total weight?

24. A fruit bar weighs 5 grams. A box of rice weighs 20 grams. How many more grams does the rice weigh than the fruit bar?

25. Which unit is greater: meter or kilometer?

362

Practice 9-1   **UNIT 9**

Fill in the missing numbers to complete the pattern.

1. 4, _?_, 12, _?_, 20, _?_, _?_
2. 5, 10, _?_, _?_, 25, _?_, _?_
3. _?_, 28, _?_, 36, 40, _?_, _?_
4. 6, 12, _?_, 24, _?_, _?_, _?_

5. 4   6. 7   7. 9
   ×6   ×7   ×8

8. 6)‾4‾8‾   9. 7)‾4‾9‾   10. 8)‾6‾4‾

Complete.

11. 8 × 7 = _?_   12. 7 × 8 = _?_
13. 56 ÷ 7 = _?_   14. 56 ÷ 8 = _?_
15. (1 × 2) × 7   16. (3 × 2) × 8

Write 4 related multiplication and division facts for each family.

17. (7, 6, 42)   18. (6, 9, 54)
19. (6, 8, 48)   20. (7, 5, 35)

21. Sarah bought 8 bunches of cherries. There were 8 cherries to a bunch. How many cherries were there in all?

22. What is the product of 9 and 4?

23. There are 4 boxes of crayons. Each box has 8 crayons. What is the total number of crayons in all four boxes?

24. Louis worked 7 days a week for 8 weeks. How many days did he work?

25. 56 rolls of paper were placed into 7 bins. How many rolls are there in each bin?

Practice 9-2

Fill in the missing numbers to complete the pattern.

1. 3, 6, _?_, _?_, _?_, _?_, 21
2. 2, _?_, 6, _?_, 10, _?_, _?_
3. 18, 21, _?_, _?_, _?_, 33, _?_
4. 24, _?_, 28, _?_, 32, _?_, _?_

Complete.

5. 8 × 6 = _?_   6. 6 × 8 = _?_
7. 48 ÷ 6 = _?_   8. 48 ÷ 8 = _?_
9. 9 × 0 = _?_   10. 8 × 1 = _?_
11. 0 ÷ 9 = _?_   12. 8 ÷ 1 = _?_

13. 7 × 9   14. 3 × 8   15. 6 × 9
16. 9 × 6   17. 4 × 7   18. 8 × 8

Write 4 related multiplication and division facts for each family.

19. (7, 4, 28)   20. (6, 5, 30)

Write the number of:

21. eights in forty-eight
22. nines in thirty-six

23. 18 balloons were divided among 9 children. How many balloons did each child receive?

24. 36 cable cars were running on 6 tracks. How many cable cars were on each track?

25. 72 books were put into 9 boxes. How many books were in each box?

363

1. 5
    ×2

2. 50
    × 2

3. 500
    × 2

4. 43
    × 2

5. 21
    × 4

6. 32
    × 3

7. 63
    × 3

8. 51
    × 4

9. 71
    × 6

10. 30
     × 5

11. 48
     × 4

12. 27
     × 6

13. 18
     × 5

14. 38
     × 2

15. $0.30
     × 3

16. $0.26
     × 2

17. $344
     × 2

18. $201
     × 3

19. $(4 \times 6) + 2$ **20.** $(5 \times 8) + 3$

21. Mario has 4 packages of markers. Each package contains 20 markers. How many markers does Mario have in all?

22. Estimate the product of 46×7.

23. How much will it cost to buy 4 pens at $0.82 each?

24. Subtract 7 from the product of 3 and 42.

25. Compare. Write < or >. The product of 3 and 34 or the sum of 26 and 76

Practice 10-2

1. $.53
    × 2

2. $.47
    × 3

3. $.99
    × 4

Estimate the product.

4. 44
    × 2

5. 23
    × 6

6. 123
    × 3

7. 114
    × 7

8. 13
    × 3

9. 37
    × 6

10. 137
     × 6

11. 25
     × 3

12. 123
     × 6

13. 160
     × 5

14. 590
     × 4

15. 351
     × 2

16. $1.65
     × 7

17. $.90
     × 8

18. $(3 \times 8) + 1$ **19.** $(6 \times 6) + 3$

20. There are 238 students in the Orchard School. If each student read 3 books, how many books were read in all?

21. Find the product of 7 and 43.

22. How many eggs are in 6 dozen?

23. Which is less: 45 multiplied by 9 or 54 multiplied by 8?

24. Estimate the product of 4 and 27.

25. Double the product of 4 and 56.

Practice 11-1

Draw the polygon.

1. square   **2.** triangle

3. hexagon   **4.** rectangle

Which shapes are congruent?

5. a. **b.** **c.** **d.**

6. a. **b.** **c.** **d.**

Which shapes are similar?

7. a. **b.** **c.** **d.**

8. a. **b.** **c.** **d.**

Which is a line of symmetry? Write "Yes" or "No."

9.   **10.**

11. How many right angles are there in a rectangle?

12. Name the plane figure that has 4 sides of the same length and 4 right angles.

13. How many sides does a pentagon have?

14. Is a rectangle a quadrilateral?

15. How many sides does a hexagon have?

Practice 11-2

Find the perimeter in units.

1.   2   3 ◼ 3   2   **2.**   4 ▲ 4   3

Find the area in square units.

3.    **4.**

5.   **6.**

Find the perimeter.

7. 2 in. ◻ 2 in.   **8.** 3 ft ▭ 2 ft

9. 4 cm ▲ 4 cm   4 cm   **10.** 3 m ◣ 5 m   4 m

Find the volume in cubic units.

11.   **12.**

13. What is the perimeter of a square with sides that measure 4 cm?

14. What is the perimeter of a triangle if one side measures 3 cm, and the other two sides measure 4 cm?

15. What is the perimeter of a rectangle with sides that measure 4 cm, 6 cm, 4 cm, and 6 cm?

Complete.

1. $11 \div 3 =$ _?_ with a remainder of _?_
2. $9 \div 2 =$ _?_ with a remainder of _?_
3. $27 \div 4 =$ _?_ with a remainder of _?_
4. $33 \div 5 =$ _?_ with a remainder of _?_

5. Dividend 12　　6. Dividend 56
   Divisor　6　　　　Divisor　7
   Quotient _?_　　　Quotient _?_

7. $3\overline{)13}$　　8. $4\overline{)29}$　　9. $2\overline{)28}$

10 $2\overline{)82}$　　11. $3\overline{)69}$　　12. $5\overline{)65}$

13. $6\overline{)84}$　　14. $3\overline{)58}$　　15. $6\overline{)74}$

Round to the nearest dollar.

16. $5.86　　　　17. $6.05

18. $5.05　　　　19. $8.50

20. How many fours are there in:
    4, 5, 8, 9, 12, 13?

21. Write which has the larger quotient:
    36 divided by 7 or $17 \div 4$?

22. Estimate the quotient of $14.32 divided by 2.

23. Four boxes hold a total of 48 crayons. If there are an equal number in each box, how many crayons are in one box?

24. How many groups of 5 are in 82? What is the remainder?

25. Len has 84 seashells to put into bags of 6 seashells each. How many bags will he fill?

Practice 12-2

1. $5\overline{)12}$　　2. $6\overline{)19}$　　3. $7\overline{)35}$

4. $4\overline{)93}$　　5. $7\overline{)91}$　　6. $3\overline{)85}$

7. $14 \div 7$　　8. $26 \div 4$　　9. $48 \div 9$

10. $44 \div 3$　　11. $61 \div 4$　　12. $94 \div 5$

Divide and check by multiplication.

13. $3\overline{)39}$　　14. $2\overline{)64}$　　15. $3\overline{)71}$

Round to the nearest dollar.

16. $6.40　　　　17. $7.80

Estimate the quotient.

18. Dividend $5.35　　19. Dividend $9.05
    Divisor　5　　　　　Divisor　3
    Quotient _?_　　　　Quotient _?_

Estimate the quotient.

20. Dividend $16.40　21. Dividend $10.02
    Divisor　4　　　　　Divisor　5.
    Quotient _?_　　　　Quotient _?_

21. If 4 apples cost $.96, how much does one apple cost?

22. Write which has the smaller quotient.
    $29 \div 6$　　or　　$32 \div 5$

23. If 72 children are divided into 9 equal groups, how many children are in each group?

24. How many groups of 5 pipe cleaners can be made from a total of 27 pipe cleaners? What is the remainder?

25. Estimate the quotient of $9.65 divided by 3.

Practice 13-1

Write the fraction.

1. 1 part out of 6.

2. 2 parts out of 8.

3. 4 parts out of 12.

Draw a picture showing each fractional part.

4. $\frac{2}{6}$ **5.** $\frac{4}{8}$ **6.** $\frac{5}{6}$

Write the fraction for the shaded area.

7.   **8.**   **9.**

Write an equivalent fraction.

10. $\frac{1}{3} = \frac{?}{6}$ **11.** $\frac{1}{5} = \frac{?}{10}$ **12.** $\frac{?}{6} = \frac{1}{2}$

Find $\frac{1}{2}$ of each.

13. 18   **14.** 6   **15.** 10

Find $\frac{1}{4}$ of each.

16. 12   **17.** 8   **18.** 16

19. $\frac{1}{3}$ of 12   **20.** $\frac{1}{5}$ of 15

21. There are 18 bicycles. $\frac{1}{6}$ of them have a racing stripe. How many bicycles have racing stripes?

22. Mildred bought 10 peaches. Jeff ate $\frac{1}{5}$ of them. How many peaches did Jeff eat?

23. Molly had 48 balloons. $\frac{1}{8}$ of them were green. How many balloons were green?

24. Mr. Collins picked 54 tomatoes from his garden. $\frac{1}{9}$ of them were ripe. How many tomatoes were ripe?

25. Is $\frac{1}{3}$ cup of milk more than $\frac{2}{3}$ cup of milk?

Practice 13-2

1. $2.4 + 3.2$ **2.** $1.9 + 2.6$ **3.** $6.1 + 8.7$

4. $5.8 - 0.3$ **5.** $9.6 - 7.5$ **6.** $2.7 - .08$

7. $3.8 - 2.4$ **8.** $4.5 - 2.2$ **9.** $7.7 - 5.4$

Write as a decimal.

10. $\frac{3}{10}$ **11.** $\frac{8}{10}$ **12.** $\frac{6}{10}$

Write as a fraction.

13. 0.5   **14.** 0.23   **15.** 0.45

Write an equivalent fraction.

16. $\frac{1}{2} = \frac{?}{6}$ **17.** $\frac{1}{3} = \frac{?}{12}$ **18.** $\frac{1}{3} = \frac{?}{15}$

19. Write one tenth as a decimal.

20. Write 0.35 as a fraction.

21. Julio has 20 cars. 4 of the cars are blue. What part of the cars is blue?

22. A farmer has 80 rows in one field. If he plants corn in $\frac{1}{2}$ of his field, how many rows are corn?

23. Alice ran 20 yards in $4\frac{4}{10}$ seconds. Write the number of seconds as a decimal.

24. How much more than 0.5 is 0.9?

25. Which is greater: $\frac{2}{5}$ or 0.8?

Brain Builders

Write the number.
1. 3 tens 4 ones

2. 6 hundreds 2 tens 5 ones

Tell what the 6 means in each number.
3. 364   4. 1634

Compare. Write < or >.
5. 64 _?_ 72   6. 403 _?_ 304

Order from greatest to least.
7. 12, 19, 6, 32

Order from least to greatest.
8. 350, 362, 240, 420

9. Write the odd number after 19.

Round to the nearest 10.
10. 38   11. 62

12. Caryn's book has 354 pages. Alice's book has 345 pages. Whose book has more pages?

13. Teresa is twelfth in line at the ticket window. Rita is 6 places after her. What place in line is Rita?

14. The third graders sold 289 tickets for the school play. Round this number to the nearest hundred.

15. Write the standard numeral for XXV.

Compute.
1. $8 + \underline{\ ?\ } = 15$ 2. $\underline{\ ?\ } + 3 = 12$

3. $16 - \underline{\ ?\ } = 7$ 4. $14 - 9 = \underline{\ ?\ }$

5. $34 + 45$ 6. $58 - 32$

7. $324 + 605$ 8. $639 - 204$

9. $6243 + 326$ 10. $7396 - 2384$

11. Ruth has 156 pennies in a jar. Patricia has 132 pennies in another jar. How many more pennies does Ruth have than Patricia?

12. Write four related addition and subtraction facts for 4, 7, and 11.

13. Compare. Write < or >.
$3 + 4 + 5 \underline{\ ?\ } 13$

14. Akemi has 67 marbles in one bag and 42 in another bag. Round the numbers to tell about how many marbles he has in all.

15. There were 26 books on the library table. Rex put 8 more books on the table. How many books are on the table now?

Compute.
1. 5 tens + 13 ones = _?_

2. 6 tens + 14 ones = _?_

3. $24 + 5$ 4. $36 - 8$

5. $32 + 49$ 6. $75 - 56$

7. $265 + 374$ 8. $378 + 547$

9. $6425 + 1796$ 10. $1205 + 326$

11. Write the standard numeral for 4 hundreds 13 tens 7 ones.

12. What is the difference between $3.75 and $5.21?

13. A box holds 36 oranges. If 14 oranges are taken from a full box, how many oranges are left?

14. Fill in the missing addend.
$32 + 19 + \underline{\ ?\ } = 116$

15. Lucio gave 10 stickers to a friend. Then he had 14 stickers left. How many did he have at first?

TEST 4

Compute.

1. 23
   + 8

2. 31
   − 7

3. 92
   −27

4. 362
   +148

5. 538
   −376

6. 724
   −389

7. 216
   +377

8. 306
   −129

9. 800
   −153

10. 4000
    + 725

11. Subtract 89 from 200 and check the answer.

12. 35 children were invited to a party. 9 did not come. How many children came to the party?

13. Round 382 to the nearest hundred.

14. Linda has 162 bird stickers. Karen has 58 more than Linda. How many stickers does Karen have?

15. How much greater than 2938 is 4659?

TEST 5

Compute.

1. Round 68¢ to the nearest dime.

2. Round $3.14 to the nearest dollar.

3. $1\frac{1}{2}$ hr = __?__ minutes

4. 1 yr 4 months = __?__ months

Compare. Write <, or >.

5. 3 half dollars __?__ 10 dimes

6. 7 nickels __?__ 2 quarters

7. $2.58 + $.63

8. $7.04 − $2.56

9. $5.69 + $2.34

10. $8.00 − $2.49

11. Alan practiced baseball from 3:30 P.M. until 5:00 P.M. How long did he practice?

12. Debbie gave the vendor 7 dimes and 1 nickel for ice cream. How much money was that?

13. Grace bought a music box for $5.90 and a rag doll for $8.75. How much did she pay in all?

14. What is the value in cents of 4 dimes, 3 nickels, and 8 pennies?

15. Ernie wants to buy a train set for $12.88 and a toy car for $5.97. Is $20 enough to pay for both?

TEST 6

Compute.

1. 63 + 54

2. 96 − 24

3. 28 + 33 + 46

4. 300 − 74

5. 8 × 2

6. 3 × 9

7. 5 × 8

8. 8 × 5

9. 5 × 7

10. 8 − 4

11. 73 people were in line to pay their gas bills. 19 people were in line to pay their electric bills. How many people in all were in line to pay their bills?

12. There are 4 boxes with 4 apples in each. How many apples are there in all?

13. Fred weighs 65 pounds. Ramon weighs 57 pounds. How much less than Fred does Ramon weigh?

14. Cereal is sold 6 boxes to a package. How many boxes are there in 5 packages?

15. Sam, Herb, and Jose each have 12 grapes. How many grapes do they have altogether?

TEST 7

Compute.

1. $1.25 + $.78   2. $6.40 − $2.85

3. 5 × 6   4. 4 × ___?___ = 24

5. 18 ÷ 2   6. 15 ÷ ___?___ = 3

7. 4)‾12   8. 1)‾6

9. 4 × ___?___ = 24 and 24 ÷ ___?___ = 4

10. ___?___ × 3 = 27 and 27 ÷ 3 = ___?___

11. Write four related multiplication and division facts for 2, 6, and 12.

12. Mack's mother baked 32 rolls. The family ate 18 rolls. How many rolls were left?

13. Teresita put 20 birthday cards into boxes, 4 to a box. How many boxes did she use?

14. How much would 3 cassette tapes cost at $6 a tape?

15. How many groups of 5 can you make with 35 pennies? 50 pennies? 100 pennies?

TEST 8

Choose the better answer.

1. The length of a nail is about 4 cm or 4 m.

2. A lump of sugar weighs 1 kg or 1 g.

3. A lake is measured in liters or kiloliters.

4. People go ice skating when the temperature is 0° C or 50° C.

5. In 1 hour Kevin rides his bicycle 2 m or 2 km.

6. Donna drank 2 cups of milk. Did she drink a pint or a quart of milk?

Compute.

7. 1 ft 8 in. = ___?___ in.

8. 1 yd 1 ft = ___?___ ft

9. 1 qt 1 pt = ___?___ pt

10. 1 gal 2 qt = ___?___ qt

11. $\frac{1}{2}$ lb = ___?___ oz

12. 1 lb 4 oz = ___?___ oz

13. 1 m = ___?___ cm

14. 1 g = ___?___ kg

15. A bucket holds 3 gallons of water. How many quarts does it hold?

TEST 9

Compute.

1. 6 × 4   2. 7 × 0

3. (3 × 2) × 8   4. (9 × 1) × 9

5. (6 × 9) + 5   6. (7 × 4) + 5

7. 8)‾32   8. 7)‾35

9. 9 × ___?___ = 54 and 54 ÷ ___?___ = 9

10. ___?___ × 8 = 48 and 48 ÷ 8 = ___?___

11. Iyo paid $2.35 for a book of games. Her brother paid $1.99 for a puzzle book. How much more did Iyo spend than her brother?

12. How many groups of 6 are there in 54?

13. At the end of 8 weeks Juanita had saved $40. If she saved the same amount each week, how much did she save in one week?

14. Marlene is baking cookies. She puts 48 on a sheet in rows of 6 each. How many rows of cookies are on a sheet?

15. Use +, −, ×, or ÷ to make this sentence true.
8 ___?___ 6 = 2 ___?___ 7

370

TEST 10

Compute.

1. 60 × 5
2. 400 × 8
3. 504 × 42
4. 630 × 23
5. 31 × 4
6. 72 × 15
7. 138 × 36
8. 3.48 × 8
9. 36 × 2
10. 64 × 5

11. About how many books are in 4 sections of a library if there are 265 books in each section?

12. 28 cans of tuna fish were on a shelf. 19 cans were sold. How many cans were left on the shelf?

13. Matt bought 24 trading cards for each of 3 friends. How many cards did he buy?

14. Which is greater: 250 × 3 or 200 × 4?

15. Add $3.58 and $4.06. Subtract the sum from $10.

TEST 11

Solve or answer each problem.

1. Make a line segment 4 cm long.

2. Which is a ray?

3. Which is a polygon?

4. Which is a right angle?

5. Which is a triangle?

6. Which is a hexagon?

7. Which is a cube?

8. How many sides does a rectangle have?

9. What is the name of a rectangle with 4 sides of the same length?

Which circle shows a diameter? radius?

10.

11.

12. Find the perimeter of a square 3 inches on each side.

How many square units are there in these figures?

13.

14.

15. How many cubic units are there in this box?

TEST 12

Compute.

1. 6)18
2. 6)22
3. 3)96
4. 4)72
5. 5)76
6. 2)232
7. 7)992
8. 4)344
9. 5)$.95
10. 4)$8.76

11. (32 ÷ 4) + (6 × 5) = ?

12. Jerry saves $15 a month. How much will he save in 6 months?

13. Write four related multiplication and division facts for 7, 6, and 42.

14. Which is more: 7 × 5 or 25 + 5?

15. Divide 19 by 4. What is the quotient? What is the remainder?

371

Drill and Mental

1 DRILL

1. $9 + 3$ $7 + 2$ $6 + 2$ $5 + 7$

2. $9 - 2$ $8 - 3$ $10 - 4$ $7 - 5$

3. Add 3 to: 4, 14, 24, 34, 44, 54, 64, 74, 84, 94

4. Subtract 3 from: 7, 17, 27, 37, 47, 57, 67, 77, 87, 97

5. 9×2 7×2 8×2 6×2

MENTAL

6. ? pints = 1 quart

7. Mr. Brown had 12 cows. He sold 5 of them. How many did he have left?

8. April has four shells, and Babs has three shells. How many shells do they have in all?

9. Three girls have 7 cents each. What is the total?

10. Pencils are 2 to a box. How many boxes are needed for 10 pencils?

2 DRILL

1. $10 - 5$ $11 - 6$ $10 - 6$ $9 - 4$

2. $8 + 4$ $9 + 3$ $8 + 5$ $7 + 6$

3. Add 5 to: 12, 22, 32, 42, 52, 62, 72, 82, 92, 102

4. Subtract 5 from: 7, 17, 27, 37, 47, 57, 67, 77, 87, 97

5. Multiply by 2: 2, 4, 8, 1, 3, 5

MENTAL

6. ? nickels = 1 dime

7. Laura has 5 white roses and 2 red roses. How many roses does she have in all?

8. Rex had 32 cents. He spent 4 cents. How much did he have left?

9. Dennis has 8 records. Ralph has 2 times as many. How many records does Ralph have?

10. Jean has 2 pencils. Ed has 4 times as many pencils. How many pencils does Ed have?

3 DRILL

1. $8 + 5$ $9 + 4$ $7 + 6$ $6 + 7$

2. $13 - 9$ $12 - 5$ $10 - 2$ $11 - 9$

3. Add 6 to: 2, 12, 22, 32, 42, 52, 62, 72, 82, 92

4. Subtract 6 from: 8, 18, 28, 38, 48, 58, 68, 78, 88, 98

5. Multiply by 5: 1, 3, 5, 7, 9, 2

MENTAL

6. Ernie has read 2 of 8 books. How many books are still to be read?

7. Teresita is 3 years old. Dad is 9 times her age. How old is Dad?

8. 14 equals $7 \times$? .

9. ? inches = 1 foot

10. ? pennies = 1 quarter

4 DRILL

1. 6 + 8   7 + 7   9 + 5   5 + 9
   6 + 7   8 + 6   2 + 5   7 + 6

2. Add 4 to: 5, 15, 35, 25, 45, 75, 55, 65, 85, 95

3. Subtract 4 from: 9, 19, 39, 29, 49, 79, 59, 89, 69, 99

4. Multiply by 2 and by 5: 1, 3, 5, 7, 9, 0, 2, 4, 6, 8

5. Multiply by 2; then add 1: 3, 6, 2, 9, 0, 1, 4, 7, 8

MENTAL

6. Harry saw 4 puppies and Dan saw 5 other puppies. How many puppies did they see in all?

7. There are 8 pictures on one page and 6 pictures on another page. How many pictures are on the two pages?

8. Mr. Sheffield has 9 pigs. If he sells 5 of them, how many will he have left?

9. There are 4 quarts in a gallon. How many quarts are there in 5 gallons?

10. How many twos are there in 18?

5 DRILL

1. 8 + 6   7 + 6   9 + 3   6 + 4
   14 − 8   13 − 7   12 − 9   10 − 6

2. Add 5 to: 15, 25, 45, 75, 95, 55, 85, 5, 35, 65

3. Subtract 5 from: 9, 19, 29, 39, 49, 79, 59, 69, 89, 99

4. Multiply by 2, by 3, and by 5: 0, 2, 4, 6, 8, 10, 9, 5, 7, 3

5. $\dfrac{?}{7} \times 2 = 4$ $\dfrac{?}{8} \times 3 = 15$
   $7 \times \underline{?} = 21$ $8 \times \underline{?} = 40$

MENTAL

6. Grace had 14 gold stars. She gave 8 of them to Brett. How many stars did she have left?

7. Olga has 15 cents and adds 5 cents. How much money does she have?

8. If there are 8 children in a row, how many children are there in 5 rows?

9. If 4 friends shared 32 baseball cards equally, how many cards would each receive?

10. One cookie costs 8 cents. How much do two cookies cost?

6 DRILL

1.
```
  9      8      8      7      8
+ 8    + 9    + 8    + 8    + 6
```

2. Add 3 to: 8, 18, 28, 38, 48, 58, 68, 78, 88, 98

3. Subtract 8 from: 11, 10, 13, 9, 12, 8, 14, 15, 17, 16

4. Multiply by 5, and by 4: 1, 3, 5, 7, 9, 2, 4, 6, 8, 10

5. Divide by 5: 5, 15, 25, 35, 45, 10, 20, 30, 40, 50

MENTAL

6. A horse trainer has 7 black horses and 9 brown horses. How many horses does he have in all?

7. There are 11 eggs in one nest and 8 in another. How many more eggs are in one nest than in the other?

8. Richard walks 3 miles a day. How many miles does he walk in 8 days?

9. Balloons are 5¢ each. How many balloons can Lucia buy for 40¢?

10. How many dimes are there in 50¢?

373

DRILL

1.
$$9 \quad 6 \quad 8 \quad 7$$
$$+7 \quad +9 \quad +6 \quad +6$$
$$16 \quad 15 \quad 14 \quad 13$$
$$-9 \quad -6 \quad -8 \quad -9$$

2. Add 4 to: 7, 17, 27, 37, 47, 57, 67, 77, 87, 97

3. Subtract 4 from: 11, 12, 13, 14, 10, 9, 8, 7, 6, 5

4. Multiply by 2, by 3, by 4, and by 5: 9, 2, 4, 6, 8, 10, 0, 3

5. Divide by 2: 4, 8, 14, 16, 2, 10, 18, 6, 12

MENTAL

6. Joan had 7 circus tickets and Eugene had 4 tickets. How many tickets did they have in all?

7. Rory has 9 tickets. If Matilda gives him 7 more, how many tickets will he have in all?

8. Trudy has 11 tomatoes. Ruth has 4. How many fewer tomatoes does Ruth have than Trudy?

9. There are 6 children in a row. How many children are in 5 rows?

10. Mario had 24 marbles. If he gave Ted $\frac{1}{6}$ of them, how many were left?

DRILL

1.
$$4+9 \quad 6+1 \quad 9+4 \quad 1+6$$
$$5+9 \quad 7+9 \quad 8+6 \quad 5+7$$

2. Add 7 to: 2, 12, 22, 42, 52, 72, 32, 62, 82, 92

3. Subtract 7 from: 9, 19, 29, 49, 59, 79, 39, 69, 89, 99

4. Multiply by 4: 2, 3, 5, 1, 7, 8, 0, 9, 6, 4

5. $9 \times \underline{\quad?\quad} = 27$ $4 \times \underline{\quad?\quad} = 16$
$\underline{\quad?\quad} \times 4 = 32$ $\underline{\quad?\quad} \times 5 = 45$

MENTAL

6. There were 9 books on a shelf. Sally added 7 more. How many books are on the shelf?

7. Bob has 16 geraniums. Tess has 9. How many fewer geraniums does Tess have than Bob?

8. Write the missing number: 4, 8, 12, __?__, 20, 24.

9. __?__ centimeters = 1 meter

10. What number comes after 24? 67?

DRILL

1.
$$8+9 \quad 9+7 \quad 8+7 \quad 6+8$$
$$17-8 \quad 16-9 \quad 15-8 \quad 14-6$$

2. Add 4 to: 8, 18, 28, 38, 48, 58, 68, 78, 88, 98

3. Subtract 8 from: 11, 13, 15, 17, 12, 14, 16, 10, 18, 19

4. Multiply by 3, and then by 6: 2, 4, 7, 8, 1, 3, 5, 6, 0, 9

5. Divide by 3: 18, 12, 3, 9, 21, 27, 15, 6, 24

MENTAL

6. Louis saw 2 bluebirds and 8 crows. How many birds did he see in all?

7. There were 17 pencils. Sam took 8 of them. How many were left?

8. Doreen has 3 apples. Her brother has 4 times as many. How many apples does her brother have?

9. 2 meters = __?__ centimeters

10. How many hours are there in 12 days?

DRILL

1.
$$\begin{array}{ccccc} 5 & 5 & 6 & 6 & 7 \\ 3 & 4 & 2 & 3 & 2 \\ +2 & +1 & +2 & +1 & +1 \end{array}$$

2. Add 2 to: 8, 18, 28, 38, 48, 58, 68, 78, 88, 98

3. Subtract 2 from: 10, 20, 30, 40, 50, 60, 70, 80, 90, 100

4.
$$\begin{array}{llll} 1 \times 6 & 3 \times 6 & 6 \times 1 & 6 \times 3 \\ 2 \times 6 & 4 \times 6 & 6 \times 2 & 6 \times 4 \end{array}$$

5. Divide by 4: 36, 16, 20, 4, 12, 24, 8, 28, 32

MENTAL

6. Veronica has 1 red car, 4 white cars, and 5 blue cars. How many cars does she have in all?

7. Eileen had 10 balloons. She gave 2 away. How many balloons did she have left?

8. There are 6 crayons in a box. How many crayons are there in 4 boxes?

9. 6 boys caught 18 fish. If they each caught the same number of fish, how many fish did each boy catch?

10. The number before 221 is ? .

DRILL

1.
$$\begin{array}{ccccc} 6 & 7 & 6 & 8 & 9 \\ 2 & 4 & 3 & 2 & 1 \\ +3 & +0 & +3 & +2 & +3 \end{array}$$

2. Add 1 to: 9, 19, 29, 39, 49, 59, 69, 79, 89, 99

3. Subtract 1 from: 10, 20, 30, 40, 50, 60, 70, 80, 90, 100

4.
$$\begin{array}{llll} 5 \times 6 & 7 \times 6 & 6 \times 5 & 6 \times 7 \\ 6 \times 6 & 8 \times 6 & 6 \times 9 & 6 \times 8 \end{array}$$

5.
$$\begin{array}{llll} 6\overline{)30} & 6\overline{)36} & 6\overline{)42} & 6\overline{)48} \\ 6\overline{)24} & 6\overline{)18} & 6\overline{)12} & 6\overline{)54} \end{array}$$

MENTAL

6. Mrs. Olsen uses 6 oranges a day. How many oranges will she use in 6 days?

7. If 36 photos are on 6 pages, how many photos are on 1 page?

8. Delores has 5 pencils, Meri has 3 pencils, and Gregory has 5. How many pencils do they have in all?

9. Julie is 10 years old. How old was she one year ago?

10. 50 cents is equal to ? dimes.

DRILL

1. $8 + \underline{\ ?\ } = 13 \qquad 9 + \underline{\ ?\ } = 13$
   $5 + \underline{\ ?\ } = 13 \qquad 7 + \underline{\ ?\ } = 13$

2. Add 7 to: 8, 18, 28, 38, 48, 58, 68, 78, 88, 98

3. Subtract 7 from: 15, 25, 35, 45, 55, 65, 75, 85, 95, 105

4. Multiply by 4, by 5, and by 6:
   9, 0, 2, 4, 6, 8, 10, 1, 3, 5, 7

5.
$$\begin{array}{lll} \frac{1}{6} \text{ of } 42 & \frac{1}{6} \text{ of } 48 & \frac{1}{6} \text{ of } 54 \\ \frac{1}{6} \text{ of } 24 & \frac{1}{6} \text{ of } 30 & \frac{1}{6} \text{ of } 36 \end{array}$$

MENTAL

6. There are 8 apple and 7 peach pies. How many pies are there in all?

7. Rosa has 15 storybooks. If she has read 7 of them, how many does she still have to read?

8. Popcorn balls are 7 cents each. How much will 6 of them cost?

9. One sixth of 54 desks is ? desks.

10. There are 5 seats in a row. How many rows will 30 children fill?

13 DRILL

1. Add 8 to: 7, 17, 27, 37, 47, 57, 67, 77, 87, 97

2. Subtract 8 from: 15, 25, 35, 45, 55, 65, 75, 85, 95, 105

3. 1×8 8×1 $8\overline{)8}$ $8 \div 1$
   2×8 8×2 $8\overline{)16}$ $16 \div 2$

4. 3×8 8×3 $8\overline{)24}$ $24 \div 3$
   4×8 8×4 $8\overline{)32}$ $32 \div 4$

5. 1×9 2×9 3×9 4×9
   9×1 9×2 9×3 9×4

MENTAL

6. What is 18 divided by 3?

7. Each girl made 7 cards. How many cards did 8 girls make?

8. _?_ nickels = 1 quarter

9. How long does it take the big hand of the clock to go from one number to the next?

10. How long does it take the small hand of the clock to go from one number to the next?

14 DRILL

1. Add 8 to: 8, 18, 24, 38, 40, 58, 68, 78, 88, 98

2. Subtract 8 from: 16, 26, 36, 46, 56, 66, 76, 86, 96, 106

3. 5×8 8×5 $8\overline{)40}$ $40 \div 5$
   6×8 8×6 $8\overline{)48}$ $48 \div 6$

4. 7×8 8×7 $8\overline{)56}$ $56 \div 7$
   8×8 $8\overline{)64}$ $64 \div 8$

5. 5×9 6×9 7×9 8×9
   9×5 9×6 9×7 9×8

MENTAL

6. Carlo saved 8 dollars this week and 8 dollars last week. How much money did he save in all?

7. _?_ minutes = 1 hour

8. What number comes next? 8, 16, 24, 32, 40, 48, _?_

9. 6 pints = _?_ quarts

10. Jane is 46 inches tall. Helene is 8 inches shorter than Jane. What is Helene's height?

15 DRILL

1. Add 9 to: 7, 17, 27, 37, 47, 57, 67, 77, 87, 97

2. Subtract 9 from: 16, 26, 36, 46, 56, 66, 76, 86, 96, 106

3. 10×8 8×10 $8\overline{)80}$ $80 \div 10$
   6×8 8×6 $8\overline{)48}$ $48 \div 6$

4. 7×8 8×7 $8\overline{)56}$ $56 \div 7$
   9×8 8×9 $8\overline{)72}$ $72 \div 9$

5. 7×9 4×9 5×9 9×8
   9×7 9×4 9×5 8×9

MENTAL

6. Joan needs 16 seals for her packages. If she has 9 seals, how many more seals must she buy?

7. 8 girls and 8 boys went to see the pet show. How many children went to see the show in all?

8. If one factor is 7 and the other factor 8, what is the product?

9. If Ronald has $.87 in dimes and pennies, he could have _?_ dimes and _?_ pennies.

10. Write the standard numeral: thirty-four thousand, two hundred.

16 DRILL

1. Add 9 to: 6, 16, 46, 36, 26, 56, 86, 76, 66, 96

2. Subtract 9 from: 15, 25, 35, 65, 55, 45, 85, 75, 85, 95, 105

3. $9\overline{)9}$ $9 \div 9$ $9\overline{)18}$ $18 \div 9$
   $9\overline{)27}$ $27 \div 9$ $9\overline{)36}$ $36 \div 9$

4. Divide by 2 and tell the remainder: 3, 5, 7, 9, 11, 13, 15, 17, 19, 21

5. Divide by 3 and tell the remainder: 16, 17, 19, 21, 22, 23, 25, 26, 18

MENTAL

6. The difference between 25 and 7 is ? .

7. Gerald is 18 years old. How old will he be 7 years from now?

8. 9 × 8 is the same as 8 × ? .

9. In 45 there are ? 5's.

10. Janet sent 8 cards to her friends. Reggie sent 16. How many more cards did Reggie send than Janet?

17 DRILL

1. Add 4 to: 9, 19, 29, 39, 69, 59, 49, 99, 89, 79

2. Subtract 4 from: 13, 23, 33, 43, 53, 63, 83, 73, 93, 103

3. $9\overline{)45}$ $45 \div 9$ $9\overline{)54}$ $54 \div 9$
   $9\overline{)63}$ $63 \div 9$ $9\overline{)72}$ $72 \div 9$

4. Divide by 3 and tell the remainder: 4, 5, 7, 8, 10, 11, 13, 14, 16, 17

5. Divide by 4 and tell the remainder: 9, 11, 15, 19, 23, 27, 31, 33, 37, 39

MENTAL

6. 63 cents was divided equally among 9 children. How much did each child receive?

7. 9 children are needed for 1 team. How many children are on 6 teams?

8. What is the sum of $.19 and $.04?

9. Ben made 13 snowballs. Steven made 4 snowballs. How many more did Ben make than Steven?

10. Sally has 1 meter of ribbon. How many centimeters is that ?

18 DRILL

1. Add 8 to: 9, 19, 49, 39, 29, 59, 89, 79, 69, 99

2. Subtract 8 from: 17, 27, 37, 47, 57, 87, 77, 67, 97, 107

3. $9\overline{)72}$ $72 \div 8$ $9\overline{)36}$ $36 \div 4$

4. Divide by 4 and tell the remainder: 21, 23, 25, 27, 29, 31, 33, 35, 37, 39

5. Divide by 5 and tell the remainder: 5, 6, 7, 8, 9, 10, 11, 12, 13, 14, 15

MENTAL

6. There are 72 players on 8 teams. Each team has the same number of players. How many players are on one team?

7. On Saturday each child earned $9. How much did 8 children earn?

8. John bought a pound of tea. How many ounces of tea did he buy?

9. Jorge is 17 years old. Tanya is 8 years old. What is the difference in their ages?

10. $.75 = ? dimes and ? pennies

GLOSSARY

addend A number to be added.

$$3 \leftarrow \text{addend}$$
$$\underline{+\ 4} \leftarrow \text{addend}$$
$$7 \leftarrow \text{sum}$$

addition (+) An operation on two numbers to find how many or how much in all. (3 + 4 = 7)

A.M. Letters that show times after midnight and before 12 noon.

area The number of square units a region contains.

bar graph A graph using bars of different lengths to compare information.

capacity The amount a container can hold.

Celsius scale Used to measure temperature in the metric system, in which 0° is the freezing point of water and 100° is the boiling point.

circle A closed figure that looks like this:

congruent figures Figures having the same size and shape.

customary system A way of measuring that uses inches, feet, yards, and miles for units of lengths; cups, pints, quarts, and gallons for units of liquid volume; ounces and pounds for units of weight; Fahrenheit degrees for units of temperature.

decimal A numeral that has a decimal point. (Example: 3.1)

degree A unit for measuring temperature.

denominator The bottom number in a fraction. The denominator names the total number of equal parts.

difference The answer in subtraction.

digit Any one of these symbols: 0, 1, 2, 3, 4, 5, 6, 7, 8, 9.

dividend The number to be divided.

division An operation on two numbers that tells how many groups or how many in each group.

$$6 \leftarrow \text{quotient}$$
$$\text{divisor} \longrightarrow 7\overline{)42} \leftarrow \text{dividend}$$

divisor The number by which the dividend is divided.

equation A number sentence that uses an equal sign (=).

equivalent fractions Fractions that name the same amount.
Example: $\frac{2}{3}$ and $\frac{4}{6}$

estimate To find an answer that is close to the exact answer.

even number Numbers that end with the digits 0, 2, 4, 6, or 8.

expanded form A way to write numbers that shows the place value of each digit. (4000 + 200 + 50 + 7 = 4257)

factor One of two or more numbers that are multiplied to form a product.

Fahrenheit scale Used to measure temperature in the customary system in which 212° is the boiling point of water and 32° is the freezing point.

family of facts Number sentences that show the relationship between addition and subtraction, or multiplication and division.

$$2 + 3 = 5 \qquad 5 - 3 = 2$$
$$3 + 2 = 5 \qquad 5 - 2 = 3$$

flowchart A list of step-by-step commands.

fractions Name the parts of a whole or a set.
Example: $\frac{2}{3}$, $\frac{1}{6}$, and $\frac{5}{4}$

gram The basic unit of weight in the metric system.

grouping property Changing the grouping of the addends does not change the sum.

graph A picture used to show information in an organized way. Types of graphs are bar graphs, pictographs, line graphs, and circle graphs.

line A set of points extending without end in opposite directions. $\overleftrightarrow{AB}$

line segment A part of a line with two points, or endpoints. $\overline{AB}$

line of symmetry A line that divides a figure into two congruent parts.

liter The basic unit of capacity in the metric system.

LOGO Is a computer language that can be used to draw figures.

measuring The process of finding how much.

meter The basic unit of length in the metric system.

metric system The system of measurement based on the meter, gram, liter, and Celsius scale.

minuend A number from which another number is subtracted.

multiple The product of a given number and any whole number. Example: Some multiples of 3 are 3, 6, 9, 12.

multiplication ($\times$) An operation on two numbers to find the total amount in a number of equal groups.

$$8 \longleftarrow \text{factor}$$
$$\times\ 4 \longleftarrow \text{factor}$$
$$\overline{32} \longleftarrow \text{product}$$

number line A line with equally spaced points shown in order.

number sentence An equation using numbers. ($1 + 2 = 3$)

numeral A symbol for a number.

numerator The top number in a fraction. The numerator names the number of parts being considered.

odd number A number that ends with the digit 1, 3, 5, 7 or 9.

opposite property of addition Subtraction is the opposite of addition.

opposite property of multiplication Division is the opposite of multiplication.

order property of addition The order of the addends does not change the sum. ($2 + 3 = 3 + 2$)

order property of multiplication The order of the factors does not change the product. ($5 \times 6 = 6 \times 5$)

ordinal number A number indicating order or position. (first, second, third)

parallel lines Lines in a plane that never meet.

perimeter The distance around a figure.

pictograph A graph using a picture to represent numbers.

place value The value of a digit depends on its position or place in a numeral. (In 45, the value of the 4 is 4 tens and 5 is 5 ones.)

plane (or flat figure) A figure that is on a flat surface.

P.M. Letters that show times after 12 noon and before midnight.

polygon A simple closed figure with sides that are line segments.

PRINT The command used to print a message or to compute.

probability The number that tells the chance of something happening.

product The answer in multiplication.

property of one in multiplication Multiplying a number by one always give the number.

quadrilateral Any four-sided polygon.

quotient The answer in division.

rectangle A quadrilateral with four right angles. The opposite sides are parallel and equal in length.

rectangular prism A shape that looks like this.

regrouping Using ten ones to form one set of ten, or using ten tens to form one set of a hundred.

remainder The number left over when a division is complete.

Roman numerals Symbols for numbers used by the Romans. (I, V, X, L, C)

rounding Writing a number to the nearest ten or hundred, and so forth.

similar figures Figures having the same shape.

space figure A geometric figure, such as a sphere, a cube, and a cone.

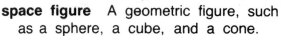

square A rectangle with all sides equal in length.

square measure The measure used to find the area of a region.

standard form The standard form for two hundred thirty five is 235.

standard numeral The name given to a number as it is written or read.

subtraction (−) An operation on two numbers to find how much larger one is than the other.

$$\begin{array}{l} 5 \leftarrow\!\!\text{minuend} \\ \underline{-\ 3} \leftarrow\!\!\text{subtrahend} \\ 2 \leftarrow\!\!\text{difference} \end{array}$$

subtrahend A number to be subtracted from another number.

sum The answer in addition.

triangle A polygon with three sides.

volume A number telling the size of the inside of a figure.

 ←————10 cubic units

whole number Any of the numbers: 0, 1, 2, 3, and so forth.

zero property of addition Adding zero to a number does not change the value of the number.

zero property of multiplication Multiplying a number by zero always gives zero.

380

Index

The Dog Lover's Companion to Florida

4TH EDITION

Sally Deneen and Robert McClure

AVALON
TRAVEL

THE DOG LOVER'S COMPANION TO FLORIDA
THE INSIDE SCOOP ON WHERE TO TAKE YOUR DOG

Published by
Avalon Travel Publishing
1400 65th Street, Suite 250
Emeryville, CA 94608, USA

Avalon Travel Publishing
An Imprint of
Avalon Publishing Group, Inc.

AVALON
publishing group incorporated

Printing History
1st edition—1996
4th edition—November 2005
5 4 3 2 1

ISBN-10: 1-56691-540-6
ISBN-13: 978-1-56691-540-3
ISSN: 1535-0312

Editor: Sabrina Young
Series Manager: Kathryn Ettinger
Acquisitions Editor: Rebecca K. Browning
Copy Editor: Valerie Sellers Blanton
Designer: Jacob Goolkasian
Graphics Coordinator: Tabitha Lahr
Production Coordinators: Mary Gilliana, Tabitha Lahr
Map Editor: Kevin Anglin
Cartographer: Kat Kalamaras
Indexer: Greg Jewett
Assistant Researchers: Aime Palmer, Courtney Bliss, Maria Goodavage

Cover and Interior Illustrations by Phil Frank

Printed in the United States by Malloy

ABOUT THE AUTHOR

Maggie Dog's lifelong pursuit of the most hound-hospitable parks, beaches, lodgings, and restaurants in Florida has sent her far and wide—from the nation's southernmost Point in Key West to the broad beaches of Greater Jacksonville, from the state's tallest "mountain" in the Panhandle to the sidewalk cafes of South Beach. As part of her research, Maggie Dog felt the wind brush her black-and-tan fur during rides in airboats, canoes, and shuttle buses. She also snoozed in historic lodgings and stared at her human companions' knees from her below-table vantage point at some of Florida's best restaurants.

Maggie never managed to learn to drive, so native Floridian and Pulitzer Prize finalist Robert McClure gladly took the wheel. As an award-winning reporter for the *South Florida Sun-Sentinel*, he wrote about Florida's environment for a decade and helped cover legislative sessions in Tallahassee. He sometimes turned over the driving task to his wife, Sally Deneen, who writes a weekly cost-cutting column for the *South Florida Sun-Sentinel* and serves as a contributing editor for *Dog Fancy* magazine. She is a freelance writer whose work has appeared in a few dozen magazines and books, and she has won several awards from the Florida Magazine Association, including Writer of the Year (1998).

The couple provided some research for another Avalon Travel Publishing guidebook—*Foghorn Outdoors Florida Camping*, considered the state's camping bible. Its offerings include hundreds of campgrounds that permit pets. The authors lived in Florida a combined 55 years before trading the Sunshine State for Washington state, where they now live near a dog park in Seattle.

CONTENTS

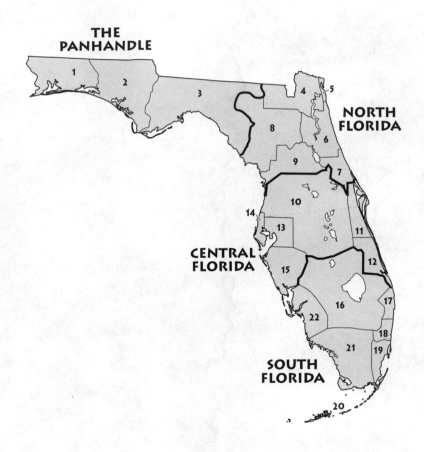

THE
PANHANDLE

NORTH
FLORIDA

CENTRAL
FLORIDA

SOUTH
FLORIDA

MAPS

MAPS

Introduction

Dogs' lives are too short. Their only fault, really.

Agnes Sligh Turnbull

A door is what a dog is perpetually on the wrong side of.

Ogden Nash

You know the look.

You're only running out to the post office. But your canine companion, your furry friend, your pal the pooch, knows all the cues: the shoes are slipped on, the wallet or purse snatched off the dresser, the keys jangled in your hands.

"I'm about to be left behind," those chocolate-brown eyes practically moan. The ears are partially aloft, alert for any sign of hope, but you can see he's prepared for the inevitable letdown. His tail is hanging, his lips drawn together in a doggy frown.

You can hear a heart breaking.

So you give in and pick up the leash.

"Oh, joy and wonderment across heaven and on earth! All is well with the world and the cosmos! We're going on a ride! We're going on a ride!"

This simple little jaunt to a drive-through postal station ranks as a major event in the average day of most dogs, a heaven-sent bit of excitement. Wind whiffles across the furry, wide-eyed visage that sticks out the side window. People are watched, dogs in neighboring cars whined at, the world examined by the pooch's sensitive sniffer.

Okay. Now take that experience and multiply it by 10. That's the kind of fun your four-legged friend can have at a local dog-friendly park. Multiply it a hundredfold, and you'll see what a road trip can do for a dog.

How do we know? We have a special source.

Her name is Maggie. Plucked off the streets of Miami as a fuzzy ball caught in traffic, Maggie is a German shepherd/husky mix (as far as we can tell). Ever playful and inquisitive, she is the smartest dog either of us has ever known; her English vocabulary has grown from "walk" and "ride" to the point where we could swear she understands half the sentences we utter. Maggie has pricked up her ears, cast a determined and knowing nose to the wind, and sniffed out the best places in the state of Florida so we could pass the news on to her doggy brethren.

She's visited the chichi sidewalk cafés of Miami Beach, the broad stretches of Jacksonville beaches where dogs run freely in the surf, the Panhandle nature trails crisscrossing woods where early settlers made their homes a hundred years ago. Some of her more offbeat explorations are included within these pages, too—everything from an archaeological dig in Tallahassee to a zoo (of sorts) at Zolfo Springs. No matter the tastes of you and your pooch, you'll find something to entertain both of you in this book.

Dogs can be wonderful traveling companions. You'll have to search a little more diligently for places to eat and sleep when you have your pal in tow. But a dog will never complain that she's bored. She'll never be a backseat driver. And you won't have to worry that she might not like the park or beach you're heading toward—dogs like all parks and all beaches! They just might prefer some over others.

Just as our Maggie grew a little too stiff to fully enjoy it, we were heartened to see a big change in communities around Florida: Dog parks. Perhaps there is hope for this state, yet, Maggie says.

These don't happen casually. They are set up when dedicated dog owners howl in indignation at the lack of off-leash running areas, bringing their concerns to the attention of elected officials such as city and county commissioners and appointed public servants in the parks departments.

In recent years, off-leash areas have been set up in Tallahassee, St. Augustine, Sanford, Sarasota, Venice, Islamorada, Delray Beach, Fort Lauderdale, Fort Myers, Naples, Orlando, West Palm Beach, St. Petersburg, Jacksonville and Jacksonville Beach. Miami, Miami Beach, and Miami-Dade County have established several dog parks between them. Tampa and Hillsborough County created several pooch-pleasing areas, too. Three free off-leash areas came on line in Gainesville, where a private, membership-only park also got going.

Don't be afraid to try this at home. City and county commissioners and particularly parks department staffers are increasingly open to so-called "paw parks." But off-leash areas are by no means a cinch. For one thing, they cost money. A price tag of $15,000 for a simple fenced-off acre or two with some running water is certainly not unheard of.

Our friend Maria Goodavage has some advice for would-be dog park organizers, based on the experience in California, where these parks were pioneered: Try to organize a key group of a half-dozen or so very committed people, perhaps by talking with dog-walking folks you see showing up at your pooch's regular haunts. Petitions help. So does figuring out a source of funding (although most Florida parks are paid for out of government funds). Emphasize that these are amenities intended to make the parks more well used by people, who are after all paying the taxes. Try to get coverage in the newspaper or on TV news. If a hearing is held, make sure you get lots of pro-dog people to show up. Be nice to the politicians and the parks department folks. And remember that this can take a while; you'll have to dig in for the long haul and be prepared to sniff out any opportunity to herd decision makers along your chosen path. To get them to roll over, you'll have to go at the task with dogged determination. Maggie says: Good luck!

Maggie would like to make one thing clear up front: This book was written from a dog's point of view. Most of the time that dog was Maggie, though we also consulted friends, acquaintances, humane societies, veterinarians, and others while in search of the widest possible range of activities for you and your pooch.

One reason we wrote this book is to help people we met while traveling, like Ron Shenk of the Amelia Island Historical Society. More than once, Ron has snuck his pooch into hound-inhospitable hotels because it was so hard to find dog-friendly lodgings.

"Okay, Missy," Ron would tell his canine companion, "get down in the back of the car while Daddy goes and rents a room." And she would. Heartbreaking, huh? (Ron is an exceptional dog owner. One of his dogs, Trixie, refused to eat after he boarded her at a kennel and left for Europe. When Ron learned of this, he says, he took the next Concorde back.)

This introduction is designed to show you how to use *The Dog Lover's Companion to Florida*, and to help you with the practical details of traveling with your dog. We hope this book will inspire you to put your dog on the right side of the door more often, and make that short life a happy one.

The Paws Rating Scale

Okay, so your ideal park features pretty paths winding around duck ponds, through richly landscaped gardens to a bunch of softball diamonds. On the other paw, your pooch probably appreciates a walk in the woods a whole lot more. She's far more inclined to trot down an honest-to-goodness nature trail, cavort in the surf at a canine-friendly beach, or perhaps even frolic in a cow pasture (ignoring or even reveling in the large cow calling cards underfoot).

Yes, it becomes clear as you crisscross Florida with one of the black-lipped set that dogs and people have divergent tastes. This doesn't mean you can't enjoy this state together, though. In this tome we tell you how much your dog is likely to enjoy a given park, beach, or other recreation area. We are indebted to Maria Goodavage and Lyle York, the originators of the Dog Lover's Companion series, for the idea of using a paws scale to reflect the value of a park from a dog's point of view.

Lowest on the scale is the fire hydrant symbol 🔥 which signifies a park that is only "worth a squat." Such places are okay for the canine with crossed legs who just won't make it to the next-closest spot o' green.

Any park, beach, or recreation area more interesting than that from a pooch's-eye view will get a paws rating. The scale starts with one paw and extends to—what else?—four paws.

A one-paw park 🐾 is nothing to be crooning to your canine about ahead of time. It's generally just a stopping-off place, a cut above make-do. There might be a playground with kids, nasty regulations about staying on the leash, and similar Oppressive Rules.

When you get up to four paws 🐾🐾🐾🐾, you're nearing nirvana, pooch-wise. Here you might be deep in the Florida woods or running leash-free in a large, open area perfect for tossing the Frisbee. These are places where your dog will strain at his leash, hoping you'll let him off the hook.

In between, we've given extra credit for shadiness, breeziness, closeness to nature, and overall dog interest.

You will also notice a foot symbol 👣 every so often. The footprint means that the park offers something that should wow humans—for instance, a waterfall, a cavern, or some special significance. You deserve a reward for being such a fine chauffeur.

There are some fairly good rules of paw for where dogs are and are not allowed. They are generally permitted in state parks, for example, and are now allowed in many parks' campgrounds. But pooches are shunned at most beachfront parks. Typically, when in state parks, dogs must at all times be on a handheld leash that does not exceed six feet.

There is no way we could list every park in the state. For one thing, the book would feel more like a dumbbell. Yet with the help of friends, acquaintances, and even dog-friendly strangers whom we met as we traveled throughout the state, we've pretty much whittled it down to the best places available in any given town. In some cases we've left out the fire hydrant-quality parks altogether because there are so many other great places to go. In other stretches of the Sunshine State, things are so doggone awful for dog romps that we've listed parks we would rather not have to mention. We know that some poor doggy will be traveling through there some day and need to make a pit stop.

We've given directions on how to reach parks near major highways and located others by their cross streets. The maps included in this book are for general reference only, and you would be well advised to pick up more detailed maps, especially if you don't know the area. We have found that some of the best maps are distributed by the American Automobile Association (AAA) and are available free to club members.

He, She, It

"It" is a word that refers to things. Animals are not things. They are like people to us, bone-i-fide family members. According to an American Animal Hospital Association pet owner survey, 62 percent of pet owners celebrate their animals' birthdays and one-third hand over wrapped gifts. Therefore, we refer to all dogs as he or she in this book. We alternate between he and she when speaking generically, because we wouldn't want any of our furry friends to feel left out.

To Leash or Not to Leash...

Some of the best places around for outdoorsy dogs who like to get away from it all are Florida's national and state forests, which are concentrated in the central and northern portions of the state. In some woodsy places, dogs are even allowed or at least tolerated off leash. However, you might want to keep your dog leashed—we do this with Maggie—because you never know what could happen.

For instance, if Maggie sees an armadillo or hears one rattling around in a thicket of saw palmetto, she's likely to go diving in headfirst—completely unaware that saw palmetto clumps are some of the favorite hiding places of the Sunshine State's rattlesnake population. Also, off-leash dogs might tear off and get lost in the wilderness. (Another concern, when you're near fresh water, is alligators. See "Natural Troubles," below.) Generally, if you're in doubt, we suggest leashing your dog.

In nearly all city parks you are required to keep your dog tethered. We find these regulations a little silly in some cases, especially in fenced, rarely used patches of green where you are the only visitors.

However, you should always keep your dog leashed if you have any doubts about his propensity to bite. Anthony Marshall, former dean of the Florida International University hospitality school, and also a lawyer, points out that the old English common law allowed you "one free bite." Once a dog had bitten someone, you were considered forewarned and could be held liable for the second bite. Now, though, you're liable for the first bite, thanks to laws passed in Florida and many other states.

This book uses the leash-free symbol 🐕 to indicate places where dogs are explicitly allowed to run free, or at least regularly tolerated. Unfortunately, there are not as many as we'd like in Florida. In some listings, we did not include the leash-free symbol but inform you when we've seen other dogs running unencumbered. Please use common sense in these places. Remember, dogs tend to get banned where owners don't follow leash laws or clean up after their pets. So in addition to common sense, employ some conscience.

There's No Business Like Dog Business

The main reason there is a need for a book like this is those odoriferous calling cards that all dogs leave in one place or another. You may see a reference here and there in this book about where it is particularly important to clean up dog waste.

Just because we remind you in some places, that doesn't mean it's any less important to clean up after your dog at any other place!

We are hereby personally baptizing you as an Honorary Florida Dog Ambassador. It is your sacred duty to carry little plastic bags with you wherever you go, stashed in your pocket, purse, or other convenient niche, and to use them when your dog does his business. You may prefer the handy-dandy new commercial scoopers, such as Dispoz-a-Scoop, a brown plastic bag attached by wire to a cardboard cover (approximately $2.50 for five scoopers). You just pop the undesirables into the bag and close the cover snugly without ever fouling your precious skin. They're available at most pet stores. Or hang on to Styrofoam cups and lids from fast-food places. They make fine little containers.

Etiquette Rex: The Well-Mannered Mutt

While cleaning up after your dog is your responsibility, a dog in a public place has his own responsibilities. Of course, it really boils down to your responsibility again, but the burden of action is on your dog. Etiquette for restaurants and hotels is covered in other sections of this chapter. What follows are some fundamental rules of dog etiquette. We'll go through it quickly, but if your dog's a slow reader, he can read it again: no vicious dogs; no jumping on people; no incessant barking; no leg lifts on surfboards, backpacks, human legs, or any other personal objects you'll find hanging around beaches and parks; dogs should come when they're called; dogs should stay on command.

Safety First

A few essentials will keep your traveling dog happy and healthy.

Beat the Heat: Florida isn't called the Sunshine State for nothing. Last we checked, St. Petersburg was the world record holder for continuous days of sunshine. And the rest of the state was not far behind. The heat and humidity here should never be taken lightly.

We hope the only hot dogs you encounter in your wanderings will be the kind you slather with ketchup and mustard. To that end, here are some guidelines:

Travel in the winter if possible. Otherwise, go in the spring or fall when temperatures are cooler.

If your pooch simply must hit the road in the summer, take *extreme* precautions. Summer heat has killed dogs and even infants who were left in cars for just a few minutes. Running the air conditioner while you dash into the store isn't practical, and besides, it's not guaranteed to work; several police dogs have died while sitting in cars with stalled engines. When it's hot, you really should leave your pal at home.

And now, some rules for traveling with your dog:

Rule No. 1: Never, but never, leave your dog in a car with the windows up—or even almost all the way up. Always park in the shade. Even in the winter, the sun can transform a car into a combination greenhouse/oven. In the summer, do not leave a dog in a parked car for *any* length of time. Even with the windows opened a little, the temperature can reach 120° F, sometimes higher, in a few minutes.

Dogs don't sweat. They release heat by panting. But when the air is hot, they just can't cool down enough. If they get overheated, it can cause brain damage or heatstroke. And don't assume the problem is limited to cars. Pooches can build up a high body temperature in any unshaded place, particularly in hot weather. Puppies and older dogs are at greatest risk.

Rule No. 2: Thou shalt at all times keep thy dog supplied with plenty of water. There are many ways to accomplish this. Our solution: Take along a cooler. In it, place a one-quart Tupperware container filled with water and lots of ice (to keep the water cool). Or use one of those one-quart take-out soup containers from a restaurant. Empty margarine or Cool Whip tubs or any lidded plastic bowl will do. Consider buying a big, heavy clay dog dish that will stay firmly rooted on the car's backseat floor to give your pooch constant access to water.

We've developed a routine with Maggie: We take along some water when we go for a hike or a walk, offering it to her periodically. Then we give her water again when we get back to the car and she knows it's time for a drink. Make sure you offer your doggy a drink at least every half hour, much more frequently when it's hot.

You may discover that your dog is partial to water from your area. Maggie, for instance, favors Fort Lauderdale municipal water. While we can't haul along enough water for a lengthy trip, we bring as much as possible when we set off, and try to keep a little container available at all times. Nevertheless, a thirsty dog will drink almost any water. The main thing is to keep plenty on hand.

Rule No. 3: Be careful about letting your dog run alongside you on a bike ride. Although some breeds need hard workouts, many dogs just aren't built for it. To please you, your loyal pooch will trot along to the point of exhaustion and can suffer physical harm—even death—from the strain. Likewise, don't jog with your dog unless she has gradually built up enough stamina to take it.

Rule No. 4: Take frequent rests when hiking or when you're involved in other outdoor activities. (Keep in mind that a four-legged critter is exposed to a lot more sun than we upright bipeds are, and that dogs are essentially wearing a fur coat all the time.) Dogs can get really pumped when they're out having fun, and will become worn out faster. Don't overdo it. Be cognizant of the symptoms of heatstroke, which can cause brain damage and even death: excessive panting, infrequent urination, glassy-eyed staring, dizziness, vomiting, and, when it's basically too late, collapse. Should you notice any of these signs, the folks at the Humane Society of Broward County say it is imperative that you get your pooch into the shade *immediately* and apply ice packs or cold towels to the head, neck, chest, and feet to slowly reduce your buddy's temperature. If the dog is conscious, give him a *small* amount of water or allow him to lick ice cubes. Most important, rush him to a veterinarian.

Rule No. 5: Establish a feeding schedule and stick to it. This seems obvious—after all, you do it at home—but on vacation, regimens can be difficult to follow. We give Maggie dog biscuits in the car at certain times of day and then her dinner when we get to the hotel room in early evening.

Car Safety: Safety is a prime consideration when you and your dog hit the highway. Traveling in an air-conditioned car should not be a problem, but remember to check periodically to see if the backseat is getting hotter than where you're sitting—a particular concern in hatchbacks. One situation to be avoiding: letting your dog ride in the bed of a truck. "Dogs can burn the pads of their feet on a hot truck bed," says Rachel Lamb, of the Humane Society of the United States. "Worse yet, they can be tossed around in the truck or thrown out entirely if the truck stops suddenly."

And no parking in the sun—even with the windows down. "Dogs can't tolerate that," stresses Dr. Susan Anderson of the University of Florida's College of Veterinary Medicine. (We discuss heat dangers more thoroughly later on.)

Always carry lots of water in the car. You don't know whether your jaunt to the grocery store will turn into a two-hour wait for a tow truck because your car has broken down. We've found that most drive-through fast-food places are happy to provide a fresh glass of ice water to anyone buying food. Maggie actually looks forward to the water when we're waiting to order fast food. Sometimes employees give her an extra treat—a bag of fries, an old bagel, or dog biscuits.

Another safety concern is whether to restrain your pet. Various pet harnesses have been devised to substitute for human seat belts, but they've received mixed reviews. Some people keep their dogs in travel kennels like the airlines use. We eschew these and allow Maggie to drink in the views of the countryside with her head outside the window. It's a personal choice. We think a dog would rather have the run of the car and really enjoy a trip, even if there's a chance that he'll trot off to that Big Doghouse in the Sky before his time.

Remember to stop for a brief walk every now and then. The actual intervals will vary according to your dog's needs. (Be sensitive to changes in your dog's usual evacuation schedule caused by the routine-shattering world of canine travel.) We learned the importance of frequent leg stretches the hard way. We vividly recall the day Maggie was having some, uh, digestive troubles in the backseat during a trip near Lake Kissimmee, and we were sent scampering to the store for Borax and other cleaning supplies.

Finally, according to some people, you should limit the amount of time your dog spends with his head hanging outside the car window, which can supposedly force too much cold air into his lungs or foul the pooch's peepers. That's never been a problem for Maggie, though.

Planes: Should you take your dog on an airplane? We don't recommend it, because air travel can be dangerous for a dog—even fatal. But if circumstances make it necessary, be sure to book a direct, early-morning or late-evening flight to avoid extreme temperatures. If you must change planes, make sure there is ample time for baggage handlers to transfer your pet from one plane to another. Freeze water in a three-quarters-full plastic margarine bowl and attach it inside a regulation-size dog carrier (big enough for your dog to stand up, lie down, and turn around). This way, water won't splash out during loading, but the ice will be melted by the time your dog is thirsty. For trips lasting longer than 12 hours, attach a plastic bag of dry food on top of the carrier along with feeding instructions addressed to the airline workers. The Humane Society of the United States advises never to ship pug-nosed dogs such as chow chows, Pekingese, or Boston terriers. Their short nasal passages don't give the hot baggage compartment air a chance to cool before it reaches their lungs.

Should you tranquilize your dog? No, say many authorities, including the American Humane Association and the American Veterinary Medical Association. While some pet owners are tempted to tranquilize their dogs, the fact is that it leaves a dog more vulnerable to injury. (A sedated dog may have trouble keeping itself balanced when its crate is moved or jostled.) And when the plane is soaring, the high altitude can create respiratory and cardiovascular problems for tranquilized dogs, warns the American Animal Hospital Association. "Although thousands of pets are transported uneventfully by air, airline officials believe that when deaths occur, they often result from the use of sedation," said Patricia Olson, a veterinarian and former director of veterinary affairs and studies for the American Humane Association.

Feed your dog a light meal six hours prior to the flight and walk her right before putting her in the carrier. Write "live animal" in letters at least one inch high in several places on the carrier. Use bold arrows to show the proper upright position of the crate. Write the name, address, and phone number of your dog's destination on top of the carrier. If your dog is small, take him on the plane with you, using a carrier that can fit under an airplane seat; check with your airline ahead of time about its animal policy.

Dog owner Bruce Batten found out the hard way what can happen to a pet who sits too long in a grounded plane. While waiting an hour for takeoff, he heard his dog dying. Nutmeg, the normally quiet golden retriever, yelped from the increasingly warm cargo hold below Batten's seat. "A dog is crying!" Batten heard a child shout. Then Nutmeg was silent. When he reached his destination, Batten learned why: Nutmeg had died of heat prostration. On airplanes, the cargo hold isn't air-conditioned until takeoff. "It was, just from what we could hear, a pretty agonizing death," says Batten. "That was the horrible part."

The Ultimate Doggy Bag

Our collection of can openers is testimony to the need to create your very own pooch travel bag. We used to rush out of town on a Friday night, remembering the can of dog food, and then, upon reaching our destination, realize we had forgotten the can opener. Maggie would look at us hungrily. So we'd head to the nearest 7-Eleven and buy our 18th or 19th can opener. We now know how convenient it is to keep doggy essentials in the car.

A simple paper grocery bag will do the trick. Among the things you should consider stashing: canned dog food, a can opener, an emergency stash of dry food, a bowl or two for food and water, a spare leash, extra heartworm pills, and other medications. You may want to purchase an Oasis, a collapsible bowl made of waterproof nylon (produced by Ruff Wear). The important thing is to bring some sort of container—even paper plates—so you can serve your dog dinner. Add to that list a brush, tennis ball, rawhide bone or another treat, spare blanket, towels (for rainy, muddy days), a first-aid kit, and pooper-scoopers. Treats and a blanket help give Maggie a sense of security.

Always bring along paperwork: your dog's registration and proof of her latest vaccination. These tend to become necessary when you're least expecting it (such as when you've suddenly realized that you've left the heartworm pills at home). It's best to have copies of the paperwork on hand. Photocopies usually suffice.

Maggie wears a dog tag that lists her name, our names, and her home address and phone number. No one intends to get separated from their dogs on vacation, but it can happen.

Bone Appétit

Unfortunately, your pooch will hear doggone few black-tied waiters in cummerbunds say "Bone Appétit" in Florida. Truly fine dining is often something pooches have to pass on here, although you can usually find a place to fill your belly while a dog rests at your ankles.

Florida restaurant regulations prohibit dogs other than guide dogs "in a public food service establishment." That gives restaurateurs a fairly loose leash when it comes to patio dining and the like. Generally, dogs may be allowed—or at least tolerated—at restaurants with outdoor seating. Proprietors at many of these places figure pooches are fine patrons as long as they stay on the fresh-air side of the building's threshold. But just because a place has outdoor seating doesn't necessarily mean your dog is welcome—be flexible in your dinner plans.

We've noticed that the availability of dog-friendly restaurants seems to vary from place to place. Judging from our conversations with restaurant managers, this variation stems from how the situation is viewed by local health inspectors. From town to town and county to county—and even week to week or month to month at the same restaurant—the rule's interpretation may differ. Sometimes the day manager is keen on King, while the night guy says no to Natasha.

Use your judgment, even at restaurants we've listed as being dog-friendly. If quarters are too close, or if your dog will make a scene with the other pooches already in the place, maybe you should look for an establishment with a better square-foot-to-whisker ratio.

Sad indeed are tales like the one from the Crab Pot in Jacksonville Beach, which happily allowed hungry hounds until a Labrador retriever bit a patron, leaving a wound that required many stitches. Management barred the four-legged set after that. So if your dog is anything but polite and gentle with people she does not know, you may want to stick to drive-throughs and picnics. Don't give up though: The more you take your dog on visits to pet stores that welcome canines and involve her in activities such as organized dog walks for fund-raising events, the more socialized she'll become. "The more you take your dog on outings, the more he becomes attuned to them and used to different things," professional dog trainer Robin Hansen of South Florida told us. Take the dog out rarely, and "he's going to act like an idiot in the car and an idiot in the waiting room."

Maggie senses that things are loosening up for hungry dogs in Florida. More restaurateurs are becoming aware that sunshine is an attraction, and are placing a few tables outside or a picnic table under a tree. Establishments that number among the most popular with the two-legged set—from the sidewalk cafés of Coconut Grove to the funky restaurants in the Panhandle's Seaside—are growing increasingly friendly to pooches. All the way from the historic eateries in Pensacola's Old Town to the salt-air-kissed bars of Key West, restaurants are going to the dogs.

We want this trend to continue. When you visit, make sure your dog doesn't cause a stir. Dog lovers statewide are counting on you.

A Room at the Inn

Just how big is your dog, anyhow? That is often what the hotel desk clerk is thinking when you arrive with your best buddy looking for a room. It's the BIG dogs who have trouble finding a place to stay. Dogs like our 50-pound Maggie. The reason, says Anthony Marshall, former dean of the respected hospitality school at Florida International University in Miami, is the way some hoteliers selectively overemphasize certain aspects of a dog's life. Marshall says many a hotelier lies awake at night wondering, "Where is that big dog going to poop? And will a guest step in it?"

"The bigger the dog," Marshall explains, "the greater the waste.... There's nothing to upset a hotel manager more than to see a nice little lady come in with a 200-pound dog."

Apparently, to some hoteliers, dogs are just walking poop machines with fangs.

In many hotel listings in this book, you will see a notation such as "Small dogs only, please," or even "Pooches under 15 pounds, please." Don't let that stop you from asking about staying, though, if your dog doesn't technically qualify. Because, Marshall says, another thing going through that hotelier's mind is, "Am I going to lose a buck by prohibiting dogs?"

We've approached a number of places that technically permitted only small dogs. As we signed in, we simply asked if having our dog along was okay. Desk clerks almost always said, "Fine." We didn't volunteer how big or mean-looking our little pride and joy happened to be, and all was well. Never a word of complaint. Rarely did they ask, "How big is it?"

Other hoteliers aren't too familiar with dog weights. One might say she accepts "small" dogs, to which Robert would reply, "Well, Maggie is *only* 50 pounds." Frequently the question would come back: "Well, is that small?" Our answer: "It's certainly not big." Or, "She's half the size of a regular German shepherd."

To help appease the hotelier who asks to see the dog, we recommend tying a yellow or red bandanna around your pooch's neck to give her an "aw, shucks" aura. If your dog is a lovable-looking breed such as an Airedale or a golden retriever, you have a good chance of winning over the manager. Emphasize how quiet and sweet your pooch is (assuming that is the case). Even Maggie, whose German shepherd face invariably reminds about half the U.S. population of a vicious police dog, has come off as docile enough to receive the blessings of previously dubious hotel owners. Must be the bandanna.

If you'll be staying at a hotel with a dog, there are other considerations, including:

• When you enter a hotel room, it becomes your dog's new home. We've seen Maggie grow territorial about a new room in a matter of hours. If this happens, you may want to keep the curtains drawn so your pooch won't be tempted to investigate every guest or housekeeper who traipses by.

• Take only house-trained dogs into hotel rooms. Praise, praise, praise when he goes outdoors. Also, keep a vigilant eye on even a reliable dog when he is first starting to sleep in hotels. He may decide he needs to mark his territory. If this happens, immediately express your displeasure. Make sure he understands that this is a big no-no. We've found it also pays to keep a newspaper handy on those first hotel stays, the better for thrusting quickly under your dog's posterior should he start to have an "accident." Take lots of walks when you arrive at a hotel or inn so your furry friend will come to realize there is plenty of territory for marking far outside the hotel room door.

• We always bring one of Maggie's blankets on a road trip. This seems to comfort her and helps prevent coating the hotel room with her fur. Some friends of ours spread a tarp or an old tent in the back of their car to cut down on fur left on the seats. Other people purchase old blankets from the Army/Navy surplus store. In addition to helping minimize dog hair in the hotel room, these blankets double as car-seat protectors, which you'll especially appreciate when your pooch hops in after a muddy hike.

• Tip the hotel's housekeeping service well. If you have a big, furry dog like Maggie, tip the housekeeper exceptionally well. The convention is $2–3 a night for a room for two people, depending on how fancy the lodging is.

• Don't leave your dog alone in the room. You may not think she cries when you're gone, but how do you know? You are, by definition, gone. Television talk show maven Oprah Winfrey once televised a few tapings of what dogs did when their owners left the house. One dog who was "taught" to never sit on the couch was secretly videotaped spending the whole day on the couch; he jumped down only when the owner's car pulled up.

Several innkeepers complained to us about whining or yapping dogs. A normally placid pooch can turn weird when left alone in a hotel room. She might gnaw on the furniture, curtains, or bedsheets, or even hurt herself while tearing around the place. A few ingenious hoteliers decided to combat the problem by having dog owners sign a waiver saying they'll take the dog with them whenever they leave the room.

If you have to leave the dog in the room momentarily, put out the Do Not Disturb sign to prevent housekeepers from knocking or entering.

• We do not recommend sneaking dogs into lodgings. Aside from making you feel like a criminal and sending your blood pressure soaring, it's generally not necessary. Hundreds of hotels are listed in this book, spread across the state from Pensacola to Key West. You don't have to settle for lousy quality. Even some of the nation's best hotels permit pets.

• If you want the security of knowing which hotel chains allow dogs in all locations, we have found a few: Motel 6 permits one (usually small) pet per room. "Small" Maggie has stayed in plenty of Motel 6s, which are located in many cities throughout Florida. You won't find minibars, but several locations have been remodeled and now feature bigger rooms. Also, every La Quinta we encountered in Florida allowed small pets. Red Roof Inns also are a good bet; nearly all permit pets. The Westin and Sheraton chains more recently announced they will accept dogs chainwide and offer to give Princess the royal treatment.

Room rates quoted in the hotel listings are for two adults and one dog per night. If a pet fee will be charged, we list that separately. When you see a price range, such as $55–105, we are referring to the lowest low-season rate and the highest high-season rate.

We've attempted to stay away from run-down motels and lodgings in less-than-savory neighborhoods. In a few cases, some make-do offerings have found their way into this guide, simply because we found so few other dog-friendly motels in that town. We included a wide range of rates so that dogs of any means can see the Sunshine State.

Natural Troubles

There is a regular laundry list of miscellaneous things in Florida that can make your life and your dog's life rough, ranging from irritations to life-threatening illnesses.

Lightning: For three decades, Florida has led the nation in lightning-related deaths. Like hurricanes, this is simply a fact of life here. About one day out of three, on average, there is a severe thunderstorm somewhere in Florida.

Protect yourself and your pooch. If you're outside, seek refuge in a building or a car, staying away from windows, doors, fireplaces, metal pipes, electrical appliances, sinks, tubs, and showers. If you're caught outside, don't hang out under a tall tree, in or near water, or alongside metal fences. The best place in this situation? Somewhere in a forest, underneath the low- to medium-profile trees and away from the tall ones.

Parvo: Parvovirus is fairly common in some locales, particularly among puppies. It is spread primarily through feces, providing another excellent reason for you to clean up after your dog. It also can be transmitted through saliva or flies, though. Symptoms appear seven to 10 days after exposure. Young puppies and very old dogs are most at risk. Symptoms typically include vomiting and bloody diarrhea. Make sure your dog is vaccinated yearly. A virulent new strain that is apparently resistant to the vaccine in some breeds—rottweilers and Doberman pinschers seem particularly susceptible—broke out in Central Florida a decade ago.

Poison Ivy: Actually, this is not a danger for your dog, but it is for you. We've heard of people petting a dog who has brushed up against poison ivy, then touching their own arm and finding themselves in agony soon thereafter. Poison ivy grows as a vine, a small plant, and a shrub. Remember: "Leaflets three, let it be." In general, if you and your dog stay on hiking trails, you'll avoid poison ivy and its cousin, poison oak. Get familiar with these plants before you go tromping off into the underbrush. If you suspect your dog has been in contact with either of them, give her a bath, preferably using rubber gloves.

Sticker Weeds: Robert once spent several days picking all the sticker weeds out of our yard, one by one, so that poor Maggie wouldn't come limping in at night with sandburs stuck in her paws.

If your dog stops, bends down, and starts biting at the bottom of his paws, look between the pads for little blond pointy balls. Pull them out with your fingers or, if they're handy, a pair of tweezers. After that, find a new place for your dog to run around. Stickers are likely to be spread throughout a field, not just in one spot.

Alligators: Imagine the puzzlement of the members of a Panhandle hunting club. They would make tracks for the Blackwater River State Forest every so often and send their hunting dogs in search of game. Then, darned if a dog didn't disappear. Again and again, trip after trip, some dog would vanish. They suspected a dog thief.

Many years passed before they figured out that a granddaddy alligator would lie in wait alongside the trail, which passed near his freshwater home, to make an easy meal of the hunters' four-legged friends. State biologists—who found several dog collars in the gator's stomach—surmised that, to the gator, the jangling collars and the barking of the hunting dogs became the equivalent of a dinner bell.

At one time, before international endangered-species trade restrictions were toughened up, poachers were wiping out Florida's alligator population. But these ancient amphibious reptiles have staged a successful comeback, and there are now so many that the Florida Fish and Wildlife Conservation Commission must keep lists of hunters who will deal with those beasts who become a problem.

One of the chief complaints, particularly at lakes ringed by suburban homes, is that alligators will eat dogs, especially small ones. You may laugh, but it's a serious threat. Don't let your pooch wander near the water's edge without supervision. And don't let your water dog scurry off to plunge into a freshwater lake. Alligators are naturally leery of humans, so if you accompany the dog, she should survive. However, some alligators who have been fed by thoughtless people have come to associate the presence of humans with food. Our advice: Keep your dog out of all bodies of fresh water in Florida. An alligator could be lurking.

Alligators usually avoid salt water, though, so it's generally safe to swim there. Brackish water also discourages them, though you may see a brave gator lolling there once in a while. (The endangered Florida crocodile does live in and around salt water in extreme southeastern Florida, at the edge of the Everglades and the Florida Keys. Some people fret that their dogs will be eaten there, but in reality crocs are quite shy and we know of no documented cases of crocs feeding on pooches.)

Of course, smaller dogs are more likely to become an alligator's breakfast. Any gator less than six feet in length should be no problem for all but the tiniest dog. At that size, alligators are still eating frogs, small fish, and the like. But a big gator can wolf down a deer or even—very rarely—a person. So big dogs are not immune. One state park ranger told us he lost a German shepherd to an alligator at the edge of a lake.

Don't be fooled into thinking an alligator isn't fast enough to catch a mutt. Even on land, they can race around at speeds that would rival the fillies at the Gulfstream Racetrack.

If you should see an alligator approach anyone, especially a dog or small child, assume it has been socialized by being given food handouts. Get the dog or child out of harm's way, then leave the area and call the local office of the Florida Fish and Wildlife Conservation Commission.

Although not as fearsome as gators, there are several other creatures to be aware of when you're outdoors with your dog in Florida:

Fleas: In Florida, fleas are a fact of life—unless you put your pets on flea treatment such as Revolution, Frontline, and Advantage, which work wonderfully. Otherwise, fleas are worst in late summer, but can be a problem any time, particularly during a mild winter. Try to look for hotels that have tile floors rather than carpets; unfortunately, these are not always easy to find. This brings to mind another reason not to sneak dogs into hotels: The hotelier needs to know whether to vacuum thoroughly, or even bug-bomb the place. At our house, we personally took up the carpet and provided Maggie with washable throw rugs to limit the places where fleas can hide.

Wash your dog frequently to help keep the problem at bay. Our routine: Wash Maggie weekly and launder her bedding in hot water at least as often.

Before the advent of oral flea treatments like Frontline, we occasionally experienced a heavy flea infestation. We found that sprinkling boric acid (Borax) on affected areas may help. Vacuum after a few hours. Avon's Skin-So-Soft also may be helpful, but it made Maggie's coat pretty oily and we jokingly called her "Elvis dog." A valuable nonchemical tool is the flea comb. When you unearth fleas this way, be sure to kill them. Wash your hands afterward.

We have found that these steps will stamp out or keep fleas to a minimum in a healthy, well-cared-for dog. When we tried powerful insecticides long ago, such as those used in flea dips, we could see that they were weakening Maggie's immune system. She sometimes seemed listless and sick afterward. So while the poisons killed those fleas that were on her at that moment, they left her vulnerable to a major infestation in the days to come. All it takes to kill fleas is a five-minute soaking in some soap and water.

Skunks: These creatures are found in many places and conditions other than lying dead in the middle of the road. One circumstance that occurs more frequently than we'd like is the canine-skunk encounter. Should your four-legged friend find herself on the losing end of this fix, give her a bath and then pour tomato juice all over her. Keep pouring on the juice until the smell begins to subside. We've even heard of people bathing their dogs in tomato juice or cans of stewed tomatoes. The possibility of crossing paths with a skunk is one of many excellent arguments for keeping your pooch leashed when you go prancing through the woods.

Snakes: We find snakes to be an infrequent problem for dogs in the Sunshine State, but you need only one encounter with a poisonous snake to make a large and sorrowful difference in your life. It's a major reason Maggie stays leashed on almost every walk in the woods.

Especially on cold days, you might find a snake sunning itself beside a rock or on top of an old log. Some poisonous snakes make their homes inside or near piles of dead wood. Also to be avoided are thickets of saw palmetto, which are interspersed through pinelands across most of the state. Keep your dog on the hiking trail here, and try to keep an eye on the trail ahead of your pooch.

Canal banks and thickets of weeds at the edge of lakes can also be treacherous. Again, the most dangerous days are the cold ones, when you might encounter a water moccasin (a.k.a. cottonmouth) soaking up some sun. As you know, your dog really shouldn't be sniffing around lakes anyway because of the threat of alligators.

If your dog is bitten, carry him if possible—letting him walk helps circulate the venom—and get to a vet as fast as you can.

Ticks and Chiggers: You are likely to encounter ticks in wooded areas anywhere north of Lake Okeechobee. They are particularly numerous in the thickest, least-visited woods. They love to live in piles of old dead wood or lurk in the leaves carpeting the forest floor. Ticks also live south of Lake Okeechobee, though we have never encountered them there in our travels with Maggie.

Curiously, ticks tend not to dig right in as soon as they jump onto you or your pup. They'll spend a few hours roaming around this new beast, looking for just the right place to settle in for dinner. So remember to inspect your pooch carefully at the end of your hikes. Don't forget to peer into his ears and snout, and to check between his toes and under his tail. A routine brushing after a hike is also a good idea. Hint: If you brush *against* the hair growth at first, you're more likely to see the small eight-legged insects.

When you find a tick walking around, crush it. Try to use something other than your fingernails. But if you must use them, wash your hands thoroughly as soon as possible to prevent the spread of Lyme disease, Rocky Mountain spotted fever, and other maladies.

If you find a tick attached to your dog's skin (the tick is usually swollen and looks like a dark corn kernel), use a pair of tweezers to grasp it as close to the skin as possible and firmly pull it straight out. Then wash the area well with rubbing alcohol or another disinfectant. If you are unable to grasp the tick close to the skin, try twisting it counterclockwise, "unscrewing" the tick's head. Frequently they will let go. Avoid leaving any tick mouth parts embedded under your dog's skin.

Chiggers don't bother dogs, as far as we know, but they can make people downright itchy. For this reason, you should avoid rolling around in Spanish moss with your pooch.

Toads: The exotic *Bufo marinus* looks ugly from a two-legged perspective, its olive-green skin splotched with weird, dark brown markings. But to many of the four-legged persuasion, they look like fun prey to hunt, torment, and kill. This is an extremely dangerous game. *Bufo marinus* toads will fight back. Just a taste of the white poison that the toads secrete from sacs behind their heads can be highly toxic to your doggy—enough so to do him in. Should you spot your furry friend toying with one of these creatures, immediately wash out his mouth very thoroughly and hightail it to the vet.

Dog Day Afternoon at the Beach

Back when *USA Today*'s smaller but older cousin *Cocoa Today* was cutting its teeth on Florida's Space Coast, reporters used to joke about one of the paper's vigorous editorial campaigns. Before that stretch of coastal Florida was beset by NASA cutbacks, pollution, overcrowded schools, and other real issues, *Cocoa Today* founder Al Neuharth's nascent newspaper editorialized against allowing dogs on the beach. Really. Neuharth's paper was more relentless than a Doberman pinscher bearing down on a burglar. And *Cocoa Today* got its way.

Today you won't find a scrap of Atlantic Ocean beachfront in Brevard County where dogs may cavort legally in the surf. (We have, however, listed some sandy stretches of causeway and other "inside" beaches as alternatives.) The reason for this is obvious: Mr. Neuharth doesn't like stepping in dog crap. Neither do millions of other Floridians. In fact, we can't think of a single person we know who likes stepping in dog crap. As a result, you'll have to search pretty hard to find Florida beaches where you can romp with Rover. But in this book, we've included at least one listing for a dog-friendly beach in the chapters on Pensacola, Panama City, Tallahassee, Jacksonville Beaches, St. Augustine, Gainesville, the Space Coast, the Treasure Coast, Tampa, St. Petersburg, Sarasota, West Palm Beach, Fort Lauderdale, Miami, the Florida Keys, and Fort Myers.

Dog-friendly beaches need to be protected. They have dwindled in number even in our lifetimes. So make sure you get rid of the No. 1 Thing People Hate About Dogs at the Beach: poop. Clean up after your dog. Bring along a plastic bag from your last trip to the grocery store or the plastic wrapper from your morning newspaper. Even better, bring several, and clean up the leavings of less-upstanding dog owners. Or buy a pooper-scooper. If you forget to bring a scooper, use a twig to prod the calling card into a fast-food cup you might find lying around. A few beaches and parks, such as Fort Lauderdale's Riverwalk and the beach in the town of Jupiter, offer disposable Mutt Mitts at posted locations. As disheartening as the diminishing number of dog beaches is, there are some encouraging signs, such as Brohard Paw Park & Beach in Venice, where dogs now run freely after years of being barred from the waterfront. Let's keep working to expand these opportunities.

In addition to accommodating your human companions at the beach, take good care of your dog. Beaches are some of the hottest places around, particularly when the midday sun is high overhead. Try to visit in the early morning or late afternoon. Happily, this also is when beaches are least crowded and you're most likely to get away with ignoring the leash law (though we don't encourage it). A prolonged stay at midday, even in the winter, may be too much for many dogs.

Always, always bring along plenty of water and offer it to your canine companion often. Your dog may be tempted to drink the salty ocean water, but don't let him. Be firm about this. Salt water can be toxic to your dog, causing him to vomit or suffer sudden bouts of diarrhea.

Also be sure to rinse your pooch with fresh water after a day at the beach. Excessive salt (and chlorine) can irritate a dog's skin. And don't let a dog run on really hot sand. It could burn her foot pads.

If you see what look like little blue balloons or silicone gel implants dotting the beach, keep your dog away from them. These are Portuguese man-of-wars, and their stingers can hurt you and your dog.

Ruffing It Together

Dogs and the outdoors go together like coffee and cream. Maggie glories in floating lazily down a Florida stream by canoe or lying around a campsite after a hard day's hike. We find that camping, hiking, and canoeing can all be great fun when you have your dog along. But you'll need to keep a few things in mind.

If you're camping, we highly recommend having the dog sleep inside the tent with you. Left chained or tied outdoors, he's more likely to try to break away and run after an armadillo, or worse. One problem, of course, is that your pooch may try to chase some critter *anyway*—and crash straight through the mosquito netting! It's best to have him lie down right next to you, so you will be quickly awakened should he stir. Also, barking dogs aggravate campers. Critics say dogs become excitable around strange sights and smells, and one barker can set off a barking frenzy. Keeping your pooch with you in your tent or camper helps safeguard against canine etiquette problems.

Boating with dogs can be a lot of fun, but not if your pooch is constantly threatening to jump overboard. He must be made to understand that he has to stay in the boat. If he dives into fresh water, he risks being eaten by an alligator. In salt water, you might run across manatees—which won't eat your dog, but are likely to lead to excitement and confusion. Other saltwater dangers: mangroves and sandbars studded with razor-sharp oyster shells that can slice a dog's legs and paws. We can take water-fearing Maggie most anywhere because she views all bodies of water as giant bathtubs. If yours is a water-loving dog, we suggest a trip in shallow, sandy-bottomed salt water until he gets used to boating.

Canoeing presents a unique challenge. Let's face it: Many paddlers have enough trouble keeping those elegant but unstable watercraft afloat even without a 100-pound dog shifting from side to side to take in the sights as cows, wading birds, and other distractions pop up like targets at a shooting range. Suffice it to say that not every pooch is made for paddling. Test yours out on a few short, easy trips in shallow salt water before setting out on a big trip.

Hiking can also be lots of fun. But make sure your dog is up to it. Start out by gradually increasing the length of your walks back home and, over a period of a week or more, work up to the distances you might be covering while on vacation.

You may want to outfit your pooch with a doggy backpack. They come in various styles and colors. Go for fluorescent orange if you can find it, as this will make your pooch easier to find if he gets lost. It also will clearly mark him as unfair game should he wander near any hunters. REI.com (800/426-4840) sells a dozen dog packs starting below $30. Another doggie backpack, by Outward Hound, sells for about $40 at PETsMART.com.

Beyond the Borders

There may be times when you and your dog find yourselves leaving Florida to visit other parts of the United States. Due to the success of *The Dog Lover's Companion to The Bay Area* (Avalon Travel Publishing), the first in the series to be published, the Dog Lover's Companion series now covers different parts of the country, including Atlanta, The Bay Area, Boston, New England, Seattle, Texas, and Washington D.C.-Baltimore. All of the authors are experts in their areas and have adventurous dogs who help them explore and rate various attractions. Keep your eyes peeled for upcoming books.

Another fun way to keep up with dog travel news around the country is through a subscription to a doggone fine newsletter called *DogGone*. As its masthead states, *DogGone* is about "fun places to go and cool stuff to do with your dog." A subscription to this informative publication is $25 per year (for six issues). For more information, contact them at: *DogGone*, P.O. Box 1846, Estes Park, CO 80517, 888/DOG-TRAVEL, www.doggonefun.com.

A Dog in Need

If you want to provide a good home for a dog, we encourage you to look over the unwanted dogs who will be euthanized tomorrow (and the next day) at the local pound. Animal shelters and humane organizations see far too many dogs walk through their front doors—and dreadfully too few walking out with happy new owners.

Our Maggie was a stray who was picked up off a busy Miami street as a pup. Shadow, a scuba-diving Lab who has made more than 25 television appearances, previously languished in a pound until Dwane Folsom of Boynton Beach picked her up and showed her the world. Brandi, a shepherd/collie mix, sat droopy-eyed in a shelter before Caroline Crane-Thomason adopted her and made the pooch the mascot of the Humane Society of Broward County. A dog is waiting to become your best pal, too. Spay or neuter your new buddy to try to lower the number of unwanted dogs. Then go for a ride! Go for a walk! Your furry confidante will devote his life to being your best friend. For more information, contact your local shelter or go to the website of the National Humane Education Society (www.nhes.org), a nonprofit organization that teaches people about the importance of being kind to animals and maintains the Peace Plantation Animal Sanctuary for dogs and cats.

THE PANHANDLE

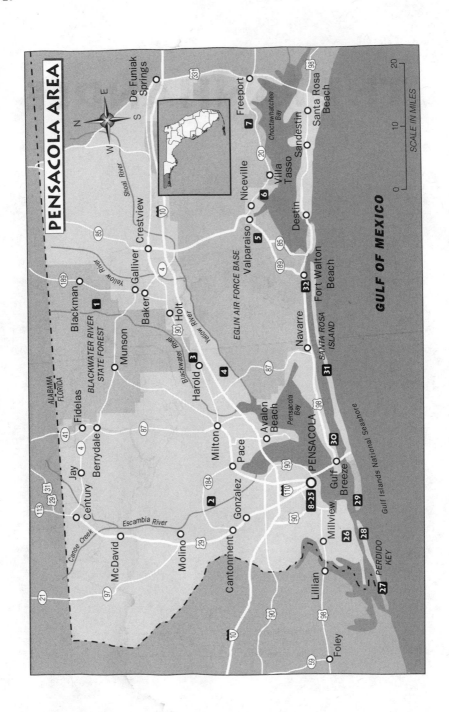

PENSACOLA AREA

N E S W

SCALE IN MILES

0 10 20

De Funiak Springs

331

Freeport

7

Choctawhatchee Bay

Santa Rosa Beach

98

Niceville

Villa Tasso

Sandestin

6

20

Valparaiso

5

Destin

85

Shoal River

Crestview

Galliver

85

10

189

Blackman

BLACKWATER RIVER STATE FOREST

Yellow River

Baker

1

Holt

90

Munson

Harold

3

4

32

Fort Walton Beach

EGLIN AIR FORCE BASE

189

Navarre

87

Blackwater River

ALABAMA FLORIDA

Fidelas

41

4

Berrydale

Jay

87

Milton

Pace

Avalon Beach

Pensacola Bay

SANTA ROSA ISLAND

31

Century

184

Gonzalez

PENSACOLA

30

98

Molino

Cantonment

2

90

170

Gulf Breeze

8·25

29

Escambia River

29

Canoe Creek

McDavid

97

Millview

26

28

GULF OF MEXICO

113

29

31

21

Lillian

PERDIDO KEY

27

Gulf Islands National Seashore

Foley

59

98

90

10

Yellow River

4

CHAPTER 1
Pensacola Area

In Florida, you have to go north to get to the South, and nowhere is this more evident than in Pensacola. Pensacola is one of the most classically Southern locales in the state. This is the Florida where grits are listed on every breakfast menu and boiled-peanut stands dot many a byway. The city hosts a Mardi Gras celebration every February, complete with parades and parties that last through Fat Tuesday, the day before Lent begins—just like in New Orleans, only a little saner.

The rest of the year, the pace of life and the demeanor of the residents are soothing and friendly. And this hospitality is extended to dogs, too. Pooches can romp along the shores of Escambia Bay at Bay Bluffs Park (see Parks, Beaches, and Recreation Areas), tour one of the South's oldest historic districts, or scarf down a scrumptious frankfurter from the Dog House Deli (see Restaurants).

While parks and activities charmed our Maggie, some of her favorite area haunts lie outside Pensacola proper: Blackwater River State Forest, Gulf Islands National Seashore, the University of West Florida, and the Eglin Air Force Base to name some of the best.

PICK OF THE LITTER—THE PANHANDLE

BEST DOG PARKS
Bayview Park Dog Park, Pensacola (page 36)
Scott Complex Dog Park, Pensacola (page 39)

BEST OFF-LEASH BEACH
Bayview Park Dog Park, Pensacola (page 36)

BEST PICNICKING
Gulf Islands National Seashore's Fort Pickens Area,
Pensacola Beach (page 48)

BEST OBSERVATION TOWER
Big Lagoon State Park, Perdido Key (page 45)

MOST UNUSUAL HIKE
Eglin Air Force Base, Niceville (page 32)

Munson

PARKS, BEACHES, AND RECREATION AREAS

1 Blackwater River State Forest

🐾🐾🐾 🐾 (See Pensacola map on page 26)

This huge tract of pines sprawls across two counties just south of the Alabama border and excites dogs with the scent of deer, wild turkeys, and Sherman's fox squirrels. Roads of red clay and sand crisscross these 190,000 acres of longleaf pine and wiregrass—the largest chunk of that once-widespread ecosystem left in the world (though 2004's hurricanes snapped a fair share of trees). Dogs without hunting licenses are allowed only in select recreation areas within Florida's biggest state forest: Bear Lake, Hurricane Lake, Karick Lake, and Coldwater. Still, there's much to explore.

The six-mile-long Wiregrass Trail sends leashed hikers through scattered pines, swampy hardwoods, and a bog with carnivorous pitcher plants. The trail begins at the west end of Hurricane Lake and intersects with a former major commerce route for Native Americans. *Backpacker Magazine* calls the 21.5-mile-long Jackson Red Ground Trail, as it's known, one of the best places to experience the South's fast-disappearing virgin pine forests.

Elsewhere, the 3.8-mile-long Karick Lake trail winds between thin pines. And the four-mile Bear Lake trail circles a lake. Notice its flooded logs, but don't let your pal jump into the lake. For dogs, this entire forest holds a special, uh, significance. Pooches would dutifully accompany their masters on hunting trips, and durned if many a hound didn't disappear. Outraged owners suspected a thief. Years later, the culprit emerged: a granddaddy alligator. When the gator was killed in 1995, seven dog collars were found in his belly, including the one with the electronic tracking device—worn by a prized hunting dog named Flojo—that led to the gator's capture.

The forest's headquarters is in Munson, on State Road 191, just south of Highway 4. You may encounter hunters from November to March, so inquire about hunting dates. 850/957-6140 or 850/265-3676.

Cantonment

PARKS, BEACHES, AND RECREATION AREAS

2 Escambia River Water Management Area

🐾🐾 (See Pensacola map on page 26)

This sprawling wilderness stretches from practically the Alabama state line to Escambia Bay, some 30 miles in all. Migrating neotropical birds in springtime flit about this government-owned land, which forms a one- to two-and-a-half-mile-wide corridor flanking both sides of the winding Escambia River and features large expanses of mature bottomland hardwood forest. You're on your own—expect no restrooms, no vending machines, no running water. You will find about 14 boat launches and possibly hunters after deer, armadillos, wild turkey, wild hogs, or other critters in season (typically mid-October through July). But if your pooch itches to escape the city, this is the place to be.

These woods are accessible from various places along U.S. 29, as well as the boat landing on County Road 184 at the river's east bank. Three boat ramps dot Highway 90A, east of U.S. 29. 850/539-5999.

Milton

PARKS, BEACHES, AND RECREATION AREAS

3 Blackwater River State Park

🐾🐾🐾 🐾 (See Pensacola map on page 26)

People come here for the white-sand beaches along the Blackwater River (which is actually greenish black), but for leashed dogs the big attraction is the hiking. While some people may try to sneak in a romp with their furry friends on the beach during off-hours, park rules forbid doing so.

DIVERSIONS

Go up the creek with a paddle and pooch: Officially, it's canoeing, yet lots of dogs jump out of canoes rented from **Adventures Unlimited Outdoor Center** in Milton so they can swim, swim, swim. Rambunctious doggies can step ashore and run on white-sand beaches during stops along the way, while their partners take a break from paddling to bask in the sun or feast on a picnic.

So many good canoeing routes are found in this part of Florida that the state legislature in 1981 designated Santa Rosa County the "Canoe Capital of Florida."

Most parties spend from a few hours to a day on the most convenient route, Coldwater Creek, where the tea-colored water runs only a few feet deep over a soft, sandy bottom. Fees are $10 for dogs, $20 and up for adults, and free for kids age 12 and under who sit in the middle of an adult-manned canoe. To reach Adventures Unlimited, take Highway 87 for 12 miles north of Milton and follow the signs to the park at 8974 Tomahawk Landing Road. Reserve at 850/623-6197 or 800/239-6864; www.adventuresunlimited.com.

Dogged swimmers, er, canoeists, may pine to explore still other Panhandle waters, such as the Perdido River. You'll pass cypress and juniper trees while enjoying a leisurely 11-mile paddle along the sandy-bottomed Perdido River after renting a canoe from Adventures Unlimited Perdido River, 160 Annex Road, Cantonment. Your well-behaved buddy must stay leashed at the canoe landing, but it's fine to take him off leash and switch to voice control during the four- to six-hour canoe trip. Be sure to clean up fastidiously after your dog. Canoes rent for $34 for up to three people; dogs ride free. Reserve at 850/968-5529.

There are two hiking routes to choose from at this 590-acre park. Try the Chain of Lakes Nature Trail, a 1.5-mile walk along the river's south side. It takes you via a boardwalk and a narrow dirt trail through a swamp to the winding Blackwater River. The Juniper River Trail leads from the campground to the old river channel and provides views of an oxbow lake. Your little buddy may pick up the scent of deer, bobcats, wild turkeys, or even otters. The forests are made up of pines and some hardwoods, including southern red cedar, and are dotted with persimmon, oak, and, yes, dogwood.

Sleeping under the stars in the 30-site campground runs $12 nightly. Reservations are especially advisable during the busy summertime and can be made at ReserveAmerica.com or 800/326-3521.

Admission for day-use visitors is $3 per vehicle. The park is 15 miles northeast of Milton, off U.S. 90, at 7720 Deaton Bridge Road in the town of Holt.

From I-10 Exit 31 (Highway 87 North), turn left onto Highway 87 and travel north one-half mile. At U.S. 90 East, turn right and go seven miles to the town of Harold, where you may begin to see directional signs to the park. Turn left onto Deaton Bridge Road, then proceed three miles to the entrance. 850/983-5363.

🐾 Yellow River Water Management Area

🐾🐾 (See Pensacola map on page 26)

Not for the faint of heart, these 8,104 acres of river floodplain are truly the Great Outdoors with a capital G and O—as in "go." And go here is precisely what hunters do, starting with archers in about mid-October to mid-November, followed by gun-toters who visit throughout the winter. The last of the legal bearded-turkey hunts here is usually held in April.

That means you and your hiking dog ought to wear fluorescent-orange vests, bandannas, hats, or other bright gear so hidden hunters don't mistake your moving bodies for deer. Your dog also may be startled by the sound of gunfire, so you may wish to avoid this place altogether during hunting season. For hunting information, call 850/265-3676.

Boating anglers fish on the Yellow River, which can be reached via any of the 15 boat ramps that dot this length of the river. Primitive camping requires a Northwest Florida Water Management District Resource Area Permit obtained through county tax collector offices. Those fishing from shore also need such a permit, unless they use natural bait and no reels, live in the county, and don't sell their catch.

From I-10, take Highway 87 (Exit 10) or County Road 89 (Exit 9) and head south about two miles. 850/539-5999 or 850/265-3676.

PLACES TO STAY

Blackwater River State Park: See Blackwater River State Park under Parks, Beaches, and Recreation Areas, above, for camping information.

Comfort Inn: Continental breakfast is free, but dogs may be more interested in stretching their legs on the big grassy area next to this 66-room poolside motel off I-10 (Exit 31). Rates range $50–110. Add $10 nightly per pet. 4962 State Road 87 South, Milton; 850/623-1511; www.comfortinn.com.

Hurricane Lake Recreation Area: Rugged pooches can hike all day, then collapse for a good night's sleep at this campground within Blackwater River State Forest (see separate park listing, above). Actually, it's two campgrounds—one on the north side, the other on the south side of large Hurricane Lake. The north side offers showers and campsites with electric hookups. You'll ruff it on the south side, where campsites are primitive; amenities are limited to a few water faucets, a boat ramp, and restrooms. Reservations aren't accepted. Primitive sites cost $5 nightly. Electric sites with water cost $13. From Baker, go 10 miles west on State Road 4, turn right onto Beaver Creek

Road, travel 8.5 miles to Bullard Church Road, turn right and follow signs to the campground. 850/957-6140.

Karick Lake: General Andrew Jackson and his troops passed through here in 1818, and now you and your leashed dog can walk in his tracks at this campground within Blackwater River State Forest (see separate park listing, above). The eastern terminus of the 21-mile-long Jackson Trail reaches this campground. Campsites offer electricity and water, as well as access to a bathhouse, restrooms, a boat ramp, and fishing on the 65-acre, bass-stocked manmade lake found in the far eastern part of the state forest. All 30 sites are first-come, first-served and cost $13 nightly. From Baker, drive eight miles north on County Road 189 to the campground entrance, at right. 850/957-6140.

Red Roof Inn: Newshounds can pick up a free USA Today and continental breakfast in the lobby of this three-story, 70-unit poolside motel off I-10 (Exit 22). One pet under 80 pounds is permitted per room, so long as he is declared upon check-in and attended at all times. Rates range $43–79. 2672 Avalon Blvd., Milton; 850/995-6100; www.redroof.com.

Niceville

PARKS, BEACHES, AND RECREATION AREAS

🔟 Eglin Air Force Base

🐾🐾🐾 (See Pensacola map on page 26)

Why go to an air base? You might well wonder that, but doggies won't quibble over the fact that this isn't a park, and it's actually one of the largest strips of wilderness in northern Florida, spanning three counties. The Department of Defense manages the base, but the military has become incredibly eco-friendly in recent years, even going so far as to try to save the endangered red-cockaded woodpecker by planting trees and protecting their homes from fires.

Your pooch probably won't care about woodpeckers, but she will be itching to romp through the tree-covered hills. Clay roads that seem to never end bisect the forest. Anglers have no fewer than 20 popular fishing ponds to choose from; alas, dogs must stay on leash and out of the swimming areas. There is much to do here, but you need to get a permit to go on base for absolutely any reason—to picnic, hunt, fish, hike, swim, bicycle, collect firewood, and even just to drive through.

To get a permit for a day visit or camping, write to the Eglin AFB Natural Resources Office at 107 Highway 85 North, Niceville, FL 32578, or drop by in person. The office is closed on Sunday, and shuts its doors at 12:30 P.M. on Saturday and 4:30 P.M. on most weekdays. You'll have to provide proof of identification for everyone in your party, and your pooch will need to wear tags showing your name, address, and phone number, as well as a current rabies inoculation tag. Best bet: Present a veterinarian certificate to prove your dog's

FETCHING NECESSITIES

Cut down your own Christmas tree with Snoopy: Your well-behaved pooch can really be a part of the family—and a family tradition—when she goes with you to cut down a sand pine tree on the dry, sandy ridges of **Eglin Air Force Base.** Indigenous to northwest Florida, these somewhat gangly trees have sparse, dark green needles that are two to three inches long. But it's your heirloom decorations and twinkling lights that really make a holiday tree (remember Charlie Brown?), and the bargain price can't be beat: $1.

After you obtain a Christmas tree permit at the base, you'll go to a designated area and cut your tree low to the ground, leaving a stump no taller than four inches. There's a limit of one tree per family. Just show up with your leashed dog on or after December 1. Eglin Air Force Base is in Niceville at 107 Highway 85 North. Call 850/882-4164.

shots are up-to-date. Recreation permits cost $7 by mail or $5 in person and entitle your party to visit the base for such fun as hiking, picnicking, bicycling, running, or taking a pleasure drive. 850/882-4164.

⬛ Fred Gannon Rocky Bayou State Park

🐾🐾🐾 (See Pensacola map on page 26)

In these quiet, out-of-the-way woods, a leashed pooch has his choice of three nature trails to explore. Should your canine companion get all tuckered out, you can just rest on one of the benches on the east side of Puddin Head Lake. (Watch your pooch carefully; there are alligators in the lake, along with wood ducks and beavers.)

The Rocky Bayou Trail is a 20-minute walk that leads under the beautifully twisted arms of young oaks and past the bayou in this 357-acre recreation area. Maggie was intrigued by the abundant birds and frogs. Bald eagles occasionally are seen, and alert dogs may notice otters or dolphins. If you'd like to picnic first, take the shorter Red Cedar Trail, located on the west side of the park in a forest of sand pine, oak, red cedar, and magnolia. It leads to some barbecue grills and stone picnic tables shaded by magnolia and live oak trees. There are also a slide and swings. The Sand Pine Trail follows the eastern shore of 7.5-acre Puddin Head Lake, home to aquatic plants such as carnivorous pitcher plants.

Some campsites overlook Rocky Bayou, and your dog can join you at any of the 42 shady sites, each equipped with water, electricity, a picnic table, and a fire ring. Sites go for $12.72 nightly. Register or call in by the 4 P.M. daily deadline, lest you be locked out. Reserve at ReserveAmerica.com or 800/326-3521.

Admission for daytime visitors is $3 per car. From Niceville, drive five miles east on State Road 20 to the park entrance at 4281 State Road 20 East. 850/833-9144.

🖤 Picnic Area/Boat Launch

🖤 (See Pensacola map on page 26)

Local dogs sometimes frolic leash-free on the red clay at this little roadside park on Choctawhatchee Bay. There are five concrete picnic tables, two of them shaded. The park is next to a busy highway, so only the best-behaved dogs should go unleashed.

The boat launch is three miles west of Villa Tasso on Highway 20.

PLACES TO STAY

Eglin Air Force Base Campground: You can camp with your pooch at a price that just can't be beat: A five-day permit for up to 10 people costs $5. What's more, the names of the 15 camping areas conjure up romantic Southern images: Buck Pond, Hickory Trees, Hammock Point, Gin Hole Landing, Rocky Creek, and so on. Your neighbors in these rustic digs are likely to be hunters, though, and these accommodations are mostly intended for folks with hunting dogs, so there is a downside: Your furry friend can't sleep with you in the tent or at the campsite, and he must be restrained at least 50 yards from your site. If you're game, get a camping permit from the Eglin AFB Natural Resources Office, 107 Highway 85 North, Niceville; 850/882-4164.

Fred Gannon Rocky Bayou State Park: See Parks, Beaches, and Recreation Areas, above.

Pensacola

PARKS, BEACHES, AND RECREATION AREAS

🖤 Baars Park

🖤🖤 (See Pensacola map on page 26)

Your leashed doggy can pad around on a carpet of leaves and pine needles in this shady, wooded area right off the Texar Bayou. The trees in this park, set amid a suburban neighborhood, are not negligible—you wouldn't want to play Frisbee here, for instance. Though we strongly suspect that the trees are teeming with squirrels, Maggie couldn't track down any when we visited. When you visit, you're likely to be the only one here.

The 13.3-acre park is at the dead end of Pintado Drive, near the intersection of 12th Avenue and Dunwoody Drive. 850/436-5670.

DOG-EAR YOUR CALENDAR

The Sunshine State's version of the famed New Orleans street party **Mardi Gras** brings record crowds to Pensacola streets every pre-Easter season to watch not just one parade, but a slew of Krewes. Tie a bandanna or slip a string of beads around the neck of your well-behaved leashed buddy, then stake a spot on a sidewalk along the parade routes to get ready for music, masks, and Mardi Gras with your mutt. For upcoming dates (usually in February, but sometimes in March), call Pensacola's visitors bureau at 850/434-1234 or 800/874-1234, or reach Pensacola Mardi Gras at 850/436-7638; www.pensacolamardigras.com.

9 Bay Bluffs Park

🐾🐾🐾 (See Pensacola map on page 26)

Follow a boardwalk down the steep bluffs to Escambia Bay—a pretty site surrounded by North Florida's signature oaks and pines and small, violet-colored flowers. Some people splish-splash through the waters of the bay and along the narrow, little-used beaches at the foot of the bluffs. The beach stretches for a mile or so.

You'll have to walk down several steps to reach the bay, so if your canine companion is little, you may want to carry her. Near the bottom you'll cross the tracks of the Louisiana & Nashville Railroad. Take care that neither you nor your leashed pooch gets sliced up on the bottles broken on the granite chunks laid for the railroad bed.

The 42-acre park is in the Mallory Heights area, on Scenic Highway at the eastern end of Summit Boulevard. 850/436-5670.

10 Baycliffs Estates

🐾 (See Pensacola map on page 26)

This neighborhood park is found within a tangle of curving streets lined with fine homes. The small grassy field is so close to niftier Bay Bluffs Park that you may wish to head to these 4.7 acres only if your pooch prefers a more suburban experience, or if your kids are dying to burn up some energy on a slide, swings, or jungle gym.

From Scenic Highway, take Wimbledon Drive West, then turn right onto Monteigne Drive. Baycliffs is about seven blocks ahead on the right. 850/436-5670.

11 Bayview Park Dog Park

🐾🐾🐾🐾🐾 🐕 (See Pensacola map on page 26)

Leash, be gone! Dogs chase balls and run with abandon at their very own one-acre fenced park, one of two leash-free areas in the city. This place remains unique for its extra perk: Furry swimmers may dog-paddle in the bay for four hours a week—10 A.M.–noon Saturdays and Sundays.

The rest of the dog park is open daily, as evidenced by devotees who flock here. Separate water fountains quench the thirsts of pets and people. As pups play, humans rest at benches or picnic tables and watch canine antics. Little Murdock likes to sit and watch, too, except for when he chases big dogs. "He's a Lhasa apso, but he thinks he's a rottweiler," jokes owner Kim Knox.

The dog park is set within a 28-acre park that also is worth sniffing (on leash). Maggie loved to race along its gently sloping, red-clay bluffs and chase squirrels up oaks, pines, and magnolias, as the human on the other end of her leash scrambled helplessly. At this favored local haunt, anglers try their luck at a pier and fitness fans can walk heel-to-toe on the wooden balance beam of an exercise course while their dogs trot alongside. Throw a steak onto a big barbecue grill at the picnic pavilions on the park's northeast end while the rest of your party enjoys the park's other offerings: tennis courts, a senior citizens center, a bocce court, and a playground. Avoid the broad expanse during special events; dogs are prohibited at festivals.

Bayview Park is at the west side of Texar Bayou at 20th Avenue and Blount Street. From Cervantes Street, head north on 19th Avenue, turn right on Blount, and continue to the park. 850/436-5670.

12 Corrine Jones Park

🐾 (See Pensacola map on page 26)

Quite big for a neighborhood park, this grassy field near downtown offers hope for those who want to have a private weekday-morning jog session with their pooch. There are basketball courts and a playground, but don't expect beauty; it's in an older neighborhood near an industrial area and railroad tracks.

The four-acre park is located two blocks north of Main Street, just off Clubbs Street. 850/436-5670.

13 Exercise Trail

🐾 (See Pensacola map on page 26)

A heart-smart exercise course is the main attraction at this small, grassy field, where leashes are the rule. Find the park on Summit Boulevard, just south of the Pensacola Regional Airport. 850/436-5670.

Lee Square

 (See Pensacola map on page 26)

Dogs may develop an irrepressible urge to sniff a 50-foot Confederate memorial at this historic square, where Union troops erected and quickly abandoned an earthen fort called Fort McClellan in 1863. The square pays tribute to Confederate soldiers. Well-traveled doggies may recognize the sculpture as a replica of one found in Alexandria, Virginia, a bronze figure looking south from Appomattox. Lucky pooches might persuade their best friends to walk south two blocks to the corner of Palafox and LaRua streets, where Fort George, built by the British in 1778, once stood. Buildings now cover much of the site, but an undeveloped parcel has been preserved. This entire neighborhood, the North Hill Preservation District, is on the National Register of Historic Places. Dogs must be leashed.

Lee Square is bordered by Palafox, Gadsden, and Cervantes streets. 850/436-5670.

 Andalusia Square

(See Pensacola map on page 26)

Maggie asked us to spread the word that this 2.5-acre passive park has squirrels there for the chasing and, with relatively few trees to provide a quick escape route, it's enough to give a dog false hopes of finally catching a furry pipe dream. Kids will enjoy the swings.

The grassy spot is known as Andalusia Square by the city government, but there's no posted sign, nor any facility other than the playground. It's just north of downtown between 15th and 16th avenues, one block north of Cervantes Street. 850/436-5670.

Granada Square

(See Pensacola map on page 26)

Leashed dogs can stretch their legs just north of downtown in this square block of open land with a few trees. The 2.5-acre passive park is called Granada Square within the city's Parks Department, though there's no posted sign, nor any amenity other than a playground for the kiddies. Find it at DeSoto Street, between 10th and 11th avenues. 850/436-5670.

 East Pensacola Heights Lions Club Park

(See Pensacola map on page 26)

You and your leashed pal will practically have this nearly treeless expanse to yourselves during weekday work hours. Basketball courts, a playground, and a fenced-in grassy field round out the amenities.

The two-acre park is at Perry Avenue and East Gonzalez Street. 850/436-5670.

18 Pensacola Naval Air Station

🐾◀● (See Pensacola map on page 26)

Forrest Sherman Field—home to those famed aerobatic pilots the Blue Angels—is located on this pleasantly landscaped base, where civilian tourists can visit a museum and an 1825 lighthouse. Alas, dogs can't join their people inside buildings. Pets, thus, are discouraged from visiting the base, lest they languish in a hot car.

Still, pets are unlikely to be outright turned away at the entrance gate if you find yourself in this area and you're itching to see the first lighthouse built on the Florida coast by the U.S. government. On a cool day (use your judgment), a dog may safely wait a short while in a vehicle with partially opened windows. Afterward, your pal might make a pit stop at the oaks near the lighthouse parking lot.

If your dog hangs her head out the window as you drive, she'll get a good view of some retired planes sprinkled like statues around the grounds. An old hospital compound on Radford Road, across from the officers' club, is an eerie reminder of the days before mosquito control: In the 1800s, victims of Florida's recurring yellow fever epidemics were treated at this naval hospital. Obey the posted 45 mph speed limit as you tool about the base; we've seen police stop speeders.

That's about all there is for dogs to do here. While a running trail leads through woods along Taylor Road and passes the military's Oak Grove Campground, it appears meant for use by campground guests. It's best to ask permission before exploring it during these heightened security times.

From Main Street in Pensacola, go west on Barrancas Avenue, turn left on Navy Road, and follow it south. At the entrance gate, you'll be handed a pass that states the areas you're permitted to visit. 850/452-0111.

19 Plaza Ferdinand VII

🐾 (See Pensacola map on page 26)

When the strange land of Florida joined the United States in 1821, General Andrew Jackson held the official ceremony right here at this Palafox Historic District park, now shaded by large oaks and magnolia trees. Inquiring leashed dogs have much to sniff here: a bust of Jackson, a fountain, a monument honoring Confederate soldier William Dudley Chipley, and magnolias that may be in bloom if you visit during spring or summer. Locals read books or munch their lunch on the park benches, but history buffs know that this spot was used by the British for drilling Native American and black troops in 1813. A succession of Spanish and British forts were built here between 1754 and 1821, and to the east you can see the foundation of one of those forts.

The 1.6-acre historic site is at the southeast corner of Government and Palafox streets. 850/436-5670.

20 Sanders Beach Community Center

🐾🐾 (See Pensacola map on page 26)

Here's your chance to wade with your leashed dog along a small, breezy beach before breaking into your picnic basket at one of four sheltered tables or on a blanket spread beneath a big oak tree. It's not picture-postcard perfect, but your dog sure won't mind admiring the local ducks or running alongside you on a large treeless field.

The 3.5-acre park is near the railroad tracks in an industrial section of town at the corner of J and Sonia streets, near the Pensacola Yacht Club. Take Main Street west, turn left on L Street, left on Cypress Street, and right on J Street. 850/436-5670.

21 Scott Complex Dog Park

🐾🐾🐾🐾🐾🐕 (See Pensacola map on page 26)

Run like the wind! Dixie the golden retriever loves to chase tennis balls and sniff other leashless dogs at the one-acre fenced area designated just for bounding pets. Some day, dogs like her may also scramble up a ramp and use other agility equipment, if the funds to buy them come through, says Jody Skelton, Dixie's owner and city parks director.

Dogs daily make good use of the little park, whose amenities match those of Bayview, Pensacola's other leash-free park. Picnic tables and benches allow owners to relax. Separate water fountains serve thirsty pooches and people. Bags are provided at the pooper-scooper station.

The dog park is located within the 52-acre Scott Athletic Complex on Summit Boulevard, just east of 12th Avenue. Find the dog park between the pool and the Roger Scott Tennis Center. 850/436-5670.

22 Seville Square

🐾🐾👣 (See Pensacola map on page 26)

No amount of sniffing will inform your leashed pooch that this well-tended land and popular setting for weddings once supported a settlement of refugees from nearby Santa Rosa Island after a hurricane flattened their homes in 1752. Not long after, the British, fresh from the French and Indian Wars, occupied a crude stockade in the area and mapped out the same streets that leashed dogs and their companions can stroll today.

With so much history, this patch of land has become part of the Seville Historic District, which is on the National Register of Historic Places. Dogs can take a walk back in time by leaving the 1.7-acre park and padding down streets named by the Spaniards who captured Pensacola in 1781.

Across the street from the park's northwest corner, notice the steamboat-shaped facade of the circa-1883 Steamboat House at 308 East Government Street. Directly west of the park, note the circa-1832 Pensacola Historical

Museum at 405 South Adams St.; this building used to be Old Christ Church, one of Florida's oldest churches.

At the southwest corner of Seville Square, walk west on Zarragossa Street to spot the Mary Perry House, with its floor-length windows, at 434 East Zarragossa Street. At 210 East Zarragossa St., you'll find the Julee Cottage; in 1805 Julee Panton became the first of several free black women to own this home. Florida has many historic districts, but the simple buildings preserved in this neighborhood have been called the most accurate representatives of the state's early days. For a walking-tour pamphlet and map, contact the visitors center at 1401 East Gregory St.; 850/434-1234 or 800/874-1234.

Seville Square is at Adams and Alcaniz streets, between Zarragossa and Government streets. Avoid the park during special events; dogs are prohibited at festivals. 850/436-5670.

23 University of West Florida

🐾🐾🐾 ◄● (See Pensacola map on page 26)

This sprawling, wooded campus offers plenty of places for your furry friend to romp, but the biggest attraction is the mile-long, wheelchair-accessible Edward Ball Nature Trail, which starts behind the romantically named Building 13, near Parking Lot 20.

Under the shade of gum, pine, and magnolia trees, your canine companion will find some 44 species of plants to sniff, as well as enough fish, salamanders, frogs, toads, alligators, birds, snakes, and mammals to keep him fascinated. Be mindful of the snakes and alligators, though they're rarely a problem. The trail quickly leads to a boardwalk that winds through a swamp. Along the way, there are benches where tired pooches can stop and rest.

Another trail leads through a less-enthralling nature preserve next to the campus entrance off North Davis Highway. Look for a parking spot on the right side as you enter. The trail passes through pine and oak woods and skirts the foundation of an old house.

The UWF campus is huge, and even if your dog doesn't favor nature trails (though we can't imagine a dog who doesn't), there are other places to have fun. You can just sit on a hill and enjoy a picnic (cheese and dog biscuits?) as you gaze down on Escambia Bay, for instance. When you arrive on campus, stop by the information booth to pick up a map and a temporary parking permit, then poke around to find a shady parking spot. Guidebooks are sold in the campus bookstore. If you come near dusk or dawn in the warmer months, be sure to bring mosquito repellent.

Take North Davis Highway/U.S. 90A north from I-10, then bear left onto University Parkway about one-half mile north of the interstate. 850/474-2000.

🐾 Veterans Memorial Park

🐾🐾 (See Pensacola map on page 26)

A magnificent bay breeze greets patriotic pooches who stop to honor (that means refraining from doing leg lifts on) the statues memorializing the country's war dead. Maggie enjoyed romping through a huge grassy area and ambling along the sizable perimeter sidewalk. A highlight for human visitors is The Wall South—a 256-foot-long replica of the Vietnam Memorial that stands in Washington, D.C., consisting of 64 blackish-gray granite panels inscribed with the names of 58,204 people from throughout the United States who died in Vietnam.

Cross the street for yet another walk that your dog should enjoy. As you stroll along the sidewalk, you'll get a better view of the bay, which is on the other side of a saltwater marsh. Your dog won't mind that the park is near some boarded-up brick apartment buildings.

The park is at 10th Avenue and Bayfront Parkway by the waterfront. 850/435-1700.

🐾 Wayside Park

🐾🐾 (See Pensacola map on page 26)

Doggies daydream about parks like this, where they can chase the many seagulls and pigeons found sitting on fences along a long, narrow strip of sun-washed, grassy land. But the big attraction for humans is Escambia Bay, with its beautiful view and merciful breezes. Leashed Maggie stopped during her stroll along the bayside sidewalk to poke her head between the fence rails for a better look at the water, temporarily oblivious to the nearby Pekingese enjoying a picnic lunch at one of the three tin-roofed pavilions with barbecue grills.

Wayside Park sits at the foot of the Three-Mile Bridge across Pensacola Bay, which leads to the town of Gulf Breeze. Take Gregory Street or Main Street east. 850/435-1770.

PLACES TO EAT

Checkers: Trot up to the window to order 99-cent Checker burgers or double-decker hamburgers to eat with your dog at a patio table shaded by a bright red umbrella. 3200 N. Pace Blvd.; 850/434-2697. Also, 5300 N. Davis Highway; 850/474-6528.

The Deli Case: A lollipop comes with your meal at this tasteful, tucked-away spot where the well-dressed crowd goes for lunch. You can tether your dog outside to an umbrella-covered table, then walk inside to order whisker-licking-good roast beef (or other) sandwiches, lasagna, quiches, salads, desserts, and soups. For your pooch, there's some refreshing water, and you can sip wine, imported beer, or excellent homemade lemonade. Far from the noisy thoroughfares, it's the perfect place for a leisurely lunch. In Cordova Square Shopping Center, 4400 Bayou Blvd., near 12th Avenue; 850/477-3354.

Dog House Deli: The motto of this weekday lunch spot and Pensacola fixture is "Over 400 ways to fix your dog." While getting fixed isn't most dogs' idea of a rousing noontime activity, you'll both probably agree that the frankfurters here are quite good. Owner Jimmy Holler once said on the local TV news that he sells 60,000 feet of wieners a year—enough, after 25 years in business, to stretch for 285 miles. Some patrons order plain dogs for their pet dogs then take a seat at one of two tables out front. The wide-ranging menu includes polish kielbasa, chicken salad, nachos, and Cajun red beans and rice. Maggie recommends the dogs. 30 Palafox St.; 850/432-3104.

Edi's Tea House: Hats, elegant gloves, and other dress-up accessories hang on the wall for human customers to slip on, if desired, to enhance the tea-luncheon experience at this historic-district bungalow. Sup soups, salads, tea sandwiches, scones, and loose-leaf teas prepared in teapots until mid-afternoon. Dinner is served on Friday and Saturday. Your dog may join you at a table on the porch. 424 E. Government St.; 850/470-0307.

Four Seasons Market & Eatery: This downtown breakfast/lunch spot serves up a daily changing menu of home-style meals, such as chicken and dumplings or beef tips over rice. Sample them with your dog at the four tables out front before the 4 P.M. closing time. 212 S. Palafox St.; 850/434-6771.

O'Brien's Bistro: Call ahead to see whether outdoor tables are available before taking your lucky dog to chef James O'Brien's continental lunch and dinner spot. French dip sandwiches and Caesar salads are among the lunch fare. Reservations are suggested for dinner, when entrées include seafood, chicken, steak dishes, and favorites like lobster-stuffed shrimp. In Cordova Square Shopping Center, 4350 Bayou Blvd., just north of 12th Avenue; 850/477-9120.

Sonic Drive-In: A carhop delivers a tray of burgers and other fast-food fare right to you and your pooch for your auto-dining pleasure at this blast-from-the-past spot north of the Pensacola Naval Air Station. If your pal wants to stretch his legs, take a far-corner table at the covered patio instead. 115 Navy Blvd./U.S. 98; 850/453-3911.

PLACES TO STAY

Ashton Inn & Suites: Every dog sleeps in a suite at this pleasant all-suite, 71-unit lodging, where the pet fee depends on the pet's size—$25 per stay for animals under 25 pounds, $50 for big'uns. A basketball court, an indoor pool, a fitness center, and free grab-and-go breakfasts number among the perks. Rates range $70–199. 4 New Warrington Road, Pensacola; 850/454-0280 or 866/ASH-TON8; www.ashtoninnsuites.com.

Comfort Inn Naval Air Station—Corry: Close to some fun dog spots such as Gulf Islands National Seashore and the Pensacola Naval Air Station, this 102-room poolside motel offers refrigerators (and microwaves) in each room, in case your pal doesn't want to devour the contents of doggy bags right away. There are limited grassy areas for dog walks. Rates range $58–100. Pet fee is $25 per stay. 3 New Warrington Road, Pensacola; 850/455-3233; www. comfortinn.com.

Comfort Inn—Davis: Designated pet rooms are set aside for furry guests under 20 pounds. Rates run $59–105, plus $20 daily pet fee, at this 115-room poolside motel located behind Shoney's Restaurant off I-10 (Exit 13). 8080 N. Davis Highway, Pensacola; 850/484-8070; www.comfortinn.com.

Crowne Plaza-Pensacola Grand Hotel: Step into a restored 1912 train station that serves as the hotel lobby to register for a room in the more modern high-rise, connected to the lobby by a glass solarium. After you've unpacked, you and your dog can take a walk around the Seville Historic District or the Palafox Historic District. The hotel is at the intersection of the two districts, but you should expect a long walk to get to the most notable buildings. Hotel perks include a gym, seasonal pool, lobby bar, restaurant, first-floor hotel library, and room service—good news for hungry four-legged travelers. Rates run $135–275. The nonrefundable pet fee is $50 per stay. 200 E. Gregory St., Pensacola; 850/433-3336 or 800/348-3336; www.pensacolagrandhotel.com.

Days Inn North: After snacking from the doggy bag you brought back from the on-site Denny's, your pooch may want to walk off the calories in back of this 80-room poolside motel off I-10 (Exit 10A). Rates are $45–90. Add $10 daily pet fee. 7051 Pensacola Blvd., Pensacola; 850/476-9090; www. daysinn.com.

Extended StayAmerica Pensacola—University Mall: Rest in a recliner after preparing dinner in your own kitchen in this all-studios lodging, which is designed for longer stays and for business travelers, though vacationers also may check in for as little as one night. While the chain's policy allows one pet per guest room, the general manager has the authority to permit additional pets, based on his or her own discretion. Studios are about $58–70; discounted weekly rates are available. Pet fee is $25 per day, up to a maximum of $75. 809 Bloodworth Lane, Pensacola; 850/473-9323; www. extendedstayamerica.com.

Holiday Inn University Mall: Cats are forbidden here, but canines may hope for an order of bacon from room service at this 152-unit hotel located next to University Mall and off I-10 (Exit 13). Every room has an ironing board, iron, and hair dryer—perfect for the pooch who wants to look her best. Dogs under 40 pounds are permitted for $25 per stay. Rates are $60–90. 7200 Plantation Road, Pensacola; 850/474-0100; www.holidayinns.com.

Hospitality Inn: Two-legged guests appreciate the exercise room and pool, but your furry pal may be more interested in crumbs from your continental breakfast. Dogs and their people sleep in designated pet rooms and take dog walks in the parking lot or green strips between the five buildings of the 124-unit lodging off I-10 (Exit 10). Rates range $55–90. Add a $25 pet fee per stay. 6900 Pensacola Blvd., Pensacola; 850/477-2333.

Howard Johnson: Dirty doggy bandannas can be washed in the coin-operated laundry of this 120-room, two-story poolside motel off I-10 (Exit 10A). Rates range $46–99. 6919 Pensacola Blvd., Pensacola; 850/478-4499; www.hojo.com.

La Quinta: Noon is checkout time and not one, but two, 24-hour restaurants neighbor this pleasant poolside motel—good news for late-sleeping canines. Well-mannered large dogs have been accepted, although officially rules call for pets under 25 pounds at this business-oriented 130-unit lodging off I-10 (Exit 13). Rates range $59–85. 7750 N. Davis Highway, Pensacola; 850/474-0411; www.lq.com.

Motel 6 East: Large grassy areas are great for letting your dog stretch her legs before you retire for the night at this 80-unit poolside motel located in the University Mall complex off I-10 (Exit 13). A spacious parcel out back is separated from the highway by woods and an entrance ramp. One pet is permitted per room. Rates are $40–55. 7226 Plantation Road, Pensacola; 850/474-1060; www.motel6.com.

Motel 6 North: The area's best Motel 6 offers 108 rooms with combination shower/bathtub and an elevator helpful for delivering pooped pooches to their rooms. Expect minimal dog-walking areas at this poolside motel off I-10 (Exit 13). One pet is permitted per room. Rates range $36–49. 7827 N. Davis Highway, Pensacola; 850/476-5386; www.motel6.com.

Pensacola Naval Air Station, Oak Grove Park Campground: Only military folk, retired military families, and their sponsored guests (and quiet pooches) may sleep here under the many shady oaks. While you won't have a water view, the beaches of Pensacola Bay are within walking distance, as is the National Museum of Naval Aviation. Creature comforts include a bathhouse, horseshoes, darts, and a gazebo with television. The 51 RV sites range $17–23. The six tent sites range $6–7 nightly. The campground is off Radford Boulevard, within the Pensacola Naval Air Station. Directions: From Main Street in Pensacola, go west on Barrancas Avenue, then turn left on Navy Road and follow it south to the Naval Air Station entrance gate, where you'll be directed to the campground. 850/452-2535.

Quality Inn: Your dog can hope for scraps from your free deluxe continental breakfast or the in-room fridge. Located off I-10 (Exit 10A), these 106 rooms range $70–75, plus $25 pet fee. 6550 N. Pensacola Blvd., Pensacola; 850/477-0711; www.qualityinn.com.

Ramada Inn Bayview: This 150-room motor inn is set on a bluff over Escambia Bay, though apparently the good bay views are reserved for the lobby. All rooms have a balcony or patio overlooking the pool and courtyard gazebo. Dogs probably are more concerned about finagling a walk along the level strip of greenery next to the woods on the hotel's south side. Only pets under 25 pounds are permitted in designated pet rooms. Rates range $65–120. Add a $25 pet fee, which covers up to seven days. 7601 Scenic Highway, Pensacola; 850/477-7155 or 800/282-1212; www.ramada.com.

Ramada Limited: Some rooms offer a microwave and fridge—all the better to handle the contents of doggy bags from the nearby Cracker Barrel. Small pets, please. You'll sleep in one of the designated pet rooms at this 92-room lodging off I-10 (Exit 7). Rates range $55–100. Add a $25 pet fee per stay. 8060 Lavelle Way, Pensacola; 850/944-0333; www.ramada.com.

Red Roof Inn University Mall: Newshounds can keep up on current events at this 108-unit poolside motel, thanks to the free weekday USA Today and in-room dataports. Located off I-10 (Exit 13), these room range $43–65. 7340 Plantation Road, Pensacola; 850/476-7960; www.redroof.com.

Residence Inn Downtown Pensacola: Room service comes from Outback Steakhouse, and all 78 pleasant apartment-style suites come with kitchens, ensuring that hungry dogs have easy access to food at Pensacola's sole pet-permissible Residence Inn. Some rooms have fireplaces. Other amenities include an exercise room, pool, whirlpool, and tennis courts. Rates range $105–159, plus a $75 nonrefundable pet fee. 601 E. Chase St., Pensacola; 850/432-0202; www.marriott.com.

Super 8: Coffee and local calls are free at this 59-room poolside budget motel near University Mall and off I-10 (Exit 13). Rates run $40–50, plus $5 daily pet fee. 7220 Plantation Drive, Pensacola; 850/476-8038; www.super8.com.

Travelodge Inn & Suites: You'll walk through an interior corridor to get to your room at this 60-unit lodging, where continental breakfast is free and dirty doggy bandannas can be washed at coin-operated washers. Located off I-10 (Exit 10A), these rooms range $45–80, plus $10 daily for the pet. 6950 Pensacola Blvd., Pensacola; 850/473-0222; www.travelodge.com.

Perdido Key

PARKS, BEACHES, AND RECREATION AREAS

26 Big Lagoon State Park

🐾🐾🐾 (See Pensacola map on page 26)

Maggie's black nose twitched as she inhaled deep breaths of air, as if she were trying to comprehend all the wondrous hidden wild animals there were to behold at this 712-acre park lined with intriguing nature trails. Leashed dogs can take a leisurely 30-minute walk along the sunny Yaupon Trail, where we picked a few boysenberries in the spring and Maggie's paws became caked with mud—a by-product of the state's frequent rains. One resident animal species is the lizard-like sand skink, whose transparent lower eyelids act like goggles as it "swims" through the sand to find food.

The observation tower at East Beach, at the eastern end of the 712-acre park, provides a spectacular view of Big Lagoon and the salt marsh meeting the beach. Maggie climbed the tower stairs but was tuckered out by the third landing, so you may want to carry your pooch, especially if he is small. Arrive early, and you might be able to snag a nearby waterfront picnic site. (Dogs must stay at picnic tables and not stray onto the beach or into picnic shelters.) Arrive late, and your reward for climbing the observation tower may be watching a great blue heron fish for dinner while the sun sets behind you.

Campsites are set amid pines on a ridge at the park's center. All 75 sites offer electricity and water. Fee is $16 nightly. Reserve at ReserveAmerica.com or 800/326-3561.

Admission for day-use visitors is $4 per vehicle. The park is about 10 miles southwest of Pensacola on County Road 292A. From Main Street in Pensacola, go west on Barrancas Avenue. Veer left and continue until the road merges into Gulf Beach Highway. Pass the Pensacola Naval Air Station, turn left on Bauer Road, and continue to 12301 Gulf Beach Highway. 850/492-1595.

27 Perdido Key State Park

🐾 (See Pensacola map on page 26)

Sup on picnic fare with your leashed pooch in this pretty spot—a picnic area with a view of the Gulf of Mexico on one side and the Old River on the other. Alas, dogs aren't allowed on the beach, and this park basically is one big beach. However, it is okay for your pup to hang out (always leashed) at the picnic area, parking lots, boat launch, and the boardwalk. After 2004's devastating Hurricane Ivan, only the boat launch remained opened for months afterward, so amenities still may be sparse.

Entrance costs $2 per vehicle. The park is 15 miles southwest of Pensacola, off State Road 292, at 15301 Perdido Key Drive. From the Florida mainland, take the Gulf Beach Highway southwest (it turns into Highway 292), cross the bridge onto Perdido Key, curve right (you'll be on Perdido Key Drive), and look for the park entrance after two to three miles. 850/492-1595.

28 Gulf Islands National Seashore, Perdido Key Area

🐾🐾 (See Pensacola map on page 26)

This sprawling haven stretches along barrier islands from Florida to Mississippi, but your leashed dog's mission here at the Perdido Key portion is to explore the woodsy nature trail by Johnson Beach. As the sun set on the spring day when we visited, the sounds of lapping waves and chirping birds accompanied Maggie as she happily followed a three-foot-wide boardwalk through pine trees and fan-shaped palmetto bushes. The trail leads to a marshy area, then turns into a dirt path covered with pine needles.

Notice the size of the trees as you walk toward the south end of the island: The wind-struck pines and oaks are smaller nearer the water than those farther away from the salty gulf breezes. Maggie wasn't that interested in the trees and preferred instead to sniff out evidence of critters in a thicket of yaupon holly. Curiously, Native Americans used to brew a strong drink from holly leaves like the ones Maggie examined so intently. Legend has it that any man who stomached large amounts of the vomit-inducing drink was held in high esteem. Use mosquito repellent at dusk or dawn. Dogs aren't allowed on the beach, but they may explore the nature trails.

An $8 entrance fee per vehicle is collected and is good for seven days. From Pensacola, take Highway 292 southwest to Perdido Key. Once on the island, turn left at Johnson Beach Road and continue to the park. 850/934-2600.

PLACES TO EAT

Flora-Bama: "The best shrimp on the Gulf" is the modest claim of staffers at this inexpensive seafood joint/lounge located right at the Alabama state line. But pizza and hot dogs also can be ordered by landlubber Lassies at an outdoor table. 17401 Perdido Key Drive; 850/492-3048.

PLACES TO STAY

Vacation rentals: Pet-permissible vacation homes seem as scarce at three-legged squirrels in these parts. Some property owners make their homes available through websites such as Vacationrentals.com and A1Vacations. com. A local company, Key Concepts Realty, has a history of representing some pet-friendly vacation rentals; while 2004's Hurricane Ivan destroyed those particular homes and caused billions of dollars in damage to others, it's possible that new pet-friendly digs since have been added to the lineup. Contact a Key Concepts agent at 13880 Perdido Key Drive, Perdido Key; 850/492-5462 or 800/955-5462; www.gulfcoastarea.com.

Big Lagoon State Park: See Big Lagoon State Park under Parks, Beaches, and Recreation Areas for camping information.

Pensacola Perdido Bay KOA Kampground: This KOA is actually just across the state line in Alabama, but your water dog will thank you for coming here, since dogs aren't allowed on the beach in Perdido Key, Florida. Voice-obedient dogs can swim in Perdido Bay, then take the short walk back to a KOA campsite to sleep contentedly in your RV or tent (not in the Kamping Kabins). The campground is set on a bluff within a grove of 200-year-old oak trees. Humans will enjoy the pool and Jacuzzi. Reservations are accepted. For two people, the fee is $25 for an RV site, $20 for a tent site. 33951 Spinnaker Drive, Lillian; 334/961-1717 or 800/562-3471; www.koakampgrounds.com.

Pensacola Beach

PARKS, BEACHES, AND RECREATION AREAS

🐾🐾🐾◆ Gulf Islands National Seashore, Fort Pickens Area

🐾🐾🐾◆ (See Pensacola map on page 26)

Maggie happily chased a squirrel up a tree and checked out the frogs along the Blackbird Marsh Nature Trail, our favorite trail in one of the nation's top 10 most-visited National Park units. This trail turns from dirt to white sand and is surrounded in places by oak-dominated sand dunes, as well as some salt marsh. Chirping birds and the sound of waves crashing on the beach erase any thoughts of civilization. The saw grass and other marsh plants often have their roots in water, so if you and your leashed friend want to keep your paws dry, stick to the dry trail. The trail also passes near the isolated beaches on the inland-facing side of this barrier island, where dogs are forbidden, as they are at the ruins of redbrick Fort Pickens, where Geronimo was held in the 1880s.

Leashed dogs are welcome in the picnic area and the 200-site campground, so long as they stay away from the water. Mostly RVs and campers are seen here, but that doesn't mean rugged tent camping is taboo. Campsites have asphalt pull-ins, running water, grills, and, due to 2004's Hurricane Ivan, fewer shade trees than previously enjoyed. Some sites have electrical hook-ups. Sites are $20 nightly. Reserve at Reservations.nps.gov or 800/365-2267.

An $8 entrance fee per vehicle is collected and is good for seven days. To reach Fort Pickens from Pensacola, follow U.S. 98 east across the Pensacola Bay Bridge to Gulf Breeze, then take Highway 399 (a toll road) to Pensacola Beach. From there, Fort Pickens is nine miles west. 850/934-2600.

PLACES TO EAT

Banana Bob's: This eatery claims to make the best pizzas on the beach. Order food to go, then grab a seat on the lower outdoor deck of this deli/pizzeria/liquor store and catch the beautiful sunsets over Pensacola Bay as you sit with your best pal. 701 Pensacola Beach Blvd.; 850/932-1124.

PLACES TO STAY

Vacation rentals: Most property owners seem to take their cats' advice and forbid dogs in their vacation homes. But we've seen a few hound-hospitable possibilities posted at such websites as VacationHomes.com and Rent101.com. Once you see a suitable vacation rental online, you'll call the property owner directly to reserve.

Gulf Islands National Seashore, Fort Pickens Area Campground: See Parks, Beaches, and Recreation Areas, above.

Gulf Breeze

PARKS, BEACHES, AND RECREATION AREAS

🐾 Gulf Islands National Seashore, Naval Live Oaks Reservation

🐾🐾🐾 🐾 ◀️🐾 (See Pensacola map on page 26)

While the town of Gulf Breeze is decidedly anti-dog (the furry creatures are forbidden at beaches and parks), a leashed pooch with a taste for history can be indulged at this woodsy, 1,300-acre chunk of waterfront run by the National Park Service.

Go to the left behind the administration building and you'll find a short nature trail that leads through a forest of oak, hickory, and magnolia trees to open views of pretty Santa Rosa Sound. The round-trip distance along the sandy, pine-needle-covered path is only two-thirds of a mile, and there are places to switch back along the loop before that should your pooch get tired. If your dog is a history buff, she might be interested in knowing that archaeologists have found 3,000-year-old Native American stone tools here. In 1829, President John Quincy Adams established the nation's first federal tree reservation here to furnish timber for our young nation's naval ships. Some of these strong, dense trees—prime leg-lift targets today—are shrouded in moss, and Maggie tugged on her leash to get a closer look at the frogs jumping around underneath.

Follow the nature trail to an observation deck, where your leashed buddy can sit under spreading oaks and look out over Santa Rosa Sound. A path leads to the isolated, little-used beach, where technically your pup isn't allowed. Instead, consider a walk down one of the other, even more remote trails on the north side of U.S. 98. Among them is the old Pensacola/St. Augustine Road, which dates back more than 100 years. Tie your dog outside the visitors center and step inside to inquire about these nature trails.

From Pensacola, take U.S. 98 across the Pensacola Bay Bridge to Gulf Breeze, then veer east and continue on U.S. 98 to the park entrance. 850/934-2600.

PLACES TO EAT

Billy Bob's Beach Barbecue: Slowly cooked, hand-pulled pork is the specialty at this barbecue joint found on the south side of Highway 98, just before the curve to the beach next to the Harbortown shopping center (on the east end of town). Barbecued ribs, slaw dawgs, "pig pudding" dessert, and a 20-odd-ingredient Brunswick stew are among other eats. Your dog may join you at one of the few outdoor tables. 911 Gulf Breeze Parkway; 850/934-2999.

PLACES TO STAY

Bay Beach Inn: Dogs may run along the private beach of this former Holiday Inn overlooking pretty Pensacola Bay. Bicycle rentals, room service, complimentary cocktail hour, two swimming pools, and prescription delivery are among unusual offerings. Two dog-walking grounds—equipped with pooper-scooper bags—sit on either side of the building. Upon check-in, a special sticker placed on your door will alert housekeeping that a pooch resides inside. Rates run $60–110 at this 168-unit, two-story hotel located about three miles from Pensacola. Pet fee is $35 per stay. 51 Gulf Breeze Parkway, Gulf Breeze; 850/932-2214; www.baybeachinn.com.

Navarre

PARKS, BEACHES, AND RECREATION AREAS

3 1 Gulf Islands National Seashore, Santa Rosa Island Day-Use Facility

😻 (See Pensacola map on page 26)

Get out of the sun and have a relaxing lunch with your leashed dog in a picnic area at the day-use portion of this National Park Service wonderland, which stretches from Florida to Mississippi. Picnicking is just about it for dogs; pooches are forbidden at the beaches. Damaged by the violent Hurricane Opal in 1995, this recreation area finally reopened in 2000, only to be walloped again four years later by Hurricane Ivan. Last we checked, the recreation area still was recovering and plans for reopening remained unclear, so call ahead.

A $8 entrance fee is collected from Memorial Day to Labor Day and is good for seven days. From Pensacola, follow U.S. 98 across the Pensacola Bay Bridge to Gulf Breeze, then take Highway 399 (a toll road) to Pensacola Beach. From there, Santa Rosa is 10 miles east. 850/934-2600.

Fort Walton Beach

PARKS, BEACHES, AND RECREATION AREAS

3 2 Liza Jackson Park

😻😻 (See Pensacola map on page 26)

Overlooking the Intracoastal Waterway, this pine-dotted park offers a large pier that you and your leashed buddy can walk on (as long as you bring a pooper-scooper). Maggie thinks it's very pleasant for a city park, and quite large—14 acres. It's also a fine place for a picnic, with some tables shaded by pavilions. Kids may find the playground with baby swings and a jungle gym hard to resist. If you're energetic, you and your pooch can chase Muscovy ducks at the creek near the nature trail.

The park is just south of U.S. 98 near the west end of Fort Walton Beach. 850/243-3141.

PLACES TO EAT

Rick's Crab Trap: Grilled snapper and grilled amberjack are popular at this eatery under Brooks Bridge. Just in case your dog is, uh, crabby around other pooches, you might try to stake out a more secluded spot on the wraparound deck. 203 Brooks St. Southeast; 850/664-0110.

Sonic Drive-In: At this 1950s retro eatery, carhops deliver the dogs (hot dogs, that is). Among other eats: burgers, fries, and soft-serve ice cream. 1166 North Eglin Parkway, in Shalimar. 850/651-6679.

PLACES TO STAY

Howard Johnson Inn: Newshounds receive *USA Today* weekdays at this 102-room poolside motel located across the street from the bay on U.S. 98. Rates vary seasonally $39–89, plus $10 daily pet fee. 203 Miracle Strip Parkway, Fort Walton Beach; 850/244-8663; www.hojo.com.

Marina Motel: Four-legged swimmers may romp along the beach behind this family-owned bayside motel, where guests arrive by car or by boat to dock at its 27 boat slips. Picnic tables and a fishing platform sit at the end of its 560-foot-long pier on Choctawhatchee Bay. All 38 rooms offer a microwave and medium-sized fridge, all the better for handling restaurant doggy bags. Regular rooms range $45–77. Two apartments run $70–125. Kitchenettes are $55–87. Add $10 nightly per dog. (Cats are forbidden.) 1345 Miracle Strip Parkway, Fort Walton Beach; 850/244-1129 or 800/237-7021.

Rodeway Inn: Located at the Intracoastal Waterway in downtown, this 36-unit two-story motel features a fishing pier and boat slips, though your dog may be more interested in scraps from your free continental breakfast. Rates range $59–119, plus $10 nightly pet fee. 314 Miracle Strip Parkway, Fort Walton Beach; 850/243-6162; www.rodeway.com.

52

ALABAMA
FLORIDA

GEORGIA

Chipola River

Chattahoochee River

331

83

Greenwood

5

Lake
Seminole

73

6

Marianna

7

Sneads

Chipley

90

1

Argyle

2

Caryville

3-4

Chattahoochee

10

De Funiak
Springs

231

167

10

331

81

71

83

79

Bloountstown

Bristol

Freeport

Ebro

20

77

12

Econfina Creek

Youngstown

9-10

West
Bay

13

APALACHICOLA
NATIONAL
FOREST

Grayton
Beach

Seaside

Dead
Lake

8

11

Lynn
Haven

79

PANAMA
CITY

Laguna
Beach

98

Cedar Grove
Springfield

Panama
City Beach

14

15

22

Wewahitchka

Apalachicola River

16

71

CROOKED
ISLAND

Mexico Beach

17

Port St. Joe

18

19

PANAMA CITY
AREA

Apalachicola

98

20

ST GEORGE
ISLAND

ST VINCENT
ISLAND

CAPE
ST GEORGE

GULF OF MEXICO

N

W   E

S

0   10   20
SCALE IN MILES

CHAPTER 2

Panama City Area

Dogs with a drawl will fit right in along the Redneck Riviera. But even if they can't drawl, they can drool, and they can sure sniff out lots of fun.

Most famous for the seemingly endless miles of sugar-sand beaches, the coastal strip in this part of Florida draws beachgoers from Alabama, Georgia, Florida, and—especially during the raucous, dog-unfriendly Spring Break—points much farther north. Around here, you can find some truly wonderful ways to pass a day with your pooch. But you'll need to know where you're going.

Like several regions in Florida, the signature city, in this case Panama City, is down on dogs. Nearby Panama City Beach, site of world-class beaches and a bacchanalian atmosphere that reminds Maggie of a college dorm party fueled by real adult salaries, is equally canine-challenged. Some of the best stuff here is off-limits to our four-legged pals. For example, rangers at St. Andrews State Park (judged by a University of Maryland beach expert to be the best beach in the country) won't let Rover rove anywhere near their precious waterfront.

PICK OF THE LITTER—PANAMA CITY AREA

BEST BEACH GETAWAYS
Indian Pass Beach, Port St. Joe (page 77)

BEST PLACE TO SPEND A DAY
Seaside, (page 62-67)

BEST PLACE TO EAT
Bud & Alley's, Seaside (page 65)

MOST UNUSUAL HIKE
Tyndall Air Force Base, Panama City (page 73)

MOST SCENIC WATERFALL
Falling Waters State Park, Chipley (page 57)

Guess folks around here are pooch-impaired. But what can you expect from a town with a billboard that advertises machine-gun rentals?

Panama City Beach's saving grace is that it's not too difficult to find a sandals-and-T-shirt kind of restaurant where you and your furry buddy can chow down.

The best advice we could give you is not to spend your entire vacation hanging around Panama City. Find a forest where both of you can chase some squirrels. Then check yourselves into a funky cottage where you can catch some ZZZs. And, yes, even make your way to one of those famous Panhandle beaches where you can soak up some rays.

The best places to go are as far away as you can get from Panama City and Panama City Beach. For a dog-friendly beach tour, head east to Cape San Blas, near Port St. Joe. If your pooch can tear herself away from the Gulf of Mexico, spend a few days exploring the wonderfully wooded hills and friendly towns closer to the Alabama border. Up there, you're likely to see local dogs lazing the day away under the shade of a moss-draped oak.

Remember that summer is the busiest time of year across the Panhandle. That's when motel rates go up, as does the crowd density on the beaches. Call ahead for reservations, especially in the Panama City area. In March and April, Spring Break is big in Panama City, and all but the most daredevil dogs will thank you for skipping the spectacle.

You might consider giving the Panhandle a try in the winter. We think there's something to be said for cradling a mug of hot chocolate as you stand on a sugar-white beach in February, draped in a warm sweater, watching the purplish clouds brood over the Gulf of Mexico while your canine companion savors the riotous fun of chasing shorebirds.

De Funiak Springs

PARKS, BEACHES, AND RECREATION AREAS

1 Lake De Funiak Park

🐾🐾 (See Panama City map on page 52)

A favorite gathering place for Independence Day events held at the amphitheater, this pine-, gum-, and magnolia-shaded park is much less used most other days of the year. Your pooch is bound to enjoy the lighted one-mile path around the lake at the center of the park, which appears to us to be the most perfectly round lake in the world. Plenty of resident ducks and squirrels will tempt your dog to give chase. Technically, there is a leash law, though locals say it is widely ignored as long as dogs are well behaved. We saw several dogs running free here. There is also a playground for any young 'uns who may be traveling with you and your dog. Picnic tables are available.

The park is on Circle Drive, just south of the railroad tracks on the south side of the historic district. From I-10, take U.S. 331 north to the second traffic light (Live Oak Avenue). Turn right and go two blocks. 850/892-3191.

PLACES TO STAY

Best Western Crossroads Inn: Set on eight acres dotted with pecan trees, this 100-unit poolside motel permits small pets to retire to the four or five pet rooms after stretching their legs on the big front lawn. A restaurant and a lounge are located on the grounds, found at the intersection of U.S. 331 and I-10 (Exit 85). Rates range $59–99, including breakfast. 2343 Freeport Road, De Funiak Springs; 850/892-5111; www.bestwestern.com.

Days Inn: A trip-weary dog can stretch her legs by padding along the large grassy area out front of this standard 60-unit poolside motel located at the intersection of U.S. 331 and I-10 (Exit 85). Rates range $50–60, including continental breakfast and local calls. Add $10 nightly per pet. 472 Hugh Adams Road, De Funiak Springs; 850/892-6115; www.daysinn.com.

DIVERSIONS

Does your pooch want to brag that he climbed Florida's highest "mountain?" Don't worry—there will be no need for a St. Bernard rescue. The red-clay **Britton Hill** is called the nation's lowest highest point, rising only 345 feet above sea level. Climbing it requires getting out of the car and walking a few yards. To get there, take U.S. 331 north from De Funiak Springs and bear right (after about 20 miles) to continue on Highway 285. A few miles up the road you'll come to Wakulla County's Lakewood Park, a small oak-shaded patch that's barely worth mentioning. Get out of the car and you're on Britton Hill, Florida's highest ground. As some people joke, don't forget to bring an oxygen tank. 850/892-8108 or 334/858-6252.

If you tire of the dizzying heights, return to Earth—or De Funiak Springs—to chew the fat with the locals at another landmark. Friendly old fellows sit and shoot the breeze at **The Opinion Place,** a small, open-air gazebo with benches located by the railroad tracks in the historic district of De Funiak Springs. The locals we bumped into here were only too happy to show a little Southern hospitality to Maggie. This informal hangout is technically named after John F. Butler, Sr., former superintendent of public schools and a protégé of the famous University of Alabama coach Paul "Bear" Bryant. The humble gazebo is at the south side of where Eighth Street runs into Baldwin Avenue, in the heart of the historic district. 850/892-3191.

Ponce de Leon

PARKS, BEACHES, AND RECREATION AREAS

2 Ponce de Leon Springs State Park

🐾🐾🐾 (See Panama City map on page 52)

Chipmunks frolic amid the oaks and gum trees that shade your eager pooch as he scampers down nature trails here. At 443 acres, this park is small compared to most Florida Park Service outposts, but there are some fine trails along crystal-clear streams. The Spring Run Trail is a sandy path with a few small "hills." The trail goes alongside a clear-water stream, where your leashed buddy might see a turtle sunning itself on a fallen log. For another dog-walk option, try the Sandy Creek Trail. Be careful of exposed roots and mud on this narrow path and expect to spend 45 minutes trekking leisurely through a river floodplain.

In the picnic area, your dog will undoubtedly be tempted to chase the chipmunks that play near the grills and tile-roofed tables. The rules require him to stay leashed, however, and he can't go to the beach.

Admission is $3 per car. This state park is so convenient to I-10 that you can hear the passing autos while walking along the nature trails. From I-10, exit onto Highway 81 and head north to the town of Ponce de Leon, where you'll turn right at Highway 90. Follow signs through this dusty little burg to the state park, whose entrance is .3 mile away at 2860 Ponce de Leon Springs Road. 850/836-4281.

Chipley

PARKS, BEACHES, AND RECREATION AREAS

🔳 Earl Gilbert Landing Park

😿 (See Panama City map on page 52)

Pine and gum trees and concrete shelters shade some concrete-and-brick picnic tables next to a lake. This is a convenient stop if you're hurrying along U.S. 10, though we urge you to hit the slightly more remote Falling Waters State Park (see below) if you have time. A busy highway borders this one-acre linear park, so don't even think about letting your pooch off leash.

From I-10, take Exit 18 south and immediately look for the park at left. From Chipley, take Highway 77 south for two miles. 850/638-6078.

🔳 Falling Waters State Park

😿😿😿 ◀● (See Panama City map on page 52)

A striking 67-foot cascade of water is the big attraction here—one of a handful of places in the state where your dog will see a waterfall, or anything like one. Called Florida's highest waterfall, it's reached by taking a .75-mile pleasant stroll through a lush hardwood hammock, then descending stairs to the viewpoint. Steps are plentiful, so you may need to carry your leashed buddy if she's not up to the task.

Consider timing your descent to the falls when crowds are thinnest. Some dog-leery patrons have complained about sharing the three-foot-wide boardwalk with pooches. The result? Some rangers flat-out say dogs are banned from the falls portion of the 171-acre park. Others advise dog owners to use good judgment. If there are crowds, gauge how others may react to your dog. (Maggie's tip: Tie on a bandanna to look friendlier!)

If it's a cool day, venture onto the two short hiking trails through the warmer pine woods. In hotter times, we recommend the Sinkhole Trail to the falls. Mastodons roamed this land thousands of years ago, pursued by our spear-bearing ancestors (and probably their dogs!). More recently, a pioneer pooch could have wet her whistle at the whiskey distillery that once operated here or hung out at the gristmill that occupied this spot for a while. Modern-day hot dogs will be thankful simply for the brisk air that flows off the falls.

Picnic tables in a longleaf pine forest allow for a cookout while the kids head to the swings. Sorry, dogs are forbidden at the beach and two-acre lake.

Entrance is $4 per vehicle. The park is three miles south of Chipley. From Exit 18 off I-10, head south on Highway 77 to 1130 State Park Road. 850/638-6130.

PLACES TO STAY

Falling Waters State Park: Set in a forest of slash pines, these 24 sites offer electricity, water, a grill, and a picnic table, though the best thing is the state park's natural wonders. It's home to one of Florida's few waterfalls, as well as short hiking trails that also can be enjoyed by pooches (see Parks, Beaches, and Recreation Areas). Unfortunately, dogs aren't allowed to follow you down the short trail to the swimming lake. Fee is $15 nightly. 1130 State Park Road, Chipley; 800/326-3521.

Super 8: If your pup has a pal in town, he can call him free from one of the 40 rooms of this one-story poolside motel off I-10 (Exit 120). Rooms go for $45–75. Add $5 daily per pet. 1700 Main St., Chipley; 850/638-8530; www.super8.com.

Marianna

Usually ignored by tourists, this area has some whiz-bang attractions for dogs and people. If you visit in the fall, keep an eye out for hillside fields where the pines thin out to reveal a sea of gold. That's the goldenrod plant, considered a weed by many but certain to produce a showy splash of intense yellow once a year.

PARKS, BEACHES, AND RECREATION AREAS

5 Upper Chipola River Water Management Area

🐾🐾 (See Panama City map on page 52)

Good for wilderness nuts like Maggie, the trail through these 7,374 acres alongside the Chipola River and its tributaries leads through mostly sunny areas between the river and the forested stomping grounds of deer. You're likely to be alone and away from all the cares of civilization, although you might spot some hunters during the cooler months, especially November, December, and the March and April turkey season. In spring, you can feast on the boysenberries that ripen here, but keep your dog out of the briar patches where these succulent black gems grow. Forget about visiting in summer, when there just isn't enough shade for hot dogs.

From Marianna, head north on Highway 71 and turn left at the small settlement of Greenwood onto County Road 162 (Fort Road), by the Junior Food Store. When you pass the bridge over the Chipola River, park on the south side of the road. 850/539-5999.

6 Florida Caverns State Park

🐾🐾🐾🐾 ⬛➤ (See Panama City map on page 52)

Dogs aren't allowed in the park's centerpiece: the underground caverns that are unique within Florida. Still, this two-square-mile park offers tons of canine fun.

Follow trails across small rises and down to the swampy Chipola River floodplain, where tupelo, cypress, and ash trees are plentiful. We saw a snake in the water, but it posed no threat to Maggie, who was leashed as required. Uphill, near the caverns, you'll pass fenced holes in the hillsides. These are minor entrances to the underground caverns. In some places, your pal can get close enough to the fence bars to enjoy cool air billowing from the dark earth. Curious Maggie stuck her nose between the bars to examine the natural air conditioning more thoroughly.

On a hot day, leave your car at the parking lot's western end (look for a shaded spot) and follow the sign indicating the Flood Plain Trail. Use the posted map to find a direct route to the Tunnel Cave Trail. This path leads about a quarter mile to where leashed dogs may walk through a tunnel cave made of limestone deposited back when ancient seas covered the area. You'll need to duck in a few spots, but the tunnel is short. Most dogs can handle the walk, even in midsummer.

A short drive away from the caverns is a picnic area with grills. Kids will like the playground and (pooch-forbidden) swimming area. The site of a Native American village when Spaniards stepped ashore in the 1500s, this area today is Marianna's biggest tourist draw. You're unlikely to be alone.

Admission is $4 per vehicle. The park is three miles north of Marianna on State Road 166, off U.S. 90. From I-10, take the Marianna exit north and follow signs to the park at 3345 Caverns Road. 850/482-9598.

PLACES TO EAT

Sonic Drive-In: At this retro 1950s-style drive-in, you never need to leave your car to enjoy vanilla Cokes, cheeseburgers, Coney dogs, wraps, salads, banana splits, malts, and other diner fare; a carhop will bring your order to you. An overhang keeps the car cool for canines. Alternatively, sit at the shaded, fire-engine-red outdoor tables. 4221 Lafayette Street/U.S. 90; 850/526-2069.

PLACES TO STAY

Arrowhead Campsites: Dominated by RVs, this campground on a bass-fishing pond by the Chipola River allows leashed dogs to arrive with tenters or people in pop-up campers. After staking out one of the 200-plus sites (150 pull-through), you might head to the pool, fishing pier, on-site store, or ask about a rental canoe for you and your canine friend. Campsites are $21. 4820 U.S. 90 East, Marianna; 850/482-5583.

Best Western: Dirty doggie bandannas can be washed in the on-site coin-operated washers, then pressed with the iron provided in each guestroom at this 74-unit, two-story poolside motel off I-10 at Highway 71. Rates are $59–69, including continental breakfast. Add $10 nightly per pet. 2086 Highway 71 South, Marianna; 850/526-5666 or 800/528-1234; www.bestwestern.com.

Comfort Inn: Your dog might end up sniffing the room for crumbs from your free continental breakfast at this 80-unit poolside motel off I-10 at Highway 71. All rooms offer dataports, irons, and coffeemakers; king rooms also include recliners. Rates range $55–89, plus $12 nightly pet fee. 2175 Highway 71 South, Marianna; 850/526-5600 or 800/228-5150; www.choicehotels.com.

Florida Caverns State Park: Sleeping under the stars in the state park's heavily wooded 38-site campground costs $17 nightly. 3345 Caverns Road, Marianna; 850/482-9598 or 800/326-3521 (reservations).

Ramada Limited: Pull back the curtains and your pal can watch people walk by on their way to the pool or the parking lot at this two-story, 70-room former Holiday Inn located a mile from the city on U.S. 90, west of Highway 71. Pooches with energy to burn can walk in the small area in front or the smidgen of greenery out back. Rates normally are $35–45. Daily pet fee is $10. 4655 Lafayette Street/U.S. 90, Marianna; 850/526-3251; www.ramada.com.

Sneads

PARKS, BEACHES, AND RECREATION AREAS

7 Three Rivers State Park

🐾🐾🐾 (See Panama City map on page 52)

Set amid wooded, rolling hills where you'll see lots of pickup trucks and mobile homes, this little-used, 681-acre park offers intriguing treats for your pooch's senses, including the scent of pine and the whine of cicadas. Lots of squirrels run amid the pines and hickory trees growing in the roomy picnic area, but remember that by law your dog is supposed to stay leashed. Deer and foxes live in these woods, which stay cool even on a hot day. You'll find plenty of picnic tables and grills, as well as swing sets, restrooms, and the three rivers that lend the park its name (Chattahoochee, Flint, and Apalachicola rivers). A fine picnic spot is available on Lake Seminole. Don't let your dog get too close to the water; alligators call this place home.

Entrance is $2 per car. From U.S. 90 in Sneads, head north two miles on State Road 271/River Road. 850/482-9006.

PLACES TO STAY

Three Rivers State Park: A dog's keen eyes can see both Georgia and Florida from these 31 tree-shaded lakeside campsites. Fishing is popular, but dogs may prefer to sniff the woods for evidence of the resident deer. All 65 sites have water, a picnic table, a grill, a fire ring, and access to showers, a fishing pier, and boat ramp. Electricity is available at some sites. Camping runs $12 nightly. 7908 Three Rivers Park Road, Sneads; 850/482-9006 or 800/326-3521 (reservations).

Grayton Beach

PARKS, BEACHES, AND RECREATION AREAS

8 Grayton Beach

🐾🐾 🐾 (See Panama City map on page 52)

This is one of those places we're not sure we really should include in this book anymore. But we thought we'd at least let you know about the possibility. At one time, any dog could romp on the sugar-white sand beach here, running over the dunes and along the length of the hard-packed sand until she was tuckered out. More recently, however, local officials issued a decree that would make visiting dogs yelp: Only dogs who belong to Walton County property owners may visit this beach. Not just any property owners, but those who buy an annual $25 dog-beach permit at the Walton County Courthouse Annex, 47 North Sixth Street, De Funiak Springs, or at a south county government office. Dogs must wear a tag and appear only during certain hours—between 6 P.M. and 8 A.M. during daylight saving time, between 3 P.M. and 9 A.M. during Eastern Standard time. What's more, dogs now must be leashed.

Last we checked, canine tourists were just plain out of luck. Maybe things will change, though. This always has been a place where people have taken their dogs to romp, and we hope that money-bearing tourists and their pooches will again be welcomed. For information on dog-beach permits, call 850/267-3066.

Beach access is available on County Road 30A, just south of U.S. 98. 850/267-1216.

Seaside

"It's a very dog-friendly town," says local chef Scott Witcoski, who welcomes dogs at one of the area's best restaurants, Bud & Alley's. (The resident cat, Jake, "holds his own" against any canine comers, Witcoski reports.) Overall, everyone else seems to get along fine with dogs in this seaside town. A happy Maggie padded all around the place and elicited no complaints.

Reminiscent of a New England town because of its similar architecture and homey feel (but with Florida's signature weather), upscale Seaside is the creation of touted architects and urban planners Andres Duany and Elizabeth Plater-Zyberk. They have designed perhaps the most livable place on Florida's Gulf Coast, for both doggies and people. You will see Old Florida-style tin roofs protecting pastel wooden houses adorned with wood-railed porches and contained by neat, white picket fences. If it looks like the idyllic setting of the film *The Truman Show,* there is good reason—Jim Carrey and crew shot the 1998 movie here. If you're lucky, you might come across a storyteller, an art show, or a concert in this laid-back, quirky burg (for schedules, call the Downtown Seaside Association at 850/231-5424). The town is engaging and very relaxing. Some, in fact, say it's a little too clean and pleasant to be part of the real world, but Maggie had a blast.

Just park in the town center and hang out at one of the restaurants, or head across the street toward the beach. Abandon your car, though, by all means. This is a laid-back, take-your-mind-off-your-worries kind of place, and that means you should leave your auto behind.

PARKS, BEACHES, AND RECREATION AREAS

🐾 Eden State Gardens
🐾🐾 (See Panama City map on page 52)
Said to be styled after a plantation home that a local lumberman saw on his way back from the War Between the States, the white-columned family home that is the centerpiece of these remote and rarely crowded gardens is off-limits to doggies. Canines can have a fine time here, anyway, picnicking on the shores of Choctawhatchee Bay. Who wants to see hundred-year-old furnishings anyway, Maggie's always saying. Instead, enjoy the spacious,

FETCHING NECESSITIES

Sun Dog Books at Seaside is a fine place for a well-read hound to hang out indoors while you peruse the shelves for beach-reading material or something weightier. Patty, the owner's black Lab, plays official store greeter most days. You'll find the bookstore in Seaside's main town square on Highway 30A. 850/231-5481.

Afterward, go window-shopping with Flopsy and sniff out the various shops housed in the Jamaica-style outdoor booths. For a break, relax at an outdoor table at a pet-friendly eatery, such as **Café Spiaggia,** a home of pizza, antipasti, and other Italian fare; 850/231-1297.

The whole concept behind Seaside is that people should be able to stroll from place to place, and that suited Maggie just fine. Dogs are always up for a walk, and she enjoyed mingling with the other browsers. If your pal pines for a longer stroll, meander north from the main town square and check out the architecture. Note the grid pattern of the small streets, which prevents what little car traffic there is from funneling onto any one byway, making the whole place a lot more pleasant for everyone concerned. Work your way west, south, then east again. If only more developers would plan communities this way!

---

breezy yard outside the house, with grills and picnic tables under tall, shady oaks and magnolia trees. It's a great place to chill out with your leashed dog. You can also walk along a small pier. A half-mile nature trail offers a taste of the park's 100 acres of woods. Just outside the park, look for a historic post office and cemetery.

Admission is $3 per vehicle. The park is on County Road 395, north of U.S. 98, in the small community of Point Washington, which is between Panama City Beach and Sandestin. 850/231-4214.

🐾 Point Washington State Forest

🐾🐾 (See Panama City map on page 52)

Rough and rugged describes the doggies who usually come to this 19-square-mile forest, which sprawls over southern Walton County and serves as home to rare gopher tortoises and a dog-pleasing hiking trail—the Eastern Lake Trail. This forest is used most often by hunters and their dogs, who do their thing during cooler months, particularly November and December, but the land is also open to nonhunters. If your pooch has visions of a rural, outdoorsy alternative to upscale Seaside, then make this a destination.

Eastern Lake Trail offers three loops for hikers and bicyclists to explore—a 3.5-mile-long loop, a 5-mile loop, and a 10-mile loop. A greenway trail system is under development to provide more than 27 miles of recreational trails crossing the forest and connecting to adjacent Grayton Beach State Park, Deer Lake State Park, Topsail Hill State Preserve, and residential developments. Lucky dogs (and their people) may find themselves alone on current trails and be tempted to run free. Officially, leashes are the rule.

By car, you're welcome to follow open roads throughout the forest, whose 10 natural communities mostly include sandhill, basin swamps, wet flatwoods, wet prairie, and cypress swamps. Much of this former private timberland has been cut down, though some sandhill areas remain intact. Warning: Hunters arrive on scattered dates between October and April. For hunting dates, call 850/265-3676.

The huge forest straddles U.S. 98 between Panama City Beach and Sandestin. The Eastern Lake Trail starts at the parking lot on County Road 395, one mile south of U.S. 98. Another way to explore the forest is to enter on County Road 395, north of U.S. 98, and take any dirt road to look for a place to romp in the woods. 850/231-5800.

11 Seaside Beach

🐾🐾 ◀▇ (See Panama City map on page 52)

This is a treat, one of the last remote stretches of beach in Florida. Too bad that the only pooches allowed to set paw on this sand are those whose owners happen to own property in this county. Everyone else is out of luck. We hope the community eventually will reconsider and once again welcome tourist dollars from visiting canines.

If you're lucky enough to own property here, then you'll stroll on sand that is as fine-textured as sugar—so fine that it squeaks under your bare feet. Sadly, your dog officially must be leashed. He also must wear a $25 beach-permit tag as he visits only during certain hours—between 6 P.M. and 8 A.M. during daylight saving time, between 3 P.M. and 9 A.M. during Eastern Standard time. For information on dog-beach permits, call 850/267-3066.

Some stretches of beach are accessible only by dirt road, and drivers should determine the road conditions before proceeding. It's worth making the trip by foot or by car, though, because many of these beaches are usually nearly deserted. Be careful about the undertow; if you haven't checked the local newspaper or television report for tide conditions, don't wade into the water above your thighs, and don't let your dog go any deeper than you. You may see other dogs romping leash-free, but their owners risk fines, we're told. Make sure that if yours goes leashless, he stays far enough away from other people that he won't bother them.

Beach access is available on County Road 30A, just south of U.S. 98. 850/622-1457.

PLACES TO EAT

Bud & Alley's: Named after a dachshund and a cat, this place was proclaimed among Florida's 200 best restaurants by *Florida Trend* magazine. As you sit perched amid the dunes overlooking the Gulf of Mexico, try such goodies as Old Florida oyster stew, arugula salad, or a wood-grilled pork chop with caramelized onion and roast portobello mushrooms. The cuisine features the cooking techniques of the Old World—Mediterranean, Basque, and Tuscan—along with Caribbean/Deep South ingredients. Your buddy will be tied to a tree next to the herb garden courtyard where you'll dine. The staff will serve him water while you sample wines from an award-winning list. Among customers who have brought dogs is troubadour Jimmy Buffett, who incidentally once penned a song about a dog, Spooner, who inherited enough dough for "growing old on steak and bacon, in a doghouse 10 foot 'round." On the gulf side of Highway 30A; 850/231-5900.

Café Spiaggia: It's a nice setting: Tables are covered with tablecloths, and you'll dine al fresco on the terrace. All the while, your dog may sit at your feet hoping you'll drop scraps of pizza, antipasti, or panini. It's possible that you may even be permitted to dine indoors together, so long as your pooch doesn't venture behind the counter. This Italian café also serves salads, biscotti, beer, wine, espresso, ice cream, and gelato. In the gulf-side shopping center across from the town center, right on the beach off Highway 30A; 850/231-1297.

Dawson's Yogurt: A good place for a cold treat on a hot day, this frozen yogurt shop serves waffle and cake cones, sugar-free and fat-free selections, milk shakes, banana splits, lemonade, and sodas. Employees brag about the yogurt's rich, creamy texture. In the main town square on Highway 30A; 850/231-4770.

Hurricane Oyster Bar: Everyone eats outside here, munching oysters, fish sandwiches, and specials such as jerk chicken sandwiches. A water bowl is presented to dogs upon request. On the gulf side of Highway 30A, below Bud & Alley's; 850/534-0376.

Modica Market: While you go inside Charles Modica's fancy deli and grocery to order some tasty light fare, your tied-up dog can peruse the front pages of the *Investor's Business Daily*, the *Wall Street Journal*, or the *New York Times*—not to mention the local papers—at the racks outside. Pick up pasta salad, roasted chicken, fine wine, imported beer, or sweet homemade baked goods, then take them outside to enjoy at a roof-covered table with your dog. He'll appreciate the wide-ranging menu, from cappuccino to chocolate baklava. If the fresh foods don't strike your fancy, by all means check out the unique canned and packaged goods that line the shelves along the market's towering walls. Maggie was enthralled watching people walk by. In the main town square on Highway 30A; 850/231-1214.

Pickles Snack Station: Everyone's excited about dogs here—hot dogs, that is. You can also munch on burgers, Philly sandwiches, shrimp, or chicken fingers. In the gulf-side shopping center across from the town center on Highway 30A; 850/231-5686.

Shades: Dogs used to be able to hang out with their bipedal friends on the covered outdoor deck here, but now they typically must be tied up 10 or 15 feet away. The motto here is "Good food and cold beer," and promising offerings include chicken wings, burgers, and grilled chicken. In the summer your dog is quite likely to find a fellow canine here. All the way at the back of the main town square on Highway 30A; 850/231-1950.

PLACES TO STAY

Emerald Waters Realty: This agency handles a few pet-permissible vacation homes and condos from Seagrove to Carillon Beach. Your canine pals must weigh no more than a combined total of 40 pounds, so you may bring one 40-pound pooch or two 20-pounders. Summer weekly rates generally range $525–6,000, lower at other times. Add a $100 nonrefundable pet fee. 8281 Highway 30A, Seacrest; 850/231-2418 or 800/226-3974; www.emeraldwaters.net.

Idyll-By-The-Sea vacation home: If money is no object, read on. This Seaside gulf-front house features two Jacuzzi tubs, Swim and Tennis Club access, and other luxuries mentioned in articles in *Dog Fancy Magazine* and *DogGone*, a national newsletter for canine travelers. Jackie the German shepherd spends winters at Idyll-By-The-Sea, thanks to his owners, Carol Irvine and Jerry Jongerius, owning the place. Your dog and family may stay, too, if you don't yelp at the rates. Nightly fee starts at a whopping $795. P.O. Box 4879, Seaside; 301/831-1345; www.Idyll-by-the-sea.com.

Santa Rosa Beach cottage rentals: Finding accommodations that welcomed their two Pekingese was always a challenge for vacationers Mark and Susan Bremer, so when they built their first of handful of vacation rentals in Santa Rosa Beach (near Seaside) a few years ago, the couple knew they'd permit pets. Small dogs are permitted, though large dogs are considered, as well, at these "cottages"—actually houses with full kitchens—located around the corner from Pets Fifth Avenue dog boutique and down the street from Bark Avenue canine boutique. The "Almost Home" house, located across the street from an outlet mall, offers gulf views from its second-floor master suite and balcony. Fee ranges $2,061–2,361 weekly in season, less in autumn. A four-bedroom, three-bathroom house on Scenic Highway 30-A ranges $1,450–1,850 weekly in season, less in fall. Cleaning fee is $150. 205/356-6776; www.findvacationrentals.com/7376/ and www.findvacationrentals.com/536/.

Seagrove Cottages: If your dog wants to swim, he's in luck. Proprietors Al and Teri Flowers got a variance from the county government, making it possible for canine guests to use the public beach, which otherwise is off-limits to anyone who doesn't own property in the county. (Of course, dogs must be leashed and limit themselves to morning hours before 8 or 9 A.M., depending on the time of year, and evening hours after 3 or 6 P.M.) All five rustic, informal cottages have linens and kitchenware but no phones. Don't expect gussied-up Seaside. The beach is across the street and a restaurant is next door. Pet fee is a flat $15. Rates for two- and three-bedroom cottages range $98–157 daily, paid "in advance on arrival." Cancellation policy calls for 10 days advance notice. 3031 E. County Highway 30A, Seagrove Beach; 850/231-4206; www.seagrovecottages.com.

Topsail Hill Preserve State Park/Gregory E. Moore RV Resort: At one of the top RV-only resorts in the nation, campers swim and beachcomb for seabeans along 3.2 miles of white quartz sand beach on the Gulf of Mexico, then can jump into a heated swimming pool, play shuffleboard, or serve up a game of tennis. The beach sits one-half mile from these 156 full-hookup campsites set amid pines, so a free shuttle runs to the beach as a service to campers who don't want to walk or bicycle the half-mile. Dogs unfortunately are forbidden on the beach. But leashed hikers can explore the 2.5-mile Morris Lake Nature Trail as it winds through dunes and scrubland, follow several miles of abandoned Jeep trails, or sniff for animals along Campbell Lake's trail. Campsites cost $38. 7525 W. Scenic Highway 30A, Santa Rosa Beach; 850/267-0299 or 800/326-3521 (reservations).

Vacation rentals: It can be simpler for a St. Bernard to climb a palm tree than for a dogged vacationer to find a beach rental that permits pets. We noticed one Seagrove Beach lodging apiece at each of these websites: Vacationhomes.com, GulfCoastRentals.com, Vrbo.com, Vamoose.com, PetFriendlyTravel.com, and FloridaVacations.com. All describe the vacation homes and ask you to contact the property owner directly. Perhaps simpler, the Beaches of South Walton Tourist Development Council can refer you to its latest short roster of pet-friendly vacation homes. Go to www.beachesofsouthwalton.com or call 800/822-6877.

Ebro

PARKS, BEACHES, AND RECREATION AREAS

🐾 Pine Log State Forest

🐾🐾🐾 (See Panama City map on page 52)

Back and forth, back and forth, Maggie paced in the car as we drove along the red-clay roads here, ever eager to get out and explore. In some areas of this 6,911-acre forest, the pines are planted in rows, plantation-style, but she couldn't have cared less. She just enjoyed getting out and hiking through the gently sloped hills.

The woods are not too thick, which makes for easy hiking, and the forest is very accessible by car: easy in, easy out. The hard red clay is generally suitable for driving, but take care not to stop on the sandy portions, or your car might get stuck. Hiking trails of various lengths wind through the forest, which is dotted with clumps of hardwoods and swampy stands of cypress.

Try the trails near the campground, which you'll pass on the paved main road. The 7.4-mile loop portion of the Florida National Scenic Trail is mostly level, passing by lakes and creeks where you can stop to swim or fish. Watch out for prickly pears, a cactus-like plant that usually stands no more than a foot high and sports inch-long spines.

This place is waaaaaaay out there, more than 20 miles from Panama City proper, and there are no facilities except at the campground, where you'll find restrooms and picnic tables. Mostly it's wilderness, so bring everything you might need while you're here, especially water for your leashed pooch. During hunting season, particularly November and December, much of the forest is crawling with hunters. But don't fret; hunting is forbidden around the campground.

Take U.S. 98 west from Panama City, turn north on Highway 79, and continue about 15 miles. The road runs through the forest, intersecting with Environmental Road and many other dirt roads. 850/872-4175 or 850/547-7083.

PLACES TO STAY

Pine Log State Forest: Twenty first-come, first-served camping spots sit around a lake within Pine Log State Forest. Swimming is allowed for humans, not canines, but dogs will have fun following forest trails (see park listing, above). Sites are $12 nightly if you want water, electricity, a picnic table, and a grill. Primitive camping runs $4 nightly. To get here from U.S. 20 in Ebro, go south on Highway 79 for 1.3 miles and enter the second forest entrance, marked Environmental Road, and watch for signs about camping. Turn west on the dirt road and continue one-half mile to the campground. 850/872-4175 or 850/547-7083.

Wewahitchka

PARKS, BEACHES, AND RECREATION AREAS

🐾 Dead Lakes Park

🐾🐾 (See Panama City map on page 52)

The name sounds ominous, but the body of water at this 83-acre county park is no more dead than it is a lake. It's actually where the Apalachicola River's current blocked the Chipola River, turning this section of the Chipola into a lake-like body that overflowed and killed thousands of trees in the floodplain. Dogs are rarely seen here, but there's plenty for them to do. Along the nature trails, your pooch's sniffer might pick up the scents of a host of animals, including foxes, opossums, deer, beavers, and rabbits. Maybe she'll even track a skunk, so keep her leashed. You can picnic here under pine trees or pavilions.

Dog-tired visitors may wish to camp beneath the pines at the 20-site campground, where half the sites have electricity (helpful for reading *Old Yeller* at night). Sites run $10–12.

From Wewahitchka, travel one mile north on Highway 71 to 510 Gary Powell Road. 850/639-2238.

PLACES TO STAY

Dead Lakes Park: See Dead Lakes Park, above, for camping information.

Panama City Beach

The problem with Panama City Beach—or one problem, we should say—is that dogs are not allowed on the beach. And the crowded sand is the big attraction here. The establishments that line the main drag give you an idea of what kind of place this is: T-shirt shops, topless bars, go-cart racetracks, and "fantasy golf" courses. Even if this isn't your dog's cup of beef broth, you still can get a bite with your pooch or find a place to sleep should you be passing through along the main drag, Highway 392, a.k.a. Thomas Drive. Warning: Spring Break madness descends on this place every March and April, and bringing dogs into this situation is not a good idea. Maggie, who long lived in Fort Lauderdale, the former Spring Break capital, can attest to that. As Maggie says, forewarned is forearmed. Or is that fore-pawed?

There is one good thing about staying in Panama City Beach any other time of the year. Locals tell us that if you head west and get outside the city limits, you can get away with letting your dog loose on the beach and the constabulary will look the other way. But the dog has to be well behaved, and you must—all together now—scoop that poop! To romp without guilt, go east, young doggies. The nearest beaches that welcome tourist dogs without question are about a two-hour drive away in the Port St. Joe area (see Port St. Joe, this chapter).

PARKS, BEACHES, AND RECREATION AREAS

14 St. Andrews State Park

😸 (See Panama City map on page 52)

Although this park has some of the country's top-rated beaches, you can't enjoy them as long as you're accompanied by your furry friend. When we visited, Maggie was made to feel quite unwelcome. However, the regulations do allow dogs to picnic on the bay side (north side) next to the boat launch. The usual oppressive rules apply: Your dog must be on a leash no longer than six feet and you must stay out of Fido-forbidden areas. Basically, that's everywhere except the parking lot, road, and bayside picnic area.

Admission is $5 per vehicle. From Miracle Strip Parkway/Alternate 98 in Panama City Beach, go east on Thomas Drive/County Road 392 about four miles to the park. 850/233-5140.

PLACES TO EAT

Beach Diner: This breakfast and lunch place features a few outdoor tables with semicircular benches fronting busy Thomas Drive, a main route to the beach. You can get doughnuts and coffee at a walk-up window, but we recommend going inside to order a tasty breakfast or lunch to go, then eating it outside with your leashed pooch at your feet. The Pulpwood Cutter's Goulash—hash brown–like breakfast potatoes with ham, cheese, and other fixings, including two eggs or sausage gravy if you prefer—is filling and yummy. Plus it seems to be a part of the Panama City Beach experience. Skip the jalapeños if you plan to share the "trash plate," as the dish also is known, with your pooch. There's no shade in the morning, so request ice water for your hot dog and consider skipping this stop on sunnier days. 104 Thomas Drive; 850/234-0250.

Big Kahuna: All the food that's not good for you comes in abundance at this laid-back, T-shirt-and-sandals kind of place. The wide-ranging, what-the-hell-I'm-on-vacation-anyway menu includes burgers, wings, stuffed jalapeños, grouper sandwiches, clam strips, and fried shrimp dinners. When we called ahead, an employee wanted to know how our dog would like her burger—rare, medium, or well. Top off your meal with yogurt or ice cream, or have a splash of something alcoholic. Sex on the Beach is advertised as a

favorite libation, though Maggie would much prefer cold milk. To find this eatery, look for the yellow-and-aquamarine outdoor tables and bar. 14896 Front Beach Road; 850/233-5706.

Billy's: Oysters, crab, lobster, and other gems of the sea dominate the menu at this casual eatery, where you'll sit on the wooden deck with concrete picnic tables. Staffers gladly provide a water dish for dogs, on request. The restaurant may be closed some weeks in winter. 3000 Thomas Drive; 850/235-2349.

Flamingo Joe's Grill: If you want a casual, Key West–style dining spot on the main route to the beach, look for the pink flamingos painted onto the green wooden building. Here you have your pick of four wooden picnic tables or two umbrella-shaded concrete benches on the outdoor wooden deck. Burgers and chicken sandwiches are popular at this lunch and dinner spot, where the cooks are also proud of their gumbo and chili. Try the Cheeseburger in Paradise (three cheeses) or the Aloha chicken sandwich (marinated in pineapple juice and served with honey mustard and sweet huli sauce). *Southern Living* called theirs the "best burger on the beach." 2304 Thomas Drive; 850/233-0600.

Shuckum's Oyster Pub & Seafood Grill: The folks who run this small place with a big menu keep a few bowls in back especially for canines, and they're happy to see a dog show up, says owner Johnny Bradley. Sit at an umbrella-shaded table on the unvarnished deck looking out across the road at the Gulf of Mexico. Shrimp is the most popular item here and comes almost any way you can imagine, including sautéed, fried, and Creole-style, yet the menu also includes steaks and burgers. Devilish hounds enjoy the contradiction in two signs here: "We shuck 'em, you suck 'em" and "Family Fun." 15618 Front Beach Road; 850/235-3214.

Sonic Drive-In: The friendly people here sometimes treat canines to a free dog biscuit. The 1950s-style drive-in features mouthwatering cheeseburgers (try one with bacon), hot dogs for any taste, chocolate Cokes, steak sandwiches, wraps, and more. 2021 Thomas Drive; 850/235-9786.

PLACES TO STAY

Camper's Inn: Favored by folks with RVs and pop-up campers but also used by some tenters, this former KOA Kampground offers such amenities as a pool, a game room, laundry facilities, a playground, picnic tables, and a community hall. This less-than-shady stopover is not ideal for dogs (they're forbidden at the beach), but it's by the beach. Rates are $18–23 for tent sites and up to $40 for RV pull-through sites. Reservations are accepted. Pets aren't accepted in cabins. 8800 Thomas Drive, Panama City Beach; 850/234-5731 or 866/872-2267.

Magnolia Beach RV Park: Fourteen of these 91 RV-only sites look onto St. Andrew Bay, while tall trees lend generous shade to many others. Saltwater fishing can be done from the pier (no license needed), though some patrons may prefer the pool or launching a boat from the concrete ramp to venture as far as the Gulf of Mexico. An adult recreation room keeps snowbirds busy in winter. Keep pets leashed at the seven-acre park. Sites are under $40 nightly. 4100 Magnolia Beach Road, Panama City Beach; 850/235-1581.

Panama City Beach Campground: Pines lend shade to this Miracle Strip-area park, where kids may love what's next door—Shipwreck Island Waterpark, open late April to Labor Day. The 200-site park mainly attracts RVs but welcomes tenters, who choose from 20 sites in a tent section. 11826 Front Beach Road, Panama City Beach; 850/235-1643.

Pineglen RV Park: Three ponds are stocked with fish for fishing at this pleasant, shady, family-owned park, where up to two small leashed pets may join you at an RV site, so long as they're not incessant barkers, they're accompanied by an adult outdoors, and they don't have guard-dog bloodlines, such as pit bull or chow chow. People-pleasers include a screened pool, horseshoes, hammocks, summertime activities for kids age 10 and under, and a wooded area for walking. Rates are $29–39, including cable TV, water, sewer, and basic electricity. 11930 Panama City Parkway, Panama City Beach; 850/230-8535 or 877/740-8535.

Vacation rentals: It can seem easier to find a one-eyed, three-legged squirrel than a pet-permissible vacation home in these parts. Last we looked, though, we did see at least one such home offered at each of these online sites: WeNeedAVacation.com, GreatRentals.com, VacationRentals411.com, and Vamoose.com. All provide details about the homes and ask you to contact the property owner directly.

Panama City

PARKS, BEACHES, AND RECREATION AREAS

15 Naju Dog Park

🐾🐾🐾🐾🐾 🐕 (See Panama City map on page 52)

Time to swim! A big pond meant for bigger dogs and a little pond for small swimmers are star attractions at this beloved off-leash area, though dachshunds, retrievers, and Great Danes tend to ignore such distinctions and gleefully dog-paddle alongside each other at both ponds. Retired racing greyhounds love the fenced broad field—a big five acres. They seem to fly at 20 miles per hour as trailing beagles give it all they've got to try to catch up.

Owners relax on swings or chairs as diggers dig in sanctioned sandy places or chase after new friends. Some agility equipment is provided, as are shelters, water, and restrooms. So is a small-dog area, though most people don't use it. The tended grounds are free of briars or sticker weeds, so paws stay briar-free as dogs play or take part in occasional flyball and agility events.

"It's nothing to see 35–40 dogs run and play together," says a pleased Polly Hunt, who saw a need for a leash-free area going unmet in the city, so in 2002 she opened the private dog park on the grounds of her grooming/boarding/obedience-training facility. The first critter to enjoy the park actually was a cat; the place wasn't yet fully fenced and ready for dogs, so a cat owner asked permission to hang out with her pal.

Dogs must be current on shots and, of course, non-aggressive to enter the membership park, whose flat fee is $18 for an entire month or any portion thereof. Hunt hopes to eventually open a pet-friendly travel-trailer park for upper-end motorhomes on adjoining property.

The park is on the grounds of Naju Boarding & Grooming at 5927 E. Highway 22, a few blocks east of Highway 30A. 850/871-1785.

16 Tyndall Air Force Base

🐾🐾🐾 (See Panama City map on page 52)

Fine, uncrowded nature trails await your pooch at this wildlife-loaded, 12-mile-long peninsula southeast of Panama City. Your first stop should be the Tyndall Visitors Center at 4027 U.S. 98. When you go inside to pick up a visitors pass, you'll be asked to show your driver's license, car registration, and tag number. You may be asked for proof of insurance, too. While there, ask for directions to the Natural Resources Office, where, on weekdays, you can get maps of hiking trails. On weekends or to save a trip, simply ask at the visitors center for directions to the popular hiking trails. Yes, it sounds like a hassle, but it's worth it.

For a pleasant stroll, try the Warbler's Way Nature Trail, an easy trek mostly along a quarter-mile-long elevated boardwalk. The trail passes a rookery where raucous egrets and herons nest from May to September. You'll reach an observation tower where your dog can get a fine view of a freshwater swamp. Maggie went bonkers on this trail, straining at her leash in clear anticipation of catching elusive mammals. If you prefer woods to swamp, take the mile-long Deer Run Nature Trail behind the Natural Resources Office. Visitors at dusk or dawn often see deer.

When you're ready to break out the picnic blanket and dog biscuits, try the Felix Lake Recreation Area, where you'll be shaded by moss-draped oaks. Nearby are a pier and the woodsy Felix Lake Nature Trail, accessible via a narrow boardwalk.

If you don't want to bother with permits or maps, you could trot along a bike path on U.S. 98, though with cars whizzing by it's not as pleasant. Dogs are forbidden on beaches.

The sprawling base is on U.S. 98, eight miles southeast of Panama City. 850/283-2641.

PLACES TO EAT

Sonic Drive-In: One of a chain of spiffy Panhandle drive-ins that remind Maggie of the movie *American Graffiti*, this eatery serves cheeseburgers, all sorts of hot dogs, wraps, salads, steak sandwiches, and more. Just sit tight in your car with your pooch and a carhop will deliver your dinner to you on a tray. Don't forget dessert: While your pooch slurps ice cream, you can have a chocolate, strawberry, or vanilla Coke. 224 W. 23rd St.; 850/763-2296.

PLACES TO STAY

Days Inn Bayside: Located on St. Andrews Bay, this 102-room former Best Western was our favorite place in town before new rules kicked in—only small pets are permitted in designated smoking rooms. Oh well, sighs big Maggie. Across the street there is a great dog walk—a sidewalk that takes you under the shady limbs of oaks and past fine waterfront homes. Amble west about half a mile to reach a stretch of road where you and your dog can splash about in the shallows of St. Andrews Bay. (If you don't want to walk that far, drive about one mile to the few parking spots on the south side of the road.) A private beach, dock fishing, and volleyball are among the motel's amenities. Rates vary seasonally, $55–150. The pet fee is $10 the first night, $5 nightly thereafter. 711 W. Beach Drive, Panama City; 850/763-4622; www.daysinn.com.

Howard Johnson By the Bay: Hold your small dog up to a window of a waterfront room to show him the sandy beach and 475-foot dock on the bay. We're told that pets may stretch their legs on the private beach; to be safe, ask staffers for the current policy. Located one mile east of the Hathaway Bridge, this 80-room, three-story motel offers a restaurant, a lounge, and a pool. Rates normally run $72–76 but can rise to $110 during Spring Break. Pet fee is $25 per stay. Check on current size restrictions (if any); you may be told that only dogs under 25 pounds are accepted. 4601 U.S. 98 West, Panama City; 850/785-0222; www.hojo.com.

La Quinta Inn & Suites: A heated pool and sundeck area with gazebo graces the courtyard of this pleasant, business-oriented hotel, where a small dog may join you in one of the 114 rooms or six suites after stretching his legs around the property's perimeter (not in the courtyard). A reclining chair, fridge, and microwave are among the amenities in extended-stay rooms, geared to pets and their people who plan to stay awhile. Rates for regular rooms normally are $85–115, including continental breakfast and local calls. 1030 E. 23rd St., Panama City; 850/914-0022; www.lq.com.

Super 8 Motel: Rates start at $51 in the off-season and can approach $80 in season at this 63-unit poolside motel, located a mile from Panama City Mall (in case your dog needs a new bandanna). There's a $15 daily pet fee. Dogs must be under 20 pounds, please. 207 Highway 231, Panama City; 850/784-1988; www.super8.com.

Mexico Beach

This is a convenient stopping point between Panama City and Port St. Joe.

PLACES TO STAY

Driftwood Inn: The inn's official greeter is a female Great Dane named Dufus, who nibbles up crumbs left by kids in the tea room and sometimes lounges in the lobby with the resident Amazon parrot, Joe, who heartily chirps "Hello!" Overlooking the Gulf of Mexico, these beachfront units come equipped with fully equipped kitchens. Cats, dogs, and birds have been known to bunk down here with their people. Although Bay County forbids dogs on the beach, there is room to walk your canine companion on the inn's grassy grounds, or ask a staffer for directions to a pet-permissible beach located a couple miles away toward Port St. Joe. Rooms are $95–140. The Street Side Victorian houses run $135–175. Add $10 daily per pet or $35 weekly. 2105 U.S. 98, Mexico Beach; 850/648-5126; www.driftwoodinn.com.

Rustic Sands Campground: Pine trees dot these 20 acres, but the rustic setting doesn't mean dogs must give up watching their favorite TV programs. Cable TV, including HBO, is piped to 50 of the 75 large RV sites at this park, which is busiest November through April. The rest of the family may enjoy the playground, shuffleboard court, heated pool, and the planned wintertime activities that keep retired snowbirds busy in the recreation hall. Sites for RVs or tents are $24–26. Reservations are recommended. The campground is a half mile from the beach and just under 30 miles east of Panama City. 800 N. 15th St., Mexico Beach; 850/648-5229.

Port St. Joe

This dog-friendly corner of the Panhandle is one of the best spots in Florida to spend a carefree, sun-drenched week with your pooch. But until 1998 it had one small problem: It stunk. "Smells like money to me," a service station worker quipped when asked about the aroma wafting from the local paper mill. Since the mill's closure, there's no more stink and just plenty of fun in the drink—the Gulf of Mexico, St. Joseph Bay, Cape San Blas, and the beaches, that is.

Cape San Blas is a 25-mile-long hook of land featuring remote, golden stretches of little-used beach that beckon dogs. Your pooch can also investigate nearby forests. The cape is clear across St. Joseph Bay from the city of Port St. Joe, and it's well worth exploring. Snorkelers can see sea horses, scallops, and sea urchins in the sea grass flats, but the main activities are sunbathing and fishing. Even mediocre anglers like us can catch something here if they stick to easy-breezy surf casting.

DIVERSIONS

Gulf County is one of those increasingly rare areas where you're actually allowed to drive on the beach and let the wind muss your fur—if you're armed with plenty of cash, that is. Tourists pay $150 for the privilege of a beach-driving permit, while Gulf County residents pay $15. Get it at the office of the county tax collector at the Gulf County Courthouse, 1000 Costin Blvd., Port St. Joe. 850/229-6652.

PARKS, BEACHES, AND RECREATION AREAS

🐾 17 St. Joe Beach

🐾🐾 (See Panama City map on page 52)

Local dogs love this long expanse of beach, located in the no-man's land between Mexico Beach and Port St. Joe. Basically stretching from the Bay County/Gulf County line to the closed-down St. Joe paper mill, this sandy romping ground will tempt pets to run like the wind. Alas, leashes are required.

From Mexico Beach, head south on U.S. 98 about one mile or two. Parking can usually be found along the paved area on the gulf-side shoulder of the road. Walk over the dunes to reach the beach, about 30 to 50 yards from your parked car. 850/227-1223.

🐾 18 St. Joseph Peninsula State Park

🐾🐾 (See Panama City map on page 52)

Ospreys, hawks, and other winged creatures will delight your alert bird-watching dog at this 2,516-acre park right off St. Joseph Bay, which ranges from 40-foot-deep troughs to above-sea-level sandbars that are exposed at low tide.

We got conflicting information on doggie-paddling here. On the phone a nice woman told us it's okay for dogs to swim on the bay side (not the ocean side) of the park. Always looking for canine swimming opportunities, we were gleeful. But when we arrived, a guard at the gate said dogs can't go in the water at all—not even on the north side in areas where people clearly don't swim. Oh, well.

You can still have a fine picnic with your leashed dog at the gulf-side picnic tables or in the back picnic area, then follow a remote nature trail that passes within a few feet of the bay, where on most days you're unlikely to see a soul. Guess that would have to do, Maggie decided. We took the St. Joseph Bay Trail near Eagle Harbor to traverse sand pine scrub, salt marsh, and the fiddler crab-covered shoreline of St. Joseph Bay. According to the sign, other common creatures here include the gray fox, raccoon, and striped skunk. Maggie loved darting after skinks on the semi-shady trail, even though she had to wear a leash. As always, bring enough water to help you and your buddy make it through the 20- to 40-minute walk. Think about packing a lunch because the trail passes by a secluded picnic table.

Admission is $4 per vehicle. Take County Road 30 as it veers off U.S. 98 just south of Port St. Joe. When you reach County Road 30E, turn right and head west 9.4 miles to 8899 Cape San Blas Road. 850/227-1327.

19 Constitutional Convention Museum State Park

🐾 🐾 ◄🐾 (See Panama City map on page 52)

Hounds with a nose for history might howl upon learning that today's little Port St. Joe was one of the Sunshine State's biggest cities back in the 1880s, behind only Jacksonville, Pensacola, and Key West. Due to its prominence, it hosted Florida's first constitutional convention.

Leashed dogs are permitted on the grounds of this park, but not in the museum where visitors can take self-guided tours through indoor exhibits about 1830s-era Port St. Joe. Museum admission is $1 per person.

From Highway 71, go south on U.S. 98/Monument Avenue for 1.3 miles, then left onto Allen Memorial Way to the museum ahead. 850/229-8029.

20 Indian Pass Beach

🐾 🐾 🐾 ◄🐾 (See Panama City map on page 52)

We used to love this place back when it remained a rare, undiscovered area where dogs could run in leash-free abandon over a stretch of isolated beach visited by horseback riders and locals. Alas, as growth has packed even the Florida Panhandle with people and their dogs—including people who don't pick up after their dogs—regulations have clamped down on the fun.

Dogs now must wear leashes. What used to be a four-paw experience now merits just two paws. Still, it's worth a stop if you're in the area. At a stretch of shore called Porpoise Run, we happened to see the arching backs of four porpoises playing a game of hide-and-seek a few yards offshore. While Maggie mostly ignored them, we were thrilled. More refined pooches might want to scour the shore for the abundant and beautiful seashells. The clumps of seaweed that are often washed ashore can delight many a canine schnozzle.

From Port St. Joe, head south on U.S. 98, then veer right on County Road 30. Turn left at the fork. Soon you'll be in Indian Pass. Go south on County Road 30B by the old raw bar. The road will twist around a bit and then run parallel to the beach. Take one of the roads to your right (in a neighborhood of beach houses), park at the end of the street, and walk onto the beach via one of the trails across the salt marsh. Or go to the end of County Road 30B, where you can park at a small boat launch and beach area. 850/227-1223.

PLACES TO STAY

Anchor Vacation Properties: This real estate office handles a few vacation homes that accept pets. Rates vary seasonally and by home. 4693 Cape San Blas Rd./County Road 30E, Cape San Blas; 850/229-2777 or 866/654-0999; www.florida-beach.com.

Donna Spears Realty vacation homes: This small real estate agency represents a few pet-friendly homes. Rates vary seasonally and by lodging. Pet fee is $75. 6335 Highway C-30A, Port St. Joe; 850/227-7879 or 800/293-0428; www.donnaspearsrealty.com.

Indian Pass Campground: Cabins and campsites are open to doggies at this rustic campground and charter fishing enterprise located all the way at the eastern tip of Cape San Blas, across from the St. Vincent National Wildlife Refuge. Fifty tree-shaded camping spots sit a few yards from the beach, and there's plenty of room for dogs (just don't plunge into the pool). Fishing is big, with a boat launch, bait sales, and charter reservations geared to fishing the Gulf of Mexico and its passes. Almost everyone brings a dog (and knows each other) in winter, when snowbirds dominate. Reservations are accepted. RV sites cost $30–40 nightly. Primitive tent sites run $17. Cabins range $75–130. 2817 Indian Pass Rd., Port St. Joe; 850/227-7203 or 800/852-1814; www.indianpasscamp.com.

Old Saltworks Cabins: Set on the water at the long-gone site of a Confederate Civil War saltworks, this collection of waterfront cabins and guesthouses pays homage to its history. Its motto: "Experience Civil War history and a Coastal Eco-Paradise at Cape San Blas, Florida." Many lodgings permit pooches; in some cases, only small pets. Rates vary by season and lodging, but expect to pay $89–119 daily, less in winter. Weekly rates are available. Pet fee is $50 weekly. The establishment reserves the right to refuse any pet that "we do not feel 'fits' in Saltworks," rules state. 1085 Cape San Blas Rd., P.O. Box 526, Port St. Joe; 850/229-6097; www.oldsaltworks.com.

DOG-EAR YOUR CALENDAR

Scalloping is a regular family affair, as locals grab their snorkels and fins and head out to the crystal-clear waters of **St. Joseph Bay** in summer to pluck up some fresh, juicy scallops. Some rent a Carolina skiff from Presnell's Bayside Marina in Port St. Joe, then head out into the bay, sometimes with the family dog along. The shallow bay is covered by grass flats and potholes—an angler's dream. Some people also enjoy bird-watching, gathering seashells, or just walking along sandbars. Skiff rentals are $75 for four hours, $95 for six hours, $125 for eight hours. As of this writing, scalloping season is limited to July through mid-September. 850/229-2710.

Presnell's Bayside Marina: After a day of scalloping or tooling around the bay in a rental boat from the on-site marina, dog-tired visitors can plop down to enjoy sunsets and sleep in a tent or RV at these two dozen campsites looking onto St. Joe Bay. Rates are under $25 nightly. Add $4–8 nightly if you bring a boat. 2115 Highway C-30, Port St. Joe; 850/229-2710; www.presnells.com.

Pristine Properties Vacation Rentals: Weekly rentals are the specialty of this agency, which at last count represented about 20 townhouses, view homes, and big houses that permit pets. Rates vary seasonally and by lodging and range $668–3135 weekly. Add a nonrefundable $100 pet fee. 155 Highway 98, Port St. Joe; 850/227-1100 or 800/215-0677; www.visitfloridabeaches. com.

Whispering Pines Cottages: Dogs may head to the beach from these pine- and palm-shaded cottages, or head the opposite direction to follow a boardwalk leading to the bay. Each cottage accommodates up to six people and offers basic amenities vital to hungry hounds—a barbecue grill, a full kitchen, and a microwave oven. Anglers can try for flounder at the shoreline and redfish in the bay. Some visitors wade into the shallow bay to pluck scallops during scalloping season (July to September). Cottage rentals run $75–85. The pet fee is $5 per stay. Weekly and monthly rates are available. 1177 Cape San Blas Rd./Highway 30E, Port St. Joe; 850/227-7252; www.cape-sanblas.com/whispine.

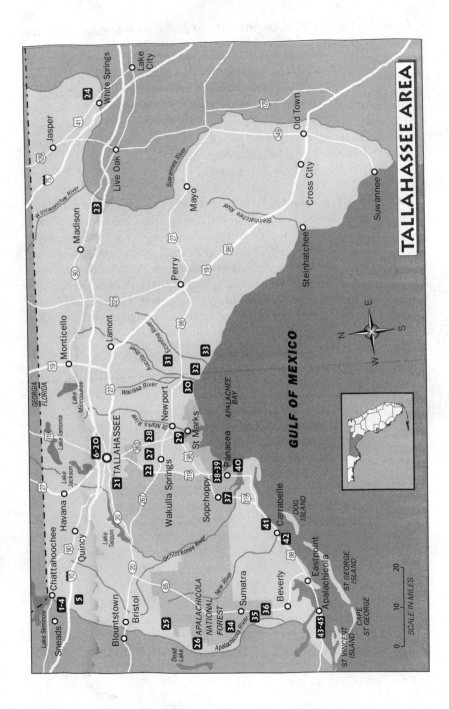

TALLAHASSEE AREA

CHAPTER 3

Tallahassee Area

Don't take offense if you and your pooch stroll up to the capitol building and a man in an expensive suit slaps another's back and says, "Now, you know that dog won't hunt."

He isn't talking about your little Muffy. That's an expression legislators and lobbyists use when they refer to a bill or amendment that just won't cut the mustard. Dogs might salivate when they hear that the popular saying dates back to the days when the Pork Chop Gang ran things around Tallahassee. A group of lawmakers from the rural north, the Pork Chop Gang ran roughshod over the interests of the majority of Floridians, who lived in the cities of central and southern Florida, for years.

Luckily for dogs and all lovers of the outdoors, the Pork Chop Gang no longer controls things in the capital, and their modern-day counterparts are much more inclined to set aside natural lands for people and animals to enjoy. These huge swaths of greenery stretch across northern Florida, providing much-needed areas where dogs may tread without fear. In the Tallahassee

PICK OF THE LITTER—TALLAHASSEE AREA

BEST BEACH VACATION DESTINATION
St. George Island (page 115)

BEST DOG PARK
Tom Brown Off-Leash Dog Park, Tallahassee (page 93)

BEST HISTORIC INN
Gibson Inn, Apalachicola (page 114)

BEST PLACE TO PEER INTO SINKHOLES
Leon Sinks Geological Area, Tallahassee (page 95)

THE ORIGINAL "GARDEN OF EDEN"
Torreya State Park, Chattahoochee (page 84)

BEST WILDLIFE VIEWING
St. Marks National Wildlife Refuge, St. Marks (page 104)

BEST "OUTDOOR MUSEUM"
Mission San Luis de Apalachee, Tallahassee (page 91)

region, the best one is undoubtedly the mammoth Apalachicola National Forest, located just outside the city limits.

The optimum place to start your visit to Tallahassee itself is the capitol building, located on Monroe Street where Apalachee Parkway dead-ends. Head to the west side of the new capitol–the sleek, white, 22-story tower rising behind the quaint old 1902 capitol building with candy-cane-striped awnings. Your dog, who will have to be tied to a railing outside, can enjoy a view of the Florida Supreme Court building while you quickly head inside to the capitol's tourism booth to get brochures and advice.

Tallahassee proper is a very dog-friendly city. Don't miss Myers Park, a woodsy retreat just a few blocks southeast of the capitol, where you might see a legislator or cabinet member jogging. Local pups prefer the leash-free dog park at Tom Brown Park. (See Parks, Beaches, and Recreation Areas in this chapter for more information on both.)

The entire region is jam-packed with places that pooches would love to visit. Take your pick among beaches, deep dark forests, rivers, or hills. Maggie's nominee for Can't-Miss-It Experience Outside Tallahassee City Limits would have to be a jaunt on the hiking trails at the Leon Sinks Geological Area in Apalachicola National Forest.

One of the biggest green spots on the Florida map, as well as one of the last bastions of the Florida black bear, the 881 square miles in the national forest are tops on any dog's list of places to visit. Just ask Kanga and Sherlock. When their alpha male, David Bruns, rumbles his truck along the logging roads, then stops, they know what comes next: time to run! "They run 'til they can't stand up anymore," says Bruns, who, along with his wife, Linda Kleindienst-Bruns, owns the dynamic duo. His advice: "Stop anywhere and let Rover out."

Leashes are required in developed picnic spots and other recreation areas, and pooches are forbidden in the beach sections of recreation areas. Most of the forest lies on the Woodville Karst Plain, which is a limestone honeycomb beneath the ground between Tallahassee and the Gulf of Mexico. This is why you see sinkholes—places where the ground has opened up and swallowed itself.

Chattahoochee

PARKS, BEACHES, AND RECREATION AREAS

1 Sneads Park

 (See Tallahassee map on page 80)

A dog with a leash and a yearning to play the national sport might want to come here and see the baseball fields, but walking around the lake and the circular path through the picnic areas may be sufficient. Most four-legged visitors stay away in season, because the fields are taken by baseball and soccer players. Dogs can't swim in the lake or take advantage of the playground, but lunch at a picnic table (some covered) or the park's two big shelters may produce a canine smile.

The park is west of town on U.S. 90 at Legion Road. 850/593-6636.

2 Jim Woodruff Dam

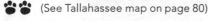 (See Tallahassee map on page 80)

Some of the least-known canine romping grounds in Florida are, like this one, recreation areas run by the U.S. Army Corps of Engineers. This place has lots of open fields that beckon dogs to run. Too bad leashes are required. You'll find a picnic table under the spreading, moss-draped limbs of a big oak tree outside the main office, and a large grassy field where your dog will want to catch a Frisbee or ball. There's another grassy field just down the road, on a bluff overlooking the river. The dam here, built across the Apalachicola River, backs up the river to form Lake Seminole on the Florida-Georgia border. You can drive out on the dam, and there may be some Canada geese to bark at.

This recreation area is a great place for a picnic. If your dog approves, you can pick up some grub at the IGA Foodliner in town on U.S. 90 by County Road 269.

From Chattahoochee, head west a few blocks on U.S. 90 and look for signs that direct you to the Jim Woodruff Dam. Or cross the Apalachicola River to the west side, where there are even more open fields. The west side gets lighter use than the east side, and your doggy will gain an even better view of Lake Seminole because the bluffs rise higher on the west bank. 912/662-2001.

❸ Clyde T. Hopkins Municipal Park

🐾🐾 (See Tallahassee map on page 80)

This three-acre picnic area looking onto the Apalachicola River offers some covered tables and a more citified experience than nearby Jim Woodruff Dam. The boat ramp explains the park's nickname among locals: "River Landing."

The park is on the east side of the river just south of U.S. 90. 850/663-2123 or 850/663-4046.

❹ Angus Gholson Jr. Nature Park of Chattahoochee

🐾🐾 (See Tallahassee map on page 80)

Trees, trees, and more trees. For at least a century, the maples, oaks, magnolias, and smaller plants here have been left intact, making for a pleasant stroll along an interpretive trail highlighting no fewer than 66 plants, including the dogwood tree. The dogtooth violet numbers among the nearly two dozen wildflowers at this prized park, formerly named Chattahoochee Nature Park.

Alert doggies will notice that the aptly named Spring Trail follows a spring. Where the spring goes underground, the trail veers northward to offer turnoffs to a shorter Ridge Trail and the Pine Trail. Lucky dogs could glimpse a wild turkey or bobwhite quail. Unlucky dogs might meet up with a poisonous rattlesnake or coral snake, as well as ticks, red bugs, and deer flies, so stay on the woodland trail. Picnic tables and grills are at the center of the park, which also features a natural spring. Fill the pet's water bowl at the restrooms.

The park is on Morgan Avenue, just west of the junction of Morgan Avenue, Bolivar Street, and Brent Street. 850/663-2123 or 850/663-4046.

❺ Torreya State Park

🐾🐾🐾 👣 (See Tallahassee map on page 80)

This part of Florida took on a special significance when the late E. E. Callaway proclaimed it the likely site of the original Garden of Eden. That's right. Callaway, a lawyer, judge, theologian, politician, real estate salesman, and fighter against communism, even wrote a 1966 book called *In the Beginning*, explaining why he believed that the eastern bank of the Apalachicola River not far south of this park is where Adam and Eve met their dear friend the snake. Whether or not they believe that story, dogs will appreciate the fabulous trails along Florida's largest river.

Considered a National Recreational Trail, the Apalachicola River Bluffs Trail provides panoramic views atop 150-foot-high bluffs—a rare sight in flat Florida. The trail leads for 7.3 miles to a hardwood forest and old Confederate gun pits. The Weeping Ridge Trail, less than one mile long, showcases a lush, deep ravine. Circling the park's east side is Rock Creek Trail, a 7.2-mile loop.

Lucky pooches might spot the Apalachicola dusky salamander, a rare creature whose bloodlines are more closely tied to the salamanders of the Great Smoky Mountains than to Florida salamanders. When your dog does his leg lifts, try to keep him away from the nearly extinct torreya tree—also known as the Florida yew—that grows only along the bluffs of the Apalachicola. Its closest relatives grow in Northern California and China, and scientists are using those to develop an anticancer drug. Locals used to call the torreya "gopher wood," which is what the Bible says Noah's ark was made of, leading Callaway to believe this was also the site where Noah built his ark. While few people took Callaway seriously, he did interest investors in an unrealized Garden of Eden theme park.

Pets are forbidden in the campground.

Admission is $2 per vehicle. The park is 13 miles north of Bristol on County Road 1641. From I-10, exit onto State Road 12 to go west about 11 miles to County Road 1641. Turn right (north). Continue about seven miles to 2576 Northwest Torreya Park Road. 850/643-2674.

PLACES TO STAY

East Bank Campground, Lake Seminole: Overlooking pretty Lake Seminole, this well-kept U.S. Army Corps of Engineers 74-site campground is actually across the border in Georgia, but near Chattahoochee. Follow a nature trail with your leashed buddy here after sharing a meal at the picnic tables, or launch your boat to try to snag fish lurking beneath the lake's submerged logs. Showers, coin laundry, a play area, and a dump station are available. Campsites with water and electricity run $16. The two tent sites cost $12 nightly. From I-10 (Exit 166), go north on Highway 269 to U.S. 90 in Chattahoochee. Turn left onto U.S. 90. Continue to Bolivar Street/Booster Club Road, where you'll turn right, go one mile, and turn left onto East Bank Road. 229/662-9273 or 877/444-6777.

Tallahassee

Tallahassee is closer to the Great Smoky Mountains than to Miami, so it's no surprise that some people call the capital "The Other Florida" or "Florida with a Southern Accent." From this hilly town, you can drive to Alabama, Louisiana, or eight other states in less time than it takes to get to Key West. The nation's largest concentration of plantations—71—is found between here and Thomasville, Georgia, 28 miles away, and your dog is welcome to frolic around the grounds of one of the prettiest, Pebble Hill in Thomasville.

An inquisitive dog might wonder why the capital is way up in Tallahassee instead of in a central spot like Orlando. In fact, in 1823, when Governor William Duval ordered his staff to find a permanent locale for the state seal, the town was in the center, more or less, for people traveling by boat from Pensacola and on horseback from St. Augustine. Back then, virtually no one lived south of Cedar Key.

Maggie loved modern-day Tallahassee. She was exuberant, running through city parks where lacy moss hung from oaks and practically touched the ground. Limbs heavy with moss arch in a canopy over five main streets: Centerville, St. Augustine, Miccosukee, Meridian, and Old Bainbridge. They make joyriding with your pooch just that—a joy. Tallahassee is "Florida's Other Magic Kingdom," as one bicycling magazine dubbed it.

PARKS, BEACHES, AND RECREATION AREAS

6 A. J. Henry Park

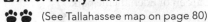 (See Tallahassee map on page 80)

These 72 acres of greenery beckon to dogs. "Come, sniff along our nature trails," they seem to say, judging by the frenzied way dogs pace upon entering the park. Follow a nature trail or cross over the lake on the boardwalk, keeping your pooch leashed. Afterward, take a break at a picnic table while the kids head to the playground.

This city park is in northeastern Tallahassee on A. J. Henry Park Drive, south of Killearn Estates and east of Arbor Hills. 850/891-3866.

7 Campbell Pond

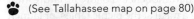 (See Tallahassee map on page 80)

At 25 acres, this park would seem to be the perfect remedy for a pent-up pooch—until your dog realizes that a lake takes up nearly all of those acres. No matter. Just roam the open spaces with your leashed pal and dream of the hot dogs you'll be throwing onto the grill later. There is also a playground.

The park is south of Four Points, off Woodville Highway/Highway 363. 850/891-3866.

8 Governor's Mansion

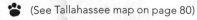 (See Tallahassee map on page 80)

Pooches can't actually tour the governor's mansion, but they're welcome to visit the very small park across the street. The park is centered on a 21-foot-long bronze statue depicting five children balancing their way along a log—accompanied, of course, by a little pooch! Recent governor Lawton Chiles, the man in charge when the private Mansion Foundation installed the sculpture, said the statue is meant to recall the importance of children: "It reminds us of those carefree days of summer when we wandered around in the woods just being ourselves." Chiles had a tear in his eye at the dedication, perhaps

FETCHING NECESSITIES

Choose a great tree, Charlie Brown: At the **Wilmar Christmas Tree Farm,** leashed Snoopy Dogs often tag along with their people for the time-honored tradition of going to the country to retrieve their own pine, cedar, or cypress for the holidays. The farm is on Highway 27 in the town of Havana.

From Capital Circle in Tallahassee, travel 4.5 miles north on Highway 27 to the tree farm, at left. 850/539-6524.

silently saying thank you for the companionship of his dog, a mutt he took in after the stray pooch wandered into the governor's yard.

The park and mansion are at 700 N. Adams St., a block west of Monroe Street. 850/413-9200.

9 Indianhead Acres Park

 (See Tallahassee map on page 80)

For dogs who are usually stuck in the backyard all day, the trail of this long, thin, 31.5-acre forested park will be a welcome treat, even though they are supposed to be leashed.

The park is on Indianhead Drive, south of Apalachee Parkway near the Governor's Square Mall. 850/891-3866.

10 Jack L. McLean Jr. Park

 (See Tallahassee map on page 80)

Humans appreciate the basketball, tennis, and sand volleyball courts, but dogs are thrilled just by the size of this park: 48 acres. That's enough room for even the biggest Saint Bernard to stretch her legs (with the requisite leash). Pack ice water in a cooler and take a break at a picnic table when your buddy has had enough fun following the nature trail.

The park, formerly known as Southside Park, is on Paul Russell Road, a few blocks west of Monroe Street and across from the Leon County Agriculture Center. 850/891-3866.

11 Lake Ella Park

(See Tallahassee map on page 80)

Maggie loved to get a small bowl of fried chicken livers at Lindy's Fried Chicken (2112 N. Monroe St.) and then head to this 19-acre popular midtown park for a picnic. The focal point is the big lake: People jog around the perimeter, sit at picnic tables and admire the view, sunbathe on the grassy area next to it, or just plain stay in their cars and gaze as if it were Lovers' Leap. After your meal, a stroll around the lake with your leashed pooch may be in order. The .6-mile walk is sure to please most pooches, especially the part where they chase the resident Muscovy ducks and pigeons. Be sure to grab (and use) a pooper-scooper bag at the posted dispensers.

The lake is a popular place to take dogs. Santa stops here for photo opportunities with the furry set during the annual Santa Paws Walk fundraiser held by TREATS, the Tallahassee-Leon County Animal Shelter support group. Hundreds of dogs and their support staffs converge on Lake Ella to circle the lake, socialize, and enjoy dog biscuits in exchange for a $25 entry fee. A dachshund, Winnie, happily arrived with her chauffeur Bruce Ritchie. Despite the throngs of dogs, he marveled that "the large flocks of resident Muscovy ducks didn't seem to mind too much." For the date of the next Paws Walk, go to http://treatsinc.org.

The park is on North Monroe Street at Lake Ella Drive, two miles south of I-10. 850/891-3866.

12 Lake Jackson Mounds State Archaeological Site

🐾🐾🐾🦴 (See Tallahassee map on page 80)

These Seminole Indian burial mounds are considered among Florida's most important archaeological sites—and dogs are welcome to climb to their top. Pets are supposed to be leashed, which makes good sense as you climb 36 feet, up many stairs, to reach the top of the mounds. These grounds served as a big ceremonial center for 13th-century Native Americans. Remains of tribal leaders have been found buried here with cloaks and copper breastplates.

Maggie seemed just as interested in the rest of the park. She ran like a major league outfielder to jump over a drainage ditch while playfully chasing two happy canines. (They apparently didn't notice the short bridge several paces away.)

A nature trail behind the mounds leads walkers on a pleasant, 30-minute stroll past remains of a gristmill dam and an earthen dike from Colonel Robert Butler's antebellum cotton plantation, once located here. Water bowls for pooches can be filled at restrooms. Picnic tables provide a place to rest. Boaters can launch into Lake Jackson from a ramp outside the park.

A funny thing happened to Lake Jackson in 1982: It disappeared. Old-timers knew it was nothing odd. The lake's 12 billion gallons of water vanished in 1907, 1936, and 1957, too. Heck, corn even grew in the lake bed in 1957. Turns out the lake is like a bathtub: When enough water washes into it, the force pushes rocks and sediment out of clogged holes at the lake bottom, causing it to drain. During droughts, not enough rain falls to replace the vanishing water and the lake eventually disappears. When you visit, though, it will probably be here.

Admission is $2 per carload. The park is off U.S. 27, two miles north of I-10, at 3600 Indian Mounds Road. 850/922-6007.

FETCHING NECESSITIES

Get a true family portrait: Outside of Tallahassee in the town of Havana, a spaniel named Max goes to work with photographer Eric Newhall, lest the pooch tear up the house while his master is away. Your dog is welcome for a photography session and to meet Max, as several families and their pets have. Max may introduce you to Kodak and Fuji, two cats whom he considers his pets. The $104 portrait-sitting fee gets you an 8-by-10 photo. 305 N. Main St., Havana; 850/224-3824.

13 Lewis Park

🐾🐾 (See Tallahassee map on page 80)

This strip of greenery is really the median of Park Avenue, a few blocks north of the capitol building and right by the federal courthouse. Moss-draped oaks shade the lunchtime crowd and serve as a source of local pride. The tree stump at Park Avenue and Gadsden Street isn't just any old leg-lift target: One of the first festivals in the South—the May Party—was centered around that stump when it was a stately oak.

Upon exhausting this spot, continue down Park Avenue to explore the Park Avenue Historic District, listed on the National Register of Historic Places. The series of greenspaces in the middle of Park Avenue form what the city calls the Park Avenue Chain of Parks, which began humbly as a dirt clearing to protect early residents from Native American attacks.

As you stroll Park Avenue, notice some historic sites. World War I soldiers were nursed at a hospital in the circa-1839 Chittenden House at 323 E. Park Avenue. Horses lived in the basement of the Murphy House (317 E. Park Ave.) back when Union soldiers slept upstairs during the Reconstruction-era occupation of Tallahassee.

Turn north onto Gadsden Street, and you'll reach the Meginiss-Munroe House (125 N. Gadsden St.), where soldiers wounded in Florida's most important Civil War conflict—the Battle of Olustee—were treated. At St. John's Episcopal Church (211 N. Monroe St.), one of the nation's few remaining hand-rung chimes hangs in its tower. The Old City Cemetery is farther west on Park Avenue. For a walking tour brochure, call 850/488-7100.

Lewis Park is at Park Avenue and Calhoun Street. The Park Avenue Chain of Parks stretches from Meridian Street to Bronough Street. The historic district stretches from Meridian Street westward to Martin Luther King Boulevard. 850/891-3866.

14 Maclay State Gardens

🐾🐾 ◀▇ (See Tallahassee map on page 80)

Follow a couple of loop trails in the recreation area at Lake Hall or take a forested 3.5-mile path that circles scenic Lake Overstreet, whose fish lure hungry wading birds hoping for a meal. Rolling hills and pretty deep ravines greet walkers on yet another trail: the 1.5-mile Ravine Trail, whose ravine system and plants would remind University of Georgia's bulldog mascot of the northern reaches of his home state or the Appalachians in North Carolina. Deer and bobcats live among its live oaks, magnolias, maple, and dogwoods.

Hopefully that's enough fun for your pooch, because she's not permitted in the 28 acres of ornamental gardens created by New York financier Alfred B. and Louise Maclay back when they wintered here and entertained the Duke and Duchess of Windsor. Nor may pets run on the beach or jump in any lake—where alligators likely lurk (keep dogs leashed).

After a walk, share a picnic lunch at tables overlooking Lake Overstreet or Lake Hall. Later, exit the park and take a joyride eastward down tree-canopied Thomasville Road.

Entrance costs $4 per vehicle. You'll pay extra to tour the gardens (where dogs are banned). The park is at 3540 Thomasville Road, less than one mile north of I-10. The entrance is at left, across from Killearney Way. 850/487-4556.

15 Miccosukee Canopy Road Greenway

🐾🐾🐾 (See Tallahassee map on page 80)

City pooches who are stuck in the house all week are sure to get dog-tired while traversing the rolling hills of this 5.5-mile-long trail through sun-dappled pine forests, large pastures, and shadier mixed hardwood forests. Shared by hikers, bicyclists, and horseback riders, the hard-packed clay and mulch trail has become "a popular place for people to walk dogs," reports local resident Bruce Ritchie, whose dachshund, Winnie, pines to join him amid the pines.

Trailside benches and picnic tables allow pooped pooches to take a break while taking in the pretty rural setting of North Florida's Red Hills Region. Lucky dogs may notice a Sherman's fox squirrel and some 46 species of birds, including herons. Bring a packed lunch. Drinking water is available at the parking areas.

The greenway runs parallel to the city's canopy roads. From Tallahassee, take Miccosukee Road east to Edenfield Road; park near this intersection, on the left-hand side of Miccosukee Road. Restrooms, drinking water, and a picnic area are found there. Another parking area is at the intersection of Miccosukee Road and Thornton Road. 850/488-0221.

DIVERSIONS

Those paws were made for walkin', and a quaint place to do it is downtown Quincy's 36-block **National Register Historic District,** where you'll find Florida's first bank. Quincy State Bank (now a retail store) sits at 22 E. Washington Street. Down the block is a 1940s theater building originally named The Leaf in honor of the area's historic crops of cigarwrapper tobacco; now shops and offices reside at 118 E. Washington Street.

Incorporated in 1828 before Florida even became a state, Quincy features a town square with a refurbished 1912 central courthouse. Plaques explain the historic significance of various buildings, such as a church that served as a makeshift hospital for Confederate soldiers during the Civil War (St. Paul's Episcopal Church, 10 W. King St.). The town's first cigars, White Owls, were produced primarily by Alsatian German immigrants in the 1890s in what now is a retail/office/residential complex at 404 Madison Street.

A Civil War-era boardinghouse numbers among the historic district's 184 town lots, as does the pooch-permissible Allison House Inn (see Places to Stay in the Tallahassee section). Homemade dog biscuits are presented to canine guests of Allison House, built by a guy who went on to become a Florida governor. To sniff out more Quincy history, contact the Gadsden County Chamber of Commerce, 208 N. Adams St., Quincy; 850/627-9231 or 800/627-9231.

16 Mission San Luis de Apalachee

🐾🐾 ◄● (See Tallahassee map on page 80)

Essentially an outdoor museum that allows leashed dogs, this former 17th-century Spanish mission and Apalachee Indian town site features an unpaved trail that connects outdoor exhibits and archaeological excavation areas. Hey, dogs dig in the backyard at home, so why not let them see how the pros do it? Your pooch can often watch researchers working in an outdoor laboratory here and learn about history.

As you stroll, you can read to her from a handful of trailside exhibits covering such things as a Spanish fort, a church where people were buried in the floor, and a council house where native ceremonies were held. All manner of artifacts have been uncovered, including pieces of a baptismal font, aboriginal pottery, religious medallions, ceramics made in far-away Spain, and animal skeletons, including of domestic dogs.

Bring a picnic lunch to fill your growling tummies afterward. Picnic tables are located by the visitors center.

The mission site is considered second in Florida only to St. Augustine in historical importance. At least 1,400 people lived in this settlement at its height in 1675. Your pet will be padding around on land that from 1656 to 1704 served as the western capital of the mission system in what then was called "La Florida."

Admission is free. From I-10, go south on Monroe Street to Tennessee Street, where you'll turn right (west). Continue on Tennessee and turn right (north) onto White Drive. Turn right at Mission Road and proceed to the 60-acre site at 2020 W. Mission Road. 850/487-3711.

17 Myers Park

🐾🐾🐾 (See Tallahassee map on page 80)

Maggie first fell in love with Tallahassee when she visited this jewel of a neighborhood park that features trees, trees, and more trees. Not far from the capitol building, the lovely retreat lures workers from the nearby government offices who eat bag lunches in parked cars overlooking the hilly 47-acre terrain and its impressive oaks. Late in the day, it wouldn't be unusual to see a member of the Florida cabinet or a legislator jogging on the long, winding fitness trail. Dogs, of course, couldn't care less about the politicians (unless, of course, they've brought some of their legendary pork!).

While pets are supposed to be leashed, we've seen well-mannered leashless pooches follow the fitness trail. Picnic tables are near the three tennis courts and a fenced ball field at the park's southwest corner.

To see where the nation's first Christmas celebration took place back in 1539, hop back into the car and motor to the nearby De Soto State Historic Site, 1022 De Soto Park Dr., just north of Magnolia Avenue, off Lafayette Street. A kiosk is the only thing that explains the historic significance of this little-noticed, otherwise nondescript spot, which these days is little more than a manicured lawn, a cute cottage, and the former country house of long-ago Governor John Martin. Here in 1539, a dozen priests—who had accompanied Spanish explorer Hernando de Soto and his 600 men—celebrated the birth of Jesus. The encampment left behind rare copper coins, a pig's jaw, and fragments of armor as evidence of their visit. Each January, cannons blast during a reenactment of that first encampment, so leave gun-shy dogs at home that day. For reenactment dates, call 850/922-6007.

Myers Park is at Lafayette Street and Myers Park Drive. 850/891-3866.

18 San Luis Park

🐾🐾🐾🐾 🐕 (See Tallahassee map on page 80)

Born free, as free as the–oh, wait a minute, that's for lions! But your pooch is free to run unencumbered here. Pooches chase each other excitedly and occasionally tussle with gusto at the city's second leash-free dog park, which is favored by pet-owning college students who live relatively nearby. A fence surrounds the densely wooded 1.5 acres. At picnic tables, humans sit and watch the scene.

It's a welcome addition to what already was one of the better city parks by canine standards, though the dog park can get crowded after work hours (around dusk), making some less-socialized animals apt to act out. Bags the boxer and his owner, Brett Gainey, actually prefer the trails found outside the dog park, especially after a few too-rough tussles at the paw park. "He just likes to run. You can't stop him," says Gainey, who often rides a bike as Bags runs alongside down the trails.

The paw park is within 69-acre San Luis Park, whose rolling hills could satisfy the cravings of any cooped-up pooch. Every time you visit, you can vary the routine: Follow a nature trail on one trip, take the boardwalk around 10-acre Lake Esther the next. On another day, try a fitness trail with your leashed buddy. Bring lunch to munch in a lakeside pavilion or picnic shelter if your pal can stand to spend some more quality time with you.

The park is in northwestern Tallahassee on San Luis Road, just south of Tharpe Street. The dog park is toward the center, just south of the lake and playground. 850/891-3866.

19 Tom Brown Off-Leash Dog Park

🐾🐾🐾🐾🐕 (See Tallahassee map on page 80)

Time to run! That's the point of this popular two-acre fenced field found within 255-acre Tom Brown Park. Dogs run to their hearts' content—chasing balls, racing each other like sprinters, or just plain socializing on the treeless field. Small dogs go downhill a little ways to enter their own nearby separate fenced area, about an acre or less in size. A shy dachshund named Winnie, however, prefers to watch the dogs for a few minutes through the fence, then go for a walk on hiking trails elsewhere (leashed, of course), says her loving chauffeur/companion, Bruce Ritchie.

The city's first off-leash dog area owes its existence to irate dog owners who were collared by pooch patrollers for letting their pets run freely in regular city parks. A committee was formed and concluded a dog park was needed. The idea took off, the city donated the land, and the Ochlockonee River Kennel Club doggedly raised money for a fence. Now visitors are asked to do their part by picking up after their dogs with the disposable bags provided at posted dispensers.

Once you leave the confines of the dog parks, be sure to snap on your pal's leash. That's the policy in the rest of Tom Brown Park, a popular destination for its ball fields, BMX track, tennis courts, playground, racquetball courts, and woodsy areas.

From Capital Circle Southeast, head east on Conner Boulevard, then left on Easterwood Drive to enter Tom Brown Park. Take the first right. Pass the playground area, cross the bridge, then find the dog-park parking area at right. 850/891-3866.

DOG-EAR YOUR CALENDAR

Your dog may turn up his wet nose at the watermelon seed-spitting contest at Monticello's annual Watermelon Festival, but he'll love its **Melon Mutt** run held most Junes. The object: You two run together and try to beat out other dog/pal teams in a footrace. Just lace up your tennies, strap on the leash, and run! Shy dogs can watch from the sidelines. Call 850/997-5552.

Just about every season, dogs can race to regional pet-friendly events and leave the boring old house behind. In October, the Blessing of the Animals draws leashed dogs and cats to St. Luke's Episcopal Community of Life church in Tallahassee; 850/385-7889. Prayers are said for each critter, though dogs most remember the free goodies.

As many as 200 howl-oweeners every October enjoy **Dog-o-ween** at Tallahassee's Tom Brown Park, where a costume contest prompts some pets and their people to wear matching costumes. Massages for hounds and humans sometimes are offered, as are ice cream sundaes for dogs. To learn this year's offerings, call 850/224-9193. Every winter, Santa arrives to town for pet photo sessions. Dogs and their people line up for portraits at PETsMART, 3220 Capital Circle NE, Tallahassee; 850/297-1500. A walk around Lake Ella is added to the portrait session at the annual Santa Paws Walk at Lake Ella Park (for dates, go to http://treatsinc.org).

Finally, cleanliness is next to dogliness, so when it's time to come clean, the Leon County Humane Society will do the dirty work for $7 during monthly **Dog Dippin' Days,** held April through September. Baths are given outdoors, a bonus for dogs like Mocha, a chow mix. "She does not like to take a bath, but she will take them outside," says Mocha's friend, Michele Taylor. "Inside, and you can forget it." Call 850/224-9193.

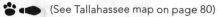

20 Vietnam Veterans Memorial

 (See Tallahassee map on page 80)

This is not a particularly dazzling place for dogs, but you may wish to make a solemn stop at this black granite memorial. The names of 1,942 Floridians who died in the war are engraved here, as are the names of 83 fighters who remain missing in action. The memorial is located across Monroe Street from the Old Capitol, which is at 400 S. Monroe St. 850/413-9200.

21 Silver Lake Recreation Area

🐾🐾🐾 (See Tallahassee map on page 80)

Dogs can do the two things they like best here—eat and go for a walk. This lightly used recreation area with a lush feel offers 65 scattered picnic tables that allow you to enjoy private meals with your family while looking onto Silver Lake. When you're ready to walk, strike off down the mile-long interpretive trail that wraps around the lake or follow one of the dirt roads just outside the pay station. Water fountains are available, as are flush toilets, hot showers, and a small boat ramp for boats with electric trolling motors. Dogs are forbidden to swim at the white-sand beach.

Admission is $3 per vehicle. From Tallahassee, drive west on Highway 20, turn south at County Road 260, and continue about four miles, following the signs. 850/926-3561.

22 Leon Sinks Geological Area

🐾🐾🐾 (See Tallahassee map on page 80)

It looks like something out of a Dogzilla movie. The ground simply caved in here long ago, creating giant sinkholes that pups today love to peer into. At this prized getaway for wilderness-minded locals, Maggie's favorite activity was following a boardwalk through the swamps of the Gum Swamp Trail. She also was partial to the Sinkhole Trail, where water covers the bottom of what essentially are big holes in the ground that resemble sunken lakes.

Set aside two hours with your leashed pooch to walk the three scenic trails: the 3.1-mile Sinkhole Trail; the half-mile Crossover Trail; and the 2.3-mile Gum Swamp Trail. You're unlikely to encounter many people most days. Lucky dogs might see fox squirrels or gopher tortoises.

A local dachshund named Winnie loves sniffing the trails. Her companion Bruce Ritchie says leashes are essential "because the walls of the sinkholes are steep, and I've seen a cottonmouth [snake] right on the trail. Winnie walked right by it and neither noticed." Swimming is forbidden; both humans and dogs have drowned in sinks, officials say.

Dogs who dig in their own backyards might be surprised to learn that, theoretically, new sinkholes could form here out of the blue—without digging (not to worry, though; there have been no reports of doggies being swallowed by the earth). Rain eats away at the hole-filled limestone that lies underground. Peer into the sinkholes to see an aquifer, a layer of water-bearing rock that supplies the water that eventually fills dog bowls.

Take a break at picnic tables. Restrooms are in the parking area.

Admission is $3 per carload. Leon Sinks Geological Area is on the west side of Crawfordville Road/U.S. 319, just north of the Leon/Wakulla county line. It's four miles south of where County Road 61 diverges from Crawfordville Highway. 850/926-3561.

PLACES TO EAT

Barnacle Bill's: Dogs and their people head to the deck of this casual local institution known for its steamed shellfish. Just poke your head inside to let a server know you're eating at the deck, then help will be on the way. Try the bacon-wrapped shrimp appetizer. 1830 N. Monroe St.; 850/385-8734.

Baskin-Robbins: For a cool break during your downtown perambulations, tether your dog outside, head inside to order frozen yogurt or hand-packed ice cream, then join your pooch to savor the treat. 904 Thomasville Rd.; 850/224-0634.

Black Dog Cafe: After a walk around Lake Ella, take a seat outside this popular spot for readers, coffee drinkers, and dog lovers to sample pastries, teas, coffee, ice cream, and more. 229 Lake Ella Dr.; 850/224-2518.

Chez Pierre: A container of dog biscuits is kept at the ready at this pet-friendly fine eatery that's been visited by a wide variety of animals over the years—dogs, lizards, ferrets, and snakes. You'll sit on the gorgeous deck of this 1920s restored home in Midtown Tallahassee and enjoy French cuisine blended with Southern hospitality. Dinners include rack of lamb, crab cakes, and tea leaf-smoked salmon. Lunch offerings include a burger with Brie cheese and a lobster BLT. 1215 Thomasville Rd.; 850/222-0936.

Dog Et Al: Hungry pups who need a hot dog pronto can head to the drive-through window of this fast-food restaurant celebrating the delights of sausages and wieners. 1456 S. Monroe St.; 850/222-4099.

Food Glorious Food: For dogs who believe variety is the spice of life, the changing daily menu at this award-winning outdoor café at shady Betton Place should keep the taste buds intrigued. Creative sandwiches, savory soups, nearly a dozen salads, fine wines, and "desserts that are da bomb" (as described by the Tallahassee Democrat) are served at outdoor tables year-round. Sample entrées include duck breast with fresh wilted greens, curried chicken with couscous, and barbecued salmon with black-bean-and-rice ragout. 1950 Thomasville Rd.; 850/224-9974.

Hopkins Eatery: Unusual sandwiches include the B.E.T.—bacon, egg salad, and tomato—but regular sandwiches, subs, salads, and sweets are served up, too. Located across the street from pooch-favorite Lake Ella Park and next door to the pet-permissible Panhandle Pet Supply store, it's a convenient place to eat at the outdoor tables. Or get a packed lunch to take to the lake. 1700 N. Monroe St.; 850/386-4258.

PLACES TO STAY

Allison House Inn: Homemade doggie biscuits perk up canine guests at this historic district home built in 1843 by A. K. Allison, a soldier/lawyer who later became governor of Florida. Decorated with antiques from the British Isles, this Georgian double-parlored structure offers pampered pooches all the comforts of the modern era: private baths, large rooms, cable television, and individually controlled heat and air-conditioning. Freshly made biscotti are a morning tradition at this bed-and-breakfast inn, hosted by Eileen and Stuart Johnson (a career hotelier). What's the overall feel? Think English country manor. *Southern Living Magazine* called it "a lovely little bed and breakfast." Rates are $85 and up. The inn is off I-10 (Exit 192) in Quincy, 23 miles from Tallahassee's Capitol building. 215 N. Madison St., Quincy; 850/875-2511 or 888/904-2511; www.allisonhouseinn.com.

Best Western Seminole Inn: Pets under 30 pounds may sleep at this 60-room poolside lodging located eight miles from downtown and hope for crumbs from their companions' complimentary morning bagels, doughnuts, and muffins. Rates run $65–139, plus $5 daily pet fee. 6737 Mahan Drive, Tallahassee; 850/656-2938; www.bestwestern.com.

Collegiate Village Inn: The name alludes to the basic motel's proximity to three learning institutions—Florida State University, Tallahassee Community College, and Florida A&M University. "Tallahassee's best year-round hotel value" is a motto of the 150-room poolside motel on busy Tennessee Street. Rates hover around $50, plus $10 nightly for the pooch. 2121 W. Tennessee St., Tallahassee; 850/576-6121; www.collegiatevillageinn.com.

Econo Lodge: After a walk at the pooch-permissible Lake Jackson Mounds State Archaeological Site, you could drive four miles to rest at this 82-unit poolside motel off I-10 (Exit 199). Rates range $50–99. Add $10 daily for the dog. 2681 N. Monroe St., Tallahassee; 850/385-6155; www.econolodge.com.

Homewood Suites by Hilton: Small pets may sleep in these 94 pleasant suites, perhaps after running at the leash-free dog park less than two miles away at Tom Brown Park (see Parks, Beaches, and Recreation Areas, above). Humans can enjoy the hotel's pool, sports court, and exercise room. Rates range $90–140, plus a big $50 pet fee. 2987 Apalachee Parkway, Tallahassee; 850/402-9400; www.homewoodsuites.com.

Howard Johnson Express Inn: As with the other lodgings that populate this stretch of Monroe Street, this 52-room poolside motel off Exit 199 of I-10 is only 10 blocks from a popular dog-walking spot for locals, Lake Ella Park (see Parks, Beaches, and Recreation Areas, above). Rates are $49–69, plus $10 nightly per pet. 2726 N. Monroe St., Tallahassee; 850/386-5000; www.hojo.com.

La Quinta Inn North: Sleepy dogs may appreciate the noon checkout time at this pleasant, 154-room poolside motel off I-10 (Exit 199), if not the proximity to pet-permissible Lake Ella Park located 12 blocks away. Humans may appreciate the free bagels, doughnuts, cereal, and muffins for breakfast. Rates run $70–99. Small pets, please. 2905 N. Monroe St., Tallahassee; 850/385-7172; www.lq.com.

La Quinta Inn South: Carry your free continental breakfast to your room to share with your small dog at this comfortable 134-room poolside motel located within four miles of the capitol building and under two miles from leash-free Tom Brown Park (see Parks, Beaches, and Recreation Areas, above). Rates range $70–110. 2850 Apalachee Parkway, Tallahassee; 850/878-5099; www.lq.com.

Motel 6 Downtown: Offering larger rooms than a typical Motel 6, this 100-unit motel features a kidney-shaped pool and is near dog-friendly Myers Park (see Parks, Beaches, and Recreation Areas, above). If you walk out to the main street with your dog, look west and you'll see the capitol. Rates are $46 and up. One pet per room, please. 1027 Apalachee Parkway, Tallahassee; 850/877-6171; www.motel6.com.

Motel 6 North: The pooch-permissible grounds of Maclay State Gardens are only about 1.5 miles from this 131-room poolside motel, where one pet may join you. Rates begin at $44 at this lodging off I-10 (Exit 203). 1481 Timberlane Rd., Tallahassee; 850/668-2600; www.motel6.com.

Motel 6 West: Every room has a combination bathtub/shower at this 101-unit poolside motel off I-10 (Exit 199). One pet may join you, perhaps after a walk around Lake Ella located 2.5 miles down the road (see Parks, Beaches,

DIVERSIONS

Pad around a plantation, Poochie: Of course leashed dogs are welcome to walk the massive grounds of the impressive **Pebble Hill Plantation,** found 28 miles north of Tallahassee. After all, the original owners adored dogs. That's made obvious by the canine visages captured in paintings hung inside the mansion, listed on the National Register of Historic Places. The outdoor kennels that remain here once sheltered nearly a hundred hunting dogs.

Your mission: Explore the grounds by following a self-guided tour map you'll be handed; it points out areas of interest. While dogs aren't permitted in the mansion, they may take this tour in the out of doors, passing a cow barn, a 1927 dairy, the old dog kennels, and more. Notice the on-site dog hospital, where the family's favorites were treated. What will you see blooming in the gardens in spring? Dogwoods.

Expect to spend 30 minutes to two hours on your outdoor exploration. Stop to munch a packed lunch at the picnic area. Admission to the grounds is $3 for adults, $1.50 for children under age 12. House tours cost $7 for adults, $3.50 for kids in first through sixth grades (younger children aren't permitted). Your pet must wait in the car if you enter the mansion. Skip the mansion tour on hot days; it takes over an hour and parking spots aren't shaded, meaning your pet could suffer from heat exhaustion in mere minutes. The plantation actually is in Georgia on U.S. 319, just five miles south of the city of Thomasville, Georgia. 229/226-2344.

and Recreation Areas, above). Rates start at $40. 2738 N. Monroe St., Tallahassee; 850/386-7878; www.motel6.com.

Red Roof Inn: Free weekday newspapers keep newshounds up on current events at this 109-room poolside motel off I-10 (Exit 199). Rates typically range $48–55 but rise during college football games. 2930 Hospitality St., Tallahassee; 850/385-7884; www.redroof.com.

Shoney's Inn & Suites: After dining a mile away at pet-permissible Barnacle Bill's or Hopkins Eatery (see Places to Eat, above), you could rest at this 113-room poolside motel. Located off Exit 199 of I-10, its regular rooms run $65–98. Pet fee is $15 per stay. 2801 N. Monroe St., Tallahassee; 850/386-8286; www.shoneysinn.com.

Madison

PARKS, BEACHES, AND RECREATION AREAS

23 Suwannee River State Park

🐾🐾🐾 ◀▶ (See Tallahassee map on page 80)

This place is pretty enough to write a song about—and, hey, someone did. Actually, Stephen Foster likely never laid eyes on the dark waters of the Suwannee River, but he used the name when he penned "Old Folks at Home" because of the way it rolls off the tongue.

Munch a picnic lunch with your leashed dog on the Suwannee's banks, where you'll enjoy the panoramic view of the river, the adjoining Withlacoochee River, and the surrounding woods. It's a bucolic scene, even on a busy day; take advantage of it and relax.

When your dog wants to stretch those legs, try the nature trails or meander around the nearly three square miles of river swamps, hills, and shady hardwood hammock. The Suwannee River interpretive trail is a good choice on a hot day, as its hardwood hammock shades pooches as they follow the path along the river and Lime Sink Run. The sunnier, pine-dotted Sandhills Trail takes visitors from the picnic area to the old Columbus Cemetery. A section of this trail follows the route of an old stage road that served as the main route between Pensacola and Jacksonville in the early 1800s.

If your pal doesn't want to leave, you don't have to. A night's sleep at the worthwhile 31-site campground runs $15. Each site offers a picnic table, a grill, electricity, and access to hot showers. Reservations are advised. Book at ReserveAmerica.com or 866/422-6735.

Admission for day use is $3 per vehicle. From I-10, take exit 275, which is west of Live Oak. Go north six miles on U.S. 90 to the park, at right. 904/362-2746.

PLACES TO STAY

Days Inn: Rates are $49 and up, plus a $10 pet fee per stay at this family-owned, 62-room poolside motel off I-10 (Exit 258). State Road 53, Route 1, Box 3329F, Madison; 850/973-3330; www.daysinn.com.

   Suwannee River State Park: See listing under Parks, Beaches, and Recreation Areas, above, for camping information.

White Springs

PARKS, BEACHES, AND RECREATION AREAS

24 Stephen Foster State Folk Cultural Center

🐾🐾🐾🖐 (See Tallahassee map on page 80)

At this 888-acre park and culture center on the banks of the Suwannee River, it's hard to beat a walk along a five-mile loop trail through the woods, followed by a picnic near the carillon tower, where the bells chime four times a day. Dogs aren't allowed in buildings, so they'll miss learning about the guy who wrote the state song, "Old Folks at Home." In the song, Stephen Foster pays tribute to the river flowing here. Keep your dog leashed.

   Oaks shade the 45 sites in the pet-friendly campground. Fee is $16 nightly. Reserve up to one year ahead at 800/326-3521.

   Admission for day-use visitors is $4 per carload. From I-10, exit onto U.S. 41 North and drive nine miles to the park, at left. The park is 13 miles north of Lake City. 386/397-2733.

PLACES TO STAY

Kelly's RV Park: Gopher tortoises live on the grounds and hiking trails surround the park, which spells excitement for canines who stay in the two-room cabins with satellite TV or the 56 shady concrete-pad RV sites (13 pull-through). This off-the-beaten-path place borders state land ribboned with several miles of bike paths that lure bicyclists from all over. Clubhouse amenities include a piano and pool table. Walk leashed dogs in the woods (not park), clean up after them, and don't leave them unattended, as rules dictate. Camping cabins cost $60 daily, $275 weekly, plus $25 for the pooch. Campsites are $27. To get here from I-10, exit onto U.S. 41 and go six miles north to the park, at left (before you cross the Suwannee River). 142 NW Kelly Lane, White Springs; 386/397-2616 or 866/355-9600.

Stephen Foster State Folk Culture Center: See park listing under Parks, Beaches, and Recreation Areas, above, for camping information.

Bristol

PARKS, BEACHES, AND RECREATION AREAS

25 Camel Lake Recreation Area

🐾🐾🐾 (See Tallahassee map on page 80)

From the lake here, strike out on the Florida National Scenic Trail with your leashed pooch, but be sure to turn around at a comfortable distance. One trail spans almost 10 miles, giving leashed visitors a close-up look at swamps and pine forest. An easier, mile-long shady loop trail circles a lake.

Afterward, grill some wieners and have a picnic near small, scenic Camel Lake, which is popular with boaters and anglers. If your dog likes it so much that he doesn't want to leave, he doesn't have to—you can camp for $5 nightly at one of the six lake-view campsites (but your dog can't swim with you). Each site offers a picnic table and a grill or fire ring, plus access to flush toilets and a cold-water outdoor shower meant for rinsing off after swimming. A volunteer host lives on-site.

Day-use fee is $3 per car. From Bristol, take County Road 12 south for about 11 miles, turn left (east) on bumpy Forest Service Road 105 and continue two miles to Camel Lake Recreation Area in Liberty County. 850/926-3561.

26 Apalachicola River Water Management Area

🐾🐾 (See Tallahassee map on page 80)

Canine noses have much to sniff at Florida's largest forested floodplain, which stretches for 19 miles along the Apalachicola River and is home to more reptile and amphibian species than any other area north of Mexico, according to the

Northwest Florida Water Management District. You'll need to be ruff and ready: Squeezed in between Apalachicola National Forest and Dead Lake, this 55-square-mile area in Gulf and Liberty counties is accessible mostly by dirt roads.

Some good hiking trails are found in the northern end at Florida River Island, which is up by the Calhoun County/Gulf County line. Birdwatchers enjoy the springtime aerial displays of Mississippi kites and hawks. Boaters explore the area after launching from the nearly 20 landings found along the floodplain's perimeter. Due to seasonal hunting, it's best to stay away in December, January, and early February. Call ahead at 850/539-5999 to ask about camping with your dog at the few primitive campsites. Every camper in your party must carry an annual Resource Area Permit purchased for under $20 apiece at county tax collector offices.

To reach Florida River Island from Bristol, take County Road 12 south, turn right at County Road 379, then right at Forest Service Road 188. Cross the bridge over the Florida River (an offshoot of the Apalachicola River), which will lead you into the northern end of the water management area. A network of dirt roads serves as good hiking trails. 850/265-3676.

PLACES TO STAY

Apalachicola River Water Management Area: See under Parks, Beaches, and Recreation Areas, above, for information on primitive camping.

Wakulla Springs

PARKS, BEACHES, AND RECREATION AREAS

27 Wakulla Springs State Park

🐾🐾🐾 🐾➔ (See Tallahassee map on page 80)

Dogs are not allowed to set paw on the biggest attraction here—the glass-bottomed boats that give passengers a view of one of the largest freshwater springs in Florida. But leashed dogs are welcome on the hiking trails, one of which has historical interpretive signs. After a visit to the woods, which serve as home to some of the state's biggest, oldest trees, a picnic is another possibility. It's a good thing that dogs aren't allowed in the water, because there are many alligators here. This is one of the few places in Florida where there has been a documented case of an alligator eating a person. Hollywood's Tarzan, Johnny Weissmuller, nonetheless braved the waters to film some underwater scenes at this 2,900-acre park.

Admission is $4 per vehicle. From Tallahassee, head 14 miles south on Highway 267 to where it meets Highway 61. 850/922-3633.

DIVERSIONS

Wander the Wakulla with tails a-wagging: Your dog may see otters and turtles along the cypress-lined **Wakulla River** as you glide along in a rental canoe. Expect a three-hour roundtrip paddle to a point just outside pretty Wakulla Springs State Park from TNT Hideaway, which rents three-person canoes for $25 for four hours from its locale on U.S. 98 at the Wakulla River in St. Marks. Gretchen, who runs the outfit, says your pooch is welcome, though don't let him jump out. "We have alligators, you know," she says. Do alligators ever get into canoes? "In 28 years, none of them have. I don't want anyone spoiling my record." 850/925-6412.

Farther west, in the canine playland of St. George Island, Jeanni McMillan's **Journeys of St. George Island** welcomes dogs on most guided treks around barrier islands and on her seven captains' sightseeing tours in small powerboats. You also may venture out alone with your dog in a rental canoe. For $20 daily, try a kayak, in which some small dogs have traveled, says son Justin McMillan, who helps run the outfit. His Labrador retriever, Blue, often tags along on trips. Blue approves of the company's motto: "We're a trip!" Find them at 240 E. Third St. (bayside), St. George Island. 850/927-3259.

Still, some canoeists daydream about yet another waterway—the Suwannee River, the focus of Florida's state song. Your dog can experience the Suwannee in a canoe rented for $4–6 hourly from **The River Rendezvous** in Mayo; 386/294-2510. As you paddle, tell your pal this tidbit: Stephen Foster really had South Carolina's Pee Dee River in mind when he wrote his song. But he substituted "Suwannee." It sounded a heck of a lot more mellifluous than "Way Down Upon the Pee Dee River."

Woodville

PARKS, BEACHES, AND RECREATION AREAS

28 Natural Bridge Battlefield Historic State Park

🐾🐾 (See Tallahassee map on page 80)

Southern doggies can take solace in a monument to Confederate soldiers here, but even Yanks will have a fine time at this picnic spot far out in the woods. It was here in March 1865 that a ragtag bunch of old men and boys from the area helped Tallahassee become the only Southern capital east of the Mississippi River never to be captured in the Civil War. This is also where the St. Marks

River disappears underground for perhaps 100 yards. Maggie loved it here and ached to run into the woods, but we kept her leashed.

The free park is six miles east of Woodville, off County Road 363. From downtown Tallahassee, go south on Monroe Street/Highway 61 for a little over three miles, then stay straight to follow County Road 363/Woodville Highway for about six miles. Turn left onto Natural Bridge Road. Proceed six miles to 7502 Natural Bridge Road. 850/922-6007.

St. Marks

PARKS, BEACHES, AND RECREATION AREAS

29 Tallahassee-St. Marks Historic Railroad State Trail

🐾🐾🐾 🐾 (See Tallahassee map on page 80)

If your pooch had walked this trail decades ago, he would've risked getting hit by a train. The 16.5-mile route was part of Florida's oldest railroad line, serving for 147 years until 1984. Today, it's an improved trail intended mostly for bicyclists and in-line skaters, who can rent gear at the northern end of the trail. But hikers leave their tracks here, too. The mostly unshaded eight-feet-wide paved path makes a good place for a short stroll. Keep your dog leashed to comply with the rules.

Admission is free. The trail leads from Capital Circle Southeast in Tallahassee all the way south to Posey's Oyster Bar, located on the water at the southern end of State Road 363. To get to the main trailhead from downtown Tallahassee, go south on Monroe Street, which will turn into Woodville Highway/ State Road 363. Upon passing Capital Circle/U.S. 319, look for the trailhead at right. 850/245-2052.

30 St. Marks National Wildlife Refuge

🐾🐾🐾 🐾 (See Tallahassee map on page 80)

This park is alive with birds, and the plentiful resident critters are sure to thrill any pooch who has been cooped up at home all week. Manatees tend to swim in the waters by the lighthouse in May. In June, turkeys flit about the woods. Wood storks often hang out at the headquarters' pond in July. Bald eagles nest here in September. Graceful monarch butterflies return in October. Cool Decembers are good for glimpsing deer, river otters, and possibly a bobcat.

A good first stop is the visitors center (leave the dog outside), where you can peruse a log noting the locations of the day's unusual wildlife sightings. Then go hiking. One primitive trail stretches for seven miles, another for 13 miles. Easily tired dogs can opt for the quarter-mile Headquarters Pond Trail, quarter-mile Lighthouse Levee Trail, or one-third-mile Plum Orchard Pond Trail.

A windshield driving tour—with several designated stopping points along Lighthouse Road—rewards canines who love to sightsee with their heads out the car window, tongues flapping. Pets will take in some of the refuge's many features: upland forests, forested swamps, marshes of fresh and brackish water, and a saltwater estuary. A self-guided auto tour booklet is sold at the visitors center bookstore; it describes sights along the seven-mile drive winding from the parking lot to Apalachee Bay, near the circa-1832 St. Marks Lighthouse (which remains in use).

The refuge is among the nation's oldest and serves as a favorite weekend retreat for Tallahassee bird-watchers, bicyclists, and boaters who use the boat ramps. Bring a cooler for a picnic with your leashed buddy.

Admission is $4 per carload. The entrance is on County Road 59, three miles south of U.S. 98. 850/925-6121.

31 Florida National Scenic Trail/St. Marks

🐾🐾 (See Tallahassee map on page 80)

Part of the Florida Trail follows the dark, clear waters of the Aucilla River north from U.S. 98. You'll pass through hardwood forests as well as swampy areas dominated by cypress and gums. Along the way, curious dogs will likely see some limestone sinkholes. The trail spans 17 miles, but we recommend turning back long before that.

Adventurous doggies may not wish to turn back, considering that the Florida Trail Association contends that this lengthy trail through the St. Marks National Wildlife Refuge traverses more varieties of forest types and wildlife zones than any other segment of the Florida Trail in northern Florida. For a trail map or further details about the St. Marks/Aucilla hike, contact the Florida Trail Association via its website, Florida-Trail.org, or 877/HIKE-FLA.

From the St. Marks area, take U.S. 98 east through Wakulla County and Jefferson County, passing State Road 59 along the way. Look for the trailhead where the road crosses the Aucilla River, which serves as the Jefferson County/Taylor County boundary. 850/925-6121 or 877/HIKE-FLA.

32 Big Bend Wildlife Management Area

🐾🐾 (See Tallahassee map on page 80)

Even the mighty Underdog himself is apt to get pooped hiking the entire 6.5-mile trail at the Hickory Mound Impoundment, considered a Wildlife Viewing Site. You may walk—or drive—atop this dike, which surrounds a large brackish body of water on the coast of the Gulf of Mexico. Swans sometimes spend winters here, while bald eagles may appear at various times of year. Wading birds normally are seen any day. Alligators bask on warm days (keep the pooch leashed). On the other side of the levee, hammocks of palms and pines dot the landscape. Hunters do their thing from about mid-March to late October, so it's best to call before you decide to head out to the 22.5-square-mile impoundment.

To reach the Hickory Mound Impoundment from Perry, drive 18 miles west on U.S. 98, then turn left on Cow Creek Grade. Proceed six miles on gravel road to the check station. Continue two miles to the impoundment. 850/838-9016.

33 Econfina River State Park

🐾🐾🐾 (See Tallahassee map on page 80)

Here in one of the state's quietest corners, your buddy's paws can pad through a wide variety of ecosystems, from salt marsh to thick oak forests. The nine miles of trails used by hikers, equestrians and off-road bicyclists are unimproved, make-do affairs, except for the Florida National Scenic Trail, which passes nearby. Several trails follow routes used long ago by since-abandoned logging trams. By taking paths to the park's southern end, you'll get a panoramic view of the coast and nearby tree-covered islands. Steer clear of any open freshwater, a ranger warns, because the gators "truly love dogs."

Deer sometimes graze beneath oaks at the adjacent Econfina River Resort, where pets may sleep at the 65 RV sites or the separate pine-shaded tent camping areas. Leashes are the rule, lest dogs scamper after wild boar, turkey, and quail in the second-growth pine forest surrounding the resort. Resort amenities include a pool, a clubhouse, a convenience store, and rentals of boats and canoes. Campsites go for $14–23. Reserve at 850/584-2135.

Admission to the seven-square-mile state park is free, though it costs $4.50 to launch a boat. The park is in Taylor County, at the end of County Road 14, south of U.S. 98. From I-10, head south on Highway 257 through Lamont. It will become Highway 14. When you get to the end you'll see the private campground. The state owns the boat ramp and land surrounding Highway 14, so just park on the roadside, a ranger advises. You'll need to walk around several gates made of a cable stretched across the road to get to the trails. Or access the Florida National Scenic Trail where it crosses Highway 14 about two miles north of the campground. 850/922-6007.

PLACES TO STAY

Best Budget Inn: Your hungry dog might sniff for crumbs from your free continental breakfast at this 61-unit poolside motel. Rates run $40–50. Pet fee is $5 nightly. 2220 U.S. 19 South, Perry; 850/584-6231.

Econfina River Resort: See Econfina River State Park under Parks, Beaches, and Recreation Areas, above, for camping information.

Newport Recreation Park: Since dogs aren't allowed to camp in the St. Marks National Wildlife Refuge, consider bedding down at this small, basic, Wakulla County–run campground about four miles up the road on U.S. 98 after a hard day on the trails. Boaters can launch into the St. Marks River from the park's boat ramp, then return to shower at the bathhouse. Campsites range $10–15. From Tallahassee, take State Road 363 south for 12 miles, then turn east on U.S. 98/319. Drive about 2.5 miles, traveling through Newport, to the park. 850/926-7227.

Steinhatchee

PLACES TO STAY

Steinhatchee Landing Resort: Set along the Steinhatchee River, these Victorian homes and cracker-style Southern cottages recall earlier times. Time moves a little slower at this 35-acre, laid-back resort, where 10 cottages accept pets (typically under 28 pounds).

"We are blessed with hundreds of squirrels, which delights both people and dogs," reports R. Dean Fowler, resort developer. The family-oriented resort is "especially pet friendly. Justin, our nine-year-old Maltese, is in charge of security and our dog activity program."

Dogs must behave around the petting zoo's goats and ducks. Guests get free seven-day passes to pooch-permissible state parks, including Peacock Springs State Park (36 miles away). This also is a good base for exploring Little River Springs, Charles Springs, and Royal Springs (see Gainesville chapter). Nightly rates range $132–270. You must post a $250 security deposit on your credit card. 228 NE Highway 51, P.O. Box 789, Steinhatchee; 352/498-3513; www.steinhatcheelanding.com.

Sumatra

PARKS, BEACHES, AND RECREATION AREAS

3.4 Wright Lake Recreation Area

🐾🐾 (See Tallahassee map on page 80)

For a pleasant walk, follow a five-mile-long interpretive trail through pine forests and past swampy areas. You may notice pitcher plants along the way. Double back at a comfortable distance for your leashed pooch, who will appreciate sharing your lunch back at the lake-view picnic tables.

Next to cypress-lined Wright Lake, a 20-site camping area provides something that many campgrounds within Apalachicola National Forest don't: hot showers, drinking water, a dump station for RVs, and a wheelchair-accessible bathhouse with flush toilets. Sites are $8.

Day-use fee is $3 per vehicle. From Sumatra, take Highway 65 south. In less than two miles, turn right (west) onto Forest Service Road 101. Continue two miles; turn right (north) at the sign. Wright Lake is a quarter mile ahead in Franklin County, not far from the Franklin/Liberty county line. 850/643-2282.

3.5 Hickory Landing

🐾🐾 (See Tallahassee map on page 80)

On the banks of Owl Creek, this scenic spot amid cypress groves offers a place to walk along a hiking trail or picnic with your leashed dog. You can bring a fishing pole or a boat, if your dog is game. Or bring a tent: At the 12 first-come, first-served campsites, you can spend the night for just $3. Expect a rustic experience at this hunt camp, where each campsite offers a picnic table and grill or fire ring, plus access to drinking water. Vault toilets and a concrete boat ramp round out the amenities.

Day-use visitors pay $3 per carload. From Sumatra, take Highway 65 south for less than two miles, then head right (west) on Forest Service Road 101 for 1.5 miles. Drive south on Forest Service Road 101B for a mile to this boat landing/hunt camp in Franklin County, near the Franklin/Liberty county line. 850/643-2282.

36 Fort Gadsden Historical Site

🐾🐾🐾 (See Tallahassee map on page 80)

This remote historical spot overlooking the Apalachicola River offers a fine place for a picnic beside oaks covered with resurrection ferns. The park sits within Apalachicola National Forest in Franklin County, and you'll probably find yourself all alone when you visit. But whoa there, dogs technically are supposed to be leashed.

Your dog can sniff around the outlines of a long-gone fort that was built by the British during the War of 1812. He'll breathe a sigh of relief that he wasn't visiting when it was a hideaway for fugitive slaves after the war. The runaways fired on American troops passing through on the river below, and most of the 300 people in the fort died when the Americans fired back a red-hot cannon ball that hit the fort's powder magazine. Interpretive signs will help you relay the tale more completely to your furry buddy. Bring water for the pooch; there is no drinking water here. Vault toilets are provided.

Day-use fee is $3 per car (or boat, if you arrive by boat). From Apalachicola, drive east on U.S. 98 about nine miles. Turn left (north) onto Highway 65. You'll pass through the hamlet of Beverly in about 12 miles, then enter Apalachicola National Forest about five miles farther north. Follow the sign directing you to Fort Gadsden up the road. 850/643-2282.

PLACES TO STAY

Hickory Landing: See Hickory Landing under Parks, Beaches, and Recreation Areas, above, for camping information.

Wright Lake: See Wright Lake Recreation Area, under Parks, Beaches, and Recreation Areas, above, for camping information.

Sopchoppy

PARKS, BEACHES, AND RECREATION AREAS

🐾🐾🐾 Ochlockonee River State Park

🐾🐾🐾 🐾● (See Tallahassee map on page 80)

This place is teeming with wild animals, in part because oak thickets and small ponds break up the pine flatwoods that dominate the relatively small 550-acre park, giving it that "edge effect" so crucial to some wild critters who need a little of this and a little of that.

But for doggies, the big thing is tromping down the wide, sandy, riverside Ochlockonee River Nature Trail and reaching a scenic point where the Dead River and the Ochlockonee meet. Or you can meander through the park interior on the slightly less shady Pine Flatwoods Trail, just off the parking lot. If you can get her attention long enough, tell your leashed pal how this used to be a shallow sea much like the Gulf of Mexico, and howl on about other interesting stuff explained on the interpretive signs.

It can get a little warm here, so fill water containers at the restrooms and plan to hike at a cooler time of day. Dusk and dawn are best, but be sure to bring mosquito repellent. Bring a canoe if you want to paddle around on the Ochlockonee River; this stretch is part of the designated Florida Canoe Trail. Picnic tables overlooking Dead River allow for a nice break afterward.

Camping costs $15 at the 30 shady sites, each with a picnic table, grill, electricity, water, and access to hot showers. Book at ReserveAmerica.com or 800/326-3521.

Entrance for day-use visitors costs $3 per vehicle. From Tallahassee, take U.S. 319 south for about 30 miles to Sopchoppy. Continue four miles south on U.S. 319 to the park, on the east side of the road. 850/962-2771.

Panacea

How can you not visit a place with a name like this?

PARKS, BEACHES, AND RECREATION AREAS

🐾🐾🐾 Florida National Scenic Trail

🐾🐾🐾 (See Tallahassee map on page 80)

If your dog has a bit of the outdoorsman in him, take a walk in the woods on this narrow, sandy, pine-scented section of the Florida National Scenic Trail. Head east or west. If you walk 3.3 miles to the east, you'll hit the Spring Creek Road, but you certainly don't have to go that far. (In fact, 3.3 miles is way too far for most dogs; Maggie says you should just take a non-goal-oriented stroll in the forest.) One spring day at dusk, Maggie enjoyed a 30-minute jaunt along this path, where she sniffed the trail incessantly. There are no facilities—not even a parking lot.

Keep your eye out for the orange-on-blue FT trail marker on either side of U.S. 98 as you head north from Panacea, then park on the side of the road. The trail crosses U.S. 98 about a half mile south of U.S. 319, near Medart. 850/925-6121.

39 Otter Lake Recreation Area

 (See Tallahassee map on page 80)

You'll pass Fishing Fool Street and Lucy Lane on your way down to this relaxing, dog-friendly outpost in the St. Marks National Wildlife Refuge, one of the nation's oldest wildlife refuges. Here, your pooch has her choice of sniffing her way down trails through pine and palmettos or lounging on the oak- and cypress-shaded shores of this large lake—a fine place for a canoe outing. Take advantage of picnic tables, some shaded. If your pet is as lucky as Maggie was, she will see a hawk, a rabbit, or even some woodpeckers during a daytime stroll (the place closes at dusk). Keep your dog leashed and out of the lake because alligators are numerous.

Take County Road 372A west from Panacea. Otter Lake is less than two miles west of U.S. 98. 850/925-6121.

40 Bayfront

(See Tallahassee map on page 80)

For a relaxing place to watch the Ochlockonee River run, head to this small roadside area where you can park and maybe even fish with your dog. It's on the west side of the U.S. 98 bridge across Ochlockonee Bay. 850/697-2585.

PLACES TO STAY

Alligator Point KOA Kampground Resort: Sleep in a cabin or at one of 115 campsites at this little peninsula on the Gulf of Mexico, then rent a boat for fishing or dolphin-watching—a pod occasionally swims nearby. You'll sleep near the gulf or by a pond. Expect little shade but lots of amenities, including a pool, playground, game room, 400-foot-long fishing pier, fish-cleaning station, and convenience store. Cabins range $51–61, plus $25 pet deposit. Campsites run $26–37. On Highway 98, go five miles west from Panacea, then south on County Road 370 to the KOA five miles ahead. 1320 Alligator Drive, Alligator Point; 850/349-2525 or 800/562-0848; www.koakampgrounds.com.

Holiday Park & Campground: Dogs, cats, birds, and even pet snakes have slept at this waterfront campground on Ochlockonee Bay. Pretty sunsets can be viewed from the on-site fishing pier, where anglers catch fish and crabs. Leashed dogs may take walks along the waterfront and some grassy areas toward the back of the park. People-oriented amenities include a pool, a recreation room, hot showers, volleyball, and shuffleboard. The camping area is mostly on open ground, but a few huge oaks offer a modicum of shade. Of the 75 campsites, 69 are for RVs and six are for tents. Camping is $22 for tent sites, $27 for waterfront RV sites. Reservations are accepted. The campground is on U.S. 98 on the east side of Ochlockonee Bay. 14 Coastal Highway, Panacea; 850/984-5757; www.holidaycampground.com.

Vacation rentals: With sweeping views of the Gulf of Mexico, the beaches of peninsular Alligator Point serve as a favorite of some vacationers. Precious few vacation homes are open to Precious, but, last we checked, we saw at least one pet-friendly property apiece posted at PetFriendlyTravel.com, FindRentals.com, and VRBO.com. View photos and descriptions online; you'll then contact owners directly. Alternatively, Fish & Grits is the name of a two-bathroom, hound-hospitable rental that sleeps eight people for $375 for the weekend or $575 for the week, plus a $100 nonrefundable pet fee. The Alligator Point home is offered via a local realty company: Ochlockonee Bay Realty, P.O. Box 556, Panacea; 850/984-0001; www.obrealty.com.

Carrabelle

PARKS, BEACHES, AND RECREATION AREAS

41 George L. Sand Field

🏃 (See Tallahassee map on page 80)

Four baseball fields are about the sum total of this place, so your leashed dog might stretch her legs here in the off-season or view some Little League action from afar when kids are playing. The park is on U.S. 98 on the east end of town. 850/697-3618.

42 Bay Beaches

🐾🐾 (See Tallahassee map on page 80)

There are a number of places where you can pull off U.S. 98 south of Carrabelle and wade in the bay waters. But these are make-do beaches and, as Maggie wonders, why eat Alpo if you can have hamburger? St. George Island is just a little farther down the road, and a half hour's drive past that is Cape San Blas, near Port St. Joe (see the Panama City chapter). But if your pooch is pooped, well, this will do. A good beach is about 10 miles south of Carrabelle, near the highway patrol station, where you'll find parking, seclusion, and some shade. Leashed dogs are tolerated here, according to the Franklin County Sheriff's Department. 850/697-2585.

PLACES TO STAY

Ho-hum RV Park: Dogs run gleefully on nearby beaches before returning for the night to this three-acre, 50-site, adult-oriented private park, where pets accompany 80 to 90 percent of guests. "We're pet lovers," says park co-owner Toni. "It gives people some way to meet and greet each other." Sites have a pretty gulf view, and anglers have access to a 250-foot fishing pier. Rates are $26 a night, plus an extra $3 for the 16 beach sites. Scattered pines lend some shade to the place, which in winter draws snowbirds who play bingo and cards. The park is located right at the Gulf of Mexico, along U.S. 98, just over three miles east of town. 2132 Highway 98 East, Carrabelle; 850/697-3926 or 888/88-HO-HUM (884-0486); www.hohumrvpark.com.

Island View Inn: Fishing is big here, as evidenced by the two 200-foot fishing piers and the free boat slips for guests. One guest caught a 47-inch redfish from a dock here. The cinder-block duplexes are nothing fancy, but they look onto St. James Bay. The few RV spots run $25 nightly, plus a flat $15 for the pooch. Rooms range $55–70, plus $15 pet fee (up to two pets). 1714 Highway 98 East, Carrabelle; 850/697-2050.

The Moorings at Carrabelle: Set on the Carrabelle River, this two-story motel/marina establishment offers pleasant rooms and counts traveling boaters among its clientele due to its amenities: a pool, barbecue grills, a private boat ramp, boat slips, fuel, laundry facilities, and a shuttle to local restaurants. Rates are $75–150, plus $10 nightly per pet. You must leave a credit-card imprint or $50 pet deposit, but it will be returned if your pooch behaves. 1000 U.S. 98, Carrabelle; 850/697-2800; www.mooringscarrabelle.com.

Apalachicola

Apalachicola is best known for its oysters, but dogs across Florida should howl their approval for a wholly different reason. This was where John Gorrie, a physician caring for yellow fever patients, created an ice-making machine that laid the groundwork for air-conditioning. Talk about changing a dog's way of life!

Unfortunately, dogs aren't allowed in the John Gorrie State Museum to learn about his patent, No. 8080, issued on August 22, 1850. But they can frolic in a small field across the street and outside the Trinity Episcopal Church, which is catty-corner from the museum. Perhaps half the buildings in this small town are on the National Register of Historic Places—pleasing news to dogs with a taste for history.

Your pooch wouldn't know it to look at little Apalachicola today, but this was once one of the most important cities in the state, a bustling port and fishing town. Because of its early start, Apalachicola still claims the greatest number of pre-Civil War homes in the state. The town faded into obscurity for a time, becoming just another small seaside settlement, but Apalachicola is again on the rise as a tourist magnet.

Walk your dog around the downtown area (it may be a stretch to call it such, but it *is* the center of town). There you both can wander the sidewalks and peer into the windows of cute shops. This is a small town, though, so your picks are limited when it comes to dog-friendly lodgings and restaurants. The best place to stay is the Gibson Inn (see Places to Stay, below), a real find. Nearby spots offering additional lodgings include St. George Island, detailed in this chapter, and Port St. Joe, covered in the Panama City chapter.

Overall, the town is an idyllic little burg, one with a lot of character that doesn't scream "tourist trap!" At least not yet. A great getaway, Maggie opines.

PARKS, BEACHES, AND RECREATION AREAS

43 Battery Park

 (See Tallahassee map on page 80)

If you're staying at the Gibson Inn or Apalachicola River Inn, this small park makes for a good turnaround point or quick stop during a neighborhood stroll with your leashed pal. There's a playground for the kids.

The park is by Sixth Street and Avenue B, next to the U.S. 98/John Gorrie Bridge on the east side of town. 850/653-9419.

44 Lafayette Park

(See Tallahassee map on page 80)

Perhaps there's not much here for a leashed pup to fantasize about, but humans appreciate the orange-glow sunsets and the pretty, well-shaded grounds covering about a square block next to Apalachicola Bay. The scenery served as the inspiration behind artist William Trotter's painting entitled "A Walk in Lafayette Park." Tired of walking? Rest your dogs at a gazebo or picnic table, or stop to read the interpretive signs. The park is at the end of Bay Avenue, just south of Avenue B, between 13th and 15th streets. 850/653-9419.

45 Trinity Episcopal Church

 (See Tallahassee map on page 80)

One of the earlier buildings constructed in the state of Florida (then a territory), this 150-year-old church is made of white pine brought here by ship from New York. We let Maggie off her leash in the grassy yard that acts as a de facto park in this quiet neighborhood.

Cross the street to see a memorial to John Gorrie, the inventor of air-conditioning and refrigeration. His headstone, erected by the Southern Ice Exchange, sits alone under the shade of a spreading, moss-draped oak. Gorrie died in 1855, long before the significance of his invention could be realized and a century before it was used to cool millions of thoroughly modern doggies.

The church is just off U.S. 98 on Sixth Street, across from the John Gorrie State Museum. 850/653-9419.

PLACES TO EAT

Boss Oysters: Sample shucked-to-order oysters prepared more than a dozen different ways at this riverside eatery. Named among the country's Top 10 Oyster Bars by *Coastal Living* magazine for its "superb seafood" despite its "ramshackle" appearance, it's located at pet-permissible Apalachicola River Inn (see Places to Stay, below). You'll tie your dog to the outside of a fence, then dine al fresco on blue crabs, bay scallops, shrimp, pizza, steak, or other eats on the opposite side of the fence in the outer deck area. Try the oyster po' boy; it'll have you dreaming of New Orleans. 123 Water St.; 850/653-9364.

The Owl Café: For lunch, sit at one of the four umbrella-shaded tables in the brick courtyard to sample fried oysters or Grandma's chicken sandwich (among others). At dinner, choose from pasta, filet mignon, crab cakes, and local seafood dishes complemented by fine wines. Don't miss the Panhandle Clam Chowder. 15 Avenue D; 850/653-9888.

PLACES TO STAY

Apalachicola River Inn: You may arrive by boat on weekdays or by car any day to stay at this inn/marina/restaurant set on the banks of the Apalachicola River. All guests sleep in river-view rooms and have access to a rooftop lounge and charter fishing. Rooms cost $95–150. Cottage Jacuzzi suites run $160–400. Add a flat $15 for the pooch. 123 Water St., Apalachicola; 850/653-8139; www.apalachicolariverinn.com.

Gibson Inn: What a place! It's not every day that pets may sleep at a 1907 lodging listed on the National Register of Historic Places. Even a bullmastiff has stayed at this gracious hostelry, a destination in itself. Staffers often present a dog biscuit to pet owners, who proceed to six pet-permissible rooms with outside entrances. With its wrap-around porches, the Gibson is a throwback to simpler times. Still, you'll get a private bathroom, cable TV, and a phone. The dining room is superb—though dogs are forbidden there (and the saloon and Common Area) to sample such treats as stuffed grouper Florentine or crab cakes. Breakfast in your room can be arranged, however. A good base for exploring the lower Florida Panhandle, these rooms range $85–169. Add a $15–25 daily pet fee; maximum $45–75 per dog per stay. 51 Ave. C, Apalachicola; 850/653-2191; www.gibsoninn.com.

Rancho Inn: A kidney-shaped pool and a picnic area set this pet-friendly, 32-unit motel apart. Find a dog-walking area outside the Mexican-style building, whose owners live on-site. Rooms run $75–90. A suite ranges $98–140. Add $6 daily per pet. 240 U.S. 98 West, Apalachicola; 850/653-9435; www.ranchoinn.com.

Sportsman's Lodge: Rates run about $50 for a regular room, $60 for a kitchenette at this motel/marina/RV park set on 14 acres overlooking East Bay. Ducks and resident peacocks are sure to excite canines, who are accepted for $3 nightly. Use the pay phone or your cell phone to make calls (rooms lack telephones). The rustic place is just east of the town of Apalachicola, across the U.S. 98/John Gorrie Bridge. 99 N. Bayshore Drive, Eastpoint; 850/670-8423.

St. George Island

We had been cruising around this laid-back resort island for only a little while when we encountered Norman, a wet, leashless, chocolate-brown pooch who, we learned, had been hitting the beach all week. Then, at one stretch of sand with public parking and volleyball nets, we saw two dogs playing in the surf and asked their human buddy if it really was okay to bring dogs to this 22-mile-long island.

"Sure it is! Just ask them," he said, motioning to his canine companions. Others at the beach confirmed that dogs regularly traipse along the beach, chasing Frisbees and hermit crabs.

Now, technically, dogs are not allowed on the beaches at St. George Island. The local sheriff will tell you that. But the law appears to be rarely enforced, with the exception of the namesake state park. Dogs playing in the water, which is an azure blue tinged with Bahamas green, are very much tolerated. Of course, scoop the poop.

Warning: Stay away from St. George Island State Park. On the map, it may look like a big, green spot where dogs can cut loose. But forget it! There is nothing here for a dog to do, with the exception of—get this—walking around on a leash in a parking lot. You'll be fined $125 if a park employee sees your pooch anywhere else. In an almost Orwellian twist to our experience here, a park worker tried to tell us that dogs were not allowed on beaches anywhere on St. George Island because the beaches are private. Maggie resisted the temptation to tell him he should check with his counterparts in the state legal offices, who have spent untold dollars defending the rights of the public to have access to Florida's beaches. Our advice: Just stay away from the state park and hit the beaches along the western part of this barrier island.

PLACES TO EAT

BJ's Pizza & Subs: Your leashed dog may sit at your feet at the outdoor tables and hope for crumbs from your sub sandwich, calzone, salad, or hand-tossed pizza. 105 W. Gulf Beach Drive; 850/927-2805.

Blue Parrot Ocean Front Cafe: Home to a tiki bar, this popular casual spot on the water has another claim to fame: large po' boy sandwiches. Take a seat on the deck, a common destination for kid-friendly leashed dogs and their owners. 68 W. Gorrie Drive; 850/927-2987.

The Market Place: Sit at the sole picnic table to share eats purchased inside the island's only grocery store, which sells deli meats, produce, beverages, and what you'd expect from a small grocery. 148 E. Pine Ave.; 850/927-2808.

PLACES TO STAY

Your best—and only—option here is to rent a house, although you might have to stay for at least two nights. In the winter there's a chance you could find a rental for under $500 a week, but in the summer a beachfront property can set you back in excess of $2,000 per week. Plus you'll pay tax and possibly a pet fee, in addition to putting down the normal damage deposit for the humans in the party.

Anchor Vacation Properties: Rates for renting one of several pooch-permissible vacation homes vary seasonally. See photos of available homes online. 119 Franklin Blvd., St. George Island; 850/927-2625 or 800/824-0416; www.florida-beach.com.

Collins Vacation Rentals: "People who travel with dogs are apt to take better care of a house," said the woman we spoke to over the phone. She figures it's because people who care for dogs learn to be responsible. So she gladly accepts well-behaved pooches at more than 100 rentals, and the agency provides an easy-to-browse list of pet-friendly homes at its website. Rates vary; expect a base rate of $1,000–2,000 weekly in summer (less other times), though a smattering of homes fall below $800 or beyond $3,000 weekly. The nonrefundable pet fee is $75 per pet; limit two dogs. 60 E. Gulf Beach Drive, St. George Island; 850/927-2900 or 800/853-9015; www.collinsvacationrentals.com.

Resort Vacation Properties of St. George Island: This realty company actively targets dog owners as vacationers and devotes a page to pet vacations at its website, where you can click on links to view photos of nearly 200 pet-friendly homes. Two Rhodesian Ridgebacks named Gypsy and Nandi are the canine companions of Helen and John Spohrer, past owners of this firm's predecessor, Prudential Resort Realty, and the two dogs routinely run happily at the beach. Vacationing pets can gleefully join them. Rental fees vary. Base rates start below $1,000 weekly in season for one-bathroom rentals that sleep four to seven people. Bigger places typically range $1,000–3,000 weekly, though some fancy beachfront digs surpass $6,000. Two pets may stay free; extra pets require a fee. 123 Gulf Beach Drive West, St. George Island; 850/927-2322, 800/332-5196, or 866/927-BEACH; www.resortvacationproperties.com.

NORTH FLORIDA

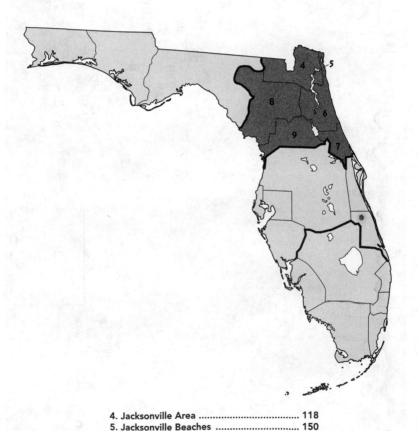

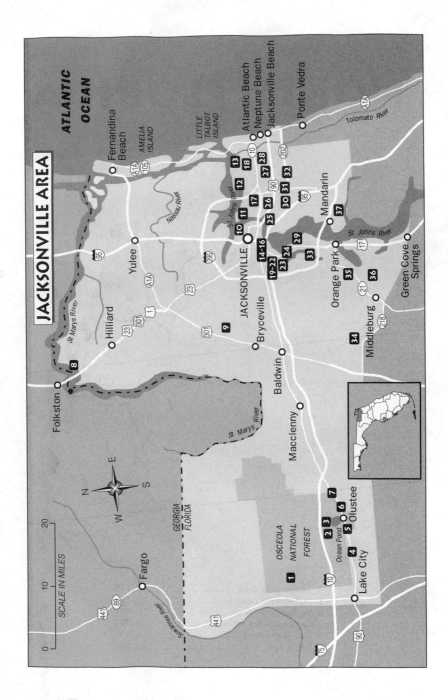

CHAPTER 4

Jacksonville Area

Some people in this town have a history of cheering for the dogs—the Georgia Bulldogs, that is. The Florida-Georgia college football game used to be the biggest football event of the year here, until Jacksonville got its own pro team, the Jaguars, in 1995.

Lots of things are looking up for Jacksonville. Our favorite is that this is now one of the most relaxing, hassle-free areas in the state to vacation with your dog. Our second favorite takes a little more explaining: It used to be that people said this city, one of Florida's oldest, was, ahem, going to the dogs. And who could yelp a note of disagreement? The paper mill dominated the landscape—and your olfactory senses. Now, though, thanks to some stiff regulations and responsible businesspeople, it's rare to catch more than the faintest whiff, and you can pass many a day here unaware of the mill. Many other good things are happening in Jacksonville, but we'll leave it to the chamber of commerce to fill you in. Suffice it to say this is one of Maggie's most unexpectedly beloved vacation destinations—a real diamond in the ruff.

PICK OF THE LITTER—JACKSONVILLE

NATION'S BIGGEST DOG PARK
Dog Wood Park, Jacksonville (page 136)

BEST PLACES TO SWIM
Dog Wood Park, Jacksonville (page 136)
Poochie's Swim and Play Park, Orange Park (page 146)
Julington Creek Animal Walk, Mandarin (page 149)

BEST FREE DOG PARK
Pooch Park, Jacksonville (page 135)

BEST PLACE TO EAT
Sterlings Cafe, Jacksonville (page 139)

FANCIEST DIGS
Club Continental, Orange Park (page 148)

BEST HIKES
Osceola National Forest (page 121–123)

City loving dogs and their people can enjoy plenty of shared adventures in Jacksonville. The two of you can eat at Sterlings Cafe, a fancy sidewalk restaurant; or watch the shrimp boats roll in to anchor while you try the seafood at La Cruise Restaurant in Mayport (see the Jacksonville Beaches chapter); or take your pick among several city parks that dot the landscape (there is a leash law, but it doesn't appear to be strictly enforced). However, it's not all good news for pooches. One of the greatest things going for the new, improved Jacksonville is Riverwalk, a spiffy riverside shopping center near the gleaming insurance towers that dominate the city's skyline. But signs here tell the same old story in three hated words: No Dogs Allowed.

But don't just stay in the city. Pack up the leash and water bowl and head for the backcountry. Outdoorsy pups can canoe on the St. Marys River as well as pad around the site where early French colonists tried to scratch out a living in a harsh new land, or they can hike the Florida National Scenic Trail past the Civil War battlefield at Olustee.

Osceola National Forest

Nearly 312 square miles of forests and swamps await inquisitive sniffing by doggies at Osceola National Forest.

PARKS, BEACHES, AND RECREATION AREAS

1 West Tower, Osceola National Forest

😊😊😊 (See Jacksonville map on page 118)

Horses sometimes mosey up to this rustic spot, which is sure to excite pooches unaccustomed to large critters. Actually a primitive camping area for horseback riders, hunters (in autumn and early winter), and other rustic sorts, this portion of the national forest is worth an afternoon visit. Park your car, then explore some of its 50 miles of horse trails with your leashed dog. The shortest trail, the five-mile-long Green Trail, mostly follows main roads. Turn around at a comfortable distance for your pal in the fur coat. Bring water. A restroom is available. Camping is free.

From Lake City, take U.S. 441 north, passing I-10. About three miles north of I-10, turn right (east) on Forest Service Road 233. Proceed about 5.5 miles to West Tower. 386/752-2577.

2 Hog Pen Landing, Osceola National Forest

😊 (See Jacksonville map on page 118)

Your dog's nose is likely to twitch at all the scents found at this rustic spot along Ocean Pond. Actually a primitive camping area, this is where hunters come in fall and winter to get a good night's sleep before trying to snag deer and wild hogs. A key attraction is the price: It's only $2 to camp. You can stop here to walk around, but don't let Tugboat run into Ocean Pond—an alligator pulled a boy underwater there in 1995. Bring water and any supplies; the only facility here is a boat ramp.

Fee is $2 to park or camp. From Lake City, drive east on U.S. 90 about 10 miles to Forest Service Road 241. Turn left (north). At Forest Service Road 241A three miles ahead, turn right. 386/752-2577.

3 Ocean Pond, Osceola National Forest

😊😊😊 (See Jacksonville map on page 118)

Ocean Pond is actually a campground set around a 1,760-acre lake. But you can just park here and walk on the Florida National Scenic Trail. A delight for dogs with active sniffers, this section ribbons through dark forests and, more typically, bright, open pine-studded areas. If you're not careful, your leashed Sherlock Holmes is apt to drag you along the wide trail in pursuit of deer, gopher tortoises, or wild turkeys ambling amid the spoonflowers and rosebud orchids.

For gonzo hikers with several days to spare, the 23-mile trail leads to the Olustee Battlefield (see separate listing, below) or, in the opposite direction, County Road 250.

The 67-site campground is fine and rustic, and many sites look onto the lake. Brush and shade trees provide privacy, so you and your leashed pooch won't have to stare into the eyes of strangers eating dinner outside a neighboring tent or motor home. Campsites with ground-level grills and concrete picnic tables range $8–18. Water and electrical hookups are available, as are hot showers, a boat ramp, a beach, an RV dump station, and flush toilets. Dogs must be leashed and kept off the beach. When we visited on a Labor Day, this place wasn't packed—surprising considering it's the sole developed campground in Osceola National Forest.

Don't get your hearts set on swimming. In 1995, an alligator pulled a 10-year-old boy underwater, punctured his chest and back, and ripped an inch-long tear in his chest after the boy apparently surprised him while swimming at the pond's northeast corner.

From U.S. 90 in Olustee, go north on County Road 250A and follow the signs. 386/752-2577.

4 Mount Carrie Wayside, Osceola National Forest

🐾 (See Jacksonville map on page 118)

The main focus at this wayside park is doing the two things Maggie loves best—eating and walking. Snack on a packed lunch at a picnic table, then follow a short interpretive trail in hopes of seeing the red-cockaded woodpeckers that nest at this day-use-only portion of the national forest. A downside: This little park is across from the Columbia Correctional Institution.

Admission is free. From Lake City, take U.S. 90 east about nine miles and look for the wayside park along the highway. 386/752-2577.

5 Olustee Beach, Osceola National Forest

🐾🐾🐾 (See Jacksonville map on page 118)

A favorite with locals who come for holiday picnics, this park is a disappointment for swimmers itching to dog-paddle on the lake. That's right, dogs aren't allowed in the park's watery focal point. When we visited, Maggie kept her eyes trained on what she thought was a big orange animal inching toward the lake from way across the park, but she never got the chance to find out that it was actually an inflatable toy being pulled on a cord by a child.

Still, this is a pleasant place to throw a few hot dogs onto a grill for a lazy afternoon picnic under moss-draped pine trees or in a pavilion. If you forgot to bring the fried chicken or fishing worms, they can be purchased nearby at the Fastway Food Store, 24116 U.S. 90 East, Olustee; 386/758-9882.

Creative canines might imagine that they can hear the hum of saws while following a short boardwalk to the site of the long-gone, 19th century Russell-

Eppinger sawmill. You'll walk on an old tram road that was used to carry trees from the forest to the sawmill. Back then, workers made $2 a day for cutting about 15 cross ties. Bring mosquito repellent.

Parking fee is $2. The entrance to Olustee Beach is at U.S. 90 and Pine Street; follow the signs. 386/752-2577.

6 Florida National Scenic Trail, Olustee Trailhead

🐾🐾🐾 (See Jacksonville map on page 118)

This hiking trail through moss-draped oaks and pines starts at the site of Florida's most important Civil War battle—the Battle of Olustee. Southern pooches may swell with pride as they sniff around the very place where, in 1864, some 5,000 Confederate soldiers unexpectedly beat 6,000 Union troops, preventing a Sherman-style invasion of Georgia from the south.

An excited Maggie pulled us along as she examined palmetto bushes for evidence of armadillos. From the battlefield, dogs can follow the Florida National Scenic Trail's "Nice Wander Loop Trail," which offers three loops of varying distances—just under one mile, 1.2 miles, and 2.1 miles. The trail follows an old road past a fire tower and through a picnic area. Then it turns to classic North Florida woods as the narrow pretty trail winds through widely spaced pines.

You may occasionally hear distant cars, but overall the walk is relaxing. We had the trail to ourselves on a Labor Day. In all, the Florida National Scenic Trail meanders through the Osceola National Forest for 23 miles and offers 20 boardwalks with views of swamps and wetlands. Keep your dog's abilities in mind. Periodically offer water from a bottle stored in a backpack. Especially on a hot day, consider turning around well before covering the 5.6-mile one-way leg to Ocean Pond.

Bring mosquito repellent, and be mindful of the blackberry brambles, which your pup may stumble into. For a backcountry map, call 800/343-1882.

Park at the Olustee Battlefield State Historic Site on U.S. 90, two miles east of Olustee, then walk to the left to the trailhead sign. Other sections of the trail are accessible where it crosses County Roads 250 and 250A (north of I-10), and Forest Service Roads 233 and 237 in the northwest portion of the forest. 386/758-0400 or 800/343-1882.

7 Olustee Battlefield State Historic Site

🐾🐾🐾🐾 🐾 (See Jacksonville map on page 118)

Your leashed buddy will walk the ground where, in four fateful hours, some 3,000 soldiers became casualties in what is considered Florida's only major Civil War battle, the Battle of Olustee. Dogs with a nose for history may find themselves sniffing the bases of cannons and monuments paying tribute to the outnumbered Confederate soldiers who soundly defeated Union troops on February 20, 1864.

Your dog may care more about the huge grassy lawn surrounding the monuments than the statues themselves at Florida's first state park. Listed on the National Register of Historic Places, this land offers a sort of city-park experience: You can eat at picnic tables beneath shady oak trees (there are no grills), then romp around a large, well-tended lawn. During our visit, a few butterflies fluttered past us, catching Maggie's eye. After reading the information on the plaques to your pal, you might walk down a portion of the more woodsy Florida National Scenic Trail that starts here or explore the grounds of the fenced state historic site. At a cemetery off to the side, a tall cross serves as a monument to those who died in the battle.

Expect a mob scene one weekend each February when cannons are blasted and gun-toting Civil War buffs don Confederate and Union uniforms to reenact the historic battle. People come from miles away to watch it. But if your dog is at all like Maggie, we recommend that she stay home. Only the most tolerant pooch can stand the noise of the cannons.

Admission is free. The visitors center is closed Tuesday and Wednesday. The site is two miles east of Olustee on U.S. 90, on the southern perimeter of Osceola National Forest. 386/758-0400.

PLACES TO STAY

East Tower Campground, Osceola National Forest: If you're not the rugged outdoorsy type, you probably should pass on this rustic campground. The words "Lost Dogs" are printed on the side of a caged pen—a clue that hunters and their sometimes-wayward hounds are the main tenants of these free digs, whose facilities are basically limited to the restrooms. If you prefer to get away from strangers, Osceola rangers allow you to camp absolutely anywhere you want in the massive forest except at Olustee Beach and at summer home sites. Camping is restricted for your safety during big-game hunting season, which usually lasts from early November to early January. East Tower is east of Highway 250 on Forest Service Road 202. 386/752-2577.

Hog Pen Landing, Osceola National Forest: See Parks, Beaches, and Recreation Areas, above, for camping information.

Ocean Pond, Osceola National Forest: See Parks, Beaches, and Recreation Areas, above, for camping information.

West Tower, Osceola National Forest: See Parks, Beaches, and Recreation Areas, above, for camping information.

Lake City

This stop off I-75 is just down the road from doggy delight Osceola National Forest, home to black bears and more.

PLACES TO STAY

Best Western: Palm trees and a fountain adorn the grounds of this pleasant 82-room poolside motel, where dogs might pine for bacon from the adjacent Bob Evans restaurant. Located off I-75 (Exit 427), the motel offers a sauna, pool, playground, and free continental breakfast. Rates run $50–95. Add a $10 daily pet fee. 4720 U.S. 90 West, Lake City; 386/752-3801; www.bestwestern.com.

Days Inn: Every room has a microwave and fridge—good news for hungry pets on the lookout for food. A small—preferably short-haired—dog may join you in a smoking room at this 46-unit poolside motel off I-10 (Exit 303). Rates range $59–75. Add $5 daily for pets. Route 16, Box 38310, Lake City; 386/758-4224; www.daysinn.com.

Driftwood Motel: For $5 nightly, a pet may join you at this 20-room budget motor inn located less than a mile east of I-75 (Exit 427). Rates range $35–60. 4380 U.S. 90 West, Lake City; 386/755-3545.

Econo Lodge South: Newshounds can keep up on current events with the free weekday paper and weather channel at this one-story, 60-room motel by I-75 (Exit 414). Rates start at $40, including continental breakfast. Small dogs, please. Route 2, Box 6008, Lake City; 386/755-9311; www.econolodge.com.

Jameson Inn: Milk and cookies are served each evening at this pleasant lodging, part of a chain of white-columned, colonial-style inns. A dog under 25 pounds may join you in these king rooms or suites off I-75 (Exit 427). Suites offer a sitting area, wet bar, fridge, microwave, and reclining chair (off, Fluffy!). Rates normally run $75–107. Pet fee is $10. 1393 Commerce Blvd., Lake City; 386/758-8440; www.jamesoninns.com.

Knights Inn: A free pass covering golf greens fees at a local course sets this budget motel apart. Located off Exit 427 of I-75, these basic rooms normally run $38–47, plus a $5 pet fee per stay. Route 13, Box 201, Lake City; 386/752-7720; www.knightsinn.com.

Motel 6: One small pet may join you at this 98-unit poolside motel off I-75 (Exit 427). Rates range $39–46. 3835 U.S. 90 West, Lake City; 386/755-4664; www.motel6.com.

Ramada Limited: Hungry hounds may have a hankering for a doggy bag from one of the 10 eateries within walking distance of this 64-unit, two-story motel, located east of I-75 (Exit 427). Rooms normally run $45–60 but rise during special events. Pet fee is $10 daily. 4670 U.S. 90 West, Lake City; 386/752-6262.

Hilliard

PARKS, BEACHES, AND RECREATION AREAS

🖪 Ralph E. Simmons Memorial State Forest

🐾🐾🐾🐾 (See Jacksonville map on page 118)

Heaven for rustic pooches, this out-of-the-way home of otters, deer, bobcats, and turkeys will set wet noses to twitching with delight during woodsy hikes. The White Trail leads through uplands and some bottomlands for 6.4 miles roundtrip, though you can follow only the north leg to White Sands Landing for a four-mile loop trip. Alternatively, follow only the south leg to White Sands Landing for a three-mile loop hike. Whichever route you choose, the White Trail follows denser forest and is easier on the feet (or paws) than the sandy-path Red Trail, named for the color of the painted blazes that mark the way.

If your dog loves water, bring a canoe for an easy paddle down the gently curving St. Marys River. You may see orchids or purple baldwina along the way. This 5.7-square-mile forest at the Georgia border isn't for the faint of heart, but it's perfect for people who like to fish, hike, ride horses, bird-watch, or (on designated dates) hunt. The birding is best around Hawkins Shop Landing, near the St. Marys River. While leashed dogs are allowed in this conservation area, you must leave the following at home: all-terrain vehicles, motorcycles, and animal traps. Call ahead to ask about staying at the designated primitive campsites along the white sandbars of the river and to check hunting dates before using the hiking trails.

Locals know the place as St. Marys River State Forest, its former name. The forest is on the south bank of the St. Marys River. From Hilliard, drive seven miles north on U.S. 1 to the town of Boulogne, then turn right onto Lake Hampton Road/State Road 121. Look for a forest entrance less than one mile ahead on the left, just past Pigeon Creek. Parking and a boat ramp are available on Pigeon Creek Road. 904/845-3597 or 904/266-5003.

Baldwin

PLACES TO STAY

Best Western Baldwin Inn: All 42 rooms are down and out—that is, downstairs and easy for a pooch to get into and out of. Hungry hounds can hope for a takeout order of bacon from the 24-hour Waffle House adjacent to this poolside motel, set 20 miles west of downtown Jacksonville off I-10 (Exit 343). Rates run $54–99. Pet fee is $8 daily. 1088 U.S. Highway 301, Baldwin; 904/266-9759.

Jacksonville

Jacksonville parks are easy on the eyes, in part because most—if not all—are devoid of those nasty signs saying Dogs Must Be Leashed. It's enough to make dog lovers leap for joy with the hope that their companions can romp leash-free everywhere. But after quite a few happy hours in the city, we spotted the first dreaded warning sign: "Jacksonville Animal Care and Control Leash Law Enforced. All animals must be under restraint. Ordinance 462.306. 904/387-8846." It was nowhere near a park but instead near the antique shops, restaurants, and other businesses on St. Johns Avenue. It can make an old dog groan. However, we did see plenty of dogs ignoring the rules and walking leash-free with their two-legged friends in the city's parks.

PARKS, BEACHES, AND RECREATION AREAS

🐾 Cary State Forest

🐾🐾🐾 (See Jacksonville map on page 118)

For city-slicker canines, this five-square-mile domain of deer and bobcats won't soon be confused with a walk around the block back home. Turkey hunters flock here in spring, and horseback riders set out through the pine flatwoods other times. Your mission: Follow a 1.2-mile nature trail and boardwalk that winds through a cypress swamp (bring mosquito repellent). A food plot near an observation tower—located in the woods, just off the nature trail—attracts wildlife in early mornings and in evenings, so keep a tight hold of the leash. An eight-mile-long Red Root Trail is intended for horseback riders, though pets are permitted on leash. Go only as far as is comfortable for your pal in the fur coat; and remember, a half-mile walk out means you'll have a half-mile trek back.

DIVERSIONS

Hey, a hayride! You may see deer, cattle, armadillos, Canada geese, and hogs during a leisurely hayride through the woods with the whole family—including the family dog. Imagine how your furry friend's whiskers will twitch with excitement on a reserved wagon from **Horse & Buggy Daze.** Fee is $200 hourly, plus tip.

Prefer a horse-drawn carriage ride? A footman can arrive to announce that your carriage is ready, then take you off to see lovely landscaping on Jacksonville city streets or spring flowers in the woods. A well-mannered pet is welcome on this ride, too. Weddings are the biggest business for Horse & Buggy Daze, but after-dinner rides are popular. Call 904/779-0632.

You can snack on a packed lunch at the picnic pavilion near the pooch-permissible camping area. Sleeping beneath the sun-dappled pines is free. Just call 904/266-5021 beforehand to request a special use permit. Amenities are few but include restrooms, picnic tables, fire rings, and hot showers.

From Baldwin, drive north about seven miles on U.S. 301, then turn right on the first dirt road after the Bryceville Fire Department. The campground is on the forest's main entrance road. 904/266-5021 or 904/266-5003.

Confederate Park

 (See Jacksonville map on page 118)

The homeless folk who hang out at this fenced downtown park tend to scare off would-be visitors, but the rooster wandering along the shores of the big lake here is a sign that the place does have some good qualities. After all, a roaming rooster is a rare sight in a downtown area. What's more, your pup will perk up when she sees the many geese and ducks eating bread crumbs thrown by locals. A war memorial and old cannons may become the targets of leg-lifting canines. If not for the smattering of trash, this six-acre park would be fairly pretty.

The park is at 956 Hubbard St., at Phelps Street. 904/630-4100 or 904/630-3500.

Arlington Lions Club Park and Boat Ramp

(See Jacksonville map on page 118)

At this sizable local park, big magnolia trees covered with velvety moss tower over a leaf-carpeted trail that delights sleuthing dogs hoping to pick up the scent of animals. Your leashed dog can follow a nearly mile-long nature path that winds through dense woods, passing the fan-shaped leaves of saw palmettos, the purple seed clusters of American beautyberry bushes, and trees that sprouted before Franklin Roosevelt was president.

The trail passes a ranger's fenced residence, which is watched by a loyal dog who will probably yelp at the perceived interlopers who've dared to set paws on the park's trail. Crosses in the ground behind the house read, "Here lies Blackie" and "Here lies Red."

Vines along the trail tend to grow upward from the forest floor to the canopy above, giving the place sort of a Grimm's fairy tale feel. You'll hear chirping cicadas and the occasional sound of aircraft, but no cars. Keep an eye out for the almost neon-blue skinks scurrying harmlessly among the dead leaves. Tired pooches can sit next to a trailside bench and admire a nearby tree whose amazing limbs stretch almost perpendicular to the trunk. One branch actually lies on the ground, creating a potential leg-lift target for your dog.

The nature trail leads to a shelter with four picnic tables. From there, a short asphalt trail leads to the St. Johns River and not-so-picturesque views of the port and paper mill. At river's edge, the path connects with a boardwalk that

DOG-EAR YOUR CALENDAR

Normally, black-tie affairs don't welcome guests who aren't wearing clothing, let alone ties. Yet dogs, and their dressed-up owners, always make the guest list at the annual **April Fur Ball Gala**. Usually a red carpet is rolled out for pets to pad along. Held in a ballroom, the fancy evening features an auction, a parade of pets, and hors d'oeuvres, as well as a cash bar and a pet version called a "pet bar." Ticket sales benefit the Jacksonville Humane Society. To get your buddy on the next guest list, call 904/725-8766.

links to 120-acre Blue Cypress Park, a former 18-hole golf course that's been turned into a smaller golf course/public park less than a mile away at 4012 University Boulevard North.

If you want to skip the nature trail, you can walk straight to the river and picnic area from the parking lot by turning right when you get to the trailhead for the nature walk. (A left turn enters the nature trail.) Bring water for your pooch and mosquito repellent for you.

Near the park's boat ramp is a fenced playground and a better picnic option: shelters with tables and grills.

These 30-plus acres sit on the south bank of the St. Johns River in the city's Arlington section. Take Arlington Expressway East over the Matthews Bridge to University Boulevard North (second ramp). Proceed 2.5 miles past Jacksonville University. Turn left onto Richard Denby Gatlin Drive just before the road is split by a grassy lane (the sign on the left says Rive St. Johns). Follow the road to its end. The park is at 4322-1 Richard Denby Gatlin Drive. 904/630-4100 or 904/630-3500.

12 Fort Caroline National Memorial

🐾🐾🐾🐾 🐾 (See Jacksonville map on page 118)

It's not every day that a dog can walk around a fort. But here at the site of what has been called the first decisive battle between Europeans for American soil, your leashed pup can putter over a moat-spanning bridge and sniff the grassy floor of an earthen fort. Grass grows on every wall—inside and out—so there is much information for your curious pup to collect.

For a little over a year, more than 300 French Huguenot colonists lived in Fort Caroline and used it as a home base to explore Florida. From time to time, they also hid here from angry Timucuan Indians, who had initially taught them how to use earth, wood, and sod to build a fort. The grassy attraction you see today is a model; the original was washed away after the St. Johns River was deepened and widened in the 1880s. Note that the fort's cannons face inland instead of toward the St. Johns River,

FETCHING NECESSITIES

Pardon me, do you have any Grey Poupon (or dog treats)?
Your well-mannered lapdog may wonder just that during a ride in a chauffeur-driven stretch limousine hired from **Dana's Limousine Service.** A trip from downtown to the airport will run about $185. A Town Car ride costs $95. Reserve at 904/744-3333 or 800/456-5466.

because back then the river was too shallow for attacking warships to use. Still, early in the morning on September 20, 1565, Spain's Admiral Pedro Menendez de Aviles and 500 soldiers managed to capture the fort and slaughter 140 French settlers.

As you walk on the elevated edges of the fort, your vertically challenged dog won't be able to peer over the berm to see the nearby saltwater marsh and the occasional great blue heron fishing for dinner, but you can admire the view.

One doggy highlight is outside the fort: the pretty, 1.25-mile-long Old French Trail, which leads through brushy wilderness. In this maritime hammock forest, your alert buddy will pick up a variety of scents in wet tidal areas, humid palmetto thickets, and moist pine woods. This type of forest once covered the riverbanks of northeastern Florida, but only small fragments remain today. Another route, the 1.5-mile Spanish Pond Trail, is almost always closed in late summer and early fall because of flooding. Either way, bring mosquito repellent.

Decently shaded picnic tables are found to the right of the visitors center. No fires or grills are permitted. Behind the visitors center is a short sidewalk leading to a deck with two benches facing the St. Johns River. At the deck, watch your dog's reaction after you push a button to hear recorded information about local history. Maggie stuck her head through the bars of the deck fence, trying to figure out where the voice was coming from.

Admission is free. The park is about 14 miles east of downtown Jacksonville. Take the Arlington Expressway east to Atlantic Boulevard, turn north on Monument Road or St. Johns Bluff Road, then go east on Fort Caroline Road to the park entrance. 904/641-7155.

13 Theodore Roosevelt Area, Timucuan Ecological and Historic Preserve

🐾🐾🐾🐾 🐾 (See Jacksonville map on page 118)

Maggie works herself into a lather at this 600-acre woodsy retreat, sort of the untamed brother of the more refined Fort Caroline National Memorial (see above). One local jogger's favorite running path, the Willie Browne Trail, narrows under mossy trees and passes a Confederate soldier's grave on a

1.75-mile trek to the old Willie Browne homestead. Approximately five miles of trails for hiking and bicycling zigzag through salt marsh and trees. Plus, this maritime hammock forest hosts some 35 acres of shell mounds that the Timucuan Indians made thousands of years ago. It was their version of a garbage can, but your dog won't try to wangle his way in for a snack—they look like little hills today. Instead, eat a packed lunch at the picnic area next to the parking lot.

Admission is free. From Jacksonville, take the Arlington Expressway east to Atlantic Boulevard, turn left (north) on Monument Road, and continue about five miles to Fort Caroline Road. Turn right onto Fort Caroline; at the bottom of the hill, go straight on Mount Pleasant Road to the park gate, which is 1.2 miles ahead, on your left. Alternate directions: From Fort Caroline National Memorial, go south on Fort Caroline Road for .3 mile, turn left at Mount Pleasant Road, and travel 1.2 miles to the park gate. Follow a bumpy dirt road for .1 mile to the Willie Browne Trailhead. 904/641-7155.

🐾 Memorial Park

🐾🐾🐾 👣 (See Jacksonville map on page 118)

This large yet refined city park is a favorite of Clay County Humane Society Director Linda Welzant, who takes her dog, Scout, to work every day and brings Scout here at other times for a special treat. A black iron fence surrounds wide-open areas rimmed by trees. Take a seat at one of the 22 benches and dig into your bag lunch (there are no picnic tables) as you gaze out onto the picturesque St. Johns River. Or walk with your leashed buddy along a wide, winding sidewalk. Your pent-up pup might make a beeline to the memorial dedicated to an American War Mothers official or to the large waterfront World War I statue, *Winged Figure of Youth*. According to the sign, the youthful figure "rises triumphant from the swirl of war's chaos, which engulfs humanity, and faces the future courageously." Maggie was more interested in the chaos of chasing doves.

The six-acre park is in the city's Riverside area at 1620 Riverside Ave., at Margaret Street. 904/630-4100 or 904/630-3500.

🐾 Powers Park

🐾🐾 (See Jacksonville map on page 118)

Not in Jacksonville's wealthiest of neighborhoods, this three-block-long passive park tempts dogs who would love to chase a passel of squirrels among the more than 100 pine trees. It's a veritable canine obstacle course. A little pit bull who lives on the boundary looked wistfully past his fence at leashed Maggie during our pleasant visit.

The 13-acre park is at Dellwood Avenue and Shearer Street in the Murray Hill section of west Jacksonville. 904/630-4100 or 904/630-3500.

16 Riverside Park

😻 😻 (See Jacksonville map on page 118)

You might admire the rose garden and the large, fenced-off pond. But your dog will probably be drawn to the stand of pine trees right along Park Street. This two-square-block neighborhood park really isn't worth a special trip unless you like to shoot hoops. But the city's second-oldest park is perfect for locals who just want to unwind with their pooches on a walk after work.

The park is in the city's Five Points section at Park and Post streets. 904/630-4100 or 904/630-3500.

17 Victory Park

😻 (See Jacksonville map on page 118)

It's nothing to bark about, but at least the grassy lawn at this 10.7-acre fenced park offers a chance to romp. Heck, hungry dogs might also appreciate a picnic beneath an oak tree. A drawback is that the picnic tables face well-traveled Fort Caroline Road. Kids will like the playground. Two tennis courts, a quarter-mile paved path, a picnic shelter, and four barbecue grills basically round out the amenities. Fill a dog water dish at the restroom.

The park is at Fort Caroline Road and Haslett Drive East in Arlington, near Fort Caroline Middle School. 904/630-4100 or 904/630-3500.

18 Leonard Abess Park

😻 😻 (See Jacksonville map on page 118)

A sidewalk winds past ball fields toward a marshy area and through some woods, eventually leading your leashed pooch to a big, grassy soccer field where she might pine to romp. This well-maintained park, built in part with federal tax dollars, should win an award for cramming the most possible uses into the available space. Ball fields dominate one corner. In another, you'll find tennis courts, a basketball court, and a fenced playground with grills and picnic tables. The soccer field closer to Girvin Road is the most alluring feature for rambunctious dogs. Five restrooms provide ample opportunity for filling dog water bowls.

The 34-acre community park is at 12743 Leonard Abess Blvd., just off Girvin Road, north of Atlantic Boulevard. 904/630-4100 or 904/630-3500.

19 Willow Branch Park

😻 😻 (See Jacksonville map on page 118)

A local favorite, this very shady park attracts a lot of canines looking for a place to enjoy an afternoon walk with their people. The place is quite large for a neighborhood park, and the mostly level ground slopes gently toward the southern end. We saw several dogs walking off leash, and no one seemed to mind. Some dogs ignored the quarter-mile paved path, basketball court,

DOG-EAR YOUR CALENDAR

Jake the Diamond Dog serves as mascot of the Jacksonville Suns minor league baseball team, so it's only fitting that one night each July he invites fellow pooches and their people to the Baseball Grounds of Jacksonville for a game dubbed the **"Dog Days of Summer."** Sometimes, prizes are awarded for the smallest, biggest, and cutest dogs. Game tickets cost $5. For the next date, call 904/358-2846.

playground, and two softball fields and instead turned their attentions to more important matters, such as munching grass. Judging by one dog's ravenous chewing, the green stuff is tasty.

The 17-acre park is in the Riverside area of Jacksonville at 2870 Sydney St., at Willow Branch Avenue. 904/630-4100 or 904/630-3500.

20 Fishweir Park

 (See Jacksonville map on page 118)

This sun-splashed spot practically screams for dogs to run like the wind on its grassy expanses, which span a few blocks. As far as we can tell, the park is virtually abandoned on many weekday afternoons. But remember: Jacksonville has a leash law, despite its welcome habit of not posting signs.

A few pines and two large oaks grace one side of the 10-acre park. People tend to flock to the other side for the playground, two soccer fields, and softball diamond. Three picnic tables and nine benches await tired pups. Fill a water bowl at the restroom.

The park is in the Avondale section of southwest Jacksonville at 3925 Valencia Rd., at Canterbury Street. 904/630-4100 or 904/630-3500.

21 Boone Park

(See Jacksonville map on page 118)

This place is so pretty, it's not unusual to see locals sitting in their cars overlooking the sizable shady park—spanning about eight city blocks—to read a paper or eat during the weekday lunch hour. Yes, dogs like it here, too, as you can tell by the many paw prints in the mud leading to a footbridge in the main part of the park. Your pup can scurry over several of these short footbridges and gently rolling hills. Eventually, you two can cross two-lane Herschel Street to reach the more-level continuation of the park, where hundreds of trees await excited pooches. While city rules require leashes, on one of our visits Maggie had a chat with a golden retriever who had no companion in sight.

Doggies concerned about their weight might want to follow a wooden fitness course or one-mile paved trail after chowing down hot dogs sizzled on one of the eight grills near the 24 picnic tables. The rest of your party might appreciate the playground and 16 lighted tennis courts.

The park is considered the birthplace of "corkball." City parks employee Chuck Rogers invented the sport in 1937 after watching two kids at this old park use a tree limb to bat around an ordinary cork as if it were a baseball. Be quiet as you commune with nature amid these 26 acres, and you might hear the rat-a-tat of woodpeckers hammering away overhead in the old trees.

Boone Park is at 3700 Park St., at Van Wert Avenue. 904/630-4100 or 904/630-3500.

22 Stinson Park

 (See Jacksonville map on page 118)

You and your special friend can lounge at one of the few benches overlooking the Ortega River as a breeze rustles the leaves of nearby trees and anglers try their luck from the bank. The view of the Ortega River is the main attraction of this narrow, triangular, two-acre park at 4050 San Juan Ave., at the foot of the Ortega Bridge in the city's Lake Shore area. 904/630-4100 or 904/630-3500.

23 Lakeside Park

😺😺 (See Jacksonville map on page 118)

Lots of squirrels and doves give your pooch good chasing opportunities in this small, sleepy, triangular park in a tree-shaded neighborhood of brick and wood homes. Indeed, as we approached, squirrels immediately scrambled up the trunks of the more than 60 moss-draped oaks. There are no picnic tables or restrooms (the place is barely an acre, if that), but it's a pleasant place to take your dog in spring to admire a few huge azalea bushes in bloom.

The neighborhood park is on Lakeside Drive, just south of San Juan Avenue and near the Ortega River in the Lakeside Park subdivision of southwest Jacksonville. 904/630-3510 or 904/630-3500.

24 Bettes Park

😺😺 (See Jacksonville map on page 118)

Just 1.6 acres in size, this shady circular neighborhood park is the kind of pleasant spot where you and your buddy can go for a walk and sit at a bench to relax beneath picturesque trees, though the lack of tables makes it difficult to picnic. Resurrection ferns cover the wide trunks of some of the more than 25 oaks here—a clue that these beauties have been around for decades, if not a century.

The park is at 3800 Bettes Circle in the Ortega section of southwest Jacksonville. It's just off the east end of the Ortega Bridge on Bettes Circle, north of Ortega Boulevard. 904/630-4100 or 904/630-3500.

25 Drew Park

 (See Jacksonville map on page 118)

If you do as the locals do, you'll burn at least 145 calories by walking for a half hour along the loop path at this ball-field-dominated park. A favorite with joggers, the paved path spans about a mile and basically circles a parking lot. Take a break with your leashed pal under the shade trees that ring the ball fields and playground. Seven grills sit near the 28 picnic tables, in case you're hungry. Fill a water bowl at the drinking fountain or restroom.

The 25-acre park is at 6621 Barnes Rd. South, at Parental Home Road. 904/630-4100 or 904/630-3500.

26 Pooch Park

 (See Jacksonville map on page 118)

Ditch the leash! Dogs dart after each other and take advantage of agility equipment at this fully fenced two-acre off-leash park located in an unusual place—it's in a shady natural setting of huge oaks on the grounds of the creekside Jacksonville Humane Society. Dogs who can tell time benefit here because the park is open only during regular shelter hours: Monday and Wednesday 9 A.M.–7 P.M.; Tuesday and Thurs.–Sat. 9 A.M.–5 P.M.; closed Sunday.

Separate areas for large and small pets, watering stations, a gazebo, and benches are provided. Among the rules: no dogs under four months old, no unvaccinated pets, no digging of holes, no kids without adult supervision, and no smoking.

Admission is free. Also known as JHS Community Pooch Park, it's located at 8464 Beach Blvd., one-quarter mile west of the Southside Boulevard underpass. From Jacksonville's North Washington Street, go toward the beach (eastbound) on the Hart Bridge Expressway/State Road 228 for 5.2 miles, then merge onto U.S. 90 East/Beach Boulevard. The Humane Society is a half-mile ahead on the south side of the road. It's set amid trees by the creek, so it's easy to miss. 904/725-8766.

27 Adolf Wurn Park

 (See Jacksonville map on page 118)

Maggie kept a close eye on the doves walking around this plain park located in a neighborhood of small houses and apartments. But with only a few pine trees here, the most noteworthy thing at this park—about the size of a small city block—is the bulldozer-shaped jungle gym, though humans also appreciate the pool, two baseball fields, basketball court, football field, and generous parking (93 spaces). You can people-watch from the 19 benches or two picnic tables. Fill a water bowl for your leashed pet at the restrooms.

The six-acre park is at 2115 Dean Rd., just south of Beach Boulevard in the San Souci neighborhood in southeast Jacksonville. 904/630-4100 or 904/630-3500.

28 Southside Estates Park

🐾 (See Jacksonville map on page 118)

Located in a neighborhood of small homes and tall trees, this large, fenced, humble park features plenty of room for a pent-up pooch to stretch his legs but not a whole lot to explore. Ball fields take up much of the space. Still, there is a stand of pine trees on a ridge at the north end of the 33-acre park, and the unleashed boxer we saw roaming around wasn't complaining about the conditions.

Don't look for a park entrance sign because there isn't one. You'll know you've found the right place when you reach a gate sporting a sign that reads No Alcoholic Beverages Allowed in Park.

The park is at the bend at 9827 Jupiter Court North, at the end of Jupiter Court, two blocks east of Southside Boulevard/U.S. 90A. 904/630-4100 or 904/630-3500.

29 Stockton Park

🐾 🐾 (See Jacksonville map on page 118)

Other parks are more scenic and have less noise from passing cars, but it's hard to beat the breeze here. Grab a bench above a bluff to look onto the broad, gray St. Johns River and the many anglers waiting patiently on a seawall. Off to your left are the insurance towers of downtown. Notice the greenery rimming the banks of the huge river. A local fisherman told us that mullet is the popular catch here. His tip for canine anglers: Use pork fat as bait for mullet. He swears it works.

Your leashed buddy may prefer romping amid the more than 50 mossy oaks and tall pines dotting the three-acre park. Surely it will be hard to resist the urge to chase squirrels up a stand of pines in one corner of the park or oaks on the other side. An open grassy field sits at the center. A 2005 renovation added a waterfront boardwalk, a pavilion, landscaping, and a possible leg-lift target—a sculpture.

The park is at 4021 Ortega Blvd., southeast of the Ortega Bridge, in the Ortega section of southwest Jacksonville. 904/630-4100 or 904/630-3500.

30 Dog Wood Park of Jacksonville

🐾 🐾 🐾 🐾 🐕 (See Jacksonville map on page 118)

Doggy nirvana! At 42 acres (25 fenced), this spread is considered the nation's largest dog park. The size of 30 football fields, "it's huge and it's awesome," says fan Sandy Golding, who arrives with her dog, Coconut.

Labs hightail it to two-acre Lake Bow Wow to swim as their people relax on hammocks, benches, or swings. Landlubbers explore Barkham Woods, a 10-acre woodsy area with nature trails. Retrievers chase park-provided tennis balls on broad fields. A four-acre shady area offers respite on hot days.

A separate small-dog area—with sunny and shady areas—will soon add a swimming pond, if it hasn't already.

A rarity: five acres are lighted for use after dark (until 10 P.M.).

Amenities also include a sand pile for diggers, tunnels and tires to exercise dogs, and a full agility course for serious students.

It's essentially a country club for canines. University of Florida librarian Lynn Badger opened a big commercial dog park in Gainesville in 1998, then opened this second, bigger spread here in 2003 hoping she could earn enough to quit her librarian job. She succeeded. "I didn't set out to have such a large dog park. The land I found was big," says Badger. "As far as I know, it is the largest dog park (single-use park) in the world."

Admission for non-members is $10.70 for one dog, $1.07 per additional dog from the same family. Non-member hours are weekdays 3–7 P.M., Saturday 10 A.M.–5 P.M., and Sunday noon–5 P.M. Dogs enjoy longer hours and free entry with membership, which costs $34–36 monthly per family. Annual plans cost $269–289.

The private park is at 7407 Salisbury Road. From I-95 (Exit 344), go briefly east on Butler Boulevard, turn right on Salisbury Road South, and continue one mile. 904/296-3636.

31 University of North Florida

🐾🐾 (See Jacksonville map on page 118)

Your homework assignment is to head to what students call "The Green"—a big grassy area toward the center of campus. You're likely to see a dog or two chasing a Frisbee there on weekends or when school is out. Don't venture onto the people-pleasing nature trails, or you'll risk getting a dunce's cap: The trails are off-limits to dogs except during the annual Paws in the Park event held by the Jacksonville Humane Society in March.

The university is at 4567 St. Johns Bluff Rd. South, a little over a mile south of Beach Boulevard. 904/620-2646.

32 Victoria Park

🐾🐾 (See Jacksonville map on page 118)

More than 100 pine trees stand to be targets for leg lifts at this eight-acre Southside park. If running around the park's grassy center isn't interesting enough for your pooch, be prepared for him to pull you by the leash into the woods that rim the field. The park is so-so aesthetically, but kids can play at the playground and four ball fields, while families like to picnic at the two shelters.

The eight-acre park is at 2948 Knights Ln. West, along Barnes Road in Southside. Find it across the street from Southside Middle School, on Barnes Road near I-95. 904/630-4100 or 904/630-3500.

🐾🐾 Westside Regional Park

🐾🐾 (See Jacksonville map on page 118)

A chocolate Lab named Scooby loves to run with the chipmunks at this heavily wooded regional park, says her person, David Alevy. Just bring a leash and water, then follow the nature trails for 2.75 miles. A wildlife observation post and a nature center pay homage to the woodsy attributes of these 357 acres. At several spots around the park, alert canine noses may notice parts of an old brick road that before 1917 linked Ortega to Jacksonville. Dogs can be glad they weren't walking the old road during World War I. That's when Camp Johnston operated right here to help train American troops, and the 16-foot-wide road carried so many cars and carriages that traffic at times could flow only one way, according to the city.

Pooped pooches and their people can rest at the 36 picnic tables or 20 benches. Fill the pet water dish at the restrooms or drinking fountain.

The park is at 7000 Roosevelt Blvd., at the intersection of Roosevelt and Yorktown Avenue, not far from the Naval Air Station Jacksonville. 904/630-4100 or 904/630-3500.

PLACES TO EAT

Cafe Carmon: Ceiling fans whirl above sidewalk-fronting tables at this casual yet stylish spot for pasta, Asian-influenced dishes, big desserts, and a goat-cheese salad that some people go wild over. French windows make up the front wall of this tasteful restaurant, which seems to draw mostly families at dinner. It's also open for lunch weekdays. A host said he couldn't foresee any problems with letting a dog dine at either of the two outside tables closest to the sidewalk (and not quite covered by a white-and-dark-green-striped awning). But he suggested that dog owners gauge the receptiveness situation upon walking up. (We suggest calling first.) Stuffed pooches who need an after-dinner walk might want to cross the street to visit a tiny triangular park with a gazebo and water fountain. 1986 San Marco Blvd.; 904/399-4488.

Checkers: Burgers, fries, and other fast-food fare can be munched at these umbrella-covered outdoor tables near dog-friendly motels such as La Quinta and Motel 6. 930 Dunn Ave.; 904/696-7777.

Harpoon Louie's: On a covered deck overlooking Fishweir Creek, well-behaved pooches can watch their people consume bulldog-size burgers and a variety of beers, as well as appetizers, homemade soups, steaks, and a few seafood choices. Nearly half a dozen tables are on the deck. Tie your buddy to your table or chair. 4070 Herschel St.; 904/389-5631.

The Loop Pizza Grill: We got interested in this place when an employee told us about an Akita who came here to eat three times a week. Pooches have their choice of thick-crust Chicago-style pizza or thin-crust California pizza, lots of specialty pizzas, and burgers—many made with gobs of cheese.

Health-conscious dogs can stick to the wraps, black-bean burger, and salads, such as the gorgonzola walnut or Cajun chicken. The Loop has locations all over the greater Jacksonville area, but only this one lets you watch Fishweir Creek empty into the St. Johns River as you sit on a shaded wooden deck. 4000 St. Johns Ave.; 904/384-7301.

Russ Doe's Sandwich Shop: If you're in the somewhat industrial area near the landmark Gator Bowl stadium, you might head to the green, wood-shingled house that is now home to a breakfast and lunch joint. You and your pooch can eat takeout orders of liverwurst, hoagies, and sandwich fare while sitting in a little gazebo under oak trees or at a small picnic table in a shady area. Breakfast is also served. 1745 E. Church St.; 904/353-9065.

Sterlings Cafe: Frank the owner loves dogs, and it's hard to beat the experience of walking your pooch up the long canopied entrance to this refined sidewalk café for a memorable meal at one of Florida's best restaurants. Maggie gulped every morsel of her share of fried green tomatoes as we sat at an outdoor table adorned with a tablecloth and linen napkins. Lunch offerings include salad niçoise, black-bean cake, and pan-seared salmon. Dinner features lamb, veal, crab cakes, tuna, and Angus steaks, including the Sterlings steak with shrimp, asparagus, and béarnaise sauce. A sidewalk and bushes separate tables from passing cars, while a concrete overhang provides shade. In back, there's a splashing fountain and a courtyard with more shaded tables. Owner Frank Gallo patted Maggie lovingly and suggested we take an after-lunch walk down nearby Talbot Avenue past the handsome riverfront homes of Richmond Street. 3551 St. Johns Ave.; 904/387-0700.

Wedge Cafe: This Floribbean eatery—meaning the chefs blend Caribbean cooking techniques with fresh Florida foods—will accommodate a pooch at the fenced patio in front by the parking lot, though dogs are an unusual sight. Besides serving sandwiches, appetizers, and salads, the lunch/dinner spot in Southpoint dishes up just about anything made with jerk seasoning, including chicken, pork, or fish. *Jacksonville Magazine* deemed the baked scallops with nutty Dijon mustard sauce one of the 75 best things to eat in the city. 5711 Bowden Road, just off I-95; 904/731-7598.

PLACES TO STAY

America's Best Inns and Suites: Chaise lounges surround the rectangular outdoor pool of this 100-room budget motel just west of I-95 (Exit 341). Rooms are $55–70, including continental breakfast. Add a flat $20 for the pooch. 8220 Dix Ellis Trail, Jacksonville; 904/739-3323; www.bestinn.com.

AmeriSuites Jacksonville Baymeadows: Dogs are okay—"just no snakes," says one staffer. Among the nicest digs for dogs in the area, all suites include mini kitchens, which are good for storing perishable canine treats. People-pleasers include a heated pool, access to a local fitness center, and a free breakfast buffet. Rates start at $79, plus $10 daily pet fee, at this six-story lodging just east of I-95 (Exit 341). Corporate policy permits pets under 30 pounds. 8277 Western Way Cir., Jacksonville; 904/737-4477; www.amerisuites.com.

Baymont Inn & Suites: A grocery store is within walking distance and the free lobby breakfast features waffles and French toast, giving hungry hounds hope for handouts. Dogs pad along interior corridors to get to the guest rooms of this three-story poolside motel located off I-295 (Exit 5). Rates are $59–90, including weekday newspapers. 3199 Hartley Rd., Jacksonville; 904/268-9999; www.baymontinns.com.

Best Western JTB/Southpoint: Multilingual staffers can say "Good dog!" in Croatian, Russian, Creole, and English at this pleasant, 184-room hotel near the Southpoint Business District off I-95 (Exit 344). People-pleasers include a steam room, an exercise room, a pool, and free continental breakfast. Pets under 40 pounds may pad along interior corridors to enter designated rooms on the first and third floors for a night's sleep. Rates are $65–159, plus $10 nightly pet fee. 4660 Salisbury Rd., Jacksonville; 904/281-0900; www.bestwestern.com.

Candlewood Suites: Everyone gets a suite with a big recliner, a CD player, and a full kitchen, plus some perks tailored to the business traveler such as two separate phone lines so you can check email and talk on the phone simultaneously. Set in a suburban office park eight miles south of downtown, the three-story, 111-suite lodging offers a fitness room and is off I-95 (Exit 344). One pet under 80 pounds is permitted per suite. Rates are $76 and up. Pet fee is $25–150, depending on length of stay. 4990 Belfort Rd., Jacksonville; 904/296-7785; www.candlewoodsuites.com.

Cary State Forest: See Parks, Beaches, and Recreation Areas, above, for camping information.

Econo Lodge Jacksonville Airport: Dogs stroll through interior corridors to reach guest rooms at this 100-unit motel off I-95 (Exit 363B). Rates are $50–60, including continental breakfast. Add $10 nightly for the pet. 14585 Duval Rd., Jacksonville; 904/741-1133; www.econolodge.com.

Flamingo Lake RV Resort: Set on a 17-acre lake stocked with bass, this 50-acre park features niceties such as a beach, golf driving range, pool, playground, and basketball hoops. Some campsites overlook the lake. The 152 paved RV-only sites each run $31 nightly, but about half the guests pay by the month. Dogs under 30 pounds are accepted. 3640 Newcomb Rd., Jacksonville; 904/766-0672 or 800/RV-AHEAD; www.flamingolake.com.

Hampton Inn Jacksonville Airport: A gated entrance marks the only Hampton Inn in town that allows dogs, though they're limited to nonsmoking designated pet rooms. Found near the airport off I-95 (Exit 363), this pleasant poolside lodging is near a Waffle House, in case your dog wants a takeout order of bacon. Rates run $65–95, including continental breakfast. 1170 Airport Entrance Rd., Jacksonville; 904/741-4980; www.hamptoninn.com.

Holiday Inn Airport: With an atrium and concierge floor, this six-story hotel off I-95 (Exit 363) isn't your normal doggy digs. A poolside lounge, gift shop, weight room, lighted tennis court, and three pools please humans. You'll be near the airport—good for doggies who like to sleep in on the day of a flight. Rates are $85–125 for the designated pet rooms. 14670 Duval Rd., P.O. Box 18409, Jacksonville; 904/741-4404; www.holidayinns.com.

Holiday Inn Baymeadows: "Don't bring a horse," a staffer says, but a dog will do. You'll find an exercise room, lobby bar, pool, gazebo, and in-room ironing board—maybe for ironing doggy bandannas—at this pleasant 240-room hotel off I-95 (Exit 341). Rates run $60–130. 9150 Baymeadows Rd., Jacksonville; 904/737-1700; www.holidayinns.com.

Homestead Studio Suites Jacksonville Baymeadows: Dogs have plenty of chances to beg for treats, thanks to the fully equipped kitchens at this pleasant lodging designed for longer stays and located just east of I-95 (Exit 341). Policy dictates that one dog may join you, though the general manager may use discretion to make exceptions for multi-pet travelers. Rates start at $68. The pet fee is $25 daily, maximum $75. 8300 Western Way, Jacksonville; 904/739-1881; www.homesteadhotels.com.

Homestead Studio Suites Jacksonville Southside: A full-size fridge is plenty big for storing doggy bags for your wistful pooch. Better yet, prepare your own dinner on the cook-top stove or in the microwave and dine in with your best pal. One dog is permitted per suite, though the general manager has the power to make exceptions for multi-pet travelers. Rates start at $65. The pet fee is $25 daily, maximum $75. 10020 Skinner Lake Dr., Jacksonville; 904/642-9911; www.homesteadhotels.com.

Homestead Studio Suites Salisbury Road: A pool and an exercise room set this place apart from the city's other pleasant Homestead Studios. As at the others, these 100 suites offer work areas and full kitchens—good for frying up the morning bacon for you and your furry companion. Officially, only one dog may join you; in some cases, the general manager may grant an exception if you have more well-behaved pooches in tow. Rates start at $85. The pet fee is $25 daily, maximum $75. 4693 Salisbury Rd., Jacksonville; 904/296-0661; www.homesteadhotels.com.

Homewood Suites by Hilton Jacksonville: A stay at this well-land-scaped, two-story hotel with heated pool and fully equipped kitchens feels more like a visit to Aunt Fluffy's townhouse. There's a small central yard with a gazebo, but the official, woodsy pet walk is off the parking lot and is apt to be soaked with standing water after a big rain. Rates are $159–199. The pet fee is $75 per stay at this upscale 116-suite extended-stay hotel just west of I-95 (Exit 341). Dogs under 40 pounds, please. 8737 Baymeadows Rd., Jacksonville; 904/733-9299; www.homewoodsuites.com.

Homewood Suites by Hilton Jacksonville South: Basketball, tennis, a fitness room, and a pool are among the people-pleasers at this upscale extended-stay hotel off I-95 (Exit 344). All 119 suites provide creature comforts such as a DVD player, television with expanded cable, and a full kitchen with dishwasher. Rates start at $160. Pet deposit is a whopping $100. 10434 Midtown Pkwy., Jacksonville; 904/641-7988; www.homewoodsuites.com.

La Quinta Baymeadows: For a grassy stroll to walk off those free waffles and muffins from breakfast, step outside with your four-legged travel companion and follow the walk described in the Quality Inn listing, below. Rates are $82–102 at this pleasant 106-room poolside motel off I-95 (Exit 341). 8255 Dix Ellis Trail, Jacksonville; 904/731-9940; www.lq.com.

La Quinta Airport North: Your dog can hope for crumbs from your free breakfast of bagels, hard-boiled eggs, sausage, and fresh fruits at this pleasant lodging, where chaise lounges surround the heated outdoor pool. Rates are $72–85 at this three-story, 128-unit motel located off the Dunn Ave. exit of both I-95 and I-295. 812 Dunn Ave., Jacksonville; 904/751-6960; www.lq.com.

La Quinta Inn & Suites Jacksonville Butler Boulevard: An exercise room, an outdoor hot tub, and some two-room suites—big enough for Fifi to fetch a toy in—set the area's newest La Quinta apart from its predecessors. Rates run $78–112 at this six-story, 131-unit lodging next to the Cracker Barrel restaurant just west of I-95 (Exit 344). 4686 Lenoir Ave., Jacksonville; 904/296-0703; www.lq.com.

La Quinta Orange Park: While human travelers are treated to such niceties as a free workout at Super Fitness and a free continental breakfast, pooches pining for a walk make do with a small sandy area and thin strip of grass next to a highway entrance ramp. Rates are $80–100 at this pleasant 121-unit, two-story poolside motel off I-295 (Exit 12). 8555 Blanding Blvd., Jacksonville; 904/778-9539; www.lq.com.

Masters Inn: Only small pets may pad along interior corridors to get to the designated pet rooms at this three-story, 100-unit motel off I-95 (Exit 344). The budget rates—$45–60—include continental breakfast. Add $15 daily for the dog. 4940 Mustang Rd., Jacksonville; 904/281-2244; www.mastersinn.com.

Motel 6 Airport: For dogs crossing their legs in anticipation of a walk, try the small strip of grass stretching to the back of this 125-room poolside motel. Rates are $43–51 at this lodging located off I-95 (Exit 360). One small pet is permitted per room. 10885 Harts Rd., Jacksonville; 904/757-8600; www.motel6.com.

Motel 6 Orange Park: All rooms have showers—not doggy-dreaded bathtubs—at this 126-unit motel off I-295 (Exit 12). Rates are $43–52. One well-behaved pet may join you. 6107 Youngerman Cir., Jacksonville; 904/777-6100; www.motel6.com.

Motel 6 Southeast: The area's best Motel 6 features combination shower/baths and bigger rooms than the typical Motel 6. Ask for Room 320 and you might get to hear croaking frogs in the on-site wetland. There is precious little room to walk your dog here, but you can head off the property and follow the curvy neighborhood trail described in the Quality Inn listing, below. One mannerly pet may join you at this 109-unit motel off I-95 (Exit 341). Rates are $42–46. 8285 Dix Ellis Trail, Jacksonville; 904/731-8400; www.motel6.com.

Quality Inn: For a $50 flat pet fee, a peewee pooch—under 15 pounds—may join you at this pleasant 127-suite hotel in the Freedom Commerce Center Business Park. For a woodsy neighborhood walk: Stroll past the hotel fountains out front, cross the street, turn left, and walk down a curvy sidewalk hugging the woods. Rates run $55–129 at this lodging west of I-95 (Exit 341). 8333 Dix Ellis Trail, Jacksonville; 904/739-1155; www.qualityinn.com.

Ralph E. Simmons Memorial State Forest: See Hilliard city for camping information.

Ramada Inn Conference Center: Many rooms overlook the sundeck and pool, and every room has a reclining easy chair—perfect for cuddling Toto. A piano bar, a comedy club, and a free breakfast buffet help set this 152-room lodging apart. Rates start at $76 at this two-story locale off I-295 (Exit 5) and a 15-minute drive from downtown. Pet fee is a flat $50. You may be asked to leave a $100 refundable pet deposit. 3130 Hartley Rd., Jacksonville; 904/268-8080; www.ramada.com.

Red Roof Inn Airport: Newshounds can keep up with current events, thanks to the free weekday newspapers and cable news station at this poolside motel off I-95 (Exit 363). Corporate policy allows one pet under 80 pounds to join you. Rates are $45–55. 14701 Airport Entrance Rd., Jacksonville; 904/741-4488; www.redroof.com.

Red Roof Inn Orange Park: One of best receptions Maggie ever had at a motel was at this Red Roof Inn, where a cigar-chomping, gray-haired motel security guard on a bike vowed, "By the end of the night, I'll have her pulling me around on my bicycle." The front desk clerk stepped outside to pet Maggie, who ate up the attention. You can expect a basic economy room with two sufficient beds and free weekday newspapers. Walk your pet on a roughly quarter-acre grassy triangle by the office. One pet under 80 pounds is permitted per room at this poolside motel off I-295 (Exit 12). Rates are $40–58. 6099 Youngerman Cir., Jacksonville; 904/777-1000; www.redroof.com.

Red Roof Inn Southpoint: Some suites are offered at this poolside motel, and both a Waffle House and Cracker Barrel are nearby, giving hungry pets hope for takeout orders. Policy dictates that one pet under 80 pounds may join you at this lodging off I-95 (Exit 344). Rates are $50–66. 6969 Lenoir Ave. East, Jacksonville; 904/296-1006; www.redroof.com.

Residence Inn Airport: If you don't want to make dinner in your kitchenette, head to the nearby riverside Chart House or opt for the free light meal served here four nights a week. Rates are $119–150 at this pleasant, apartment-style establishment off I-95 (Exit 363). The nonrefundable pet fee is a whopping $75. 1310 Airport Road, Jacksonville; 904/741-6550; http://marriott.com.

Residence Inn Baymeadows: With a kitchen, fireplace (in some rooms), and other homey amenities, your pup may think he's at Uncle Turbo's house rather than a hotel. Walk your furry friend along the curvy sidewalk described in the Quality Inn listing, above. Free beverages are served in the early evenings most weekdays at this pleasant 112-suite lodging off I-95 (Exit 341). Rates are $99–199. The nonrefundable pet fee could make budget-minded dogs yelp: It's $75 per stay. 8365 Dix Ellis Trail, Jacksonville; 904/733-8088; http://marriott.com.

Residence Inn Jacksonville Butler Boulevard: People-pleasers include a free buffet breakfast in the gatehouse and a weekly hotel cookout, as well as a sport court, pool, and fitness facility. Your dog is welcome to pad along the interior corridors to reach your suite. Rates are $99–159. The pet fee is a biggie: $75. 10551 Deerwood Park Blvd., Jacksonville; 904/996-8900; http://marriott.com.

Studio 6 Baymeadows: At this corporate sister of Motel 6, rooms have fully furnished kitchens and larger sleeping areas than the typical budget accommodation offers. Rooms measure at least 280 square feet and are intended for economical extended stays, though you're welcome to spend just one night, with one well-behaved pet. Rates run $49–53 daily or around $230 weekly at this 119-unit poolside lodging off I-95 (Exit 341). Add a pet fee of $10 daily; maximum $50. 8765 Baymeadows Rd., Jacksonville; 904/731-7317; www.staystudio6.com.

Macclenny

PLACES TO STAY

Econo Lodge: King might ask for a king suite with a Roman tub at this 53-unit poolside motel off I-10 (Exit 335), though small pets are sometimes preferred as guests. Rates range $50–90. Add a flat $11 pet fee. 151 Woodlawn Rd., Macclenny; 904/259-3000; www.econolodge.com.

Travelodge: Rates are $65–85 at this 51-unit poolside motel south of I-10 (Exit 335). Pet fee is $5 daily. 1651 S. 6th St., Macclenny; 904/259-6408; www. travelodge.com.

Orange Park

PARKS, BEACHES, AND RECREATION AREAS

34 Jennings State Forest

🐾🐾🐾 (See Jacksonville map on page 118)

A veritable amusement park for outdoorsy pooches who ache to escape the dog-eat-dog world of the city, these 37 square miles are home to eastern cottontail rabbits, gray foxes, white-tailed deer, and other critters whose scents may put a spring in your pup's step. Take a deep breath and listen as you walk; you may hear the occasional trill of a pine warbler or the "poor-bob-WHITE" whistle of a bobwhite quail.

Lanky longleaf pine trees tower over the wire-grass floors of the sand hills here. Choose from two loop hiking trails: The 1.7-mile Fire and Water Nature Trail offers interpretive signs. The North Fork Black Creek Trail stretches five miles roundtrip. Though these woods are quite removed from civilization, you're supposed to keep your pooch leashed.

If you'd like, bring your own canoe for a lazy trip with your dog. This forest protects the headwaters of the Black Creek, as well as tributaries such as the North Fork and Yellow Water Creek. Locals come here to hike, fish, canoe, ride horses and bikes, hunt (with permit), and admire birds. Three cemeteries lie within the forest's nearly 8,000-acre Upper Black Creek Conservation Area. This place is ruff around the edges, yet four canoe landings are available on the north fork of Black Creek; call for directions to the landings.

The forest is southwest of Orange Park, between Cecil Field Naval Air Station and Camp Blanding. From Kingsley Avenue/Highway 224 in Orange Park, go south five miles on Blanding Boulevard/Highway 21. Turn right onto Old Jennings Road/Highway 220A, go four miles to Live Oak Lane, and turn right. Use the first parking area for the North Fork Black Creek Trail. The second parking area is for the longer hiking trail. 904/291-5530.

DIVERSIONS

Browse a bakery for Bowser, or maybe a boutique: At **Petibles** dog bakery in Orange Park, leashed pets can choose from an array of freshly made, preservative-free treats shaped like alligators, pretzels, sushi, lollipops, squirrels, and even "freedom fries." Founder Shirley Tate started the company after daughters Ana and Angie tried in vain to find a birthday cake for their Pekingese, Buttons Michele. Tate started experimenting with recipes. Now, other doggies benefit and know where to go for birthday cakes: 2131 Park St., Orange Park; 904/269-1259.

Elsewhere, a cat named Sylvia wanders around the **Unleashed** pet boutique at 4495 Roosevelt Blvd., Jacksonville. Well-mannered, leashed shoppers are welcome to investigate the shop and its unique pet toys, handmade leather leashes, animal doormats, coffee mugs, tote bags, breed-specific key chains, original works of art, and other unusual things canine and feline. Co-owner Mary Mathis is active in agility training with her Australian shepherd, Chili, so the little shop doubles as a local source of information for dog training, rescue, and boarding. For hours, call 904/384-9922.

Still other pet boutiques and bakeries open their doors to leashed shoppers, including Bark Avenue Pet Boutique, 1008 Atlantic Ave., Amelia Island, 904/261-2275; and Stix & Bonz, 815 Beach Blvd., Jacksonville Beach, 904/246-3266. Some even offer free sample treats, as is the case at Redbones Dog Bakery and Boutique, 809 S. 8th St., Amelia Island; 904/321-0020.

35 Poochie's Swim and Play Park

🐾🐾🐾🐾 🐕 (See Jacksonville map on page 118)

Practically a theme park for canines, this 7.5-acre retreat bowls dogs over with its astounding features—a big swimming lake, a full course of agility equipment, acres and acres of fenced areas for all-out running, and a rarity: an eight-foot-tall digging mountain. Dogs can dig to China and never face rebuke, making it an object of devotion among diggers. Yet the sand mound was formed by happenstance; it's simply the sand dug from the ground to create the popular swimming lake.

Owners can watch the antics from hammocks, swings, and benches or toss complimentary tennis balls, flying discs, and squeaky toys for retrievers to chase. Kids entertain themselves at a separate playground area. Small, shy, disabled, or elderly dogs can use a separate rear entrance to access their own designated area. Watering stations at different areas of the park quench dogs' thirsts. At day's end, sandy shepherds can be rinsed off at rinsing stations.

"It's a dog's dream," says owner David Kophamer, who in 2004 bought the park from its founders shortly after his discharge from the Marines. He introduced doggy daycare and boarding, allowing boarded hounds to run at will in their own portion of the leash-free park.

It's a membership park, but non-members can enjoy it Saturday and Sunday 10 A.M.–4 P.M. Fee for non-members is $10 per family, including all dogs and people in the household. Membership allows daily access and costs $30 per month, $85 for three months, $150 for six months, $250 for a year. All dogs must be up to date on vaccinations.

The park is on Oak Lane, near the intersection of Blanding Boulevard and Knight Bo118 Road. Find the park directly behind the Walgreen's located at 1320 Blanding Blvd. 904/272-4545.

36 Black Creek Ravines Conservation Area

🐾🐾🐾 (See Jacksonville map on page 118)

Set on the south bank of Black Creek, these 965 acres of woods and wetlands certainly provide a natural escape for Jacksonville city dogs. Gopher tortoises, bald eagles, otters, deer, and bobcats make their home here, and the land to offers a remarkable range in elevation by pancake-flat Florida standards—from five feet above sea level at the banks of Black Creek to an unusual 90 feet above sea level on the sandhills in the southern portion of this conservation area.

Curvy trails for hiking and horseback-riding ribbon this Clay County retreat, starting at the parking area at the southwestern corner of the property. Two prongs eventually end up at Black Creek, where some people fish and alligators may sun on the banks.

Bring water, supplies, food, mosquito repellent, a pet water bowl, and anything else you'll need. Since the goal of this conservation area is to protect the creek, rather than cater to human needs, there are no bathrooms or running water.

The conservation area is one mile east of Middleburg at 5645 Green Rd., about .75 mile north of County Road 218. 904/529-2380.

PLACES TO EAT

Checkers: Dogs on the go can grab a 99-cent burger to eat beneath red metal umbrellas here. You'll find the fast-food chain along busy streets around Greater Jacksonville, including one at 853 Blanding Blvd.; 904/276-4909.

Larry's Giant Subs: The restrooms are marked "Fay" and "Kong" at this local King Kong–motif chain where messy, all-beef kosher chili dogs come piled high with slaw, sauerkraut, onions, cheese, mustard, and ketchup. You'll find branches of Larry's around Greater Jacksonville, and they all serve good subs. But this is the only one with two concrete tables under a porch overhang where you and your pooch can eat. 700 Blanding Blvd.; 904/272-3553.

McDonald's: Not your usual Mickey D's, this western-themed home of cheap eats has a wagon wheel out front, a tin roof, and a gray wood exterior. Canine cowpokes can mosey up to the few unshaded concrete tables outside while their pardners order up a mess of burgers indoors. 2485 Blanding Blvd., Middleburg; 904/282-9303.

Ramirez Restaurant: Small well-mannered dogs have been known to accompany their people on the patio to watch them eat moderately priced cuisine hearkening to distant lands such as Cuba and the Caribbean. 1237 Park Ave./Highway 17; 904/278-9040.

Whitey's Fish Camp: Order gator tail, turtle, or the local favorite—catfish—to go, then eat it by the on-site dock on Swimming Pen Creek. Dogs aren't regulars here, but they do drop by every now and then. 2032 County Road 220, between Orange Park and Green Cove Springs; 904/269-4198.

PLACES TO STAY

Club Continental: Lapdogs who expect estate-style digs will feel at home in this 1923 Mediterranean-style mansion, which, along with its accompanying buildings overlooking the St. Johns River, is owned and run by heirs to the Palmolive Soap fortune. Huge 200-year-old oaks grace the common areas of the breathtaking compound, and several walls are covered in ivy. Arrive by car or boat; this occasional wedding site offers dock space by prior arrangement. You'll sleep in Room 101 or 102, equipped with TV, phone, and one king-size or two queen-size beds. Tennis, fine dining, three pools, volleyball, and free continental breakfasts entertain guests. For a pleasant walk, leave the compound and stroll along the St. Johns River, where lucky dogs may notice a manatee, an occasional visitor. Rates range $80–225, plus $15 nightly for your pet (under 10 pounds). 2143 Astor St., Orange Park; 904/264-6070 or 800/877-6070; www.clubcontinental.com.

Comfort Inn: Every room at this pleasant motel has a microwave and fridge—good for hungry hounds. An on-site tennis court and the pari-mutuel dog track next door set this place apart. Rates range $70–129 at the poolside 119-unit motel off I-295 (Exit 129). Pet fee is a flat $30 for up to three days. 341 Park Ave., Orange Park; 904/264-3297; www.comfortinn.com.

Days Inn: A Cracker Barrel restaurant is next door, in case your dog wants a takeout order of bacon in the morning. Each room features a mini refrigerator and microwave at this 62-unit motel off I-295 (Exit 10), where pets under 40 pounds are accepted. Rates run $59–90. Add $25 per stay per pet. 4280 Eldridge Loop, Orange Park; 904/269-8887; www.daysinn.com.

Mandarin

PARKS, BEACHES, AND RECREATION AREAS

37 Julington Creek Animal Walk

🐾🐾🐾🐾🐕 (See Jacksonville map on page 118)

More resort than mere dog park, this place wows bow-wows with its amenities, particularly its bone-shaped swimming pool. Labrador and golden retrievers swim joyously in the climate-controlled waters. Toys are provided, as are towels for drying off.

Lots of regulars also make good use of the generous nine acres of fenced off-leash running room, which is about the size of 6.5 football fields. Nature trails ribbon the wooded portion so owners can walk with their dogs or take a seat on a bench as their pets chase squirrels or run in the play field. An obstacle course awaits in the agility field. There, owners can take a break in a gazebo.

A pet bakery sells goodies such as Ginger Pups and party-sized Woofy Cakes. This pet campus also offers doggy daycare, boarding, grooming, training, and veterinary care; it's actually on the grounds of the Julington Creek Animal Hospital.

Admission is $12 per family, meaning all dogs and humans in a household; maximum three dogs per adult. Long-term passes cost $50 monthly, $250 yearly. Kids must be at least four feet tall to enter (lest dogs knock them down). You must bring proof that your pets are current on these annual vaccines: rabies, parvo, bordetella, and DHLP. You also must sign a liability waiver.

The park is on the campus of Julington Creek Animal Hospital, 12075-300 San Jose Blvd. From I-95, get onto I-295 and head west for five miles to the exit for San Jose Boulevard (Exit 2B). Head south on San Jose Boulevard about two miles to the facility, at left. 904/338-9480.

150

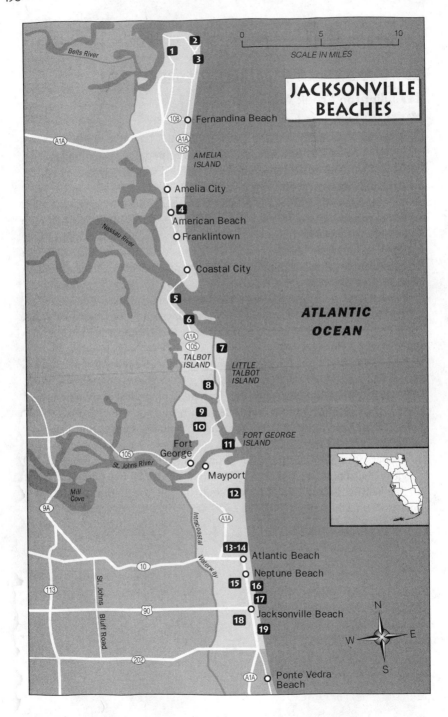

SCALE IN MILES

JACKSONVILLE
BEACHES

Bells River

Fernandina Beach

AMELIA
ISLAND

Amelia City

American Beach

Franklintown

Coastal City

ATLANTIC
OCEAN

Nassau River

TALBOT
ISLAND

LITTLE
TALBOT
ISLAND

FORT GEORGE
ISLAND

Fort
George

Mayport

St. Johns River

Mill
Cove

Intracoastal Waterway

Atlantic Beach

Neptune Beach

Jacksonville Beach

St. Johns Bluff Road

Ponte Vedra
Beach

CHAPTER 5
Jacksonville Beaches

If your dog is the beachgoing type, she'll howl with delight in this corner of Florida. With only a few restrictions, dogs are allowed at most beaches, and the seashore here boasts much wider, lesser used stretches of sand than anywhere elsewhere along the state's east coast. This is still the kind of place where, at certain times at least, you'll be all alone with your dog on a remote piece of waterfront. Seagull chase, anyone?

Too much sand getting in your pooch's paws? The town of Fernandina Beach, featuring one of the state's oldest and most quaint downtowns, sits at the north end of Amelia Island. Amelia is one of those barrier islands that makes developers drool, but luckily most of it has been developed tastefully. Your furry friend also will discover lots of Old Florida history—including plantations, forts, and Native American sites—at Florida Park Service facilities on Talbot and Fort George islands. Highway A1A is the main drag through this section.

All in all, this is one of the most enjoyable parts of the state for dogs, particularly those who love to swim.

PICK OF THE LITTER—JACKSONVILLE BEACHES

BEST BEACHES
Huguenot Memorial Park, Fort George Island (page 161)
Kathryn Abbey Hanna Park, Atlantic Beach (page 162)

BEST DOG PARK
Sandy Paws Park at Wingate Park, Jacksonville Beach
(page 165)

BEST PLACE TO SPEND A DAY
Fernandina Beach, (page 152-156)

MOST HISTORIC LODGING
Florida House Inn, Fernandina Beach (page 156)

BEST PLACE TO CATCH FIREFLIES
Fort Clinch State Park, Fernandina Beach (page 152)

Fernandina Beach Area

PARKS, BEACHES, AND RECREATION AREAS

❶ Central Park

 (See Jacksonville Beaches map on page 150)

This large, unfenced open field is on a fairly busy street, so keep hold of your buddy's leash. Ball fields, tennis courts, and restrooms are provided—but not much else (not even signs about leashes). The park is at Atlantic and 11th streets in Fernandina Beach. 904/277-7350.

❷ Fort Clinch State Park

👣👣👣 ◀ (See Jacksonville Beaches map on page 150)

With the soothing sound of lapping ocean waves and the candlelight tours of an impressive Civil War fort, we can see why this is considered one of Florida's best parks. Covering nearly two square miles at the northern end of Amelia Island, it invites leashed pooches to follow hiking trails, camp, and picnic at one of Florida's oldest state parks.

Watch for wading birds, deer, and alligators on the Willow Pond nature trail, whose two loops encircle freshwater ponds. The smaller loop is a 20-minute walk. The longer trail through a shady coastal hammock takes 50 minutes.

A six-mile trail shared by hikers and cyclists begins at the fort parking lot. Alert dogs will notice that it simply runs parallel to the park road for about three miles before crossing the road and doubling back to the fort. But trees provide a heavy cover on parts of the trail, enhancing the experience, and you'll reach some steep ancient dunes.

If you have a boat, you can use a nearby boat ramp for a side trip to Georgia's Cumberland Island National Seashore, a 17.5-mile-long barrier island just east of St. Mary's, Georgia; 912/882-4336. Wild horses run in its woods. An eerie island attraction is the ruins of Dungeness, the home of the Carnegie family.

Regrettably, dogs are forbidden at Fort Clinch's beaches and on fort tours, during which rangers in costume do the daily chores of an 1864 soldier.

Admission is $5 per car. Take I-95 to the Fernandina Beach/Callahan exit (Exit 373), and stay to the right. You'll be traveling east on Highway A1A, which doubles as 8th Street within Fernandina Beach. Stay on Highway A1A/8th Street for 16 miles to Atlantic Avenue. Turn right. Continue two miles to the park at 2601 Atlantic Avenue. 904/277-7274.

🐾 Beachfront Park, Fernandina Beach

🐾🐾 (See Jacksonville Beaches map on page 150)

An old, unleashed dog was seen dozing lazily on the sun-bleached boardwalk here, oblivious to the big S-formation of pelicans flying overhead. There are plenty of pigeons to chase at this relatively large, grassy city park, home to a playground, restrooms, and some worn concrete picnic tables sheltered by concrete roofs. But the beach is the highlight. Even at 4 P.M., people are still roaming the beach, heads bent, eyes down, studying the gray sand for good shells to cull from the many broken, lackluster pickings. A sign says that dogs must be leashed here. With three wood-covered gazebos, there are plenty of places to get your overheated pooch out of the sun. Some neighborhood shops are boarded up, but dogs don't care if this isn't the French Riviera.

Fernandina Beach's public beach is just north of the point where Highway A1A veers west toward Yulee. 904/277-7350.

PLACES TO EAT

Amelia Island Coffee & Ice Cream: Relax with coffee, tea, or dessert here after strolling with your furry friend along quaint Centre Street. The drill: Tie your dog to one of the sidewalk tables, then walk inside to retrieve a treat. 207 Centre St., Fernandina Beach; 904/321-2111.

DIVERSIONS

All pups want to go for a walk, and it's hard to find a quainter historic Florida downtown to do it in than **Fernandina Beach.** Of all the streets, **Centre Street** takes center stage. Fifty-plus specialty shops, boutiques, restaurants, and historic buildings along cobblestone walkways await tourists' window-shopping and sniffing. Start at the western tip of Centre Street at the petite brick train depot (now the chamber of commerce), which long ago served as the terminus of Florida's first cross-state railroad. Tie your dog to a lamppost and walk inside for brochures or information. Then begin your walking tour: Marina Restaurant at 101 Centre St. is in a former customs house built way back in 1882, more than 800 years ago in dog years.

Even older, the Palace Saloon at Second and Centre streets served libations to the Carnegies and Rockefellers and is said to be the oldest saloon in continuous operation in Florida. Up ahead is the 1891 courthouse, considered one of the state's two oldest courthouses still in use. The nearby 1910 post office building was modeled after the Medici Palace in Florence.

For a break, stop at the wrought iron benches along the street or a sidewalk table outside **Amelia Island Coffee & Ice Cream,** 207 Centre Street. Tie your pooch to a table and walk inside for a takeout order of dessert and coffee or tea. You and your citified canine can people-watch while enjoying a treat. Afterward, you may return to Florida's oldest surviving tourist hotel, the **Florida House Inn,** an 1857 landmark whose guests have included Ulysses S. Grant, Cuban freedom fighter Jose Marti, comedians Laurel and Hardy, and many a happy dog.

Down Under: During warm months when outdoor service is provided—say, March through autumn—your pooch can join you on the wooden deck of this rustic casual spot for Dungeness crab and fresh local seafood. On Highway A1A at the Intracoastal Waterway, Amelia Island; 904/261-1001.

Taco Bell: Dogs are allowed at the scattering of unshaded tables outside this fast-food Mexican eatery. 1858 S. Eighth St., Fernandina Beach; 904/277-2263.

PLACES TO STAY

All-Service Realty Inc.: Dog-paddlers itching to jump into the ocean will appreciate the convenience of staying at one of these beach cottages or duplexes at the water's edge or perhaps a block away. In this laid-back resort region, some vacationers book a home for a month or two. Sandy Mick handles pet-permissible reservations and has high praise for her canine clientele.

"We love our dogs," she says. "We also encourage families to visit with their pets, as this is a nice family vacation place." Sleep in an oceanfront vacation house for $100–350 nightly. The nonrefundable pet fee is $200. 1925 South 14 St., Fernandina Beach; 904/277-0907 or 800/477-8922.

Amelia Inn at Amelia Island Plantation resort: On your private patio facing the ocean, you can watch the sun rise or eat a room-service breakfast with your small dog. Part of the famed Amelia Island Plantation resort, the Amelia Inn permits small pets in a dozen first-floor luxury rooms offering nice views of the ocean. Pet sitting is available (for a fee) so you can try out the three golf courses, 23 clay tennis courts, golf school, spa, pools, restaurants, shops, and other amenities of the 1,350-acre resort. Oceanview hotel rooms run $240–350 nightly. Add a $150 pet fee, $100 of which is refundable barring doggy destruction. 6800 First Coast Hwy., Amelia Island; 904/261-6161 or 800/874-6878; www.aipfl.com.

Amelia Island Plantation vacation rentals: Andre Agassi and Martina Navratilova have volleyed balls at this secluded resort with 25 tennis courts, but your leashed pup will enjoy the nature trails that honeycomb the island or romping along four miles of broad, private beach. Forty-five holes of golf set amid marshland, dense greenery, and the ocean are just a part of the refined experience. Don't call the resort directly; instead you'll stay at a vacation home offered by Unique Realty. "We've had very good luck with animal owners. Love 'em," says Mariann Dahl, Unique's resort manager. She considers Amelia Island a good place for dogs. Weekly rates range $1,050–4,000. Add a nonrefundable pet fee of $150. All stays require a $100 cleaning fee and $400 refundable security deposit, with or without a pet. Unique Realty, 3955 Amelia Island Pkwy., Amelia Island; 904/261-3900 or 800/940-3955; www.uniqueameliaisland.com.

Ash Street Inn bed-and-breakfast: Not your ordinary doggy digs, this compound of two historic homes treats human guests to a three-course gourmet breakfast, freshly baked cookies and lemonade in the afternoon, and use of bicycles, beach towels and beach chairs—all complimentary. It's a place where guests can lounge in the hot tub, get a massage at the spa (for a fee), or relax on the deck of the pretty, retreat-like pool. The video library has more than 200 movies to watch with your small well-mannered dog back in one of the three designated ground-floor pet rooms, including a Hemingway-style suite with marble fireplace, wrought-iron king bed, and two-person whirlpool tub. Rates range $159–299 nightly. The pet fee is a nonrefundable $50, and pets must be declared at reservation time. 102 S. 7th St., Amelia Island; 904/277-4941 or 800/277-6660; www.ashstinn.com.

Best Western Inn at Amelia Island: You can walk to pet-permissible Beachfront Park from this 130-room lodging, which features two lighted tennis courts, a Jacuzzi, volleyball courts, Shoney's restaurant (next door), and an Olympic-size pool with sundeck and a poolside lounge. Rates range $40–130.

Add a $25 nonrefundable pet fee, plus an extra $10 daily for the dog. 2707 Sadler Rd., Fernandina Beach; 904/277-2300; www.bestwestern.com.

Florida House Inn: The Carnegies, Rockefellers, and Ulysses S. Grant stayed at what is considered Florida's longest continually running inn. Dogs, too, are welcomed at this 1857 charmer listed on the National Register of Historic Places. They may sit with their owners on the spacious porches or in the brick courtyard, featuring a 200-year-old oak tree. Better yet, your pal can run (on leash) on Amelia Island beaches. Ten of the 18 guest rooms have fireplaces. The dining room at lunchtime serves family-style meals for a fee; at night, the room offers fine dining. A fireplace glows in winter in the pub. Lodging rates range $99–259, including country breakfast, free use of bicycles, and limited use of a touring scooter. Pet fee is $25 for dogs over 40 pounds, $15 for others. 20 & 22 South Third St., P.O. Box 688, Amelia Island; 904/261-3300 or 800/258-3301; www.floridahouseinn.com.

Fort Clinch State Park: Camping at this worthwhile state park is a memorable experience. Maggie gladly rested next to a picnic table one night while we counted the lightning bugs that glowed and flitted about our heavily shaded campsite. We slept under oaks and cedars that gave an Old Florida feel to the 41 sites on the Amelia River. The park has a second camping area, too. Its 21 breezy, oceanside sites are set back in the dunes about 75 yards from the beach on Cumberland Sound. All sites offer campfire rings, water, and electric hookups. Amenities include showers and lots of woods to explore with a well-rested leashed pooch in the morning. Sites are $22. 2601 Atlantic Ave., Fernandina Beach; 904/277-7274 or 800/326-3521 (reservations).

Hampton Inn Amelia Island at Fernandina Beach: Canine beachcombers can pad around Beachfront Park one block away before retiring to one of the designated pet rooms at this pleasant 77-room lodging, where pets under 25 pounds are accepted for a $25 fee. Rates range $99–170, including continental breakfast. 2549 Sadler Rd., Fernandina Beach; 904/321-1111; www. hamptoninn.com.

Amelia City

PARKS, BEACHES, AND RECREATION AREAS

🐾 Burney Beachfront Park

😊😊😊 (See Jacksonville Beaches map on page 150)

Maggie had oodles of fun romping along this broad beach in the vain hope of catching ever-fleeting sandpipers. (Later, a state naturalist gently pointed out that this isn't a good idea because it tires out the poor birds.)

You and your dog likely will have a mile or more of beach to yourselves on weekday afternoons. If anglers are fishing in the surf, you may be able to stake out your own territory farther down the shell-strewn beach. The big parking lot suggests that this place may be packed on sunny weekends.

The trees in the parking lot have a prehistoric look, with gnarly, windswept branches. Two picnic pavilions between the parking lot and beach each shelter one wide and one regular-size picnic table. If your pooch quivers at the sight of stairs, get ready to scoop him up and descend at least a dozen steps from the boardwalk to the sandy beach. Dogs often are seen swimming here. A sign says pets must be leashed.

From Amelia City, take Highway A1A south and turn left at the sign marking the road to the beach, also known as the historic African-American beach, American Beach. 904/548-4689.

Talbot Island

PARKS, BEACHES, AND RECREATION AREAS

5 Nassau Sound

 (See Jacksonville Beaches map on page 150)

Beach diehards may have an irrepressible urge to stop at the unmarked beaches where Highway A1A crosses Nassau Sound. Not as pretty as the area's official parks, these beaches are basically for anglers and those visitors who just can't get enough of the sandy stuff. But dogs have been known to swim here. You'll likely see cars parked on either side of the sound on weekends. To reach the sound, head south of Fernandina Beach on Highway A1A. 904/261-3248.

6 Big Talbot Island State Park

(See Jacksonville Beaches map on page 150)

Huge, bleached logs almost form an obstacle course of driftwood at the water's edge, making this beach much more interesting for sleuthing dogs and photographers than your average stretch of oceanfront. One leg-lift target for your leashed pooch might be the dead tree we saw when we visited; it somehow was balanced upright on its exposed ball of roots, as if it were growing in the sand.

Picnic tables sit beneath the swooping arms of oaks. Although the beach isn't visible from these dune-top tables, you can hear waves lapping the shore.

The Blackrock Trail, one of five marked trails, leads to the beach. To find the trail, exit the park's main entrance, drive south about a mile, and park at a pulloff by the chained posts on the street's east side. A sign marks the start of the trail, which explores other parts of Big Talbot. Dogs may pick up scents of raccoons, opossums, or bobcats.

Bird-watchers are partial to the miles of dunes, beaches, coastal hammocks, and marshland, while boaters launch into Nassau Sound for a $3 launch fee. Somehow, this pretty, remote park tends to be nearly deserted much of the time. At 2,000 acres, there's enough room to stake out your own spot along Nassau Sound even if a few parties arrive.

Keep an eye on your pup as he frolics on the beach. He may trip on the giant driftwood. As Maggie chased an osprey flying overhead, she suddenly stopped to bite a submerged log at water's edge as if she thought it were an animal. Sometimes we just can't fathom what's going on in that pooch's mind!

Admission is $2 per car. The park is 20 miles east of downtown Jacksonville on Highway A1A, just north of Little Talbot Island State Park. 904/251-2320.

7 Little Talbot Island State Park

😺😺 (See Jacksonville Beaches map on page 150)

If you were stranded on an island, who would you want with you? Your trusty pooch, of course. So here's your chance. This popular park covers an entire island and is prized as one of the few remaining undeveloped barrier islands in the state. The scent of otters, gopher tortoises, or marsh rabbits may excite pent-up pets while following trails used long ago by English and Spanish soldiers. Alas, dogs are verboten at the 5.5 miles of beach, where throngs of people plunge into the waves.

A hiking trail starts several yards in front of the Little Talbot Ranger Station. It winds beneath trees and past palmetto thickets on a path to the beach. When your pooch reaches the sandy beachfront portions of the trail, you're supposed to double back (dogs aren't allowed on the sand). The beach is 2.4 miles from the trailhead, or 4.8 miles round-trip. Bring water and mosquito repellent and rest occasionally to ward off heat exhaustion.

Look up into the branches of centuries-old cedar and live oak trees as you walk along the coastal hammock; over the years, bird-watchers have spotted no fewer than 194 species within the park's four square miles.

Hungry dogs can eat in the sun-washed picnic areas. The heat can be unrelenting, so the 13 reservable picnic pavilions provide a welcome refuge. If it's a busy beach day, you'll probably share a pavilion with other families. The view is so-so; you won't see the ocean from your table because of the ecologically essential tall dunes.

Entrance is $4 per car. From I-95 (Exit 358A), go east on Heckscher Drive for 22 miles. 904/251-2320.

8 Wayside, Big Talbot Island State Park

😺😺 (See Jacksonville Beaches map on page 150)

What's notable about this picnic pulloff is the big marsh that spreads out like a prairie near the picnic tables. Although the area is not as picturesque as the spots you'll find if you head to the main entrance of Big Talbot Island State Park about a mile north, these picnic tables can be used free by leashed pooches and their dining companions. A boat ramp suitable for small watercraft is available on the east side of Highway A1A.

Wayside is just west of the bridge over Simpson Creek on Highway A1A, between Big Talbot Island State Park and Little Talbot Island State Park. 904/251-2320.

PLACES TO STAY

Little Talbot Island State Park: Campers sleep along Myrtle Creek on the island's west side, a quarter mile from the beach. Moss-draped oaks and dense palmettos lend shade to most of the 40 pet-friendly campsites, each with water, electricity, picnic table, and fire ring. Amenities include hot showers, a small boat ramp, a playground, a dump station, and rentals of bikes or canoes from the ranger station. Camping is $19 nightly. Reservations are advised. 12157 Heckscher Dr., Jacksonville; 904/251-2320 or 800/326-3521 (reservations).

Fort George Island

PARKS, BEACHES, AND RECREATION AREAS

🐾 Kingsley Plantation

🐾🐾🐾 🐾 (See Jacksonville Beaches map on page 150)

The bent arms of oak trees create a canopy over the narrow dirt road leading to the former cotton and sugar plantation of Zephaniah Kingsley, setting the tone for a get-away-from-it-all afternoon. The silence and woodsy feel of the drive is remarkable. We saw a huge snapping turtle pull himself out of a watery hole to prepare to cross the road, only to plop back into the water when our car approached.

Once you arrive, your leashed dog can explore the grounds (though not buildings) of what is considered Florida's oldest standing plantation. A loop trail leads from the planter's home to the slave quarters, then winds into the woods for a .3-mile walk. Dogs can sniff the outer remains of slave cabins and an old barn run by Kingsley, a slave trader, in the early 1800s.

An astute pooch might wonder why the main house faces the river, not the road. Back then, it was easier to get around by boat. Even today, the broad marsh makes walking the entire preserve impossible.

For another walk, exit the main entrance gate, turn left, drive about a half mile, and look to your left for the sole parking space for the broad grassy pathway called Point Isabella Spur Trail. Bring water. The trail has little shade.

Admission is free. The plantation, run by the National Park Service, is at the northern tip of Fort George Island at the Fort George inlet, off Highway A1A.

From the St. Johns River Ferry, take Highway A1A northeast for three miles and look for the sign marking the turnoff to the Fort George State Cultural Site. After the turnoff, a dirt road cuts to the left. Take it; the road leads to the plantation. 904/251-3537.

DIVERSIONS

Be merry on a ferry: In a rush-rush world, kicking back and taking a brief ferry ride is a simple pleasure. Maggie loved sitting in our car and watching sandpipers land on the **St. Johns River Ferry,** a car ferry that connects Fort George Island and Mayport by crossing the St. Johns River Inlet.

Sure, you could drive to your destination by veering inland instead of taking a coastal ferry. But the shortest distance between two points is a straight line. In this case, that means taking the fun ferry. As you cross the St. Johns River Inlet, look closely; you may see the curved backs of dolphins arching above the water. Mayport is among the nation's oldest fishing villages, and you'll probably see commercial shrimp boats. The ferry itself is no-frills; don't expect the *Love Boat.* And dogs must remain in cars, so arrive early to get a spot with a better view instead of being in the dark belly of the vessel. The ferry costs $2.50 for two-axle vehicles. It departs from 4610 Ocean St., Mayport, and from 9560 Heckscher Dr., Fort George Island. For ferry times, call 904/241-9969.

Once off the ferry, your buckaroo will be on the Buccaneer Trail. That's the nickname for Highway A1A—specifically, the 52-mile-long historic stretch between Amelia Island and St. Augustine. Northbound from the ferry, you'll pass various pooch-permissible parks; the first is the grounds of Kingsley Plantation, called the oldest standing plantation in Florida. Cross the Fort George River and you'll reach Little Talbot Island State Park, a barrier island whose trails beckon dogs. Farther north, you'll reach Big Talbot Island State Park, where toppled oaks serve as giant driftwood. Your trek on the Buccaneer Trail ends at Amelia Island's northernmost point and a great hiking/camping park, Fort Clinch State Park.

10 Fort George Cultural State Park

🐾🐾🐾 (See Jacksonville Beaches map on page 150)

Walk up to Mount Cornelia here, and your pooch can brag to his friends back home that he did leg lifts on the highest point on the Atlantic coast south of North Carolina's Outer Banks. No need to tell him that this "mountain" is a series of remnant dunes rising only 65 feet above sea level.

Proud rangers consider this park and its island the cradle of local history, if not American history. Seven Spanish missionaries were martyred here when killed by Native Americans. And see the huge shell mounds? About 7,000 years ago, Native Americans shucked oysters to eat, then tossed the shells onto these piles—forerunners of today's landfills.

Accompany your leashed buddy on a 4.4-mile self-guided history walk to soak up lore. Rangers occasionally spend their lunch hours walking this pretty loop, but you can also drive it. Pick up an interpretive brochure near Marker 1, then follow the partially paved, partially gravel loop all the way along to Marker 28 to learn about Florida history. You can make a day of it by leaving the loop trail to take in more sights. Historians know that a fort called Fort Saint Georges was built somewhere on this island in 1736, but no one knows where. Maybe your sleuthing pooch will stumble onto the answer.

Keep in mind your dog's abilities while walking on this fairly remote island. She wants to please you, and even if she's tired will likely try to match your pace. For her sake, bring water and rest occasionally.

Admission is free. The park is about 16 miles east of downtown Jacksonville on Highway A1A. From the St. Johns River Ferry, take Highway A1A north about three miles, look for the sign marking the turnoff, and continue to the park. 904/251-2320.

11 Huguenot Memorial Park

🐾🐾🐾🐾 (See Jacksonville Beaches map on page 150)

This is doggy heaven, probably the biggest Florida beach that allows dogs. Broad stretches of sand seem to span as far as the eye can see. There's a magical quality about the place: While the view from many Florida beaches inevitably includes high-rises or houses, once you get to the easternmost part of the park here, you see just grayish tan beach and the Atlantic Ocean. From the southern end, however, the view across the St. Johns River Inlet is of the Mayport Naval Air Station. Unconcerned, dogs get their thrills by chasing seagulls and sandpipers, as much in their element as the surfers who ride waves on prime surfing days.

You and your pooch can drive directly on the beach just like folks in the car commercials do. The beach narrows and broadens with the tides, which explains why four-wheel-drive vehicles sometimes appear to be parked on their own islands. Their drivers follow the curving peninsula at low tide and, as the tide rises, the surrounding lower sandy areas flood. As you look toward the park from Highway A1A, those vehicles appear to be marooned—an optical illusion. As you drive, follow tire tracks left in the hard-packed sand. Venturing onto billowy sand will bury tires.

A wet, unleashed springer spaniel was seen sitting 15 feet from a sign that read: "Jacksonville Animal Care and Control Leash Law Enforced." His human friend told us the local wisdom is this: If you drive to remote areas and let your dog run free, keep a leash ready and the dog under control in case police appear. Of course, it's no guarantee you won't be ticketed.

Park admission is 50 cents per person. The park is just south of Little Talbot Island State Park on Highway A1A at 10980 Heckscher Drive. 904/251-3335.

PLACES TO STAY

Huguenot Memorial Park: When asked whether dogs can camp here, an employee patted Maggie's head and enthused, "Yeah! We let pretty dogs camp here!" Her three rules: Arrive before 9 P.M., keep your dog leashed, and don't bring alcohol. The bargain camping fees—$5.65–7.91 nightly— are a clue that this is a rustic, no-frills place. Don't expect a recreation hall or hookups, just shower facilities and a fantastic view of the Atlantic Ocean. You'll be able to find a secluded spot, but it may mean packing in your gear on foot. Tides rise quickly, and you don't want to park in a spot that will later be flooded. So ask about tide conditions and where you can safely park and camp. Campsites are first come, first served. The park is just south of Little Talbot Island State Park on Highway A1A at 10980 Heckscher Drive. 904/251-3335.

Atlantic Beach

PARKS, BEACHES, AND RECREATION AREAS

12 Kathryn Abbey Hanna Park

🐾🐾🐾🐾 (See Jacksonville Beaches map on page 150)

This 450-acre park—one of the biggest in the area—is a true find, as a Saint Bernard named Megan can attest. Leashed dogs can run along 1.5 miles of beach any time. Megan frolics in the surf as happily as a child. Maggie, too, loved the grayish tan beach, where the hard-packed sand feels firm under paws. It's a fine place for humans to lie back and be lulled by the sound of the frothy waves. Frankly, we don't understand why more tourists don't flock to Jacksonville-area beaches instead of the more-crowded, typically narrower ones in southern Florida.

More than a great beach, this park offers something to do for just about any-one: The adventurous can race mountain bikes down off-road trails, anglers can snag channel catfish at a 60-acre freshwater lake, canoeists can paddle their own craft around the same lake, and anyone can explore the extensive hiking trail system that winds beneath trees. Picnic tables offer a place to rest afterward. Find them by the beach or overlooking the big lake.

Leashed dogs may join you in any of those activities, though trotting behind mountain bikes on rugged trails can be treacherous, so use your judgment. Pets can quench their thirst at a ground-level pet water fountain at the park-ing lot by the park entrance.

Admission is $1 per person; children five and under are free. The park is near the Mayport Naval Air Station and is run by the City of Jacksonville. From Atlantic Beach, go north about 2.4 miles on Mayport Road, then right onto Pioneer Drive, which soon becomes Sherry Drive. Continue a short distance to Wonderwood Drive, where you'll turn right and proceed to 500 Wonderwood Drive. 904/249-4700.

13 Atlantic Beach

🐾🐾🐾 (See Jacksonville Beaches map on page 150)

At any time of day, furry swimmers can dog-paddle leash-free alongside their loved ones in the ocean here. Only when they step ashore must they be reattached to a leash.

Locals have told us that not everyone abides by the mandatory leash laws, even though a city employee sometimes rides up and down the beach looking for scofflaws to ticket. On many days, they say, Mother Nature smiles on dogs: The tide rises too high for the official's vehicle to make it down the shrunken strip of beach, so dogs can breathe a sigh of relief. We saw several pooches and their people ambling to the beach on a late afternoon. Some dogs wore leashes, others didn't.

It isn't easy finding a place to park near a public access point. Homes are packed side by side along the two miles of beach here, so look for narrow beach access points off Seminole Beach Road. 904/247-5828.

14 Jack Russell Park

🔥 (See Jacksonville Beaches map on page 150)

Dominated by ball fields and sports courts, this small park in the center of town may not be a Jack Russell terrier's idea of big-time fun. But it's popular among humans who head to its six tennis courts, two racquetball courts, two playgrounds, ball fields, and reservable picnic pavilion. The 12-acre park is next to City Hall, 800 Seminole Road. 904/247-5828.

PLACES TO EAT

Al's Pizza: Many a local dog fancier stops here for lunch or dinner with her pooch after a jog or a walk along the beach. Blow your diet with any number of specialty pizzas or try the lasagna or calzones. Sandwiches, homemade bread, wine, and imported beer also can be enjoyed at the covered outdoor seating in front. 303 Atlantic Blvd.; 904/249-0002.

PLACES TO STAY

Kathryn Abbey Hanna Park: At this terrific beach park, campsites—nearly 300 in all—permit two leashed pets apiece and are set in the woods along a ribbon of paved roads. Amenities include hot showers, 24-hour security, a laundry facility, restrooms, and a general store. Fee is $13.50 nightly for tents, $18 for RVs with water, electricity, and sewer hookups. Reservations are advised, though normally unnecessary. 500 Wonderwood Drive, Atlantic Beach; 904/249-4700.

Mayport

PLACES TO EAT

La Cruise Dockside Restaurant: A server automatically brought Maggie a water bowl as we watched seagulls fly overhead and boats tool alongside this casual eatery's sun-bleached deck. Sitting at one of the dozen tables on the waterfront deck is the highlight. Maggie tilted her head at the sound of a loud horn signaling the next run of the casino ship *La Cruise,* which departs from its namesake restaurant. This is a working port community, with the occasional rusty freighter in view. While the all-you-can-eat food bar is popular for lunch, dinners include a small range of somewhat heavily breaded seafood, plus grilled chicken breast or the half-pound Dockside Burger. Bring mosquito repellent at dusk. The outdoor tables where your dog can sit aren't shaded, so consider avoiding this place at midday. The restaurant is busy right before cruise departures. 4738 Ocean St.; 904/246-8384.

Neptune Beach

PARKS, BEACHES, AND RECREATION AREAS

15 Jarboe Park

🐾🐾 (See Jacksonville Beaches map on page 150)

More than 100 ducks hang around the two ponds at this park, a sight that may send your dog tugging at his leash with excitement. Follow a trail around the ponds for a pleasant walk. Kids will like the little playground, and there are picnic tables with grills, a basketball court, and three tennis courts. The size of a city block, this park is named for James Jarboe Sr., who probably saw many a dog in his days as city marshal from 1933 to 1974. Dogs must be leashed here. The park is at Highway A1A and Florida Boulevard. 904/270-2400.

16 Neptune Beach

🐾🐾🐾 (See Jacksonville Beaches map on page 150)

Canine swimmers are welcome to hit the beach with their people after 5 P.M. and before 9 A.M. In other words, dogs are taboo during prime sunbathing times. That may be just as well for four-legged beachgoers in fur coats, considering Florida's considerable midday heat.

A little more than a mile of beach spans the Atlantic Ocean in Neptune Beach. Signs say dogs must be leashed, but a surfer told us that many a dog saunters around leashless after the lifeguards leave. Of the two dogs we saw on the beach shortly after 5 P.M., neither was leashed. Local wisdom says that if you're daring enough to be here before 5 P.M. and you see a red law enforcement truck coming down the beach, grab your dog and leave or you'll face trouble. Of course, it's a lot simpler to keep your dog leashed and arrive after 5 P.M. Locals consider Neptune Beach the strictest spot around these sandy parts when it comes to enforcing the law—including the ban on wearing string bikinis.

To get to the beach, drive along Highway A1A and look east for beach access points. It seems that at the end of every street there are a few parking spaces for beachgoers. 904/270-2400.

PLACES TO EAT

Mezza Luna Vagabondo: Dogs occasionally are seen sitting at the outdoor tables here as their companions munch goat-cheese pizzas, more traditional pies, pasta, veal specialties, chicken, and desserts such as tiramisu. An employee suggests you try the great appetizers. Note: Outdoor seating may not be available during cold weather, so call ahead. 110 First St.; 904/246-5100.

Shelby's Coffee Shoppe: Voted best coffeehouse in at least one local competition, this coffee bar and people-watching spot serves breakfast and lunch by day, then switches to desserts, pastries, and other diet-blowing goodies alongside espresso drinks in the afternoon and evening. Dogs can join their owners at the outside tables under the palm trees. 200 First St., 904/249-5182.

Sliders Seafood Grille: A local dog, Coconut, likes to join her chauffeur at the covered outside dining area of this popular unpretentious eatery, whose specialty is fresh fish prepared to order, plus ubiquitous oysters. Its key lime pie clinched a Best of Jacksonville competition. Dinner is served daily; lunch is offered on weekends. 218 First St., 904/246-0881.

Jacksonville Beach

PARKS, BEACHES, AND RECREATION AREAS

🔟🔽 Seawalk Pavilion

🐾 (See Jacksonville Beaches map on page 150)

Enjoy a cooling breeze while sitting at a gazebo-like structure with your leashed pooch at this small park next to City Hall and the police station. The park is at First Avenue North and North First Street. 904/247-6236.

🔟🔽 Sandy Paws Park at Wingate Park

🐾🐾🐾🐾🐾 🦮 (See Jacksonville Beaches map on page 150)

As sailors at nearby Mayport might say, "Liberty Call!" Unsnap the leash and your dog can run freely at Jacksonville Beach's first dog park, while you cool your heels at a nearby bench. Automatic watering bowls quench canines' thirst, and spigots with hoses make it easy to clean canines before they clamber back into cars. The small park is grassy, and some of its space unfortunately is devoted to a stormwater retention pond (no swimming). Big dogs and small dogs play in separate areas. Restrooms for people are nearby.

Coconut, a pound dog, inspired her owner Sandy Golding to research potential park sites and spearhead a citizen's campaign to petition the city for a dog park, notwithstanding the city's lack of available land. The paw park opened in 2005, two and a half years after the citizens submitted a detailed proposal, complete with videotaped footage of happy hounds running leash-free at dog parks in Sarasota. To Golding's way of thinking, visiting a dog park makes humans happy, too: "It can't help but put you in a good mood."

The leash-free area is the newest addition to 16-acre Wingate Park, which is dominated by ball fields but also has a picnic area. To swim off leash and find more room to run, head inland to the city of Jacksonville's private paw parks, including Dogwood Park of Jacksonville, called the nation's largest.

Admission is free. From Beach Boulevard, turn south onto Penman Road South. Turn right past the concrete wall surrounding the City Operations and Facilities property. The dog park is at the road's end. 904/247-6236.

19 Jacksonville Beach

🐾🐾🐾 (See Jacksonville Beaches map on page 150)

Grayish-white sand feels soft underfoot (or paw) along this family beach, where leashed dogs are welcome daily from 5 P.M. to 9 A.M. That's the law. Practically speaking, tourist dogs are pretty much limited to a three-or four-hour window for romping in the cushy sand. That's because signs at nearby parking spaces forbid parking between 9 P.M. and 6 A.M., so that effectively shortens a trip the beach. The other alternative is to walk here from a motel or far-off parking spot.

We saw a black Lab happily breaking the rules by running leashless with his person one evening. A native walking her leashed pooch told us she often lets her dog run untethered but will keep the leash attached if kids are playing nearby. Her M.O.: On the odd day when she encounters a police officer cruising the beach in a car, she escapes confrontation by running into the water with her leashless pooch. For those who play fast and loose with leash laws, locals say the regulations seem to be much more stringently enforced when the crowds arrive in summer. Of course, we're not advocating breaking the law.

Nearly four miles of beach span the Atlantic Ocean in Jacksonville Beach. Drive along Highway A1A and look toward the ocean to find one of many beach access points. 904/249-9141.

PLACES TO EAT

Beachside Seafood and Sandwich Company: A local dog, Coconut, likes to bring her support staff to this seafood market. They order fresh seafood sandwiches and salads to eat at the open-air covered dining area on the second floor, which has a nice view. The *Philadelphia Daily News* reported that it serves the area's best cheese steak sandwich, as determined by a transplanted native Philadelphian. 120 Third St. South, 904/241-2702.

Bukket's Baha Beach Club: Everyone from "wiener dogs to rottweilers" visits this place, an employee tells us. Arrive during warm weather—about March through October—when outdoor service is offered, though the patio is open sporadically in winter. You can sit at the outside row of tables by the latticework on the boardwalk, and your dog can sit next to you. You'll just be off the deck and on the other side of the eatery's fence. Bukket's serves seafood, wings, burgers, ribs, and the like. Its slogan: "Where the food is great and the service shucks." 222 N. Oceanfront St.; 904/246-7701.

First Street Grille: New Orleans–style muffaletta sandwiches, fine seafood, and lots of other goodies are featured at this spot, where well-mannered dogs are permitted to sit on the concrete boardwalk next to their human buddies seated at the tiki bar. Outdoor service generally is offered March to November, good news for dogs whose thicker coats can ward of the slight chill here. 807 N. First St.; 904/246-6555.

PLACES TO STAY

Quality Suites Oceanfront: Salty dogs can view the frothy waves of the ocean from the private balconies of this pleasant six-story hotel, where smoking is forbidden in all 72 suites, but pets are accepted. Convenient to hound-hospitable public beaches, the new lodging (opened in 2002) also pleases people with such amenities as valet service, a heated outdoor pool, and an afternoon guest reception. Rates are $150–299, including a hot breakfast buffet. The non-refundable pet fee is $50 daily for pets over 50 pounds, $35 daily for smaller pets. 11 N. First St., Jacksonville Beach; 904/435-3535; www.qualityinn.com.

Surfside Inn: After sunbathing at the pooch-permissible public beaches, your dog may join you in the designated pet rooms of this 32-unit, two-story poolside motel located 150 yards from the ocean. Rates range $70–199, including continental breakfast. Pet fee is $15 daily. 1236 N. First St., Jacksonville Beach; 904/246-1583.

168

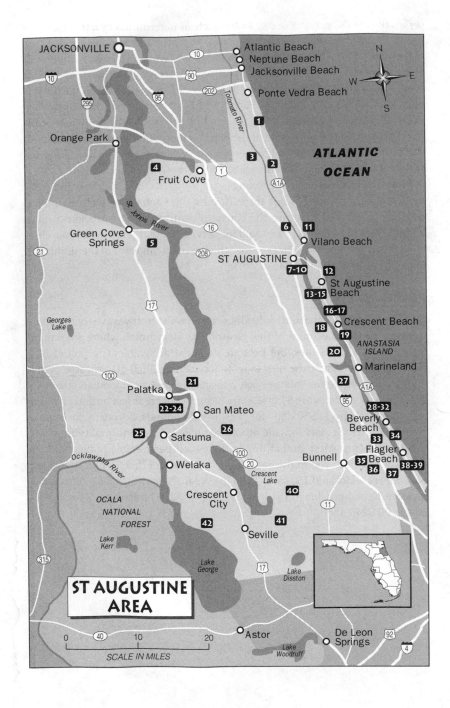

JACKSONVILLE

Atlantic Beach
Neptune Beach
Jacksonville Beach

Ponte Vedra Beach

1

ATLANTIC OCEAN

Orange Park

4 Fruit Cove

Green Cove Springs **5**

3 **2**

6 **11**
Vilano Beach

ST AUGUSTINE

7-10 **12**

13-15 St Augustine Beach

16-17

18 **19** Crescent Beach

ANASTASIA ISLAND

20

Marineland

27

28-32

Beverly Beach

33 **34**

Flagler Beach

35 **36** **37** **38-39**

Palatka **21**

22-24 San Mateo

26

25 Satsuma

Welaka

Ocklawaha River

Bunnell

Crescent Lake

40

OCALA NATIONAL FOREST

Crescent City

42 **41** Seville

Lake Kerr

Lake George

Lake Disston

ST AUGUSTINE AREA

0   10   20

SCALE IN MILES

Astor

De Leon Springs

Lake Woodruff

Georges Lake

CHAPTER 6

St. Augustine Area

The nation's oldest city is beloved by sophisticated dogs. Dogs can join the tourist throngs on sightseeing trains. They can feel the breeze flow through their fur on a carriage ride or a boat tour. They can sniff the ground where the nation's first successful European settlers set foot in 1565 and roam the site of the nation's first Catholic Mass. And just like any two-legged tourist, they can stroll streets dating back hundreds of years, then stop for a bite at dog-friendly restaurants.

You'll have to venture beyond the city boundaries to run with your dog along some of the most remote beaches on Florida's east coast. When you leave, you'll have wonderful memories of these environs: touring the ruins of a plantation mansion burned long ago by angry Seminoles, or trekking through the peaceful stomping grounds of the Florida black bear or bobcat.

There's one important historical tidbit that you probably won't hear during your stay in St. Augustine. Yes, folks will tell you that this city was founded 55 years before the Pilgrims landed at Plymouth Rock. Yes, Juan Ponce de León reputedly believed he had discovered the Fountain of Youth right here. Yes,

PICK OF THE LITTER—ST. AUGUSTINE

BEST BEACH
Flagler Beach, (page 199)

BEST DOG PARKS
Davis Paw Park, Ponte Vedra Beach (page 172)
Paws Park at Treaty Park, St. Augustine (page 175)
Bark Park, Flagler Beach (page 198)

BEST STROLL IN A TOURIST AREA
St. George Street, St. Augustine (page 176)

BEST INN FOR FURRY SWIMMERS
House of Sea and Sun, St. Augustine Beach (page 185)

MOST SACRED ACRE
Shrine of Our Lady of La Leche, St. Augustine (page 177)

MOST HISTORIC INN
St. Francis Inn, St. Augustine (page 181)

Florida got its name when Ponce de León arrived here in 1513, calling this new land *Pascua Florida* for its Easter-time Feast of Flowers.

But what about the story of Bill? Bill was loved by fellow World War II sailors so much that they had him sit front and center in group photos. His best friend had an easy time convincing him to join the Navy. They traveled the world together on a landing vessel that stopped at exotic ports that Bill's relatives never got to see. Bill managed to escape harm from the suicide planes that attacked his ship and was a fine sailor in that he didn't chase women. He did jump ship a couple times, and he had a weird habit of chasing a ball to kill time. But he served honorably. Heck, his story even made the St. Augustine newspaper. Who was Bill? A Chesapeake Bay retriever. His best pal, a St. Augustine man, still thinks of him fondly.

Ponte Vedra Beach

Forget the laid-back atmosphere of Jacksonville Beach. Just to the south, this stretch of stately columned homes and immaculate landscaping caters to the country club set. Bring your Sunday clothes if you want to feel at home; we saw a woman in a stylish checkered dress and heels walking her dalmatian along a grassy median. We, however, came dressed in T-shirts, shorts, and sandals.

PARKS, BEACHES, AND RECREATION AREAS

1 Ponte Vedra Beach

🐾🐾🐾 (See St. Augustine map on page 168)

The shelly, brownish-beige sand crinkles underfoot (or paw) here. It felt slightly sharp on our bare feet, but Maggie plodded along contentedly. Homes line the ocean, so you may get the mistaken impression that you're walking in someone's backyard. However, the broad beach is open to the public up to the high-water line, and leashed dogs are welcome any time.

Of course, you may notice the occasional scofflaw dog running leash-free here. A local couple told us that they often let their well-mannered husky run unencumbered in the surf, but they keep a leash in hand and make a point of avoiding the beach at the strictly protected Guana River State Park.

Finding an access point to the beach isn't easy in Ponte Vedra Beach, with its sometimes wall-to-wall private properties. Try the 100 block of Ponte Vedra Boulevard or Mickler Road. Also, drive along Highway A1A and look toward the ocean for public beach access points between Guana River State Park and Ponte Vedra Beach. 904/471-6616.

2 Guana River State Park Dam-Use Area

🐾🐾🐾 (See St. Augustine map on page 168)

This marshy magnet for anglers hoping to pull up flounder and red bass may look sort of homely from the parking area, but just wait: The dark, thick woods about a quarter mile from the parking area are achingly pretty and a dream for forest-loving dogs. Maggie chased a frog next to the big marsh and practically pranced with anticipation along the berm leading to the woods.

Your leashed buddy can follow several trails—the Shell Bluff Road Trail (one mile), the South Point Loop (2.8 miles), the Timucuan Trail (3.1 miles), and the Guanaloop (over one mile)—which wind past oaks so wide that two people can't link their arms around the trunk. Dusk is a great time to hear the cacophony of cicadas while walking alongside palmetto bushes—just be sure to bring a flashlight. Observant pooches may notice tracks of foxes, bobcats, or deer.

For a brief stroll, simply walk from the parking lot to the levee and scan the marsh for great blue herons. According to a park checklist of more than 170 birds, you can't miss seeing a mourning dove, a blue jay, or a cardinal somewhere amid these 2,200 acres.

Most visitors prefer to fish from the riverbank or from kayaks or boats launched here. On one side of the dam is Guana Lake. On the other is marshland blending into the Guana River—bring mosquito repellent. Picnics are make-do affairs, as there are no picnic tables. The beach bans dogs.

The park is just north of the Gates Gas Station on Highway A1A, 10 miles south of Ponte Vedra Beach's Micklers Road. Park your vehicle and walk along the berm for about a quarter mile to the trailheads. Several paces to your right is a boardwalk leading to an observation deck. 904/825-5071.

❸ Davis Paw Park

🐾🐾🐾🐾🐕 (See St. Augustine map on page 168)

Unclip the leash! The largest dog park in St. Johns County gives pets room to run and swim, swim, swim. About the size of six football fields, the park actually is two paw parks. The biggest exceeds five acres and is dominated by a three-acre pond with two fountains. In short, "it's basically a fenced area around a pond," sums up area resident Sandy Golding, chauffeur of Coconut, a Jack Russell mix.

Nearby is a second fenced area meant for small dogs, though pets and people have yet to use that 3.5-acre area (with one-acre pond) that way. They treat it like a second park suitable for any size pooch. Benches and mutt mitts are provided.

Dogs swim in the ponds. Of course, ponds can attract alligators, which prompts the question: Why build a leash-free park here, as if pups were giant reptile appetizers? Don't worry, says park director Wil Smith. The ponds are checked daily, he assures. If any gator is seen, a trapper is called and arrives that day. Smith once saw a 3.5-foot-long gator, but he assures that's too small to cause trouble (plus, it was captured promptly).

The free off-leash areas are found within 138-acre Davis Park, an athletic park with lots of ball fields, four stocked fishing ponds for kids only, and pedestrian footbridges. Find it at 2455 Palm Valley Road/County Road 210, about a mile west of the Intracoastal Waterway. 904/280-1860 or 904/471-6616.

PLACES TO EAT

Manuel's Deli and Fine Wines: While hundreds of wine labels are on hand here, your pooch will be more interested in the Reuben, the Cuban, and other sandwiches made from Boar's Head meats and imported cheeses. Grab a table under an outdoor awning. 880 Highway A1A South; 904/273-4785.

Fruit Cove

PARKS, BEACHES, AND RECREATION AREAS

◼ Julington Creek Plantation Park

🐾🐾 (See St. Augustine map on page 168)

Dominated by fields for football and soccer, this 53-acre park in northwestern St. Johns County offers picnic areas where leashed dogs can join their people. A promising development: As of 2005, there was talk of adding an off-leash paw park. Call to see whether it's now a reality.

The county park is at 3060 Race Track Road, next to Fruit Cove Middle School. 904/471-6616.

Green Cove Springs

PARKS, BEACHES, AND RECREATION AREAS

◼ Bayard Conservation Area

🐾🐾🐾 (See St. Augustine map on page 168)

Pent-up pooches might fantasize about these 15 square miles on the west bank of the St. Johns River. They have many scents to sniff in this home of turkeys, deer, and gopher tortoises. If you hang out by the river long enough, your very lucky dog might also notice a lumbering endangered manatee as its whiskery nose juts from the water.

Anglers fish from the seven-mile-long riverbank, and some visitors bring bicycles or horses to follow the same trails that you can explore with your leashed dog. This area was established to preserve and store water in the Lower St. Johns River Basin, but that doesn't mean you'll have a solely marshy experience. You'll find pinelands, sand hills, and riverine bottomland hardwood forests that ring with the rat-a-tat-tat of woodpeckers and the songs of warblers.

Bring your canoe to paddle along the St. Johns River with your dog. If you don't mind the lack of restrooms, ask about camping in the designated primitive campsites by the Area 4 parking area or two sites near the river (Area 1). Seasonal hunting occurs mainly in marshy areas but is prohibited north of Bayard Point Road. The popular Pearl's Trail and Lindsey Lane are off-limits to hunters, and both end near an on-site security station next to a parking area.

The conservation area is near Reynolds Airpark, just southeast of Green Cove Springs and 12 miles south of Jacksonville. From Green Cove Springs, take Highway 16 east; the conservation area is about half a mile west of the Shands Bridge. 904/529-2380.

St. Augustine

PARKS, BEACHES, AND RECREATION AREAS

6 Stokes Landing Conservation Area

🐾🐾 (See St. Augustine map on page 168)

Alert dogs might pick up the scent of otters while following interpretive trails at this 274-acre conservation area. Gaze out from an observation platform, and you may see a red-tailed hawk flying overhead or wading birds waiting to pounce on unsuspecting fish in the broad marsh. Stop for a break at the picnic tables offering views of both the marsh and the Tolomato River.

Locals sometimes fish or bicycle here. While there is on-site security and a parking area, expect an outdoorsy experience without such niceties as snack bars. Bring water and mosquito repellent. Bird fans will find binoculars helpful.

The conservation area is located within the coastal basin of the Tolomato River. From St. Augustine Regional Airport, take U.S. 1 north, turn right at Venetian Boulevard, then right at Old Dixie Road. Turn left onto Lakeshore Drive and continue to the entrance on the right. 904/529-2830.

7 Castillo de San Marcos National Monument

🐾🐾🐾 🐾 (See St. Augustine map on page 168)

Maggie looked down into the moat of the oldest intact masonry fort in the continental United States. Head bent and paws planted on the coquina-rock border, she could see that although the water wasn't too deep, the drop-off was steep. Even if she could swim across, she'd have to contend with the tall walls of the fort. She could never climb it. Nope, there's just no way to get over there, she determined and then ambled away. Oh, well. Dogs aren't allowed in the fort anyway.

Still, your leashed dog can romp in the massive grassy field surrounding this bayfront fort dating to the 1600s, where Seminole leader Osceola once was held prisoner. Easily one of the largest open expanses in St. Augustine, this unfenced field lures picnickers who stretch out on blankets on weekend afternoons as pleasant breezes waft in from Matanzas Bay. You can get away from the crowds by staking out a spot by the eastern coquina-rock wall. Golden retrievers will be tempted to chase Frisbees here. The catch? Legally, dogs must be leashed. Think of this place as a city park, and enjoy the greenery outside the fort. That'll lessen the sting of not being allowed to walk the wooden bridge into one of the area's biggest tourist attractions with your dog.

The fort is at 1 Castillo Drive, north of the Bridge of Lions off Avenida Menendez. 904/829-6506.

DIVERSIONS

Search for the Fountain of Youth: What could be more important than beating the clock when your pooch's one year equals seven human years? Your leashed buddy is welcome in the park portion of **Ponce de Leon's Fountain of Youth,** 11 Magnolia Ave. (off San Marco Avenue North), St. Augustine.

Lore has it that this is the exact spot where Ponce de Leon landed in 1513 while searching for the fountain of youth. He claimed this very land for Spain. As you pass through the gardens and walkways, you'll see a statue of Ponce, as well as cannons, anchors, native plants, and an Indian-style barbecue. The actual fountain is off-limits to pooches, but hopefully the grounds alone will have a rejuvenating effect. Call 904/829-3168 or 800/356-8222.

8 Paws Park at Treaty Park

🐾🐾🐾🐕 (See St. Augustine map on page 168)

Run free! After all, that's the point of this three-quarter-acre fenced park. Dogs from as far away as Jacksonville have arrived to scamper and sniff each other while their people look on from picnic tables or chat with other pet owners. This park marks a first for St. Augustine: Here, leashes are banned.

Inspired by California leash-free parks enjoyed by Meg, a whippet, and Daisy, a spaniel mix, during their travels with St. Augustine residents Leo and Kathleen O'Farrell, the park never would've opened in 2000 without help. Donations for the $1,500 fence poured in from veterinarians, residents, and businesses. County officials set aside the land after fears of doggy mayhem were allayed by watching a videotape of dogs playing happily together at Sarasota's leash-free park; the O'Farrells traveled there to shoot it.

Today, retirees and their pets are known to arrive at this beloved spot by the carload and younger people have made visits a weekly ritual. For some, it's a place to socialize. Small dogs can use a special fenced area just for them, while big dogs have the run of the remainder. Trees lend some shade. Water is provided for thirsty canines.

The off-leash area is immediately inside the entrance of the larger Treaty Park, which itself is notable for being near the spot where Seminole Indians and U.S. government officials met in 1823 to settle their conflicting claims to Florida lands. That meeting resulted in the treaty of Moultrie Creek; hence, the park's "treaty" name. Still, most locals know the big county park for its tennis courts, ball fields, skate park, picnic areas, and now dog park.

Admission is free. The park is on the south side of St. Augustine at 1595 Wildwood Drive, between U.S. 1 and Highway 207. 904/471-6616 or 800/653-2489.

DIVERSIONS

All dogs love a walk, and a great place to do it is where all tourists go—**St. George Street in St. Augustine's historic district.** From the visitors information center on San Marco Avenue, walk south to pass through the old stone city gates of St. George Street. Many a leashed pooch has ambled along this wide, cobblestone pedestrian mall lined with shops, historic sites, and some dog-friendly restaurants.

Maggie marveled at all the people and sights. Together, we followed history: We passed the Oldest Wooden Schoolhouse—built before 1763—at 14 St. George Street. At 23 St. George Street, we admired the exterior of Casa de Gomez, where a Spanish soldier lived in the 1750s. Up ahead, the St. Photios Shrine at 41 St. George Street pays tribute to the first Greeks to settle here.

If your pooch is hot, stand near the open door of St. George's Row, south of Hypolita Street, to take advantage of the cool breeze that usually pours out. For a break, order food to go at Columbia Restaurant to eat in its courtyard at 98 St. George Street. Or try other eateries mentioned in the St. Augustine chapter.

End your trip at the grassy Plaza de la Constitucion, at St. George and Cathedral Place. Notice the cathedral facing the plaza; it's home to the nation's oldest Catholic parish. If your dog begs for more, head west one block to reach Flagler College, which hosted several presidents in its original incarnation as the Ponce de Leon Hotel. Considered the first major U.S. building constructed of poured concrete, it was built by railroad tycoon Henry Flagler. He's buried inside the

🐾 Plaza de la Constitucion

 (See St. Augustine map on page 168)

Great for dogs who enjoy people-watching, this historic district park features a Confederate memorial that your leashed pup may feel compelled to investigate. It's a pleasant place to sit on a bench or under a central gazebo and enjoy the breeze from Matanzas Bay. Tourists often ride by in horse-drawn carriages—a sight that sent Maggie into a barking frenzy. Otherwise, she was captivated by the many passing cars and people walking quickly through the park via its crisscrossing paths. Slaves were once sold at the roofed structure at Charlotte Street and Cathedral Place, at the northeast corner of the park. A sign says that a guardhouse and watchtower stood at the site from 1605 to

DIVERSIONS

Take a sightseeing tour—by horse-drawn carriage, boat, or trolley: A good way to tour St. Augustine's historic district is in a carriage provided by **Avalon Carriage Service**. Are dogs welcome? Certainly. "The horses don't care," an employee told us. Horses and drivers line up by the bayfront near the Bridge of Lions and Castillo de San Marcos National Monument to offer this popular excursion. As you travel, your driver will indicate points of interest. For a peaceful ride, it's best to test your dog's compatibility with horses first by walking past the waiting liveries to see whether he barks fanatically. A ride for four people runs about $20 apiece; for two people, it's about $30 per person, plus tip. Call 904/824-7722.

Prefer a boat tour? The owners of the *Victory III* accept well-mannered lap dogs free on their 75-minute narrated tours of Matanzas Bay. Just call ahead to declare your companion. You'll enjoy views of the Castillo de San Marcos, the Bridge of Lions, and other sights. The narrators descend from Minorcans who arrived in St. Augustine in 1777. Prices: $12 for adults, $7.50 for kids 13 to 18, $5.75 for ages four to 12, and free for younger kids. Boats depart from the City Yacht Pier. 904/824-1806.

Prefer a trolley tour? A lap dog—under 10 pounds—may accompany you on an hour-long **St. Augustine Sightseeing Train** tour that takes in more than 80 sights. If you miss hearing the juicy ending of a story when your dog showers you with affection, just take the seven-mile tour again—your ticket is good for three consecutive days. Basic tickets are $18 for adults, $5 for ages six to 12. Leashed pooches and younger kids ride free. The depot is at 170 San Marco Avenue. 904/829-6545.

1765, but later, under British rule, it became known as the Slave Market, a place for public auctions. Today, it is a favorite festival site.

The plaza is at St. George Street and Cathedral Place. 800/653-2489.

🔟 Shrine of Our Lady of La Leche

🐾🐾🐾 (See St. Augustine map on page 168)

They call it America's most sacred acre, so maybe it's no surprise that leashed dogs are welcome to cross a short bridge and retrace the steps of the nation's first founding fathers along an oak- and cedar-shaded path. Your angelic dog never does anything wrong, right? Spanish explorer Pedro Menéndez de Avilés landed on this site on September 8, 1565. Near the site of the first Mass celebrated in the United States, you'll find the Shrine of Our Lady of La Leche.

According to a sign, the nation's first permanent Christian settlement was formed right here, 55 years before Pilgrims set foot on Plymouth Rock.

We saw two small pooches who seemed to be in dog heaven, so to speak, during a shady walk past the 208-foot-tall Great Cross, a rustic altar, a shrine of St. Francis, a number of graves, and a statue of Father Francisco Lopez de Mendoza Grajales, the first priest to give Mass in this country. Watching a great blue heron fish for dinner in a narrow waterway here provides a peaceful break from the touristy hubbub farther south. Pioneers named this site *Nombre de Dios* (Name of God) and founded the nation's first mission here.

The site is at 101 San Marco Avenue. From Castillo de San Marcos National Monument, go north on San Marco Avenue a few blocks and the site is on your right. 904/824-2809.

PLACES TO EAT

Columbia Restaurant: A sister of the famous 1905 Columbia Restaurant in Tampa's historic Ybor City, this place is a real treat. Try the *caldo gallego,* a Spanish bean soup with pork and a special sausage called chorizo. Also heavenly is the Cuban sandwich, a tasty hot treat featuring pork, ham, and cheese on daily-baked Cuban loaves. Order food to go from the bar, then sit

DIVERSIONS

Here is the church, here is the steeple.... St. Augustine is home to several historic churches, so if you enjoy architecture, here's your chance to take a tour while your doggy stretches his legs. Start at the home of the nation's oldest Catholic parish, **Cathedral Basilica of St. Augustine,** at 38 Cathedral Place. Facing the Plaza de la Constitucion at Cathedral Place and St. George Street downtown, the original 1797 cathedral was rebuilt in 1887 after a fire left only some original walls standing.

Next, cross the plaza and tell your pooch to look up if she wants to see the original cypress-shingle spire of the 1825 **Trinity Episcopal Church** at King and St. George streets. Walk west one block, turn right at Cordova Street, then left at Valencia Street to approach Memorial Presbyterian Church. Railroad tycoon Henry Flagler built this 1890 Venetian Renaissance church at Sevilla and Valencia streets in memory of his daughter, Jennie, who had died during childbirth. Flagler is buried in a mausoleum here.

Your pooch will probably be pooped by this point, so you can end the tour here. Rest assured that you will probably pass two religious shrines elsewhere during your visit: St. Photios Shrine at 41 St. George Street and the Shrine of Our Lady of La Leche at 101 San Marco Avenue. For information, call 904/829-5681.

outside in the iron-gated courtyard to enjoy it away from the teeming crowd on St. George Street. 98 St. George St.; 904/824-3341.

Florida Cracker Cafe: Coconut fried shrimp is a popular dinner item at this historic-district eatery, where your leashed dog is welcome to sit with you at one of the eight picnic tables covered with gingham tablecloths. The cuisine is Florida coastal—gator tail, shrimp po' boys, conch fritters, jerk chicken sandwiches—but burgers, sandwiches, and salads are served, too. In summer, try the fresh-squeezed lemonade. All tables are covered by a roof or white cloth umbrellas, a welcome treat to a hot pooch at high noon. 81 St. George St.; 904/829-0397.

Harry's Seafood Bar & Grill: Well-behaved pooches are rewarded for their good behavior here with a real treat: the chance to drink in views of the bayfront and the Bridge of Lions while their people wolf down Cajun-style dinners and listen to blues music. The century-old building seats about 600, but you'll have to stick to the courtyard. Dogs may be turned away when the crowds are thickest. 46 Avenida Menendez; 904/824-7765.

Mi Casa Cafe: Dogs who dream of changing the world might want to hang out in the outdoor garden/patio here to draw inspiration from the live folk music offered on varied days each week. Righting all those wrongs takes a lot of fuel, and this place has plenty to fill your tank: red or black beans and rice, picadillo, tacos, chicken wings, burgers, hot dogs, and chili con carne. 69 St. George St.; 904/824-9317.

Nobby's Sports Tavern: Sit on the deck out front to sample burgers, turkey sandwiches, catfish, and roast beef platters before 5 P.M. Chicken wings of "all different temperatures" are also served here, an employee told us. You can order water for your dog, then belly up to the full bar for some draft beer—so long as your pooch "is not in the way," says an employee. After 5 P.M., only libations are served. 10 Anastasia Blvd.; 904/825-4959.

O. C. White's: Fanciful locals claim that this 1791 former home of General Worth (of Fort Worth, Texas, fame) is haunted, but that doesn't stop people from showing up for blue crab cakes, Dutch garlic shrimp, charbroiled filet mignon, and other creations at this popular restaurant overlooking the city marina. Your dog is welcome to join you for lunch or dinner in the courtyard. 118 Avenida Menendez; 904/824-0808.

St. George Street Eatery: Eat dogs with your dog on the patio of this historic-district luncheonette, which also serves subs, salads, chicken tenders, and other simple fare. 3 St. George St.; 904/824-8914.

PLACES TO STAY

Beach Cottages Company vacation homes: Dogs may sleep at nearly all vacation homes represented by this company, thanks to the owner's Labrador retriever, Ella. She inspired the outfit's pet-friendly attitude, says company owner Win Kelly. Homes run the gamut—from a five-bedroom oceanview house with a chef's kitchen and 14-foot ceilings in Flagler Beach to a two-bedroom lodging in an oceanview funky 1920s former motel said to have been used in the filming of "The Revenge of the Creature of the Black Lagoon." Vacation homes are scattered along the coast from Jacksonville Beach through the St. Augustine area to points farther south. Weekly summer rates range $952 to just over $3,000; most prices drop in fall and winter. Pet fee is $140 for one or two pets; add $75 per additional pet. Some homes accept only small pets. 6899 A1A South, St. Augustine; 888/963-8272; www.beachcottagerent.com.

Best Western I-95: Pets under 20 pounds may stay in designated rooms at this 114-unit poolside motel located seven miles west of the tourist district and just west of I-95 (Exit 318). Rates range $50–100. Pet fee is $10 daily. 2445 State Road 16, St. Augustine; 904/829-1999; www.bestwestern.com.

Conch House Marina Resort: Looking for something tropical? Palm trees surround the curvy pool here, and the on-site namesake restaurant is notable for its tiki-like tree houses serving as outdoor dining areas. Set in a 200-slip marina complex overlooking Salt Run, these 24 motel rooms and efficiencies aren't too far south of the historic district. Rates range $95–225. Pet fee is a flat $50, and pooches may sleep in all but six units. 57 Comares Avenue, St. Augustine; 904/829-8646 or 800/940-6256; www.conch-house.com.

The Cozy Inn: Located both on the east and west side of San Marco Avenue near the historic district, this notable establishment offers a mix of lodging types: a Victorian house with a honeymoon penthouse suite and three other deluxe suites whose full kitchens are equipped down to the spices; five townhouses with similarly equipped kitchens; and motel rooms with minifridges, microwaves, coffee service, cable television (with HBO), and free local calls. The place aims for a homelike ambience. Small pets, please. Rates range $50–200 daily, plus $25 pet fee. A separate $100 pet security deposit will be refunded, barring doggy damages. 202 San Marco Ave., St. Augustine; 904/824-2449 or 888/288-2204; http://thecozyinn.com.

Days Inn Historic: The sightseeing trolley stops at this 124-room, two-story motel, where a sunny yard packs in a little gazebo, a fenced-in pool, and an umbrella-covered picnic table. The closest Days Inn to the historic district permits pets under 40 pounds. Rates are $55–100. Pet fee is $10 nightly. 2800 North Ponce de Leon Blvd., St. Augustine; 904/829-6581; www.daysinn.com.

Days Inn West: You'll sleep in one of the designated pet rooms with tile floors at this 120-unit motel located next to the St. Augustine Outlet Center off I-95 (Exit 318). The historic district is six miles east. Rates typically range $45–75 but can surpass $100. Add $10 nightly per pet. 2560 State Road 16, St. Augustine; 904/824-4341; www.daysinn.com.

Faver-Dykes State Park: Set in a shady hardwood hammock, this 30-site campground offers ample brush between most sites, offering pups privacy from neighbors. Hot showers and restrooms are available for people, as are scenic park trails where leashed hounds may hope to pick up the scent of deer. Sites are $14, and each has water, electricity, a ground grill, and a picnic table. 1000 Faver-Dykes Road, St. Augustine; 904/794-0997 or 800/326-3521 (reservations).

Howard Johnson Express Inn: A 600-year-old live oak tree sets this budget option apart. Everyone sleeps in a ground-floor room at this 77-unit motel located within walking distance of the historic district. Rates range $50–110. Pet fee is $10 daily. 137 San Marco Ave., St. Augustine; 904/824-6181; www. howardjohnson.com.

La Quinta Inn: Your dog can hope for crumbs from your free breakfast of waffles, fruit, and other eats before walking to the historic district and its pet-friendly restaurants. Rates are $95 and up at this 115-unit poolside lodging. 1300 Ponce de Leon Blvd., St. Augustine; 904/824-3383; www.lq.com.

North Beach Camp Resort: "Sunrise on the ocean— sunset on the river" is a slogan of this 60-acre campground set on a barrier island that stretches from the North River to the ocean. Moss-draped oaks lend shade to the 125 campsites, which are dominated by RVs and trailers, though tents are welcome. You won't really be ruffing it—a pool, lending library, game room, playground, tackle shop, fishing pier, and a restaurant on the ocean are among the amenities. Rates range $36–40. Reservations are advised. 4125 Coastal Highway, St. Augustine; 904/824-1806 or 800/542-8316; www.northbeachcamp.com.

Ramada Inn: Walk two blocks from this historic-district, five-story lodging to reach the pooch-permissible grounds of the Fountain of Youth. Rates range $60–100. 116 San Marco Ave., St. Augustine; 904/824-4352; www. ramada.com.

Ramada Limited: Two pools—one for small children, the other for everyone else—are offered at this 141-room motel near the St. Augustine Outlet Mall off I-95 (Exit 318). After a morning stop at the free breakfast bar, you might walk your dog at the open field across the way. Rates range $60–170 at this 141-room poolside motel off I-95 (Exit 95). Add a flat $15 for the pooch. 2535 State Road 16, St. Augustine; 904/829-5643; www.ramada.com.

St. Augustine/Jacksonville South KOA Kampground: Sleep in a cabin or at a campsite at this campground, set on a shady 10-acre lake just east of I-95 (Exit 323). Creature comforts include a pool, snack bar, bike rentals, and miniature golf. Cabins run $45–70. Campsites range $22–59. Reservations are accepted. 9950 KOA Road, St. Augustine; 904/824-8309 or 800/562-3433; www.koakampgrounds.com.

St. Francis Inn bed-and-breakfast: The fountain in the courtyard pond is fed by an artesian well, and homemade pastries are available at all times at what is called St. Augustine's oldest continually operating inn, dating from 1791. Cats and dogs (under 45 pounds) have stayed in select few rooms at this lovely bed-and-breakfast inn, a place that draws kudos from *The New York Times* and various Florida periodicals. Upon prior arrangement, your well-behaved small pet may join you in a room furnished with antiques or reproductions, a phone, and cable television. You'll sign an agreement guaranteeing payment to cover damages from any doggy misdeeds. Rates range $100–230, including a buffet breakfast, bicycle use, an evening social hour, and admission to the St. Augustine Lighthouse. Pet fee is $10 nightly. 279 St. George St., St. Augustine; 904/824-6068 or 800/824-6062; www.stfrancisinn.com.

Scottish Inn Historic Downtown: From this 27-room poolside motel, you can walk about two blocks to the pooch-permissible stomping grounds of the Fountain of Youth or the equally hospitable Shrine of Our Lady of La Leche (see Parks, Beaches, and Recreation Areas, above). Rates range $40–90. Add $10 daily for your pet under 30 pounds. 110 San Marco Ave., St. Augustine; 904/824-2871; www.bookroomsnow.com.

Super 8: Pets under 25 pounds are permitted in smoking rooms at this 64-unit poolside motel, located next to an outlet mall off I-95 (Exit 318). Rates are $48–79. Add $6 daily per pet. 2550 Highway 16, St. Augustine; 904/829-5686; www.super8.com.

Vilano Beach

PARKS, BEACHES, AND RECREATION AREAS

🐾 Vilano Beach

🐾🐾🐾 (See St. Augustine map on page 168)

Swimming time! Here you can frolic in the surf with your leashed pal after enjoying a picnic together. Locals tell us that dogs have been known to get away with swimming without a leash, but you'd be wise to keep the leash on. If not, then certainly snap it on as soon as all four paws hit dry land. The picnic pavilion is about two miles north of Vilano Beach. Beach access is available in various spots between Vilano Beach and Ponte Vedra Beach. 904/471-6616 or 904/829-5681.

PLACES TO EAT

Cap's Seafood: Your pooch can romp on the beach between your waterfront table and the Intracoastal Waterway, but she can't sit on the deck. You'll sit at picnic tables by some trees next to the restaurant to sample local fish. This is a good place to visit in the warmer months. 4325 Myrtle St.; 904/824-8794.

Oscar's Old Florida Grill: At this quintessential Florida seafood place on the Intracoastal Waterway, dogs are tied up next to the deck where people eat. Shrimp is popular here, but you can also get catfish, steaks, burgers, and a variety of seafood. Motor up to the restaurant by boat or car. By car, head west on Euclid Avenue from Highway A1A (turn by Compton's Restaurant) and go all the way to the end of Euclid. By boat, head north along the Intracoastal Waterway from the St. Augustine Inlet about 3.5 miles. 614A Euclid Ave.; 904/829-3794.

PLACES TO STAY

Vilano Beach Motel: From the street, you're unlikely to miss this 1950s Art Deco–style poolside motel, thanks to its rooftop pink flamingo and the neon lights outlining its architecture. The beach—where leashed dogs are welcome—is 100 feet away down a sidewalk. All rooms feature murals of historic St. Augustine and other scenes painted by local artist John George. Amenities include microwaves and fridges, if not full kitchenettes. Rates range $45–100. Pet fee is $10. 50 Vilano Rd., St. Augustine; 904/829-2651 or 866/327-3529; www.vilanobeachmotel.com.

St. Augustine Beach

PARKS, BEACHES, AND RECREATION AREAS

12 Lighthouse Park

🐾🐾 (See St. Augustine map on page 168)

Your curious pooch can sniff around the base of an old lighthouse, which in its earlier incarnation as a wooden lookout tower was used to warn Spanish sentries of approaching English raiders in 1586. The light shining in the stone tower today was last changed when Ulysses S. Grant was president—in 1874.

In the park-like area next door, windswept trees shade eight picnic tables with grills—perfect for an impromptu cookout. A stand of gnarled cedars and oaks dominates the small field between the lighthouse and the waterfront Lighthouse Park Restaurant. To spice up your picnic, you can order thick burgers and Minorcan clam chowder to go from the restaurant. (If you're lucky, the staff will let you eat on the restaurant's porch with your pooch, but cats tend to hang out there, stubborn creatures that they are.)

To reach the park from downtown St. Augustine, go east on the Bridge of Lions, follow Anastasia Boulevard, and turn left at Old Beach Road. 904/829-8807 or 800/653-2489.

13 Anastasia State Park

🐾🐾👣 (See St. Augustine map on page 168)

Just about everyone who visits this oceanfront park raves about the beach, the sailboarding, and the swimming. Sadly, dogs aren't allowed to enjoy those things. Still, this is a fine place to take your leashed pup for a picnic or a morning walk before sleeping at a campground that attracts campers from around the world.

For a short walk back in time, hit the quarry trail to see the source of rocks used in the 1500s to build downtown's formidable Castillo de San Marcos, the nation's oldest standing masonry fortress. Indians used hand tools to hew and pry out squares of coquina rock—a soft, porous limestone filled with shell and coral pieces. They lugged the blocks by ox-drawn carts, then shipped them across the bay. Your dog walk starts near the park entrance gate and takes maybe five minutes to complete. Bring mosquito repellent.

Hungry dogs can enjoy a cookout at picnic tables overlooking the sailboarders on the slowly flowing Salt Run Lagoon; beyond the lagoon is marsh, then a barrier island. You'll hear the occasional car on a nearby road, but overall this is a pleasant picnic spot. Prickly sandburs sometimes sprout up in the picnic area by Salt Run Lagoon; if your dog starts to limp, check his paws for the pea-sized spiky balls. The pain will be short-lived.

Sleeping in the oak-shaded, 139-site campground is a treat, so reserve early at 800/326-3521. Sites cost $25. Don't plan on ditching your dog at the campsite then running off to the park's four miles of beach. Rules state dogs can't be left alone for more than 30 minutes.

Admission is $5 per vehicle. The state park is off Highway A1A at Highway 3. 904/461-2033.

14 St. Augustine Beach

🐾🐾🐾 (See St. Augustine map on page 168)

Leashed dogs are welcome to frolic anytime along St. Johns County beaches. We even saw a woman carrying an iguana here. A sign says that dogs must be on an eight-foot leash, but there wasn't a word about iguanas.

The sand is packed hard enough to drive on, and people do—with a permit. Get yours, if desired, at any tax collector's office for $5 daily or $30 yearly. You and your pooch can see beautiful wildflowers during a springtime walk along some of the roads leading to this beach. We met two locals walking with a leashless dog, and they told us the leash law isn't strictly enforced. Of course, we don't recommend breaking the law.

From St. Augustine's quaint historic district, cross the Bridge of Lions and look for marked access points on the left side of Highway A1A. Access roads include Ocean Trace and Dondanville Road, south of where Highway 3 and Highway A1A meet. North of the intersection, try A Street. 904/471-6616 or 800/653-2489.

15 Ron Parker Dog Park

🐾🐾🐾🐕 (See St. Augustine map on page 168)

Leash, be gone! Dogs run happily in this leash-free area, which is about the size of three basketball courts (around 15,000 square feet). Trees lend shade over the mulched grounds. A ground-level water fountain quenches the thirsts of pooped pets.

The paw park is within Ron Parker Park, a ball field dominated recreation area developed and named in honor of a local police officer killed in the line of duty in 1979.

The free park is at the corner of Pope Road and Old Beach Road. 904/471-6616.

PLACES TO EAT

Bono's Pit Bar-B-Q: The pork sandwich is a highlight at Bono's: "It has the best flavor," an employee told us. Choose from two octagonal picnic tables outside on a wooden deck next to the takeout window. Afterward, your dog can walk off the meal in a small grassy area next door. 1001 A1A Beach Blvd.; 904/461-0157.

Sunset Grille: Small, well-mannered dogs show up for seafood at tiled and shaded counters outside this casual restaurant with a sea breeze. You can check out the sautéed fish or crab legs, but your furry friend would probably opt for a hand-cut steak. Dogs are tied to a fence next to the stools where their human buddies eat. 421 A1A Beach Blvd.; 904/471-5555.

PLACES TO STAY

Beach Properties and Management of St. Augustine: Smoking is forbidden but pets get the green light at most vacation homes represented by this agency, as clearly noted by a big paw mark next to each pet-friendly home described at its website. Expect to pay a base rate of $1,000–2,000 weekly, though some charge less. The last we checked, the three-bedroom, three-bath, partial-view house dubbed the Lighthouse charged $700–850 weekly. All require a nonrefundable $150 pet fee. 5120 Highway A1A South, St. Augustine Beach; 904/471-8110; www.bpmstaug.com.

Bryn Mawr Ocean Resort: Bragging that it's the only RV park directly on the beach in Greater St. Augustine, this resort offers creature comforts such as lighted tennis courts, a pool, shuffleboard, and a playground. Sites accommodate only RVs (not tents). Fee is $40–49 nightly. Trailer-like "park models" with one or two bedrooms and a private deck cost about twice that, with a three-day minimum stay required. In some cases, pets are permitted in park models. Add $2 daily per pet. 4850 Highway A1A South, St. Augustine Beach; 904/471-3353 or 888/768-9638; www.brynmawroceanresort.com.

Holiday Inn St. Augustine Beach: If your small dog can't see the ocean from the window of your designated second-floor, partial-view pet room, just go downstairs and walk to the beach, where dogs are welcome. Rates at this 151-room, five-story hotel range $105–160, plus $20 nightly per pet. 860 A1A Beach Blvd., St. Augustine; 904/471-2555; www.holidayinns.com.

House of Sea and Sun: At this notable oceanfront bed-and-breakfast establishment, innkeeper Patty Steder lends guests boogie boards, beach chairs, and beach towels to add to the experience of hanging out at the pet-friendly beach,

where dogs "bodysurf the waves just like people. It's funny," says Windy, an assistant innkeeper. "Labradors love it." Dogs—not cats—are accepted at the inn's two one-bedroom condominium suites, each with a full kitchen, private bath, and an oceanfront balcony where pretty sunrises can be enjoyed. Daily rate is $169, including breakfast for two. Weekly rate is $850, plus $5 per person daily for breakfast. Add a flat $25 pet fee. Two B St., St. Augustine; 904/461-1716; www.houseofseaandsun.com.

Ocean Grove Camp Resort: Walk across the road to admire the ocean. Or walk your leashed dog to the back of this 20-acre campground to watch anglers trying their luck in the marsh (if you neglect to clean up after your pet, you'll have to face the wrath of the fishermen). Among the amenities: a pool, movies, basketball, volleyball, a recreation hall, and shuffleboard. Babysitting is offered in summer. Rates are $35 for tents, $42 for RVs. Reservations are accepted. 4225 Highway A1A South, St. Augustine Beach; 904/471-3414 or 800/342-4007; www.oceangroveresort.com.

St. Augustine Beach KOA Kampground: Sleep in a cabin or at a campsite, then wake up to follow the bike path to the beach. The ocean is less than a mile from this 12-acre campground, which features a daily shuttle to St. Augustine's historic district (3.5 miles away), a pool, a fishing pond, and paddleboats. Cabins run $51–80. Campsites are $26–50. 525 West Pope Rd., St. Augustine; 904/471-3113 or 800/562-4022; www .koakampgrounds.com.

St. Augustine Beachfront Resort: Hold your pooch up to the window in one of the 144 rooms to show him the Atlantic Ocean. Better yet, walk along the resort's beach or head about five blocks to a pooch-permissible public beach. An oceanside pool with a curlicue 116-foot-long water slide helps set this place apart. Rates vary seasonally $60–200. Dogs under 60 pounds are accepted for $20–55 per stay. 300 Beach Blvd./Highway A1A, St. Augustine Beach; 904/471-2575 or 800/752-4037; www.floridabeachresort.com.

Super 8: Set across the street from the beach and a fishing pier (but lacking ocean-view rooms), this 50-room poolside motel charges a flat fee of $15 for pets. Rates are $49–130, including continental breakfast. 311 Beach Blvd./ Highway A1A, St. Augustine Beach; 904/471-2330; www.super8.com.

Crescent Beach Area

Although a hefty crop of condominiums has sprouted up here in the last 30 years, Crescent Beach is distinct from touristy St. Augustine. Bring a copy of *Old Yeller* or other reading material—it's a quiet town.

DIVERSIONS

Put out the Gone Fishin' sign: If your salty dog is angling for a few hours of fun on the **Intracoastal Waterway**, she may join you in sightseeing or fishing for trout, bass, flounder, snook, or sheepshead from a 16-foot Carolina skiff. Rent it for $115 a day or $75 for four hours from **Devil's Elbow Fishing Resort,** 7507 Highway A1A South, 1.25 miles south of the Highway 206 bridge, south of Crescent Beach; 904/471-0398. Family-owned for four decades, the rustic place invites people to hang out at its bait shop and talk about the big one that got away.

Of course, some people erroneously call fishing an excuse for drinking. You could skip the fishing altogether and go straight to having a brew with Blue. They don't serve food at the **Sand Bar** in Crescent Beach, but you're welcome to have a beer with your dog at a picnic table outside the pub at 7025 Highway A1A South, also south of Crescent Beach. 904/461-4671.

PARKS, BEACHES, AND RECREATION AREAS

16 Frank Butler Recreation Area

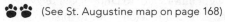 (See St. Augustine map on page 168)

The sand feels very flat and hard under the paws at this St. Johns County park, where leashed dogs are welcome to play. This recreation area is for doggies who want a taste of it all: beaches, broad grassy areas, picnic spots, fishing, and a boat ramp so they can get out on the water and let the wind flow through their fur.

A boardwalk leads to the beach from two treeless picnic pavilions that aren't very scenic. To find the newer-looking picnic area with large grills, leave the park's one-acre beachside area and follow a bumpy dirt road into the recreation area's five-acre western portion, known as Frank Butler Park West. If you want to picnic on the Matanzas River, head there. A large field awaits leashed dogs pining to run. While the recreation area may not be aesthetically pleasing to some people, dogs certainly like it.

From Crescent Beach, head north on Highway A1A to just north of Dune Street. The park is one-half mile north of the Highway 206 bridge. 904/471-6616.

17 St. Johns County Beaches

(See St. Augustine map on page 168)

Some of the least-crowded beaches on the Florida coast are found in these parts. Perhaps that's because the access points aren't simple to find. Try Mary Street and Matanzas Road, 1.5 to two miles north of Highway 206 in Crescent

Beach. Just south of the Matanzas Inlet, we veered southeast off Highway A1A to follow Old A1A. Eventually, the pavement ended, and we saw locals enjoying big waves whipped up by a far-off storm. Leashes are the law, but the lack of crowds raises the paw rating.

For the easiest beach access, go to Fort Matanzas National Monument or Frank Butler Recreation Area (see above). 904/829-5681 or 904/471-6616.

18 Moses Creek Conservation Area

🐾🐾🐾 (See St. Augustine map on page 168)

Look for fox and deer while following the canopied dirt roads that serve as trails at this 2,042-acre preserve. You'll walk beneath huge oaks, through scrub, and onto the sandy bluffs overlooking Moses Creek during a day trip that is certain to leave your leashed pal dog-tired.

More than eight miles of former Jeep roads ribbon this home of gopher tortoises and otters; they are now used as trails for hiking, bicycling, and horseback-riding. The purpose of this marshy rustic spot is to preserve one of the last undeveloped tidal creeks in the region, so expect no amenities. Bring water, food, supplies, and mosquito repellent.

Primitive hike-in camping with your pooch is allowed at two sites on the north side of the creek. Sites are free and first-come, first-served. There are no facilities. Parties of seven or more campers need a permit; call 904/329-4410.

From St. Augustine, drive about eight miles south to Dupont Center, where you'll turn east (left) onto State Road 206. Continue one mile to the two parking areas at left. 904/529-2380.

19 Fort Matanzas National Monument

🐾🐾🐾 (See St. Augustine map on page 168)

Dogs can't take the ferry to see the circa-1740 stone fort standing where stranded French soldiers were slaughtered by Spaniards in 1565. Spain dominated Florida for nearly 235 years after that bloody event. But pooches don't care about such things. They'd rather romp on the beach, which they can do at the mainland portion of this park, even though they're supposed to be leashed.

A half-mile nature trail passes through a forest of cedar trees, ferns, and saw palmetto, then opens into a sun-washed area where delicate wildflowers sometimes bloom. Maggie thinks that hardly anything tops chasing the occasional lizard-like skink here, except maybe sniffing at the edge of the boardwalk to see what's lurking beneath. Several endangered species live here, including the Anastasia beach mouse and eastern indigo snake (no, they don't bite). A small monument to the 1565 massacre stands at the end of the trail, which overlooks water. Still wondering how the fort got its name? Matanzas is Spanish for "slaughters."

Beautiful live oaks lend shade to the picnic area of this 300-acre park, where admission is free. Find the park south of Crescent Beach on Highway A1A, .25 mile north of Matanzas Inlet. 904/471-0116.

20 Faver-Dykes State Park

🐾🐾🐾 (See St. Augustine map on page 168)

Completely different from the sophisticated tourist haven of St. Augustine, this remote diamond in the ruff might send your dog frantically following the trails of bobcats, turkeys, or deer in the early morning or at dusk. It's an extraordinarily peaceful place. During our sunset visit, a pinkish-purplish hue softened the sky over Pellicer Creek and the surrounding marsh as an osprey flew overhead. The silhouettes of pine trees served as a pretty backdrop. All the while, Maggie seemed to be saying, "When are we going to hike, already?"

From the pine-shaded picnic tables and grills near the boat ramp, join your leashed dog on a half-mile walk along a wide loop trail through stands of pine trees and palmetto bushes. Maggie loved sniffing the ground here, and lucky dogs might see river otters in Pellicer Creek, where anglers try for amberjack, drum, sheepshead, snook, and snapper. Another half-mile loop nature trail begins in the pooch-permissible campground and leads hikers through hardwood hammock to the banks of Pellicer Creek. After rains, you might encounter puddles that will muddy feet and paws alike—bring hiking boots and mosquito repellent.

You'll have to drive along a dirt road leading to the entrance of this 75-acre, off-the-beaten-path park. Despite the remote location, the pine-dotted picnic area along Pellicer Creek does include restrooms and a playground.

Admission is $3 per vehicle. The park is 17 miles south of St. Augustine. From I-95, take the U.S. 1 exit (Exit 298), go north on U.S. 1 for 300 yards and turn right onto Faver-Dykes Road. Continue 1.5 miles to the park at 1000 Faver-Dykes Road. 904/794-0997.

PLACES TO STAY

Channel Marker 71/Barrier Island Inn: Arrive by boat or car to stay at this bed-and-breakfast inn, whose notable features include an outdoor swimming jet spa offering views of the inn's barrier-island setting and a Middle Ages-style labyrinth that guests can follow to find inner peace. The building's Mediterranean-style exterior gives it the appearance of a century-old mansion, but the inn actually was built in recent years by owners/contractors Heather and Warren Michael, who designed it to have river and ocean views. A gift shop, a restaurant, a 750-foot-long boardwalk, marshes, and two boatlifts (for craft weighing up to 7,000 pounds) number among amenities. People-friendly, quiet, housebroken small pets are accepted and may rejoice that the beach is within walking distance. Rates range $118–298 daily, including breakfast. 7601 A1A South, 1.4 miles south of Highway 206, just south of Crescent Beach; 904/461-4288 or 866/461-4287; www.barrierislandbb.com.

Palatka

PARKS, BEACHES, AND RECREATION AREAS

2 1 Causeway Park

🐾 (See St. Augustine map on page 168)

Locals enjoy picnicking at this wee park overlooking the St. Johns River. Weeds choke the water, so only the most single-minded pooch will ache to jump in. Instead, follow the exercise course with your leashed pup. The park is on U.S. 17 at the St. Johns River causeway in East Palatka. 386/329-0100.

2 2 Hank Bryan Park

🐾🐾 (See St. Augustine map on page 168)

Oak, palm, and cherry trees serve as leg-lift targets for leashed dogs at this four-acre park, which has a playground and picnic tables. The park is at Highway 20 and 14th Street. 386/329-0100.

2 3 J. C. Godwin Riverfront Park

🐾🐾 (See St. Augustine map on page 168)

Frisbee fans will enjoy the wide-open spaces at this six-acre park with picnic tables. The catch? Dogs are supposed to be leashed. The park is just off St. Johns Avenue at Laurel Street. From U.S. 17, turn east at Second Street. Go to the second stop sign and enter the park. 386/329-0100.

2 4 Ravine State Gardens

🐾🐾🐾 (See St. Augustine map on page 168)

A favorite of joggers, this pretty 82-acre park is one of the best places to take your dog in Palatka. The steep ravine—a fairly unusual sight in Florida—was created by water flowing from beneath the sandy ridges that flank the St. Johns River. You can make a day of it by following one of the nature trails with your leashed dog and then picnicking at one of the park tables. A 1.8-mile paved loop road is shared by joggers and walkers. It's unclear whether the gardens are open to your flower-sniffin' pooch; past policy said nay, yet leashed pooches have been seen in the gardens.

Admission is $4 per vehicle. Take U.S. 17 south into Palatka. Turn right at Mosley Avenue (by the Suwannee Swifty store), then cross Highway 20. Turn left at Twigg Street and continue one block to 1600 Twigg Street. 386/329-3721.

DOG-EAR YOUR CALENDAR

Go on a doggie bone hunt, then walk with cows: People from as far away as Daytona Beach and Jacksonville show up at the Palatka waterfront for the state's oddest pet walk—**the Putnam County Humane Society Pet Walk,** an annual benefit held every February or March. A dog-bone hunt—like an Easter egg hunt, except dogs retrieve hidden dog bones—starts the day off. Whoever finds the golden bone wins the grand prize. Afterward, enroll your dog in a fun pet show that declares winners in oddball contests, such as the fattest pet. (Don't worry, chubby cows enter, too.)

Then it's time to walk! Pooches line up to trod a mile along the waterfront, joined by a few cows, goats, snakes, lizards, horses, cats, llamas, and maybe even a skunk. For the date of the next walk, call 386/325-1587.

25 Caravelle Ranch Wildlife Management Area

🐾🐾🐾 (See St. Augustine map on page 168)

Your leashed pup stands a chance of seeing the wide, dark nose of an endangered manatee poke out of the Ocklawaha River here. But if he doesn't, he won't be disappointed: There is much to explore along the roughly 20 miles of hiking trails that wind through this 13,400-acre area bounded by the St. Johns River to the east and the Ocklawaha River to the south.

Bird-watchers will be delighted as well: Bald eagles nest in the hammock islands here, and the eerie wails of the goose-sized limpkin can often be heard. Gopher tortoises, herons, egrets, and the secretive Florida black bear pass through or live in these woods. This partially marshy terrain connects the Cross Florida Greenway with Ocala National Forest, providing dogs who like to rough it the chance to fish with their boating companions in the Rodman Reservoir to the west or the Ocklawaha River. Boat ramps are available here and nearby.

There are some drawbacks, though. Hikers and horseback riders are forbidden to traverse the trails during the pleasantly cool hunting season (better safe than shot); there are no restrooms; and you'll have to watch out for alligators. Plus, a U.S. naval reservation bombing range borders the area to the southwest.

The conservation area is six miles southwest of Palatka. From Palatka, go south on Highway 19 (don't turn onto County Road 310), cross the Cross Florida Greenway, and you will be in Caravelle Ranch. The parking area is about a mile north of the Ocklawaha River and its boat ramp. To reach the Rodman Reservoir boat ramp, turn west from Highway 19 onto Rodman Road before entering Caravelle Ranch and follow the road to its end. 352/732-1225 or 904/529-2380.

26 Dunns Creek Conservation Area

🐾🐾🐾 (See St. Augustine map on page 168)

You might share the trail with horseback riders or bicyclists while hiking with your dog, but walking on a dry trail through Long Swamp offers its own rewards. Many creatures whose scents may excite your leashed pooch live in this off-the-beaten-path area, including bobcats, white-tailed deer, foxes, wood ducks, and herons. You'll pass mostly through floodplain swamp, with scattered patches of drier pine flatwoods and upland forests.

Most people who know about this 3,182-acre conservation area are either locals or hunters (who are restricted to certain hunt dates). If you're the outdoorsy type and don't mind the absence of such niceties as restrooms, ask about camping with your pooch at the designated primitive campsite at Long Swamp. Bring a canoe for a long paddle down Dunns Creek to Crescent Lake, where anglers come to try their luck. Wherever you see a closed gate during a hike—such as at the end of Tram Road—feel free to walk around it. The four-pawed and two-legged set can go on, but four-wheeled types can't.

This marshy land is a floodplain located immediately east of Dunns Creek. Watch out for alligators and snakes, and bring mosquito repellent. There are no snack bars, so pack whatever you'll need, including water for your dog.

From Palatka, go about eight miles south on U.S. 17, then east on State Road 100. Continue about three miles to Tram Road. Turn right. The entrance is about a half mile ahead. 904/529-2380.

PLACES TO EAT

Angel's Dining Car: Sit at the sole picnic table with your pooch and a server will come out to take your order. If you don't want to wait, a waitress suggests that you walk inside to order or beep your car horn for service. Burgers, fries, and onion rings are popular. 209 Reid St.; 386/325-3927.

PLACES TO STAY

Budget Inn: Small pets are preferred at this economy motel, where every room has a microwave and a fridge—good for storing doggy bags. Rates usually range $50–55, including continental breakfast. Add a flat $10 pet fee. 100 Moseley Ave. (in the business district), Palatka; 386/328-1533; www.budgetinnofpalatka.com.

Kenwood Recreation Area: Anglers try for bass at this rustic, state-run recreation area on the western end of the Rodman Reservoir. You'll find a double concrete boat ramp, picnic tables, and vault toilets—but no showers or running water, so bring water. Leashed dogs are permitted only with registered campers. From Palatka, go south about 10 miles on State Road 19, then west six miles on County Road 310. Turn south when it dead-ends into County Road 315. Proceed one mile to the park access road, where you'll turn left to the campground at 300 Kenwood Boat Ramp Road. Each of the 16 first-come, first-served campsites costs $6 nightly. 352/236-7143.

Rodman Reservoir: Fishing is king at these 39 woodsy first-come, first-served campsites, 13 with electricity and water, located in a state-run recreation area at the eastern end of Rodman Reservoir. Facilities include grills, restrooms, showers, and limited picnic tables near a boat ramp. Built as part of the Cross Florida Barge Canal, the reservoir is a favorite of local bass anglers, while environmentalists want the river returned to its natural, free-flowing state. Dogs care more about heading east to the nearby hiking grounds of Caravelle Ranch Wildlife Management Area (see Parks, Beaches, and Recreation Areas, above). To get to the campground from Palatka, take State Road 19 south about 12 miles, cross the Cross Florida Barge Canal, turn right to head west 2.5 miles on Rodman Dam Road. Turn right at Rodman Dam Access Road, which leads to the campground at 410 Rodman Dam Road. Sites are $10 nightly. 352/236-7143; http://rodmanreservoir.com.

Palm Coast

PARKS, BEACHES, AND RECREATION AREAS

27 Princess Place Preserve

🐾🐾🐾 (See St. Augustine map on page 168)

Dogs may sniff excitedly for wild turkeys and other critters while following trails here and within the surrounding 3,865-acre Pellicer Creek Conservation Area. But the county park is best known for its namesake, Princess Estate, an 1887 coquina-rock lodge with wraparound porches designed by William Wright. It's the oldest building in Flagler County and it's thought to be the only building of this style of architecture in Florida.

Set on the southern shore of Pellicer Creek, the park offers various scenic observation points. Moss-draped oaks and cabbage palms shade the short (.68-mile) paved Blue Trail, which leads to an observation deck where you can view pretty sunsets over the confluence of Styles and Pellicer creeks. The 1.45-mile-long Orange Trail and 2.29-mile long Red Trail lead to observation decks offering views of Pellicer Creek and huge wetlands where herons look for meals and alligators hang out. Dogs who follow the interconnecting Orange and Red trails may be tempted to make leg-lift targets of all five species of pines native to Florida: longleaf, slash, loblolly, pond pine, and sand pine.

Wild hogs have been seen running through the woods of the short (.67-mile) Green Hiking Trail, where birds noisily chatter as they nest seasonally in its rookery. Pines and saw palmetto bushes dominate the sun-dappled, nearly mile-long Yellow Trail, which provides fishing docks along the way for those who want to try to catch red bass.

Bring food, mosquito repellent, and any supplies you'll need for a long walk. You can fill a pet's water bowl at the restrooms near the main parking lot.

The preserve is closed Mondays and Tuesdays. From St. Augustine, go south on U.S. 1 about 16 miles, passing Highway 204 along the way. Turn left (east) onto Old Kings Road and follow the signs. 386/329-4883 or 904/437-7474.

28 Bing's Landing Preserve

🐾 (See St. Augustine map on page 168)

Set along the Intracoastal Waterway, this palm- and oak-shaded county park is a pleasant place to eat at the picnic tables after sniffing the ruins of Mala Compra Plantation. This green spot was originally part of a 724-acre cotton plantation bought for $1,500 in 1818 and immediately named Mala Compra (Bad Purchase) Plantation. By the 1960s, Bing's Fish Camp operated right here. By the time the county bought these four acres in 1989, land values soared, making it far from a bad purchase for Charles Yant and his wife; the county paid $1 million to the couple, who were said to have been living in a mobile home at the time.

Today, some people fish the Intracoastal Waterway from the pier, while others launch boats here for joyriding or fishing. One drawback is that a highway borders the park, so, from that vantage point, it's not terribly picturesque.

Once you exhaust this park, notice the pretty oaks as you drive along Highway A1A. They're part of the Mala Compra Plantation Greenway, a 323-acre greenway preserving the oak hammock along Highway A1A from the Intracoastal Waterway to the ocean—or, basically, between Bing's Landing and another pooch-permissible park, Malacompra Park. A walking path hugs much of Highway A1A, providing leashed pooches further options for stretching their legs.

A sign at Bing's Landing doesn't exactly roll out the red carpet for dogs, stating that dog waste is "a threat to the health of our children, degrades our town, transmits disease." So remember to leash, curb, and clean up after your dog—it's required by law.

The park is at 5880 N. Oceanshore Blvd./Highway A1A, about four miles south of Marineland. 386/437-7490.

29 Jungle Hut Road Beach

🐾🐾 (See St. Augustine map on page 168)

For one of the area's more remote beaches, drive your leashed pooch to Jungle Hut Road. You may have the place to yourselves for an important reason: There are rocks on this course-sand beach and in the surf. A rambunctious pup could get hurt, and there are no lifeguards around to help you. Forget about driving on the beach, because your car will sink in the red sand. Still, this two-acre county park is a fine place for pedestrians and quadrupeds to see the ocean without stumbling over people stretched out on beach blankets. Restrooms offer an outdoor shower.

Jungle Hut Road Park, as it's also known, is at 100 Jungle Hut Rd., less than a mile north of Hammock Dunes Parkway. From Highway A1A, take Jungle Hut Road east to the beach. 386/437-7490.

30 Malacompra County Park

🐾🐾 (See St. Augustine map on page 168)

The coarse sand is reddish brown and the waves help mask offshore boulders at Malacompra, one of the more remote beaches in these parts. A sign warns: Danger, Rocks in Surf. Swim at Own Risk. You may be alone with your leashed dog, especially on a weekday, but remember to scoop the poop. Fill a dog water bowl at the restrooms.

The 36-acre park is on Malcompra Road at the Hammock, just east of Highway A1A/Oceanshore Boulevard. It's about four miles south of Marineland. 386/437-7490.

31 Varn Park

🐾🐾🐾 (See St. Augustine map on page 168)

We once saw leashless dogs run merrily along this brownish-red, coarse-sand beach. We were exultant. Could this be that rarest of finds—a Florida beach that permits dogs to run like the wind without being tethered to a too-slow two-legged friend?

But no. According to the local parks department, leashes are the law. Arrgh.

On a good beach day in September, we saw few people—but several dogs—at this eight-acre county park, which tends to be visited mainly by locals. Much of the area is taken up by a parking lot; the point is to leave your car here, then stake out your favorite part of the beach. It stretches a long way in both directions. Fill a dog water bowl at the restrooms, which also offer an outdoor shower.

The park is at 3665 N. Oceanshore Blvd./Highway A1A, south of Palm Coast and north of Painters Hill. 386/437-7490.

32 Washington Oaks State Gardens

🐾🐾🐾 (See St. Augustine map on page 168)

Shhhh! We're walking on the Jungle Road hiking trail and are about to pass a big hole—home to a gopher tortoise. The car-width trail is dark. Towering oak trees and spiky sabal palms shield us from the dipping sun. Grotesquely twisted vines call to mind Tarzan movies. We're in a lush coastal hammock that once was part of the Bella Vista Plantation owned by a Second Seminole War militia general, Joseph Hernandez. Maggie is crazy about the place.

Nearly three miles of hiking trails honeycomb this 400-acre coastal park. While dogs are forbidden at the boulder-strewn beach and the popular ornamental gardens, the four short nature walks are worth trying after you've chowed down on burgers cooked on the grill. If hiking with your leashed pal on forest floors isn't your thing, yet you want to get out into an Old Florida forest, try the half-mile-long Old A1A Road, which has been converted into a hiking trail. Visit the park in the early morning or close to dusk for the best chance to see deer. Bring mosquito repellent.

Admission is $4 per vehicle. The park is off North Ocean Shore Boulevard/Highway A1A, two miles south of Marineland. 386/446-6780.

PLACES TO STAY

Microtel Inn: Located three miles from the beach and next to a Cracker Barrel restaurant, this 82-unit economy motel promises chiropractic-approved beds in every room. A pet weighing 20 pounds or less may join you in one of the designated pet rooms. Rates start at $59. Add a flat $27.50 for the pooch. 16 Kingswood Dr., Palm Coast; 386/445-8976; www.microtelinn.com.

Ocean Shore Villa: These basic, one-room efficiencies with refrigerators and stoves are adjacent to dog-pleasing Washington Oaks State Gardens. Rates are $58–62. 6287 North Ocean Shore Blvd./Highway A1A, Palm Coast; 386/445-3033.

Palm Coast Villas: Dogs who stay in these pleasant 1930s renovated coquina-rock rooms are no more than a half-mile, leashed walk away from the surf. After returning from the ocean, you can wash beach duds at the on-site guest laundry, rent a movie, or whip up dinner in the kitchenette. You'll sleep in one of the designated pet rooms. Rates range $54–94. 5454 North Ocean Shore Blvd./Highway A1A, Palm Coast; 386/445-3525; www.palmcoastvillas.com.

Flagler Beach Area

PARKS, BEACHES, AND RECREATION AREAS

🐾🐾 Graham Swamp Conservation Area

😺😺 (See St. Augustine map on page 168)

Your pooch may have heard tales about the Florida swampland, and here he can experience it firsthand. With all the wading birds and waterfowl in the area, it can be a tail-waggin' time for bird-watchers. The scents of deer, otters, and foxes may also perk up city pooches, but keep your pal leashed, lest he encounter another resident animal—the alligator.

A short loop trail—about a mile, at most—is tucked into the drier northwestern corner of this nearly five-square-mile conservation area located in eastern Flagler County. It's best to stick to this trail with your leashed dog. The rest of this rustic place is mostly wetland hardwood swamp.

From State Road 100, go north on Old Kings Road about 4.5 miles to a parking area on the east side of the road. 386/329-4883.

🐾🐾 Beverly Beach

😺😺😺 (See St. Augustine map on page 168)

We saw a wee happy pooch sitting atop a streetside picnic table while his two-legged companions ate a leisurely lunch here. Picnic tables are spaced far apart from each other, allowing beachgoers to enjoy relatively private moments (if you ignore the cars passing close by). A beach sign warns that you can swim at your own risk. Dogs are welcome but, according to another sign, the leash law is strictly enforced.

For beach access, drive down Highway A1A in the city of Beverly Beach. Picnic tables are available north and south of the 2600 block of Highway A1A. 386/437-0106 or 386/439-6888.

🐾🐾 Wadsworth Dog Park

😺😺😺😺🐕 (See St. Augustine map on page 168)

Unsnap the leash! Dogs race and chase balls at this fenced broad grassy area with some trees. All told, it measures bigger than a football field (60,000 square feet). Small pets get their own section, so they aren't forced to mingle with gentle giants. Owners watch the antics from benches.

This popular destination is set within a 45-acre county park that seems to have something for everyone: ball fields, a skate park, tennis, playgrounds, pavilions, racquetball, soccer, horseshoe pits, a launch for canoes or kayaks, and elevated boardwalks. When you venture into those areas, keep pets leashed.

The park is at 2200 Moody Blvd. From I-95, take the Flagler Beach/Bunnell exit to proceed east on State Road 100 about two miles to Wadsworth Park, at left. 386/437-7490.

36 Bulow Plantation Ruins State Historic Site

😸 😸 😸 (See St. Augustine map on page 168)

All that is left of a gracious mansion and what was once Florida's most prosperous sugar plantation is this: the towering coquina-rock ruins of the sugar mill, several wells, a springhouse, and the crumbling foundation of the mansion. It sort of looks like a medieval castle in ruins (albeit a small one). An exciting event occurred here in the 1830s, when plantation owner John Bulow ordered a cannon pointed at state militiamen who swarmed his seven-square-mile plantation and later took him prisoner. Indians became more hostile after Bulow was freed. He abandoned the plantation, which was soon razed by the Seminoles.

Maggie was less interested in history than following the quarter-mile, pine-needle-carpeted trail leading to the ruins, ignoring a woodpecker hopping up a tree trunk. Leashed Maggie sniffed the ground, probably hoping to find evidence of resident bobcats.

This is a good destination for a pleasant afternoon. Eat at the picnic area near the parking lot. Visit the former site of slave quarters, where 159 slaves lived in 46 wood cabins measuring a mere 12 by 16 feet. Read interpretive signs at the mill ruins.

The Florida National Scenic Trail leads through jungly forest, salt marsh, and pines to connect this park with Bulow Creek State Park in Ormond Beach (see the Daytona Beach Area chapter). It spans six miles one way—too long except for the hardiest dogs. So walk a portion, then double back. Otherwise, arrange for a driver to pick you up at the other end at Bulow Creek State Park.

Admission is $3 per vehicle. From I-95, exit at Moody Boulevard/Highway 100, heading east. Turn right at Old Kings Road, and follow it about 3.5 miles to the park entrance. A four-wheel-drive vehicle may be helpful on the single-lane dirt road after heavy rains. 386/517-2084.

37 Bark Park

😸 😸 😸 (See St. Augustine map on page 168)

Swim? Or run freely? Dogs have their choice at the biggest paw park in Flagler County. Fans come from around the county to dart around trees and run at full speed on the open grassy areas of these 2.5 fenced acres, nearly the size of two football fields. A separate side yard is for shy dogs and people who want one-on-one time with their pets, perhaps by playing fetch with balls (some provided by the park).

Hammocks and gliding benches offer unusual places for humans to rest, by dog-park standards; other owners have a bite to eat at picnic tables.

A pool for pooches debuted in 2005 and requires a $3 fee. One side provides a beach walk-in so swimmers can gradually step into the L-shaped pool; another beach walk-in is more of a play area where retrievers frolic in the water.

Free prime rib bones from Martin's restaurant are presented to dogs at this private park located on the grounds of Bed & Biscuit Inn, a doggy daycare/lodging/grooming/dog-training establishment presided over by Rosemary Williams, who lives on-site. Son Richard Steele came up with the idea of opening Flagler Beach's first dog park. He lives in California, where there are bark parks aplenty, and saw an unmet need here. "We did it for the doggies, so they can play," says sister Alex, manager.

Bark Park is open daily 8 A.M.–6 P.M. It's busiest after 5 P.M. and on weekends.

Admission is free for landlubbers; only pool users must pay a fee of $3. The park is at Bed & Biscuit Inn, 711 John Anderson Hwy., Flagler Beach, one-half mile south of Moody Boulevard/Highway 100. 386/439-4006.

38 Flagler Beach

🐾🐾🐾 (See St. Augustine map on page 168)

We had a long stretch of sand just south of Beverly Beach practically to ourselves during a Sunday visit here one September. Wow. Four miles of beach are open to leashed dogs in the city of Flagler Beach. Only a mile-long stretch is off-limits, dangling out there like a forbidden apple in the Garden of Eden. So stay away from this stretch—between 10th Street North and 10th Street South. Succumb to the temptation or ignore the leash law on any stretch of beach, and you risk being slapped with a $500 fine. That's a lot of dog biscuits.

Officials have threatened an all-out ban on dogs on the beach if owners don't rigorously leash pets and pick up their calling cards. Some irate residents are pushing for the ban and have complained of dog-bite incidents, being knocked down by dogs, and general disregard of others. So, please, do your part for the sake of all pooches.

When your dog needs a break from running in the sun, take refuge under the shelters on the dunes. We like Flagler Beach, where we saw a sign that says, "Make new friends on Flagler's peaceful beaches." Yes, they are peaceful. But we predict that they won't stay that way if Flagler grows like the rest of Florida. So now is the time to take your dog there to romp. Finding a sandy area for frolicking doesn't seem to be a problem, but parking is another matter. Your best bet is to head to the northern part of the city of Flagler Beach along Highway A1A and grab a streetside spot. 904/437-0106.

39 Gamble Rogers Memorial State Park

🐾🐾🐾 (See St. Augustine map on page 168)

One of the most lively nature trails we've traversed in a Florida state park is right here, and it's only a 15-minute walk. Maggie almost stumbled onto a tortoise sitting smack in the middle of the Dune Trail when she finally realized, Hey! That's an animal! While she strained at the required leash, the alert tortoise was safe, having long ago tucked his head into his shell at the sight of the approaching monster. Maggie encountered several more critters along the trail: a second tortoise, a blue heron, a squirrel (just three feet away), and a complaining blue jay. Oak trees and palmettos close so tightly onto the narrow, short trail that anyone taller than six feet will have to duck in a few places. Over time, these bent, stunted trees were shaped by winds.

A short distance away, picnic shelters are available near the sunny Intracoastal Waterway. A playground can entertain the kids nearby. Your leashed dog is welcome in the picnic area, campground, and on the sole nature trail, which starts just inside the entrance to the 144-acre park, before you get to the entrance booth. Dogs are forbidden at the beach.

Admission is $4 per vehicle. From I-95, take exit 284 to travel east on State Road 100 for about three miles to Highway A1A; turn right. Go three miles south to the park at 3100 South Highway A1A. 386/517-2086.

PLACES TO STAY

Beach Front Motel: Sleeping right on the ocean, a mile south of the fishing pier, makes this a good choice for dogs who can't wait to run along the nearby beaches the next morning. Just fuel up on the food you'll store in your in-room refrigerator, then go. Rates usually range $57–72 at this 20-unit lodging found about four miles east of I-95 (Exit 284). Pet fee is $15 per stay. You'll sleep in one of the designated pet rooms. 1544 S. Ocean Shore Blvd./Highway A1A, Flagler Beach; 386/439-0089 or 888/221-4722 (reservations only); www.beachfrontmotel.com.

Beverly Beach Camptown RV Resort: Wake up on the beach at this sunny campground that stretches for 1,500 feet along the ocean. Dogs may play joyously in the surf or swim, though management strictly enforces the leash rule. Amenities include a restaurant, a bait shop to serve surf anglers, a convenience store, laundry facilities, and wintertime bingo. There are no trees to speak of—just full-hookup spots for RVs and a few tent sites overlooking the Atlantic Ocean. Tent sites cost $35. RV sites range $45–68 but can rise to $93 daily during special events. Reservations are advised. 2816 N. Ocean Shore Blvd./Highway A1A, Flagler Beach; 386/439-3111 or 800/255-2706; www.beverlybeachcamptown.com.

Bulow Resort: Sleep in a cabin or at a campsite at this 90-acre campground near dog-pleaser Bulow Plantation Ruins State Historic Site (see Parks, Beaches, and Recreation Areas, above). The place offers a pool, shuffleboard, an all-purpose hall, hot showers, and peace and quiet. Dogs must be leashed here. Cabins sleep four to six people and run $38. Camping at the 300-plus sites ranges $18–24. Reservations are accepted. From I-95, go east on State Road 100, then right at Old Kings Road. 3345 Old Kings Rd. South, Flagler Beach; 386/439-9200 or 800/782-8569.

Flagler by the Sea Campground: There's no need to drive to the beach here—your tent or camper will be sitting right on it. You and your dog can sit up late by a beachside campfire, then spend the day fishing and swimming. If you camp with a television, look for *Rin Tin Tin* reruns on the free cable channels. Small pets are preferred; vicious dogs are forbidden. Rates range $30–50. 2982 N. Ocean Shore Blvd./Highway A1A, Flagler Beach; 386/439-2124 or 800/434-2124.

Gamble Rogers Memorial State Park: You'll sleep on the dunes at these 34 campsites, which all overlook the Atlantic Ocean. Expect no shade; bring a canopy to serve as shelter from the unrelenting sun. Each site offers electricity, water, a picnic table, a ground grill, nearby showers, and a nearby RV dump station. Unfortunately, dogs are forbidden on the park's beach. To satisfy your water dog, exit the park and drive to pet-permissible Flagler Beach (see Parks, Beaches, and Recreation Areas, above). Sites are $23. Bring proof of your dog's current rabies vaccination. 3100 S. Highway A1A, Flagler Beach; 386/517-2086 or 800/326-3521 (reservations).

Luxury Suites on the Ocean: With a Jacuzzi bath and fireplace in every suite, these are not your run-of-the-mill doggy digs. Pets can step through each suite's sliding glass doors to gaze at the ocean from a balcony or patio. Better yet, they can exit the place and walk a few steps to the beach to scurry along the sands (on leash). Be careful not to let your pal dig up the eggs laid here in summer by sea turtles. Rates for these 900-square-foot ocean-view suites are $190, plus a flat $35 cleaning fee. Add $25 daily for the well-behaved pooch. Sorry, no credit cards are accepted. 2815 S. Ocean Shore Blvd./Highway A1A, Flagler Beach; 386/439-1826; www.suitesonthebeach.com.

Topaz Motel: Your pooch can rejoice: Those dastardly cats are forbidden at this oceanfront motel featuring antique rooms with balconies. Built in the 1920s, the place is historic by Florida standards, so you'll notice a player piano in the Victorian parlor. Yet, the updated rooms feature TVs, VCRs, and private baths, and the outdoor swimming pool overlooks the ocean. Rates range $65–155. Pet fee is $11. 1224 S. Ocean Shore Blvd./Highway A1A, Flagler Beach; 386/439-3301 or 800/555-4735.

Bunnell

PARKS, BEACHES, AND RECREATION AREAS

40 Haw Creek Preserve
😺😺😺 (See St. Augustine map on page 168)

Set on the northern bank of Haw Creek in western Flagler County, this rustic spot with herons and ospreys has much to offer a bored pooch. After sharing a packed lunch in the picnic area, your pet can hike in a sun-dappled patch of longleaf pines. A boardwalk winds through swamp and provides overlooks to view Haw Creek. About two miles of trails loop around the eastern portion of this 1,005-acre preserve and recreation area, while visitors on horseback favor the western portion.

Bring a canoe or boat to launch at Russell Landing. You'll wind along marsh-lined Haw Creek for about four miles before reaching the broad fishing waters of Crescent Lake. Alligators may sun themselves on the banks, so keep your pet leashed.

From Bunnell, take Highway 100 west about six miles, turn left at County Road 305, and proceed about 3.5 miles to County Road 2006. Turn right (west). In a mile, turn left at County Road 2007. Continue less than two miles to park at Russell Landing. 386/329-4883.

41 Crescent Lake Conservation Area

☙☙☙ (See St. Augustine map on page 168)

Shhhh. Here, observant dogs might spot bald eagles, ospreys, or wading birds. Nothing like a refined city park, these 5.5 square miles offer the chance to hike with your leashed pooch along a loop pathway near marshes in the Crescent Lake floodplain.

From the parking area, hikers and bicyclists enter through a pedestrian-only gate to follow about three miles of trails at the edge of marsh. Much of this property serves as a floodplain for nearby Crescent Lake and provides water storage and protection. In other words, you may get wet. If it's been raining a lot lately, this place could be quite soggy. Wait for a drier week.

Bring food, mosquito repellent, water, and any supplies you think you'll need while visiting this rustic area. Many trails offer no hint of shade, so bring a hat and be prepared for lots of sun, as well as potentially excessive heat and sudden thunderstorms. Best bet: Avoid the place in summer.

From Bunnell, take Highway 11 south for nearly nine miles. Turn right at County Road 304. Proceed less than three miles to County Road 305, where you'll turn left. Travel nearly 11 miles to U.S. 17; turn right. Go 2.3 miles to North Raulerson Road, turn right, proceed 1.9 miles to the parking area. 386/329-4883.

Crescent City

PARKS, BEACHES, AND RECREATION AREAS

42 Lake George Conservation Area

☙☙☙ (See St. Augustine map on page 168)

Alert canine hikers may notice bald eagles soaring overhead—proof that these 19,831 acres are home to one of the region's largest concentrations of bald eagles. Set on the eastern shore of Lake George, the land is a mixed bag of hardwood swamp and sun-dappled pine forest. You can hike with your leashed pooch along the many dirt roads and trails crisscrossing the northern portion of the conservation area, found in Putnam County. Elsewhere, restrooms and fewer trails—although, at more than seven miles, still enough to tire out a pooch—are found in the central portion of the conservation area, reached via Lake George Road/Highway 305 from Seville in Volusia County.

Nature comes first and visitors second at this conservation area, where gopher tortoises, otters, and the elusive threatened Florida black bear number among the critters who call this place home. This land provides a "wildlife movement corridor" that's over 20 miles long—sort of a highway that wild animals can use to get from one place to another without stumbling into suburban backyards.

Facilities are practically nonexistent as a result, so bring water, food, mosquito repellent, and any supplies. Watch out for alligators near the lake. Bicyclists and horseback riders share several miles of roads and trails here, as do seasonal hunters. Wear fluorescent orange clothing if you visit during hunting season or avoid the place then. For hunt dates, call 352/732-1225.

From County Road 308 in Crescent City, go south one mile on U.S. 17, then turn west (right) onto Georgetown-Denver Road. Continue about four miles to the entrance. 386/329-4483.

PLACES TO STAY

Crescent City Campground: Tent campers sleep by a stream, while folks in RVs follow wide paved roads to park at oak-shaded sites (some pull-through) with concrete patios, picnic tables, and free cable TV. Guests don't exactly rough it at the oak-shaded park: a pool, lighted shuffleboard courts, a playground, and a pool table are among the amenities. Reservations are essential in winter when snowbirds dominate. Rates range $20–25 for tents, $24–29 for RVs. 2359 U.S. 17 South, Crescent City, FL 32112; 386/698-2020 or 800/634-3968; www.crescentcitycampground.com.

Lake View Motel: Everyone gets a first-floor room at Dale and Hema's single-story 19-unit motel. Located in town and across the street from a shopping center, it offers a bit of a view of Crescent Lake. The lake actually is about two blocks away, so human swimmers may prefer jumping into the rectangular motel pool. Rooms range $55–65 daily, $315 and up weekly. 1004 North Summit St., Crescent City, FL 32112; 386/698-1090; www.lakeviewmotelfl.com.

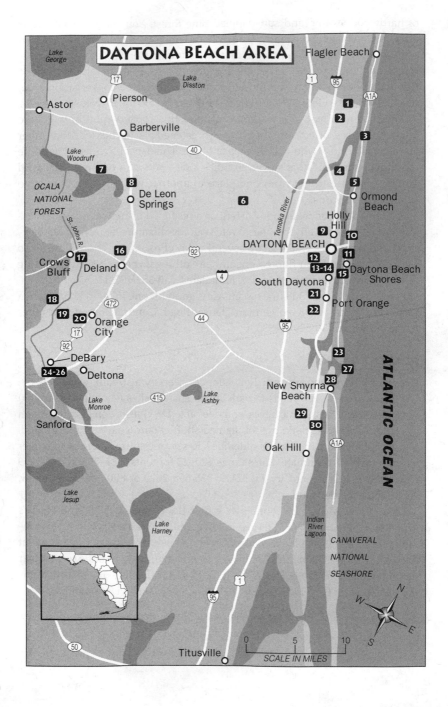

DAYTONA BEACH AREA

CHAPTER 7

Daytona Beach Area

It's enough to make a dog yelp in disbelief. The renowned, laid-back beach town of Daytona Beach encourages Harley-riding bikers to roar through here at a deafening volume for the annual Bike Week in March. About the same time, MTV camera crews film hordes of college students who invade each spring, drinking beer, baking on the beach, and doing other things that are probably best left unsaid. Meanwhile, city regulations allow 2,000-pound cars to drive on 18 miles of broad, hard-packed beach, forming ribbons of tire tracks in their sandy wake.

So, to review: Bikers, drunken college students, and exhaust-spewing vehicles are allowed on the beach. Dogs are not. Pooches can't even legally ride in a car traveling on the beach.

We recommend a quick pass at the city's Boardwalk area, but the better stuff for pooches is located much farther inland. Head west, young dog owner!

Four-legged pals who appreciate the untamed outdoors will love the area's state parks, where wild turkeys and deer run free. In this pretty country, you can sit comfortably, even on a summer day, inside thick hammocks of oaks

PICK OF THE LITTER—DAYTONA BEACH AREA

BEST DOG PARK
The Dog Park at Riviera Oaks Park, Holly Hill (page 213)

BEST BEACHES
Lighthouse Point Park, Ponce Inlet (page 226)
Smyrna Dunes Park, New Smyrna Beach (page 228)

BEST NATURE TRAILS
De Leon Springs State Park, De Leon Springs (page 212)
Bulow Creek State Park, Ormond Beach (page 207)

MOST UNUSUAL ATTRACTION
Daytona Beach Drive-In Christian Church, Daytona
Beach (page 215)

MOST UNUSUAL PLACE TO STAY
Sunny Sands Nudist Resort, Pierson (page 213)

whose branches sport resurrection ferns. You'll also find some uniquely Floridian stretches of wilderness that are becoming increasingly rare around the state.

In a city where motels are nearly half empty on average, Maggie has advice for Daytona Beach leaders who want to boost tourism year-round: Let dogs go to the beach. You have a family town, right? So don't leave out the family dog. Give families an extra excuse to spend more time here instead of high-tailing it 53 miles west to Mickey Mouse territory. You'll have a dog leg up on the Space Coast to the south, where dogs are banned from the beach. Other tourist-oriented communities are opening up their beaches to the furry set: Key West has a Dog Beach, Sanibel Island and St. Johns County allow leashed dogs on their beaches, and the former Spring Break town of Fort Lauderdale has freed up a 100-yard section of waterfront.

With 23 miles of oceanfront, Maggie wonders, why can't Volusia County spare even a sliver of Atlantic sand for dogs?

Astor

PLACES TO STAY

Parramore's Fantastic Fish Camp & Family Resort: The pace is slow at this self-described nature lover's paradise on the St. Johns River, across the river from dog-friendly Ocala National Forest (see the Ocala Area chapter). Bring a boat and a fishing pole so you and your dog can catch dinner. Meanwhile, the rest of the family can head to the pool, playground, exercise room, or barnyard with donkeys, hogs, and Billy the goat. Rental boats are offered, but pets can't enjoy them "due to a lawsuit we had over one causing a person to fall out," says Reva, park owner. Pets may sleep in most cabins, which include kitchens, bed linens, microwaves, coffeemakers, and, for the hot dog, central air-conditioning. Cabins range $85–175. Campsites run $26.50–33.50. 1675 S. Moon Rd., Astor; 386/749-2721 or 800/516-2386; www.parramores.com.

Ormond Beach

PARKS, BEACHES, AND RECREATION AREAS

◘ Bulow Creek State Park

🐾🐾🐾 🐾 (See Daytona Beach map on page 204)

Dogs may howl in horror if you tell them that bobcats number among the wild animals who populate this peaceful stretch of forest north of town. So we'll keep it our secret. In fact, the park itself is a secret treasure, with only a few locals making it to these 3,230 rugged, remote acres.

The highlight is the massive Fairchild Oak, a stately tree that has been rooted since the time of Jesus and is so old that a few fern-covered branches dip down to rest on the ground. Named in memory of famed Florida botanist David Fairchild, the tree has withstood fires, hurricanes, droughts, and war for centuries, so give it well-deserved respect, doggies. *Do not climb on the limbs.*

Instead, go for a walk. A short loop trail, the Wahlin Trail, starts at the Fairchild Oak. Energetic dogs may prefer the Florida National Scenic Trail, which connects the Fairchild Oak site to the Bulow Plantation Ruins State Historic Site (see the St. Augustine chapter). The six-mile (one-way) hike is too long for all but the hardiest of hounds, so turn back at a comfortable distance. If you have two cars and can use one as a shuttle, the trail would make a good longer hike. Maggie was excited to see an armadillo and also tried to chase a grasshopper here, but, being nature lovers, we restrained her. Three miles up the trail is a cutoff to the Bulow Woods Trail, which leads through coastal hammock, salt marsh, and pines.

Bring water, insect repellent, and everything that you'll need, as there's no store. Restrooms are available.

DIVERSIONS

All dogs love a joy ride, and a pretty place to do it is along a 23-mile, tree-canopied loop that has sparked a campaign called **"Save the Loop."** Big oaks line streets favored by bikers and bicyclists, yet concerned citizens bristle at the encroachment of subdivisions, so they're campaigning to protect this bit of Old Florida. Your mission: Drive the loop to sniff out what all the fuss is about.

Start in Ormond Beach at State Road 40, where you'll go north on North Beach Street. Notice the estates. See sailboats on the Halifax River. Four miles down, a woodsy feel takes over as you pass beneath the oaks of pooch-permissible **Tomoka State Park** (see Parks, Beaches, and Recreation Areas under Ormond Beach). Notice marshland as you continue north. Houses come next, followed by two more hound-hospitable parks: **Ormond Tomb Park** and, after Beach turns into Old Dixie Highway, the worthwhile **Bulow Creek State Park.** Stop here. Your dog may sniff around the massive **Fairchild Oak,** estimated to be 2,000 years old.

Continue driving north on Old Dixie Highway to pass Halifax Plantation, a housing development. Further construction plans for this area sparked "Save the Loop." Turn right at Walter Boardman Road, and right again at curvy Highbridge Road, where you may see oodles of birds. Cross a drawbridge over the Halifax River. Turn right onto John Anderson Drive to travel south to the tour's end at State Road 40 in Ormond Beach, passing many homes along the way.

To recap the route: You'll start at State Road 40 in Ormond Beach. Go north on North Beach Street, then Old Dixie Highway. Go east on Walter Boardman Lane, then Highbridge Road to cross the Halifax River. Go south on John Anderson Drive to Ormond Beach. For a map, go to www.savetheloop.org.

To reach the free Fairchild Oak site, head north from Ormond Beach on Old Dixie Highway, passing through Tomoka State Park, until you see the turnoff sign at right. 386/676-4050.

➋ Ormond Tomb Park

🐾🐾 (See Daytona Beach map on page 204)

Near this county park lies the tomb of James Ormond II, a Scotsman who moved here, via the Bahamas, sometime around 1804. It's right near the Bulow Creek State Park Fairchild Oak site, but this place makes up for what that spot lacks in picnic facilities. In the dog days of summer, pooches will be glad to know that shaded tables are available, along with grills, restrooms, and, for kids, volleyball facilities and a playground. Dogs won't be happy when they hear that they must be leashed.

The 13-acre park is north of town at 3268 Old Dixie Highway. 386/736-5953.

❸ Seabridge Riverfront Park

🐾 (See Daytona Beach map on page 204)

This pleasant riverfront park is just what an old dog might request. Here, a leashed dog could share a packed lunch at the shaded picnic area, then follow a winding boardwalk over the Halifax River. Nothing too tough, but it sure breaks the boredom of everyday life. Anglers like this county park for its long, shaded fishing pier on the Halifax.

The three-acre park is north of town at 3270 John Anderson Drive, just east of Highway A1A. 386/736-5953.

❹ Tomoka State Park

🐾🐾🐾 (See Daytona Beach map on page 204)

This started out as a simple sandbar between the Tomoka and Halifax rivers, but today it is covered with lush green forest that stirs up the hunting instinct in even docile doggies. (Keep yours on a leash, as required.)

Here, Timucuan Indians built a village they called Nocoroco—a place where the fish were plentiful and the hurricanes held at bay by the inland location. In short, living was easy. Europeans eventually showed up, transforming the site into the Mount Oswald Plantation. Richard Oswald, a wealthy Scotsman, got the land after the American Revolution and planted indigo, a plant used to make a blue dye that was popular at the time, along with sugar and rice.

Five picnic areas are scattered around the 914-acre park, and a half-mile interpretive nature trail provides a 15-minute scenic walk through a shady coastal hammock between the museum and the north picnic area, which is bordered by a beach. Bring mosquito repellent. If you think you'll be the first person on the trail that day, consider carrying a stick to knock down the abundant spiderwebs. Observant pooches may notice the wide variety of plants to sniff; the park is home to about 150 types of wildflowers, shrubs, and other plants. Swimming is forbidden for both dogs and people.

The worthwhile 100-site campground features huge moss-draped oaks. Campsites cost $22.50 and fill up quickly. To reserve a spot for your tent or RV (under 34 feet long and 11 feet tall, due to trees), call 800/326-3521.

Entrance is $4 per vehicle. From the intersection of North Beach Street/Old Dixie Highway and Granada Boulevard, travel four miles north on North Beach Street. Look for the entrance on your right at 2099 N. Beach Street. 386/676-4050.

5 Bicentennial Park

😺😺 (See Daytona Beach map on page 204)

Gopher tortoises and raccoons call this scrub habitat home, and their scents are certain to enliven leashed pooches who follow the nature trail and boardwalk at this popular 40-acre county park. At the western end of the short nature trail, you'll find the Riv-Ocean Drive fishing dock on the Halifax River. To fuel up for the walk, perhaps share a lunch by the barbecue grills in the picnic area.

The park is better known for its Fido-forbidden beach and other people-pleasers: ball fields, basketball court, fishing dock, playground, and courts for racquetball, tennis, and shuffleboard. Fill a water bowl for your pooch at the restrooms.

The park stretches from the Halifax River to the Atlantic Ocean. Find it north of Ormond Beach at 1800 N. Oceanshore Boulevard. 386/736-5953.

6 Tiger Bay State Forest

😺😺 (See Daytona Beach map on page 204)

Nearly 37 square miles in size, this wildlife corridor for the secretive, nocturnal Florida black bear should tire out even the most energetic of leashed hikers. For starters, the two-mile Buncombe Hill interpretive trail is found near little Indian Lake and its lakeside primitive campsites. Not enough? Then follow the nearly six-mile-long Rima Ridge Road, a strip of high ground that forms a long spine through this extensive wetland forest. Horses share the Rima Ridge trail; for harmony's sake, be sure your pal gets along with hoofed critters before striking out. In all, at least 16 miles of hiking can be had in this forest located seven miles west of Daytona Beach.

The rustic place features its namesake wetland, Tiger Bay, as well as a large sandy pine ridge, and lots of swampland dotted with pine islands. Wildfires in 1998 burned two-thirds of the area; since then, timber has been salvaged and young trees have been planted. Bring water, food, mosquito repellent, and any supplies. Primitive camping—in a tent or little camper—is first-come, first-served. Sites cost $5.

Bicyclists share designated roads. Hunting occurs seasonally. To avoid hunters, call 352/732-1225 for hunt dates.

From I-95 (Exit 268), go west on U.S. 92 for 4.3 miles to Indian Lake Road, turn right, and proceed 2.7 miles to the hiking trail sign. Turn left and follow signs to the Indian Lake Recreation Area. To reach the Rima Ridge trail, return to U.S. 92, go west about another mile, turn left onto Rima Ridge Road, and park one-half mile ahead. The state forest's headquarters is on U.S. 92, 6.5 miles west of I-95. 386/226-0250.

PLACES TO STAY

Comfort Inn On the Beach: Only peewee pets—under 10 pounds—may join you at this 47-unit, four-story oceanfront lodging with a pool. Your dog can see the ocean from her room window, even if she isn't allowed on the beach. For the nearest off-leash fun, travel 6.4 miles to the Dog Park at Riviera Oaks Park (see under Holly Hill, below). Rates range $75–195, plus $10 nightly pet fee. 507 S. Atlantic Ave., Ormond Beach; 386/677-8550; www.choicehotels.com.

Jameson Inn: Recliners, free weekday newspapers, a fitness center, and deluxe continental breakfasts with waffles number among the main perks at this pleasant three-story poolside lodging off I-95 (Exit 268). The closest leash-free action is five miles away at the Dog Park at Riviera Oaks Park (see Holly Hill, below). Rates range $78–85. 175 Interchange Blvd., Ormond Beach; 386/672-3675; www.jamesoninns.com.

Tomoka State Park: See Parks, Beaches, and Recreation Areas, above, for camping information.

De Leon Springs

PARKS, BEACHES, AND RECREATION AREAS

7 Heart Island Conservation Area

🐾🐾 (See Daytona Beach map on page 204)

Surrounding little Dan George Lake, this 19-square-mile chunk of natural land is home to deer, otter, foxes, and raccoons whose scents will enliven most leashed visitors. Cabbage palms and ruler-straight pine trees lend shade to the upland areas, while wispy cypress trees and thick-leafed wax myrtle thickets are scattered about the wetlands.

Wildfires in 1998 ripped through a third of these woods, and staffers soon set about replanting longleaf pines and other plants. Roads with names such as Deep Creek Road and Bee Road crisscross this rustic place and have been turned into hiking trails—about five miles in all. Look for woodpeckers and songbirds as you hike.

You may share the roads with horseback riders and bicyclists. Hunters head here seasonally. To avoid them, check official hunting dates by calling 386/758-0525.

Primitive tent campsites are reached by walking about one mile from the southwestern parking area. Camping is free, and sites are first-come, first-served. Parties of seven or more people need a reservation and permit; call 386/329-4410 at least one week ahead. Be sure to pack out trash.

Bring water, food, and everything else you'll need, even for a short daytime visit. There are no facilities here, not even bathrooms. Overseen by the St. Johns River Water Management District, this land's main purpose isn't recreation, but the protection of water resources and the buffering of the uplands east of Lake George.

The conservation area is at the Volusia-Flagler county line in northwestern

Volusia County. From the intersection of U.S. 17 and State Road 40, go south about one-quarter mile to the parking area at left. 386/329-4883.

8 De Leon Springs State Park

😺 😺 😺 😺 🐾 (See Daytona Beach map on page 204)

Dogs with a flair for the dramatic can follow a half-mile nature trail traveled by elephants and giraffes back when the Clyde Beatty Circus wintered here and used this road to get to a nearby railroad siding.

Today, interpretive signs describe the trail's floodplain forest and swamps. Several spur trails await exploration, including the Monkey Island Trail; its name alludes to the escaped circus monkeys that once lived along an island here.

Ruff-and-rugged dogs may follow the narrow 5.2-mile Wild Persimmon Trail, which signs describe as "not for the casual walker." You must check in at the office before and after this hike, lest staffers fear you're lost. Possible obstacles include fallen trees and water. Be prepared with sturdy footwear, lots of drinking water, and insect repellent. Go slow; don't overtax your leashed pooch. To stay on the trail, follow the white rectangular blazes painted on tree trunks and the four-by-four-inch posts with raccoon paw prints on top. The trail branches off the main nature trail mentioned above.

Stately oaks shade the pleasant picnic area. Maggie eagerly sniffed the crevices at the base of a tree, where an animal apparently lived. Pooches are forbidden in the swimming area, where 19 million gallons of springwater bubble upward every day. People have visited the springs since 8000 B.C. (before cats). A late-1800s advertisement extolled the virtues of the springwater, "impregnated with a deliciously healthy combination of soda and sulfur." Yum!

Kids will enjoy the playground and making pancakes at the 603-acre park's Old Spanish Sugar House Grill and Griddle House (see Places to Eat, below).

Admission is $5 per car. The park is at 601 Ponce de Leon Blvd., off Burt Parks Road. From Deland, take U.S. 17 north six miles, turn left at Ponce DeLeon Boulevard, and proceed about one mile. 386/985-4212.

PLACES TO EAT

Old Spanish Sugar House Grill and Griddle House: This snack bar is housed in an old sugar mill at De Leon Springs State Park (see Parks, Beaches, and Recreation Areas, above). Your pooch will gladly help you eat sandwiches, hot dogs, ice cream, fruit smoothies, cookies, and other goodies ordered at the walk-up window. If the window is closed, order inside while your pooch is tied to a shaded picnic table. The main attraction is that customers can grill their own pancakes using grain ground on-site with a French buhrstone. But skip this indoor-only activity unless someone in your party will wait outside with your dog or walk him. The snack bar is in De Leon Springs State Park, 601 Ponce de Leon Blvd., which requires a $5 admission per carload; 386/985-5644 or 386/985-4212.

Pierson

PLACES TO STAY

Sunny Sands Nudist Resort: Pooches never bother with garments, and here you won't have to, either. Moss-draped oaks shade campsites at this clothing-optional resort in the boondocks, which is designed for families acquainted with, or exploring, the nudist lifestyle. This is near the Lake George Conservation Area (see Crescent City in the St. Augustine chapter), which is chock full of hiking trails. You'll find more trails within the 49-acre resort, where nudity is absolutely required only in the pool area. Dogs are tolerated. Campsites for tents and RVs start at $34.70. 502 Central Blvd., Pierson; 386/749-2233; www.sunnysands.com.

Holly Hill

PARKS, BEACHES, AND RECREATION AREAS

🖲 The Dog Park at Riviera Oaks Park

🐾🐾🐾🐾 🐕 (See Daytona Beach map on page 204)

Run, Spot, run! Dogs come from miles around to run freely at Volusia County's first off-leash park. Actually it's two parks: One fenced woodsy play area is for big dogs, and another smaller fenced area is for small dogs. Owners sit at benches beneath big shade trees as their pets chase each other, sniff trees, and hope in vain for squirrels to magically fall from tree branches overhead. A walking path and restrooms are available, as are water fountains for both humans and hounds.

Canine swimmers are out of luck at this two-acre domain of landlubbers. To swim, pets must leave town for Smyrna Dunes Park (see New Smyrna Beach section, below). The off-leash area of Riviera Oaks Park is the result of a joint effort by several government agencies: the cities of Holly Hill, Daytona Beach, Ormond Beach; Volusia County; and the St. Johns River Water Management District. We hope it's a sign of more good things to come.

From Daytona Beach, take State Road 430/Seabreeze Boulevard west. The state road will become Mason Avenue; continue following it west for 1.5 miles to Nova Road. Turn right. Go 2.5 miles to Alabama Avenue, where you'll turn right and proceed one-half mile to 980 Alabama Avenue. 386/248-9460.

Daytona Beach

For off-leash fun, head northwest to nearby Holly Hill. Daytona Beach may welcome bikers and rowdy college kids, but the world-famous city bans pets from beaches and offered no leash-free parks the last we checked. For the latest status, call the city at 386/671-3400.

PARKS, BEACHES, AND RECREATION AREAS

🔟 J. L. Saxton Riverfront Park

😻 (See Daytona Beach map on page 204)

Your pooch will find plenty of leg-lift targets in the form of date palm trees at this breezy strip of green overlooking the river. (Respect the monument to members of the armed services, pooches.) For contemplative pups looking for a spot to ponder whether there is a Dog, the gazebo with picnic tables will do. Nearby City Island Park may be a better choice.

The park is on the Halifax River and stretches from 101 S. Beach St. to 301 N. Beach Street. 386/671-3400.

🔢 City Island Park

😻😻😻 (See Daytona Beach map on page 204)

Lots of squirrels call this small downtown waterfront park home. After chasing a few, your whiskered wanderer can enjoy a bite to eat under tin-roofed pavilions with large grills. It's not a large park, but there is a playground and a large pavilion out on a dock on the Halifax River. There are also some decent grassy areas, but not much shade.

You'll also find a large field at the library adjacent to the park. You're supposed to keep your pooch on a leash here but—wink, nod—you're unlikely to encounter anyone, especially on a weekday. Picnic or just watch the world go by, and enjoy the breezy waterfront space. On Saturdays, you may find a farmers market here. Your pooch will be glad to sniff around and meet people, and maybe get a snack.

The park is at 115 E. Orange Street. Find it on the Halifax River at the intersection of Beach Street and Orange Avenue. 386/671-3400.

12 Tuscawilla Park

🐾🐾🐾 (See Daytona Beach map on page 204)

Stunning for a city park, this large, partially wooded expanse is a favorite with local pooches. We saw a few roaming leash-free in the forest preserve, though leashes are the rule. For a more citified experience, let your pal wander around the Frisbee golf course that is crisscrossed by shallow canals. It's a peaceful place, the kind of spot where a bicyclist might stop to read a book.

One local told us that this woodsy home of the Museum of Arts and Sciences is his pooch's favorite park in town. As he walked with his tiny leashless pal obediently in tow, a woman across the park strolled with her boxer. If the place isn't going to the dogs, it should be.

As they explore this unfenced land, dogs will find plenty to sniff and lots of

DIVERSIONS

For the traveling pooch with spiritual leanings, nothing beats Sunday church service at the **Daytona Beach Drive-In Christian Church** (Disciples of Christ). A sign says: "Welcome, friends," and several members of the car-bound congregation take that sentiment to heart, bringing their dogs, cats, and even birds.

"We have a parrot that comes every Sunday. He's one of our most faithful," says minister Larry Deitch, chuckling.

He certainly knows how to welcome animals to the flock: At the entrance, cats are handed catnip and dogs get canine treats. Humans get a Communion packet and printed bulletin. Cars pull into grassy parking spots, then the faithful tune their radios to a low-power station to hear the service. Rev. Deitch speaks from a balcony below where a movie screen hung decades ago, back when this was the Neptune Drive-In Theater. Its congregation has been worshipping outdoors since 1953; the 12-acre church features a broad expanse of lush lawn flanked by palms. Arthur Frommer's *Budget Travel* magazine numbered it among the nation's 59 Jaw-Dropping Roadside Attractions.

Oh, and you can get married at the **Little Chapel by the Sea** out front. If you want your dog to watch you tie the knot, be sure to say so when reserving the chapel. Services are held at 8:30 A.M. and 10 A.M. on Sundays at 3140 South Atlantic Ave., near Peninsula Drive, Daytona Beach Shores. 386/767-8761.

leg-lift targets to choose from, including some decorative limestone boulders where lizards may hide in nooks and crannies. Beware of the poison ivy that grows in the woods. To help make sure you don't break out in a rash from petting a pup who has rubbed against the plant, stick to the open areas.

The inland park is at 1000 Orange Avenue. Find it at the intersection of U.S. 92/International Speedway Boulevard and Nova Road/Highway 5A. 386/671-3400.

PLACES TO EAT

Pizza Hut: Your dog may join you at one of the four shaded concrete tables out front and watch you dive into a Meat Lover's Pizza or other flavorful pie. 500 South Atlantic Ave.; 386/255-7234.

PLACES TO STAY

Aruba Inn: You can show your small dog the beach from your room window at innkeeper Harry Biser's 32-unit, two-story oceanfront motel. But pets pining to run leash-free can't do it on Daytona's beaches. Instead, travel 6.5 miles to the nearest off-leash park: the Dog Park at Riviera Oaks Park (see Holly Hill, above). Some rooms are efficiencies with kitchens—good for hungry hounds. Shuffleboard entertains guests, as does a heated pool that overlooks the broad beach and ocean. Rates vary seasonally $40–200. Add $10 nightly for your small dog. 1254 N. Atlantic Ave., Daytona Beach; 386/253-5643 or 800/214-1406; www.arubainn.com.

The Bermuda House: This recently renovated, full-service resort offers 143 rooms with kitchenettes or mini kitchens and views of the pool or the Atlantic Ocean. Water dogs, though, must travel 14.8 miles south to Lighthouse Point Park (see Ponce Inlet, below). For the nearest off-leash fun, head 7.7 miles northwest to the Dog Park at Riviera Oaks Park (see Holly Hill, above). Rates range $69–240, plus $10 nightly pet fee. An additional $30 pet deposit is refundable, barring doggy damages. 2560 N. Atlantic Ave., Daytona Beach; 386/672-1440 or 800/792-7309; www.thebermudahouse.com.

Best Western La Playa Resort: Every room overlooks the ocean, so your pet may step onto the private balcony to view the forbidden beach. People-pleasers at the 238-unit resort include an oceanfront deck with pool, whirlpool, and kiddie pool. Indoors, find a heated pool, whirlpool, sauna, and steam shower. Canine swimmers, though, must leave town for Lighthouse Point Park, located 14.4 miles south (see Ponce Inlet, below). Rates range $60–190, plus $10 nightly pet fee. 2500 N. Atlantic Ave., Daytona Beach; 386/672-0990; www.staydaytona.com.

Budget Host Inn The Candlelight: You'll park by your room door at this 25-unit economy motel, whose amenities include coffee and danish at breakfast, truck parking, shuffleboard, and the ability to throw burgers on a grill in its picnic area. Rates start at $39 and can rise to $175 during special events. A $20 pet deposit is refundable, barring doggy damage. 1305 South Ridgewood Ave., Daytona Beach; 386/252-1142; www.budgethost.com.

Days Inn Speedway: A bonus for leashed canines is they have the run of a 7.5-acre wooded lot at this otherwise-basic 180-unit poolside motel, located off I-95 (Exit 261), one mile west of the Daytona International Speedway. Rates range $49–250, plus $10 nightly pet fee. Discounts may be offered to dog show attendees, and a staffer reports, "One night we had 90 Spuds McKenzies here." 2900 International Speedway Blvd., Daytona Beach; 904/255-0541; www.daysinnspeedway.com.

La Quinta: Dog-tired travelers may opt for takeout orders from the Daytona Ale House across the street or from the Outback Steakhouse, Red Lobster, and other eateries located within a mile of this poolside motel off I-95 (Exit 261). Rates are $72–105, including continental breakfast and local calls. 2725 International Speedway Blvd., Daytona Beach; 386/255-7412; www.lq.com.

La Quinta Inn & Suites: Oceanfront rooms allow pets to peer out the window or step onto the balcony to see the ocean. Jacuzzi suites come with wet bars, and all 77 rooms offer a microwave, refrigerator, and cable TV including HBO. People-pleasers include an outdoor pool with a mushroom fountain and a hot tub overlooking the ocean. Canine swimmers, though, need to travel 12 miles south to Lighthouse Point Park (see Ponce Inlet, below). For off-leash exercise, travel six miles to the Dog Park at Riviera Oaks Park (see Holly Hill, above). Rates range $99–270. 16 N. Atlantic Ave., Daytona Beach; 386/944-0060; www.lq.com.

Miss Pat's Inn—A Bed & Breakfast: Innkeeper John Dunn says many dogs, cats, and even a bird has stayed in the Island Room, a 540-square-foot suite that takes up the entire first floor of the carriage house of this notable inn located blocks from the ocean. Listed on the National Register of Historic Places, the circa-1898 property has been restored as a bed-and-breakfast inn with modern amenities such as whirlpool tubs, high-speed Internet access, and expanded cable television. For off-leash fun, the Dog Park at Riviera Oaks Park is 6.7 miles away (see Holly Hill, above). Regular rate is $150, higher during special events. Dunn suggests checking his website for occasional special rates. 1209 S. Peninsula Dr., Daytona Beach; 386/248-8420 or 866/464-7772; www.misspatsinn.com.

The Plaza Ocean Club: Oceanfront and ocean-view rooms let small pets gaze onto the forbidden Atlantic Ocean at this former Radisson Resort. The place offers several extras: a large T-shaped oceanfront pool, a fitness facility, a game room, a restaurant, summertime room service, and 68 kitchenettes—good for hungry hounds. Dogs can stretch their legs in the parking lot or travel 5.5 miles to the Dog Park at Riviera Oaks Park (see Holly Hill, above). For canine swimming, you'll need to travel 12.5 miles to Lighthouse Point Park (see Ponce Inlet, below). Rates typically range $90–149. Add $10 nightly per pet. Pets under 30 pounds, please. 640 N. Atlantic Ave., Daytona Beach; 386/239-9800 or 800/874-7420; www.plazaoceanclub.com.

Ramada Inn Speedway: If your dog wonders where the famous Daytona International Speedway is, just point your pointer across the street. Volusia Mall is next door and Pizzeria Uno is on the motel property—handy for picking up a takeout pizza to share back at the room with your best pal. The 127-room lodging is two miles east of I-95 (Exit 261). Rates vary seasonally $79–360. Pets under 35 pounds are accepted for a flat fee of $25. 1798 W. International Speedway Blvd., Daytona Beach; 386/255-2422; www.ramada.com.

Scottish Inns: Only peewee pooches—under 10 pounds—may sleep in designated rooms at this economy motel found 2.5 miles east of I-95 (Exit 260). Rates are $40 and up, plus $5 pet fee. 1515 S. Ridgewood Ave., Daytona Beach; 386/258-5742; www.bookroomsnow.com.

Super 8 Speedway: Hungry hounds may have a hankering for a takeout meal from the adjacent McDonald's or 24-hour Denny's. But don't eat too much, doggies—the pet weight limit is 30 pounds at this 112-room poolside motel located off I-95 (Exit 261). Rates range $50–75. Add $10 nightly per pooch. 2992 W. International Speedway Blvd., Daytona Beach; 386/253-0643; www.super8.com.

South Daytona

PARKS, BEACHES, AND RECREATION AREAS

13 Reed Canal Park

🐾🐾 (See Daytona Beach map on page 204)

A local rottweiler/basset hound mix named Maximus Black-Treblas thoroughly enjoys the pleasant trail that leads to the lake—the park's featured attraction. We saw a chow chow running off leash at the lake, but signs make it clear that pooches must stay tethered.

Hundreds, if not thousands, of tall trees shaded the park before three hurricanes—Charley, Frances, and Jeanne—tore through in 2004. Since then, pavilions, a playground, a lakeside trail, and other amenities were added. New landscaping serves as new doggy leg-lift targets.

The park entrance is on Reed Canal Road, just east of Nova Road. The lake is accessible via Nova Road, just south of Reed Canal Road. 386/322-3070.

14 Riverfront Park

🐾 (See Daytona Beach map on page 204)

This pretty yet poorly shaded park covers about two acres and is good for a waterfront picnic away from town. A small playground will please kids, while leashed dogs will long to chase seabirds or trot out onto the dock on the Intracoastal Waterway. Tennis and shuffleboard courts are across the street.

Take heed: You may be smacked with a $500 fine if you fail to scoop the poop. So do your duty.

The park is northeast of the intersection of Big Tree Road and Palmetto Avenue, on the Halifax River. 386/322-3070.

PLACES TO EAT

Dairy Queen: Dine on burgers, fish sandwiches, hot dogs, and ice cream at one of the four umbrella-shaded picnic tables to the side of this fast-food joint. 2270 S. Ridgewood Ave.; 386/761-8590.

Daytona Beach Shores

PARKS, BEACHES, AND RECREATION AREAS

15 Lula M. McElroy Park

🐾 (See Daytona Beach map on page 204)

Windswept oaks provide some shade for the lazy pooch who wants to take a nap near the concrete picnic tables here. Bear in mind that local animal-litter and leash ordinances are strictly enforced. You can relax at the shady picnic area, but dogs are barred from the tennis and handball courts.

This eight-acre park is by the Daytona Beach Shores Community Center, at the end of Esperanza Avenue. The street dead-ends into the park at its north

DIVERSIONS

Fetch freebies with Fido: If you asked a rottweiler/basset hound mix named Maximus Black-Treblas, he'd say sniffing the aisles of pig ears, rawhide, toys, and treats at **PETsMART** is more fun than going to his favorite park, Reed Canal Park in South Daytona Beach. Maybe that has to do with the free little treat a staffer invariably hands him.

"Everybody loves him," says his human companion, Joyce Black.

Your leashed dog will also enjoy fetching a free snack at 1900 International Speedway Blvd., Daytona Beach; 386/254-7555. PETsMART stores throughout the state (and nation) welcome leashed pets, as do outposts of Pet Supermarket, Petco, and some independent stores. Freebies notwithstanding, a quick stop at any store further helps socialize your pal and exercises his mind. As you drive around the city and state, keep a lookout for pet-supply stores. Some post signs on their glass front doors stating those three words all dogs long to read: Leashed Pets Welcome.

end. From Highway A1A, turn right on Vann Avenue, take the third right, and continue one block. 386/763-5353.

PLACES TO STAY

Atlantic Ocean Palm Inn: One of the better pet-permissible places in the area, Stanley and Pamela Obrochta's 49-unit motel fronts the Atlantic Ocean— hence, the name. All rooms—and the rectangular pool—have a view of the ocean. That's as close as your canine pal will get to the forbidden beach. Instead, water dogs can swim 6.5 miles from here at Lighthouse Point Park (see Ponce Inlet, below). A dog under 30 pounds may join you in designated first-floor rooms with tile floors. Rates run $40–100 but can rise as high as $250 during special events. Pet fee is $15 per stay. 3247 S. Atlantic Ave., Daytona Beach Shores; 386/761-8450 or 800/634-0098; www.atlanticoceanpalm.com.

Day-Star Motel: Overlooking a gloriously car-free stretch of beach, this 15-unit independently owned and operated motel features fully equipped kitchens in all rooms, golf specials, a shuffleboard court, and barbecue grills. Only a fence divides the heated, kidney-shaped pool from the broad beach, so guests simply turn their poolside chaise lounges around to view the waves lapping ashore. Canine swimmers can't exercise here but may dog-paddle at Lighthouse Point Park located 5.2 miles away (see Ponce Inlet, below). Rates run $48–85, plus a $15 pet fee per stay. 3811 S. Atlantic Ave., Daytona Beach Shores; 386/767-3780 or 800/506-5505; www.daystarmotel.com.

Manatee Suites: A big heated pool overlooks the beach, and your dog may be lucky enough to join you on a private balcony to take in the ocean view from this worthwhile 45-unit lodging. Everyone gets a suite with a fully equipped kitchen for whipping up meals. Several restaurants are within walking distance for those too dog-tired to cook; Denny's, Red Lobster, and Subway sit across the street. Pets are welcome at management's discretion. If your pooch qualifies, enjoy a barbecue at the landscaped ocean-view yard. Shuffleboard, two pools, free movies, and in-room VCRs are available. Pets can dog-paddle at Lighthouse Point Park located 6.9 miles away (see Ponce Inlet, below). Rates are $40–109. 3167 S. Atlantic Ave., Daytona Beach Shores; 386/761-1121 or 800/378-6826; www.manateesuites.com.

Quality Inn Ocean Palms: Most rooms overlook the ocean at this pleasant 110-unit lodging, one of the better dog-permissible options in these parts. Look below your balcony and you'll see the big beachside pool and snack bar. Pets can't swim here, but may dog-paddle at Lighthouse Point Park located 9.2 miles away (see under Ponce Inlet, below). Rooms normally run $55–169, though they can rise to $325 during special events. Pets under 35 pounds are accepted for $10 nightly. 2323 S. Atlantic Ave., Daytona Beach Shores; 386/255-0476; www.choicehotels.com.

Sand Castle Motel: A large sundeck overlooks the heated pool and broad beach at this 31-unit oceanfront motel, where owners Vic and Lonnie Patrenko permit small pets in efficiencies that include kitchens with microwaves. Barbecue grills are available and restaurants are within walking distance, in case you want to fetch a takeout order and dine back at your room with your retriever. One of the city's better lodgings for pets and their people, this establishment is 5.8 miles from a park where dogs may swim: Lighthouse Point Park (see Ponce Inlet, below). Rates normally range $39–95, higher during special events. Add a $15 pet fee per stay. 3619 S. Atlantic Ave., Daytona Beach Shores; 386/767-3182 or 800/967-4757; www.sandcastlemoteldaytona.com.

Deland

PARKS, BEACHES, AND RECREATION AREAS

16 Cypress Lake Park

🐾🐾 (See Daytona Beach map on page 204)

Set on the east bank of Cypress Lake, this nine-acre park is great for doing what old dogs like best—hoping for handouts from the barbecue grill or picnic table, then falling asleep on a comfortable grassy spot. Cypress trees are scattered around the picnic pavilion, which is a few yards from the lake's edge. Look for turtles and wading birds.

Kids will prefer the playground and basketball court. If you bring a boat, you can launch into Cypress Lake.

The county park is at 1700 First Ave., east of Kepler Road and east of Deland Municipal Airport. 386/736-5953.

17 Ed Stone Park

 (See Daytona Beach map on page 204)

At this county park on the St. Johns River, there's precious little room for leashed dogs to stretch their legs, but there are a few trees to inspire thoughts of leg lifts. The main features are a boat ramp, a waterfront picnic pavilion, and a few picnic tables on a wooden boardwalk by the river. If your dog is of the patient angler persuasion, you can join the many visitors trying to snag a bass here—and maybe see the occasional bald eagle while you wait.

The seven-acre park is on the St. Johns River at 2990 W. State Road 44, west of Deland. 386/736-5953.

18 Hontoon Island State Park

 (See Daytona Beach map on page 204)

For adventurous dogs who love to go for rides, a trip to this state park offers a bonus: To reach the 2.5-square-mile island on the St. Johns and Huntoon Dead rivers, you must take a park ferry; dogs are allowed aboard for the short ride. The other option is for you and your pooch to get out to the island on a private boat.

There, the main attraction for dogs is picnicking on an island. The picnic area features grills, picnic tables, a playground for kids, and restrooms that overlook the St. Johns River. Before its 1967 purchase by the state, this island was home to a boatyard and cattle ranch. Nowadays, it attracts people who camp or stay in cabins; unfortunately, those amenities are off-limits to dogs. Timucuan Indian mounds are visible on the nature trail, but a park employee said dogs should stay out of that area, too.

"We prefer that you don't take your dog down the nature trail," he explained. "Even the smell of your dog will disturb the wildlife. Your dog is an exotic." (We imagined Maggie in a Carmen Miranda–style headdress, instead of the leash she was required to wear.)

Admission is free. From Deland, take State Road 44 west and follow the signs, which will direct you to Hontoon Road. The ferry is at the end of Hontoon Road. 386/736-5309.

PLACES TO EAT

Belly Busters: Subs are the big thing at this casual eatery, where you and your hungry dog can dine at the picnic tables in back. The eight-inch sandwiches come with roast beef, cheese, and other doggy favorites. 930 N. Woodland Blvd.; 386/734-1611.

Checkers: Head to the walk-up window at this downtown locale to order chicken sandwiches, 99-cent burgers, chili-cheese fries, and other eats, then take a seat at any of the tables shaded by bright red umbrellas. 133 S. Woodland Blvd.; 386/943-9653. A second location is at 2490 S. Woodland Blvd.; 386/943-9277.

DIVERSIONS

To see Florida as it used to be, try viewing the **St. Johns River** from a rented houseboat. Herons stand as still as statues at river's edge, waiting to pounce on a fish. An alligator may bask in the sun on a distant bank lined with moss-draped trees. A slow-moving manatee may poke its whiskery snout above water as an osprey circles overhead.

Rivers served as roads long ago, as settlers and Indians traveled from place to place by boat or canoe. Today, a houseboat trip still affords some back-to-nature views not seen by motorists, as the craft putts along at 8 to 10 miles per hour.

Some vacationers spend a lazy day fishing for bass. Dogs under 35 pounds are permitted to join vacationers on air-conditioned houseboats rented from Holly Bluff Marina, 2280 Hontoon Rd., Deland. A week in a 38-foot houseboat (for four people) costs $1,175–1,275. Two weekend nights ranges $675–775. Add a $10 daily pet fee. Reserve at least a month ahead by calling 386/822-9992 or 800/237-5105.

PLACES TO STAY

Holiday Inn: This pleasant 148-room hotel on the way east toward the world-famous Daytona Beach Speedway is good for pooches who'd like to check out one of the various state parks around here. Otherwise, walk around the big field next to this six-story hotel. Sorry, dogs—only humans have access to the pool, sundeck, fitness center, bar, and restaurant. Maybe an order of bacon from room service will suffice. Rates range $68–140, plus a flat $25 pet fee. 350 E. International Speedway Blvd., Deland; 386/738-5200; www.holidayinns.com.

Howard Johnson Express Inn: Two pools—one for adults, one for kiddies, and none for doggies—are offered at this 113-room motel off I-4 (Exit 118). Rates range $55–275. Add $10 nightly for the pooch. Pets under 35 pounds, please. 2801 E. New York Ave., Deland; 386/736-3440; www.howardjohnson.com.

University Inn: Walk to Deland's historic district with your leashed pal after waking up to your free continental breakfast at this 57-unit lodging, located next to Stetson University. A large outdoor pool, fitness room, and a hair salon are offered. Every room includes a mini-fridge—good for storing doggy bags. Rates range $60–175. 644 N. Woodland Blvd., Deland; 386/734-57111 or 800/345-8991; www.universityinndeland.com.

Orange City

PARKS, BEACHES, AND RECREATION AREAS

19 Blue Spring State Park

🐾🐾🐾 🐾 (See Daytona Beach map on page 204)

Leashed dogs can follow four miles of nature trails to view marshes and partially shady pine forests in this popular park. They also can pad along a portion of boardwalk between the concession building and the river. Pets can't, however, do what most tourists do: follow the rest of the boardwalk to reach an observation platform and gaze onto the namesake spring where manatees gather in winter to stay warm. (Manatee-watchers had spotted more than 60 of the creatures on the day we visited.) We noticed that a ranger didn't mind when leashed Maggie trotted down a part of the boardwalk somewhat removed from the actual spring. Visitors can also take part in ranger interpretive programs to learn more about the endangered manatee.

Hounds with a nose for history will be interested in the Thursby House, a two-story wooden affair with verandas on both stories. Perched on brick stilts, the tin-roofed white house has a real Old South flavor. Visiting U.S. presidents and Union gunboats have traveled down the St. Johns River here. Maggie was more intrigued by the squirrels running around in the field in front of the house, but, much to her chagrin, her desire to give chase was curbed by a rule requiring her to stay on a leash.

Sleeping in the park's 51-site pine-dotted campground near the river and spring costs $22.50. Bring proof of your pet's rabies vaccination. Reserve early; sites can be reserved up to 11 months ahead at 800/326-3521.

Entrance costs $5 per car. From I-4, take Exit 114 and follow signs to the park. You'll go south about 2.5 miles on U.S. 17/92 to Orange City, turn right onto West French Avenue, and follow to the dead end at 2100 W. French Avenue. 386/775-3663.

20 Pooser Park

🐾🐾 (See Daytona Beach map on page 204)

Good for a lazy day with Lassie, this six-acre park is a local favorite for picnics. Just grab a table atop the bluff, then munch a lunch with your leashed Lab while taking in the view of a small pond below. Afterward, follow a short circular nature trail that offers pretty views of the pond. Keep your dog leashed—violators can be fined $55.

The county park is at 100 E. Elm Drive, just west of U.S. 17/92. 386/736-5953.

PLACES TO STAY

Blue Spring State Park: See Park, Beaches, and Recreation Areas, above, for camping information.

Port Orange

Good news, doggies: There is talk of the city building an off-leash park. For its current status, tell your people to call City Hall at 386/756-5200.

PARKS, BEACHES, AND RECREATION AREAS

21 Veterans Memorial Park

🐾🐾 (See Daytona Beach map on page 204)

This little park would be a great place for Beetle Bailey's sergeant to spend an afternoon with his dog, Otto. A concrete walking path winds under the canopy of pines and deciduous trees, making it a popular trail for joggers. At the pretty lake, leashed Maggie whimpered at the sight of black anhingas drying their wet wings by fanning them outward.

The county park is at 1000 City Center Circle, the street that surrounds the City Hall complex. 386/756-5388.

22 Spruce Creek Park

🐾🐾 (See Daytona Beach map on page 204)

Set on the banks of pretty Spruce Creek, this 23-acre county park packs in several passive pursuits for laid-back pooches and their people. After following a half-mile nature trail, you could stop for a picnic at a pavilion or picnic table, then take in views from the boardwalk or fishing dock. The highlight of the park is exploring the scenic bluffs overlooking Spruce Creek, though kids may appreciate the playground and horseshoe pits. Whatever you choose to do, remember that you're standing at what once was the site of a Timucuan Indian civilization, as evidenced by the Indian mounds still found here.

Campers and their leashed canines can pitch tents at the 17-site primitive camping area, which offers restrooms with showers. The tent-only sites range $10–20.

The park is south of Port Orange at 6250 S. Ridgewood Ave., less than two miles south of Dunlawton Avenue. 386/322-5133 or 386/736-5953.

PLACES TO EAT

Boston Market: Try ham, chicken, and other comfort foods at the three picnic tables off to the side, overlooking a four-lane road. 1037 Dunlawton Ave.; 386/322-6801.

PLACES TO STAY

Daytona Beach Campground: A 50-foot kidney-shaped pool is the focal point at this shady 224-site campground, which, despite its name, is actually in Port Orange, not Daytona Beach. A general store, playground, and laundry facility are offered on these 17 acres. Dogs are expected to be quiet here. Among other pet rules: "All leashes must be accompanied by a dog. The county sure has a mean dogcatcher." Campsites for tents or RVs range $30–34. From I-95, exit onto Highway 421/Dunlawton Avenue, head two miles east, then north one mile on Clyde Morris Boulevard. 4601 S. Clyde Morris Blvd., Port Orange; 386/761-2663; www.rvdaytona.com.

Nova Family Campground: Leashed dogs may marvel at the stone dinosaur replicas down the street from this 12-acre, 350-site campground, shaded by palms and oaks. Amenities include a pool, shuffleboard, horseshoes, a camp store, a laundry facility, showers, and a game room with pool tables and pinball. Rates typically range $18–30 but during special events rise to $32–57. Add $2–5 nightly per dog. 1190 Herbert St., Port Orange; 386/767-0095; www.novacamp.com.

Spruce Creek Park: See Parks, Beaches, and Recreation Areas, above, for camping information.

Ponce Inlet

PARKS, BEACHES, AND RECREATION AREAS

23 Lighthouse Point Park

🐾🐾🐾 (See Daytona Beach map on page 204)

From a dog's viewpoint, Ponce Inlet is a tremendous place to swim, despite the leash rule. From the viewpoint of piping plovers, a bird protected under the Endangered Species Act, this beach is a lousy place for dogs to run freely, lest they trample nests. In ever-more-populous Florida, this park, in federal terms, is "a critical habitat for wintering piping plovers."

So, keep your dog-paddler on a retractable leash or regular lead. The rule is strictly enforced, says Wes Hewson, manager of the Volusia County–run park. The place, he says, is essentially "a wildlife sanctuary for birds," which "do come occasionally."

"We don't want to be the bad guys. I want people to come to the park and enjoy the park. It's great: You can bring your dog and be in the saltwater," Hewson says.

Just keep dogs leashed.

That rule bothers some locals. Chances are you'll see a few leashless swimmers. Owners risk a $55 fine.

There are other paws-itive aspects to this 52-acre park. Because it's geologically older than Smyrna Dunes Park (see Parks, Beaches, and Recreation Areas in New Smyrna Beach, below), it offers more of the relatively cool and shady maritime forest that occupies some coastline here. Almost a mile's worth of trails and elevated boardwalks thread through maritime hammock and coastal dunes. It's also easy to find this park—right next to the Ponce Inlet Lighthouse. Facilities include pavilions, barbecues, restrooms, and showers. A final plus: You're less likely to find crowds here, unless you count the possums, raccoons, and armadillos that your pooch may notice.

Admission is $3.50 per vehicle. From Daytona Beach's Boardwalk, take Highway A1A south about 11 miles to 5000 S. Atlantic Ave., Ponce Inlet. Nicknamed Ponce Inlet Park, the park is on Ponce de Leon Inlet's north side. 386/756-7488.

Debary

PARKS, BEACHES, AND RECREATION AREAS

24 Gemini Springs Park

😺😺 (See Daytona Beach map on page 204)

The main attraction for humans at this 210-acre county park is the 6.5 million gallons of fresh water that bubble up in the two springs every day. The idea is to admire the springs, not swim; that's prohibited. Landlubber dogs can enjoy a .75-mile nature trail or a .25-mile bridge loop trail, so long as they're leashed (violators may be fined $52). As you explore the park, you'll notice arched bridges, a stone barbecue building, and an earthen dam. These were put here by Saundra and Charles Gray, who raised cattle on this land before selling it to the government in 1969. If your pooch isn't dog-tired after a day at this park, consider padding along the nearby Spring to Spring Trail (see below).

Campers can stake a spot in the big primitive camping area or at one of the park's 21 tent-only sites, which run $17. A $25 refundable cash deposit is required. No hookups are available, but there's a source of water nearby. You'll sleep on land that was used in the 1800s for timber and citrus operations, before John H. Padgett and his family used it to raise cattle and grow sugar cane.

The park is at 37 Dirksen Drive, between the towns of Enterprise and DeBary. From I-4 (Exit 108), go west toward DeBary for about two miles to the park at left, on Dirksen Drive. 386/736-5953 or 386/668-3810.

25 Lake Monroe Park

😺 (See Daytona Beach map on page 204)

Lake Monroe meets the St. Johns River at this 42-acre county park, where anglers cast for bluegill from the pier and dogs appreciate the occasional breeze wafting from the lake. Expect little room for pooches to romp. Still, there is fun to be had: Have lunch with your leashed pooch at a table or a picnic pavilion, follow a nature trail, or bring a boat to launch into Lake Monroe. Kids will appreciate the playground and volleyball court.

Pets may spend the night in an RV or tent at the oak-shaded campground. The 44 campsites were improved during a 2004 park renovation, which also brought in new docks, restrooms, pavilions, and showers. Camping reservations are advised; sites fill quickly in summer and winter. Campsites are $19.

The lakeside park is at 975 U.S. 17/92, in the shadow of an electricity plant. From I-4 (Exit 104), go north on U.S. 17/92. Cross the St. Johns River and the park is ahead at right. 386/668-3825.

26 Spring to Spring Trail

🐾🐾 (See Daytona Beach map on page 204)

A favorite of joggers, bicyclists, and plain old pedestrians, this paved trail runs beneath the lovely bent branches of oaks and past streets landscaped with oleander. The great thing about this 1.3-mile-long trail is that it links pet-permissible Gemini Springs Park with the impressive DeBary Hall Historic Site, 210 Sunrise Blvd., a former hunting retreat that hosted millionaires.

The parking area for the trail is near the intersection of U.S. 17/92 and Dirksen Drive in DeBary, just west of the entrance to Gemini Springs Park (see above). Alternatively, park at Gemini Springs Park, 37 Dirksen Drive. From I-4 (Exit 108), go west toward DeBary about two miles. 386/736-5953.

PLACES TO STAY

Gemini Springs Park: See Parks, Beaches, and Recreation Areas, above, for camping information.

Lake Monroe Park: See Parks, Beaches, and Recreation Areas, above, for camping information.

New Smyrna Beach

PARKS, BEACHES, AND RECREATION AREAS

27 Smyrna Dunes Park

🐾🐾🐾 (See Daytona Beach map on page 204)

This is one of the few places in this region where dogs are actually allowed on the beach, though technically they're supposed to stay leashed even while swimming or risk a $55 fine. Maggie eagerly bounded down the raised wooden boardwalk, which loops around dunes and the Indian River at Ponce de Leon Inlet. It's a pretty place: Dolphins and manatees swim past at times, and nice boats often glide by. Portions of the boardwalk are unsheltered, so be sure your eager pup takes it easy on a hot day.

Dogs love the place. They're allowed at the riverside beach and the inlet-side beach, but not on the oceanside beach favored by surfers, sunbathers, and migrating piping plovers. We didn't stay long on the inland side of the inlet, at the Indian River, because a fisherman's dog gave Maggie a hard time. We headed east on the 1.38-mile boardwalk toward the ocean, where there's a bit more shade. A local corgi named Dingho loves this trail and the entire 73-acre park, "except the water," says owner/local innkeeper John Miller. Sidekick Joe, a standard poodle, swears by the swimming, however.

Picnic shelters with grills are available, and if your pooch needs a washing, there are outdoor showers. Boxes containing pooper-scooper bags are posted next to walkways, so please be sure to grab one. Violators can be fined $55.

Admission is $3.50 daily per carload; alternatively, buy a $20 annual pass. To reach the park from downtown, take Highway A1A/Lytle Street east. As soon as you cross the Indian River, make a left onto Peninsular Avenue and continue to the end. 386/424-2935.

28 Callilisa Park

(See Daytona Beach map on page 204)

Local dogs like this thumbprint of a park, where they can wade in the brackish waters of the Indian River or enjoy a meal at the four concrete picnic tables beneath pine and cedar trees. Dogs are officially supposed to be leashed.

The park is at Highway A1A and Peninsular Avenue. 386/424-2175.

29 Sugar Mill Ruins Historic Site

(See Daytona Beach map on page 204)

Once run by the state, this small piece of green with remnants of a sugar mill has since been turned over to Volusia County. It's a pleasant place for a picnic at one of several tables shaded by towering oaks, and the view of the old mill ruins makes it offbeat for the two-legged set. Maggie was unimpressed by the eroding 1820s coquina-rock walls and the big iron vats (once used to boil sugarcane juice into crystals), but was happy enough to wolf down bits of sandwich. You can also see where a boiler, steam engine, and other machinery were once used to make sugar until the Second Seminole War forced the closure of 16 sugar mills between here and St. Augustine. Leashes are required at the free 17-acre park.

From downtown, head west on Highway 44 from its intersection with U.S. 1, then turn left at Mission Drive. The entrance is on the west side of the road at 600 Mission Dr., where the road angles east toward Ingham Road. 386/736-5952.

30 River Breeze Park

(See Daytona Beach map on page 204)

Bring a boat and your furry sailor can join you in a search for bald eagles and playful dolphins at this 37-acre county park near the Intracoastal Waterway.

Some people also watch space shuttle launches from the water, while kayakers put in here to travel across a tidal estuary and admire its wading birds. Landlubber pets may prefer to take in the surroundings from the boardwalk or just eat a packed lunch at the picnic area and pavilion. A pier stretches over Mosquito Lagoon, where egrets, mergansers, and loons hang out. Lucky dogs may glimpse a migrating American white pelican.

A 17-site campground near the Intracoastal Waterway is open to tent campers only. Sites cost $10–20 nightly, and you'll sleep on grounds that long ago were part of a Colonial-era plantation. Kids can head to the playground.

The county park is at 250 H. H. Burch Rd., east of U.S. 1 in Oak Hill. From I-95 (Exit 231), go east one mile to U.S. 1. Go north (left) for about eight miles, then turn right on H. H. Burch Road. The park is ahead on the left. 386/345-5525 or 386/736-5953.

PLACES TO STAY

Buena Vista Inn Vacation Apartments: Step out the back door and you're right on the Indian River, with two fishing piers, a picnic area, and a play area at your disposal. Proprietors Kathy and Robert Standing live at this eight-unit, single-story lodging located six blocks from the beach, and they'll willingly lend bikes to pedal. Canine swimmers can make a day of it at Smyrna Dunes Park, located farther up the beach at the tip of the peninsula (see Parks,

Beaches, and Recreation Areas, above). Rates range $65–85, higher during special events. Pet fee is $10 nightly for big dogs, $5 for small dogs; maximum $30 weekly. If your dog won't stay off the furniture, ask for a blanket to use as a cover. 500 N. Causeway, New Smyrna Beach; 386/428-5565; www.buenavistainn.com.

Inn Paradise: A standard poodle named Joe and a little corgi named Dingho greet guests at this 14-unit establishment overlooking the Indian River. From your room, you can view the river or step outside to enjoy it from the dock or deck. Hosted by John and Joyce Miller, the place offers a pool, barbecue grill, and nine suites equipped with kitchens. An adjacent pet spa offers doggy daycare, boarding, and grooming. Water dogs can't swim here but instead can travel to the tip of the peninsula to reach Smyrna Dunes Park, as recommended by Joe and Dingho (see Parks, Beaches, and Recreation Areas, above). Rates run $48–160, plus a variable pet deposit. 1157 N. Dixie Freeway/U.S. 1, New Smyrna Beach; 386/423-3812; www.motelinnparadise.com.

River Breeze Park: See Parks, Beaches, and Recreation Areas, above, for camping information.

232

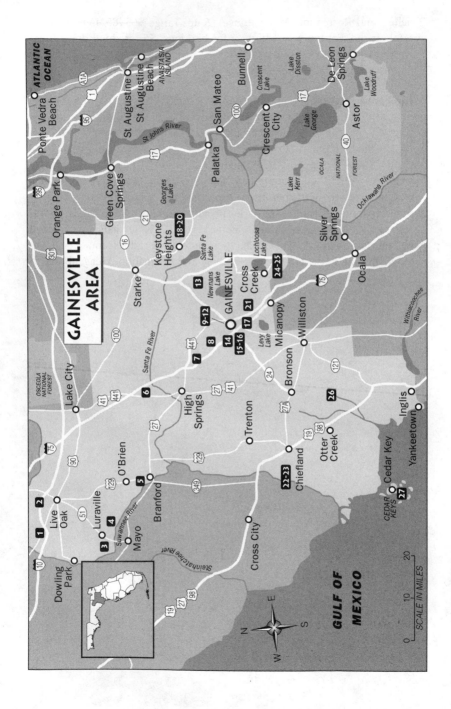

GAINESVILLE AREA

ATLANTIC OCEAN

GULF OF MEXICO

Ponte Vedra Beach
St Augustine
St Augustine Beach
ANASTASIA ISLAND
San Mateo
Bunnell
Crescent Lake
Lake Disston
De Leon Springs
Lake Woodruff
Astor
Lake George
OCALA NATIONAL FOREST
Ocklawaha River
Crescent City
Palatka
St Johns River
Orange Park
Green Cove Springs
Georges Lake
Keystone Heights
Santa Fe Lake
Lochloosa Lake
Newnans Lake
Silver Springs
Ocala
Lake Kerr
Starke
GAINESVILLE
Cross Creek
Micanopy
Levy Lake
Williston
Withlacoochee River
Lake City
OSCEOLA NATIONAL FOREST
Santa Fe River
High Springs
Bronson
Trenton
Inglis
O'Brien
Chiefland
Otter Creek
Yankeetown
Luraville
Branford
Cedar Key
CEDAR KEYS
Live Oak
Mayo
Suwannee River
Cross City
Steinhatchee River
Dowling Park

18-20
13
9-12
8
7
14
15-16
17
21
24-25
5
6
22-23
26
27
1
2
3
4

SCALE IN MILES
0   10   20

N E S W

CHAPTER 8

Gainesville Area

Gainesville and the surrounding stretches of rolling, oak-shaded hills punctuated by peaceful lakes and ice-blue springs are quite canine-cordial.

Although the University of Florida dominates the region in many ways, much of this part of the state is just plain country. So if your dog longs for the rural life, she won't be disappointed. More citified pooches can stick to Gainesville proper, where there's plenty of stuff to keep any dog entertained— including Florida's second-largest off-leash dog park, Dogwood Park.

Live Oak

PARKS, BEACHES, AND RECREATION AREAS

1 Falmouth Spring Conservation Area

😊😊😊 (See Gainesville map on page 232)

The folks at Ripley's Believe It or Not have called it the world's shortest river, but dogs call this swimming hole just plain fun. At this local favorite, the

PICK OF THE LITTER—GAINESVILLE AREA

BEST CANINE "COUNTRY CLUB"
Dogwood Park, Gainesville (page 244)

BEST HISTORIC INN
Herlong Mansion, Micanopy (page 251)

BEST GIANT HOLE IN THE GROUND
Devil's Millhopper Geological State Park, Gainesville
(page 240)

BEST SPOT FOR LITERARY LITTERMATES
Marjorie Kinnan Rawlings State Historic Site, Cross
Creek (page 253)

WORLD'S SHORTEST RIVER
Falmouth Spring Conservation Area, Live Oak (page 233)

BEST HIKE
San Felasco Hammock Preserve State Park, Alachua
(page 239)

BEST GARDEN
Kanapaha Botanical Gardens, Gainesville (page 245)

inland spring boils up above the surface and runs about 100 yards—then disappears underground. Observant doggies will notice something else: "When the water level of the river is up, it will actually flow backwards," says county parks employee Greg Scott. In short, when the river waters are running low, the water flows down from the spring to the river. When the river waters are running high, water flows from the river to the spring.

Fishing, hiking, nature study, and bicycling are all possible at this 276-acre conservation area, but the waters of the spring—a comfortable 72 degrees Fahrenheit year-round—are the focal point. Out of courtesy to other visitors, try to stake out an uncrowded part of the spring to help ensure your fuzzy swimmer doesn't bother others. Duck beneath the shady branches of oaks and pines surrounding the springs to protect your leashed pal from the sun. Note: An alligator once appeared in this spring (and was quickly removed)—a big surprise to authorities, considering this spot is three miles from the Suwannee River, where gators usually live. Even though the likelihood of another gator appearing here is quite small, you may wish to be on the lookout, just in case.

From Live Oak, go west on Highway 90 past the I-10 intersection to the community of Falmouth. Look for the conservation area on the south side of the road, past 185th Street. 386/362-1001.

2 Suwannee Springs

 (See Gainesville map on page 232)

Time to swim! Sure, this spring is pretty small. And like many springs in the area, it can virtually dry up during a drought (call ahead for conditions). But the place is doggy nirvana for Labrador retrievers and other natural born swimmers. Here, they may dog-paddle to their hearts' content. Authorities just ask you and your pooch to display courtesy toward other visitors: If the spring is wall-to-wall people, please stay out of the water until crowds thin. Should you have the swimming hole to yourself, no problem. Go have a ball!

If your dog had visited a century ago, she would have seen people from around the nation plopping their bodies in the "medicinal" sulfur water of the now-defunct Suwannee Springs tourist attraction. Believers thought the water would cure many ills—gout, constipation, and rheumatism, to name a few. Dogs with tender noses might have sneezed at the sulfur scent, but it didn't prevent three hotels and nearly 20 homes from sprouting up here in the springs' heyday.

Although the last hotel burned down in 1925, leashed dogs may still notice railroad pylons and a spring house during a hike around these approximately 100 acres. Swim at your own risk (there are no lifeguards) or venture onto the backwoods trails that tend to attract locals in four-wheel-drive vehicles (be on alert so you don't get hit). A gradual slope leads to the Suwannee River, making this a perfect place to launch your own canoe. Be alert for alligators in the river.

From Live Oak, go north on U.S. 129 to Old Highway 129 before the agriculture inspection station. Follow a dirt road to the tract sign on the right. Suwannee Springs is part of the Woods Ferry Conservation Area of the Suwannee River Water Management District. 386/362-1001.

PLACES TO STAY

Best Western Suwannee River Inn: A peewee pet—under 15 pounds—may join you at this two-story, 64-unit poolside motel found behind the Huddle House restaurant off I-10 (Exit 283). Rates run $40–130. Pet fee is $10 per stay. 6819 U.S. 129, Live Oak; 386/362-6000; www.bestwestern.com.

Econo Lodge: Tall oaks shade the back of this poolside motel, located one block south of I-10 (Exit 283). Dogs of any size are accepted for a nightly fee of $5–10. Rates range $50–100. 6811 U.S. 129 North, Live Oak; 386/362-7459; www.econolodge.com.

DIVERSIONS

Row, row, row with Joe: Your dog can see firsthand why canoeing is such a popular activity on the Suwannee River, with its pretty scenery and wildlife—and relatively easy paddling.

Observant pooches may notice Robb's Waterfall (actually just a trickle) and horses and cows at the Florida Sheriff's Boys' Ranch. The canoe livery for this area warns: "Alligators are attracted to dogs. Large dogs can upset a canoe. For these reasons we recommend that you leave your dog at home." Being experienced canoeists, we personally aren't deterred by that, despite Maggie Dog's to-and-fro motion in a canoe. But it's something you might want to consider, particularly if your dog loves water (Maggie doesn't).

Suwannee Canoe Outpost offers canoeing day trips on the Suwannee River for $10–17 per adult, $5–8.50 for children. Overnight trips include a shuttle fee. The office is based at Spirit of the Suwannee Music Park (see Places to Stay) on U.S. 129 North in Live Oak, about 4.5 miles north of I-10. Reserve a canoe at 386/364-4991 or 800/428-4147.

Spirit of the Suwannee Music Park: Your dog will find plenty of rustic trails to follow at this woodsy, 700-acre campground before retiring for the night at one of the 1,250-plus campsites. This retreat routinely offers country-music concerts (dogs prohibited there), as well as other people-pleasers such as playgrounds, a pool, a miniature golf course, and horseback riding with JK Stables (guided rides start at $25 hourly). Non-event rates for campsites range $15–35. Reservations are advised. The park is on U.S. 129, about 4.5 miles north of I-10 (Exit 283). 3076 95th Dr., Live Oak; 386/364-1683; www.musicliveshere.com.

Luraville

PARKS, BEACHES, AND RECREATION AREAS

🐾 Charles Springs

😊😊😊😊😊 🐕 (See Gainesville map on page 232)

Get ready to dog-paddle! If you happen to be in the area, a stop to swim at the springs here is a treat to consider. Locals head here to relax with their dogs, despite this sad fact: Technically, pets are banned. In practice, however, the 1985 ordinance has been little enforced. While sheriff's deputies could stop by and lay down the county law—meaning a fine of up to $500 and up to two months in jail for the second-degree misdemeanor—they normally are busy

with bigger issues. Should you visit? Use your judgment. And keep a leash handy in case other visitors get nervous being around your pooch.

From Gainesville, take I-75 north to Exit 399, then head west on U.S. 27/441 about 50 miles to Mayo. Turn right (north) on Highway 51 and go about five miles. Turn left onto 152nd Street/Charles Spring Road. When you have a choice of making a 90-degree turn or continuing straight on a dirt road, take the dirt road. The springs are about a half mile down. 904/362-1001.

◪ Peacock Springs State Park

🐾🐾 (See Gainesville map on page 232)

At this remote scuba-diving destination, where the underwater caves are among the nation's longest, your leashed dog may walk along the half mile of shady dirt roads used by cars or head into the hardwood forest where a nature trail and boardwalk were under construction last time we checked. Afterward, eat at two small picnic areas that are no bigger than some people's front yards.

Disappointed locals recall the days when dogs could jump into the springs. That was before the state took over management of the 288-acre park. While the current setup sounds like no great shakes for pooches, dogs who like to walk on dirt roads would probably appreciate stopping here on an uncrowded weekday if you're in the area.

Admission is $3 per vehicle. The park is 17 miles southwest of Live Oak on State Road 51 and two miles east of Luraville on Peacock Springs Road. 386/776-2194.

PLACES TO STAY

The River Rendezvous: Set along a quarter-mile stretch of the Suwannee River and connected to Convict Springs, this oak-shaded campground keeps people busy with diving, canoeing, and offerings not found just anywhere: a steam room, hot tub, dive shop, game room, bar, and restaurant. Formerly known as Jim Hollis' River Rendezvous, the park charges $15–17 for RV sites,

$10 for shady primitive tent sites on the river. From Luraville, take Highway 51 south for 4.5 miles to U.S. 27. Turn left (east) onto U.S. 27; continue three miles to Convict Springs Road; turn left; go two miles to the campground. 828 NE Primrose Rd., Mayo; 386/294-2510 or 800/533-5276.

Branford

PARKS, BEACHES, AND RECREATION AREAS

5 Little River Springs

🐾🐾🐾🐾 (See Gainesville map on page 232)

For years, dogs jumped gleefully into the long, oval-shaped springs and sat around with the two-legged crowd on the beach here. Today, this county-owned spot continues to be a favorite of dog-loving locals, despite this sad news: Officially, pets are forbidden at this spring.

In practice, the rule was for years little enforced. Sheriff's deputies were always able to stop by and fine dog owners $500 or even throw them in jail for two months. It's a second-degree misdemeanor. While they were seldom seen in years past, it remains unclear since a recent renovation how strictly they'll now be enforcing the rules.

Another warning: The spring's run leads about 200 feet out into the Suwannee River, but don't go in the river or you might meet up with an alligator.

The small parking area here gets crowded in summer, and you'll pass many visitors on the stairs leading to the water. The beach can get crowded, too, so keep a leash handy in case any other visitors get nervous. For smaller crowds, consider Charles Springs in Dowling Park or Royal Springs in O'Brien (see separate listings).

From U.S. 129 north of Branford, turn west at County Road 248, then follow the signs. You'll go about 1.5 miles until the road dead-ends; turn left into the entrance. 386/362-3004.

High Springs

PARKS, BEACHES, AND RECREATION AREAS

6 O'Leno State Park

🐾🐾🐾 (See Gainesville map on page 232)

Shady trails spanning three to five miles are the highlight for dogs at this scenic spot, where the Santa Fe River disappears to flow underground. Alas, dogs aren't allowed near the water (or horseback trails or campground), so it's off to the picnic areas and hiking trails for pooches. History-minded hounds might notice artifacts left by early settlers along former road beds. But they're more likely to see a deer sprinting in the distance.

DIVERSIONS

You can howl at the moon, and your dog will howl with delight when she hears that she is welcome to join you on an organized moonlight canoe trip down the lazy, gently curving Santa Fe River—a pretty river flanked by oaks, pines, and cypress. Jim and Sally Wood of High Springs–based **Santa Fe Canoe Outpost** begin the trek every month at about 7 or 8 P.M. on the Saturday closest to a full moon. It's a romantic experience, and the signature trip of this outfitting service. Paddling ends late in the night and is followed by a big bonfire. Fee is $22 per person, minimum $44 per canoe. Reserve at 386/454-2050.

Earlier risers can tip a canoe with Tipper, too, any day. Water-loving dogs have much to cheer about: While they are routinely turned away from popular Poe Springs and Ginnie Springs, they don't have to put up with second-class status at Rum Springs and Lily Springs. You'll float down the Santa Fe River and pass moss-draped oaks that make up deep, dark forests where you can get out to take a short walk. In all, you can choose from seven routes, ranging from 90 minutes (three miles) to five hours (15 miles). Santa Fe Canoe Outpost rentals cost $12–19 per person; kids under age 12 free. Want to camp out? Consider the three overnight trips, ranging from 19 to 39 miles; fee is $55 daily. Whatever the route, ask about alligators and bring water for your dog. Reserve at 386/454-2050.

The entrance fee is $4 per vehicle. From High Springs, head six miles north on U.S. 441 to the park entrance. 386/454-1853.

Alachua

PARKS, BEACHES, AND RECREATION AREAS

7 San Felasco Hammock Preserve State Park

🐾🐾🐾 (See Gainesville map on page 232)

A favorite of local golden retriever Jessie and her companion collie, Lucy, this nearly 11-square-mile preserve offers more than 11 miles of nature trails that weave through a dense hardwood forest and make for a shady, cool walk—a treat in summer, when the temperatures tend to make dog-walking prohibitive.

A quick look at the map at the entrance should help you plan a walk that is the perfect distance for you and your dog. The San Felasco hiking trailhead, located on County Road 232/Millhopper Road, offers three trails of varying lengths—0.9 mile, 4.8 miles, and 5.6 miles. Jessie and Lucy's favorite path starts on the south side of Millhopper Road. It's deep woods here, so the two-some has plenty to smell; their two-legged buddy, Mitch, sometimes lets them lead him off-trail to pursue particularly compelling scents. Bobcats, deer, foxes, and turkeys live in these woods. Park rules say dogs must be leashed (though the rules seem loosely enforced and loosely obeyed).

Entrance is $2 per vehicle. The park is at 12720 NW 109 Lane. From I-75 (Exit 390), drive west 2.9 miles on County Road 222. At County Road 241, turn right and drive two miles. At County Road 232, turn right and go 2.2 miles to the park at right, just east of the I-75 overpass. (Note: There is no interchange at this I-75 overpass.) 386/462-7905.

PLACES TO STAY

Comfort Inn: Once fortified by a free continental breakfast at this 60-room poolside motel off I-75 (Exit 399), you could strike out for a hike with your hound at San Felasco Hammock Preserve State Park. Rates typically range $65–90, higher during special events. Pet fee is $10 daily. 15920 NW U.S. 441, Alachua; 386/462-2414; www.choicehotels.com.

Quality Inn: Microwaves and refrigerators are available on request at this 90-room poolside motel off I-75 (Exit 399), where pets may sleep in designated rooms. Rates range $60–95. 15960 NW U.S. 441, Alachua; 386/462-2244; www.choicehotels.com.

Gainesville

When it comes to grumbling around the University of Florida, the big issue is parking—not barking. Watch out for signs warning you that city decals are required; you could be towed if you don't have one. Probably the best place to park if you're just passing through is a pay lot behind the shops and bars just north of campus across 13th Street. You'll find some metered spots on the streets in that neighborhood, but do not park where you see the black-and-white signs depicting a car being towed. Heavy-handed, yes, but that's the way it's been for more than a decade.

If your pooch wants to rub noses with the scholars on campus, consider parking at the J. Wayne Reitz Student Union, where there is a parking garage. It's on Museum Drive, just east of North-South Drive.

PARKS, BEACHES, AND RECREATION AREAS

🐾 Devil's Millhopper Geological State Park

🐾🐾🐾 🐾➧ (See Gainesville map on page 232)

Furry flatlanders won't soon forget the walk to the bottom of this 120-foot-deep sinkhole—if only because of the 232 stairs involved. The bones of extinct

DIVERSIONS

Give your dog a bone—or a trip to a day spa: People bring bottles of wine to share and socialize with others while their dogs sample fresh-baked organic biscuits—made of rolled oats, carob chips, and other sugar-free ingredients—at the weekly socials held at **Earth Pets,** 500 NW 60th St., Gainesville. But leashed customers are welcome to shop any day at the 3,000-square-foot natural pet food store, stocked with gift baskets, organic treats, aromatherapy supplies, and other things dogs are unlikely to sniff out just anywhere. People drive from hundreds of miles away with their coolers and pets to buy "raw diet" refrigerated canine food, say store proprietors Guy Webster and Joy Drawdy, who are well known in the local dog community because of their connections to dog-obedience and dog-show folks. A holistic veterinarian/acupuncturist provides consultations here by appointment for $50. For information, call Earth Pets at 352/331-5123.

Prefer a day spa for Spot? Imagine taking a saltwater bath and maybe toning up that dry skin with moisturizers. No, not you—it's your pooch who will be luxuriating at **Nature Pets Day Spa,** also at 500 NW 60th St. Proprietor Lisa Jordan tailors her grooming services to the four-legged crowd, offering, among other things, hydrotherapy to accelerate healing and provide comfort for pets suffering from hip disorders. Make an appointment at 352/331-8681.

Elsewhere, leashed shoppers are likely to run into free-roaming cats whenever they stop at the little pet supply boutique found inside the **Alachua County Humane Society,** 2029 NW 6th St., Gainesville. Yes, leashed dogs are welcome to pad along the same terrain in search of collars, leashes, toys, and premium food. For hours, call 352/373-5855.

animals have been found at this national natural landmark, and the lush surroundings are bound to keep wet noses twitching. You'll probably have relatively little trouble walking with your leashed pup down the steep stairs, so skip the frequent stops at the interpretive signs until your laborious trip back up. Resting with your pooch will give you time to admire plants similar to those found in the Appalachian Mountains. Shady much of the year, the bowl-shaped, 500-foot-wide cavity gets lots of sun—even at the bottom—in winter. So bring water for your dog.

Admission is $2 per vehicle. From I-75 (Exit 390), drive east 3.8 miles on County Road 222. At 43rd Street, turn left. At the next traffic light, turn left onto Millhopper Road. The park is 1,000 feet ahead, at right, at 4732 Millhopper Road. 352/955-2008.

9 Northeast Park Off-Leash Area

😺😺😺🐾 (See Gainesville map on page 232)

Time to run! This little one-acre fenced area has gone to the dogs, quite intentionally. As the city government's first official leash-free park, this space is reserved for pooches, who race each other, chase slobbery balls, and generally have a great time.

At this grassy field dotted by large pines, you'll find water for pooches, a double-gated system to ensure no dog escapes, several benches, pooper-scooper bags, and a bulletin board for posting doggy-related information. And, yes, there's an actual fire hydrant. "We grabbed an old fire hydrant and put it in there just for laughs," Pat Burn, then head of the city's recreation division, said after the park's opening.

Be sure to pick up after your pooch: This field serves as a pilot project, and the better the results, the more likely it is other city parks will open off-leash areas (hopefully bigger ones). If the place fails, then this patch of land could close. Still, the city spent about $6,500 to fence the area, so this bark park's future looks bright. Besides, some high-ranking dogs love roaming freely. Upon voting on whether to open this off-leash area, then-city commissioner John Barrow quipped, "I can't go home if we don't pass this. My dog is watching this [vote]."

The off-leash area is inside 22.5-acre Northeast Park, which itself is a fairly decent place to walk a leashed dog. A path winds around ball fields and a playground, so there usually is plenty to see and bark at.

Northeast Park is at 400 NE 16th Ave., just east of North Main Street. The off-leash area is on the park's south side, behind a softball field. 352/334-2171.

10 Plaza of the Americas

😺😺😺 (See Gainesville map on page 232)

A popular place to hang out and soak up the sun when the weather is agreeable, this University of Florida plaza reflects the diverse enrollment of the largest college campus in the southeastern United States. When the people are out, the dogs usually are, too, thanks to the plentiful open areas for games of Frisbee and fetch—and the easygoing folks who'll stop and give a pup some affection. Stop by at lunch and share a vegetarian meal with your dog, compliments of the Hare Krishna. The suggested donation is $3, and cash-strapped students rely on the organic "Krishna-roni," as they've nicknamed it. (Since your dog will probably sniff wildly in vain hopes of finding meat, a trip to the Burrito Brothers' takeout shop at 16 Northwest 13th St. for a bag lunch of huge, meat-packed burritos might be in order. Robert thinks they're the best burritos in the state, bar none.)

Remember, the city leash law is in effect at the plaza. But you'll probably see more dogs without leash than with.

The plaza is about a block southwest of the intersection of the town's two main roads, University Avenue and 13th Street/U.S. 441, south of the George Smathers Libraries at the University of Florida. 352/392-1148.

11 University of Florida Gardens

🐾🐾🐾🐾 (See Gainesville map on page 232)

Especially beautiful in spring and summer, this 14-acre botanical garden is beloved by dogs for a big reason: There is just so much room to roam. The botanical garden is outfitted with a boardwalk, but you can go off-trail in many spots and play in open spaces. The gardens open into the University of Florida intramural athletic fields, which, if not in use, are a great place to play fetch, Frisbee, or other doggy games that beg for room. However, the citywide leash law technically is in effect here. That's OK by Jessie, a golden retriever who prefers to roll around in mud puddles.

A favorite of local dogs, the gardens nonetheless raise a red flag. At the western border, Lake Alice teems with the live version of the university mascot—the alligator. Keep your dog leashed here, especially if she normally makes a beeline for water. Many a small dog learned the hard way that racing after the lake's ducks isn't a good idea. "Usually once, twice a year, a dog gets eaten by a gator—with an owner at the end of the leash," Dr. Gail Kunkle, of U.F.'s college of veterinary medicine, told us.

The gardens are on Museum Road at Fraternity Row. From Southwest 34th Street, turn east on Radio Road, then north on Museum Road. 352/392-1148.

12 Westside Park

🐾🐾 (See Gainesville map on page 232)

A pleasant 1.5-mile running trail winds past this 27-acre park's tennis courts, baseball fields, picnic area, and playground. That means there is plenty for leashed dogs and their humans to see—including, usually, other leashed dogs and their humans.

An old golden retriever and canine cancer survivor named Knick Knack Paddywack for years showed up here in a red wagon, drawing instant attention from everybody. The park is at Northwest 34th Street and Northwest Eighth Avenue. 352/334-2171.

13 Gum Root Park

🐾🐾🐾 (See Gainesville map on page 232)

Leashed pooches who keep their noses to the ground might pick up the scents of otters, squirrels, foxes, or deer—and totally miss out on the eagles and woodpeckers perched above them. This remote refuge for wild animals is 369 acres in size, dwarfing the neighborhood parks where most dogs go. The landscape also is more varied, including floodplain swamp, pasture, and sun-dappled pine flatwoods.

The park is on State Road 26 at Northeast 27 Avenue. From Main Street, go east six miles on State Road 26, following it as it curves northeasterly, to the park. 352/334-5000 or 354/334-2231.

14 Forest Park Off-Leash Area

🐾🐾🐾🐾🐕 (See Gainesville map on page 232)

Dogs run like the wind at this off-leash park, where many of Gainesville's dog people gather to socialize and let their pooches play together. Many friendly folks come each evening after work, and it's become quite a little subculture. Pups revel in the room to run, play ball, chase Frisbees, and roll around.

The off-leash area backs onto a creek, and for a long time the county relied on the creek to serve as a border and simply fenced the three other sides of the park. But water-loving dogs obviously romped in the creek, which in 2001 led to the unthinkable—an alligator killed a pooch. A month later, another small dog was killed by a gator. "The gator actually carried the dog away," said Vernest Legree, who oversees Alachua County parks. "It's just one of those things you don't think is going to happen until it happens."

That second death did it: The county finally decided to fence the fourth side of this off-leash area. Alligator warning signs now are posted.

The free county park is at 4501 SW 20th Avenue. From Archer Road/State Road 24, turn north onto Southwest 34 Street/State Road 121, then left onto Southwest 20th Avenue and proceed to the park. The off-leash area is in the park's northwest corner and is clearly posted. 352/374-5245.

15 Dogwood Park

🐾🐾🐾🐾🐕 (See Gainesville map on page 232)

Howl-elujah! These 15 acres of leash-free fun are worth a weekend visit. Originally Florida's largest dog park (a sister park in Jacksonville now surpasses it), it truly is hound heaven: retrievers swim in two ponds, small dogs run in two areas just for them, and big dogs bound along their own fields. A "dog mountain" sand pile satisfies diggers.

Shady walking/jogging paths and fitness stations are geared to people and pooches. Hammocks, benches, picnic tables, and swings provide nice places to sit and read. Big trees provide glorious shade.

Since it was started in 1998 by owner Lynn Badger, this park has become a destination. A self-service dog wash is open during office hours. A gift shop sells leashes, treats, and so on. A dog photography studio takes photos by appointment. Doggy daycare is offered weekdays at Kelly Meyer's on-site Camp Wag-a-Lot. Obedience and agility training are offered. Special events for the furry set also happen here; at one Halloween party, some dogs showed up as University of Florida cheerleaders.

Dogs must wear license tags and be current on shots. Kids must be at least four feet tall, though carried babies are acceptable. Male dogs must be neutered, though exceptions occasionally are made during weekend visiting hours (except for large aggressive breeds).

Admission for nonmembers is $9 for one dog, $1 per additional dog in the same family. Nonmembers may visit Saturday and Sunday 10 A.M.–5 P.M. and weekdays during office hours (Mon.–Tues. 4–6 P.M., Wed.–Fri. 2–6 P.M.). Members can use the park daily from dawn to dusk; membership costs $30 monthly for one dog, $33 monthly for a multi-dog family. From I-75 (Exit 384), go west one mile on Archer Road/State Road 24 to 5505 SW Archer Road. 352/335-1919.

16 Kanapaha Botanical Gardens

🐾🐾🐾 🐾 (See Gainesville map on page 232)

Not only is this lovely 62-acre botanical garden much more elaborate than the University of Florida Gardens, it is also one of the few nature parks in the county that welcomes dogs. The proprietor, the North Florida Botanical Society, loves pups—as long as they're leashed. This winding path is plenty enjoyable for dogs and humans, and large watering dishes are placed along the trail "for our canine friends," according to the sign. Dogs welcome the water break, and Jessie, the golden retriever of our friend Mitch Stacy, managed to soak the entire front half of her body in a bowl.

The paved, sometimes-narrow trail winds through a butterfly garden, a sunken garden, and past a water lily pond. The trail also runs along the edge of Lake Kanapaha, where a five-foot alligator has been spotted sunning himself on the bank. Bring a picnic basket—a picnic area in the shady grove is perfect for lunch. Jessie, the soaked retriever, and her collie companion, Lucy, attracted attention from well-wishing visitors on a Saturday visit. But few local dogs seem to take advantage of this park and its plentiful benches and gazebos that offer fine opportunities to sit and enjoy the flowers.

DIVERSIONS

Get a gander at Gainesville's past: Urban dogs who prefer sidewalks to woods should head to the downtown Clock Tower at East University Avenue and Northeast First Street to start a daytime walking or driving tour of the 63-block **Northeast Historic District,** listed on the National Register of Historic Places.

Look for Victorian homes and the stately Mediterranean Revival–style Thomas Center, along with the Kirby Smith School, named for a Confederate general. Your pooch may not care that the 290 buildings here give onlookers a taste of the state's architectural styles from 1880 through the 1920s, but he'll appreciate the change of scenery. For a printed guide, call 352/374-5231.

Admission is $5 per adult, $3 for kids, free for children age five and under. The park is at 4700 SW 58th Drive. From I-75 (Exit 384), go west one mile on Archer Road/State Road 24. Look for the Kanapaha park entrance sign at right. 352/372-4981.

🐾 Squirrel Ridge Off-Leash Area

😺😺😺😺🐕 (See Gainesville map on page 232)

Run, Spot, run! Dogs do just that at this grassy off-leash area, where trees provide shade toward the western end. Measuring about 500 feet by 250 feet, this county-run paw park is a favorite of locals. It's fenced, it offers parking, and water is available to quench canine thirsts. But that's about it for amenities. Some locals call this a poor man's Dogwood Park, referring to the membership bark park requiring an entry fee (see Dogwood Park, above).

The dog park is within 17-acre Squirrel Ridge Park, which offers fields for football and soccer, picnic areas, a playground, and a fitness trail. Dogs must be leashed in those areas.

Squirrel Ridge is at 1603 SW Williston Road. 386/374-5245.

PLACES TO EAT

Bageland: At this no-frills, budget breakfast and lunch spot, folks at the four plastic tables outside were blasé about Maggie as we sat in the breeze under a shady overhang. The drill: Tie your dog to a bike rack, then walk inside to order bagels or sandwiches with egg salad, smooth chicken salad, lox, pastrami, turkey, and more. Robert practically lived on the food at this place when he was a Florida Gator, and it still serves a tasty bagel. 1717 NW First Ave; 352/372-2435.

Book Lover's Cafe: At this café inside Books Inc., you may tie your dog outside, walk in to pick up a three-salad sampler, lasagna, or other vegetarian or vegan meal, then rejoin your pal at the outdoor seating. 505 NW 13th St.; 352/384-0090.

Cafe Gardens: The kind of place where penny-scraping University of Florida students go for lunch when they feel like spending some money, this home of salads and burgers has a pleasant courtyard setting with wrought-iron fences. The catch is that dogs are merely tolerated, if that. "If you're here with a dog, we won't turn you away, but we don't like them here," said one server. So, tie your dog on the outside of the fence. While you sup in the courtyard, your pooch may watch from the other side of the bars. 1633 NW First Ave.; 352/376-2233.

El Indio: Dogs on the run can grab tacos, burritos, fajitas, and other Southwestern/Mexican dishes at the drive-through window of this college student favorite. Or slow down and take a seat at the outdoor patio. 407 NW 13th St.; 352/377-5828.

Krispy Kreme: When the neon sign lights up, that means doughnuts have just been pulled from the oven at this 24-hour chain locale. Devotees swear by the pillows of hot dough. To get yours, tie your dog to an outdoor table, go order a doughnut and coffee, then rejoin your buddy. 310 NW 13th St.; 352/377-0052.

Leonardo's Pizza: A favorite of cash-strapped college students and the tattooed crowd, this budget pizza joint sells pizza by the slice, as well as pasta and whole thick-crust or New York–style pies. Perhaps the most unusual pizza is the Florentine—spinach, sun-dried tomatoes, and cheese. To Maggie Dog's relief, the usual meats and other toppings are offered, too. Take an outdoor table with your leashed pooch. 1245 W. University Ave.; 352/375-2007.

Maude's Classic Café: Locals are known to wait nearly an hour on Friday and Saturday nights to get a table at this popular downtown dessert and coffee spot in Sun Center, next to the Hippodrome. Cheesecake, pies, and cakes are the draw. Take an outdoor table on the brick patio with your leashed dog. Just ask, and a staffer will scrounge up water for your dog. 101 SE Place, Suite 101; 352/336-9646.

Shamrock: In some circles, this casual Irish spot is better known as a bar offering occasional live music by local bands than as a grill. But former resident Cathy Goodwin vouched for the food, just as her keeshond, Keesha, was tickled to be served a bowl of ice water at an outdoor table. "I didn't even have to ask," Goodwin reports. The broader-than-expected menu includes Irish fare—such as shepherd's pie, corned beef and cabbage, and, of course, Guinness stout—as well as burgers, salads, and chicken pot pie. 1017 W. University Ave.; 352/374-6777.

Starbucks: From just about any spot in downtown, alert doggies can see the five-story landmark building in which this coffee franchise is set: Union Street Station. Tie your pal to one of the outdoor tables, then go inside to retrieve a takeout order of espresso drinks, regular coffee, tea, and limited desserts made by local bakers. The drill is the same at an alternate location in Magnolia Park, 4780 NW 39th Ave.; 352/379-7787. The Union Street Station store is at 201 SE First St.; 352/374-8227.

Steamers: Following, as the sign says, "a 1950s Iowa tradition of loose hamburger," this ruff and ready place (aesthetically speaking) near the University of Florida specializes in beef that's been pounded into small bits and splashed with spices. As your dog sits on the asphalt pavement beneath the worn picnic tables out front, she will pray that you drop bits of your burger, chicken breast, Philly cheese steak, or salad. Call ahead on weekends to be sure it's open; the place is closed Sunday and closes early on Saturday. 1618 NW First Ave.; 352/374-9920.

The Swamp: This bar/eatery is right in the middle of the University of Florida action, and dogs are regularly seen at the outdoor tables. The food, which ranges from appetizers and sandwiches to full dinners, is a cut above tavern fare. Philly cheese steaks and the swamp bayou pasta (a chicken and pasta dish with a Creole sauce) are popular. 1642 W. University Ave.; 352/377-9267.

PLACES TO STAY

Baymont Inn & Suites: Newshounds sleep in designated pet rooms and keep up on the latest happenings with the free weekday newspaper at this pleasant chain motel off I-75 (Exit 384). Hungry pets can hope for doggy bags from the adjacent Cracker Barrel or the nearby Outback Steakhouse. Rooms run $80–160. Pet fee is $10 the first night, $5 daily thereafter. 3905 SW 43rd St., Gainesville; 352/376-0004; www.baymontinns.com.

Best Western Gateway Grand: This place calls itself Gainesville's most elegant and affordable full-service hotel, with its sundeck, pool, hot tub, and massage therapy in the fitness room. Dogs may be more interested in your left-overs from the on-site restaurant or other eateries near this pleasant, 152-room, three-story lodging off I-75 (Exit 390). Rates range $79–99. Pet fee is $15 daily. 4200 NW 97th Blvd., Gainesville; 352/331-3336; www.bestwestern.com.

Econo Lodge: Small dogs and their companions are permitted in smoking rooms at this poolside motel located about two miles east of I-75 (Exit 382). Rooms range $49–105. 2649 SW 13th St./U.S. 441, Gainesville; 352/373-7816; www.econolodge.com.

La Quinta: Among the amenities at this pleasant business-oriented motel are a fitness trail, an exercise room, and a heated pool, though your pooch may be more interested in sniffing for crumbs from your free continental breakfast. Small, short dogs—"below knee level," one staffer told us—are preferred at this 134-room, four-story lodging off I-75 (Exit 387). Rates run $75–90. 920 NW 69th Terrace, Gainesville; 352/332-6466; www.lq.com.

Motel 6: Set back from a major road, this 121-unit motel doesn't have an official dog walk, so head to the grassy swales off the side street or to the unde-veloped lot next door. Canine light sleepers might request Room 106, deep in the bosom of the pool area and sheltered from the interstate. Rates normally are $42–52 but rise during football weekends at this motel off I-75 (Exit 384). 4000 SW 40th Blvd., Gainesville; 352/373-1604; www.motel6.com.

Quality Inn: You can store a doggy bag in the in-room fridge, then heat it later in your microwave at this pleasant 88-room, two-story poolside motel located on a hill just west of I-75 (Exit 382). Small dogs are preferred. Rates normally run $70–85. 3455 SW Williston Rd., Gainesville; 352/378-2405; www.choicehotels.com.

Red Roof Inn: Hungry hounds can hope for doggy bags from nearby eateries—Bob Evans, Cracker Barrel, Outback Steakhouse, and Olive Gar-den, among others. One pet under 50 pounds may join you at this poolside motel off I-75 (Exit 384). Rates range $45–80. 3500 SW 42nd St., Gainesville; 352/336-3311; www.redroof.com.

Residence Inn: In these townhouse-style suites, dogs can stretch their legs by wandering from the kitchen to the living-room fireplace, then to the bedroom. People-pleasers include an exercise room, a whirlpool, an outdoor pool, laundry valet service, free continental breakfast, and in-room hair dryers and irons. Rates normally range $114–145. Add a flat $75 pet fee. 4001 SW 13th St./U.S. 441, Gainesville; 352/371-2101; http://marriott.com.

Keystone Heights

PARKS, BEACHES, AND RECREATION AREAS

18 Mike Roess Gold Head Branch State Park

🐾🐾🐾 (See Gainesville map on page 232)

Dogs can pretend that they've been sent back to the days of the Downing & Burlington—a narrow-gauge railroad—by walking down an old tram road once used for transporting logs and other freight. Better yet, the canine-pleasing Florida National Scenic Trail passes through here. Follow the car-width path and your lucky pooch may hear the soft clatter of a white-tailed deer as it darts through the mossy woods. Maggie just about went nuts trying to chase one—a good reason to keep your pooch leashed.

At this three-square-mile park, your dog can climb soft rolling hills that once were ancient sand dunes. That's right—the sea was much higher then. You're likely to have the place to yourself on weekdays, and it's always a relaxing spot to throw burgers on a grill for a picnic in pavilions or at tables scattered around the park. As fine as it is here, it's a howling shame that dogs aren't allowed on the beach or the Ravine Trail—the park's most fascinating hiking trail. Still, you and your buddy should enjoy looking for "cat faces"—long scars on old pine trees that can be traced back to the days when turpentine makers slashed open the trunks to obtain sap. Also, look up for woodpeckers flying onto the pointy tips of the bleached-white dead trees along the Florida Trail.

When we called to check recently, an employee said dogs are limited to the picnic areas and always have been. This didn't square with our experience though. Use your judgment.

The entrance fee is $3–4 per vehicle. From Keystone Heights, head six miles northeast on State Road 21. The park will be on the right at 6239 State Road 21. 352/473-4701.

19 Lowry Lake, Camp Blanding Wildlife Management Area

🐾🐾 (See Gainesville map on page 232)

This big lake has a certain no-frills charm. A swing—actually an old tire attached to a rope—dangles from a tree limb above the water, making it tempting to swing out and make a splash. (Don't let your pooch join in though—alligators live here!) Beneath a tree, a memorial marker honors the lake's namesake: Lieutenant General Sumter L. Lowry, decorated veteran of both world wars. We spotted raccoon footprints along the sandy road that doubles as a makeshift walking trail into the woods.

Expect no restrooms, no water fountains, no picnic tables—just a lake and some woods. You're likely to have the place to yourself, but dogs are supposed to be under restraint. (Hunting dogs must follow hunting rules.) It's not worth the long drive from Gainesville if you want a typical city-park experience. Still, solitude-seeking dogs and anglers like it.

From Keystone Heights, head north on Highway 21 for about three miles, watching for the green-and-yellow sign on your left that marks the entrance. (If you reach Gold Head Branch State Park on the right, you've gone too far.) Turn left into the wildlife management area. The road will turn to dirt, heading west, then it turns right and heads north. You'll pass the entrance to Magnolia Lake on your right; it's another mile or so to the entrance to Lowry Lake. 386/758-0525.

20 Magnolia Lake, Camp Blanding Wildlife Management Area

🐾🐾🐾 (See Gainesville map on page 232)

Soft sand seems to melt underfoot (or under paw) on the few tree-canopied sandy roads that double as make-do walking trails at this secluded, woodsy retreat. Even in hot months, a cooling breeze may waft from fairly small Magnolia Lake, making a walk beneath the moss-draped, arching oak limbs a pleasant experience. Along the way, you may spot bald eagles, red-cockaded woodpeckers, gopher tortoises, or one of the 75 species of butterflies that are among the threatened and endangered animals living here.

This place won't please big-city sensibilities, as it lacks restrooms, picnic tables, official walking trails, permissible camping, and even an asphalt parking lot. (Instead, park on the hardest sand you can find.) That doesn't stop some anglers from using the boat launch here to try for the daily limit of six channel catfish. And Maggie enjoyed trampling a carpet of dead leaves on the spongy forest floor.

It's a shame that with 55,195 acres in the wildlife management area, dogs are limited to this lake and the less-pretty Lowry Lake nearby.

From Keystone Heights, head north on Highway 21 for about three miles, watching for the green-and-yellow sign on your left that marks the entrance. (If you reach Gold Head Branch State Park on the right, you've gone too far.) Turn left into the wildlife management area. The road will turn to dirt, heading west, then turn left and head south. Look for the entrance to Magnolia Lake on your right. 386/758-0525.

Micanopy

PARKS, BEACHES, AND RECREATION AREAS

🐾1 Paynes Prairie State Preserve

🐾 (See Gainesville map on page 232)

Although people may rave about this 22,000-acre preserve, you won't hear a peep from your dog. Walking pooches must stick to the parking lot or the park's four or five miles of roads (shared with cars and the occasional pedestrian). They cannot set foot in the deep woods, swamps, ponds, wet prairies, and other stomping grounds of hawks, otters, and wild American bison. What a letdown. When you're in the area, a better alternative might be the Lochloosa Wildlife Conservation Area (see Parks, Beaches, and Recreation Areas in Cross Creek, below).

Admission is $3–4 per car. From Gainesville, head 10 miles south on U.S. 441 to the preserve. 352/466-3397.

PLACES TO STAY

Herlong Mansion: Pretty enough to host weddings and anniversary parties, this 1800s mid-Victorian mansion allows small dogs to sleep in a cottage called the Pump House, provided they're on Advantage or Frontline flea protection. While Spot isn't allowed to pass the impressive columns of the main house to gaze at its 10 fireplaces and romp amid antiques, the cottage should provide a cozy getaway with its queen-size bed, Jacuzzi tub, and robes. The mansion is a local landmark surrounded by oaks and pecan trees. For a dog walk, stroll one block to window-shop at antique stores. Tell your dog that the House of Hirsch Too Antiques, 209 NE Cholokka Blvd., was used to film the hospital scenes in the Michael J. Fox film *Doc Hollywood*. Rates range $139–159, and you must make advance arrangements to bring your pooch. 402 NE Cholokka Blvd., Micanopy; 352/466-3322 or 800/HER-LONG; www.herlong.com.

Chiefland

PARKS, BEACHES, AND RECREATION AREAS

🐾2 Clay Landings

🐾 (See Gainesville map on page 232)

It's simply a county boat ramp, but some locals let their pooches swim here—including a few Labrador retrievers seen having a blast during a high-water winter day. You're taking your chances, though: Alligators may be present.

From U.S. 98 at Chiefland, head nearly six miles west on Highway 320. About one-quarter mile shy of Manatee Springs State Park, turn right onto Clay Landing Road. Follow it about a mile to the road's end at the boat ramp. 352/493-6072.

🐾 Manatee Springs State Park

🐾🐾🐾 ◀▣ (See Gainesville map on page 232)

Only a canine Arnold Schwarzenegger wouldn't tire on the sandy 8.5-mile hiking/biking trail weaving through this three-square-mile park. Seeing the whiskery noses of lumbering manatees poke out of the water is the park's star attraction, but dogs are limited to the picnic area, boardwalk, and trails—meaning they can't get a close look at the springs that produce 117 million gallons of water daily. Still, after a long hike on shady trails, your leashed pal won't have a clue that he's missing out on anything.

Live oaks shade one of Florida's nicest campgrounds, where dogs may sleep at all 92 sites. A more rustic setting is enjoyed at the tent-only campsites in the Magnolia 1 camping loop, though all sites offer water, electricity, a grill, a table, and access to hot showers. Sites cost $17. Reserve up to 11 months ahead at ReserveAmerica.com or 800/326-3521.

Park admission is $4 per vehicle. From U.S. 98 at Chiefland, head six miles west on Highway 320 to the end of the road. 352/493-6072.

PLACES TO STAY

Best Western Suwannee Valley Inn: Once fortified by a free breakfast at this pleasant 60-room poolside motel, you can strike out for hike with your dog at Manatee Springs State Park. Rates range $79–109, plus $10 daily fee for a small pet. 1125 N. Young Blvd., Chiefland; 352/493-0663; www.bestwestern.com.

Holiday Inn Express: This pleasant two-story poolside motel offers humans a whirlpool and free breakfasts. Pooches can hope for a drive to the hiking trails at Manatee Springs State Park. Rates range $58–72. Pet fee is $15 nightly. 809 NW 21 Ave., Chiefland; 352/493-9400; www.holidayinns.com.

Manatee Springs State Park: See Parks, Beaches, and Recreation Areas, above, for camping information.

Cross Creek

Cross Creek is famous because of Marjorie Kinnan Rawlings, who wrote about all manner of animals and the people who populated this hamlet when she came here seeking refuge from big-city life in 1928. The town where Rawlings wrote her books, including *The Yearling* and *Cross Creek,* remains an oasis of greenery and calm.

PARKS, BEACHES, AND RECREATION AREAS

🐾 Lochloosa Wildlife Conservation Area

🐾🐾🐾 (See Gainesville map on page 232)

City dogs stuck at home all week will burn pent-up energy at this whopping 27,333-acre area. More than 10 miles of trails thread through this home of endangered or threatened animals, such as fox squirrels, wood storks, and sandhill cranes. Just about any outdoor activity can be enjoyed here, including hiking, bird-watching, fishing, horseback riding, boating, hunting (seasonally), and bicycling.

The trick is to first call ahead to make sure it's not hunting season. Next, bring everything you need, including equipment, food, and water. This rustic retreat has no restrooms or snack bars.

From its southern parking area on County Road 325, about three miles west of U.S. 301, a short walk leads to an observation deck for a view of Lochloosa Lake and surrounding wetlands. This conservation area is considered regionally significant for large populations of bald eagles, ospreys, and wetland-dependent wading birds.

For a long hike along the northern perimeter, try the Gainesville-Hawthorne State Trail shared by hikers, bicyclists, and horseback riders. You can pick up the east-west trail by parking at Lochloosa's northeastern parking area on County Road 2008, about 1.5 miles west of U.S. 301.

Enough trails crisscross these woods that your dog could return a few times and still be sniffing new territory on each visit. Call ahead for tips or stop at the information kiosk at the parking area near the Cross Creek fire station.

From Gainesville, take U.S. 441/13th Street south through Paynes Prairie State Preserve. In Micanopy, turn left on County Road 346, proceed for a bit, then turn right at County Road 325/Cross Creek Road. The entrance is on the left near the fire station, not far from the Marjorie Kinnan Rawlings State Historic Site. 386/329-4404.

25 Marjorie Kinnan Rawlings State Historic Site

🏛 ◀🐾 (See Gainesville map on page 232)

Because mallard ducks and game chickens run freely on the grounds of the Cracker-style house where in the 1930s Marjorie Kinnan Rawlings wrote *The Yearling*, dogs aren't exactly encouraged to visit. But dogs can tour the grounds. If you bring your pooch, please keep him leashed, asks a gracious employee of the restored historic home. Only well-behaved dogs who are small enough to carry in your arms have a shot at joining a tour of the interior of Rawlings' house. Oh, well, at least your dog can brag that he's been to the home of a woman who helped put the state on the literary map with her gifted portrayal of the Florida Cracker lifestyle.

Admission to the grounds is free; the tour costs $3 for adults, $2 for children ages 6 and older. Younger children may tour for free. From Gainesville, take U.S. 441/13th Street south through Paynes Prairie State Preserve. In Micanopy, turn left on County Road 346, proceed for a bit, then turn right at County Road 325/Cross Creek Road. The site is off County Road 325 at Cross Creek. 352/466-3672.

Bronson

PARKS, BEACHES, AND RECREATION AREAS

2 6 Goethe State Forest

🐾🐾 (See Gainesville map on page 232)

Go thee to Goethe! If your pooch pines for some serious fun in the fresh air, away from all your city cares, try these woodsy 53,000 acres. Leashed dogs can tromp through one of the state's largest remaining stands of longleaf pine flatwoods—-an ecosystem that once covered much of the South but now is reduced to a few meager pockets. Note that if your dog is a hunting breed, he may not be allowed during hunting season. Dates vary from year to year but fall mostly on weekends from late October to early December. The rest of the year you're likely to share more than 60 miles of backcountry paths and dirt roads with horse riders and backwoods cyclists.

Bring supplies, especially water, because no facilities are available.

There are two main sets of trails. To reach the trailhead for the Black Prong Trails, head south from Bronson about 10 miles on County Road 337. Turn right at Camp Road, a dirt road, and look for the trailhead on your right. To reach the Tidewater Trails, head south from Bronson on County Road 337 about 20 miles. Just before County Road 337 crosses County Road 336, turn left onto Saddle Pen Road. You'll see the trailhead soon. 352/465-8585.

Cedar Key

This charming fishing village off the Florida coast was once one of the most important towns in the state. (Back before they had roads, everyone got around by water.) By today's standards it's so small that your dog will have trouble finding a place to stretch his legs.

PARKS, BEACHES, AND RECREATION AREAS

2 7 Beach

🐾🐾🐾 (See Gainesville map on page 232)

With no grassy public expanses on the tiny island, the beach is the main place to take leashed pooches to stretch their legs—and dogs aren't complaining. Some people may be, however. A city hall worker expressed chagrin at seeing free-running dogs indiscriminately leaving calling cards and swimming around kids. Dogs are supposed to be leashed, and the matter will probably come to a head one day soon. The prospect of encouraging dogs to visit the island made this person so tight-lipped about the locales of dog parks that all we could get was, "We really don't have room for all of them."

The beach is on Second Street in downtown. 352/543-5600.

DIVERSIONS

See Cedar Key, see? Stop at the bright pink **Cedar Key Historical Society Museum** at 609 Second St. in Cedar Key to pick up a $4.50 walking-tour brochure. Then stroll the streets of this fishing town with your leashed buddy, taking in the fishing boats, the bustling waterfront street, and the historic buildings.

Alternatively, float your dog's boat as you show him Cedar Key's watery side from a four-passenger covered boat rented at the downtown **City Marina,** near the waterfront restaurants. The folks there will give you a map showing how to get to area islands (although dogs may not be welcome on some little-patrolled islets that are designated as part of the Cedar Key National Wildlife Refuge). Salty dogs will enjoy the watery spray whipping through their fur.

For a real treat, try your angler's luck by dropping a live shrimp over a grass bed at high tide, then watch the fun as your pooch contemplates a trout or redfish flopping around on the deck. For boat reservations, call Island Hopper at 352/543-5904. The historical museum is at the intersection of Second Street and Highway 24; 352/543-5549.

PLACES TO STAY

Old Fenimore Mills: Some condo owners in this pleasant downtown-area lodging alternative allow dogs in their vacation units. Dogs who stay here walk only one block to reach the surf and sand. Rates vary, with daily, weekly, and monthly rates available. Pet fee is a flat $10. 11 Old Mill Drive, Cedar Key; 352/543-9803.

Park Place Motel & Condominiums: Your dog can step onto a private balcony to scan the skies for birds flying over the nearby Gulf of Mexico. Rates run $70–90. Add $7 daily for your small pet. 211 Second St., Cedar Key; 352/543-5737 or 800/868-7963.

256

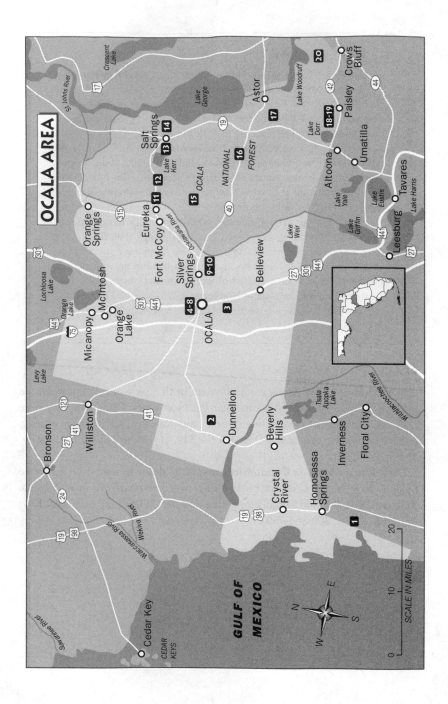

OCALA AREA

CHAPTER 9
Ocala Area

People in this part of Florida tend to turn their eyes north and west toward green hills dotted with horses. Known statewide for producing fine racehorses, the Ocala area is the state's answer to the bluegrass country of Kentucky.

Doggies, though, turn their snouts eastward, toward Ocala National Forest. It's green there, too, but in a shaggy dog kind of way. You could spend weeks in these nearly 600 square miles of national forest—hiking the Florida National Scenic Trail, canoeing the crystalline streams that flow from springs, plopping down to sleep at plentiful campgrounds in and around the forest, or dog-paddling in the watering hole at the Juniper Wayside Park.

Even if you have just one afternoon to explore the area, it's worth a small detour so your pooch can follow trails through lush oak hammocks and across pine-studded hills. This stretch of forest is one of the most dog-friendly in Florida.

One big drawback of the national forest is that two of its most popular recreation areas, Juniper Springs and Alexander Springs, allow dogs only in

PICK OF THE LITTER—OCALA AREA

BEST DOG PARK
Millennium Dog Park, Ocala (page 262)

BEST LODGING WITH A RESIDENT HORSE
Hilton Ocala, Ocala (page 265)

BEST WALK IN THE WOODS
Ocala National Forest, (page 269-275)

BEST HIKE INTO HISTORY
**Marjorie Harris Carr Cross Florida Greenway Hiking
Trails,** Ocala (page 261)

BEST CANOEING
Rainbow Springs State Park, Dunnellon (page 260)
Ocklawaha Canoe Outpost & Resort, Fort McCoy
(page 278)

their campgrounds, nowhere else. Similarly, pooches are barred from enjoying the privately owned Silver Springs, the area's largest tourist attraction,
which is located a few miles west of the national forest near Ocala. Still,
there are enough canoeing and hiking opportunities elsewhere to keep a
pooch busy.

If you're not camping and want a motel within jumping-off distance of the
forest, consider staying in Silver Springs, covered in this chapter, or Deland
(see the Daytona Beach chapter). Farther away, the city of Ocala has plenty of
lodging, as well as a popular leash-free park.

On the drive out to the national forest, you can regale your pooch with
tales of Samantha, a local rottweiler who grabbed her 15 minutes of fame
by saving the life of three-year-old Blake Weaver. The little boy and his
dog wandered away from their home and into the national forest one January afternoon; the boy was lost in the woods all night wearing only shorts
and a T-shirt. Authorities credited Samantha with keeping Blake warm
when the windchill factor dropped temperatures into the 30s. "Samantha
stayed with him all night, kept him warm, and more or less she's the one
who led him out of the woods," the boy's mother, Dawn Weaver, of Salt
Springs, told a reporter. Samantha was rewarded with a hard-won, rare-
cooked steak.

Chassahowitzka

PARKS, BEACHES, AND RECREATION AREAS

⓵ Chassahowitzka Wildlife Management Area

🐾🐾 (See Ocala map on page 256)

Wow. This 53-square-mile tract feels well off the beaten track, though it's really just off U.S. 19. It's been called the largest hardwood swamp along the Gulf coast south of the Suwannee River basin, and plenty of hiking trails and some boating opportunities are available for leashed pooches. To penetrate the tract, you'll follow an eight-mile driving loop through upland pinelands, transitional zones, and hardwood swamp, following roads with names like Gopher Road, Rattlesnake Camp Road, Swamp Grade, and Indigo Lane. Two short, marked hiking trails start near the Indigo Lane parking area and lead through flatwoods, sandhills, cypress domes, and scrub. A longer hike or bike ride along old tram roads leads through the hardwood swamp, home to woodpeckers, songbirds, and red-shouldered hawks.

Dogs who hope to glimpse manatees (occasionally seen here) can arrive via the southern entrance off State Road 50 and hike trails through scrub to an overlook at the Weeki Wachee River. Restrooms and picnic tables are found here. The best time to visit is mid-winter through spring, but avoid the place when hunters vie for deer and the area's few wild hogs, which usually happens from November to early January. Call ahead for hunt dates. These woods are part of a nearly unbroken string of public lands that stretches for 200 miles from the Apalachicola River to Pasco County. Bring mosquito repellent, food, and any supplies you'll need.

From I-75 (Exit 61), go west on State Road 50 to US 19. Turn right (north) and go about nine miles to the northern entrance, at left. Alternatively, reach the southern entrance at Weeki Wachee by going west on State Road 50. Pass U.S. 19 and continue west on what will now be called County Road 550 to the entrance, at left. 863/648-3203.

PLACES TO STAY

Chassahowitzka River Campground and Recreation Area: Rent a canoe with your leashed pooch for $15 for four hours, or just strike out from this tree-shaded 40-acre campground—a popular weekend destination—to explore nearby pooch-permissible Chassahowitzka Wildlife Management Area (see Parks, Beaches, and Recreation Areas, above). Quiet canine canoeists will see statuesque wading birds at streamside and possibly an otter while exploring four-mile-long Chassahowitzka River and its peaceful side streams. The 88 campsites are open to RVs or tents, and up to four leashed dogs are permitted per campsite. Bring proof of rabies vaccination. Sites range $15–22. From U.S.

19 in Chassahowitzka, turn west onto Miss Maggie Drive/County Road 480 and drive 1.8 miles to the county-run campground. 8600 W. Miss Maggie Dr., Homosassa; 352/382-2200.

Dunnellon

PARKS, BEACHES, AND RECREATION AREAS

2 Rainbow Springs State Park

😺 😺 (See Ocala map on page 256)

This place drew many a Florida visitor—a few with their dogs—in the early 20th century. If your inquiring doggy asks why, tell her that the park is home to Florida's third-largest spring. Unfortunately, pets are not permitted at the spring itself any longer. But the park is a fine place for a picnic with a pooch, and leashed dogs will appreciate following a 2.5-mile-long nature trail that winds beneath oaks and through sandhills to provide views of a river and phosphate pits. A separate brick/concrete pathway winds for 1.5 miles through another destination, the shady gardens, which bloom with pretty azaleas in February and March.

Dogs also may canoe along the gin-clear Rainbow River, designated by the state "An Outstanding Florida Waterway." Trees line the soft curves of the six-mile-long, spring-fed river, which some canoeists consider among Florida's clearest. Look for otters and ducks as you paddle leisurely, passing some homes and docks and plentiful trees. Just one rule, doggies: Don't jump into the river. "We have gators," summed up a ranger. Bring your own canoe, if you prefer, and be ready to carry it 1,000 feet to the launch. Canoe rentals at the separate park campground run $15 for one hour, $25 for two hours for two people and a dog, plus a $25 deposit. Inquire at 352/465-2100.

Admission is $1 per person age 6 and older. The main entrance to the 1,000-acre park is at 19158 SW 81st Place Rd., three miles north of town on the east side of U.S. 41. 352/465-8555.

PLACES TO STAY

Rainbow Springs State Park: Dogs may stay at these 93 campsites, which are found a few miles away from the state park's day-use area. Hot showers, bass fishing, and worthwhile canoeing are the main amenities. In the privacy-deprived grassy half of the campground (near the office), there are no trees, and a lot of people would just call it a field. So inquire about shady spots, if you prefer. Camping costs $20.62. Reservations are advised. From I-75 (Exit 352), go west on Highway 40 about 14 miles, then south three miles on Southwest 180th Avenue Road. 18185 SW 94th St., Dunnellon; 352/465-8550 or 800/326-3521 (reservations).

Ocala

The good news is that leashed dogs are allowed at all city parks, even those not listed below. When you're looking for a place for your dog to rest his weary body after all that exercise, you'll find most decent motels concentrated near I-75 or east of town in Silver Springs, which provides better access for day trips into Ocala National Forest (see Places to Stay in Silver Springs, below).

PARKS, BEACHES, AND RECREATION AREAS

🐾 Marjorie Harris Carr Cross Florida Greenway Hiking Trails

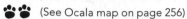 (See Ocala map on page 256)

Hikers certainly will be dog-tired after spending time on this green corridor stretching an astounding 110 miles. One sunny mile-long trail reaches I-75, where a land bridge landscaped with native plants lets hikers cross the highway and continue the westward trek. The trail continues for 2.4 miles through scrub and scattered longleaf pines to reach Southwest 49th Avenue. Whew. A pooch could get the idea he's walking across the state of Florida. Incidentally, he is.

This trail is a historic remnant from the days when the Great Communist Threat loomed off the Florida coast—a specter raised by the Soviet Union's increasingly friendly relations with Cuba. In those days, crack U.S. strategists determined that we should protect our barge traffic. Their answer: Gouge a huge waterway through the belly of Florida, à la the Panama Canal, and link the Atlantic Ocean to the Gulf of Mexico.

It was a dumb idea—federal pork of the highest order. (Pork? Maggie asks. Mmmmm.) Not only would the Cross Florida Barge Canal incredibly damage the Ocklawaha River and other natural areas, but the concept was slightly humorous, considering the long odds that tiny Cuba would attack American ships. Environmentalists stopped the project after a 16-mile section of river was dammed.

Today, dogs and human hikers benefit: They now can follow trails stretching from the Gulf of Mexico to the St. Johns River—exactly where the canal was intended to run. To see evidence of canal digging, hike between Southwest 49th Avenue and I-75. There, carved areas look like reforested small-scale valleys. Bring water.

To reach the 49th Avenue Trailhead, take Exit 341 of I-75. Head west on County Road 484 about 2.5 miles. Turn right onto Marion Oaks Trail. Turn right at Southwest 49th Avenue to the trailhead, at right. 352/236-7143.

🐾 Clyatt Park

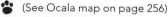 (See Ocala map on page 256)

Although almost covered by handball courts, tennis courts, and baseball fields, this spot of green has a small, heavily wooded area where leashed dogs can romp at its northwest corner. For a better alternative, you might want to

DIVERSIONS

Take a furry surrey: Here in the heart of horse country, a horse-drawn carriage ride underscores why this area of rolling hills is Florida's answer to the bluegrass country of Kentucky. You'll travel through working horse farms and see impressive animals up close: Thoroughbreds, Tennessee walkers, Paso Finos, and quarter horses, among others. You'll pass hundreds of horses, some trotting, playing, bobbing their heads.

Sometimes carriages leave from downtown Ocala Square, making for a nice ending to a meal at pooch-permissible eateries. **Ocala Carriage** may accept canine riders (preferably small dogs) after special accommodations are made—either a blanket will cover the seat so the dog's nails won't make a hole, or the pooch will sit on the floor between his human companions. At reservation time, be sure to say that you'd like your pet to join you instead of showing up with a furry surprise. A good idea: Test your buddy beforehand—if he goes ballistic at the mere sight of a horse as you pass by in a car, then this diversion definitely isn't for him. If he is blasé, then great. Don't forget the camera.

"We've taken a bunch of little dogs and a couple of big dogs," says Andrew, who co-owns Ocala Carriage. "Most of them have been pretty good." Reserve at 877/996-2252 or 352/867-8717.

head across the street to Robert Ritterhoff Rotary Park (see below). Both are on Southeast 17th Street next to 14th Avenue. 352/351-6696.

5 Downtown Ocala Square

 (See Ocala map on page 256)

This square-block park has benches, some shade trees, and a gazebo where old pooches can plop down and sit a spell. Your leashed buddy can also accompany you on a stroll along the perimeter sidewalk to walk off a calorie-laden dessert enjoyed at the nearby pet-permissible eateries or to take in the sights on the town square, including a building that has stood here since 1885.

The city park is at the southeast corner of Silver Springs Boulevard/State Road 40 and Magnolia Avenue. Park on Broadway, the street south of the park that runs parallel to State Road 40. 352/351-6696.

6 Millennium Dog Park

(See Ocala map on page 256)

Leash, be gone! Dogs can run as fast and far as they want to stretch their strong legs at this fenced, five-acre, broad grassy field—bigger than many paw parks in Florida. A separate three-quarter acre fenced area with lots of trees caters to small pets. Between the two parks is open space with memorial bricks honoring hounds who've departed to the great Doghouse in the Sky.

Onlookers sit at plentiful benches, some beneath a pavilion. Pets slurp fresh running water from watering stations. It's such a pretty place that some people actually show up without dogs. It has become a place where people make and rekindle friendships. Park president Letty Towles was touched when a caller offered thanks for what the park means to her retired mother: "The park has given her somewhere to go, to look forward to."

A veteran dog trainer, Towles in 1998 had homeless dogs on her mind when she approached the city with the idea of building Ocala's first dog park and opening it on the first day of the new millennium. So many dogs end up in shelters due to barking and other behavior problems caused by lack of exercise and socialization; she wanted dogs without yards to have a place to run freely.

People started calling it the Millennium Dog Park project. Kids sent $1 donations toward fences, a pavilion, the property lease. Pet Supermarket, the biggest donor, gave $4,000. Due to red tape and other delays, the park opened in November 2003. But the New Millennium name stuck.

Entrance is free, though donations are accepted. You must show proof of up-to-date vaccinations. The dog park is at 2513 SE 32nd Ave., at the corner of Southeast 24th Street and Southeast 34th Avenue. It abuts the southern end of Jervy Gannt Park. 352/351-6696.

🐾 Robert F. Ritterhoff Rotary Park

😺 (See Ocala map on page 256)

Paws here a while and let your dog watch the ducks and swans swimming in the small pond next to busy 17th Street. Locals come here to eat lunch or just while away the hours with a sweetie (furry and otherwise). The ducks are definitely the highlight, but you should keep your dog leashed so she doesn't ruffle too many feathers. When the thrill of the ducks wears off, your buddy can take advantage of a small grassy field or a picnic table shaded from the sun. Kids will appreciate the playground.

The park is on Southeast 17th Street near 14th Avenue. 352/351-6696.

🐾 Tuscawilla Park

😺 (See Ocala map on page 256)

A lake in the southwest portion of this city park is home to alligators, so make sure your leashed dog doesn't plunge in. Also shoehorned onto the property are an American Legion post, tennis courts, racquetball courts, basketball courts, the Tuscawilla Arts Center, the City Auditorium, the armory, and a pool. Whew! We wish they'd left more room for doggies to stretch their legs.

The park is in a neighborhood of aging homes mixed with some light industry. From the main drag (Silver Springs Boulevard/State Road 40), head north a few blocks on Watula Avenue to Northeast Third Street and the park entrance. The park is at 300-899 NE Sanchez Avenue. 352/351-6696.

PLACES TO EAT

Checkers: Eat 99-cent burgers and other fast-food fare at distinctive outdoor tables topped with red umbrellas. For hungry hounds in a hurry, there are twin drive-throughs. 1239 E. Silver Springs Blvd.; 352/351-1199. Other locations are at 2701 SW College Rd., 352/237-0071, and 8585 SW Highway 200, 352/873-4760.

Harry's Seafood Bar and Grill: Cajun, seafood, and grilled eats are the favorites at this hip place at the downtown square. The jambalaya is popular for good reason, but don't give any to your pooch—too spicy! Better to stick to the oyster po' boys, doggies. You'll sit at umbrella-shaded tables out front. 24 SE First Ave.; 352/840-0900.

Hops Restaurant and Brewery: The Jamaican top sirloin steak—marinated in pineapple, soy, and ginger—is a popular choice at this chain microbrewery/eatery, where your dog may join you outdoors. Burgers, loaded nachos, meatloaf, chicken tenders, and grilled shrimp number among the other menu items. Oh, so does freshly brewed beer. 2505 SW College Rd.; 352/237-8182.

Juicy Lucy's: Hamburgers are the specialty at this fast-food joint, but hungry hounds can sniff out chicken sandwiches, polish sausages, hot dogs, and more. Sit at umbrella-covered picnic tables outside or use the drive-through window. 101 SW 60th Ave.; 352/873-2660.

Lee's Famous Recipe Chicken: Order your chicken fried, pressure-cooked, roasted, or skinless at this drive-through eatery. For a side dish, choose from the 14 vegetables or salads. 2303 E. Silver Springs Blvd.; 352/732-7981.

O'Malley's Alley: The lunch menu at this decidedly casual watering hole/live boxing venue on the downtown square features a garden club salad and a few sandwiches, including three chicken sandwiches—chicken breast, chicken fingers, or chicken salad. Your dog may join you at the outdoor tables and hope for bites of your sandwich. 24 S. Magnolia Ave.; 352/690-2262.

Reno's Grille: One-pound sirloin steaks, spicy ribs, and appetizers such as bacon-wrapped shrimp are served up at this Southwest-inspired eatery on the downtown square. Your leashed, well-mannered pal may join you at the outdoor tables. 30 S. Magnolia Ave.; 352/402-0097.

PLACES TO STAY

Budget Host: Watch HBO with your pooch in a designated pet room at this modest 21-unit poolside motel, found two blocks west of I-75 (Exit 354). Rates range $45–75, including continental breakfast. Add a $10 nightly pet fee. 4013 NW Blitchton Rd., Ocala; 352/732-6940; www.budgethost.com.

Comfort Inn Ocala: When asked whether the motel has a size limit for pets, a staffer said no, adding, "that would be like saying someone can't stay

DOG-EAR YOUR CALENDAR

Holidays mean howling fun at Ocala's Millennium Dog Park, starting with the **Easter Dog Hop** pet parade. Pooches wear their versions of Easter bonnets, such as rabbit ears or flouncy veils, though a four-legged joker named Vinny once won honors for his formal top hat with a baby chick perched on top.

Dogtoberfest means it's time to think up a cute costume—you know, like the grass hula skirt once worn by an Australian shepherd. Judges for the annual Dogtoberfest costume contest include a K-9 officer, so you know there's no funny business.

At **Canine Christmas at the Park,** Santa arrives for pet photo sessions and may slip on sunglasses for sunny shoots, underscoring just how balmy Christmas is in Ocala, compared to the North Pole. Park president/professional dog trainer Letty Towles sniffs out still other fun Fido events to raise money for maintaining or improving her brainchild, the city's first dog park; they include the Dog Park Dog Walk. For the date of the next event, get the scuttlebutt at Millennium Dog Park, located at the corner of Southeast 24th Street and Southeast 34th Avenue, or go to www.millenniumdogpark.com.

If your bearded collie misses the bearded man from the North during his single day at the dog park, then take her to see Santa during holiday weekends at PETsMART, 3500 SW College Rd., Ocala; 352/237-0700.

here because their child is too fat." Amen. Continental breakfast is free, and some whirlpool suites are offered at this 134-unit poolside motel just west of I-75 (Exit 352). Rates run $65–150, plus $5 daily per pet. 4040 W. Silver Springs Blvd., Ocala; 352/629-8850; www.comfortinn.com.

Days Inn Ocala: A playground area and shuffleboard set this poolside motel apart. Checkout time is noon—good for sleepy shepherds. Rates range $60–125, including a limited hot breakfast at its on-site restaurant off I-75 (Exit 354). 3811 NW Bonnie Heath Blvd./Blitchton Rd., Ocala; 352/629-7041; www.daysinn.com.

Days Inn Ocala West: Each room has a balcony, so your canine companion can scan the night skies for its brightest light, the Dog Star. A sizable field for a pit stop is found at the northeast corner of the 100-unit poolside motel off I-75 (Exit 352). Rooms cost $53–95. Add $10 daily per dog. 3620 W. Silver Springs Blvd., Ocala; 352/629-0091; www.daysinn.com.

Hilton Ocala: Set on six acres, this full-service high-rise hotel with a marble-tile lobby stands out. Two lighted tennis courts, beach volleyball, horseshoes, a fitness room, and a fine-dining restaurant are offered at the 193-room lodging. Emphasizing its horse-country location, the place offers sunset rides in a white

Victorian carriage pulled by Buddy, a Clydesdale. From the outdoor heated pool and hot tub, you might see thoroughbreds tossing back their heads. Leashed pets may walk in the paddock (the open field out back). The gift shop has been known to offer doggy gift baskets. Rates range $79–208. 3600 SW 36 Ave., Ocala; 352/854-1400 or 877/602-4023; www.hiltonocala.com.

Howard Johnson Inn: King can reserve a king room or save his money for dog treats and choose a regular room at this 125-unit, three-story poolside motel off I-75 (Exit 354). Miniature golf sets the place apart. A fitness facility and whirlpool also are offered. Rooms range $41–200. Add $10 nightly per pet. 3951 NW Bonnie Heath Blvd./Blitchton Rd., Ocala; 352/629-7021; www.hojoocala.com.

La Quinta Ocala Inn and Suites: Dog-tired travelers might opt for a takeout order from the adjacent Chili's restaurant or one of the dozen other eateries within a quarter mile of this pleasant, six-story, 117-unit motel. People-pleasers include a workout room, pool, spa, and a sundeck area in a landscaped courtyard. A pet smaller than 25 pounds may join you in one of the designated sixth-floor rooms. Rates run $79–110. 3530 SW 36th Ave., Ocala; 352/861-1137; www.lq.com.

Ocala/Silver Springs KOA Kampground: Sleep in a cabin or beneath oaks and magnolias in your RV or tent. At this 20-acre wooded campground, dogs are likely to perk up around the two duck ponds while people appreciate the pool, hot tub, sauna, shuffleboard court, volleyball net, rental bikes, camping kitchen, and TV lounge. It's convenient to I-75 (Exit 350) but not very close to Ocala National Forest. Cabins range $62–72. RV sites run $41–55; tent sites $35–44. Reservations are accepted. 3200 SW 38th Ave., Ocala; 352/237-2138 or 800/562-7798; www.koakampgrounds.com.

Quality Inn: A fitness room and a cocktail lounge with big-screen TV are offered at this two-story, 269-room motel just east of I-75 (Exit 352). Your companion can stretch her legs along a small grassy strip. The fair-sized landscaped courtyard—which overlooks the pool—is only for emergencies. Rates range $53–100. Add $20 per stay for the pooch. 3621 W. Silver Springs Blvd., Ocala; 352/629-0381; www.choicehotels.com.

Steinbrenner's Ramada Inn & Conference Center: At one of the nicer pooch-permissible places in these parts, pets can hope for a room service order of bacon or maybe a doggy bag from the on-site Pinstripe Bar & Grill. People-pleasers include live entertainment in a lounge decorated with New York Yankees memorabilia, a fitness center, a playground, and a heated pool. Rates range $70–140 at this 124-unit lodging off I-75 (Exit 354). Add a flat $25 for your pet weighing 50 pounds or less. 3810 NW Bonnie Heath Blvd./NW Blitchton Rd., Ocala; 352/732-3131 or 800/715-1070; www.ocalaramadaatsteinbrenners.com.

Super 8: Morning cereal and coffee cakes are free, but your pooch may pine for bacon from the Denny's or Waffle House across the street from this 96-room poolside motel off I-75 (Exit 352). Rates run $65–115, plus a $5 nightly pet fee. 3924 W. Silver Springs Blvd., Ocala; 352/629-8794; www.super8.com.

Silver Springs

Tarzan's signature yell rang through here long ago. Actually, it was actor Johnny Weissmuller shooting *Tarzan Finds a Son*. And he was hardly the first to set foot here. In prehistoric times, people hunted the mastodons that drank from the 23 million gallons of crystal-clear water that gush hourly from a 780-square-foot cavern known as Silver Springs—Florida's original tourist attraction. More recent visitors have included Thomas Edison, Henry Ford, and Harvey Firestone.

The tourism business really got booming when a huckster from the Buffalo, New York, area showed up in the 1930s and decided to import Asian rhesus monkeys. Colonel Tooey (his real name was Colonel) had it all figured out: He had an island dredged in the middle of the Silver River, just downstream from the springs. There he would exhibit the monkeys to tourists, who would pay for boat rides to the island. He built a special house that only the monkeys could enter to protect them from bobcats, panthers, and other native predators. When the big day arrived, Tooey had a box filled with monkeys lugged out to the island amid great fanfare. The box was opened, and Tooey immediately discovered that he should have done a little more research: Rhesus monkeys can swim.

Swim they did, to the north and south banks of the river. All these years later, descendants of those first monkeys still live in nearby woods and have split into three separate bands. Should you encounter them—most likely at Silver River State Park—do not go near them. Some may carry herpes B, a potentially fatal simian virus that can be transmitted to people. We walked freely and happily through the woods here, though, knowing that the monkeys generally fear people and keep their distance, and they rarely bite unless cornered. (Besides, herpes B is common only in monkeys used for research purposes.) Do not feed the monkeys; it encourages them to approach people. And keep your pooch away from them, too. State records reveal that in a few instances the monkeys have attacked dogs, though supporters of the simians—a cause célébre among locals—dismiss these tales as overblown.

Alas, doggies are not welcome in the Silver Springs Natural Theme Park tourist attraction, though park kennels are available. Instead, we recommend heading a few miles east to the natural splendors of Ocala National Forest or taking a hike at nearby Silver River State Park.

PARKS, BEACHES, AND RECREATION AREAS

🐾 Marshall Swamp Scenic Hiking Trail

🐾🐾 (See Ocala map on page 256)

Eat a packed lunch at picnic tables after following a .6-mile-long interpretive loop trail around a seasonal pond. If that's not enough, burn off more of your leashed pal's pent-up energy by continuing on from the pond to follow a sort of zigzag course southwesterly through hardwood swamp. The three miles of gravel trail end at a parking area at Southwest 64th Avenue in Silver Springs Shores. There, another trail begins—this time, a paved five-mile multi-loop trail shared by pedestrians, cyclists, in-line skaters, and wheelchairs. It leads farther southwest through former pastures that are being returned to pinelands, and it ends at Baseline Road/Highway 35, just north of State Road 464.

Of course, a short walk around a pond will do for many a pooch. No matter what distance you travel, the entire time you'll be enjoying a portion of the Marjorie Harris Carr Cross Florida Greenway. This system of trails follows a course once intended to become a canal that would slice the entire state of Florida into two (see Marjorie Harris Carr Cross Florida Greenway Hiking Trails in Ocala, above).

Fill a pet water bowl at restrooms by the parking area. Picnic tables also are found by the trailhead. Marshall Swamp is best enjoyed during the dry season, when mosquitoes aren't an issue.

From I-75 (Exit 352), go east a little over seven miles on State Road 40/Silver Springs Boulevard to State Road 35/Baseline Road. Turn right; continue to the next stoplight. Turn left onto Highway 314 and continue about two miles to the trailhead, at right. If you prefer the paved trail through former pasture, start at the Baseline Road Trailhead found on Baseline Road/Highway 35, a quarter-mile north of State Road 464. 352/236-7143 or 850/245-2052.

10 Silver River State Park

🐾🐾🐾 (See Ocala map on page 256)

Maggie was excited as we wheeled into this park alongside the Silver River, just downstream from Silver Springs Natural Theme Park. From the parking area at the end of the entrance road (by the Silver River Museum and Nature Center), a winding foot trail leads east beneath sabal palms and shiny-leaved magnolias before connecting with a car-width trail. Maggie strained at her leash here in

anticipation of meeting up with the animals whose scent she had picked up. We also saw groups of schoolchildren, who stopped to pet Maggie and ask us about the sock on her foot (she was recovering from leg surgery on this trip).

Much of the trail will leave your leashed pooch exposed to the sun, so on hotter days you may not want to go all the way to the Silver River—a round-trip jaunt of more than a mile. If you do reach the river, you'll be rewarded with the sight of huge fish swimming under the blue-tinted, crystalline surface. Keep an eye out for otters, particularly early or late in the day. Keep the other eye peeled for alligators. After your hike, stop for a snack at the covered picnic shelter. In all, the park offers about 15 miles of trails and paths for cycling or hiking.

Dog-tired visitors may sleep in the 59-site campground, where sites are arranged along four loops and cost $21. Each offers water and electricity for RVs, a picnic table, grill, and fire ring, plus nearby showers. Reserve at ReserveAmerica.com or 800/326-3521.

Admission is $4 per carload. From State Road 40/Silver Springs Boulevard, head south on State Road 35 (also known as 58th Avenue or Baseline Road). Go about 1.2 miles to the park, at left. 352/236-7148.

PLACES TO STAY

Days Inn: In front of this 56-unit poolside motel, there is a bit of room for your dog to walk around near the silver statue of a horse rearing up on its hind legs. Kids may like the playground. Rooms cost $50–89. Add $10 nightly per pet. 5001 E. Silver Springs Blvd./State Road 40, Silver Springs; 352/236-2891; www.daysinn.com.

Econo Lodge: This two-story poolside motel has an economy-sized stretch of green in the front courtyard where you can walk your dog (under 30 pounds). Rates run $53–99, plus a $10 nightly pet fee. 5331 E. Silver Springs Blvd./State Road 40, Silver Springs; 352/236-2383; www.econolodge.com.

Sun Plaza Motel: Collier County's Emergency Management agency keeps this basic, 47-room poolside motel on its Rolodex as a place that accepts pets during a hurricane. The one-story motel is near pooch-permissible Silver River State Park, just 1.2 miles south from here on County Road 35. Rates run $55–75. Add a $10 nightly pet fee. 5461 E. Silver Springs Blvd./State Road 40, Silver Springs; 352/236-2343.

Ocala National Forest

Ahhhh. This nearly 600-square-mile forest is one of the most dog-friendly wooded areas in the state and is well worth the drive if you're in the vicinity of Orlando or Daytona Beach. If you're howling down I-75 toward Disney World or points south, Maggie highly recommends that you slow your pace around Ocala, jump on State Road 40, and head east to Ocala National Forest.

A favorite stop for canine swimmers Earnhardt and Roxy of Palm Beach County is the watering hole found at Juniper Wayside Park on Highway 19, four miles north of U.S. 40, basically between Juniper Springs and Salt Springs. "They had a blast there—clean, knee-high water and no gators to be seen," reports their chauffeur, Ellen Markwood. "It doesn't get much better than that."

PARKS, BEACHES, AND RECREATION AREAS

🐾🐾 East Eureka Dam & Boat Ramp

🐾🐾🐾 (See Ocala map on page 256)

These woods in the Eureka/Fort McCoy area are bound to soothe your frazzled buddy's nerves after a long car ride—and they'll leave a bit more at peace, too. Maggie was in heaven, sniffing the ground furiously. She spooked a deer and refused to leave when it was time to go.

This is a primitive area, so bring water, mosquito repellent, and any supplies. Depending on the weather, you may hit pockets of water; also watch for vines on the ground that can trip up your leashed dog.

To start your tour, drive east from Fort McCoy and across the Ocklawaha River on County Road 316. Turn right onto the access road on the south side of the street, following a sign that directs you to the East Eureka Boat Ramp. Double back and head west toward the riverbank, then drive through what was intended to be a deep boat channel when the Cross Florida Barge Canal was designated to go through here. If you follow the road all the way down, you'll come to the East Eureka Boat Ramp area, where you'll see the meandering Ocklawaha River. Look for deer and wild turkeys at dusk.

For a higher, drier, sunnier visit, drive to nearby hills. When you cross the river heading east on County Road 316, continue past the sign on the right that directs you to the boat ramp. Look to the left for an unmarked road known as River Road. Take that left. As you proceed up the road, take the next left. This road leads along hills overlooking the Ocklawaha River floodplain. Drive far enough and you'll see the huge, unused lock and dam that was intended to become part of a cross-state canal. Roads and trails crisscross the sands of these reddish white hills. Park on a roadside. 352/236-0288.

🐾🐾 Florida National Scenic Trail/Eureka

🐾🐾 (See Ocala map on page 256)

Cutting from one end of the forest to the other in a southeast-northwest direction, this sandy portion of the 67-mile-long Florida National Scenic Trail is covered with pine needles and follows orange blazes painted on pine trees and turkey oaks. You're high above the world here, up where water percolates down quickly through the sand hills. Your leashed pooch will have to hunt hard to find good shade, and the terrain is neither lush nor particularly green. Those spindly puffs of vegetation you'll see on the forest floor are wire grass, one of the few plants these sandy hills will support.

FETCHING NECESSITIES

Retrieve a tree: For a new family experience, take the family dog with you to fetch a fresh holiday tree from the **Ocala National Forest.** An antidote to high-price store-bought firs, a permit to cut down your own Florida-grown tree costs a mere $7. It'll be a sand pine, which is wispy, not bushy. But, heck, add strings of lights and ornaments of bears, gators, and horses for a novel yule tree, Sunshine State–style. Besides, an old dog eventually realizes that the best part about holidays is making memories together, not searching stores for the perfect tree. Perfect *treats*, sure. But not perfect trees. For permit details, call 352/625-2520 or 352/236-0288.

This is primitive country, and you'll need to bring all the necessities. Water is most important, followed by food, mosquito repellent, and rain gear. You can walk as far as your pooch's condition will permit, but remember to take it easy on a hot day. And keep checking her paws for sandburs. If she starts limping, stop immediately and use your fingers to pull out the pea-sized spiked balls. If you plan to spend several days backpacking with your leashed dog, get trail advice from the Florida Trail Association at 800/343-1882.

The trailhead is on County Road 316, immediately west of Forest Service Road 88 (3.5 miles east of Highway 301). You can head north or south on the trail. If you go north about 1.5 miles, you can camp at Grassy Pond Campground (see Places to Stay, below), also accessible via Forest Service Road 88, just north of Highway 316. 352/625-2520 or 352/236-0288.

Florida National Scenic Trail/Salt Springs

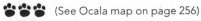 (See Ocala map on page 256)

Sun-dappled pinelands and palmetto habitat line the hiking trail here. On hotter days, shadier portions of the Florida National Scenic Trail are found at the Juniper Prairie Wilderness and Alexander Springs. In this location, your leashed pal can lead you on the trail either north or south from County Road 314, about a quarter mile west of its intersection with Forest Service Road 88. For backpacking advice, call the Florida Trail Association at 800/343-1882. For general information, contact the forest service. 352/625-2520 or 352/669-3153.

Salt Springs Observation Trail

(See Ocala map on page 256)

This three-foot-wide dirt path dips and winds its way for one mile to an observation platform on the Salt Springs Run, the river that carries water from Salt Springs into Lake George. Your leashed pooch will pad through sand pine scrub, slash pine flatwoods, bayheads, cypress, and clusters of oaks with branches that sometimes hang low enough to knock a basketball player in the head. Luckily, no dogs we know are taller than three feet.

Nature-loving dogs should be on the lookout for deer and raccoons at dusk or dawn. Remember that on the return one-mile-long walk, you'll be hiking uphill. We recommend that you rest up by picnicking at the observation platform. There, you'll likely see herons and alligators.

We encountered a hunter along this trail. As you hike, you should make some noise to ensure that hunters don't mistake you or your dog for deer, particularly if you visit in the cooler months.

From the south end of Salt Springs, head southeast on Highway 19. (Don't take County Road 314, which veers off to the right.) After about three-quarters of a mile, look for a sign on your left directing you to the trailhead parking lot. 352/236-0288 or 352/669-3153.

15 Lake Eaton Sinkhole and Loop Trails

🐾🐾🐾 (See Ocala map on page 256)

Let's say your pooch is not exactly in the kind of shape Lassie was when she forded mighty rivers, climbed mountains, and performed her famous can't-you-see-I'm-barking-to-tell-you-there's-something-wrong routine. But let's also say he wants to see the Real Florida up close and personal—away from other four-legged friends. If so, Lake Eaton, with its honeycomb of uncrowded trails not far off the main road, is for you.

The offbeat Sinkhole Trail leads leashed pooches through palmetto and down steps into an 80-foot-deep, 450-foot-wide dry sinkhole where oaks and dogwoods thrive. Three routes lead to the rim of the sinkhole, which can be viewed from an observation deck.

For a traditional walk in the woods, hit the Lake Eaton Loop Trail. Padding over mulch and sand, you'll set off down the hill toward Lake Eaton, passing through various natural communities, including an unusually dry xeric hammock and the very wet upland lake margin. Fire is a key factor in the evolution of this place, killing some trees and sparing others. Look for odd, dwarfed oaks and pointy palmettos. (Also watch for exposed roots that could trip you or injure your dog.)

Maggie was reluctant to turn back when we visited. A better alternative—on a cooler day—is to not turn around at all. You can follow the two-plus-mile loop and find yourself back at the car.

Both trails share a parking area near Grahamsville. From Silver Springs, head east on State Road 40. When you get to the first major intersection inside the national forest, turn left (north) onto County Road 314. Head northeast for about 3.5 miles, turn right (south) onto Forest Service Road 86, then south (right) onto Forest Service Road 79, another limerock road. Soon you'll come to the parking area. 352/236-0288 or 352/669-3153.

16 Florida National Scenic Trail/Juniper Prairie Wilderness

🐾🐾🐾 (See Ocala map on page 256)

Juniper Springs Recreation Area is probably the most popular place in the forest. Alas, dogs are forbidden in the swimming areas and on its nature trails; they must stay back at the campsite (see Places to Stay, below). A great injustice, Maggie observes.

However, leashed doggies can tread where few visitors bother to go, and they shall be all the richer for the experience. They can hike the Florida National Scenic Trail north into the Juniper Prairie Wilderness from near the Juniper Springs parking area. If you're backpacking, head about three miles up the trail to where it crosses Juniper Creek for a pleasant place to camp.

For a shorter but still beautiful day hike, park where the Florida Trail crosses State Road 40, about a mile east of the entrance to Juniper Springs, and head south. Hop over small logs that block the narrow, shady path, passing through several oak hammocks and crossing a slough on a small footbridge within the first mile. Maggie walked energetically, sniffing the ground in the hopes of finding animals. You could camp back here, perhaps 100 yards south of State Road 40, at the campsite just before you reach the wooden footbridge.

Dogs should take the footbridge slowly because there are gaps between the boards. Carry small dogs across, but be careful not to lose your balance. For advice about backpacking in this area, reach the Florida Trail Association at 800/343-1882.

The trail crosses State Road 40 about a mile east of the Juniper Springs Recreation Area, 26701 E. State Road 40, Silver Springs. If you're heading north on the trail, park at the recreation area; fee is $4 per person. If you're heading south, park free alongside State Road 40 by the trailhead sign about a mile east of the Juniper Springs entrance. 352/625-3147 or 352/236-0288.

17 Alexander Springs

🐾🐾 (See Ocala map on page 256)

Maggie whimpered at the sight of a wild baby hog scampering into the woods from the roadway leading to this popular recreation area. Yes, that does sound tempting to adventurous dogs, but pooches aren't allowed in the picnic areas or the springs that churn out 80 million gallons of crystal-clear water every day. In fact, dogs are pretty much restricted to the parking lot and campsites, although they're free to wander into the woods surrounding the recreation area.

The best part about the 67-site campground is that it's across the street from some decent hiking trails that pass through sandy, sunny hills. In the campground, Rover is limited to roving around the four paved road loops. Consisting of mostly pine-tree dotted open spaces, this campground offers less privacy than many other forest campgrounds and attracts more RVs than tents, though there are no full-hookup sites. Campsites cost $19 and come with a picnic table, grill, and fire ring, plus access to hot showers, canoe rentals, and a small convenience store. Book a site at ReserveUSA.com or 877/444-6777.

Admission for day-use is $4 per person. From I-75 take Highway 40 east through Ocala and Silver Springs for about 40 miles to Highway 19. Go south on Highway 19 about five miles to County Road 445. Turn east on County Road 445; continue five miles to the entrance at 49525 County Road 445, Altoona. 352/669-3522.

18 Clearwater Lake Recreation Area

🐾🐾🐾 (See Ocala map on page 256)

Look for deer or raccoons across the hill in the morning as you follow part of the national forest's 67-mile stretch of Florida National Scenic Trail, which passes through here. It's a pretty hike, best at dusk or dawn but always pleasant.

The trailhead is located alongside the road leading into the pet-permissible campground, also known as the Clearwater Recreation Area. Dogs here bed down beneath oaks whose branches are twisted into unusual shapes. A natural swimming lake delights people, though furry swimmers are forbidden. Some of the 42 shaded sites have concrete pull-ins for RVs. Set along two loop roads, all sites offer a picnic table, grill, and fire ring—but no electricity. Creature comforts are limited to hot showers, flush toilets, a dump station, and ice and firewood for sale. Bears and raccoons may pass through, so food must be stored in animal-proof containers. Sites cost $13.32 and can be reserved at ReserveUSA.com or 877/444-6777.

Bring water, food, and any supplies. A small convenience store is less than three miles away in Paisley. If you plan to spend several days in the outback with your leashed dog, get trail advice and help planning your backpacking trip from the Florida Trail Association at 800/343-1882.

Day-use fee is $3 per person. From the Intersección of Florida Highway 19 and Highway 42 at Altoona, go east on Highway 42 (toward Paisley) about six miles to the entrance, at left. 352/669-0078.

19 Paisley Woods Bicycle Trail

🐾🐾 (See Ocala map on page 256)

Much more open and less shaded than the nearby Florida National Scenic Trail, this 22-mile rugged dirt pathway through oaks, pines, and sun-washed grassy prairies is intended for those of the two-wheeled persuasion. Tell your leashed pooch to stay out of the way of bikes. Shaped like a figure eight, the trail essentially forms two loops. Double back at a comfortable distance. Bring lots of water.

The trailhead is alongside the road into the national forest's Clearwater Lake Recreation Area, where the day-use fee is $3 per person. From the Intersection of Florida Highway 19 and Highway 42 at Altoona, go east on Highway 42 (toward Paisley) about six miles to the Clearwater Lake entrance. 352/669-0078 or 352/236-0288.

20 St. Francis Interpretive Trail

😺 😺 😺 😺 🐾 (See Ocala map on page 256)

In the little-used southeastern portion of the national forest, near Orlando and Daytona Beach, there's a true gem of a trail. Here your leashed pooch will pick his way through lush hammocks and cross makeshift wooden bridges spanning small creeks. The array of Florida ecosystems that your four-legged friend can experience is impressive—riverine swamp, pine flatwoods, oak hammock, and open flatwoods. Look for red-tailed hawks.

If your pooch is up to a 8.5-mile historical adventure—a feat that should never be attempted on a hot day—consider a hike to the site of the old town of St. Francis. Over a century ago, this was a bustling timber and citrus port. The St. Johns River then was akin to today's Florida's Turnpike, and steamboats came through here laden with clothes and other goods bound for settlements farther south. Eventually, railroads took over the freight business and St. Francis became a ghost town. Today, wilderness reigns again. Still, traces of the early settlement remain, including a levee built to flood an area where rice could be grown. The trail—marked by blue blazes painted onto tree trunks— may be too much for inexperienced hiking dogs.

A shorter walk will please many a pooch. A small offshoot trail leads to a natural spring and back to the main trail, allowing hikers to see the spring and return to the car with much less wear and tear. Bring lots of water for either hike.

The trail is in an area called Crows Bluff. From Altoona, take County Road 42 east, turn left (north) onto Forest Service Road 542, and look for signs. From Deland, take Highway 44 west, turn right onto County Road 42, then right almost immediately onto Forest Service Road 542 and look for signs. 352/236-0288 or 352/669-3153.

PLACES TO EAT

Roger's Bar-B-Que: Roger's is home to some of the best barbecue around, though its claim of serving the "best barbecue in the South" is pushing the point a tad far. The baked beans, coleslaw, and pork sandwich are particularly good. There is no outdoor seating, so you must get food to go for a picnic with that special pup at nearby Lake Eaton. (Instead of doggy bags, Roger's gives out piggy bags.) This restaurant is in the same shopping center as the visitors center for the national forest, so it's a convenient place to stop for food and maps to help you get the lay of the land. It's just east of the Ocklawaha River, near the western boundary of the national forest. 10863 E. State Road 40, Silver Springs; 352/625-2020.

PLACES TO STAY

Alexander Springs: See Parks, Beaches, and Recreation Areas, above, for camping information.

Buck Lake/National Forest Campground: Easily reached by car, this 50-person campground on the Florida National Scenic Trail is used by backpackers and hunters. Camping is primitive—only a hand-pump provides water—but the site will do if you can't get into the more modern campgrounds at Juniper Springs or Alexander Springs recreation areas. There's also something to be said for the solitude you're likely to enjoy here in western Ocala National Forest. Sites are first come, first served. Fee is $5 nightly. From Umatilla, drive 13 miles north on Highway 19, turn left on Forest Service Road 595, and go about 2.5 miles to the campground at left. 352/236-0288.

Farles Lake/National Forest Campground: This 75-person campground in southwestern Ocala National Forest is next to a lake and a wet prairie. Better yet for dogs, it's on the Florida National Scenic Trail. Hike seven miles north, and you'll be at Juniper Springs. Camping is primitive—with chemical toilets and hand-pumped drinking water—but it will do if you can't get into the more modern campground at Alexander Springs. Sites are first come, first served. Fee is $5 nightly. You may share the place with hunters in winter, and a U.S. Naval Bombing Range lies a couple miles west. From Umatilla, go north on Highway 19 for 13 miles. Turn left on Forest Service Road 535, which will jog south into Forest Service Road 595. The campground is ahead. 352/236-0288.

Fore Lake/National Forest Campground: A 250-foot beach on Fore Lake attracts swimmers (sorry, no dogs). Anglers may drop lines from a fishing pier on the 77-acre lake. All 31 first-come, first-served campsites have picnic tables, fire rings, and access to restrooms and a pay phone. Fee is $10 nightly. From Ocala, go east about 12 miles on State Road 40, then north (left) on County Road 314 for about six miles to the entrance. 352/236-0288.

Juniper Springs Recreation Area/National Forest Campground: Natural springs that pump out 13 million gallons of water daily are the attraction for human swimmers at this popular 79-unit campground in central Ocala National Forest. Dogs can't swim, but they may sleep here and follow the nearby Florida National Scenic Trail. Hot showers, an amphitheater, a laundry facility, a dump station, and a lot of privacy in a peaceful setting help set this camping area apart. Canoe rentals and a small convenience store are available. All sites have a picnic table, fire ring, and grill, but none has full hookups. Rates are $16.28–18.45. From Ocala, drive east on State Road 40 about 28 miles to the entrance at left. 352/625-3147 or 877/444-6777 (reservations).

Kerr City Cottages: Art Brennan's houses and cottages on the northeast shore of Lake Kerr appear on the National Register of Historic Places. Brennan actually owns the entire town of Kerr City—what's left of it—including the 1925 Texaco station, which he calls Florida's oldest Texaco. People deserted Marion County's second-oldest town by 1895 due to crop-killing freezes, but Brennan's kin stayed and gradually bought up some of the ghost

town. Now, your dog may sleep in renovated original homes. Guests may borrow rowboats to take their dogs out on Lake Kerr, where some folks fish and swim. Watch out for gators should your pooch fall into the drink. Rates are $95 nightly or $400 for six nights. Pet fee is $20 "or bring a flea bomb," Brennan says. The cottages are on County Road 316, three miles west of Highway 19 (Salt Springs). 22850 E. Highway 316, Kerr City; 352/685-2557.

Lake Dorr/National Forest Campground: Anglers, canoeists, and boaters use nearby Lake Dorr, and four-legged hikers can pick up the Florida National Scenic Trail a few miles up Highway 19 at Alexander Springs. This place offers more amenities than some alternatives—restrooms, warm showers, picnic tables, and two boat ramps. Still, this small, not-so-scenic spot is our least favorite campground in the national forest, though we did see a man going for a walk with two happy-looking hounds. Watch out for rattlesnakes in the saw palmetto. Sites are first come, first served and cost $8. From Deland, go west on County Road 42 for 24 miles to Highway 19, turn right, and continue three miles to the entrance. 352/236-0288.

Lake Eaton/National Forest Campground: Set on the southern end of Lake Eaton, these 14 primitive campsites in western Ocala National Forest are a short drive away from the pooch-permissible Lake Eaton Sinkhole and Loop Trails (see Parks, Beaches, and Recreation Areas, above). Amenities include picnic tables, fire rings, vault toilets, a fishing pier, and a boat ramp, but last we checked the water was unreliable so you'll need to bring your own. Sites are first come, first served. Fee is $6 for a single site, $8 for a double. From Silver Springs, go east 12 miles on State Road 40, turn north (left) onto County Road 314A, then east (right) onto Forest Service Road 95. After about .5 mile, turn left onto Forest Service Road 96A. The camping area is about one mile ahead. 352/236-0288.

Ocklawaha Canoe Outpost & Resort: Sure, friendly pets are invited to these cabins and campsites. In fact, a proprietor told us, "I don't stay anywhere my dog can't go." A monkey and a potbellied pig have camped here, just as many regulars have been brought here by their dogs. If your spoiled pooch gets tired of the competition, the two of you can take a rental canoe onto the Ochlawaha River and look for critters on the heavily tree-shaded banks. Cabins cost $89–129, plus $10 nightly per pet. A separate $50 pet deposit is refunded, barring doggy damage. Tent sites at this seven-acre shady retreat on the Ocklawaha River are $16.50. RV sites are $21.50. Reservations are advised. The campground is on County Road 316 at the Ocklawaha River. 15260 NE 152nd Place, Fort McCoy; 352/236-4606 or 866/236-4606; www.outpostresort.com.

Salt Springs/National Forest Campground: Warm showers and the chance to swim in the Salt Springs (sorry, no dogs) attract campers to this 160-site campground found in a forest of pine, mixed hardwoods, and oaks in northeastern Ocala National Forest. You'll enjoy more amenities than at most forest campgrounds, including restrooms, a boat ramp, limited groceries, nearby laundry facilities, picnic tables, fire rings, and grills. A concession stand is open in warmer months. This campground is convenient to the hound-hospitable Salt Springs Trail (see Parks, Beaches, and Recreation Areas, above). Rates are $14 for tent sites, $20 for RV sites with full hookups. The recreation area is on State Road 19 near the junction of County Road 316. 14152 State Road 19 North, Salt Springs; 352/685-2048 or 877/444-6777 (reservations).

CENTRAL FLORIDA

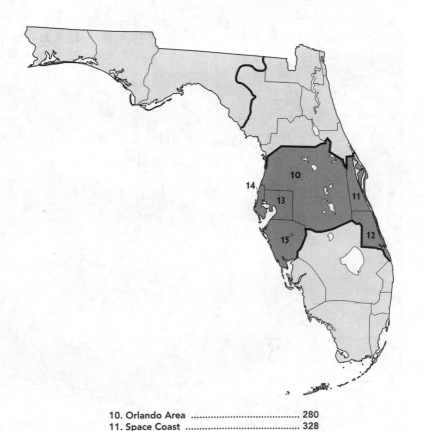

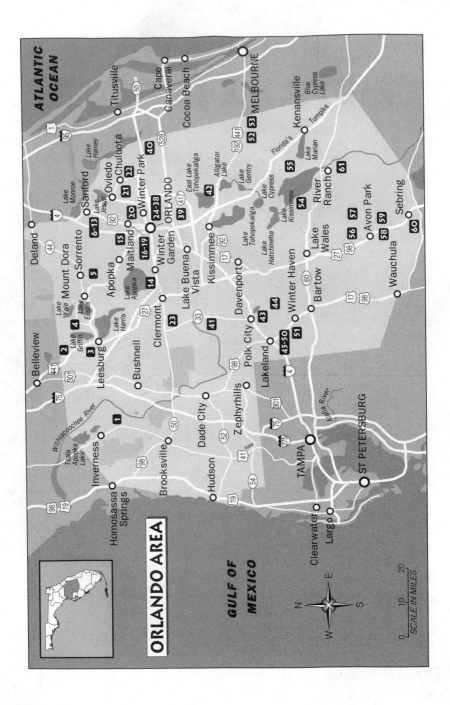

ORLANDO AREA

CHAPTER 10
Orlando Area

Mickey Mouse certainly comes to the minds of those who visit the world's number one vacation destination, but pooches think of the rodent with the high-pitched voice in slang terms—as in, "Boy, for dogs, this is a Mickey Mouse town." As long as you stay near Disney World, Sea World, and Universal Studios, this is a lousy place for the canine set.

Even though people have arranged Cinderella weddings complete with stagecoaches at Disney World, fairy-tale endings aren't extended to those with tails. That's true at any of the region's six main amusement parks. Though they rank among the nation's top 10 in visitor numbers, you'll have to put your pup in an on-site kennel if you want to visit Sea World, Universal Studios, or any of Disney World's four parks.

Still, you absolutely can have fun here with your pooch—as long as you strike out from the theme parks. How many times can you stand to hear mechanical children sing "It's a Small World," anyway? Instead, canoe in Orlando's near-pristine streams. Eat at sidewalk tables. Hike through lush oak hammocks and prairies of pine and palmetto—not to mention along the

PICK OF THE LITTER—ORLANDO AREA

MOST POPULAR DOG PARKS
Paw Park of Historic Sanford, Sanford (page 290)
Downey Dog Park, Winter Park (page 295)

MOST SCENIC PARK FOR AN OFF-LEASH WALK
Fleet Peeples Park at Lake Baldwin, Winter Park
(page 295)

WORLD'S BEST HOTELS
Westin Grand Bohemian, Orlando (page 309)
Portofino Bay Hotel at Universal Orlando, Orlando
(page 308)

MOST OFFBEAT HIKE
Avon Park Air Force Bombing Range, Avon Park (page 323)

banks of the Kissimmee River. This is where you'll find out that Florida's only major inland city and its environs are great for dogs.

Inverness

PARKS, BEACHES, AND RECREATION AREAS

🟦 Fort Cooper State Park

🐾🐾 (See Orlando map on page 280)

Soldiers in the Second Seminole War had to leave behind the family—and the family hound. It's too bad, because the pooches would have loved sniffing around the forts that protected soldiers from hostile Indians, as today's pooches do with this partial reproduction of the original Fort Cooper.

Hounds can also enjoy hiking on three miles of nature trails near the shores of spring-fed Lake Holothikaha. The trails pass through swamps and marshy areas as well as hardwood hammocks.

The walking paths used to stretch some 10 miles, but state biologists cut that back to give a breather to colonies of the gopher tortoise, whose numbers are dwindling. Because of this, you won't pass through as many sandhill/scrub–type communities as in the past. Still, it's a nice, long, tiring walk for all but the friskiest dog.

Entrance costs $2 per carload. The park is at 3100 S. Old Floral City Road.

From Inverness, head south on U.S. 41 for about a mile, turn left onto Eden Drive, then turn right onto Old Florida City Road. Continue 1.1 mile to the park. 352/726-0315.

Lady Lake

PARKS, BEACHES, AND RECREATION AREAS

🐾 Lady Lake Dog Park

🐕 (See Orlando map on page 280)

Every morning at 6:45, a black Lab named Kelli starts to hound her human companion, as if to say, "It's time to go to the dog park!" That's because Kelli accompanies her owner, Noreen Stein, to open Lady Lake's sole dog park for the morning.

Run by volunteers, the park basically is a fenced grassy open field measuring a little over an acre. It's divided into one section for dogs under 22 pounds and a bigger fenced area for bigger pooches to chase plentiful park-provided balls and toys. Water dishes quench thirsts. On hot days, dogs can plunge into a kiddie pool to cool off, as Kelli recommends. "She loves the water and playing ball. Her life is chasing a ball and bringing it back," says Noreen, president of the Lady Lake Dog Park Association. "She loves the park. They all do."

Two shelters provide human companions a place to sit at picnic tables and chairs while avoiding the hot sun.

The paw park is open 7 A.M.–noon daily, so it's visited mainly by retirees on weekdays and working folks on weekends. Admission is $5 weekly, $30 for six months, or $50 for one year. Lifetime membership costs $150. Find it at the Rolling Acres Sports Complex on Rolling Acres Road, between U.S. 441 and Highway 466. 352/751-1507 or 352/751-1500.

PLACES TO EAT

TCBY Treats: Lots of tables beneath a big overhang await people and pooches with a hankering for frozen yogurt or hand-dipped ice cream. 1000 Bichara Blvd.; 352/750-0010.

PLACES TO STAY

Holiday Inn Express: Cocker spaniels and other dogs under 40 pounds may walk along interior corridors to sleep at this pleasant three-story lodging. Rates start at $80. Pet fee is $35 per stay. 1205 Avenida Central N., Lady Lake; 352/750-3888; www.holidayinns.com.

Microtel Inn & Suites Lady Lake: Jack Russell terriers may stay here, but dogs over 20 pounds are turned away from these 80 guest rooms and suites. Rates range $61–85. Add $25 per pet. 850 U.S. 27/441, Lady Lake; 352/259-0184; www.microtelinn.com

Fruitland Park

PARKS, BEACHES, AND RECREATION AREAS

🖪 Lake Griffin State Park

🐾 (See Orlando map on page 280)

Maggie longed to chase a scrawny squirrel she saw dashing into the palmetto understory of this heavily wooded 460-acre park on the west side of Lake Griffin. The place is filled with oaks, and lucky pooches who visit can do leg lifts onto the state's fifth-largest live oak tree, standing 150 feet tall.

Enjoy a walk on a short nature trail before plopping down for a picnic or a night's sleep in the 40-site wooded campground, which features a boat ramp, picnic area, and warm showers. Fee is $16.65. Reserve at ReserveAmerica.com or 800/326-3521.

Beware, Labs: Alligators linger in Lake Griffin (although state scientists have been studying them because they seem to be having some trouble reproducing). Swimming is forbidden everywhere in the park, whether you're of the canine or human persuasion.

Admission is $4 a carload. From Leesburg, drive about two miles north on U.S. 441/27. The park is on the right side of the road at 3089 U.S. 441/27. 352/360-6760.

PLACES TO STAY

Lake Griffin State Park: See Parks, Beaches, and Recreation Areas, above, for camping information.

Leesburg

PARKS, BEACHES, AND RECREATION AREAS

🖪 Emeralda Marsh Conservation Area

🐾🐾🐾 (See Orlando map on page 280)

Unlike the state park located on the other side of Lake Griffin, this tract is the answer to a high-energy doggy's prayers. The St. Johns River Water Management District has purchased and set aside these 10 square miles to help restore the headwaters of the Ocklawaha River. But a by-product is a great place to go walking and wildlife-watching for you and your pooch. Migratory birds are often seen here, including a large population of sandhill cranes, as well as ducks, wading birds, and other waterfowl.

The hiking trails skirt the sides of big man-made lakes and marshy areas between Lake Griffin and Lake Yale. Take care to stay a good ways away from the water's edge, as alligators are common. The water district warns that these lakes and wetlands "support one of the highest alligator production areas in central Florida." Stay near your dog and a healthy distance away from the water. (Carrying a sturdy walking stick isn't a bad idea, either.)

Warning No. 2: There are no facilities, so bring everything you will need, including water, toilet paper, food, and mosquito repellent. If you come during the cooler months from November to January, hunting season may be in effect. We'd recommend calling ahead to find out whether you and your pooch need to wear orange-blaze clothing for protection.

To reach the conservation area, head east from Leesburg on U.S. 441. Turn north (left) onto Highway 44, then left again onto Lisbon Road after about three miles. At the end of Lisbon Road, turn left onto Goose Prairie Road, which leads to the parking area. 352/821-2066 or 386/329-4404.

PLACES TO EAT

A&B Hot Dogs: Dogs can get dogs (or even Italian sausage) if they sit at the garden tables outside this white, no-frills lunch spot. Or buzz through the drive-through and take the goodies north to pooch-permissible Lake Griffin State Park in Fruitland Park for a ready-made picnic. 1322 N. 14th St., at U.S. 441/27; 352/315-0995.

PLACES TO STAY

Guesthouse International: Newshounds can keep up on the latest events with the free weekday paper and cable news channels at this 13-unit, two-story hotel at the junction of U.S. 441 and U.S. 27. A fitness room, a heated outdoor pool, and a lounge entertain humans. Rates range $59–130. Add $15 per stay for a small pet, $25 for a large dog. 1308 N. 14th St., Leesburg; 352/787-3534; www.guesthouseintl.com.

Super 8 Motel: Once fortified by your complimentary continental breakfast, your pet hopes for a hike at Emeralda Marsh Conservation Area or at Lake Griffin State Park, about three miles away (see Parks, Beaches, and Recreation Areas in Fruitland Park, above). Afterward, he may hope for a doggy bag from the Sonny's Real Pit BBQ near this 52-room poolside motel, found at the junction of U.S. 441 and U.S. 27. Rates range $50–100. 1392 North Blvd. W., Leesburg; 352/787-6363; www.super8.com.

Tavares

PLACES TO STAY

The Inn on the Green: About a dozen of the 77 rooms here are designated to accommodate traveling pets, but only those weighing 50 pounds or less. Rates are $58–79. The hotel is on U.S. 441. 700 East Burleigh Boulevard, Tavares, FL 32778; 352/343-6373 or 800/935-2935.

Sorrento

PARKS, BEACHES, AND RECREATION AREAS

5 Rock Springs Run State Reserve

🐾🐾🐾 (See Orlando map on page 280)

In this canine equivalent of Disney World, very little of the nearly 14-square-mile wilderness seems accessible by automobile, which makes the foot trails and horse trails irresistible to furry forest fans. We spotted deer tracks and raccoon prints while hiking on Shell Mound Road. A lucky leashed dog might sniff the tracks of the secretive Florida black bear (we didn't see any).

If one can judge how much fun a place is by a dog's unwillingness to turn back, then this remote landing site of scrub jays and sandhill cranes ranks high with Maggie. Compared to the lushness of nearby Wekiwa Springs State Park (see Parks, Beaches, and Recreation Areas in Apopka, below), this sunnier park isn't necessarily breathtaking—with its sparse-limbed pine trees and understory of pointy-bladed palmetto bushes. But people and dogs will enjoy keeping an eye out for animal tracks. A lot of open sky hangs over sandy Shell Mound Road; in summer, opt for shadier Wekiwa Springs State Park.

The entrance fee is $2, on the honor-pay system. Rock Springs Run State Reserve borders more than 12 miles of the Wekiva River and Rock Springs Run. There is foot access to both. From Sorrento, take Highway 46 east. The entrance is on the right, just short of where the road is raised to let bears pass underneath. 407/884-2008.

DIVERSIONS

Pig out with Piglet: Piglet is a retired racing greyhound who brings her owners, Edson and Carla Pereira, to work with her at her dog bakery in historic downtown Mount Dora, called **Piglet's Pantry.** Inspiration for the bakery came from her very sensitive stomach. "I started cooking for her and then I started baking for her," explains Edson.

Today the trio cranks out treats, including dog-enticing "pizza pies," liver bites, half-pound bones, carob biscuits, and—the best seller—peanut butter cookies. They even can accommodate wheat-sensitive pups. Piglet now has two greyhound sisters: Tigger and Kricket. A Dog on Duty sign posted on the front door lets people know who is working each day. (Two dogs stay home to watch TV while one comes to work). Carla says that 10 percent of the shop's profits are donated to Greyhound Adoptions of Florida to help retired racers find loving families. 400 N. Donnelly St., Mount Dora; 352/735-9779.

Sanford

PARKS, BEACHES, AND RECREATION AREAS

6 Centennial Park

😊 (See Orlando map on page 280)

This square-block park with a gazebo, moss-draped oaks, and sabal palms gives your leashed pooch a chance to pad along brick-paved sidewalks in a charming section of town featuring well-tended homes. It's a picturesque spot, often used for weddings. Doggies can take their pick from several dozen trees to sniff, mostly at the perimeter.

The park is on Park Avenue between West Fourth and West Fifth streets. 407/330-5687.

7 Fort Mellon Park

😊 😊 (See Orlando map on page 280)

On the shores of Lake Monroe, this green spot is large for a city park. It also has the most amenities of any park in town: picnic tables, barbecue grills, lighted softball fields, lighted shuffleboard courts, horseshoe pits, basketball courts, lighted tennis courts, a playground, and a mile-long fitness trail to keep your leashed pup in shape.

Fort Mellon Park is located in Sanford at East First Street and San Juan Avenue. 407/330-5687.

8 Lake Jesup Conservation Area

😊 😊 😊 (See Orlando map on page 280)

When your pooch trots into these remote open fields, she's likely to think, "Hmmm—this looks like an old cow pasture." Here's news for her: It may still be!

When we last visited, this easy-on-the-eyes green spot was still pastureland, complete with cows that tend to stick together in one corner or another. They're allowed to stay here by the property owner, the St. Johns River Water Management District, which sometimes permits low-impact agriculture to continue on conservation lands. Without the cows, this easily would be a four-paw experience. Eagles, ospreys, hawks, and alligators may be seen here, along with other birds and mammals. Maggie was quite impressed.

These 5.36 square miles are divided into three areas around Lake Jesup. The North Lake Jesup tract—home to cows—comprises nearly two square miles. The slightly larger Marl Bed Flats tract to the southwest mainly contains wet prairie grasslands that extend from the lake's northern bank to thick woods in an area called Caldwell's Field. A third area, East Lake Jesup tract, is on the southern bank of the lake and features a two-mile-long loop trail with a lakeside observation tower. Hiking is best there and at North Lake Jesup, though bird-watchers may be rewarded near the southern lakeshore of Marl Bed Flats.

Your canine companion will need to be amenable to working her way around any bovines who still tromp across North Jesup. She will have to step over cow poop and put up with uneven footing on the cow paths that lead back to the lake. Also watch out for fire ant mounds. Bring food, water, insect repellent, and anything else you might need, as this conservation area is far from any facilities. Technically, dogs are supposed to remain leashed.

To reach North Lake Jesup from U.S. 17/92 in Sanford, go east on State Road 46 about 3.5 miles to Cameron Avenue, where you'll turn right (south) and continue two miles to the parking area. To reach Marl Bed Flats from U.S. 17/92 in Sanford, go east on State Road 46 about one-half mile to Sanford Avenue/State Road 425, where you'll go right (south) for nearly three miles to Pine Way Road. Turn left onto Pine Way, then right after a mile at South Mellonville Avenue, then left a short distance later at Oakway Lane. The parking area is ahead. To reach East Lake Jesup, take U.S. 17/92 south from Sanford about five miles and head east on Highway 434/Florida Avenue. Go about eight miles and turn left (north) onto Elm Street. The trailhead is about two miles ahead on the left. 407/897-4311.

🆚 Lake Monroe Conservation Area

🐾🐾🐾🐾 (See Orlando map on page 280)

Follow a three-mile-long loop trail from the southern parking area to the St. Johns River and your leashed pooch will be traversing terrain where Native Americans once hunted and fished. Look for sandhill cranes, turkey, and deer as you explore this floodplain—marsh, wet prairie, and floodplain swamp—protecting Lake Monroe.

Even if your pooch is too pooped to hike all the way to the St. Johns River—a one-way distance of about 1.5 miles—you still can let her stretch her legs in the big field by the northernmost parking area. This open space offers perhaps 10 acres, directly next to the road.

Ninety-four percent of these 11.5 square miles are classified as wetlands. Here your pooch will have a chance of spying eagles, ospreys, and the inevitable alligators. No swimming for Sam here! This wide-open space can be used by horses and their riders, so if your pooch normally clashes with his hooved cousins, consider skipping this stop.

Also skip this place in the hottest months. Even in the coolest times, bring water, food, mosquito repellent, a hat, and anything else you'll need, as there are no facilities. Technically, dogs are supposed to remain leashed in this remote area.

From Sanford, head east about 4.5 miles on Highway 415 to the parking area, at right. To reach the northern parking area, continue east on Highway

415 another half-mile to Reed Ellis Road. Turn north (left) to the parking area .9 mile ahead. 407/893-3127 or 909/329-4404.

🔟 Little-Big Econ State Forest

🐾🐾🐾 (See Orlando map on page 280)

A good ways east of Sanford, this forest is way out in the country. Bisected by a blackwater stream called the Econlockhatchee River, these 4,600 acres offer the adventurous pooch the opportunity to walk and walk, and then walk some more. On a cool day your leashed dog may want to go the whole 2.1 miles up to the Econ railroad bridge, along an abandoned railroad track that has been turned into a hiking trail. Maggie sniffed the dead, curly grass intently, apparently convinced that furry creatures lurked nearby. Keep an eye out for waterfowl, wading birds, deer, turkeys, eagles, hawks, ospreys, and sandhill cranes. Opt for a shorter walk in the woods on a warmer day.

Camping with your pooch is permitted here, and it's free. It's primitive-style camping, though, so bring absolutely everything you'll need, including water.

From Sanford, take Highway 46 east for 13 miles and turn right (south) onto Highway 426. About four miles down, turn left on Barr Road and continue to the entrance. Look for the green-and-yellow sign for the Florida Department of Agriculture and Consumer Services Division of Forestry, and turn left into the parking area. Another entrance to the area is reached by taking Highway 46 east and turning south onto Highway 426, as described above, but then veering left off Highway 426 onto Snow Hill Road less than a mile south of Highway 46. Take Snow Hill Road south another two miles to the first trailhead (which you may share with horseback riders), or go three miles to the second trailhead (which you may share with mountain bikers). 407/897-4311.

1️⃣1️⃣ Lower Wekiva River State Preserve

🐾🐾🐾 (See Orlando map on page 280)

Amid the widely spaced pines and sparse oaks that grow in these seven square miles of sandy rolling hills, a dog can see far in all directions. He'll appreciate that, because otters, bears, and other secretive critters traipse through here.

Don't expect your walk to turn into a big workout: The loop Sandhill Nature Trail leads past a sinkhole and gopher apple trees, providing an easy 50-minute walk—less if your leashed dog decides she's in a hurry. If she sniffs around marker No. 4 of the interpretive trail early in the morning, she may notice a pocket gopher turning up fresh, moist ground (don't let her bother it). At marker No. 8, a dog who looks up may notice a fox squirrel nest in the crook of three branches of an oak tree. The longtime nest is obvious in winter.

You'll never get far enough from the road here that you won't hear cars going by. Still, the park is a fine rustic stop-off point if you happen to be in the area. With no picnic tables or concession stands, no access to the river, and no chance of swimming (this is alligator country), your dog's sole activity is hiking. You might want to skip this sparsely shaded park on a hot summer day.

From Sanford, drive nine miles west on Highway 46. The park is at 8300 West Highway 46. 407/884-2008.

12 Memorial Park

😊😊 (See Orlando map on page 280)

At this fun destination for anyone staying in town, Maggie pined to chase a great blue heron wading in Lake Monroe. The park amounts to a palm-dotted grassy strip, perhaps 15 feet wide, extending a long, long way along the lake's shoreline. A peninsula of about one acre, marked by a flagpole, juts into the water. Take a seat at a waterfront bench to enjoy the breeze and soon your pooch will be itching for a waterfront walk.

The lakefront park is across from the modern-looking city hall at West Seminole Boulevard and Park Avenue. 407/330-5687.

13 Paw Park of Historic Sanford

😊😊😊😊🐾 (See Orlando map on page 280)

Run, Spot, run! That's the point of this two-acre fenced area, where dogs run freely like so many four-legged outfielders. Bordering Sanford's historic downtown district, this park made history of its own with its 2001 opening—marking the first official dog park in Central Florida. These two acres are renowned. Lots of dogs of all sizes show up on weekends to take advantage of separate running areas for small pets and big dogs. People chat at tables and benches in an oak-shaded park setting (though 2004's Hurricane Charley walloped some trees).

This piece of land became a city park way back in 1886. Recently, the park had been frequented mostly by druggies, so the city closed it—then, with the urging of the citizen's group Friends of Paw Park, reopened it as a revitalized wheelchair-accessible dog park. As highlighted in *Landscape Architecture* magazine, the park features dog showers, self-watering bowls, a time-out area for pets who need to chill out, and historic lighting.

The park—formerly Jaycee Park—is at 427 French Ave., off U.S. 17/92, between 3rd and 4th avenues. 407/330-5688.

PLACES TO STAY

Best Western Marina Hotel and Conference Center: From your room's window, you can show your dog a view of the lake or marina. Arrive by boat or car to stay at this 96-room lodging, featuring a restaurant, a lounge, a pool, exercise facilities, and an on-call physician. Rates are $69–90, plus a $20-per-stay pet fee. 530 North Palmetto Ave., Sanford; 407/323-1910; www.bestwestern.com.

Days Inn: Kindly put your Do Not Disturb sign on the door if you plan to step out to use the on-site coin laundry or grab food while your dog stays in the room during housekeeping hours. At this 119-unit poolside motel, rates are $50–105. Pets are $5 nightly. 4650 State Road 46, Sanford; 407/323-6500; www.daysinn.com.

Little-Big Econ State Forest: See Parks, Beaches, and Recreation Areas, above, for camping information.

Super 8: Dog-tired travelers can retrieve takeout orders from the nearby Outback Steakhouse or Cracker Barrel before retiring at one of four pet-permissible smoking rooms at this 104-unit poolside motel. Rates are $55–85, including local calls. 4750 State Road 46 West, Sanford; 407/323-3445; www.super8.com.

Winter Garden

PARKS, BEACHES, AND RECREATION AREAS

🐾🐾🐾🐾 West Orange Dog Park and Trail

🐾🐾🐾🐾🐕 (See Orlando map on page 280)

The two plastic fire hydrants are a funny touch at this off-leash park, which might only rate three paws except that it comes complete with a walking trail next door. The dog park itself is separated into two sections, each with a drinking fountain. Opened in late 2003, the park is well used and sometimes gets a little crowded. Each of the sections—one intended for small dogs, the other for big pooches—comes with a time-out area for participants who get a little too rowdy. Really energetic dogs can also partake of a doggie obstacle course.

Outside the dog park, the focus here is doing exactly what dogs love—walking. Your leashed buddy is bound to share the asphalt trail with cyclists, joggers, and in-line skaters as you follow the scenic former railroad corridor. The trail stretches 17 miles to link downtown Apopka, Ocoee, Winter Garden, and Lake County, and if that's not enough for your pooch, he can take a spur trail and lengthen the distance to 20 miles. Hungry? Eat a bag lunch at a picnic table after your walk. Doggie bowls are found all along the trail.

The trail's Winter Garden entrance is near the intersection of Dillard Street and Highway 438. The dog park's address is 150 Windermere Rd., but this is the easiest way to get there: From West Colonial Drive, head south on Beulah Road, by the gas station. Turn left onto Marshall Farm Road. It's up ahead about a quarter-mile on the right.

Apopka

PARKS, BEACHES, AND RECREATION AREAS

15 Wekiwa Springs State Park

🐾🐾🐾 (See Orlando map on page 280)

At this 12.5-square-mile jewel, dogs may picnic, camp, and follow fun the fun Sand Lake Trail, which informally tests a dog's IQ by seeing how he reacts to a couple of obstacles. Quick: A fallen tree blocks the trail. Will your leashed dog decide to climb over or under the tree trunk—or instead give up and turn back? Maggie did the limbo to get under the trunk, her body scraping the ground. Quick: Which way to cross a four- to six-foot stretch of river, by straddling along two four-by-four planks of wood or, as Maggie chose, just plowing right through the fairly shallow river? What will your dog do? Be ready to carry a small dog over the bridge. Apparently disliking the experience of wading through nearly shoulder-high water, Maggie allowed us to carry her across the bridge on the trip back.

Bring water, snacks, and mosquito repellent for a hike along the 13.5-mile Sand Lake Trail. You can make the walk as short or long as you'd like; at the trailhead, a sign details several options. The East-West Cross Trail segment is almost a mile long. Scattered pines provide little shade, but a bench provides a place to rest. To follow a portion of the 5.3-mile Volksmarch Trail, look for orange diamonds painted onto tree trunks. The sandy trail wends through six different plant communities. Keep a towel in the car to wipe your dog's potentially muddy paws.

At the 60-site campground, some sites are wide open while others are woodsy, though the 2004 hurricanes toppled some trees. Fee is $20. Reserve at ReserveAmerica.com or 800/326-3521.

Admission is $5 per vehicle. From Apopka, head east on Highway 436, turn north on Wekiwa Springs Road, and continue to the park. 407/884-2009.

PLACES TO STAY

Crosby's Motor Inn: Canine guests may play fetch off-leash in the fenced pet area behind this 61-unit, two-story, family-owned and -operated poolside motel in northwestern Apopka. Rates range $69–125. Add $10 nightly per pooch. 1440 W. Orange Blossom Trail/U.S. 441, Apopka; 407/886-3220 or 800/821-6685; www.apopkafoliage.com.

Wekiwa Springs State Park: See Parks, Beaches, and Recreation Areas, above, for camping information.

Maitland

PARKS, BEACHES, AND RECREATION AREAS

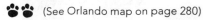 16 Community Park

 (See Orlando map on page 280)

Happy dogs are a common sight in the early morning at this 23-acre, heavily wooded park. It's the best dog haunt in town, thanks to the nature trails and other attributes. "I'm on a first-name basis with so many of the dogs," says a park employee, "that I would miss them if I didn't see them."

Stop with your leashed buddy at workout stations along a half-mile trail, or simply follow joggers along the paths before throwing burgers onto a grill and eating at a tree-shaded picnic table. A 200-yard boardwalk leads through a swampy, dog-intriguing portion of the park, which also has volleyball and basketball courts.

The park is at the north end of town at 1400 Mayo Ave.—a short detour off North Orlando Avenue/U.S. 17/92. 407/539-0042.

17 Lake Lily

 (See Orlando map on page 280)

The gazebo at Lake Lily seems like a fine place to gaze onto the lake and ponder life's mysteries, which, for Maggie, include how to capture one of the many birds here. Aside from a welcome change of dog-walking routine, this place offers little in the way of romping room for a leashed pooch.

The lake is on South Orlando Avenue/U.S. 17/92 at Maitland Avenue/Highway 427. 407/539-6247.

18 Lake Sybelia

(See Orlando map on page 280)

Local dogs, bicyclists, and plenty of pedestrians follow the mile-long sidewalk that circles the small park's lake. Fill up a water bowl at the restrooms here to quench your tired, leashed pup's thirst.

From I-4, go east on Maitland Boulevard, then turn right on Maitland Avenue. Turn right on Packwood Avenue and continue to the lake. 407/539-6247.

PLACES TO EAT

Edy's Grand Ice Cream: To split a banana split with your dog, sit at one of the two outdoor tables and give her some banana while you eat the rest. 111 South Orlando Ave.; 407/644-9528.

Altamonte Springs

Sadly, dogs are banned at city parks, so canines can't commune with nature at Lake Lotus Nature Park or go to Crane's Roost Park. Best bet: Head to Orlando's Lake Eola for a leashed walk.

PLACES TO EAT

Little Dairy Manor: We all bark for ice cream! Sample malts, floats, sundaes, or other frozen concoctions at the outdoor tables. 1109 W. State Road 436; 407/862-3223.

PLACES TO STAY

Candlewood Suites: Maybe the movie *Beethoven* will be available at the video library for a quiet night with your small pooch (under 40 pounds) at this pleasant all-suite hotel. Rates range $79–109. The $75 pet fee is non-refundable. 644 Raymond Ave., Altamonte Springs; 407/767-5757; www. candlewoodsuites.com.

Club Esprit Apartments: If you're here on business for the week or maybe a few months, your dog (under 35 pounds) may join you in a luxury apartment with access to a heated pool, fitness center, sauna, and whirlpool next to the Altamonte Mall. Weekly rates range $525–833. The nonrefundable pet fee is $75 for one week. 525 One Center Blvd., Altamonte Springs; 407/331-3131.

Days Inn: Outdoor fountains make a statement at this tropically land-scaped hacienda-style former La Quinta Inn. Rates range $60–100. Pet fee is $10 daily. 150 S. Westmonte Dr., Altamonte Springs; 407/788-1411; www. daysinn.com.

Embassy Suites Orlando North: Every dog sleeps in a suite, some over-looking a lake, at this full-service hotel located at pet-permissible Crane's Roost Park. Remember to give scraps from your free, cooked-to-order break-fast to your pooch before your visit to the sauna, pool, or whirlpool. Rates range $109–180. Add $20 daily per pet. 225 E. Altamonte Dr., Altamonte Springs; 407/834-2400; www.embassysuites.com.

Holiday Inn: A waterfall cascades into the Olympic-size pool at this pleas-ant 263-unit lodging, where the exercise room offers television and video equipment, and the lounge features live entertainment a few nights a week. Rates range $70–160. 230 W. Highway 436, Altamonte Springs; 407/862-4455; www.hialtamonte.com.

Residence Inn: Offering the comforts of home, these townhouse-like apartments might make a dog think he's visiting Uncle Spot. Rates range $99–180. You must pay a $75 nonrefundable pet fee. Ouch! Dogs over 25 pounds may be refused. 270 Douglas Ave., Altamonte Springs; 407/788-7991; http://marriott.com.

Winter Park

This oak-shaded, lake-dotted suburb is one of the more tasteful burgs surrounding the central core of Orlando, and a very good place to be a dog.

PARKS, BEACHES, AND RECREATION AREAS

19 Fleet Peeples Park at Lake Baldwin

🐾🐾🐾🐾🐕 (See Orlando map on page 280)

This park is a testament to dedicated dog lovers—so don't you and your pooch blow it! For a long time, the park was officially off-limits to pooches. But the 23 acres, often deserted on weekdays, beckoned for dogs and their owners to visit, and authorities basically looked the other way. Then the issue of the dreaded canine calling cards came up, and the ban was enforced.

Eventually, animal lovers prevailed on the town to allow them a six-month trial period in the park. Everyone behaved themselves, and dogs became welcome visitors.

Most recently, the town mothers and fathers have agreed to an off-leash provision. However, there's a big "but": Your dog must obey your voice commands. That means leaving all the other parkgoers alone. "It's a little trial and error thing, so make sure you clean up after your dog," a city parks staffer warns. And make sure she doesn't bother any two-leggers who aren't into the four-leggers.

Completely covered with trees, this shady, scenic lakeside park is perfect for a picnic, even on a hot summer day. You can canoe on Lake Baldwin if you like, or just sit and contemplate the spooky-looking twisted oak branches that block out the sun.

The park is sandwiched between the Veterans Administration Clinic and the former site of the Orlando Naval Training Center on Lakemont Avenue, in the extreme southeastern section of Winter Park. From the Bee-Line Expressway, take Highway 436 north about 10 miles, turn left at Aloma Avenue, then left at Lakemont Avenue. The lake is ahead about two miles. 407/599-3334.

20 Downey Dog Park

🐾🐾🐾🐕 (See Orlando map on page 280)

At just 1.25 acres—an acre for the big dogs, and a quarter-acre of the puny pooches—this leash-free, county-run park is a good place to see dogs chasing balls and each other. There are time-out pens in each section, but "you don't see too many people using them," says Mark, the acting site supervisor, when we inquired. We guess these are just real friendly dogs!

The park is quite well used, a testament to its popularity. People come out here with their dogs all the way from downtown Orlando. "I've probably seen 100 or 150 out there at once" on weekends, Mark says, and it's nothing

DIVERSIONS

Pass mansions with your Manchester terrier: For more than half a century, **Winter Park Scenic Boat Tour** has run narrated cruises that take passengers past mansions, the Kraft Azalea Gardens, the Isle of Sicily, and other sites. During a one-hour chartered tour that starts at Lake Osceola, you and your curious pup will learn about local history as the boat wends for 12 miles through a pretty chain of three lakes and two canals. Charters are $100 hourly. Head to 312 E. Morse Blvd., Winter Park. Reserve at 407/644-4056.

to have 30 dogs even if it's drizzling. When the park opens in the morning, there are often dogs and people waiting to get in. The Schnauzer Club meets there monthly.

People will appreciate the picnic tables, water fountains, and benches, and we're not quite sure what dogs will make of the decorative fire hydrants.

The park is 10107 Flowers Ave., near the corner of Dean Road and Colonial Drive/Highway 50. 407/249-6195.

PLACES TO EAT

Brandywine's Deli Restaurant: At this home of meal-size deli sandwiches, ice cream, cold beer, and wine, you'll need to walk inside to order after tying your dog to a post (a helpful employee may volunteer to watch your buddy). Take your meal outside to share at your choice of tables—covered or sunny. 505 North Park Ave.; 407/647-0055.

Hot Dog Heaven: At the city's best hot dog shack (as named by *Orlando Weekly*), your dog can eat a dog dressed Chicago style—topped with onions, relish, mustard, dill pickles, and two hot peppers. Sit at one of the little red picnic tables out front. 5355 Colonial Blvd./Highway 50; 407/282-5746.

Park Plaza Gardens: Your dog won't be the first to visit this award-winning restaurant known for serving continental cuisine in a New Orleans–style courtyard on Winter Park's main thoroughfare. The "regional American cuisine" is all over the map: Florida Caesar salad (with key lime-and-mustard dressing), Asian noodle stir-fry, filet mignon, chicken sandwiches, and so on. You'll sit with your pooch at the very front of the outdoor seating area. After lunch, dinner, or Sunday brunch, your dog might appreciate window-shopping at Park Avenue's specialty shops. 319 South Park Ave.; 407/645-2475.

Steak-n-Shake: Try the spaghetti with chili, the chicken, or the popular Steakburgers at this all-night eatery. Use the drive-through or sit at an outdoor table with your dog. 443 North Semoran Blvd./Highway 439, 407/678-9527.

Tijuana Flats Burrito Company: Order inside and bring the Mexican-style bounty out to your patient pooch waiting at the brown tables in front of this storefront restaurant. 7608 University Blvd.; 407/673-2456.

Twistee Treat: Try ice cream or hot dogs at the concrete table outside. 3000 North Goldenrod Rd.; 407/671-8809.

PLACES TO STAY

Langford Hotel: After chartering the Scenic Boat Tour a block away (see Diversions in this chapter), you could sleep at this Park Avenue-area hotel if your pooch is small enough—10 pounds or less. Rates are $90 and under. The pet fee is $25 per stay. 300 East New England Ave., Winter Park; 407/644-3400.

Motel 6 Winter Park: One pet per room is allowed at this 121-unit motel three miles from downtown Orlando. Rates normally are $40–49. 5300 Adanson Rd., Orlando; 407/647-1444; www.motel6.com.

Oviedo

PARKS, BEACHES, AND RECREATION AREAS

🐾 Riverside Park

🐾🐾 (See Orlando map on page 280)

Play fetch to your heart's content at the open central field of this 25-acre park, which is surrounded on three sides by water and woods. From downtown, take Central Avenue south and turn left on Mitchell Hammock Road. Proceed to the end, turn right on Lockwood Boulevard, and continue south about .75 mile. 407/977-6081.

Chuluota

PARKS, BEACHES, AND RECREATION AREAS

🐾 Florida National Scenic Trail

🐾🐾🐾 (See Orlando map on page 280)

If you asked three Labrador retrievers named Hershey, Cookie, and Rolo where they most like to go—and we did—they'd think of this woodsy trail. Ahh, the great outdoors. Better yet, leashes are optional for dogs on strong voice control. Of course, these three pooches obey commands; their friend, Amy Gagnon, is an Oviedo dog trainer. Gagnon says the Florida Trail is better than the best city park back home.

The Florida National Scenic Trail traverses Seminole County from Chuluota to Sanford. One section stretches 17 miles from Snow Hill Road to the

Seminole County Environmental Studies Center in Longwood. Double back at a comfortable distance for your pal in the fur coat. Bring water, snacks, and any supplies.

To reach the Snow Hill Road Trailhead, take State Road 417 to Red Bug Lake Road. Turn east onto Red Bug Lake Road, which becomes Mitchell Hammock Road, then turn left (north) onto Lockwood Road. At County Road 419, turn right (east) and follow to Snow Hill Road. Turn left. Continue until you see the sign for Flagler Trail South. Alternatively, start at the Seminole County Environmental Studies Center, whose parking area is Soldier's Creek Park, 2400 State Road 419, Longwood. 407/665-5601 or 800/343-1882.

Clermont

PARKS, BEACHES, AND RECREATION AREAS

23 Lake Louisa State Park

🐾🐾 (See Orlando map on page 280)

This remote 4,372-acre park bordering the Green Swamp is a nice place for a placid picnic on the shores of Lake Louisa. Leashed dogs afterward may follow a series of sandy horse trails to cobble together a hike as long as 30 miles. Double back at a comfortable distance for your pooch.

Four-legged hikers may collapse for a night's rest at the park's 60-site campground, nestled between Dixie Lake and Hammond Lake (no swimming allowed). Getting there requires a 1.5-mile drive from the ranger station. Set along three loops, the campsites have access to warm showers, two fishing piers, and a pavilion. Most sites offer water and electricity; 15 include sewer hookups. Fee is $21. Reserve at ReserveAmerica.com or 800/326-3521.

Admission costs $4 per carload. The park is at 7305 U.S. 27, which is 7.3 miles south of State Road 50. 352/394-3969.

DIVERSIONS

No whining allowed… On a personal tour of **Lakeridge Winery & Vineyards in Clermont,** you may carry your lapdog. The tour begins when you show up; no need to wait for a crowd to gather. You'll taste wines made from a strain of Muscadine grape developed at the University of Florida. Bigger dogs can join you at the outdoor picnic area at this 127-acre estate in gently rolling countryside. Bring water for your pooch to sip. The winery is at 19239 U.S. 27, about three miles south of Florida's Turnpike (Exit 285). Call 352/394-8627 or 800/768-WINE.

PLACES TO STAY

Vacation Village Resort: Set on 44 acres at Lake Louisa, these condominium villas and lofts offer people such pursuits as swimming in an Olympic-size pool and playing tennis, shuffleboard, and basketball. Kids head to a wading pool or playgrounds. Dogs under 25 pounds might search for scraps in the kitchens. Rates start at $89 in season, $68 in fall. Minimum stay normally is three nights, five nights during special events. Pet fee is $50–100 per stay. 10301 U.S. 27, Clermont; 352/394-4091 or 800/962-9969; www.floridavacationvillage.com.

Orlando

It's a law that anyone who sets foot in Orlando must go to the theme parks at some point. At least it seems that way. But here's the dreaded poop for pooches: At Universal Studios, dogs stay at kennels found in the parking garage for $10 per day and it's up to you to bring food and walk your dog periodically (staffers don't). The theme park is at 1000 Universal Studios Plaza, off I-4 (Exits 74B and 75A). Call 407/363-8000.

Sea World charges a similar fee for its on-site kennel. Bring food and stop by once in a while to walk your dog. The theme park is at 7007 Sea World Dr., where I-4 and the Bee-Line Expressway intersect. Call 407/351-3600.

Don't leave pets in the car. The scorching sun turns vehicles into death chambers in mere minutes in summer, and there is no shade at any time of year. It's also wise not to leave pets alone in motel rooms, lest they bark from boredom or cause doggy destruction. Greater Orlando and Las Vegas compete for the distinction of having the nation's biggest stock of hotels, with more than 84,000 rooms each. Dogs may not be happier in a kennel, but keeping hoteliers happy means hotels in this vacation mecca will continue to allow doggies.

PARKS, BEACHES, AND RECREATION AREAS

🞂🞂 Cady Way Trail

🐕 (See Orlando map on page 280)

This 3.5-mile asphalt exercise trail and bikeway, which links Winter Park and Orlando, is best on a winter day or when the sun is low in the sky. Even on a hot day, though, you will find an occasional rest stop where you can drink from a fountain, give your leashed dog water, and get out of the sun. Maggie loved sniffing around by the water fountain at the beginning of the trail and also along the little strips of green that line the path. She was eager to keep going when we turned around on a chilly afternoon. The trail winds mostly along golf courses and suburbs.

From I-4, go east on Colonial Boulevard/Highway 50, then turn left on

DOG-EAR YOUR CALENDAR

Head to a festival for everyone in the family—including the family pet: Kids love the carnival rides and Arabian Nights horse shows while dogs love taking in all the commotion and taking part in silly pet contests at the annual **Pet Fair Family Fun Day** held each December at the Orlando Science Center.

A mountain of snow was dumped here one year, to the delight of young 'uns. Santa swoops in for photo opportunities with kids or pets. The exact agenda changes from year to year but generally includes live music by local musicians, free pet health mini exams, and cute contests such as the best doggy costume and the person who looks most like his or her hound. A nice amenity: Pet-sitting services are available for two-legged attendees who want to check out the science center, which is also the beneficiary of profits from the $8–10 tickets. For Pet Fair Family Fun Day dates, call 407/514-2000.

Dog-ear your calendar for yet another cool event: Sometimes called the **"Bark Brunch"** or "Bark Breakfast Buffet," the SPCA of Central Florida throws the annual shindig at a fancy hotel. One year, Universal Studios' Portofino Hotel served as the sumptuous setting, offering several tables that seat 10—five dogs, five people. The dogs had two bowls in front of them, one for water and one for food. And they ate better than many people we know, scarfing down filet mignon and salmon, we're told. If it sounds extravagant, bear in mind that it's a fundraiser for the shelter, which can provide details if you call 407/351-7722, ext. 233.

Herndon Avenue. The best place to park is at the shopping center a quarter mile ahead. Find the post office; the bike route (Cady Way Trail) parking is immediately to the north. 407/836-6200 or 407/249-6194.

25 Cypress Grove Park

 (See Orlando map on page 280)

Some romantic couples have tied the knot with their best dog at their side at a gazebo overlooking Lake Jessamine here or in the park's 1925 renovated estate house. Dogs, meanwhile, are smitten with the park's little-used open spaces. Never mind the basketball court, playground, lakeside gazebo, volleyball court, and tennis courts, hounds would say. But, oh, a burger browned on a grill here would do just fine.

The 80-acre county park is a favorite of local Labs and dog people because of its big expanses. It's too bad that pooches are supposed to stay leashed. Follow the nearly mile-long path found on one side of the park. The pathway itself is nothing fancy, but the park is pleasant.

From downtown, take Orange Avenue/Highway 527 about three miles south. Turn right at Holden Avenue and continue a quarter mile to 290 Holden Avenue. 407/858-2295 or 407/836-6200.

26 Dickson Azalea Park

🐾🐾 (See Orlando map on page 280)

People have been married at this pretty, heavily shaded park—an unusual sight in the middle of a city. In these parts, water drainage from Highway 50 and the East-West Expressway passes for a creek. Maggie liked the idea of combining a trip here with a visit to Mayor Carl T. Langford Park to the south, where picnic tables, a playground, and a walking trail are found. Central Boulevard separates the two.

Leashes are the rule at 3.4-acre Dickson Azalea Park, found at 100 Rosearden Drive. From East Colonial Drive/Highway 50, go south on North Hampton Avenue, right (west) on East Washington Street, then left (south) on Rosearden. 407/246-2150 or 407/246-2283.

27 Hal Scott Preserve

🐾🐾🐾 (See Orlando map on page 280)

Follow the nature trail through prairie and flatwoods, keeping your eye out for the eagles, sandhill cranes, bobcats, otters, and red-cockaded woodpeckers who call this wild park in eastern Orange County their home. The Econlockhatchee River divides these 14 square miles of untamed country, preserved by the county and by the St. Johns River Water Management District. Hiking trails crisscross the property, leading past the old Yates Homestead to Cowpen Branch and back for an all-day hike. Or turn back sooner after a picnic lunch at the Econlockhatchee.

A grassy area immediately west of the parking lot will tempt Frisbee dogs. They are supposed to stay leashed, though this area is quite isolated. The matted-grass hiking trail, which begins at the parking area, is narrow, and it can be difficult in places to tell that a trail exists amidst the sun-washed fields of pointy-bladed saw palmetto bushes; follow the blue blazes on tree trunks to make your way toward the river. In spring, you'll pass wildflowers with pearl-size dots of white or orange.

Arrive early or late in the day to protect your pooch from the sun. Bring water and anything else you'll need, as there are no facilities here.

From Orlando, go east on Highway 50 to Highway 520. Turn right (south). A few miles down, turn right again into the Wedgefield subdivision on Maxim Parkway. Turn left at Bancroft Street, right at Meredith Avenue, and left on Dallas Boulevard. The park entrance is 1.6 miles from the intersection of Meredith and Dallas. There is also an exit for Dallas Boulevard from the eastbound Bee-Line Expressway. 407/836-6200.

28 Jay Blanchard Park

🐾🐾 (See Orlando map on page 280)

Here we saw a German shepherd trotting alongside his master, who was jogging in this 412-acre linear park bordering the Little Econlockhatchee River. If it's not crowded, maybe your dog will like to run in the soccer fields, though he is technically supposed to be leashed. He can check out the basketball courts, lounge under spreading oaks, or try to get a closer look at the wading birds in the pretty, meandering river. The four-mile-long Little Econ Greenway Trail begins here.

The county park is at 2451 Dean Road. From Orlando, head east on Highway 50/Colonial Drive. Turn left (north) on Dean Road and continue one mile. 407/249-6194.

29 Shadow Bay Park

🐾🐾 (See Orlando map on page 280)

Convenient for tourists visiting nearby theme parks, this 111-acre park gives you a chance to reward your dog without driving a zillion miles to find a hiking trail. The park is better known for its 13 tennis courts and a pro shop than its less-than-postcard-perfect hiking trails, but your leashed pal will want to walk anyway, particularly if he has been cooped up in a theme park kennel (yikes!). Take a break at one of the picnic areas while the kids head to the fishing lake, basketball courts, or playground.

The park is at 5100 Turkey Lake Rd., at the intersection of Conroy and Turkey Lake roads. From I-4, go north on Kirkman Road/Highway 435, then turn left (west) at Conroy Road. The park is ahead on the left. 407/254-9175.

30 Lake Cherokee Park

🐾🐾 (See Orlando map on page 280)

If you're tired of Lake Eola (see separate listing), head to this historic neighborhood to walk beneath old-fashioned lampposts and admire the homes representing a mix of styles, including ranch, old Southern, and modern. Maggie couldn't care less about architecture, but she does love the idea a walk that takes in not one, not two, but three parks.

Start at scenic Lake Cherokee, a nearly four-acre open park that overlooks the lake of the same name. Walk south to the next small park, Cherokee Park, at Cherokee Drive and Summerlin Avenue. Next, head east one block to the walking path circling the lake at Lake Davis Park, a 3.5-acre park at South Summerlin Avenue and Lake Davis Drive. Big dogs will appreciate the exercise.

Lake Cherokee Park is at 474 Palmer St., at Cherokee Circle. Find it a few blocks south of the East-West Expressway and east of Orange Avenue. 407/246-2283.

31 Lake Eola

🐾🐾🐾 (See Orlando map on page 280)

Locals love this landmark 43-acre park, where folks with leashed dogs follow the nearly mile-long sidewalk encircling the scenic lake, dotted at the edge by shaggy cypress trees. They pass azalea bushes and huge moss-draped trees—and dogs sniff at each other. "It's a great place to socialize a dog," says Amy Gagnon, a dog trainer in neighboring Oviedo.

Rest at a bench in the lakeside red pagoda and watch the lighted fountain at the lake's center shoot water like a geyser at Yellowstone National Park. Most of the path is unshaded, so skip walking on hot afternoons.

At a manicured area with chairs and brick sidewalks on the park's southeast side, the spreading arms of oaks shade outdoor tables. Bring a bag lunch to eat near a circle of English ivy (there's no water view here). On the west side, the ice cream, salads, and sandwiches at the concession stand provide an excuse for a break.

An open grassy area will tempt dogs to run, but leashes—and cleaning up after your pet—are required. Maggie recommends that dogs try to pull off the arm at the other end of the leash by chasing ducks at the lake's edge.

Check into special performances—such as *The Nutcracker*—at the outdoor amphitheater. If your dog is well mannered, consider taking him along. When asked whether dogs are permitted at performances, a parks employee paused briefly, then replied, "We don't really like it, but we can't stop it if they're on a leash."

The park is at 195 N. Rosalind Ave., at East Central Boulevard. Find it just east of the downtown high-rises. 407/246-2827.

32 Lake Underhill

🐾 (See Orlando map on page 280)

A nearly mile-long walking course with exercise stations runs along the southern bank of Lake Underhill, a beautiful little lake surrounded by cattails and cypress trees. It's a narrow 8.8-acre park. Well-traveled roads surround the course, which is near the East-West Expressway—not quite a wilderness experience. But it will help vary your dog-walking routine, and your leashed pooch is likely to keep an eye on the birds.

The park is at 4355 Lake Underhill Road. Exit the East-West Expressway at Conway Road heading south and make an immediate right onto Lake Underhill Road. Park at the boat ramp found northwest of the intersection of Conway and Lake Underhill. 407/246-2283.

33 Orlando Festival Park

🐾🐾 (See Orlando map on page 280)

Maggie enjoyed prancing in this grassy, wide-open field, her mouth cracked open as if she were smiling. With the relatively ample room and squirrels to chase up the smattering of cabbage palms and oaks, it's no wonder that a local woman told us she drives her dogs here two or three times a week to let them run free. Technically, leashes are in order on these unfenced grounds surrounded by streets, but we can see how the Frisbee golf course would tempt pent-up pooches to run.

The 16-acre park is at 2106 E. Robinson St., at North Primrose Drive, southwest of Orlando Executive Airport. 407/246-2283.

34 Orlando Loch Haven Park

🐾🐾 (See Orlando map on page 280)

You always claimed your dog was smart, so why not head to this grassy 45-acre park that houses the city's brainy museums? Male pooches may be tempted to make a beeline to a famous oak tree dating back almost to the days when the Pilgrims landed at Plymouth Rock. Called "The Mayor," it's one of Central Florida's oldest and largest oaks.

Sit at an oak-shaded bench to take in views of the three surrounding lakes: Lake Estelle to the north, Lake Rowena on the east, and Lake Formosa on the south. Fill a water bowl at the restrooms or at the drinking fountain.

The park is at 900 E. Princeton St., at the northwest corner of North Mills Avenue/U.S. 17/92 and Princeton Street. This scenic open parkland is by the Orlando Museum of Art and Orlando Science Center, among other museums. 407/246-2283.

35 Park Lake

🐾🐾 (See Orlando map on page 280)

If your lapdog thinks it's too much to expect his wee legs to handle a walk around nearby Lake Eola, try the .75-mile walk around this smaller lake. You can picnic at this scenic park, just like at Lake Eola. And you can fish here, which you can't at the other, more popular park. Just remember: Alligators live in lakes—keep your dog leashed.

The narrow 1.7-acre park is on the north side of East Colonial Drive/Highway 50 at Park Lake Circle. 407/246-2283.

36 Signal Hill Park

🐾 (See Orlando map on page 280)

This neighborhood park is maybe two acres in size, tops, and worth a visit only if you're already in the area. Follow a fitness trail with your leashed dog.

Then take a rest at the pavilion while the kids enjoy the playground, basketball court, or ball field.

The park is at 3877 Watch Hill Rd., off Center Lane. From Ocoee-Clarcona Road and Pine Hills Road/Highway 431, go south on Highway 431 to Watch Hill Lane, turn left (east), then right (south) on Watch Hill Road to the park. 407/246-2283.

37 Turkey Lake Park

 (See Orlando map on page 280)

Dog-tired is what your leashed pooch will be after exploring eight miles of woodsy hiking trails and two miles of bike trails at this local favorite of the two-legged set. He also may tag along with you at the 18-hole Frisbee golf course or follow the "five senses nature trail" for disabled visitors. Humans head to the 300-acre park for still other reasons—the ball field, a pool, an elaborate playground, and a farm complete with animals. But four-legged visitors who want to visit those spots receive an all-too-familiar command: "No!"

No matter, says Maggie. The hiking trails are fun enough. Just be sure to bring water, as fountains are few and far between.

One furry pal may join you in a camper (but not a tent) in the park's 32-site campground for $18 nightly. Reservations are required and you must prepay for your stay.

Admission is $4 per carload. The city park is at 3401 Hiawassee Road. From I-4, exit onto Conway Road. Go west on Conway to Hiawassee Road, where you'll turn right. The park is one mile down on the right. 407/299-5581.

38 University of Central Florida

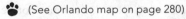 (See Orlando map on page 280)

Dogs are just tolerated, not welcomed, as they walk around the campus of this branch of the state university system, which is dominated by the large white-and-black U.C.F. water tower. With 1,142 acres, there's a lot of room for stretching those doglegged legs! You'll have to stay at the perimeter of the campus to dodge the 26,000 students, though. Get a visitor parking pass at the visitors information booth, found near the campus main entrance, or take a metered spot nearby. There are quite a few walking trails in the southeastern portion, by Central Florida Boulevard and Andromeda Drive East; keep your dog leashed. The interior areas are partially shaded, but the thick woods are out past the parking lots.

Located northeast of Orlando, the university is at University Boulevard where it dead-ends into Alafaya Trail/Central Avenue. 407/823-2000.

39 Meadow Woods Dog Park

🐕 (See Orlando map on page 280)

The groundbreaking ceremony at this new dog park took place the day before this book went to print, so it's difficult for us to rate it for you. Still, it sounded promising: A dog park as part of a 19-acre expanse that was to also include playground, tot lot, basketball courts, picnic pavilions and open playing fields, all nestled next to Meadow Woods Middle School in unincorporated Orange County south of Orlando. Like other county-run dog parks, it was to include small- and large-dog areas, water fountains, agility equipment and time-out areas for naughty pooches.

The park is located on Rhode Island Woods Drive, a few miles east of the intersection of U.S. 441/92 and Highway 417/Central Florida Greenway. 407/836-6243.

PLACES TO EAT

Fazoli's Italian: For drive-through Italian fare, try fettuccine, salads, or pizza. 3922 E. Colonial Dr., 407/894-7006. Another location: 12025 Collegiate Way; 407/380-3737.

Hot Dog Heaven: Lots of dogs watch their people eat dogs, er, frankfurters, at the outdoor concrete tables of this casual joint. 5355 E. Colonial Dr.; 407/282-5746.

PLACES TO STAY

Baymont Inn and Suites: Pets usually sleep in rooms on the first floor or near exits at this pleasant three-story hotel located south of the Bee-Line Expressway and west of Orlando International Airport. Dogs must not be left alone in the room and should be restrained or kept in a crate should a

housekeeper arrive while you're present. Rates run $64–80. 2051 Consulate Dr., Orlando; 407/240-0500; www.baymontinns.com.

Best Western Orlando West: Boston terriers may stay here, but breeds over 25 pounds are turned away from this 109-room downtown-area motel located eight miles from Universal Studios. Rates range $49–125. You'll be required to leave a $25 pet deposit. 2014 W. Colonial Dr., Orlando; 407/841-8600; www.bestwestern.com.

Days Inn North of Universal Studios: Located near Universal Studios, this four-story lodging provides a free continental breakfast and accepts housebroken pets. Rates range $45–70. Pet fee is $10 nightly. 2500 Caravan Ct., Orlando; 407/351-3800; www.daysinn.com.

Hard Rock Hotel at Universal Orlando Resort: Special treatment for dogs begins with a special note from the general manager providing inside tips on good dog-walking routes and other information. Doggy beds, a pet room-service menu, a pet bowl, and treats continue the pampering. All Loews Hotels aim to be the most pet-friendly hotels around (including nearby Portofino Bay Hotel and the Royal Pacific Resort). By requesting the "Pampered Pet Package," you'll also get a movie to watch back at the room and dinner for two people at an on-site restaurant. At the seven-story, California mission–style resort, visiting rock musicians fix their favorite recipes at The Kitchen restaurant, music is piped underwater into the 12,000-square-foot pool, and rock memorabilia is displayed throughout. Rates start at $210. Pets are accepted with proof of current vaccinations. 5800 Universal Blvd., Orlando; 407/503-2000; www.loewshotels.com.

Howard Johnson Plaza Resort: Found south of Universal Studios, this two-story hotel offers a playground, shuffleboard, two pools, a kiddie pool, and a game room. Rates run $40–120. Add $10 nightly for a pooch under 35 pounds. 7050 S. Kirkman Rd., Orlando; 407/351-2000; www.hojo.com.

La Quinta Inn Airport: Local calls and continental breakfast are free at this comfortable business-oriented poolside motel off the Bee-Line Expressway's Tradeport Drive exit. Rates range $60–85. 7931 Daetwyler Dr., Orlando; 407/857-9215; www.lq.com.

La Quinta Inn International Drive: A putting green sets this pleasant four-story hotel apart. Located off I-4 (Exit 74A), the lodging offers a free continental breakfast and rooms equipped with refrigerators—good for hungry hounds. Rates range $80–100. 8300 Jamaican Ct., Orlando; 407/351-1660; www.lq.com.

Masters Inn: Two pets under 20 pounds may join you at this four-story hotel off I-4 (Exit 74A), between Sea World and Universal Studios. Just don't leave them alone in the room, staffers ask, echoing the refrain heard from area hoteliers. Rates range $49–80. 8222 Jamaican Ct., Orlando; 407/345-1172; www.mastersinn.com.

Motel 6 International Drive: With larger rooms featuring a combination shower/bath, this is the area's roomiest Motel 6. The 112-unit poolside motel is two miles from Universal Studios. Small dogs are preferred, but medium-size pets typically are accepted. Rates run $46–56. 5909 American Way, Orlando; 407/351-6500; www.motel6.com.

Portofino Bay Hotel at Universal Orlando: Located on the grounds of Universal Studios, this grand hotel will deliver a special room service meal, plus treats and toys—all for your dog. A wide selection of dry and canned pet foods is available, as are a dog-walking service, leashes, and doggy beds. By requesting the "Pampered Pet Package," you'll get many of those perks, plus a movie to watch back in the room and dinner for two humans at an on-site restaurant. Called one of "the world's best places to stay" by *Conde Nast Traveler* magazine, this Loews hotel is a re-creation of the seaside resort village of Portofino, Italy. A ballroom, a spa, three themed swimming pools, a supervised children's activity center, and eight restaurants and lounges number among the human amenities. Nightly rates range $265–550. Pets are accepted with proof of current vaccinations. 5601 Universal Blvd., Orlando; 407/503-1000; www.loewshotels.com.

Quality Inn International Drive: Store doggy bags in your room fridge at this 728-room lodging off I-4 (Exit 74A), near Universal Studios. A pool, game room, and gift shop are offered. Rates range $39–99. Add $11.15 nightly for your dog (50 pounds or less). A separate $50 pet deposit will be refunded, barring canine indiscretions. 7600 International Dr., Orlando; 407/351-1600; www.choicehotels.com.

Quality Inn Plaza: At this 1,020-room hotel within walking distance of the Orange County Convention Center, amenities include a big pool, a playground, and a 24-hour mini market. Rates range $40–90. Add $10 daily for the dog (under 50 pounds). 9000 International Dr., Orlando; 407/345-8585; www.choicehotels.com.

Red Roof Inn Convention Center: Free weekday newspapers and a range of cable TV stations make it easy for newshounds to keep up on national affairs from this International Drive–area motel, located a mile from Sea World and near the Orange County Convention Center. Rates range $40–99. 9922 Hawaiian Ct., Orlando; 407/352-1507; www.redroof.com.

Residence Inn: This all-suite hotel off I-4 (Exit 74A) may make dogs feel like they're visiting Grandpa Spot—except here, a maid visits daily to clean up the fully equipped kitchen and the rest of the suite. Some units offer fireplaces, and all Human guests enjoy a whirlpool, a pool, an exercise room, and complimentary full breakfasts and weekday evening beverages (on certain days). Rates range $110–199. Pet fee is a flat $75. 7975 Canada Ave., Orlando; 407/345-0117 or 800/331-3131; http://marriott.com.

Royal Pacific Resort at Universal Orlando: Located within walking distance of Universal Studios, this Loews resort offers signature pet bowls, doggy beds, and a pet room-service menu developed by a veterinarian. Beverage carts offer bottled water for pets (or people), and a wide selection of dry and canned pet foods are available. A concierge can line up a pet sitter or dog walker. From its swaying palms to weekly luaus, the 1,000-room hotel has a tropical feel. Human amenities include a lagoon-style pool with sandy beach, and weekly luaus. Restaurants include TV chef Emeril Lagasse's Tchoup Chop. Nightly rates range $199–620. Pets are accepted with proof of current vaccinations. 6300 Hollywood Way, Orlando; 407/503-3000; www.loewshotels.com.

Sheraton Suites Orlando Airport: Dog beds are available for the small pets accepted at this pleasant lodging, where all 150 suites offer two televisions, a microwave, and a fridge. Rates start at $59. Pet fee is $25. 7550 Augusta National Dr., Orlando; 407/240-5555; www.sheraton.com.

Sheraton World Resort: Dog bowls are offered for canine guests of this resort set on 28 acres within walking distance of Sea World and a half mile from the Convention Center. Three pools, a fitness center, a miniature golf course, and restaurants number among people-pleasers. Rates start at $200. Pets weighing 50 pounds or less are accepted. A $100 deposit is refunded, barring canine indiscretions. 10100 International Dr., Orlando; 407/352-1100; www.sheraton.com.

TraveLodge Orlando Downtown: Wash dirty doggy bandannas at the on-site laundry of this downtown-area, two-story, poolside motel. Rates range $45–85. Add $10 daily per pet up to 50 pounds. 409 N. Magnolia Ave., Orlando; 407/423-1671; www.travelodge.com.

Turkey Lake Park: See Parks, Beaches, and Recreation Areas, above, for camping information.

Veranda Inn Bed and Breakfast: Small pets are accepted with prior approval at these downtown-area poolside suites and cottages, which are close enough to the Church Street Station shopping complex to W-A-L-K there. From the veranda of this Key West–style B&B, you can look out over lush foliage. Guests are welcome to a free continental breakfast that's a bit heartier than many we've seen, and guests receive a free bottle of wine upon check-in. All rooms have a private bath and phone. Rates are $99–159; cottages go up to $199. 115 North Summerlin Ave., Orlando; 407/849-0321 or 800/420-6822.

Westin Grand Bohemian: Dog beds and pet bowls number among the perks at this downtown Orlando landmark, called one of the world's best hotels by *Conde Naste Traveler*. A collection of more than 100 rare works of art are housed at the 250-unit luxury hotel. Its lobby's barrel-tiled ceiling is adorned with gold-flecked Italian mosaic tiles, setting a tone for your stay. In-room massages are available for humans, as are a heated pool, fitness room, spa, and fine dining. Rates start at $140. The pet fee is a whopper: $100. Pets 50 pounds or less are accepted. 325 S. Orange Ave., Orlando; 407/313-9000 or 866/663-0024; www.grandbohemianhotel.com.

Kissimmee

In this land of neon and wall-to-wall budget motels, heed this safety tip: Do not walk your dog across wide, treacherous, well-traveled U.S. 192. It's a sad sight when a poor tourist tries to cross busy U.S. 192 as if it were a sleepy Main Street. Walk your dog at the grassy patches around your motel or drive to a park. Even if you merely want to get to a restaurant right across the street on U.S. 192, drive there.

Although farmers started quietly selling their land to Disney World three decades ago, turning this former farm town into what seems like a giant budget motel for people going to the Magic Kingdom, there is still a small-town core here. Just look for it around the lake a few blocks south of U.S. 192.

PLACES TO EAT

Checkers: At the outdoor tables shaded somewhat by red umbrellas, your pet would love to watch you eat burgers, chicken sandwiches, fries, and other fast food fare in hopes that some nibbles fall to the ground. Since the eatery is located on a very busy multi-lane road, you may wish to opt for a drive-through order to take back to a motel or to a park. 5780 W. Irlo Bronson Memorial Highway/U.S. 192; 407/396-0069.

PLACES TO STAY

Amerisuites: Every dog sleeps in a suite at this pleasant 151-unit lodging, whose people-pleasers include a free breakfast buffet, an outdoor pool, and a fitness center. Guests normally walk their pets in the parking lot or along adjacent sidewalks instead of driving to Mill Slough Dog Park. Rates range $80–150. Pet fee is $25 per stay. 4991 Calypso Cay Way, Kissimmee; 407/997-1300 or 866/499-1300; www.amerisuites.com.

Country Inn & Suites: Three pools, an 18-hole miniature golf course, a fitness center, and free continental breakfast greet guests at this 162-room, seven-story lodging. Walk the dog in the yard or along sidewalks. Rates range $80–170. Add $25 per pet. 5001 Calypso Cay Way, Kissimmee; 407/997-1400 or 800/456-4000; www.countryinns.com.

Fantasy World Club Villas: Every four-legged vacationer wakes up in a two-bedroom suite with a kitchen at this 334-unit lodging. Unusual amenities include six lighted tennis courts, three pools, a lobby lounge, and a pool bar. Regular rates range $165–200, though discounts may be available. 5005 Kyngs Heath Rd., Kissimmee; 407/396-1808; www.fantasyworldresort.com.

Flamingo Inn: An economical choice for pets who'd rather save their money for dog biscuits, this 40-unit poolside motel offers rooms with microwaves and refrigerators. Small pets, please. Rates range $30–50. 801 E. Vine St./U.S. 192, Kissimmee; 407/846-1935 or 800/780-7617; www.flamingoinn.com.

Homewood Suites by Hilton: The pet fee is enough to make you yelp: $100. However, these apartment-style suites feature fully equipped kitchens, a pool, a cabana, an on-site convenience store, and free continental breakfast. Rates range $90–180. 3100 Parkway Blvd., Kissimmee; 407/396-2229; www.homewoodsuites.com.

Howard Johnson Express Inn Parkside: Century-old oaks serve as leg-lift targets for canines walking outside this 172-unit poolside lodging set back from busy U.S. 192. Rates range $49–100. Pet fee is $10 nightly. 4311 W. Vine St./U.S. 192, Kissimee; 407/396-7100 or 800/388-7698; www.hojokissimmee.com.

Howard Johnson Kissimmee Inn: Grassy areas for a dog walk are few and Irlo Bronson Memorial Highway is busy, so a staffer suggests a drive to Lake Toho to stretch the legs. Room service is available from the on-site diner—good for hungry dogs. Small pets are preferred. Rates range $49–96. Add $10 nightly or a maximum $20 weekly for pets. 2323 E. Irlo Bronson Memorial Highway/U.S. 192, Kissimmee; 407/846-4900; www.hojo.com.

Magic Castle Inn & Suites Maingate: Every room has a fridge and microwave and you can cook up goodies at barbecue grills outside this poolside motel set back from busy Irlo Bronson Memorial Highway. You'll sleep in a standard smoking room. Rates range $35–55. Add $6 per pet. A $50 refundable pet deposit is required for patrons who pay cash. 5055 W. Irlo Bronson Memorial Highway/U.S. 192, Kissimmee; 407/396-2212 or 800/446-5669; www.magicorlando.com.

Masters Inn: Two dogs under 20 pounds may share your room. Just keep them leashed in public and don't leave them unattended in your room (unless they're crated). Rates range $49–70. Add $20 weekly per pet. 2945 Entry Point Blvd., Kissimmee; 407/396-7743 or 800/633-3434; www.mastersinn.com.

Motel 6 Maingate East: This 347-unit poolside motel five miles from Disney World permits one dog under 20 pounds per room. Rates run $30–46. 5731 W. Irlo Bronson Memorial Highway/U.S. 192, Kissimmee; 407/396-6333; www.motel6.com.

Motel 6 Maingate West: Located behind a Perkins restaurant and five miles from Disney World, this 148-unit poolside motel accepts one pet per room. Rates range $30–46. 7455 W. Irlo Bronson Memorial Highway/U.S. 192, Kissimmee; 407/396-6422; www.motel6.com.

Red Roof Inn: Newshounds can keep up on current events with the free weekday paper available in the lobby of this three-story motel located at the junction of U.S. 192 and Highway 535. A whirlpool, heated pool, and game room entertain guests. Rates range $40–80. 4970 Kyng's Heath Rd., Kissimmee; 407/396-0065.

Seralago Hotel & Suites Maingate East: At this family-oriented 614-unit former Holiday Inn, amenities include two heated pools, two whirlpool spas, two playgrounds, two tennis courts, and a fitness center. Small pets are preferred, though pets up to 50 pounds have been accepted. Rates range $55–90.

Pet fee is $25. 5678 W. Irlo Bronson Highway, Kissimmee; 407/396-4488 or 800/366-5437; www.orlandofamilyfunhotel.com.

Summerfield Condo Resort: Cook dinner in the complete kitchen and serve your lapdog in the formal dining room of these 38 two-bedroom town houses, which feel like a home away from home. Watch television in either bedroom or the living room, or go outside for a barbecue. You'll sleep in one of the designated pet units, where the flat fee is $25 for a small animal, $50 for a medium-size dog. Rates range $99–180. 2425 Summerfield Way, Kissimmee; 407/847-7222.

Tropical Palms Resort: A big heated pool is open 24 hours at this tree-shaded campground property bordering Disney World. A poolside café, a kiddy pool, a game room, and a business center are offered, so you're not ruffing it at these campsites for tents and RVs. Sites range $24–49. 2650 Holiday Trail, Kissimmee, FL 34746; 407/396-4595 or 800/647-2567; www.tropicalpalms.com.

Lake Buena Vista/Disney World

If you don't have a pet-sitter, you can take your dog to Disney's kennel for the day or—gasp!—overnight. You've probably noticed that we rarely mention kennels in this book, because kennels are to dogs what sunlight is to those other fanged beings, vampires. Still, we realize that many among the two-legged set will insist on stopping here.

So here's the kennel deal: Rates are $6 for the day, $9 overnight if you're sleeping at a Disney resort, $11 overnight if you're sleeping outside Disney World. The kennels are at the entrances to Disney's Animal Kingdom, Disney-MGM Studios, and EPCOT Center, as well as adjacent to the Magic Kingdom Park Transportation and Ticket Center. Another kennel is near the entrance to Disney's Fort Wilderness Resort & Campground. The pleasant employees will feed your buddy whatever food you bring, but you're expected to walk him. At EPCOT, though, staffers will do the job for $2.50 per walk. You must show proof of vaccinations, including parvo, bordatella, distemper, and rabies. Call first to check on policy updates: 407/827-7200.

PLACES TO STAY

Comfort Inn: This pleasant 640-room hotel—located a mile from EPCOT Center—is a refreshing surprise for anyone who believes an affordable hotel that allows pets must be way below par. A gift shop, a playground area, and two pools are available. Dogs 50 pounds or less, please. Rates are $49–90. Add $10 nightly per pet. 8442 Palm Pkwy., Lake Buena Vista; 407/239-7300; www.choicehotels.com.

Disney's Fort Wilderness Resort & Campground: The only way a dog may go inside Disney World is to magically transform into a human—or sleep at this massive, worthwhile, frontier-theme campground with 1,192 campsites. Up to four pets may share your camper (but not a tent, unfortunately) in certain loops of Disney World's only campground. Seminole Indians once hunted and fished among the tall pines, moss-draped cypress, and white-flowering bay trees. Now, guests who pry themselves from Disney theme parks can fritter the day away here—visiting a petting farm, riding horses, swimming, canoeing, pedaling or paddling rented bikes or boats, and hitting the tennis courts. Leashed dogs are to walk along canalside pet paths. Campsites range $43–89. Pet fee is $5 daily. Since pet campsites are limited, you must declare your dogs at reservation time. The campground is off U.S. 192 in Disney World. P.O. Box 10000, Lake Buena Vista; 407/827-7200; www. disneyworld.com.

Holiday Inn Sunspree: Mini-kitchens allow you to cook up treats, and the maids will leave you alone unless you specially order maid service. Dogs under 25 pounds are accepted at this six-story hotel with a large pool. Rates range $70–130. Add a flat $25 pet fee. 13351 State Road 535, Orlando; 407/239-4500 or 800/366-6299; www.sunspreeresorts.com/dis-buenavista.com.

Christmas

Inquiring canines may wonder: Why do front yards and houses display Christmas decorations year-round? The reason is an avid appreciation of the town's name, which actually alludes to Fort Christmas, built here on Dec. 25, 1837, back during the Second Seminole War. Nowadays, the town is best known for its post office, not erstwhile fort. Some people (perhaps accompanied by their dogs) travel hundreds of miles to mail holiday packages or cards from the Christmas post office so they'll bear the coveted postmark, "Christmas, FL."

PARKS, BEACHES, AND RECREATION AREAS

40 Tosohatchee State Reserve

🐾🐾🐾 (See Orlando map on page 280)

The sound of our approaching car sent three wild turkeys scampering off the sandy road to hide in the surrounding brush. That's a clue that these 28,000 remote acres offer great rewards for anyone pining to escape the hubbub of Orlando. During a drive-by tour, Maggie craned her neck out the car to gape at turkeys, an armadillo poking around the base of a pine tree, and ducks paddling around Jim Creek. The result: one happy dog!

With nearly 44 square miles open to hiking, a lucky leashed pooch might spot a deer, bobcat, or fox in the forested uplands. At the 10,000 acres of marsh, long-legged wading birds stand as still as statues while waiting to pounce on a fish dinner. In the hot afternoons, the chirps of cicadas resound from the thickest parts of the woods. Other areas are sunny with few trees and thick stands of squat saw palmetto bushes. About all there is to do here is hike, ride your own horse, or fish along 19 miles of the St. Johns River.

Driving the sandy roads is not for the faint of heart. Keep moving so your car won't become bogged down in sand, but don't travel so fast that you'll hit a tree. Four-wheel drive is recommended. On a Saturday afternoon, we saw only two other cars—one belonging to a reserve employee. Bring water, mosquito repellent, and any supplies.

Admission is $3 per car. The park is at 3365 Taylor Creek Rd., east of the hamlet of Christmas. From Titusville, take Highway 50 about 14 miles west, then turn south on Taylor Creek Road. From Orlando, head east about 20 miles on Highway 50 and turn south on Taylor Creek Road. 407/568-5893.

Polk City

PARKS, BEACHES, AND RECREATION AREAS

41 Green Swamp

🐾🐾🐾 (See Orlando map on page 280)

The brown faces of cows peered out from behind a fence when we hiked here with Maggie near dusk one day. Maggie's head tilted as the cows mooed, as if to ask, "What's that?" The exciting thing for her, though, was spotting a bobcat stealthily dashing across the General James A. Van Fleet State Trail, part of the Green Swamp area that forms the headwaters of several rivers. Although it's bordered by deep, dark forest, most of the trail itself is unshaded. That's because it's a former railroad bed and part of the nationwide "rails to trails" movement. Expect to see horses and their riders, as well as cyclists here. There are no facilities, so be sure to bring water and other supplies.

The trail is 29 miles long and is accessible in a number of places by simply heading north on Highway 33 from Polk City, then turning left (west) and driving a few miles to the old railroad bed that forms the trail. We took Green Pond Road, but the trail is also accessible from Lake Erie Road, Poyner Road, and Dean Still Road. To use the north end of the trail, head west from Clermont on State Road 50 for about 10 miles and look for the Mabel Trailhead on the south side of the road. 352/394-2280.

St. Cloud

PARKS, BEACHES, AND RECREATION AREAS

42 East Lake Toho

🐾🐾🐾 (See Orlando map on page 280)

Locals like Shane Belson love to bring their dogs here to follow the two-mile stretch of sidewalk alongside Lake Toho. Belson says he keeps his Rhodesian Ridgebacks, Tara and Ricoh, on leash, although there are plenty of grassy areas around where well-behaved pooches might get away with roaming untethered.

"It's a great place," says Belson, who sometimes relaxes there after a hard day at the "office"—he's a biologist at the Tosohatchee State Reserve.

The south shore of the lake is great for Tara and Ricoh because they like to see and sniff other dogs and sometimes romp around a grassy area by the lake. People in-line skate, cycle, and walk along the sidewalk, so your pooch will have to be civil. You, too: Pooper-scooper bags are provided, so you know what to do!

From U.S. 192 at the south end of St. Cloud, head north on any street named after one of the 50 states (New York and Indiana are big ones) and proceed to the lake. Park along Lakeshore Drive and walk to your heart's content.

Auburndale

Leashed Labs may visit any city park, so strap on a lead and join pedestrians for a pleasant stroll around little Lake Stella north of downtown on County Road 559.

PARKS, BEACHES, AND RECREATION AREAS

43 Lena Vista Lake

(See Orlando map on page 280)

This is no great shakes, but if your pooch is passing through and wants to stretch her legs, give it a whirl. It's a short walk to the lake, where you might see otters, Muscovy ducks, or wood storks, as we did. The "park" is really just a one-acre plot covered with moss-draped oaks, but it's shady and fairly cool, even on a sunny day.

The park and lake are immediately east of Lena Vista Elementary. From town, go west on Highway 92 and turn north (right) onto Berkley Road, which leads past the elementary school. Park on the street by the empty lot; avoid the places that have No Trespassing signs by the lake; just walk by on the road as you circle the lake. 863/967-3400.

44 Lake Myrtle Park

(See Orlando map on page 280)

Call first to make sure the off-leash area has opened at this city park. Plans called for opening a sizable park—maybe three acres or more—sometime in 2006. Small dogs would play in their own fenced field. Big dogs would chase balls in the bigger fenced area.

Outside the bark park, leashed pets may follow walking paths. Kids appreciate the soccer fields.

From U.S. 92, turn north onto Berkley Road/County Road 655 (by the Super Wal-Mart). Go about 2.5 miles to Lake Myrtle Road. Turn left. Continue about 100 yards to the park. 863/965-5545.

Lakeland

All Lakeland city and Polk County parks are open to dogs on leashes. There is talk about building a dog park, but lack of money appears to be the sticking point. Want an off-leash area? Tell elected officials. Reach county commissioners at 863/534-6000. Call city commissioners at 863/834-6000.

PARKS, BEACHES, AND RECREATION AREAS

45 Crystal Lake

 (See Orlando map on page 280)

This small park consists mostly of a large boardwalk leading out onto Crystal Lake, one of dozens of lakes that give Lakeland its name. The boardwalk makes a semicircle, connecting one piece of shoreline to another.

The park is at 2500 N. Crystal Lake Drive. Take Crystal Lake Drive west from Highway 98. You'll see the park when you reach Combee Road. 863/534-4340.

46 Curtis Peterson Park

 (See Orlando map on page 280)

Set on Lake John and located immediately behind the Cleveland Heights Animal Clinic, this 38-acre park, named after a former president of the Florida Senate, is mostly dominated by sports fields. But dogs can trot around the edges and Maggie seemed to enjoy the break after a long car ride.

The park is at 3700 Cleveland Heights Boulevard. Head south from downtown on Florida Avenue to Edgewood Drive and turn left (east). At Cleveland Heights Boulevard, turn right (south). Look for the park entrance at left, just beyond the YMCA. 863/834-6035.

47 Lake Hollingsworth Park

(See Orlando map on page 280)

The boxy Frank Lloyd Wright architecture of Florida Southern College is the backdrop for a 2.7-mile-long walking trail around Lake Hollingsworth, which is encircled by a sidewalk and perfect for as long or short a walk as your dog desires. We even saw dogs running off leash here, though technically they're supposed to stay on the lead. Alert pooches might notice the botanical palm collection. Public parking is available on the south side of the lake, on the opposite side from the college.

The 18.4-acre park is at 920 Lake Hollingsworth Drive. From U.S. 92, take Ingraham Avenue South to McDonald Street. 863/834-6035.

DIVERSIONS

Head to a doggy oasis: In a city devoid of dog parks (so far), **The Doggie Bag** pet boutique serves as a focal point for Lakeland terriers and other four-legged lovables looking for a place to go or shop. Every week, leashed dogs show up for Sample Saturday to try out cakes and treats created by a local baker. Every day, owner Heather Moran offers treats and water to visiting canines—and to their people. Once a year, the place holds a Yappi Hour picnic. "We encourage people to bring their dogs in," says Moran. "We cater to the dogs and to their owners."

Cats occasionally arrive, too, to browse the 850-square-foot upscale boutique's aisles of collars, leashes, pet argyle sweaters, comfy beds, and pup T-shirts. A shop kitty lives here but moves to the back when Moran's bichon frise mix, Lily, or West Highland terrier, April, decide to work that day. (They let her know by standing by the door as Moran prepares to depart for work.) The boutique is at 1745 E. Edgewood Dr., Lakeland; 863/683-6220 or 888/683-6220.

48 Lake Parker Park

🐾🐾🐾 (See Orlando map on page 280)

This 100-acre park on sprawling Lake Parker is said to offer something for everyone, but we'll bet doggies will be happiest trotting down the walking trails that crisscross the woodsiest portions of the tree-shaded park, north and east of the soccer fields. Another path encircles the six soccer fields. Picnicking is also popular.

The park is at 910 E. Granada Street. Take Granada Street north from central Lakeland and look for entrances to the park on your left, just before Lake Parker. 863/834-6035.

49 Saddle Creek Park

🐾🐾🐾 🐾 (See Orlando map on page 280)

Dogs have to remain leashed at this favorite bird-watching spot, but they'll still have an experience to remember trodding the trails around the man-made lakes left over from when this area was mined for phosphate. Even though the area hasn't been totally restored, it still provides habitat for birds and other wildlife.

Maggie munched on grass in the park-like area before hitting a grassy trail that leads back to the wilder parts of the park. Once there, she was confused by the green, algae-like growth on top of the ponds, thinking that she could step onto the green stuff just like she did with the grass she'd been on earlier. Ploosh! Maggie was soaked. Smart as she is, though, Maggie failed to realize her mistake and took a second plunge at another little pond. Of course, you'll want to keep your dog out of these waters, as they could harbor alligators. The little lakes are pretty deep, and you'll see big, old cypress trunks lying in and near the water, a holdover from before this area was logged.

Pooches less eager to see wilderness but trying to keep their weight down might partake in the fitness trail here. There's also a boat ramp, picnicking facilities, and a playground.

To reach the county-run park from downtown Lakeland, take U.S. 92 east to Fish Hatchery Road, and turn left (north). At Morgan-Combee Road, turn right (east). The road will take you to the park at 3716 Morgan-Combee Road. 863/534-4340.

50 Sertoma Park

🐾 (See Orlando map on page 280)

Perhaps the best thing about this conveniently located 1.8-acre park is that it has three little picnic shelters where you could have an informal lunch with your pooch. You'll have a gorgeous view of the Larsen power plant right down the shore of Lake Park, the biggest of Lakeland's lakes. It's basically a boat ramp—and one where you're likely to see alligators—but a pleasant stop nonetheless.

The park is at 1800 E. Memorial Boulevard. Head east on U.S. 92/Memorial Avenue from Florida Avenue, the main north-south drag through town. You'll see the park on the left before you reach East Lake Parker Drive. 863/834-6035.

PLACES TO EAT

Steak-n-Shake: They don't really have steaks here, just Steakburgers, which basically are hamburgers. Chicken and turkey sandwiches also can be sampled at the four tables out back, which are protected by a rain shelter. 819 E. Memorial Blvd.; 863/683-9352.

PLACES TO STAY

Amerisuites: Maggie would never slide under the weight limit of 20 pounds required by this six-story, all-suite lodging located at Lakeland Center. Pets sleep in smoking rooms for $10 daily. Rates range $80–160. 525 W. Orange St., Lakeland; 863/859-2866; www.amerisuites.com.

Baymont Inn and Suites: At this pleasant four-story hotel off I-4 (Exit 33), pets under 40 pounds may pad along interior corridors to reach rooms—some with kitchens. Rates range $72–111. Pet fee is $20 per stay. 4315 Lakeland Park Dr., Lakeland; 863/815-0606; www.baymontinns.com.

Comfort Inn: Yorkshire terriers are accepted, but breeds over 20 pounds aren't, at this nicely landscaped 100-room hotel off I-4 (Exit 32). Rates range $50–150. Pet fee is $15 nightly. 3520 N. Highway 98, Lakeland; 863/859-0100; www.choicehotels.com.

Jameson Inn: Peewee pets—under 10 pounds—are accepted automatically, while larger dogs require approval from the general manager of this 67-unit pleasant lodging off I-4 (Exit 33). Rates range $60–90. Add $10 nightly pet fee. 4375 Lakeland Park Dr., Lakeland; 863/858-9070; www.jamesoninns.com.

La Quinta: King can sleep in a king room with a recliner at this pleasant six-story hotel off I-4 (Exit 32) and dream of doggy bags from the nearby Lone Star Steakhouse, Olive Garden, or Chili's. Rates range $81–119. 1024 Crevasse St., Lakeland; 863/859-2866; www.lq.com.

Motel 6: An economical choice for dogs who'd rather spend their money on rawhide treats, this basic 124-unit poolside motel is located off I-4 (Exit 32). One small or medium-size pet is permitted per room. Rates range $46–58. 3120 U.S. 98 North, Lakeland; 863/682-0643; www.motel6.com.

Winter Haven

PARKS, BEACHES, AND RECREATION AREAS

🟦 Lake Howard Park

🐾 (See Orlando map on page 280)

Maggie happily chased the Muscovy ducks that hang out in this extended grassy area alongside Lake Howard. Even though it's in an area in the middle of town, Lake Howard offers lucky pooches the opportunity to spot all manner of wildlife, including eagles, ospreys, alligators, otters, herons, frogs, water snakes, and marsh rabbits. Don't let your dog hang out too close to the water, though; you never know how well the local alligators have been eating. Lake Howard is one of 30 lakes inside city limits, but it has a distinction: This is where a guy named A. G. Hancock invented *barefoot* waterskiing in the 1940s (though it was later popularized by Dick Pope Jr.).

The park has a parking area and some nice, shaded lakeside picnic tables. It's located at Avenue A Southwest and Tower Drive. 941/291-5656.

Holopaw

PARKS, BEACHES, AND RECREATION AREAS

52 Triple N Ranch Wildlife Management Area

🐾🐾🐾 (See Orlando map on page 280)

Your dog's mission here is to do what he does best—walk! About 10 miles of walking trails spiderweb these 15 square miles, which are sliced up by Crabgrass Creek, Boggy Branch, Cabbage Slough, and West Branch. This property is a veritable mosaic of habitats, including oak and cypress woods, hardwood swamps, Florida prairies, and pine flatwoods. Plus they're filled with wild animals, such as bobcats, sandhill cranes, deer, turkeys, and—Robert's favorite—otters.

Like at neighboring Bull Creek Wildlife Management Area, you may encounter hunters here in winter. Call ahead to see if you and your pooch should wear orange-blaze clothing to alert hunters that you aren't prey. Bear in mind that you may also encounter horses and riders.

There are no facilities, so bring everything you will need, including water, toilet paper, food, and mosquito repellent.

To reach the area from Holopaw, head east on U.S. 192 about 3.5 miles and look for the entrance on the south side of the road. 352/732-1225.

53 Bull Creek Wildlife Management Area

🐾🐾🐾 (See Orlando map on page 280)

These 36 square miles aren't for the faint of paw, but the attractions are many for the outdoorsy pooch: the possibility of seeing wild creatures, including deer, turkeys, wading birds, and rabbits; an old cemetery; a historic railroad bed; or even canoeing (if you bring your own canoe). Your pooch can hoof it around an eight-mile loop trail or even go 17 miles on the Florida National Scenic Trail. However, we'd recommend a much shorter hike—for the sake of the dog, if not you.

Brochures at the check-in stations will help you navigate the trails and backcountry roads of this tract, which is owned by the water management district.

There are no facilities, save for a few on-site, hand-pumped wells for drinking water. Bring snacks, a hat, sunscreen, mosquito repellent, and any other supplies. Take care if you come during the cooler months from November to

January, when hunters may be present. Call ahead to find out whether you and your pooch need to wear orange-blaze clothing to warn hunters.

To reach the area from I-95, go west on U.S. 192. One entrance is on the south side of the highway about two miles after it passes Highway 419. To reach the other entrance, keep heading west on U.S. 192. When you are between 21 and 22 miles west of I-95, turn left (south) on Crabgrass Road, which will dead-end at the entrance to the tract. This area borders on the Triple N Ranch. 352/732-1225.

Lake Wales

PARKS, BEACHES, AND RECREATION AREAS

54 Lake Kissimmee State Park

😺😺🐾 (See Orlando map on page 280)

A drive past the cattle in the park's cow camp—where on weekends a costumed "cow hunter" pretends to be a Floridian cowboy from 1876—will launch any bored city dog into alert mode. Your leashed cowpoke may walk 50 yards from the parking lot to the 200-acre cow camp to sit around the campfire with you and swap stories with rangers. Just frame your questions without using modern-day references (such as Alpo) so the ranger, who appears to be straight out of the 1800s, can understand what you're talking about.

Staffers aren't crazy about dogs taking this trip back in time because the pooches tend to get a bit excited by all those big hooved creatures, and then the big hooved creatures tend to get excited, and, well, you get the idea. Mellow dogs on their best behavior have occasionally been tolerated.

That doesn't describe Maggie, though, and she longed to rush headlong into the woods elsewhere in this nearly eight-square-mile home of bobcats and deer. The place offers 13 miles of hiking trails. Dogs are permitted anywhere in the shady park except the campground. For private meals with your pal, eat under a moss-covered oak tree or at a creekside picnic table.

Even just driving into Lake Kissimmee State Park will titillate city pooches. You'll pass pastures and possibly hear croaking frogs.

Admission is $4 per vehicle. The park is at 14248 Camp Mack Road. From Lake Wales, take Highway 60 east for eight miles. Turn left (north) on Boy Scout Road and follow the signs. 863/696-1112.

PLACES TO STAY

Super 8: Local calls are free at this 62-room motel at the intersection of busy U.S. 27 and Highway 60. Rates run $45–79. 541 W. Central Ave., Lake Wales; 863/676-7925; www.super8.com.

Kenansville

An hour south of the family vacation haven of Disney World and just a few hours north of the party-hearty capital at southern Miami Beach, Kenansville gives you an idea of what Central Florida looked like for a long, long time, when most of the area was cattle country. Your dog will see fields of cattle seeking shelter from the hot sun under pines and palmettos.

PARKS, BEACHES, AND RECREATION AREAS

55 Three Lakes Wildlife Management Area

😋😋😋😋 (See Orlando map on page 280)

Maggie sounded like Darth Vader as she strained at her leash to bolt after wild turkeys at this exceptional backcountry hiking location. We also saw lots of deer prints in the sand as we traversed a small stream and ultra-thick oak hammocks along part of the Florida National Scenic Trail.

Hunters use this area in late fall and winter, so you'll want to be careful when you come here with your pooch, for your safety and your dog's. Call ahead to check hunt dates.

The roads here leave a lot to be desired. Four-wheel drive would be helpful but is not necessary, as we have proved. Still, it's best to check with the Florida Fish and Wildlife Conservation Commission about conditions before you come out. You can camp here, too, though we're unclear on how your dog would get any sleep out here with all the wild critters cruising the woods day and night. The primitive campsites are free for a reason—there are no facilities. Sites are first-come, first-served and require a free permit from the Florida Fish and Wildlife Conservation Commission, reached at 352/732-1225. When requesting a permit, ask for a map of the area to aid in finding your campsite.

From U.S. 441 at St. Cloud, turn right and head south on Canoe Creek Road/Highway 523. You'll see an entrance after about 25 miles. Continue another mile and take the second entrance on the right, a better road. It will lead to the Parker Slough parking area, where you can access the Florida National Scenic Trail. 352/732-1225.

Avon Park

PARKS, BEACHES, AND RECREATION AREAS

56 Lake Wales Ridge State Forest

😋😋 (See Orlando map on page 280)

Stay on the trail, Fido! Some of Florida's rarest plants are found at this 26,488-acre state forest. Nearly the size of Newark, New Jersey, the forest helps protect an ecosystem that evolved over eons. This ridge in the middle of Florida was one of the few places not covered by water as sea levels rose and fell over the millennia.

Alert pooches may notice rare scrub jays, a gray-and-blue bird whose closest relatives live in the deserts of the Southwest. Two dozen plants and 19 animals are classified as threatened or endangered, including the gopher tortoise, gopher frog, indigo snake, and the legless sand skink (look for the sand trails where the skink "swims"). As your pooch hikes the ancient sandhills and lusher areas, keep her leashed—you never know what she might trample.

Bring a hat, sunscreen, and water. Expect little shade, especially since 2004's hurricanes toppled a stand of tall pines.

To reach the 3.6-mile Bay Loop hiking trail, take U.S. 27, then turn east onto County Road 630. Follow it through Frostproof for three miles. Bay Loop Trail is the second trailhead on the road's north side. The 2.5-mile-long Scrub Jay Loop Trail is the third trailhead on the road's north side.

To reach the Reedy Creek Trail, which stretches at least 11 miles, take U.S. 60 east from U.S. 27 in Lake Wales. Travel 9.5 miles to Walk in the Water Road. Turn right. Go nine miles, cross County Road 630A, and continue south on what now will be called Blue Jordan Road. In two miles, turn left onto North Lake Reedy Boulevard. Go 1.6 miles to Lake Arbuckle Road, turn left, go 1.5 miles to unpaved Rucks Dairy Road, and turn right. The trailhead kiosk is on the left at the fork in the road. 863/635-8589.

57 Avon Park Air Force Bombing Range

🐾🐾🐾 (See Orlando map on page 280)

Weird as it may seem, this Air Force bombing range is a jaw-droppingly beautiful place to pal around with the outdoorsy pooch in your life. The size of a small county, it encompasses everything from deep, dark forests to desert-like scrub areas subject to occasional flooding.

Maggie was enthralled here, her sniffer going a mile a minute as she made her way along trails hemmed in by prehistoric-looking ferns. This is a popular place for bird-watchers, and you may spot the endangered red-cockaded woodpecker.

Now the details: Yes, this is a bombing range. But 82,000 of the 106,000 acres are open to the public. You have to stop by the security office on the way to pick up a free permit and sign a waiver. If you or your pooch should fall into a shell hole or gun emplacement, that's tough luck. Just stick to the portions of the Florida National Scenic Trail that run through here and you'll be okay.

Pooches are supposed to be leashed, and we recommend that you follow the rules even when you're way out in the wilds of this little-used area to minimize the chance of snakebite. Bring everything you'll need, especially water.

Dogs who are scared of gunfire may want to steer clear during hunting season, from mid-September to early January. Dogs are prohibited on weekends during the spring turkey season, from mid-March to mid-April.

From Orlando, head south for about an hour on U.S. 27. Next, head west from the town of Avon Park on Highway 64 for approximately 10 miles. Look for the signs for the Natural Resources Office, where you must go to pick up a permit. 863/452-4254 or 863/452-4119.

Donaldson Park

 (See Orlando map on page 280)

Set at Lake Verona across from City Hall, this small sleepy downtown park is named for the Depression-era mayor who developed the mile-long Mall (see separate park listing below). Covered concrete picnic tables provide a place to eat; afterward, take kids to the playground or beach area. Fill a water bowl at the restrooms.

The park is across from City Hall, 110 E. Main St., at the east end of Main Street as you're leaving downtown. 863/452-4414.

59 The Mall

 (See Orlando map on page 280)

This little linear park along Main Street features a small gazebo under the spreading arms of ancient oaks, with quaint, historic buildings on either side. 863/452-4400 or 863/452-4414.

PLACES TO STAY

Econo Lodge Sebring: After your morning swim in the outdoor pool (open in season) and complimentary breakfast of pastry and coffee, your four-legged explorer hopes to leave the 57-unit motel for a day of hiking at Lake Wales Ridge State Forest, the Avon Park Air Force Bombing Range, or Sebring's Highlands Hammock State Park. Rates range $60–150. 2511 U.S. 27 South, Avon Park; 863/453-2000; www.econolodge.com.

Sebring

PARKS, BEACHES, AND RECREATION AREAS

60 Highlands Hammock State Park

 (See Orlando map on page 280)

Don't tell your dog, but a catwalk—yikes!—wound through the cypress swamp of this gem of a park as early as 1933. Today, leashed dogs love the 20-minute walk down the rebuilt Cypress Swamp Trail, where the brown waters act somewhat like a mirror reflecting the tall cypress trees. Maggie lunged at an armadillo, then followed two itsy-bitsy dogs and a German shepherd along a boardwalk made from two-by-fours spaced about an inch apart. Dogs with tiny paws need to walk carefully to make sure their feet don't slip between the boards. Stop to rest at the interpretive signs to learn, for instance, that giant dragonflies with three-foot wingspans fluttered around the world's first swamps. (Thank goodness no Chihuahuas were around back then.)

This nearly six-square-mile park is a favorite of some Miamians, who travel a few hours to flee life in the city. Your dog could visit several times before she'd be able to follow all the short trails here: the Fern Garden Trail, the Memorial Trail, the Wild Orange Grove Trail, the Hickory Trail, and the Young Hammock Trail. The other options—the woodsy Ancient Hammock Trail and the Big Oak Trail—should protect dogs from the afternoon sun better than the sunnier Cypress Swamp Trail.

Just driving through one of Florida's few large remaining virgin hammocks feels like a trip through a jungle, and Maggie thoroughly enjoys the ride. When she spotted her first deer sniffing at fallen orange rinds in an orange grove near dusk, she mightily craned her neck through the partially open car window. When her barking frenzy began, we pulled away. Deer and alligators are seen every day at the park.

Dogs may eat in the picnic areas, and later bed down in the campground. It's $13 a night for the humans and $2 for the canines. Camping dogs need written proof of rabies vaccination.

Entrance costs $3.25 per vehicle. From Sebring, head four miles west on Highway 634 to the park entrance. 863/386-6094.

PLACES TO STAY

Highlands Hammock State Park: Camping with dogs is allowed. See Parks, Beaches, and Recreation Areas, above, for camping information.

Inn on the Lakes: Rates are $65–150, plus $40 per stay for the dog. The motel is on U.S. 27/98, north of Highway 17. 3100 Golfview Rd., Sebring; 863/471-9400.

River Ranch

A city dog will perk up when you take him on a drive down Highway 60 to River Ranch, his head bobbing out the car window, tongue flapping in the breeze. Maggie peered at black cows with white faces and brown cows with ivory markings. She ogled the big trucks stacked full of Christmas-colored red and green bell peppers and oranges plucked from the green-tufted trees we passed.

PARKS, BEACHES, AND RECREATION AREAS

61 KICCO Wildlife Management Area

🐾🐾🐾 (See Orlando map on page 280)

The antithesis of Disney World, the 27-mile hiking trail that winds south across this remote wilderness and through the nearby Avon Park Air Force

Phil Frank

Bombing Range will tire any energetic dog. Of course, a short walk will do for most leashed pups visiting the nearly 12 square miles of KICCO (pronounced KISS-oh)—a name that comes from this land's 1920s incarnation as the Kissimmee Island Cattle Company. The Florida National Scenic Trail starts here in a beautiful oak hammock, where, after a rain, the resurrection ferns on the tree trunks unfurl into tiny green tufts. Maggie, however, was more interested in sniffing the ground for evidence of raccoons, armadillos, and deer.

Follow the orange blazes painted on the sides of trees and you'll pass through shady oak forests and sunny pinelands. Hunters share the lower part of these woods during limited hunting seasons, but they're prohibited in a sizable portion of the wilderness—south of Highway 60 to the Eight-Mile Canal. From the Outdoor Resorts River Ranch (see Places to Stay, below), day hikers can easily walk two miles south toward the Eight-Mile Canal or more than two miles north toward a navigational lock on the Kissimmee River and rest assured that the territory is closed to hunters. Dogs classified as hunting breeds are prohibited in the woods except when accompanying hunters during hunting season. Other dogs must be "restrained" at all times. Groan.

Bring water, food, and mosquito repellent.

From Yeehaw Junction off Florida's Turnpike, take Highway 60 west and turn south at the Outdoor Resorts River Ranch entrance on River Ranch Road. Pass the security kiosk (tell them you're going to hike on the trail). Soon, you'll see a KICCO sign on the right. Drive about a mile to the trailhead of the Florida National Scenic Trail. 863/648-3203 or 800/432-2045.

PLACES TO STAY

Outdoor Resorts River Ranch: This standout RV park has 367 sites (no tents, please). Leashed dogs may roam around the massive fields of this pleasant getaway, but don't even think about taking a dog into the hotel or horseback-riding area. Far from the big city, this resort nonetheless offers such creature comforts as a pool, a game room, shuffleboard courts, a snack bar, and a dining room where you may request doggy bags. Two dogs are allowed per campsite. Rates are $30–40, and reservations are recommended. The resort is at 24700 Highway 60, five miles east of Indian Lake Estates and halfway between Lake Wales and Yeehaw Junction. P.O. Box 30421, River Ranch; 941/692-1321.

328

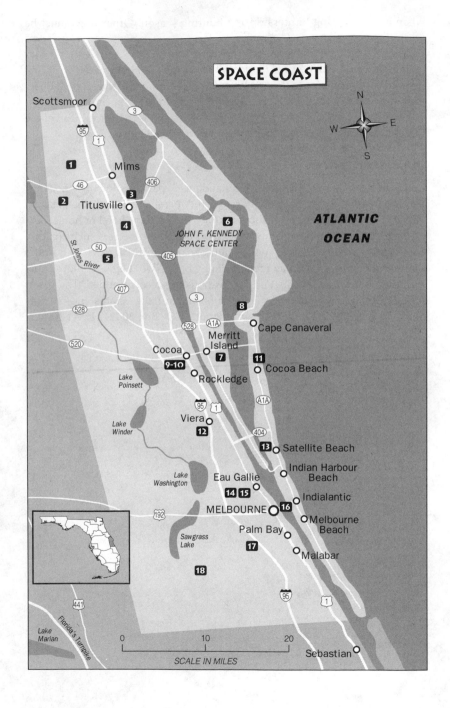

SPACE COAST

N
W · E
S

Scottsmoor

(3)

{95}
(1)

1

Mims

(406)

(46)

3

2   Titusville

4

JOHN F. KENNEDY
SPACE CENTER

6

ATLANTIC
OCEAN

St Johns River

(50)

5

(405)

(407)

(3)

(528)

(A1A)
(528)

8

(520)

Merritt
Island

Cape Canaveral

Cocoa

7

9-10

Rockledge

11

Cocoa Beach

Lake
Poinsett

(A1A)

{95} (1)

Lake
Winder

Viera

12

(404)

13

Satellite Beach

Indian Harbour
Beach

Lake
Washington

Eau Gallie

14 **15**

MELBOURNE

16

Indialantic

(192)

Palm Bay

Melbourne
Beach

Sawgrass
Lake

17

Malabar

18

{95}   (1)

(441)

Florida's Turnpike

Lake
Marian

0   10   20

SCALE IN MILES

Sebastian

CHAPTER 11
Space Coast

The first warm-blooded mammal to rocket into outer space wasn't Neil Armstrong, but Laika the dog. That's right, Laika became the envy of all dogs who ever pined for a ride when she blasted into space on the Soviet Union's *Sputnik II,* 12 years before Armstrong uttered his memorable words on the moon.

So, if a man—or a dog—can go to the moon (or somewhere reasonably near it), then why can't a dog go to the beach? In this hotbed of rocket scientists, solving the riddle of how to reserve at least 100 yards of beach for dogs should be a simple task. But for now, dogs are banned from one of Florida's longest stretches of beachfront, not to mention many of the parks run by Brevard County. They also can't set paw inside the boundaries of the Canaveral National Seashore. And they can't sniff around the retired spaceships next to the parking lot at the popular Kennedy Space Center visitors center. Dogs there are ushered into free kennels.

In short, this region is doggone ruff on pooches.

PICK OF THE LITTER—SPACE COAST

BEST DOG PARKS
Satellite Beach Dog Park, Satellite Beach (page 342)
Wickham Park Dog Park, Melbourne (page 344)

BEST BED-AND-BREAKFAST INNS
Crane Creek Inn, Melbourne (page 346)
Wisteria Inn, Melbourne (page 347)

BEST LODGING FOR SWIMMERS
Surfcaster Motel, Melbourne (page 347)

BEST PLACE TO EAT AND ADOPT A DOG
Mustard's Last Stand, Melbourne (page 345)

BEST LODGING FOR SPACE BUFFS
La Quinta, Cocoa Beach (page 341)

BEST HIKES
Merritt Island National Wildlife Refuge, Merritt Island (page 335)

A key reason dogs are taboo at beaches? Blame a crusade against furry beachgoers waged in the 1970s by the local paper *Cocoa Today* (now *Florida Today*), long before its founder, Al Neuharth, launched *USA Today*. While newspapers elsewhere printed editorials concerning the political crises of the moment, this paper campaigned to get dogs off the beach—a matter of some embarrassment for at least a few staff reporters. Today, many parks bear the dreaded No Animals sign, and we're told that the beach ban is ardently enforced with hefty fines.

It's enough to make a dog wish that a real-life Major Nelson and his genie lived here, as they did in the television sitcom *I Dream of Jeannie.* That way, Jeannie could blink her eyes and signs saying Yes, Dogs Are Allowed would appear along the beach and in county parks. Until then, Maggie has sniffed out some other suggested stops—including the outstanding Merritt Island National Wildlife Refuge (see Parks, Beaches, and Recreation Areas under Merritt Island, below).

Mims

PARKS, BEACHES, AND RECREATION AREAS

1 Buck Lake Conservation Area

🐾🐾🐾 (See Space Coast map on page 328)

This is sort of the little-brother partner to Seminole Ranch Conservation Area (see below), and these 15 square miles on the opposite side of State Road 46 are equally fascinating for woodsy dogs. Bobcats, owls, alligators, and wild turkeys live on this former cattle ranch, and your pal can get dog-tired tromping on the hiking trails that wind throughout. A small ridge of 200 acres in the eastern part of the property provides conditions dry enough that you might see the rare scrub jay. Your pooch can also sniff through marshy areas located mostly near Buck Lake.

Bring water, mosquito repellent, and hiking boots.

These woodlands and wetlands stretch from southeastern Volusia County to northwestern Brevard County. From I-95 (Exit 223), head west on State Road 46 nearly one mile to the first parking lot, at right. A second parking area is about 6.5 miles west of I-95 on State Road 46. A boat ramp is 3.5 miles west of I-95 on State Road 46 at Six Mile Creek. 386/329-4500 or 386/329-4404.

2 Seminole Ranch Conservation Area

🐾🐾🐾 (See Space Coast map on page 328)

At this 45-square-mile marshy wilderness that stretches into four counties, a leashed dog can feel like he's getting away from it all during a short hike. Lucky dogs might see white pelicans, sandhill cranes, roseate spoonbills, or bald eagles. Not-so-lucky dogs could be mistaken for game by seasonal hunters, so check hunting dates by calling ahead at 352/732-1225.

A 4.3-mile-long section of the Florida National Scenic Trail passes through here. With neighbors such as the Tosahatchee State Reserve and the St. Johns National Wildlife Refuge, this place is unmistakably un-urban. The conservation area includes 12 miles of the St. Johns River, and many of the salt-tolerant and marine-dwelling creatures found here live nowhere else along the river. Almost all of this wilderness serves as a floodplain for the St. Johns River, so paws may be muddied (keep a towel handy in the car). Trails flood seasonally.

Bring water, mosquito repellent, hiking boots, binoculars, and any supplies you'll need for your hike.

To reach the hiking trails, go west on State Road 50 from I-95 for 10 miles, turn right onto County Road 420, then right at Wheeler Road. 386/329-4500.

Titusville

This is the town closest to the space shuttle launchpad, and it's here that your dog can feel the ground rumbling beneath her paws on launch days.

PARKS, BEACHES, AND RECREATION AREAS

3 Sand Point Park

😾😾 (See Space Coast map on page 328)

Pelicans are sure to grab the attention of your leashed dog at this popular 30-acre park overlooking the pretty Indian River. Anglers sometimes fish for their dinner from the shoreline, and the big-billed birds hang out in hopes of consuming fishy leftovers. A blacktop walkway cuts through the open and shaded portions of the park, giving dogs and their human companions a view of the broad river and the Max Brewer Causeway. You can follow a stationed exercise trail, but don't worry about getting too winded— it measures two-thirds of a mile. At the park's south entrance stands the Astronaut Memorial, which honors those who gave their lives for the NASA space effort.

Barbecue grills, picnic tables, 11 pavilions, and a playground are available, and you can fill a water bowl for your thirsty dog at the restroom. The unfenced park is at busy U.S. 1, so you'll hear the noise of passing cars and want to keep your pal leashed.

The park is at 10 E. Max Brewer Causeway, at the intersection of U.S. 1 and the causeway. 321/264-5105.

4 Brevard Community College North Campus

😾 (See Space Coast map on page 328)

A few big fields dot this campus on the north end of Titusville, and leashed dogs unofficially stretch their legs there when students aren't around. Technically, dogs are banned. Look for big fields by the John Henry Jones Gymnatorium, the faculty and staff parking lot, and the campus entrance. The campus is at 1311 N. U.S. 1. 321/632-1111.

5 Canaveral Marshes Conservation Area

😾😾 (See Space Coast map on page 328)

The best part of this tract managed by the St. Johns River Water Management District is the wildlife. Lucky dogs may notice a deer, wild turkey, feral pig, or soaring eagle. Wading birds and alligators are a pretty good bet at the marshes within these 10.5 square miles.

Leashed dogs may follow the 3.9-mile moderately difficult Florida National Scenic Trail here as it traverses the pancake-flat floodplain of the St. Johns River, crosses cattle pasture, and reaches scattered hammocks of oaks, pines,

DIVERSIONS

Take Rocky to see a rocket: If your dog is steamed about being turned away from the Kennedy Space Center visitors center, he can see an actual Titan 1 rocket perched horizontally in front of **Titusville High School,** 150 Terrier Trail South. The rusting rocket is a source of civic pride, prompting citizens and businesses to pull together to raise money to restore it to its former glory. First developed in 1955, the Titan 1 rocket—the nation's first two-stage rocket—launched Gemini astronauts into space and has blasted exploratory robots off to Mars and Saturn.

As for watching the launch of an unmanned rocket or a space shuttle, you could walk into any parking lot or stand almost anywhere on launch day to track the shuttle's fiery plume as it fades away in the sky. While space fans stake out viewing spots at such places as Space Shuttle View Park and along the Max Brewer Memorial Causeway, many dogs would be too scared to tag along. If your pet is afraid of fireworks or thunder, then the ground-trembling roar of a space shuttle launch isn't for him. Just hearing the muffled roar while safely ensconced inside a motel room would suffice. For shuttle launch dates, call 321/452-2121.

and red cedar. Much of the land is poorly drained, making it muddy during rainy times (wear hiking boots).

About midway through the hiking trail, you'll cross the Allison-Addison Canal—basically a canal to nowhere. Envisioned to connect the St. Johns River with the Indian River, it never was completed. Money ran out when the rock on the east shore of Indian River proved too expensive to dig through, according to the Florida Trail Association, which maintains the hiking trails. Much of the trail is sun-washed, so arrive early or late in the day and avoid the place in summer. Turn around at a comfortable distance for your pooch. For a Canaveral Marshes Trail hiking map, contact Florida Trail at 877/HIKE-FLA.

This conservation area is far southwest of Titusville, out on State Road 50 by the Great Outdoors Resort. From I-95, go west on State Road 50 for 2.6 miles to reach the hiking trail's north entrance, at left. 407/349-4972 or 877/HIKE-FLA.

PLACES TO EAT

Kloiber's Cobbler Eatery: Quiche, soups, specialty salads, and sandwiches are the mainstays of this downtown-area lunch spot. When you and your pooch arrive at the couple of outdoor tables, just let the staff inside know you're out there so they can serve you. 337 S. Washington Ave.; 321/383-0689.

Moon Light Drive-In: Everyone is supposed to eat in the car at this 1950s throwback, so dogs don't have to feel like second-class citizens. Burgers, fried mushrooms, onion rings, chicken sandwiches, and fried shrimp are among the menu items. You'll recognize the eatery by its neon sign with three stars and a sliver of moon. 1515 S. Washington Ave.; 321/267-8222.

PLACES TO STAY

Best Western Space Shuttle Inn: Humans appreciate the dry sauna, pool, shuffleboard, lounge, and fishing pond (with resident alligator). Pooches will appreciate any handouts from the on-site eatery or others neighboring this pleasant, 129-unit motel off I-95 (Exit 215), where you'll sleep in a smoking room. Rates range $69–135. Add $10 daily per small pet. 3455 Cheney Hwy., Titusville; 321/269-9100; www.bestwestern.com.

Comfort Inn: Six rooms are set aside for pets at this pleasant 117-room poolside lodging off I-95 (Exit 215), where continental breakfast and local calls are free. Rates range $59–255. Add $10 daily per pet. 3655 Cheney Hwy., Titusville; 321/269-7110; www.choicehotels.com.

Days Inn: This pleasant 149-unit poolside motel is about 15 miles from the wonderful pooch-permissive Merritt Island National Wildlife Refuge (see Parks, Beaches, and Recreation Areas under Merritt Island, below). If your pal's bandanna gets dirty while hiking there, you can wash it at the guest laundry here. Shuffleboard and an exercise room also are offered. Rates run $60–135. Add a $10 daily pet fee. 3755 Cheney Hwy., Titusville; 321/269-4480; www.daysinn.com.

The Great Outdoors RV Resort: Deer and wild turkeys are known to scamper within this roughly 4.5-square-mile, amenity-packed RV park geared to older campers. That's sure to get your dog's sniffer twitching. Only self-contained RVs at least 18 feet or longer are accepted at these manicured sites. No tents, truck campers, or pop-ups. Sites run $30–40. 135 Plantation Dr., Titusville; 321/269-5004 or 800/621-2267; www.tgoresort.com.

Hampton Inn: A kidney-shaped outdoor pool, a free breakfast bar, and a fitness room are offered at this high-rise lodging off I-95 (Exit 215). Rates start at $99. Add a flat $25 pet fee. 4760 Helen Hauser Blvd., Titusville; 321/383-9191; www.hamptoninn.com.

Holiday Inn Riverfront: Set on the Indian River, this pleasant, 117-room motel has a clear view of the space shuttle launchpads, but your furry pal might be more interested in an order of bacon from room service. Guests can fish from the seawall or take advantage of the lounge, restaurant, exercise room, pool, and kiddie pool. Rates run $79–145. Add a flat $25 pet fee. 4951 S. Washington Ave., Titusville; 321/269-2121; www.holidayinnksc.com.

Manatee Hammock Campground: The canopy of oaks is a godsend for dogs tired of Florida's hot sun, and the setting on the Indian River is good for boaters and canoeists who want to use the small boat ramp. But NASA fans may appreciate this 26-acre, 147-site, county-run campground for another reason: It's less than 10 miles from space shuttle launches. Locals use this place as a day-use area for fishing, and some bring along their dogs to play by the river. Technically, dogs only are permitted with registered campers, however. Camping is $14–22. 7275 S. U.S. 1, Titusville; 321/264-5083.

Ramada Inn & Suites-Kennedy Space Center: Another good option for those traveling with pooch, this place offers a playground, whirlpool, fitness room, 24-hour restaurant, sauna, and heated outdoor pool just east of I-95 (Exit 215). At this 124-unit lodging, rates range $70–130. Pet fee is $25 per stay. 3500 Cheney Hwy., Titusville; 321/269-5510; www.ramada.com.

Riverside Inn: Arrive by boat or car at this 104-room motel on the Indian River. It offers a restaurant, lounge, and exercise room, yet the big deal here is the view of the Kennedy Space Center launch sites. For the few dogs who miraculously don't mind the sound of thunder, this may be a good spot to watch the much more thunderous space shuttle launches. Rates start at $40. Pet fee is $10 daily or $12.50 weekly. 1829 Riverside Dr./U.S. 1, Titusville; 321/267-7900.

Merritt Island

Looking for an off-leash park? A bark park is in the works for Mitchell Ellington Park, 4110 N. Tropical Trail. For current status, call the Brevard County Parks & Recreation Department at 321/255-4400.

PARKS, BEACHES, AND RECREATION AREAS

6 Merritt Island National Wildlife Refuge

🐾🐾🐾🐾 (See Space Coast map on page 328)

To Maggie, a four-paw rating isn't good enough for this 219-square-mile birder's paradise. She awarded it four paws and a wagging tail. While Merritt Island is best known as the home of the Kennedy Space Center, most of the government land remains natural.

Leashed dogs can follow four nature trails. On the half-mile Oak Hammock interpretive loop trail, the path alternates between a gravel and dirt walkway and a boardwalk with inch-wide gaps between its boards. Maggie watched her footing so her paws wouldn't slip through the open spaces—which happened once when she was distracted by her pursuit of an armadillo. Ferns provide a beautiful understory. Leafy oaks and maples protect dogs from the hot sun. At one point, you can leave this trail to follow a straight, car-width trail, but it has no shade. As you approach the marsh/oak transition zone, look at the muddy floor beyond the boardwalk for signs of raccoons, wild hogs, and squirrels.

The two-mile Palm Hammock loop trail is more challenging and muddy after recent rains. The boardwalks span seasonally flooded marshes and connect three cabbage palm/oak hammocks.

The five-mile Allan D. Cruickshank loop trail to the Indian River features an observation tower located only a five-minute walk from the trailhead parking lot. There is precious little shade, so hike in the early morning or late afternoon.

Bring water, mosquito repellent, and binoculars. Most trails have no nearby restrooms. Biting insects, high water, and sudden thunderstorms may be a problem, particularly from May to September.

From I-95, go east on Highway 406. After you cross the Indian River on Max Brewer Memorial Parkway/Highway 402, you'll be in the refuge. The visitors center is four miles ahead on the right. The Oak Hammock and Palm Hammock trailheads are near the information center. 321/861-0667.

🟦 Brevard Veterans Memorial Center

🔥 (See Space Coast map on page 328)

This small park overlooking Newfound Harbor is a good place for you to sit on a bench with your leashed dog, but there's precious little else for a pooch to do. The park is at 400 S. Sykes Creek Pkwy., behind the Merritt Square Mall at 777 E. Merritt Island Causeway/Highway 520. 321/453-1776.

PLACES TO EAT

Brevard Seafood Crab Shack: Not an actual restaurant, this retail market nonetheless will boil up some savory garlic crabs for you to take outside to eat at an uncovered table with your dog. 580 W. Merritt Island Causeway; 321/459-3759.

Dairy Queen: Munch hot dogs, barbecue sandwiches, or ice cream with your dog at one of the half-dozen picnic tables shaded from the sun. 265 N. Courtenay Pkwy.; 321/452-1610.

Shuttles Bar & Grill: The half-pound burgers named for space missions are popular, but the cook, Ken, prides himself on his barbecue technique—he cooks chunks of pork for 20 to 26 hours as an occasional special. Astronauts are known to hold parties here before their launches, and Kennedy Space Center employees sometimes head here after work. Space memorabilia decorates the walls inside, but you and your pooch will sit outside at a small picnic table. You may run with your leashed dog in the yard or even play horseshoes. Just tie up your pal near you before you play or eat. Note: Horses sometimes are hitched here, too. The casual eatery is outside the gates of the Kennedy Space Center. 6100 N. Courtenay Pkwy.; 321/453-2320.

Sinbad Mediterranean Fast Food: It's not every day that a dog can order falafel, hummus plates, gyros, or beef kabob sandwiches at a drive-through restaurant. You may eat with your pooch at one of the three outdoor tables in the parking lot out back, but the view is far less interesting than the tasty food whipped up at this family operation. The kafta is like a Mediterranean meat loaf made of ground beef, spices, and onions, served in pita bread with lettuce and tomatoes. Too daring? Try a hot dog, burger, or salad. 1450 N. Courtenay Pkwy.; 321/459-9815.

DIVERSIONS

Take a wildlife tour by car: Canine couch potatoes will find **Merritt Island National Wildlife Refuge** great for windshield explorers. During our self-guided driving tour (pamphlets are available at the visitors center or the trailhead), Maggie paced the backseat and poked her head out a window. She panted happily as she took in Black Point Wildlife Drive.

At stop No. 1, bald eagles nest in pines to the left, but Maggie instead ached to rush after ducks about 10 feet from the car. At stop No. 2, you'll learn about mosquito control efforts that hurt seven species of birds but benefited 22 others. At stop No. 7, you'll discover why thousands of birds from as far away as Alaska spend winters here or stop on their way to the tropics. Among them are at least 50,000 ducks and 100,000 coots. Some arrive as early as September, but the peak time to hear the cacophony of chirping is January and February.

Bring binoculars to zoom in on the birds in the huge, wet prairie. At least 310 species have been noted.

Max Holk Creek Wildlife Drive offers another windshield tour. It's closed frequently due to NASA operations, so it's best to stop first at the visitors center to plan your visit.

A drive through any part of the refuge is a treat for a city dog. He may notice an osprey sitting on a pole or a turtle lumbering alongside the road. Space buffs at some point are sure to notice in the distance NASA's boxy Vehicle Assembly Building, which appeared in the movie *Apollo 13*.

From I-95, go east on Highway 406. After you cross the Indian River on Max Brewer Memorial Parkway/Highway 402, you'll be in the refuge. The visitors center is four miles ahead on the right. 321/861-0667.

Cape Canaveral

PARKS, BEACHES, AND RECREATION AREAS

🐾 Port's End Park/Canal Locks

🐾🐾 (See Space Coast map on page 328)

This is actually three parks in one, with a four-acre picnic area for hungry hounds, a make-do beach-like area for water dogs, and a set of canal locks for pooches who are engineering-minded. Port's End Park is little more than a glorified boat ramp, but it does offer a few picnic tables shaded by shelters. An observation tower provides a view of the harbor. Fill a pet water bowl at the restrooms.

Next door, the U.S. Army Corps of Engineers operates locks on the canal. The public is allowed to come in and sniff around. But the best part is that you're right across the canal from a makeshift beach area favored by anglers and their dogs. Here, there are plenty of sandpipers and gulls for chasing. It's a beach of broken-up shells and mud—nothing to howl about by human standards, but we saw several happy dogs romping here.

To reach the picnic area, head east on the Bennett Causeway/State Road 528/Highway A1A/Bee-Line Expressway from Merritt Island. Where the road bears right, make a left onto Dave Nisbet Drive, which will immediately put you onto George J. King Boulevard. (You have to make a left or right onto George J. King Boulevard; make a left.) Then make an almost immediate left onto Mullet Drive, which leads through an industrial section to the park. That's also where you'll find the locks. If instead you want to take your dog to the beach, head east on the Bennett Causeway and take the Highway 401 exit heading north. You'll pass Port's End Park on your right just before crossing the port canal. As soon as you cross the bridge, park on the right side of the road on the grassy berm and climb down the rutted shell-and-sand path to the beach. 321/783-7831.

Cocoa

For leash-free fun, head to Cocoa Beach's Lori Wilson Park (see Cocoa Beach, below).

PARKS, BEACHES, AND RECREATION AREAS

🖤 Florida Solar Energy Center

🐾 (See Space Coast map on page 328)

The fact that we're even listing the large grassy field behind this government building tells you about the sad state of canine affairs on the Space Coast. But this field will do in a pinch for a leashed dog who simply must

stop somewhere for a few moments. For another alternative, explore the grounds back by the planetarium at Brevard Community College, or head to the banks of the college's Clear Lake. Alligators lurk in the lake, so keep your dog leashed. Note: Leashed dogs are tolerated at these areas of the college campus, but technically pets are banned. Use your judgment. The campus is immediately behind the energy center.

The energy center is at 1679 Clearlake Rd./Highway 501; 321/638-1000. The college is at 1519 Clearlake Road. 321/632-1111.

Travis Park

🐾 (See Space Coast map on page 328)

A local black Lab mix named Quincy highly recommends his favorite routine: Follow the mile-long paved path around Clear Lake that extends from this park to the nearby Florida Solar Energy Center. Explore a patch of natural Old Florida woods along the way. "You really feel like you're in Florida," says Quincy's two-legged companion, Susan Rieff.

Dominated by a community center building, this three-acre park also offers volleyball courts. Kindly avoid the front of the park, where kids play. The park is at 2001 Michigan Blvd., just east of Clear Lake and just west of Clearlake Road/Highway 501. 321/633-1871.

PLACES TO EAT

Arbetter Hot Dogs: Eat dogs with your dog at an outdoor table. *Spacecoast Living Magazine* calls them "the best dogs in the central Coast." 816 Dixon Blvd.; 321/636-0763.

PLACES TO STAY

Best Western Cocoa Inn: Toss a few dogs—frankfurters, of course—on the two barbecue grills at the picnic pavilion of this 120-unit poolside motel just east of I-95 (Exit 201). If the free continental breakfast won't do, then pass the on-site lounge and cross the parking lot to reach the International House of Pancakes, where your dog might request a takeout order of bacon. Pets under 20 pounds are accepted for $10 nightly. Rates range $59–99. 4225 W. King St., Cocoa; 321/632-1065; www.bestwestern.com.

Days Inn Cocoa Expo: A dog under 40 pounds may join you at this 115-unit poolside motel west of I-95 (Exit 202), near an Outback Steakhouse and McDonald's. Rates range $55–79. 5600 State Road 524, Cocoa; 321/636-6500; www.daysinn.com.

Econo Lodge Space Center: Queenie can request a queen room at this 150-room poolside motel, provided she weighs 40 pounds or less (the motel limit). Amenities include a cocktail lounge, shuffleboard, and a restaurant. Rates run $55–150, plus $10 per stay for the pooch. A separate $30 pet deposit will be refunded, barring doggy damage. 3220 N. U.S. 1, Cocoa; 321/632-4561; www.choicehotels.com

Ramada Inn: Set on 17 acres featuring a walking/jogging trail that circles a fishing lake, this 99-room poolside motel off I-95 (Exit 202) accepts dogs under 45 pounds. Rates range $60–99, plus $5 daily pet fee. A separate $50 pet deposit is refunded, barring canine mishaps. 900 Friday Rd., Cocoa; 321/631-1210; www.ramada.com.

Super 8 Cocoa: Next door to the Ramada Inn, this 53-unit motel shares ownership and a people-pleaser: a walking/jogging trail that circles a bass-stocked fishing lake. A restaurant is next door, too, in case your pooch requests an order of bacon. Deemed a "superior small lodging" by an independent local panel, the motel is just southwest of I-95 (Exit 202). Rates run $40–90, plus $5 daily pet fee. A separate $50 pet deposit will be refunded in the absence of terrier trouble. Pets under 45 pounds, please. 900A Friday Rd., Cocoa; 321/631-1212; www.super8.com.

Cocoa Beach

PARKS, BEACHES, AND RECREATION AREAS

11 Lori Wilson Park

🐾 (See Space Coast map on page 328)

The two-acre off-leash area of this Brevard County park may not yet be open when you read this, so call first. County commissioners approved Cocoa Beach's first dog park in January 2005. Plans called for separate fenced areas for big dogs and small dogs, as well as restrooms for people.

Making it happen took teamwork, including grassroots help from the Community Problem Solving Team of Future Problem Solvers at Cocoa Beach High School. Resident Chris Albergo, a member of the Brevard Animal Recreation Club, also worked with city commissioners to retrieve city money for fencing and restrooms, then turned to the county to provide land within popular Lori Wilson Park. All the while, Albergo's dogs Buddy and Max crossed their legs in anticipation of the grand opening.

The off-leash area is to open at 1500 N. Atlantic Avenue. From State Road 520, go south 1.4 miles on State Road A1A. Remember: Call first to make sure it's open. 321/455-1380 or 321/633-1874.

PLACES TO EAT

Taco City: This beachside eatery located a mile north of Patrick Air Force Base claims to serve the best in Tex-Mex cuisine, though its claim to fame on Surfline.com is that "almost every pro or otherwise surfer from Cocoa Beach has worked there for at least a day or two (including the Slater brothers)."

Sample nachos, tacos, burritos, fajitas, or enchiladas at an outdoor table with your dog. 2955 S. Atlantic Ave.; 321/784-1475.

PLACES TO STAY

Holiday Inn Cocoa Beach Oceanfront Resort: Not your normal doggy digs, this full-service oceanfront hotel is set on 27 acres and packs in a lot of people-pleasers: room service, a gift shop, a fitness center, a poolside eatery, two tennis courts, boogie-board rentals, shuffleboard, a whirlpool, a kid-pleasing Pirate Ship pool, and so on. If your dog wants to see the ocean, just open a curtain or step onto a balcony. She can't use the beach though; for off-leash exercise, try Wickham Park in Melbourne or Lori Wilson Park in Cocoa Beach. Dogs under 50 pounds are accepted at these 499 rooms and 119 suites (including lofts and villas). Rates run $108–220. Pet fee is $10 daily, plus a $50 deposit, $25 of which will be refunded barring doggy damages. 1300 N. Atlantic Ave., Cocoa Beach; 321/783-2271; www.holidayinns.com.

La Quinta: Once owned by NASA's seven original Mercury astronauts, this 127-room motel across the street from the beach features a tiki bar, shuffleboard, free breakfasts including sausage and waffles, and an on-site restaurant. Guests may use a nearby 21,000-square-foot fitness center. One of the better pet-permissible options in the area, the pleasant motel accepts medium to small pets in designated rooms, provided owners sign a pet waiver. Despite the lure of the beach, Brevard County forbids dogs on beaches; for leash-free fun, try Wickham Park in Melbourne or Lori Wilson Park in Cocoa Beach. Rates range $65–130. 1275 N. Atlantic Ave., Cocoa Beach; 321/783-2252; www.lq.com.

Motel 6: Horseshoes and shuffleboard are offered at this poolside lodging, where the 151 rooms are bigger than at most Motel 6s. Rates range $50–70. One small to medium-size pet is permitted per room. 3701 N. Atlantic Ave., Cocoa Beach; 321/783-3103; www.motel6.com.

South Beach Inn: Set on the ocean—where people swim, surf, and watch space shuttle liftoffs—this two-story motel has been deemed a "superior small lodging" by a local independent panel. All 18 units have kitchens with cooking utensils and dishes. Palm trees lend a bit of shade to the picnic area. Instead of daily maid service, you'll exchange linens and towels as needed. Despite the call of the ocean, pooches must find off-leash fun elsewhere; try Lori Wilson Park in Cocoa Beach or Wickham Park in Melbourne. Rates range $60–150. Add $15 nightly for a "well-disciplined small pet." A $50 pet deposit is refundable barring doggy damages. 1701 S. Atlantic Ave., Cocoa Beach; 321/784-3333 or 877/546-6835; www.southbeachinn.com.

Surf Studio: Hammocks, picnic tables, and a stone barbecue grill lend a laid-back feel to this family-owned and -operated motel, set on 250 feet of ocean beach. From the rectangular pool and its surrounding deck with chaise lounges, you'll enjoy an ocean view. All 11 efficiencies and apartments have refrigerators or full kitchens—good news for hungry hounds. Despite the tempting beach, pooches must walk in designated areas elsewhere or take a ride to the off-leash areas of Lori Wilson Park or Melbourne's Wickham Park. Rates range $75–185. Nightly pet fee is $20 per dog (under 80 pounds). 1801 S. Atlantic Ave., Cocoa Beach; 321/783-7100; www.surf-studio.com.

Viera

PARKS, BEACHES, AND RECREATION AREAS

12 Dog Park at Viera Regional Park

🐕 (See Space Coast map on page 328)

Call first to make sure this off-leash park has opened at the totally new $8.2 million Viera Regional Park, which itself remained under construction at press time. Soccer fields were expected to open in fall 2005, giving hope that the dog park might open by then, too, though one never can be sure, says Fran Gorecki, co-founder of the off-leash-area advocacy group called Brevard Animal Recreation Club.

Once you know the paw park is open, you can reach it from I-95 (Exit 191) by going west one-half mile on Wickham Road. Turn right on Lake Andrew Drive and go two miles to the park, at right, just before the School Board Complex. 321/255-4400.

Satellite Beach

PARKS, BEACHES, AND RECREATION AREAS

13 Satellite Beach Dog Park

🐾🐾🐾🐕 (See Space Coast map on page 328)

Go, dog, go! Pets chase each other and retrieve park-provided dog toys at this popular 1.25-acre field encircled by a six-foot-tall fence. Small dogs play in a separate quarter-acre field. A construction pipe serves as a fun obstacle for dogs to leap over or crawl through. Dog-wash areas are provided, as are pooper-scooper bags, drinking water, and a memorial brick path that pays homage to pets who've departed to the Great Doghouse in the Sky. Kiddie pools offer relief on hot days.

Tree-shaded tables and benches allow humans to relax as they watch or chat. "It's not only a doggy park," says Kerry, a park staffer, "it's a social experience for the owners, too."

Dog advocates say there is talk of eventually adding a water feature, which would be good news to furry swimmers. The off-leash area abuts natural scrub where gopher tortoises lumber, though a fence ensures that pets don't have access to that area. They may, however, snap on a leash to sniff out the rest of the Satellite Beach Sports & Recreation Park, known among humans for its skate park and soccer field. Leashed walkers can follow a path that encircles the sports park and covers less than a mile.

Entrance costs $2 for up to three dogs accompanied by one or two people. Fee is $3 for more dogs or people (limit three dogs per adult). Dogs must wear a rabies tag and an animal license; owners also must show proof of current vaccinations. Annual memberships allow unlimited visits at a cost of $100–150 if all pets are spayed and neutered; up to $200 if even one dog is intact.

The city park is at 750 Jamaica Blvd., within Satellite Beach Sports & Recreation Park, west of the Satellite Beach Library. From Highway A1A at the south end of Satellite Beach, turn west at Pine Tree Drive and follow the signs to the library to the north. 321/777-8004 or 321/773-6458.

PLACES TO EAT

Long Doggers: Clams, ribs, half-pound burgers, and salads number among the offerings, but the casual joint is probably best known for its Hebrew National hot dogs served 11 ways, including the county's "Best Chili Cheese Dog," as named by readers of *Florida Today*. Staffers will be glad to bring your dog a water bowl at the outdoor tables. 1201 S. Patrick Dr.; 321/773-5558.

PLACES TO STAY

Days Inn: The ocean is across the street from this 104-unit poolside motel, though the beach bans four-legged friends. Perhaps lounging in a king room will suffice. Drive 4.4 miles for off-leash exercise at Satellite Beach Dog Park (see Parks, Beaches, and Recreation Areas, above). Rates range $60–110 but may be lower at Daysinn.com. Pet fee is $10 daily for the first pet, $5 daily per additional pet. 180 Highway A1A, Satellite Beach; 321/777-3552; www.daysinn.com.

Melbourne

PARKS, BEACHES, AND RECREATION AREAS

14 Brevard Community College South Campus

🐾🐾 (See Space Coast map on page 328)

Weekend visitors will find few cars at this sizable campus, with the possibility of a solitary romp in the pine-dotted field at the northwest corner of campus or in the sunny sea of grass outside the ball field in the southeast corner. Another large open field is available to the northeast by the Justice Center. Leashes are essential: While officially dogs are banned from campus, in practice leashed pets are tolerated, particularly in the wooded area. Skip this stop on school days.

From I-95, follow Eau Gallie Boulevard/Highway 518 east. Turn north at Wickham Road/Highway 509. The college is about three miles up at 3865 N. Wickham Road. 321/632-1111.

15 Wickham Park Dog Park

🐾🐾🐾🐾🐾 🐕 (See Space Coast map on page 328)

Unsnap the leash! Dogs run joyously at this fenced grassy area with some trees for shade and a decorative fire hydrant for, uh, sniffing. Small pets head to a separate fenced area. Benches, pooper-scooper bags, and water bowls pretty much round out the amenities. Its size is unclear; we were told 1.75 to three acres, depending on whom we asked. Regardless, "it's a nice setting," says Mike Pavlick, who brings his Australian shepherds, Sunny and Frankie.

An attendant will make sure your dog is wearing tags and is current on his shots; otherwise, you won't be allowed in the off-leash area. The paw park is within a nearly 400-acre county park whose other areas are also worth exploring (on leash). Maggie whimpered when she saw the horses at the stables during our inaugural drive through the park, which features two lakes (where dogs are banned). Forget about eating in a picnic area—pets are forbidden there. Leashed dogs are permitted anywhere else, so bring a blanket to spread out your packed lunch. Afterward, follow a 1.5-mile-long workout trail or head to the nature trails on the park's east side. At night, you may camp in a pine forest at the 88 water-and-electricity sites or 22 rustic spots with your leashed pal. Sites are reservable. Fee ranges $14–20.

The free park is at 2500 Parkway Dr., just east of North Wickham Road/Highway 509. From southbound I-95, take Exit 191 (Wickham Road) and proceed east 8.4 miles on Wickham Road, curving south to Parkway Drive. Turn east on Parkway Drive. The entrance is one-half mile ahead. If you're northbound on I-95, take Exit 183 (State Road 518) and go east to the second light. Take Wickham Road north 2.5 miles to Parkway Drive, turn right, and continue one-half mile. 321/255-4307.

PLACES TO EAT

Burger Inn: Get curbside service in your car or, if management is smiling on you, eat at one of the concrete picnic tables under an overhang at this eatery on U.S. 1, less than a mile north of Eau Gallie Boulevard. Burgers are king for King, but your pal might also sample corn dogs, Philly cheese steaks, sandwiches, or even some bacon. "Reminder: You cannot live on the minimum wage alone. Please tip the staff," says a sign on the wall. 1819 North Harbor City Blvd.; 321/254-2211.

Checkers: After a romp down the road at the off-leash area of Wickham Park, munch a 99-cent burger with your dog at this fast-food chain's umbrella-covered outdoor tables. 2505 N. Wickham Rd.; 321/259-2222.

DIVERSIONS

Sniff out thrift-store bargains: Leashed, budget-conscious canines actually are encouraged to join their people in tracking down deals among the aisles of clothes, tools, furniture, pet supplies, children's goodies, books, tools, boutique items, and bric-a-brac at two shops nicknamed "Burdines West." Instead of the bargains, dogs seem more interested in the patrons.

"They're looking for a lot of attention, and they get it," says a staffer at **Molly Mutt II** thrift shop, 728 E. New Haven Ave., in Old Downtown Melbourne; 321/951-3607.

Molly Mutt I thrift shop, a sister store, is at 2525 N. Courtenay Parkway, two blocks south of State Road 528 in Merritt Island, 321/459-1525. Run by the Central Brevard Humane Society, the shops are named for Molly, a plain brown mutt who 25 years ago waited at the shelter for months while flashier pups swiftly went to new homes. Finally, Molly gained a home—after a seven-month wait. "She kind of symbolizes all the plain little brown dogs who have wonderful hearts," says Clara Gunde, former humane society executive director.

Dogs, cats, and other critters have shopped at the store, including what looked like an oversized pet rat perched on a patron's shoulder. Are pets really that welcomed? "Of course! We're a humane society," says executive director Theresa Clifton.

Island Pasta Co.: Set in historic downtown Melbourne, this lunch/dinner/happy-hour spot offers a foliage-lined courtyard where pooches have been known to join their people. Sample shrimp-and-crab cakes, grilled Mahi Mahi, sushi-grade tuna, steak, and several pasta dishes with a Caribbean twist. 903 E. New Haven Ave., Melbourne; 321/723-1584.

Mustard's Last Stand: Princess gets the royal treatment at this converted gas station, home to Brevard County's "Best Hot Dogs," as voted by *Florida Today* readers. The menu not only includes people-pleasing Chicago-style Vienna beef franks, Italian beef sandwiches, and polish sausage, but also the $1 "dog for a dog"—a plain frank served with dog biscuits. The patio's dog-friendly atmosphere is renowned and has 10 tables used by people with and without pooches. A wall displays pictures of canine regulars. "We really wanted to make it dog-friendly," says Mike Pavlick, who, along with co-owner/wife, Sheila, arrived from hound-hospitable California and wanted to foster animal hospitality in their adopted community. Monthly, folks from the Central Brevard Humane Society showcase a few adoptable dogs here. The hot dog stand awards a gift certificate to any showcased dog who goes home with a new family. 1288 N. Harbor City Blvd., Melbourne; 321/254-5776.

Pineda Inn: "Everyone does," the waitress replied when we asked about bringing a dog. Then, on reflection: "Well, not everyone. But everyone who wants to." The outdoor riverfront seating with plenty of beer, burgers, Brevard County's best chicken wings (as voted by *Florida Today* readers), and other snacky offerings is sometimes complemented on weekends with live blues or jazz. It's a grooving-on-a-Sunday-afternoon kind of place. Leashed, well-mannered dogs may be allowed at the back bar, too, provided no one complains. 6533 U.S. 1 (off Suntree Boulevard), Rockledge; 321/242-9666.

Pizza Gallery and Grill: "Where food becomes art" is the motto of this eatery serving lunch and dinner across from Brevard Community College. At the eight outdoor tables, munch pizza sold by the slice (at lunch) or an entire pie. Salads, appetizers, fish, chicken, beef, and calzones number among other offerings. 3700 N. Wickham Rd.; 321/259-8852.

PLACES TO STAY

Baymont Inn & Suites: After munching free breakfast waffles and French toast at this pleasant poolside motel off I-95 (Exit 191), consider giving your dog his treat—namely, a leash-free romp at nearby Wickham Park. Cracker Barrel restaurant neighbors this 103-unit, four-story motel, where small pets are preferred. Rates range $80–145. 7200 George T. Edwards Dr., Melbourne; 321/242-9400; www.baymontinns.com.

Crane Creek Inn Waterfront Bed & Breakfast: At Gillian and Bob Shearer's worthwhile inn in historic downtown Melbourne, a pretty pool and all guest rooms overlook Crane Creek. A hot tub sits at water's edge. Fishing can be done off the dock after your complimentary afternoon snack or morning breakfast. Winner of several beautification awards from the city of Melbourne, the adults-only inn also is deemed a "superior small lodging" by an independent local panel. Well-behaved dogs may sleep in two rooms for $10 nightly, $20 minimum per dog. Rooms range $100–199; a two-night minimum is in effect on weekends and holidays. Dogs under 65 pounds are preferred. 907 E. Melbourne Ave., Melbourne; 321/768-6416; www.cranecreekinn.com.

Hilton Melbourne Rialto Place: A lobby bar with marble water fountains sets the tone at this eight-story tower, featuring tennis, basketball, a pool, a fitness room, a restaurant, and 24-hour room service. Rates range $117–230. A $50 pet deposit is refundable, barring misdeeds by the pooch (under 50 pounds). 200 Rialto Pl., Melbourne; 321/768-0200; www.hilton.com.

Long Point Park Campground: Otters, bobcats, and manatees live in or around this 84.5-acre conservation area and urban district river park. But the county-run camping park is popular for another reason—its 113 campsites are at the shoreline of the Indian River Lagoon. Nature trails, volleyball, horseshoe pits, showers, laundry facilities, playground, swimming pond, boat ramp, small fishing dock, and fish cleaning station number among the amenities. Two leashed dogs are permitted per campsite. Camping runs $15–25. Reservations are recommended. 700 Long Point Rd., Melbourne Beach; 321/952-4532.

Outdoor Resorts Melbourne Beach: Two-legged guests of this civilized RV park enjoy three pools and six tennis courts—oh, and the ocean across the street. Walk your leashed dog along a path on Highway A1A. Sites are $26–40. 3000 Highway A1A South, Melbourne Beach; 321/724-2600 or 800/752-4052; www.outdoor-resorts.com.

Super 8: Your pooch might sniff for crumbs from your free continental breakfast at this 55-unit poolside motel. Small dogs are preferred; fee is $10 nightly. Rates normally run $40–70. 1515 S. Harbor City Blvd., Melbourne; 321/723-4430; www.super8.com.

Surfcaster Motel: South Florida dog trainer Robin Hansen told us about this beachfront motel, a rarity in that management actually encourages guests to bring their canine companions. Robin loved how they allowed dogs to swim in the ocean right here (in early morning or late evenings) as long as their people cleaned up after them. There are only eight units—three rooms, three efficiencies, two suites—so reserve early. The proprietor, Susan, has three cats and a dog named Tiger herself, which she says helps explain why she rolls out the welcome mat to traveling pets. Rooms cost $65; efficiencies $75. The oceanview suite costs $110. Add $5 nightly per pet. 5935 South Highway A1A, Melbourne Beach; 321/723-1967; www.surfcastermotel.com.

Wickham Park: See Parks, Beaches, and Recreation Areas, above, for camping information.

Wisteria Inn: This 1920s Spanish Revival house has nine-foot-tall ceilings, heart of pine floors, and an elegant dining room where guests gather for gourmet breakfasts that might include crepes and fruit grown on the inn's citrus trees. Complimentary afternoon high tea is served at 4 P.M. Beach towels, games, books, and beach chairs are available for use. Innkeepers Judi and Jeff William welcome well-behaved dogs of seemingly all sizes in the carriage house, whose rooms are decorated with antiques and custom fabrics, and which comes equipped with a mini-refrigerator, microwave, dishes, sink, VCR, and television. Deemed a "superior small lodging" by an independent local panel, the inn has a large treed yard where dogs may stretch their legs. The innkeepers offer dog-walking services for business travelers and concierge services for doggy-related needs that might arise. Rates range $95–125, plus $10 pet fee. 1924 Catterton Dr., Melbourne; 321/727-0717 or 888/787-0717; www.wisteriainn.net.

Indialantic

PARKS, BEACHES, AND RECREATION AREAS

16 Melbourne Causeway

🐾🐾🐾 (See Space Coast map on page 328)

We saw a pooch happily dog-paddling away in the Indian River along the south side of this causeway. You can stake out a shaded spot under a shaggy Australian pine or follow a path with your leashed pal. Cars zip by here, so don't let your dog wander freely.

The Melbourne Causeway/U.S. 192 links Indialantic and Melbourne. As you reach the part of the causeway just west of Indialantic, head to the south side of the causeway and park. 321/724-5400.

PLACES TO EAT

Bizzarro's Famous New York Pizza: Fans love the thin-crust pizza, though the busy eatery also serves up subs, salads, and Italian pasta dinners. The outdoor tables on the deck out back overlook the beach, so your pal can get an eyeful people-watching the surfers and retired tourists. 4 Wavecrest Ave., Indialantic; 321/724-4799.

Long Doggers: Hebrew National hot dogs are served 11 ways, including Brevard County's "Best Chili Cheese Dog," as judged by readers of *Florida Today*. Clams, ribs, half-pound burgers, sandwiches, and salads number among other eats. Take a seat at the covered picnic tables. 890 Highway A1A; 321/725-1115.

Ocean View Diner: Besides patty melts, Reuben sandwiches, and Greek salads, the wide-ranging menu includes tamer offerings such as bagels, meat loaf, club sandwiches, and breakfast omelettes. Sit at any of half a dozen umbrella-covered plastic tables for breakfast, lunch, or dinner. 1 Fifth Avenue; 321/723-2270.

PLACES TO STAY

Oceanfront Cottages: Toss a log in the fireplace, then settle in with your small dog to watch satellite TV or gaze through the nine-foot-tall sliding glass doors at the blue-green ocean. Most of the six units have French doors looking onto a pool; all offer full kitchens and niceties like a VCR and a blender. Guests have free use of beach umbrellas, beach chairs, and the laundry facility at this "superior small lodging," a label given by an independent local panel. Just two blocks down is a path leading to an unofficial dog beach. Robert and Carol Randazzo, the inn-keepers, show up to work with their dog, Amber; a bird named Rio is the resident winged ambassador. Nightly rates range $125–170. Pet fee is $15 nightly, $50 weekly. A $100 pet deposit is refunded barring Fido fiascoes. 612 Wavecrest Ave., Indialantic; 321/725-8474 or 800/785-8080; www.oceanfrontcottages.com.

Palm Bay

PARKS, BEACHES, AND RECREATION AREAS

17 Dog Park at Palm Bay Regional Park

🐕 (See Space Coast map on page 328)

Call before you head to this long-awaited dog park—with restrooms, light-ing, and parking—to make sure it is open. Its groundbreaking ceremony took place in November 2004 and officials expected construction to take 18 months. It can't open soon enough for Scooter and Rusty, two corgis who expect to be driven here by owner Fran Gorecki, co-founder of an off-leash-area advocacy group called the Brevard Animal Recreation Club.

Dogs otherwise are forbidden at the massive 200-acre regional park, whose many people-pleasers include ball fields, courts for volleyball and basketball, a picnic area, a playground, a walking/bicycling trail, a fishing deck on a lake, and one of the few cricket courts in central Florida.

Palm Beach Regional Park is at 1951 Malabar Road Northwest. From I-95 (Exit 173), head west on Malabar Road/Highway 514 for six miles to the park, at right. 321/255-4400.

18 Three Forks Marsh Conservation Area

🐾🐾 (See Space Coast map on page 328)

Measuring 81 square miles, this marshy area is more than twice as big as Miami. Look for wading birds in the massive marsh as you follow two trails. From the picnic area and parking lot, you'll walk about 1.5 miles one-way to reach a 10-mile-long rectangular loop trail for hiking, cycling, and seasonal hunting through the marsh.

Alternately, follow a ruler-straight levee at the eastern boundary of a lake called Stick Marsh, popular for fishing and boating. Hikers and cyclists can

follow the levee south for four miles, starting from the southernmost parking area on Fellsmere Grade. Alligators are known to sun themselves on the banks of this conservation area, so keep your dog leashed.

From I-95, go west about eight miles on Malabar Road/Highway 514 to the dead end at the C-1 water retention area, then curve south to the parking lot about one mile ahead at the Thomas O. Lawton Recreation Area. A hiking trail leads east, then south, from the parking area. To reach the conservation area's southern entrance from I-95, go east on Malabar Road/Highway 514 to Babcock Road/Highway 507, turn right, continue to Fellsmere Grade, turn right, and proceed to the parking lot. 321/676-6614 or 386/329-4500.

PLACES TO EAT

Checkers: Your leashed dog will hope for table scraps from your meal of burgers, french fries, or chicken sandwiches at the umbrella-shaded tables outside this fast-food eatery. 4840 Babcock St. NE; 321/952-4267.

Woody's Bar-B-Q: When your dog is howling for you to keep driving on I-95 but your stomach is growling, take the Malabar Road exit (Exit 173) to pick up barbecued pork, chicken, beef, or ribs at this drive-through window.

Sandwiches include burgers, as well as catfish or pulled pork. 1109 Malabar Rd. NE; 321/726-8804.

PLACES TO STAY

Motel 6: For a morning dog walk at this 118-room former Knights Inn, head to the grass-rimmed lake of nearby Brevard Community College or drive down the road to the Dog Park at Palm Bay Regional Park (see park listing above). One small pet may join you at the poolside motel west of I-95 (Exit 173). Rates range $43–58. 1170 Malabar Rd. SE, Palm Bay; 321/951-8222.

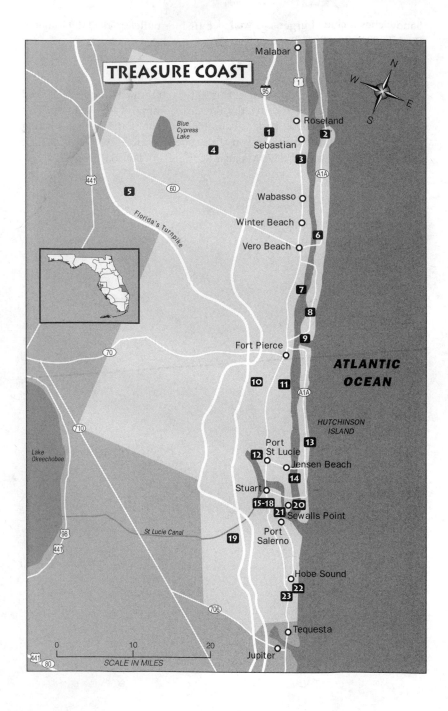

CHAPTER 12

Treasure Coast

Inquiring canine minds might want to know why this stretch of lesser-used beaches and deserted inland citrus groves is known as the Treasure Coast.

If your dog should give you that puzzled look, tell her it's because hurricanes clobbered and sank so many treasure ships near these shores in the 1500s and 1600s—the days of the Spanish conquistadors. Some folks are still hunting for ocean-washed gold doubloons just off this coast between Palm Beach and Sebastian.

This area is not exactly a treasure chest for adventure-seeking doggies, though. The region offers some pluses and minuses for the whiskered set. With just one ocean beach still legal for dogs and only two "inside" beaches at Hobe Sound and Fort Pierce, the Treasure Coast has grown alarmingly like Palm Beach and Brevard counties on either side of it, at least as far as beach access goes.

Landlubber doggies can head inland to explore some of the least-spoiled expanses of Old Florida. For a quick glimpse of Florida marsh that's sure to get your pooch's sniffer in high gear, try a sunset hike on the levee at nearby

PICK OF THE LITTER—TREASURE COAST

BEST OCEAN BEACH
Walton Rocks Beach, Jensen Beach (page 365)

BEST INLAND BEACHES
Fort Pierce Inlet State Park, Fort Pierce (page 361)
Hobe Sound National Wildlife Refuge, Hobe Sound (page 370)

BEST WEEKEND CAMPING GETAWAY
Jonathan Dickinson State Park, Hobe Sound (page 372)

FANCIEST DIGS
Hutchinson Island Marriott Beach Resort & Marina, Stuart (page 369)

Blue Cypress Conservation Area (see Parks, Beaches, and Recreation Areas under Vero Beach, below).

On the negative side, looking for a decent place for a dog and his people to eat on the Treasure Coast is like... well, searching for buried treasure. Hound-hospitable lodgings also are in short supply. Finally, some hard-hearted little towns such as Port St. Lucie seem downright dog-unfriendly. Maggie asks, "What's with these people? Do cats run the place?"

Sebastian

PARKS, BEACHES, AND RECREATION AREAS

🚹 St. Sebastian River Preserve State Park

🐾🐾 (See Treasure Coast map on page 352)

Nearly the size of Miami, this 35-square-mile preserve is quite the opposite in feel. Several miles of trails used for hiking, bicycling, and horseback riding wind through three-quarters of this chunk of woods, where bobcats, otters, and turkeys reside. Here, a leashed dog can explore sun-dappled pine forests, seasonal wetlands, and scrub.

Nature comes first and visitors second at this preserve. Its goal is to protect manatees, red-cockaded woodpeckers, and the Florida scrub jay by providing a buffer to the creek and limiting development in this area. To glimpse manatees in winter and early spring, head to the observation platform at the eastern dead-end of Buffer Preserve Drive. Bring a fishing pole or a canoe to paddle along the St. Sebastian River and possibly set your sights east to the Indian River Aquatic Preserve. A big alligator hangs out in the preserve, so no swimming, doggies.

You may also ruff it with your dog at several designated primitive campsites. These first-come, first-served sites cost only $4 per person for a reason—there are no bathrooms, facilities, or drinking water. Bring everything you'll need, including water and sunscreen to hike in the open, sunny areas. Pack out trash.

Admission is free. The preserve is bisected by the Brevard/Indian River county line and straddles I-95. From I-95 (Exit 173) in southern Brevard County, go east on Malabar Road/State Road 514, then south (right) onto Babcock Road/County Road 507. Continue 11.5 miles and turn east onto Buffer Preserve Drive. The manatee viewing area is at the road's end. Alternately, enter the southern entrance off Fellsmere Road/County Road 512, 1.8 miles east of I-95 Exit 156. 321/953-5004.

2 Easy Street Park

😼 (See Treasure Coast map on page 352)

If your pooch wants to live on Easy Street (or at least cavort there), this is the place for him. Actually, this square block is taken up mostly by a lake. Use the jogging/walking path that circles it, or just sit on an oak-shaded bench while your leashed pooch longs to run after the plentiful Muscovy ducks. The white ibises roosting in the middle of the lake might also raise an inquisitive ear or nose.

The park is on Easy Street at Lake Drive. From I-95 (Exit 156), go east on County Road 512 and continue following it as it veers northeast. Look for Easy Street to your left after passing Collier Creek. Turn left and continue two blocks. 772/589-5330 or 772/589-5490.

3 Sebastian Inlet State Park

😼😼 (See Treasure Coast map on page 352)

Picnicking and camping pretty much sums up what dogs may do at this popular park drawing a half-million visitors a year to its three miles of Atlantic Ocean beaches. Beloved by surfers and sunbathers, the park unfortunately forbids pets at its beaches, as well as the pier, concession stand, and its McLarty Treasure Museum. The beach ban may not be such a bad thing. The day we visited, a handwritten sign at the entrance gate read Sharks 5, Humans 0.

Better picnic facilities—including grills—are found on the park's south side. It's a sunny place, so wear caps. Fill a water bowl for the pooch at the restrooms.

If you don't want to pay the park entrance fee, there is an alternative. As you proceed south on Highway A1A from the park, you can pull over onto the west shoulder, which borders the Indian River. There are a few picnic tables nearby, next to the McLarty Treasure Museum.

Dogs may sleep at the worthwhile campground, where the 51 sites each go for $25.53 nightly. The beach is a short walk away from the campsites, each offering water, electricity, a fire ring with grill, a picnic table, plus nearby showers, laundry facilities, and a dump station. Reservations can be made up to 11 months ahead at ReserveAmerica.com or 800/326-3521.

Day-use admission is $5 per vehicle for up to eight people or $3 for a single-occupancy vehicle. From I-95 (Exit 156), go east on County Road 512 a short distance, then right onto County Road 510. Continue east to Highway A1A, turn left (north), and travel seven miles. The state park is at the Indian River/Brevard county line, on both sides of the Sebastian Inlet. 321/984-4852.

PLACES TO EAT

Checkers: Grab fast-food burgers and fries at the walk-up window, then take them to an umbrella-covered table to share with your dog. 7850 Roseland Rd.; 772/589-7661.

PLACES TO STAY

Donald MacDonald Park & Campground: Pets must be leashed at this quite heavily wooded campground set on the Sebastian River and operated by Indian River County. Tall pines, scraggly oaks, sabal palms, and southern red cedars shield the 30 sites from each other, providing privacy. Each camping spot has some shade, a concrete picnic table, a ground grill, and access to a restroom with showers. There's also a boat ramp for launching onto the Sebastian River. Dogs may be more interested in the short nature trail and observation boardwalk. Sites are first-come, first-served; only one offers electricity. Fee is $16.65. From I-95 (Exit 156), go east on State Road 512, then turn left (north) on Roseland Road/County Road 505. The entrance is north of Dale Wimbrow Park on the left side of the road. 12315 Roseland Rd., Roseland; 772/589-0087.

Sebastian Inlet State Park: See Parks, Beaches, and Recreation Areas, above, for camping information.

Vero Beach Kamp: Shade is only moderate and the 120 sites are spaced fairly close together at this former KOA Kampground. You'll find a pool among the cabbage palms and pines, as well as an activities building, showers, and a small playground reminiscent of giant toy Legos. While a four-foot-wide perimeter dog walk sounds boring, Maggie loved eating the tall grass and sniffing in a hole (probably home to a crab). Tent sites start at $26. RV sites start at $36. 8850 N. U.S. 1, Sebastian; 772/589-5665.

Vero Beach

There aren't many places to take a dog here, which explains why a former resident beagle named Sparky became a frequent flier, logging 3,000 miles on a trip to the Grand Canyon and another 3,000 to San Francisco, for instance. "It's not a good place to be a dog, really," Sparky's companion, Wendy Ballard, says of Vero

Beach. Indeed, the dearth of dog-friendly spots sparked Sparky and Wendy to launch *DogGone,* a newsletter about fun places to go with dogs nationwide.

It also sparked the opening of the first private off-leash dog park in Indian River County: 4-H Best Friends Off-Leash Dog Park, 1230 16th Ave., Vero Beach; 772/567-8969. A resident donated 2.5 acres of land for the membership-only park at 12th Street and 16th Avenue. A nonprofit group called Dogs for Life manages the wide open fenced field, which offers lots of room to run, separate small-dog and big-dog areas, running water, an exercise trail, and events such as an Easter Bonnet Parade. No visiting dogs are accepted, but occasionally short-term memberships of three months are offered; for details, call 772/567-8969.

PARKS, BEACHES, AND RECREATION AREAS

4 Blue Cypress Conservation Area

🐾🐾🐾 (See Treasure Coast map on page 352)

The attraction out here in the boonies is an unshaded, car-width hiking trail atop a levee that runs west from the parking lot. This mosaic of wetland communities is dominated by maidencane, saw grass, and willows. Maggie tugged at her leash, stopping every few steps, her nose atwitter as she searched in the blondish grass for clues about the marsh's inhabitants. For people, the trail may be a little monotonous, but to dogs it is a place of hidden treasures. It's not bad for bird-watching, either, if that's what your canine companion is into. Maggie was eager to chase a coot that sounded something like a squeaky dog toy. The sunsets are pretty stunning here, too.

If you arrive on a weekend, you're likely to be around airboaters who gather to drink beer, cook out, and have a good time. When we visited on a Saturday night, some of them had dogs in the backs of their pickup trucks. Maggie seemed excited by the spectacle of airboats roaring up out of the water onto the land, like something out of an old science fiction picture.

There are no facilities, so bring everything you'll need—water, food, suntan lotion, etc. Mosquito repellent is a good idea in the warm months. Most important: *Stay on the trail.* Alligators live in this 82-square-mile conservation area, but if you stick by your pooch and stay out of the water, they shouldn't bother you.

From the Vero Beach exit of I-95 (Exit 147), head west about 7.5 miles on State Road 60, then turn right (north) on County Road 512 to proceed about one mile to the parking area. 321/676-6614.

5 Fort Drum Marsh Conservation Area

🐾🐾 (See Treasure Coast map on page 352)

Waaaay out west of Vero Beach, ruler-straight trails stretch for about 16 miles along the perimeter of this massive conservation area, home to deer, turkeys, and wild hogs. At 32.6 square miles, this marshy area is bigger than Miami.

DIVERSIONS

See a manatee—if you can find a place in Florida where you and your dog are allowed. Most attractions and parks featuring the endangered sea cows prohibit pets, but two Treasure Coast spots serve as exceptions. **Vero Beach's Manatee Viewing Area** next to the Vero Beach Power Plant isn't fancy, but it is dog-accessible. A fence keeps dogs (and children) from joining the slow-moving sea cows for a swim in warm winter waters. Find the parking lot on Indian River Boulevard, just north of the 17th Street Causeway. The viewing area is just north of the parking lot.

In Fort Pierce, manatees tend to gather in the waters outside the **Henry D. King Municipal Electric Station** from early November through mid-April. These warm-blooded creatures show up in the cool months because they enjoy lolling in the warm water being discharged from the power plant into the Indian River. There's an outdoor viewing station where small crowds gather to watch the whiskered mammals.

Maggie shared the platform with motorcyclists who rode up on Harley-Davidsons, and she even tried to sniff one biker's butt. He apparently didn't notice. We were very glad. Maggie didn't seem too intrigued by the dark outlines of the manatees in the water, but your dog might be. The station is just north of the power plant, at 480 N. Indian River Dr., south of Seaway Drive. Just head to the boat ramp area to see the manatees with your dog. For information, call 772/466-1600, ext. 3333.

Look for wading birds as you follow the boundary line, where trails for hiking and bicycling form three sides of this conservation area, featuring dry prairie, pine flatwoods, marsh, and hardwood swamp.

For a more picturesque walk, skip the perimeter hiking grounds and instead circle Horseshoe Lake, where a loop trail stretches less than a mile. Afterward, stop for a break at the lakeside picnic tables or picnic pavilion. Another longer hike leads south from Horseshoe Lake to link up with Hog Island, where a boardwalk leads through hardwood swamp and reaches primitive campsites.

Lake Cara provides another nice picnic spot. It's easy to reach; just park by the lake and walk to a table. Bring water, mosquito repellent, sunscreen, hats, food, and any other supplies you'll need.

The conservation area is at the southwestern corner of Indian River County, about 20 miles west of Vero Beach. From the Vero Beach exit of I-95 (Exit 147), go west on State Road 60 to just shy of the 20 Mile Bend, turn left into the conservation area, then park by Lake Cara or by Horseshoe Lake. Hiking trails lead from the parking areas. 321/676-6614.

FETCHING NECESSITIES

Go shopping with Shep: A pretty pink script on the door declares Pets Are Welcome at **Jasmine of Vero Beach,** a beachside boutique for humans at 3403 Ocean Drive. Namesake Jasmine, a miniature poodle, gets on well with visiting dogs who let her be the boss. The boutique sells fashions, accessories, and art. For hours, call 772/231-3899.

6 MacWilliams Park

 (See Treasure Coast map on page 352)

Locals let their dogs run off-leash in the unfenced area toward the Indian River, behind the ball field known as Bob Summers Field. Pooper-scoopers are provided, along with a special garbage can where you can dispose of your dog's handiwork.

Elsewhere, leashed pets are permitted at picnic tables. Dogs are forbidden on the ball field. Overall, "the best thing I can say about this park is that it's shady," says former local resident Wendy Ballard, who sniffed out the park with her beagles, Sparky and Iggy.

The park is on the north side of the Merrill P. Barber Bridge, which spans the Intracoastal Waterway. From Vero Beach, take Highway 60 across the bridge to the east end. 772/567-2144.

7 Oslo Riverfront Conservation Area

(See Treasure Coast map on page 352)

For a walk through lush, forest-like terrain, it's hard to beat the two loop trails that wind for less than a mile through these 336 acres. Tall, vine-strangled palms and oaks lined with resurrection ferns cover a jungly understory. Look for wild tangerines growing in some trees in winter.

Within earshot of well-traveled U.S. 1, this is a real slice of Old Florida, including 20 rare plant species (such as the coral root orchid) and a virtually undisturbed example of mature coastal hammock. Maggie kept her nose to the ground here and was particularly interested in sniffing around the bottoms of some trees. An observation tower overlooks the Indian River Lagoon, called an "estuary of national significance" by the federal government.

Take a break at the small picnic area by the parking lot. If you forget to bring water for your tired dog, the South Vero Beach Square Shopping Plaza is about one block west.

From Vero Beach, head south on U.S. 1, then turn east on Oslo Road. You'll reach the easily overlooked entrance almost immediately, on your left behind the shopping center. (If you see the state entomology lab building, you've gone too far.) 321/676-6614 or 772/567-8000, ext. 249.

PLACES TO EAT

Cravings: Sandwiches are served, but this place is known for sweets—ice cream, pastries, cookies—that can be enjoyed at the outdoor tables. 3149 Ocean Dr.; 772/231-0208.

Hibiscus Coffee & Tea: Enjoy your lunch of bagels and sandwiches alfresco. You'll have to tie Sparky's leash to the wrought iron rail on the opposite side of the tables to meet with owner approval. 2205 14th Ave.; 772/778-4138.

PLACES TO STAY

Vacation rentals: Rates vary for renting a hound-hospitable vacation home. If you plan to stay at least a month, try Beach & Beyond Rentals, 2945 Cardinal Dr., Vero Beach; 772/234-3379; www.verobeachrental.net.

Vero Beach Resort: King can ask for a king room at this poolside motel offering a restaurant, lounge, fitness room, and laundry facilities off I-95 (Exit 147). Not to be confused with Disney's Vero Beach Resort, this economical alternative is both a former Days Inn and a former Super 8. Rates range $39–70, plus $10 daily for each four-legged pal. 8800 20th St., Vero Beach; 772/562-9991 or 800/960-7707; www.verobeach.com/VeroBeachResort/.

Fort Pierce

The most fun for dogs around here is, of course, the beaches. Find an ocean beach at Walton Rocks Beach in Jensen Beach and an inland beach at Fort Pierce Inlet State Park, both below.

PARKS, BEACHES, AND RECREATION AREAS

🐾 Jack Island State Preserve

🐾 🐾 🐾 (See Treasure Coast map on page 352)

In addition to being a bird-watcher's paradise, this little-used island—which seems, in fact, to be frequently deserted—promises hiking galore. There isn't much shade, though, so plan your trip for early or late in the day, or during cooler months. Older dogs might prefer a peaceful picnic at the observation tower on the island's west end, right beside the Indian River. It's a good place to see ducks and herons.

From the parking area, a concrete bridge leads to Jack Island, where a display shelter outlines round-trip hiking routes of 2, 4.2, and 4.4 miles, all leading to the observation tower. We recommend the two-miler; the others are just too much for most dogs to handle. On a hot day, or with a tired dog, you can opt for a simple nature hike that's as short as .1 mile.

Look for interpretive brochures at the display shelter at the west end of the concrete bridge. Maggie went bonkers in anticipation of finding otters and raccoons

DOG-EAR YOUR CALENDAR

Celebrate the dog days of summer with the Dodgers: Dogs like to play ball, so why not take them to a ball game? The **Minor League Vero Beach Dodgers** may have thought just that when in 2000 they began welcoming leashed pets for one particular game each year (more or less). Poodles, Chihuahuas, and the Sheriff's K-9 units have numbered among the four-legged fans. Pets accompany their owners in a designated section of the stadium. "They were very accommodating to the dogs," says Shelly Ferger, who helped sponsor the first game. "It was great."

For the next Dog Days of Summer event, inquire at the ticket office at 772/569-6858.

along these trails. If your pal looks skyward, he might see storks, ospreys, or loons. Also, if you walk far enough on the narrow, soft-sand trails, you'll read signs about how attempts to control mosquitoes have altered the natural environment.

Admission is free. Facilities are nonexistent, so you must bring everything you'll need, particularly water for your dog. The preserve is on North Hutchinson Island, four miles east of Fort Pierce via the North Causeway. Look for the entrance on the west side of Highway A1A, less than .5 mile north of Pepper Park and 1.5 miles north of Fort Pierce Inlet State Park. 772/468-3985.

🟦 Fort Pierce Inlet State Park

🐾🐾🐾 (See Treasure Coast map on page 352)

Time to swim! The beauty of this place is that it's one of the few locations we've found around here where dogs are officially, legally, and without any question allowed to dog-paddle to their heart's content. However, they must be leashed (retractable leashes are fine). They also must stick to the inland portion of the 340-acre state park, on the Fort Pierce Inlet. Mainly accessible at low tide, it's a runner-up beach, but it'll do. If you take your retriever out to the Atlantic Ocean, you'll be sent home with your tail between your legs.

Leashed pooches may eat in the picnic area, located next to the cove and the inlet. As you snack beneath a shady pavilion, tell your canine historian about nearby Dynamite Point, which earned its name during World War II when the Navy's underwater demolition team set off big watery explosions here.

Do your pooch a favor and explore the nature trail off the parking lot. It threads through a densely shaded coastal hammock of strangler fig trees and live oaks, one of the few scattered remnants of a lush, life-sustaining ecosystem that once ran along much of Florida's east coast. In warmer months, be sure to bring mosquito repellent. As always, bring water for your canine companion. The leisurely 30-minute walk along a dirt path is enhanced by interpretive

DIVERSIONS

Shoot a picture of your leashed pooch in front of a life-size model of an Apollo space capsule at Fort Pierce's outdoor **UDT-SEAL Museum.** Then you can lend some credence to your claim that your pup is out of this world.

As long as you clean up after your leashed pal, you may show him the space capsule and the unusual military hardware stored outdoors, including a real horned scully—one kind of offshore obstacle that U.S. Navy engineers built in the ocean off Fort Pierce when they used this area as a base of operations from 1943 to 1945. A Seabee (construction) battalion installed many obstacles in the ocean waters off Fort Pierce to mimic the defenses put up by the Japanese and Germans in World War II; then Navy frogmen would practice blowing up the thingamajigs. Some 140,000 members of the U.S. Armed Services were stationed in Fort Pierce during World War II, and some were forerunners of today's Navy SEAL divers. Whatever obstacles remained in the ocean off Fort Pierce when the war ended were left there—until 1991.

Some now are displayed at the outdoor museum, along with models of torpedoes, Navy landing craft, and the like. Maggie was less than impressed with the military hardware. She just figured it was another place to take a walk.

The museum is at 3300 N. Highway A1A, less than one mile north of the Fort Pierce Inlet on North Hutchinson Island. Humans can enjoy the indoor museum, too, which calls itself "the only museum in the world dedicated exclusively to the elite warriors of Naval Special Warfare." Fee for the indoor museum is $5 for adults, $2 for children. It's free to visit the outdoor museum. 772/595-5845.

---

signs. Consider skipping this walk in summer: "Too hot and buggy," says former local Wendy Ballard, past publisher of the dog travel newsletter *DogGone*.

Admission is $3 for one person, $5 for a party of two to eight people. The state park is at 905 Shorewinds Dr. on North Hutchinson Island, four miles east of Fort Pierce via the North Causeway. 772/468-3985.

10 White City Park

🐾🐾🐾 (See Treasure Coast map on page 352)

A lush, woodsy island park along the North Fork of the St. Lucie River, this place is so crowded with trees that an overenthusiastic dog could get a leg cramp. Plop down with your leashed buddy for a waterside picnic at one of several picnic tables, some of which are sheltered from the sun. Don't let your pooch get too close to the water, though, or she might become alligator food.

The 17-acre county park is south of Fort Pierce at 1801 W. Midway Rd./County Road 712, just west of Sunrise Boulevard. 772/462-1519 or 772/462-1521.

🐾 The Savannas Recreation Area

🐾🐾🐾 (See Treasure Coast map on page 352)

"Oh, no!" we thought when we spied an entrance sign warning that dogs are not allowed in the day-use area of this informal county park/camping getaway, a favorite of locals. But a man at the gate said dogs are permitted as long as they're well behaved. After all, he reasoned, dogs may camp here (for $11–22), so why discriminate against dogs visiting for the day? Even if you show up on a day when employees take a different attitude, you still can have a picnic here. Simply pull off at the day-use areas along the east side of the dirt road leading up to the entrance gate. You'll have to park by the side of the road, then cross some footbridges.

Inside the gate, in day-use area No. 2, you can picnic with your pet and then walk along the Everglades-like marsh on a hiking trail that's shaded by Australian pines. The trail leads to a sort of makeshift observation tower where your pooch can peer out over the saw grass and cattails. You'll hear frogs croaking—after all, this place is wild—but the lack of dry land leaves something to be desired when it comes to getting your pooch out into the wilderness. You see, while the park is large (550 acres), it feels fairly small because it's hemmed in by the watery prairie. Still, this place is fine for an afternoon visit or camping. Hot showers, laundry facilities, canoe rentals, and 52 campsites—primitive, full-hookup, and water/electric sites—are available.

Entry is $1 per vehicle. The park is at 1400 E. Midway Rd./County Road 712, 1.5 miles east of U.S. 1. From I-95 (Exit 126), drive 6.2 miles east on Midway Road/County Road 712 to the entrance. 772/464-7855 or 800/789-5776.

PLACES TO EAT

Checkers: Fetch fast-food fare to chow down at outdoor tables shaded by red umbrellas. 2050 S. U.S. 1; 772/468-8822.

Donut Circus: Don't let the name fool you. Yes, this 24-hour spot has the jelly- and cream-filled goodies that will clog your pooch's arteries. But light sandwiches also are served. Leave your canine companion outside by the overhang-sheltered plastic chairs, pick up the food indoors, and return to feast. Although not picturesque, it is convenient. 2404 U.S. 1, just north of Highway 70; 772/461-8017.

PLACES TO STAY

Days Inn South Hutchinson Island: Set on the Intracoastal Waterway and 300 yards from the Atlantic Ocean, this small one-story motel offers a fishing pier and a heated pool overlooking the waterway. Leashed dogs can walk alongside the jetty, which spans one-half mile. Rooms cost $95. Add $10.65 nightly for the pooch (under 40 pounds). 1920 Seaway Dr., Fort Pierce; 772/461-8737; www.daysinn.com.

Days Inn Fort Pierce: Dogs may hope for a takeout order from the Steak-n-Shake restaurant by this 125-unit poolside motel off I-95 (Exit 129). Rates range $45–95. Add a $10.65 nightly pet fee. 6651 Darter Ct., Fort Pierce; 772/461-8737; www.daysinn.com.

Holiday Inn Express: If Fluffy's bandanna is wrinkled, you can press it with the iron provided in all 100 rooms of this comfortable poolside lodging off I-95 (Exit 129), the best pooch-permissible option in these parts. Rates range $77–110. Pets under 25 pounds are accepted for $25 or less (depending on weight). 7151 Okeechobee Rd./Highway 70, Fort Pierce; 772/464-5000; www.holidayinns.com.

Motel 6: At this 120-unit poolside motel off I-95 (Exit 129), you can bring back doggy bags from three restaurants within walking distance. One pet is permitted per room. Rates range $44–56. 2500 Peters Rd., Fort Pierce; 772/461-9937; www.motel6.com.

Road Runner Travel Resort: This destination park—favored by RVers who tend to stay for a month, a season, or even a year—will also accept overnighters, including those with tents. Most of the 38-acre park is shaded by pines or oaks, with fewer than a quarter of the 450 sites open to much sun. People-pleasers include a pool, golf, a tennis court, a petanque court, shuffleboard, and a bass-stocked catch-and-release pond. "Pets with good attitudes are always welcome to walk their owners on a leash," states park policy. Sites are $33.45 and up. 5500 St. Lucie Blvd., Fort Pierce; 772/464-0969 or 800/833-7108; http://roadrunnertravelresort.com/.

The Savannas Recreation Area: See Parks, Beaches, and Recreation Areas, above, for camping information.

Port St. Lucie

This is a terrible place to be a dog, with a severe lack of opportunities for canine carousing.

PARKS, BEACHES, AND RECREATION AREAS

12 Oak Hammock Park

(See Treasure Coast map on page 352)

Don't actually go inside the park, where dogs are forbidden. Instead, set your sights on the canal outside the park. That's where folks take their leashed pets for a tinkle. Stop here only if you happen to be in the area.

The park is at 1982 SW Villanova Road. You'll head to the canal outside. 772/878-2277.

PLACES TO EAT

McDonald's: Eat fast-food fare at the half-dozen tables shaded by an awning (good for extra-furry diners). 1750 SW Saint Lucie West Blvd.; 772/871-2600.

Jensen Beach

PARKS, BEACHES, AND RECREATION AREAS

13 Walton Rocks Beach

🐾🐾🐾🐾 🐕 (See Treasure Coast map on page 352)

Time to swim! Like a treasure chest located after a long search, this rare stretch of Treasure Coast beach lets dogs swim in the Atlantic Ocean legally, without question. Pooches plunge to their hearts' content.

The brown-and-tan sand at this 24-acre unguarded beach isn't the most comfortable in the world for sunbathers since it contains rough bits of shells, but dogs are happy as clams.

Relax afterward at the 18 picnic tables or two picnic pavilions. Fill a water bowl at the restrooms. Showers are provided for human swimmers.

Three dogs are permitted per owner. The beach is south of the St. Lucie Power Plant, 6501 S. Highway A1A, on South Hutchinson Island. From the power plant, continue south a short distance on Highway A1A to Walton Rocks Beach Road, then turn left to the free beach parking area. Walk across any of the three dune crossovers. 772/462-1521.

🔟 Jensen Beach Causeway Waterfront Park

 (See Treasure Coast map on page 352)

Maggie pined to run after the seagulls she spotted along the water's edge at this park. The waterfront is okay for wading and swimming as long as you choose a sandy area and dogs stay leashed (retractable leashes are fine). A few sections have submerged rocks, so don't tear into the water without looking first. If your pooch is the fishing type, you might also check out a pier at the western edge of the park in the Indian River.

Leashed dogs are welcome to enjoy a casual picnic here, and we saw an elderly woman and her chocolate-colored hound taking advantage of the shade provided by sheltered picnic tables. We also saw a black Labrador retriever hanging out with his people, who were in a van listening to rock and roll.

The park is along the North Causeway, a.k.a. Jensen Beach Causeway, between Jensen Beach and Hutchinson Island. From I-95 (Exit 101), head east on Highway 76/Kanner Highway to Stuart. Turn left at U.S. 1 and head north across the Roosevelt Bridge, veering right where the road splits onto Savannah Road/Highway 723. Turn right at Jensen Beach Boulevard, proceed to Indian River Drive/Highway 707, turn left, and then turn right on the causeway. 772/288-5690.

PLACES TO EAT

Strawberry's Deli: Retrieve an order of sandwiches and ice cream, then return to your pal to share your bounty at one of the outside benches. 11037 S. Ocean Dr.; 772/229-9356.

PLACES TO STAY

Holiday Out/Venture III: This huge, ocean-to-river resort—with two pools—is more of a residential community than a campground, but your dog may join you in your RV if a spot is open (reserve early). Pets use a dog walk along Ocean Drive. One pet is permitted per RV site. Weekly rates in season start at $390. Reserve through VNI Realty, 9803 S. Ocean Dr., Jensen Beach; 772/229-1300; www.vnirealty.com.

River Palm Cottages & Fish Camp: Pet dishes are found under the kitchen or bathroom sinks in the cottages of this pleasant retreat favored by a tiny terrier named Cricket. Set on the west bank of the Indian River Lagoon at Marker No. 222, these cottages are reachable by boat or car and are scattered among 7.2 acres of tropical plants. Seven boat slips, a nature walk, a children's play area, a kidney-shaped pool, and a sandy beach entertain humans. Leashed dogs walk in designated areas across the street and in the park's northern section, and they likely will notice the grounds' plentiful squirrels along the way. About half of the 23 units are considered river-view or waterfront. Nightly rates range $79–410. Small pets are accepted for a per-pet fee of $10 daily, $50 weekly, or $150 monthly. 2325 NE Indian River Dr., Jensen Beach; 772/334-0401 or 800/305-0511.

The Village at Nettles Island: Some RV sites overlook the Indian River Lagoon at this residential-style resort, which stretches from the lagoon to the Atlantic Ocean and offers a café, pool, and other amenities. Pets use a dog walk out front along Ocean Drive. Weekly rates in season start at $390. Reserve through VNI Realty, 9803 S. Ocean Dr., Jensen Beach; 772/229-1300; www.vnirealty.com.

Stuart/Sewalls Point

Every Stuart city park permits leashed pets, including more than a dozen parks (mainly small ones) not listed below. To sniff out other locations, call 772/288-5335.

PARKS, BEACHES, AND RECREATION AREAS

15 Colorado Avenue Mini-Park

🔥 (See Treasure Coast map on page 352)

This contender for the tiniest bit of manicured green anywhere in Florida is located at the north end of Colorado Avenue in the town of Stuart's funky, renovated downtown shopping district. It's a good spot for cooling off by the St. Lucie River after you and your leashed dog have done some window-shopping. Shady and tasteful, this park nevertheless allows no real room for pooches to stretch out.

The park is at 99 S. Colorado Avenue. From I-95 (Exit 101), go east on Highway 76/Kanner Highway, which becomes Colorado Avenue near downtown. Follow it to the end. 772/288-5398.

16 Hospital Pond Park

🔥 (See Treasure Coast map on page 352)

Hmmm… no hospital here, Maggie noticed. (She is, after all, a bright dog.) Turns out this thumbprint of a park got its name because this was the site of the first hospital in what is now Martin County—a two-story frame affair called St. Lucie Sanitarium. You won't see it today. Instead, you'll find only four wooden picnic tables under some sabal palms, a small wooden deck on a smidgen of a pond, and a postage-stamp patch of grass—just right for a pit stop.

The park is at Palm Beach Road and East Ocean Boulevard/Highway A1A. From I-95 (Exit 101), go east on Highway 76/Kanner Highway nearly seven miles to downtown. Turn right at Ocean Boulevard and continue one mile. 772/288-5398.

Kiwanis Park

 (See Treasure Coast map on page 352)

This small park by the railroad tracks has pavilion-shaded picnic tables and a playground to please the kids. Attentive dog owners will be happy to note that the park is fenced only on the two sides that face semi-busy streets. The third side of the triangular park is bounded by a dead-end street and railroad tracks. Maggie, who had been cooped up in the car for more than an hour when we arrived here, thought the park was great. Still, it is too small for anything but a confined game of fetch, and the grab bag of trees provides only sparse shade.

The park is on East Fifth Street, next to the railroad tracks between South Dixie Highway/Highway A1A and Colorado Avenue. 772/288-5398.

18 Memorial Park

 (See Treasure Coast map on page 352)

Largely occupied by shuffleboard courts and other sports courts, this park offers a pleasant patch of green right along Stuart's main road, East Ocean Boulevard. The park has many trees, some shade, and no fences. A memorial to soldiers and a small, brightly painted amphitheater round out the picture. The Stuart water tower, which dominates the landscape, is next door.

The park is on East Ocean Boulevard at Georgia Avenue, next to Stuart Middle School. 772/288-5398.

19 St. Lucie Lock and Dam

(See Treasure Coast map on page 352)

Peer down at the boats passing through this popular (if somewhat make-do) picnicking and camping spot. A pooch who squints hard enough can make out the names of the home ports spelled out on the boat transoms below. And then he can daydream about faraway places where his people will take him someday.

A nice breeze often flows through the area, so it's a decent enough place to camp with your leashed pal in winter. In summer, you'll bake in the sun, even at the three waterfront sites. Showers, a playground, a boat ramp, a dump station, fishing areas, and a picnic shelter are available. Nine sites have water and electricity; fee is $16 nightly. Three primitive tent-only sites go for $12. Boaters and their furry mates can pull into eight boat campsites for $16 nightly. A gate separates the campground from the free day-use area. Reservations for the St. Lucie South Campground, as it's also called, can be made up to 240 days ahead at ReserveUSA.com or 877/444-6777.

The lock is at 2170 SW Canal Street. From I-95 (Exit 101), go west on Highway 76 a short distance. Turn right at Locks Road. At the end of the road, turn left at Canal Street and continue to the park. 772/287-1382.

Sewalls Point Park/Jaycee Park

🐾🐾 (See Treasure Coast map on page 352)

These two causeway parks attract a laid-back, Jet Ski–riding/rock-and-roll crowd and are good for a sunny picnic. (Some picnic shelters are shaded in case it gets too warm.) Part of the beach is rocky, but wading shouldn't be too much of a problem, as glass containers are prohibited. Cars are usually whirring by on a busy road, so leashes are necessary.

Both parks are alongside the South Causeway between Hutchinson Island and the mainland. From downtown Stuart, follow Ocean Boulevard/Highway A1A east and north to the causeway. 772/287-2455.

PLACES TO EAT

Twistee Treat: You'll know you've found this spot when you see the building shaped like an ice-cream cone. They sell—what else?—ice cream. Take a seat with your buddy at an outdoor table. 3639 SE Cove Rd.; 772/287-5954.

PLACES TO STAY

Hutchinson Island Marriott Beach Resort & Marina: This 200-acre slice of luxury on Hutchinson Island features 276 rooms and suites, some on the river or ocean. It's not every day that you can order a plump shrimp cocktail from room service to share with your pooch. Rent boats here or just walk around the spacious grounds, outfitted with three heated pools, tennis, a few restaurants, a fitness center, and 18 holes of golf. It's an excellent spot to simply relax—with an Old Florida flair and modern amenities. Rates range $139–330. Pets are permitted in first-floor rooms for a flat fee of $75. The complex is on a barrier island east of Stuart, about 45 minutes north of West Palm Beach and two hours south of Orlando. 555 NE Ocean Blvd., Stuart; 772/225-3700 or 800/775-5936; http://marriott.com.

Pirates Cove Resort & Marina: Arrive by boat or by car to sleep at these 50 comfortable rooms and mini suites, each with a balcony and water view. You'll sleep in a first-floor room at this casual spot, whose amenities include a lounge with nightly entertainment, a heated freshwater pool, a poolside bar, and boat charters. Rates range $110–190, plus $20 pet fee. 4307 SE Bayview St., Stuart; 772/287-2500 or 800/332-1414; www.piratescoveresortandmarina.com.

St. Lucie Lock and Dam: See Parks, Beaches, and Recreation Areas, above, for camping information.

Port Salerno

PARKS, BEACHES, AND RECREATION AREAS

🐾🐾 Sand Sprit Park

🐾🐾 (See Treasure Coast map on page 352)

The signs tell the story: Pet Leash and Waste Removal Laws Are Enforced Here. At one time, pets were completely banned at this breezy, manicured 14-acre park on the St. Lucie River, but that has changed. Go, dogs! There is a large boat ramp here and a playground, but the attraction for your pooch will be the series of picnic shelters and lots of wide-open spaces to sniff out. And if this isn't enough space, there's a bike trail outside the park where we saw a couple jogging with their rottweiler at dusk. Except for a thick grove of oaks and sabal palms by the entrance, the place offers no shade trees.

From I-95 (Exit 101), take Kanner Highway/Highway 76 east to Indian Street and turn right. Cross U.S. 1 and Highway A1A. You'll enter a residential area, and the street will become St. Lucie Boulevard. Follow signs. 772/288-5690.

Hobe Sound

Dogs come from far and wide to enjoy the beach at Hobe Sound National Wildlife Refuge.

PARKS, BEACHES, AND RECREATION AREAS

🐾🐾 Hobe Sound National Wildlife Refuge

🐾🐾🐾🐾 (See Treasure Coast map on page 352)

Time to dog-paddle! This slice of mangrove swamp, scrub, and coastline is notable because it's one of those fast-fading places where you can still take Bowser to the beach. Sergio and Silvana Cortella have done just that, driving from two counties away to bring their enthusiastic canine family of 10: six greyhounds, two rottweilers, and two Italian greyhounds. "With a family like this one, it is not easy to find places to go," says Sergio, who, along with his wife, finds homes for retired racing greyhounds at their nonprofit Hollydogs Adoption Center in Hollywood.

This beach is a salvation for pent-up pooches, with a trail that ends on a narrow beach that is quiet and safe. The shallow water makes for excellent dog-paddling. Strangely, you have to keep your dog leashed, even in the water (at least theoretically). Some visitors try to get around that by strolling as far north as possible, away from others, and staking out a stretch of sand of their own. Another drawback: Parking, even at $5 a pop, is limited and tends to run out early in the day on weekends. If that happens, though, you can head to

the refuge headquarters, about two miles south of Hobe Sound on U.S. 1, to follow a half-mile-long nature trail with your leashed buddy.

To reach the beach portion of the refuge, head east on Highway 707 from Hobe Sound, turn left onto North Beach Road, and follow it to the end. 772/546-6141.

🐾 Jonathan Dickinson State Park

🐾🐾🐾 (See Treasure Coast map on page 352)

Maggie spent many a happy hour following hiking trails that run over the ridgelike rises of sand pine scrub at this popular picnicking and camping park—which, at 18 square miles, is half the size of Miami. These ridges are really ancient beach dunes, dating from the days when the Earth's temperature was much hotter and the sea level much higher. Since then, pines and even a few hardwoods have sprouted, providing some shade for hiking doggies.

The Florida National Scenic Trail's Kitching Creek backpacking trail easily spans 9.3 miles. Maggie loved following a short portion of the trail, starting at the parking lot near the Loxahatchee River. She sniffed at every turn and padded eagerly toward undiscovered terrain. The first three miles run through ancient beach dunes, now taken over by scrub oaks, then flattens into pine forests. It's best to turn around long before then for the comfort of your four-legged companion. Elsewhere in the park, Kitching Creek lends its name to a separate, more popular, 1.5-mile nature trail that offers two loops to explore.

The short Hobe Mountain Trail, another alternative, is a boardwalk that climbs through the sand pine scrub to an observation tower where dogs can view the entire park from above. A self-guiding leaflet is offered for yet another trail: the half-mile Sand Pine Scrub Nature Trail, which doubles as a segment of the Florida National Scenic Trail.

Picnickers share a huge, grassy, sunny field. If you forget to bring snacks or basic supplies, the concession stand may suffice. Fill your pal's water bowl at restrooms there.

Our gripe with this getaway is that dogs aren't allowed to enjoy a rental canoe trip on the park's main waterway, the Loxahatchee River—the first Florida waterway federally designated as a Wild and Scenic River. You can bring your own canoe, but the reason behind the dog ban shouldn't be taken lightly: Dogs who won't stay in the boat will face alligators. (In fact, one of the few recent documented cases of an alligator killing a human happened here when an old, sick gator mistook a boy for an animal. So stay out of the water.)

Admission is $4 per vehicle. Find the park at 16450 SE Federal Hwy., 12 miles south of Stuart. From I-95 (Exit 87A), follow signs to the park, which will direct you east on Highway 706, then left on U.S. 1 to the park. 772/546-2771.

PLACES TO STAY

Jonathan Dickinson State Park: Dogs may sleep at most campsites within one of Florida's best state-park campgrounds, which serves as a weekend retreat for South Floridians. Maggie enjoyed sitting on the carpet of pine needles as we grilled a chicken dinner, then crawled into a tent to sleep beneath tall pines in the park's 90-site Pine Grove Campground. A second camping area—the River Campground—forbids pets. All sites have water, electricity, a picnic table, a grill, and access to hot showers and a dump station. In 2004, hurricanes Frances and Jeanne walloped the pet-permissible campground, which promptly began reconstruction from the ground up. Camping costs $22. 16450 SE Federal Hwy., Hobe Sound; 772/546-2771 or 800/326-3521 (reservations).

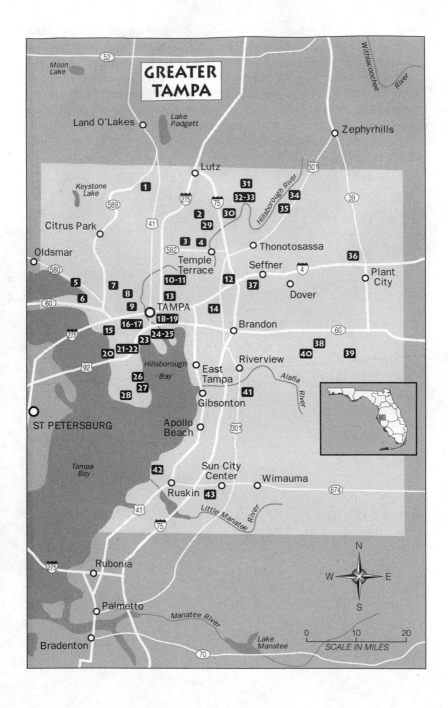

GREATER TAMPA

Moon Lake

52

Withlacoochee River

Land O'Lakes

Lake Padgett

Zephyrhills

Lutz

Keystone Lake

589

1

275

75

31

32-33

301

Hillsborough River

34

35

Citrus Park

41

2

29

30

39

Oldsmar

580

5

7

8

9

582

3

4

10-11

12

13

TAMPA

14

18-19

Temple Terrace

Thonotosassa

Seffner

4

37

Dover

36

Plant City

60

6

16-17

15

23

24-25

21-22

20

Brandon

60

38

40

39

Hillsborough Bay

275

92

26

27

28

East Tampa

Riverview

Alafia River

41

Gibsonton

ST PETERSBURG

Apollo Beach

301

Tampa Bay

42

Sun City Center

Wimauma

674

Ruskin

43

Little Manatee River

41

75

275

Rubonia

Palmetto

Manatee River

Lake Manatee

Bradenton

70

N
W E
S

0   10   20
SCALE IN MILES

CHAPTER 13

Greater Tampa

Tampa and surrounding Hillsborough County offer a little bit of everything Floridian, both old and new. Your pooch can walk among gleaming downtown skyscrapers, swim at Davis Islands Dog Park, dine at South Tampa sidewalk cafés, window-shop in quaint old Hyde Park, and picnic under moss-draped oaks in many places. He even can see a T-Rex at Dinosaur World.

Tampa was the original urban destination for Cuban exiles heading for Florida, and you still can enjoy a taste of the Caribbean island in old Ybor City. The district is as close as the city comes to being blatantly tourist-hungry, yet it manages to be charming. How can any pooch resist dinner at its pet-friendly eateries?

In one way, Tampa is best known for taking care of animals—more than 2,700 of them at Busch Gardens, the safari-themed amusement park. Unfortunately, your pooch won't be able to snarl at the lions or ape the monkeys there, because dogs are not allowed inside. (Free kennels are provided if you feel you can't miss it. But this book isn't about putting dogs in kennels.)

PICK OF THE LITTER—TAMPA

BEST BEACH
Davis Islands Dog Park, Tampa (page 385)

BEST DOG-FRIENDLY DINING DISTRICTS
East Davis Boulevard on Davis Islands, Tampa
(page 388-390)

BEST LIGHTED DOG PARK
Mango Dog Park, Seffner (page 398)

WHERE TO SNIFF CUBAN SOIL
Parque Amigos de José Martí, Tampa (page 384)

Tampa

South Tampa is going to the dogs, thanks to its dog parks, pet-friendly eateries, and shops catering to canines. East Davis Boulevard on Davis Islands is a particularly hound-hospitable place to stop to eat with a pooch after romping at the leash-free beach of Davis Islands Dog Park.

Good news for New Tampa: There is talk of building a leash-free area in Tampa Palms. For current status, call the city at 813/274-8615.

PARKS, BEACHES, AND RECREATION AREAS

1 Lake Park

🐾🐾🐾 (See Greater Tampa map on page 374)

With five lakes, pine forests, swampy terrain, and shady hardwood trees to investigate, a pooch's sniffer will twitch with delight as she tries to pick up scents at this nearly one-square-mile park. Some trails, such as those used by horses, may not be open to dogs. Bring a packed lunch to eat at a picnic table and maybe a boat so you and your pooch can go fishing. Dogs are not allowed at the locations that tend to draw the most people: the radio-controlled-car track, archery range, and bicycle motocross track.

Entrance is free, but donations are requested. The park is at 17302 N. Dale Mabry Highway. Take North Dale Mabry Highway north and look for the park on the left, just before Van Dyke Road. 813/264-3806.

❷ Lettuce Lake Park

 (See Greater Tampa map on page 374)

Locals tend to coo when they mention Lettuce Lake, a green retreat from the dog-eat-dog world for the quarter-million people living within an eight-mile radius. Your leashed pal is welcome to follow a 1.25-mile jogging trail through pine-and-palmetto flatwoods, hardwood forests, and cypress swamp; she can try to complete a four-station fitness course along the way. After your walk, you can eat a bag lunch in the woodsy picnic areas or head to the large field, which will please dogs who like to play fetch.

The park's most popular feature—its boardwalk—is off-limits to dogs. At least in some measure, this may be due to the actions of one leashed dog, said to have bitten a passerby when on the boardwalk. Just another reminder that one bad canine ambassador can ruin future fun for other dogs.

Entrance is free, but a $1 donation per car is requested. And you must show proof that your dog has a current rabies vaccination. The 240-acre park is near the banks of the Hillsborough River. From I-75, head west on Fletcher Avenue for a short distance until you reach the entrance at 6920 E. Fletcher Avenue. 813/987-6204 or 813/975-2160.

❸ Copeland Park

 (See Greater Tampa map on page 374)

Maggie doesn't much care for chin-up bars. She tries to bite the soles of our shoes as we strain to pull ourselves up. (So much for exercising.) But while your leashed pooch may not care that this park's jogging path is lined with the most exercise stations in Hillsborough County—26 in all—he'll be happy that the trail spans two miles. He'll also like roaming through the woods here. Bring burgers to cook on the grills in the picnic area.

From I-275, take the Fowler Avenue exit and head east. Turn left at 15th Street, pass the elementary school, and look for the park at left at 11001 N. 15th Street. 813/975-2733.

❹ University of South Florida

 (See Greater Tampa map on page 374)

Furry exercise fanatics who don't mind staying on a leash can stop at a dozen exercise stations along the 1.4-mile jogging trail at Florida's second-largest university. Start at Holly Drive, which is closest to the university entrance on 50th Street. Across the street from the jogging trail there's a big field, which will tempt dogs who want to run free. Ditto for several open fields in the vicinity of the big orange *Tyrannosaurus rex* replica by Fowler Avenue and 50th Street, just off campus.

The university is at 4202 E. Fowler Ave., east of I-275. 813/974-2011.

DIVERSIONS

"Pardon me. Do you have any Grey Poupon—or liver treats?"
Your dog could use that line on his next limousine ride. After all, three dogs who were filmed in Tampa for the movie *Edward Scissorhands* showed up for the grand premiere in a chauffeured $80,000 limo, says Ken Lange, owner of the celebrity canines' limo company of choice, **Royal Limousine.**

Other pooches bound for dog shows or other destinations have taken quick jaunts to or from the airport in these eye-widening limos, equipped with an $8,000 sound system, a mirrored ceiling with fiber optics, and cellular phones. Imagine your dog riding in style, his expression saying, "More liver, Jeeves."

Uniformed chauffeurs are available 24 hours a day. Lange reserves the right to turn down shedding dogs (even his son's pit bull, Lange says, "which is a wonderful dog"), very large dogs, and pooches who desire trips that are too long. Don't be too worried: A cougar mascot for Lincoln Mercury car ads has taken a ride. ("We had to invest in a $700 ozonator to get the [gamey] smell out," says Lange.)

Rates range $45–90 hourly. A ride from the airport to downtown costs $45 and up, depending on whether you choose a sedan or a stretch limo. Reserve at 813/288-9225.

5 Upper Tampa Bay Park

(See Greater Tampa map on page 374)
Tiny fiddler crabs are so numerous here that they make a low, rumbly roar as they scurry sideways along the Eagle Trail's tidal marshes. This lush trail may be Maggie's favorite in Greater Tampa, and judging by the looks on the faces of the four dogs we saw embarking on the trail with their human couple, other dogs love it, too. It's not often that a pooch can see so much nature on such a short walk (.6 mile). Starting in a pine forest, the Eagle Trail quickly enters a hardwood hammock and offers glimpses of a freshwater marsh before you and your leashed pooch emerge into the sun to cross a boardwalk over a wet prairie. At one point, the bay stretches far into the distance, providing a good place to stop and daydream. Farther on, moss clings to the gnarled arms of shady oak trees.

This 3.35-square-mile park also has a paved nature trail, picnic shelters, a playground, and a canoe launch (bring your own canoe). Leashed dogs are welcome anywhere in the park.

The county park is at 8001 Double Branch Rd., off Hillsborough Avenue and five miles west of Memorial Drive. From Hillsborough Avenue/Highway 580, turn south at Double Branch Road and follow the signs. 813/855-1765.

6 Ben T. Davis Municipal Beach

😸 (See Greater Tampa map on page 374)

Dogs aren't allowed on the beach at this favorite haunt of personal watercraft riders. But your leashed dog can picnic with you at concrete shelters and take in a view of Old Tampa Bay. For a walk, stroll out of the park and follow the long sidewalk spanning the sunny Courtney Campbell Causeway, which affords broader views of the bay. Bring water and turn around long before you exhaust your easily overheated buddy. It's best to skip this walk if it's hot or if your dog tends to cower when cars whiz nearby.

The park is on the Tampa side of Courtney Campbell Causeway, about two miles west of Eisenhower Boulevard. 813/274-8615.

7 West Park

😸😸😸🐕 (See Greater Tampa map on page 374)

This long, narrow park is located in an industrial section that nevertheless includes quite a few trees. The shade of oaks and pines would make this a pleasant enough place even if there were no leash-free area. But there it is—about three acres set aside for the four-legged stretch.

Following the lead of nearby Sarasota (and, later, colleagues in Tampa city government), Hillsborough County parks officials planned this off-leash park to include some shelter for humans, fresh water for pups, disposable pooper-scooper mitts, and a dog-wash area.

From Hillsborough Avenue, head north on North Dale Mabry Highway/U.S. Highway 92. After a little less than a mile, turn left on Lambright Avenue, which will become Pine Crest Manor Boulevard, which, in turn, will become West Sligh Avenue. Follow that street to its intersection with Occident Street. 813/975-2160.

8 James Urbanski Dog Park at Al Lopez Park

😸😸😸😸🐕 (See Greater Tampa map on page 374)

Tree-shaded Al Lopez Park has been a great place for dogs to visit for a long time, but it got a lot better in 2001, when city authorities gave the green light to construct Tampa's first off-leash area. Partially wooded and surrounded by a four-foot-tall chain-link fence, the 1.5-acre park offers the usual amenities: drinking fountains for hounds and humans, picnic tables, benches, and dispensers for doggy-doo cleanup. Small and elderly dogs use a separate fenced area about the size of a tennis court (8,000 square feet).

Leashed pets also may venture elsewhere in the oak- and pine-shaded park to sniff plaques and exhibits at the inspirational Cancer Survivor Plaza or join joggers along a 2.2-mile exercise trail. Tailored to wheelchair athletes, the course features modified versions of balance beams, ropes, ladders, bridges, and other exercise equipment. Take a break at picnic tables. Fill a water bowl at the restrooms. Kids will enjoy the playground.

The park is at 4810 N. Himes Avenue. From the intersection of Dale Mabry and West Hillsborough Avenue, head east one block, turning south onto Himes Avenue. Al Lopez Park is ahead at right. Enter and proceed deep within the park to the far side to reach the dog park. 813/274-8615.

❾ MacFarlane Park

🐾🐾 (See Greater Tampa map on page 374)

Athletes often show up before dawn to hit the 1.2-mile jogging trail at one of Tampa's oldest major parks. Your leashed dog is welcome to sniff along this trail and try out the 20-station exercise course along the way. Afterward, pooped pooches can rest at the hilltop gazebo.

The city park is at 1700 N. MacDill Avenue. Take North MacDill Avenue south from Columbus Drive. Look for the park a few blocks before you get to I-275. 813/274-8615.

❿ Rowlett Park

🐾🐾🐾🐾 ✖ (See Greater Tampa map on page 374)

Wow! What a great place to run! The city of Tampa has found room amid these 40 acres on the Hillsborough River for two off-leash areas. One is intended for big and strong dogs, and the other for small, frail, or elderly pooches.

Rowlett is in the middle of civilization but still manages to feel like a wild, wide-open space in places. For one thing, the river is here; it's dammed at the park's edge, creating a spot where in the winter your little furry friend may sometimes spy manatees, which congregate near where the fresh water from upstream flows into the brackish downstream.

Bring a packed lunch to share at the picnic area while the kids head to courts for basketball, tennis, or racquetball. Fishing is also possible here.

From Busch Gardens, head west on Busch Boulevard about four blocks. Turn left onto North 26th street and proceed one block to the park. 813/274-8615.

⓫ Woodland Terrace Playground

🐾 (See Greater Tampa map on page 374)

Dominated by ball fields, this medium-size, fenced city park attracts kite fliers and cricket players. Spreading oaks provide shade for panting dogs at the park's north and southeast corners, but overall it's not terribly scenic. Kids may appreciate the playground as you rest at picnic tables or fill a water bowl at the restrooms. Keep your dog leashed.

The park is at 6408 32nd St., near Tampa Community Bible Church and a few blocks north of Hillsborough Avenue. 813/274-8615.

12 Eureka Springs

🐾🐾🐾 🐾 (See Greater Tampa map on page 374)

Horticulturally minded hounds can sniff plants to their hearts' content in the walk-through flower garden and butterfly garden at this 31-acre county-run park. Hey, is that a dogwood tree or a dogtooth violet? Leashed dogs are allowed on the boardwalk and in the picnic area of the only botanical garden among Hillsborough County's regional parks. Only the greenhouse is off-limits.

Entrance is free, though donations are accepted. From I-4, take Exit 7 toward U.S. 92/Zephyrhills. Go 1.6 miles to Sligh Avenue, turn right, continue to Maple Lane, and turn right. Maple Lane soon will become Eureka Springs Road; continue 1.2 miles to 6400 Eureka Springs Road. 813/744-5536.

13 Giddens Dog Run

🐾🐾🐕 (See Greater Tampa map on page 374)

Big enough for a Border collie to play fetch endlessly, this half-acre off-leash area is smaller than a typical dog park. Retrievers make good use of it any-way—chasing balls and sniffing other canines. Drinking water, pooper-scooper bags, and seating for humans round out the amenities.

Locals had been letting their dogs off-leash here anyway before the neigh-borhood requested making a small dog park official. The fence was deteriorat-ing, so the city put in a new fence and amenities for the 2004 opening.

The dog run is across from Giddens Playground, a neighborhood park with a playground, community center, picnic tables, restrooms—and no parking lot. Skip this dog run unless you're in the neighborhood. The park is at 5209 N. 12th Street. 813/274-8615.

14 Veterans Memorial Park

🐾🐾 (See Greater Tampa map on page 374)

Leashed dogs are welcome to follow a three-quarter-mile bike trail along a sunny canal, then take a respite under oaks. Home to a veterans museum, this county-run fishing spot has picnic tables, grills, and shelters for hungry canines.

The park is at 3602 U.S. 301, south of Martin Luther King Boulevard. Take I-4 to U.S. 301 and head south to the park, at right. 813/744-5502.

15 Swann Circle Park

🐾🐾 (See Greater Tampa map on page 374)

Found in a quiet neighborhood, this small, shady park is a good place to spread out a blanket for a picnic. No cars or bikes are allowed within the grassy expanse, so park on Swann Avenue.

The breezy park is on Swann Avenue in the South Tampa community of Beach Park. Find it one block east of South Westshore Boulevard, a few blocks south of Kennedy Boulevard, and east of Old Tampa Bay. 813/274-8615 or 813/223-1111.

16 Plant Park

🐾🐾 (See Greater Tampa map on page 374)

This small riverfront garden spot amid the sea of concrete in downtown Tampa lures picnickers who come to munch bag lunches on park benches. Leashed pooches are welcome, too. From a bench at the edge of the Hillsborough River, the view is of pastel skyscrapers across the way. In the opposite direction are the silver Moorish spires of the University of Tampa's administration building.

When we visited, wild green parrots squawked and fled as we plopped down on a bench shaded by large sabal palms. Maggie particularly enjoyed the bounty of squirrels and pigeons that provide a good chase. This well-landscaped park is a pleasant place to visit, despite the occasional homeless person sleeping on a blanket.

Before leaving, walk up to the ornate University of Tampa administration building, formerly a grand old 1891 resort hotel that housed Teddy Roosevelt's Rough Riders during the Spanish-American War. Notice the crescent moons adorning the silver spires. Outside the building, a big statue with mermaids and fish pays tribute to its builder, Henry Plant, a pioneer Florida railroad builder. Don't miss the statue of the two pointing hunting dogs between the building and the parking area. Maggie sniffed them, at first, as if they were real.

The park is at 401 West Kennedy Blvd., about one mile off I-275. From I-275, take Ashley Street south for seven traffic lights to Kennedy Boulevard. Turn right on Kennedy, cross the river, and look for the park on your right. 813/253-3333 or 813/274-8615.

17 Riverfront Park

🐾🐾 (See Greater Tampa map on page 374)

Small hills to climb and a fair amount of shade trees distinguish this park on the Hillsborough River. A large soccer field at one end will tempt leashed dogs who like to chase Frisbees. Spreading oaks shade some parts of the park, which also features a baseball diamond, a swimming pool, tennis courts, racquetball courts, and a playground. Many times of year, you're unlikely to see anyone playing on the large ball fields, which are tucked away from busy streets. It's not in the best section of town, but with the Performing Arts Center across the river, it's not the worst.

The park, at 1001 North Blvd., is also called Julian B. Lane River Front Park. Take North Boulevard north from Kennedy Boulevard. Look for the park on your right just shy of I-275. 813/274-8615.

18 Ybor Centennial Park

 (See Greater Tampa map on page 374)

Watch where you raise those legs, doggies. The main statue at this park is dedicated to immigrants seeking freedom and economic opportunities. However, your pooch isn't likely to find freedom here; it's too small for quality romping. Mostly paved, this park offers just a few green patches of lawn. Oaks and a few date palms lend some shade as you admire a statue of Tampa's first Latin mayor, Nick Nucio, as well as the flags of the United States, Florida, and Ybor City. Listen to live music with your leashed dog during periodic events; for dates, call 813/248-3712.

The park is at 1800 Eighth Ave., at the intersection of 18th Street and Eighth Avenue in Ybor City. 813/274-8615.

DIVERSIONS

Sniff out Tampa's Latin roots: Back when Teddy Roosevelt and his Rough Riders walked these streets and José Martí helped plot ways to free Cuba from Spain, **Ybor City** was a vibrant place. Shopkeepers lived above their stores and people relaxed on their balconies at night. Today, the Tampa neighborhood is a national historic landmark district with cobblestone streets and globe streetlights. Spiffed up quite a bit in recent years, it's turned into a shopping and dining district.

Walk your dog along the broad sidewalk of 7th Avenue, the main drag. You'll pass some establishments that sustain the neighborhood's Cuban roots, including a couple of shops that sell cigars hand-rolled in Tampa. Cuban sandwiches still are served at the century-old Columbia Restaurant at 2117 E. 7th Avenue.

Stop to read historic markers during your stroll. You'll pass the century-old Italian Club at 1729 E. 7th Ave., whose façade appeared in the movie *Long Gone*. Across the way at 1602 7th Ave. is the century-old Gavino Gutierrez Building, built by the guy who persuaded Vicente Ybor to move the cigar industry from Key West to Tampa, according to FloridaHistory.org. Buffalo Bill's cousin once ran a theater downstairs.

Leave bustling 7th Avenue to visit a piece of land owned by the Cuban government: José Martí Park (Parque Amigos de José Martí), at the corner of 8th Avenue and 13th Street.

For a break, dine at dog-friendly eateries such as the Green Iguana, 1708 E. 7th Avenue. No longer in this part of town but remembered by some is the Silver Ring Cuban sandwich shop, where a poster used to read: Lost dog, three legs, blind in one eye, missing right ear, tail broken, recently castrated. Answers to the name of "Lucky."

19 Parque Amigos de José Martí

🐾◀● (See Greater Tampa map on page 374)

Plenty of doves and a larger-than-life statue of Cuban revolutionary hero José Martí may attract your leashed dog's attention at this wee fenced park, which contains soil from every province in Cuba, according to the local film commission. Maggie's visit was kept lively by a swooping mockingbird that thought Maggie was out to get her babies. Without dive-bombing birds, though, your dog may soon grow bored in this postage-stamp park across from the three-story Ybor Square mall.

For humans, though, it's a good place to soak in Cuban culture. Notice how the edging around a clump of ferns is shaped like the Cuban state of La Villas, while the border of a nearby tree looks like Camagüey. In the 1890s, people used to gather a few blocks away, at 13th Street and Ninth Avenue, when hero José Martí stayed at the home of a supporter, Paulina Pedrosas. They would watch Martí, known as "the apostle of freedom," through the windows.

The park's gates were locked the last time we visited. If you encounter the same, peer through the gates, then continue your dog's walk by exploring this Ybor City neighborhood. The memorial park is at the southeast corner of Eighth Avenue and 19th Street. 813/248-3712.

20 Cypress Point Park

🐾🐾🐾 (See Greater Tampa map on page 374)

Despite risk of fines, some people let their dogs swim at this 43-acre woodsy beach park located on a former landfill. At the request of the neighborhood, the city parks department was considering opening a leash-free area here as early as 2005, though likelier later. Niggling decisions remained, such as its location and whether to give pets water access so they could swim.

Even without an off-leash area, the place remains a favorite of some dog owners. Follow a nature trail with your leashed pet, who may stop to sniff the bases of plentiful trees. Launch a canoe, or eat at the picnic tables.

The park is at 5620 W. Cypress Street. 813/274-8615.

21 Fred Ball Park/Bayshore Boulevard

🐾🐾 (See Greater Tampa map on page 374)

Across from scenic Hillsborough Bay, Fred Ball Park sports a gazebo and some picnic tables amid pines, palmetto trees, and oaks. But perhaps the best part for dogs is when they get to leave the car behind and stroll the long sidewalk that stretches for more than four miles along the pretty bay across the street. City promoters call Bayshore Boulevard the world's longest continuous sidewalk, and the pleasant, sun-washed path attracts cyclists and in-line skaters who love the bay view on one side of the street and the stately homes on the other.

Few trees dot the bayshore, so limit your walk to protect your dog from heat exhaustion in warm months. Bayshore Boulevard is technically considered its own linear park, but parking isn't simple to find, so go to Fred Ball Park first.

Fred Ball Park is at 2629 Bayshore Boulevard. Take Bayshore Boulevard south to Rubideaux Avenue, where the park is on the right. Bayshore Boulevard Linear Park is based at 312 Bayshore Boulevard. 813/274-8615.

22 Palma Ceia Dog Run

🐾🐾🐕 (See Greater Tampa map on page 374)

It measures just .6 acre, but perhaps no other piece of ground this size is more loved by neighborhood dogs. With enough room to play fetch and sniff other canines, the grassy park is encircled by a four-foot-tall fence and includes drinking fountains for humans and dogs. It got its start when neighborhood dog owners noticed a ball field went practically unused. Why not turn it into a dog park? The city went on to turn half of it into a dog run.

Some yowls of protest ensued after the 2004 opening. Some neighbors complain the dog run is too small, attracts too much traffic, and should be used by kids, not pets. The park neighbors Palma Ceia Playground, which offers a playground, picnic tables, grills, and restrooms.

It's too small to merit a trip across town, so skip this place unless you're in the neighborhood. The park, which has no parking lot, is at 2200 Marti St., off West San Nichols Street. 813/274-8615.

23 Anderson Playground

🐾 (See Greater Tampa map on page 374)

Perhaps the tiniest picnic tables in Florida are found here. They don't quite reach knee height on an adult, which is a clue that the playground at the Kate Jackson Community Center is for kids. While children head to the swings, slides, and basketball courts, your pooch might tug at her leash to chase squirrels. The numerous trees provide a pleasant retreat from nearby sun-splashed Snow Avenue after a day of window-shopping in Old Hyde Park Village. It's best to visit on weekends or late in the day, after school's out and the kids have gone home.

The park is at 821 South Rome Ave., two blocks south of Swann Avenue. 813/274-8615.

24 Davis Islands Dog Park

🐾🐾🐾🐕 (See Greater Tampa map on page 374)

Swim or run? Dogs get their choice at this beloved destination, which actually offers two parks: a 1.5-acre beach with 200 feet of waterfront for swimming fun and a separate dry field for landlubbers. The sun-washed, one-acre grassy field lacks trees and abuts a small airport. (Indeed, you can see where a plane's wheels once hit the six-foot fence, causing damage, a park staffer points out.)

Davis Islands officially became a dog park offering a picnic table, pet shower, and drinking water in 2002, though locals have been exercising Labs here for years. We first heard about it from Jim Craven, a television news cameraman and former resident whose Australian shepherd, Jo, loved to romp along the island's south end.

That was before things got ruff. Eventually some residents of nearby upscale neighborhoods complained about dogs running free. That led to a crackdown, which led to a dog lovers' backlash, which led to the establishment of a sanctioned off-leash area. In the debate that raged, neighbor turned against neighbor. Some pro-dog islanders even boycotted a pharmacy operated by an islander who howled loudly about the pooch problems.

The biggest of the bugaboos? Poop. Now that the city has established this off-leash area, make sure you clean it up. Also bend over backwards to be nice to islanders. Much of the original controversy stemmed from the fact that "outsiders" from other Tampa neighborhoods were coming to the island.

The dog park is at the southern tip of Davis Islands, just beyond the Peter O. Knight Airport. Take the Davis Islands Bridge south from the intersection of Plant Avenue and Bayshore Boulevard. Continue south almost two miles on what now will be Davis Boulevard. Bear right onto Severn Avenue. Go one half mile to 1002 Severn Avenue. 813/274-8615.

25 DeSoto Park

🐾🐾 (See Greater Tampa map on page 374)

At this very big park, a spit of land leads into McKay Bay, allowing dogs to lounge lazily while looking out at the water from a picnic shelter. Energetic

dogs will want to follow a jogging trail or romp in the large grove of shady oaks, though they'll need a leash to stay legal. Kids may prefer the pool, basketball court, ball fields, or the tree-shaded playground. Fill a pet water bowl at the restrooms.

From I-4, head south on 22nd Street. Turn left at Stuart Street and continue to 2601 Stuart Street. 813/274-8615.

26 Ballast Point Park

🐾🐾 (See Greater Tampa map on page 374)

If your dog's antics make you think he's a bit spacey, this might be just the place for him. This tree-shaded park once bore the name of writer Jules Verne, who more than a century ago chose "Tampa Town" as the launching site for the imaginary rocket featured in his novel *From the Earth to the Moon*. Right on Hillsborough Bay, this popular holiday picnic site features little room to run with your leashed dog but plenty of places to eat together. Throw ribs onto one of the grills, then relax at picnic tables shaded by trees or shelters, or visit the playground. Dogs aren't allowed at the fishing pier. The plentiful squirrels and birds will intrigue many a dog.

The park is at 5300 Interbay Blvd. in southern Tampa. Take Bayshore Boulevard south from Gandy Boulevard, veering left onto Interbay Boulevard where it splits off. 813/274-8615.

27 Gadsden Dog Park

🐾🐾🐾🦴 (See Greater Tampa map on page 374)

Freedom! Retrievers run full blast to fetch balls and chase each other on this sunny, grassy field. The two-acre park is split in two, allowing pets access to only one acre at any given time so that the other acre—a little smaller than a softball field—has time to rejuvenate. A clump of big trees provides shade on the northern border, so owners can congregate there to watch the canine antics. Little terriers and other small dogs can head to a separate fenced area, which measures less than one-quarter acre.

Even before the bark park opened in June 2003, people ferried their pooches here for years. The park is within 87-acre Gadsden Park, whose people-pleasers include ball fields, a playground, picnic tables, a boat ramp, and a pier. The dog park introduced drinking water for pets and pooper-scooper bags.

The park is at 6901 S. MacDill Avenue. From Gandy Boulevard/U.S. 92, go south on Dale Mabry Highway. At Interbay Boulevard, turn left. Go right onto South Himes Avenue, left onto West Van Buren Drive, right onto South Sheridan Road, left onto West Marcum Street, then right onto South MacDill Avenue to the park ahead. The dog park is in the southwest corner of Gadsden Park. 813/274-8615.

28 Picnic Island Dog Run

🐾🐾🐾🐾 (See Greater Tampa map on page 374)

Between the boat ramp and canoe launch sits a long, long, humble shoreline, a no man's land that went unused—until the city decided to open up the unfenced area to dogs. This "beach" is actually a rough native-vegetation strand, so there's not much sand between it and the water. But dogs don't care how it looks. The narrow leash-free area is about 1,200 feet long and 1.4 acres in size.

Located in Port Tampa, it's part of 96-acre park that already attracted dog lovers. Snap on your pet's leash to explore the rest of Picnic Island Beach, and you'll enjoy a pretty view of the city. Picnic areas with grills offer the chance to cook up some grub for yourself and the pooch. Fill a water bowl at the restrooms. The park tends to attract anglers to its fishing pier around the clock. Kids will like the wavy sliding board at the sandy playground.

The park is at 7404 Picnic Island Boulevard. Take West Shore Boulevard south from Gandy Boulevard, bearing right at Commerce Street. Continue past Port Tampa to Picnic Island Boulevard and head south. 813/274-8615.

PLACES TO EAT

Adobe Gila's: This people-watching spot offers a view of Ybor City's 7th Avenue as you munch a lunch of burgers, pizza, nachos, or other bar fare. More bar than eatery, the open-air place offers some outdoor tables with stools. Dogs are welcome during the day, but not at night, particularly on weekends, when the place is mobbed. A sandwich board outside depicts a zonked Mexican fellow in a sombrero sitting in a margarita glass and reads, This Place Bites. Another sign: Live Dangerously—Drink Tequila. 1401 E. 7th Ave.; 813/241-8588.

Barley Hoppers International Ale House & Grille: Sit on the patio of this Central Ybor eatery to sample barley brews and appetizers from around the world, including potstickers with ponzu sauce and samosas. Entrees include filet mignon, penne pasta, and the Voodoo Mojo, a pork chop with a special sauce that gives it a little bite. Staffers have been known to bring bowls of water to canine guests. 1600 E. 8th Ave.; 813/242-6680.

Bernini of Ybor: At this elegant Ybor City bistro set in the handsome former Ybor City Bank, your dog may join you at one of four first-come, first-served outdoor tables. He can hope for scraps from your wood-fired pizza, calamari appetizer, or gourmet renditions of lamb, pasta, pork, or duck. 1702 E. 7th Ave.; 813/248-0099.

Carmine's: This decades-old Ybor City "home of the Cuban sandwich" serves up Cuban fare, as well as American and Italian. Order at the walk-up window and sit on a stool at the outdoor counter. An odd featured appetizer is the devil crab, a fried thing involving potatoes, crab, and bread served with spaghetti sauce. The Cuban sandwich—roasted pork, smoked ham, Swiss cheese, and other items—is authentic, though if you're not careful they'll add lettuce and tomato (which isn't authentic). 1802 E. 7th Ave.; 813/248-3834.

Checkers: Not far from some dog-friendly motels, this fast-food eatery offers a handful of umbrella-covered outdoor tables where you can sample burgers, chicken sandwiches, and fries with your pooch. 1509 Fowler Ave. East; 813/971-9765.

Fresh Mouth: Big taste, big attitude sums up this Central Ybor home of burgers, fries, Philly cheese steak sandwiches, chicken fingers, club sandwiches, and hand-dipped ice cream. Burgers seem to be the main event. As you sip beer at the outdoor tables behind a little black iron fence, a staffer is likely to present a bowl of water to your canine pal. 1600 E. 8th Ave.; 813/241-8845.

Green Iguana: After an afternoon of walking around the historic Cuban community of Ybor City, dogs sometimes plop down at the four tables outside this casual lunch-and-dinner spot to slurp from a bowl of ice water. You can order your own beverages, plus fajitas, grouper nuggets, sandwiches, burgers, pizzas, wraps, salads, and chicken wings sold by the pound. Late at night, the place turns into a dance club. 1708 E. 7th Ave.; 813/248-9555.

Java and Cream: Free dog biscuits make this a favorite destination of canines, while humans favor the many flavors of hand-dipped ice cream, plus other desserts and coffee. Water for canines is available on request. The shop is located on a particularly pooch-friendly business district, so you could head here for dessert after eating a meal elsewhere on the street or after fun at the off-leash beach at Davis Islands Dog Park. 225 E. Davis Blvd.; 813/254-8162.

Jax Grill at Gameworks in Central Ybor: Few people bring their leashed pets to this patio, but dogs are permitted to accompany their owners as they dine on tri-tip steak, baby-back ribs, burgers, pizzas, pastas, sandwiches, soups, appetizers, and salads, including a New York Strip salad. 1600 E. 8th Ave.; 813/241-9675.

Little Sicily: A pleasant Ybor City alternative for those who want to avoid the traffic on 7th Avenue, this Italian-style deli on a sleepy, brick-paved street serves pizza, homemade Italian sausage, Cuban sandwiches, and other goodies. Sit with your dog at any of the half-dozen outdoor tables set behind a small fence. Both the Italian and American flags fly here. 1724 8th Ave.; 813/248-2940.

Mad Dogs and Englishmen: This casual home of Sunday brunch and daily dinner gleans its moniker from dogs, so of course your pet may join you at an outdoor covered table to watch you dine on lamb chops, curried shrimp, flank steak, pan-seared cod, stilton cheese fondue, or other eats. "We come here all the time," said a guy sitting next to his yellow hound dog, Cody. "A lot of people bring their dogs here." For something different, consider the

Mad Dog salad with mixed greens, toasted pecans, blue cheese crumbles, and mustard-raspberry vinaigrette dressing. 4115 S. MacDill Ave.; 813/832-3037.

Marble Slab Creamery: Sit at the four tables out front of this ice cream shop to share banana splits, frozen yogurt, or a cone. 1600 E. 8th Ave.; 813/247-4406.

Pink Flamingo Cafe: Open for breakfast and lunch, this café is among several on this block offering outdoor tables perfect for pooches and their people bound for off-leash fun at nearby Davis Islands Dog Park. Pets have been known to get a free dog biscuit here, and they slurp heartily at provided water bowls. Sit at picnic tables to enjoy buttermilk pancakes or lunch fare. 210 E. Davis Blvd., 813/251-2928.

Red Dog Bar & Grill: Burgers, chicken sandwiches, and wings complement what the informal establishment is best known for—many varieties of cold beer, plus indoor activities such as darts and pool. A bartender recommends the "great fajitas." You'll sit in the patio in front of the "Best Slow-Night Bar" and "Best Bar," as named in past years by the local alternative paper, *Weekly Planet.* 3311 W. Bay-to-Bay Blvd.; 813/835-4347.

Rick's Italian Café: Take a seat in the patio to sample spaghetti, baked ziti, and other traditional Italian dinners or two kinds of pizzas: Neopolitan and thick-sliced Sicilian. A convenient place to stop before off-leash fun at Davis Islands Dog Park, the eatery can provide water bowls to thirsty canines. 214 E. Davis Blvd.; 813/253-3310.

Tate Brothers Pizza: Dogs head to the outside deck to watch their people sip beer and eat pizza by the slice or by the pie at this informal eatery located in a particularly pooch-friendly business district in South Tampa. Salads, calzones, and sandwiches number among other offerings. 233 E. Davis Blvd.; 813/251-2767.

PLACES TO STAY

AmeriSuites Busch Gardens: The in-room fridge may interest your dog, who must weigh 25 pounds or less to stay at this comfortable hotel offering a pool, exercise room, and free breakfast buffet. Rates range $85–130. Pet fee is $10 daily. 11408 N. 30th St., Tampa; 813/979-1922; www.amerisuites.com.

AmeriSuites Tampa Airport: Most dogs would need to diet to meet the weight limit at this pleasant lodging: just 15 pounds. Rates range $115–160. 4811 W. Main St., Tampa; 813/282-1037; www.amerisuites.com.

Baymont Inn & Suites-Tampa Busch Gardens: Don't yelp, Scottie—the knock on the door may be your companion returning with a free continental breakfast. Small dogs are accepted in smoking rooms at this pleasant poolside motel west of Busch Gardens. Rates range $60–109. 9202 N. 30th St., Tampa; 813/930-6900; www.baymontinns.com.

Baymont Inn & Suites-Brandon: Walk your pet in the grassy area in back after enjoying the free breakfast buffet. Dogs under 60 pounds may pad along interior corridors to sleep in smoking rooms at this three-story lodging. Rates start at $69. 602 S. Faulkenburg Rd., Tampa; 813/684-4007; www.baymontinns.com.

Baymont Inn & Suites-Tampa Fairgrounds: This poolside motel is across the street from the fairgrounds and near an industrial park, so you'll find grassy areas to walk your dog after your free breakfast buffet. Rates run $60–99. 4811 U.S. 301 North, Tampa; 813/626-0885; www.baymontinns.com.

Best Western All Suites Hotel Behind Busch Gardens: Everyone sleeps in a two-room suite at this comfortable 150-unit lodging with a tiki-style grill/bar, free country breakfast buffet, and big sundeck/pool area. Dogs under 75 pounds are accepted for $25 every three days. Rates range $70–129. 3001 University Center Dr., Tampa; 813/971-8930 or 800/SUNSHINE; www.bestwestern.com.

Chase Suite Hotel by Woodfin: All dogs sleep in suites at this pleasant two-story lodging, which offers humans free breakfasts and light dinners including beer and wine, plus amenities such as a pool and boat dock. Walk your dog along the causeway. Rates range $90–200. Pets weighing 50 pounds and under are accepted for $50, plus $5 every other day. 3075 N. Rocky Point Dr., Tampa; 813/281-5677; www.woodfinsuitehotels.com/tampa/.

Clarion Hotel Tampa Westshore: Overlooking Tampa Bay, this hotel tower offers a restaurant, a gift shop, an outdoor pool, an exercise room, a cocktail lounge, and bellmen to show your pup and family to your room. Rates range $125–169. Pet fee is $50, half of which is refundable barring doggy

mishaps. 5303 W. Kennedy Blvd., Tampa; 813/289-1950; www.clarionhotel. com/hotel/FL748.

Days Inn Airport Stadium: After your dip in the kidney-shaped heated pool, your dog hopes you'll order room service from the on-site Bennigan's or carry your complimentary breakfast to your room at this pleasant 285-unit motel. Rates range $79–150. The pet fee is $25 per stay. 2522 N. Dale Mabry Hwy., Tampa; 813/877-6181; www.daysinntampa.com.

Holiday Inn Express & Suites Tampa Stadium: The New York Yankees play spring-training games a block away at Legends Field, and the Tampa Bay Buccaneers play at another stadium within walking distance of this two-story poolside motel, which has an on-site lake. Rates range $104–140. Add a $25 pet fee. 4732 N. Dale Mabry Hwy., Tampa; 813/877-6061; www. holidayinns.com.

Holiday Inn Tampa Near Busch Gardens: With a snack bar and T.G.I. Friday at this two-story motel, canine dieters might ask, "Won't you raise the 20-pound weight limit for dogs, please?" Rates range $69–170. Pet fee is $25 per stay. 2701 E. Fowler Ave., Tampa; 813/971-4710; www.holidayinns.com.

Hampton Inn Tampa-Veterans Expressway: Newshounds will appreciate the free weekday paper at this comfortable lodging, where pets under 50 pounds may walk along interior hallways to reach guest rooms. Rates start at $99. Pet fee is $8 nightly. 5628 W. Water Ave., Tampa; 813/901-5900; http://hamptoninn.hilton.com.

La Quinta Inn Airport: A pavement-and-stone driveway leads to a porte cochere and pretty landscaping at the office of this pleasant 122-room poolside motel. Only a smidgen of grass out back is available for dogs looking for greenery. Rates run $79–110. 4730 Spruce St., Tampa; 813/287-0440; www.lq.com.

Motel 6 Downtown: At the Motel 6 closest to Busch Gardens, rates run $42–52. Corporate policy allows one well-behaved pet per room. 333 E. Fowler Ave., Tampa; 813/932-4948; www.motel6.com.

Motel 6 East Fairgrounds: At this 106-room poolside motel, rates range $44–58. Company policy permits one well-mannered pet per room. 6510 N. U.S. 301, Tampa; 813/628-0888; www.motel6.com.

Red Roof Inn Brandon: Newshounds will appreciate the free weekday newspaper and CNN channel at this poolside motel off I-75 (Exit 257). Rates range $50–90. 10121 Horace Ave., Tampa; 813/681-8484; www. redroof.com.

Red Roof Inn Busch Gardens: A picnic area is found by the pool of this motel off I-275 (Exit 50), where dogs who keep up on current events will enjoy the free weekday newspaper and CNN channel. Pets 70 pounds and under are accepted. Rates range $42–71. 2307 E. Busch Blvd., Tampa; 813/932-0073; www.redroof.com.

Red Roof Inn Fairgrounds: Local calls are free, so go ahead and call a pooch-permissible eatery to check tonight's specials. One pet under 80 pounds may join you at this 109-room poolside motel. Rates range $42–80. 5001 N. U.S. 301, Tampa; 813/623-5245; www.redroof.com.

Tahitian Inn Hotel and Spa: This boutique hotel offers such amenities as a fitness facility, masseuse, heated tiki pool, whirlpool tubs, coffee shop, restaurant, and full bar. Pets tend to walk in the grassy area out back. Rates range $99–200, plus a $25-per-stay pet fee. 601 S. Dale Mabry Hwy., Tampa; 813/877-6721; www.tahitianinn.com.

Temple Terrace

PARKS, BEACHES, AND RECREATION AREAS

29 City of Temple Terrace Rotary Riverfront Park

(See Greater Tampa map on page 374)

There are Muscovy ducks for dogs to chase and oak trees to enjoy picnics beneath at this little park, where we saw a small white pooch walking on leash with his two-legged companion. More of a boat launch than anything else, this park nonetheless makes a pleasant setting for a riverside picnic lunch beneath a stand of oaks. If you forget to bring food, you could order takeout meals from Shoney's, next door at 8602 Morris Bridge Road.

From I-75, head west on Fowler Avenue. Look for the park on the right when you cross the Hillsborough River. 813/989-7180.

30 Trout Creek Park

(See Greater Tampa map on page 374)

This park is part of the five-site Lower Hillsborough Wilderness Park, the county's largest regional park. Bring a canoe—or whatever craft you can lug with a friend—to launch into the Hillsborough River for a day of fishing with your dog. Afterward, toss hot dogs onto a grill at one of the picnic shelters. Twenty-eight miles of trails connect this park with Flatwoods Wilderness Park and Morris Ridge Wilderness Park, so hikers are certain to leave dog-tired.

From I-75, go east on Morris Bridge Road/Highway 579, then turn north at Trout Creek Park Road. 813/987-6200 or 813/975-2160.

PLACES TO STAY

Residence Inn: With a kitchen, fireplace (in some rooms), and other homey amenities, your pup may think he's at Aunt Queenie's house rather than a hotel suite. Rates range $104–170. The nonrefundable pet fee is a whopping $75. 13420 N. Telecom Pkwy., Temple Terrace; 813/972-4400.

Thonotosassa

PARKS, BEACHES, AND RECREATION AREAS

31 Flatwoods Wilderness Park

🐾🐾🐾 (See Greater Tampa map on page 374)

Attractive to joggers and bicyclists, the asphalt loop trail built here in 1990 covers 7.8 miles—long enough to leave even the most energetic pooch dog-tired. Just in case that wasn't enough, a 4.3-mile lane was added in 1992. In all, 19 miles of bicycle paths now ribbon this park and neighboring Morris Bridge Wilderness Park.

For an alternative, try a woodsy nature trail. Afterward, have lunch with your pal at the picnic shelters, grills, and tables. Dogs can feel very welcome here: While they are taboo in portions of most of the other parks in the five-site, 16,000-acre Lower Hillsborough Wilderness Park, they are okay anywhere in Flatwoods as long as they stay leashed.

From I-75, take the Fletcher Avenue exit and follow Fletcher, then Morris Bridge Road, east. Look for the entrance on your left. 813/987-6211 or 813/975-2160.

32 John B. Sargeant Sr. Memorial Park

🐾 (See Greater Tampa map on page 374)

A canoe or boat ride (you bring the vessel) is most likely to capture the attention of your furry friend at this tiny park, part of the five-site Lower Hillsborough Wilderness Park. Sure, you can eat a bag lunch at the sole picnic shelter. And yes, you can take in the view of the confluence of the Hillsborough River and Flint Creek. But there is little room for dogs, who must be leashed, to stretch their legs, and the pier is off-limits.

Don't let your dog jump into the river. Not known to be good spellers, alligators might mistake your dog for one of the wild hogs they are accustomed to eating.

The park is northwest of Tampa on U.S. 301, about 1.5 miles west of Mango Road/Highway 579. 813/987-6208 or 813/975-2160.

33 Morris Bridge Wilderness Park

🐾🐾🐾 (See Greater Tampa map on page 374)

Dogs who have a hankering for the outdoors can investigate nature trails at this county park on the Hillsborough River, part of the five-site Lower Hillsborough Wilderness Park. For lunch, grill hot dogs next to scattered picnic tables or at the sole picnic shelter. A boat ramp, restrooms, and docks are available.

From Tampa, drive north on I-75, then turn right (east) on Morris Bridge Road/Highway 579 and continue about four miles to the park. 813/987-6209 or 813/975-2160.

🐾 Dead River Wilderness Park

🐾🐾🐾 (See Greater Tampa map on page 374)

Ranger Jack Coleman said his Staffordshire bull terrier, Bo, loved sniffing around this woodsy home of raccoons and other creatures until he died a natural death under a tree here at age 13. Your dog will like the place, too. "It'd be a great spot to walk a dog," Coleman said.

Leashed dogs may sniff along the two-mile river trail, an abandoned road along the Hillsborough River. The drill: Friday through Sunday, the park is open to car traffic. So drive in, park, and enjoy the trail. Other days, you must park at the locked gate and hike for two miles on the tree-shaded entrance road to get to the normal parking area. It's best to turn around partway to avoid taxing your pooch, but you'll still have a pleasant walk.

Bring your own canoe to float down the Hillsborough River with your dog, but don't let her go in the water. One of Coleman's dogs, a chow chow/Labrador pup named Bear, was sniffing at the river's edge when an alligator suddenly pulled the pup under—and Bear was gone for good. A previous ranger lost a German shepherd to a gator. Don't be alarmed—just be cautious, Coleman suggests. He knew of only two canine casualties in 16 years and says, "The chances of that happening are very minimal."

Dead River is part of the five-site Lower Hillsborough Wilderness Park, the county's largest regional park. While the five parks technically are linked and can be reached on foot—if you have the stamina of Paul Bunyan—dogs are forbidden to wander outside the parks' boundaries. Picnic and restroom facilities are available.

From Tampa, head northeast on U.S. 301 until you reach Dead River Road. Turn left (west) and continue to the park. 813/987-6210 or 813/975-2160.

🐾 Hillsborough River State Park

🐾🐾🐾 (See Greater Tampa map on page 374)

Ruff-and-ready pups will leave dog-tired after a trot along this park's nature trails—eight miles in all. No barking allowed as you walk through the stomping grounds of wild turkeys, deer, and otters, or you won't catch a glimpse of these creatures. The trails meander through forests of oaks, magnolias, and hickory trees, and rim a river named for the Earl of Hillsborough, who secured England's control over Tampa Bay in the 1700s. Your pup can catch up on more history at the park's wooden replica of Fort Foster, which dates to the 1830s, when federal troops were fighting the Seminoles.

You can picnic with your pooch at the 4.7-square-mile park. While dogs are verboten in the pool, concession area, and rental canoes, your dog may ride in a canoe that you bring to the park. Watch out for alligators, though—a dog was eaten here a few years ago.

Dogs may camp at some sites at this park. (These are the sites farthest from the river, thankfully.) Fee is $22.40 nightly. Reserve at ReserveAmerica.com or 800/326-3521.

Admission is $4 per vehicle. From Tampa, head northeast on U.S. 301 for 12 miles until you reach the park on your left, at 15402 U.S. 301 North. 813/987-6771.

PLACES TO STAY

Camp Lemora RV Park: Your leashed buddy can hike into the worthwhile Dead River Wilderness Park (see Parks, Beaches, and Recreation areas, above) from this campground, but he must stay inside your camper if you ever leave him alone. A heated pool, shuffleboard, horseshoes, showers, and laundry are among the amenities. Campsites cost $23. No tents, please. From I-75 (Exit 265), go east on Fowler Avenue for 1.2 miles to U.S. 301. Turn north. Continue eight miles to the camp sign. 14910 Dead River Rd., Thonotosassa; 813/986-4456.

   Hillsborogh River State Park: See Parks, Beaches, and Recreation Areas, above, for camping information.

Lutz

PLACES TO STAY

Lake Como Club Nudist Resort: Dogs don't wear clothes, and you won't either if you camp or stay in a motel room at Florida's oldest nudist resort. Pets do wear a leash, however, to follow trails through this 200-acre retreat. Ask about the dog beach at the park's 35-acre Lake Como. Cats, birds, and a chimpanzee named Daisy number among pet guests. First-time visitors are asked to take a tour before trying the resort, which features an Olympic-size pool, tennis courts, a billiards hall, an 18-person hot tub, and an old 90-acre citrus grove. Motel rooms and suites range $35–65. Cottages and travel trailers range $65–70. Pet fee is $10. Add a daily grounds fee, which typically ranges $10–20. Campsites range $10–36, plus grounds fee. Rottweilers and pit bulls are not accepted. 20500 Cot Rd., Lutz; 813/949-1810 or 877/TRY-LAKE; www.lakecomoresort.com.

Plant City

It's too bad the annual Florida Strawberry Festival, which draws folks from around the state to this small town, isn't dog-friendly. Maggie didn't mind, though, when she figured out that strawberries taste nothing like bacon.

PARKS, BEACHES, AND RECREATION AREAS

36 Mike Sansone Park

😊 (See Greater Tampa map on page 374)

This is the biggest city park around, with fields, trees, and ball fields to tempt pent-up pooches, although going off leash is officially prohibited. Take Park Road north from town and look for the park on the right, a half mile before you reach I-4. 813/659-4200.

PLACES TO STAY

Comfort Inn: Cocker spaniels and other pets under 35 pounds may pad along interior corridors to sleep at this pleasant 61-room poolside lodging off I-4 (Exit 22). Rates range $55–120. Add a $40 pet fee. 2003 S. Frontage Rd., Plant City; 813/707-6000; www.choicehotels.com.

Days Inn: Walk your dog in the little field behind this three-story poolside hotel off I-4 (Exit 22), which features volleyball, shuffleboard, a playground,

DIVERSIONS

See a T-Rex with Rex: An orange life-size Tyrannosaurus Rex stands alongside I-4 to encourage motorists to take Exit 17 and go to **Dinosaur World,** an outdoor museum opened in Plant City in 1998 by Swedish immigrant Christopher Svensson, a maker of dinosaur replicas for theme parks in other countries.

Leashed friendly dogs are welcome to walk through the semi-tropical setting of the roadside attraction to see more than 160 life-size dinosaur models. A beagle named Iggy was quite nervous until he realized these dinosaurs did not move or roar, says his companion/chauffeur, Wendy Ballard.

Definitely low-tech, Dinosaur World nonetheless has expanded to offer kid-friendly, hands-on activities, such as digging for fossils. The staff welcomes dogs throughout the entire place—from the gift shop to the exhibits. Admission costs $9.75 for adults, $7.75 for kids ages 3 to 12, and free for younger children and dogs. 5145 Harvey Tew Rd., Plant City; 813/717-9865.

and a restaurant—good news for hungry hounds. Rates run $56–120. Add $20 per pet the first day, $10 daily thereafter. 301 S. Frontage Rd., Plant City; 813/752-0570; www.daysinn.com.

Ramada Inn Plantation House: Pets and their people sleep in designated rooms at this 150-room lodging, which offers a fitness room, a lounge, a dining room, and a pool area with a veranda off I-4 (Exit 21). Rates start at $105. Pet fee is $25 nightly. 2011 N. Wheeler, Plant City St.; 813/752-3141; www.ramada.com.

Seffner

PARKS, BEACHES, AND RECREATION AREAS

37 Mango Dog Park

🐾🐾🐾🐾🐾 (See Greater Tampa map on page 374)

Liberty call! This five-acre leash-free park was authorized by the Hillsborough County Commission in 2001, just as the local leash laws tightened and enforcement beefed up. "The timing was good," said Phil Evans of the county parks department. Also convenient, if a little unsettling (and unsettled): This park is laid out atop an old dump, where the ground periodically shifts. Buildings just wouldn't work here.

This running field surrounded by a six-foot fence was designed to offer pavilions for people, picnic tables, a few trees (offering a modicum of shade), water fountains for people and pets, disposable pooper-scooper mitts, and a dog-wash area for those inevitably muddy days. Small pets enter a separate entrance for their own romping room.

A welcome amenity: Lights shine for use at night. Retrievers from all over come to run or take part in occasional events such as a Doggy New Year Celebration with games, vendors, and contests.

Pooches must have their shots and a tag to prove it. No food, treats, aggressive animals, or kids under age six are permitted. Children ages 6 to 15 must be accompanied by an adult.

The bark park may be closed Wednesdays for maintenance. Find it next to a sports complex at Mango Recreation Center, located on the southeast corner of Clay Pit Road and County Road 579/Mango Road. From I-4, exit onto County Road 579/Mango Road. Turn a slight right onto Mango Road, then left onto Clay Pit Road. The park is up ahead at 11717 Clay Pit Road. 813/975-2160.

Brandon

PARKS, BEACHES, AND RECREATION AREAS

3 8 Edward Medard Park and Reservoir

🐾 🐾 (See Greater Tampa map on page 374)

This park's 770-acre reclaimed phosphate mine is one of Hillsborough County's most popular bass and pan fishing spots. Sadly, though, furry swimmers can't romp on the white-sand beach. Plus, they're discouraged—but not forbidden—from walking along the several miles of marked bridle paths for fear of spooking horses.

So what's a leashed dog to do at this county park? Try picnicking at the several sheltered tables and grills. According to a park employee, if you bring your own canoe (or boat), a dog can go along for the ride, provided he stays out of the water. You also can camp for $12 a night at any of 51 campsites (some a little shady, others not). All sites are first come, first served and include tables, water, electricity, and fire rings. RVs can be accommodated at some sites. Restrooms and showers are available.

The park is at 5726 Panther Loop. Take Highway 60 east through Brandon and Valrico. When you pass the railroad tracks, turn right (south) on South Turkey Creek Road and look for the entrance on the left. 813/757-3802.

3 9 Alderman's Ford

🐾 🐾 🐾 (See Greater Tampa map on page 374)

Historically a popular place for politicians to campaign (hence the name), this fording spot on the Alafia River democratically lets doggies and bicyclists share a 1.8-mile asphalt loop path dotted with wooden footbridges. The path winds through the park, crosses the Alafia River, and provides a close-up look at a swamp. Along the way, the trail connects several picnic areas on the Alafia River, where you're welcome to eat with your leashed buddy. The loop also links up with natural trails, each more than one mile long. There's even a playground for the kiddies.

The nearly two-square-mile park is pretty: Lacy moss hangs from the gnarled branches of big oaks. And here, the Alafia River branches into its northern and southern prongs. No wonder the river is popular with canoeists; bring your own canoe if your dog enjoys paddling, but beware of alligators. Dogs aren't allowed on the beloved boardwalk.

The regional park is at 9625 Canoe Launch Loop, in eastern Hillsborough County. Take Highway 60 east from Tampa and pass through Brandon. Turn right on County Road 39 and look for the park in five miles. 813/757-3801.

🔟 Lithia Springs Park

🐾🐾🐾 (See Greater Tampa map on page 374)

It's hard to find such varied terrain in one county park, with cypress swamps, hardwood hammocks, and sand hills among the many ecosystems here. If you enjoy it so much you don't want to leave, camp with your dog at one of the 40 first-come, first-served campsites for $12. While your leashed pooch is forbidden to take a dip in the 72°F waters of the popular spring-fed swimming hole here, he can join you for a picnic lunch or walks in this 160-acre park.

Entrance is $1 per person. Take Highway 60 east through Brandon. Bear right on Lithia-Pinecrest Road. After about seven miles, cross a bridge and look for a sign directing you to Lithia Springs Road. Follow it to the park at 3932 Lithia Springs Road. 813/744-5572.

PLACES TO STAY

Behind The Fence Bed & Breakfast: Dogs are welcome at this replica of an 1800s saltbox-style New England farmhouse. "It is really an experience," says proprietor Larry Yoss. Furnished with the pre-1850s antiques that Yoss's wife, Carolyn, collected through the years, the inn has an Amish feel. Guests sleep in the main house or a poolside private cottage, then wake up to a breakfast of homemade Amish sweet rolls, pastries from a nearby berry farm, fresh fruit, cereal, juice, tea, and coffee. Larry is often asked whether his five guest rooms have queen-size beds. He reminds inquirers that his beds are a century old—and queen-size beds weren't made back then. The inn is set amid oak trees in a residential development called Countryside in the southeast suburb of

Brandon. For a dog walk, head to the county park behind this lodging. Rooms cost $89. Add $10 nightly for the pooch. 1400 Viola Dr.; 813/685-8201.

Edward Medard Park and Reservoir: See Parks, Beaches, and Recreation Areas, above, for camping information.

Homestead Studio Suites: Everyone sleeps in a studio with fully equipped kitchen—good for hungry hounds. At this pleasant 141-unit lodging, per-night rates are lower if you stay a week instead of just one night. Rates range $65–100. Pet fee is $25 daily, maximum $75. 330 Grand Regency Blvd.; 813/643-5900; www.homesteadhotels.com.

La Quinta: The landscaped courtyard features a pool, spa, and sundeck area while breakfast time brings free waffles, pastries, and fresh fruit at this pleasant lodging. Guest rooms are bigger than at older La Quintas—meaning more room for Fifi to stretch her legs. At night, dog-tired travelers can dine in with Spot; just order takeout from any of five nearby eateries, including Olive Garden and Red Lobster. Rates range $79–125. 310 Grand Regency Blvd., Brandon; 813/643-0574; www.lq.com.

Lithia Springs Park: See Parks, Beaches, and Recreation Areas, above, for camping information.

Riverview

PARKS, BEACHES, AND RECREATION AREAS

41 Riverview Civic Center

🐾🐾🐾 (See Greater Tampa map on page 374)

A favorite of two local Yorkshire terriers named Angie and Pebbles, this two-acre park overlooking the Alafia River has hosted several weddings. Bring a bag lunch or launch a boat to see the pretty Alafia with your leashed pooch. Angie and Pebbles revel in running around the town's biggest park to fetch a ball thrown by their companion, Sandra Lott.

Take U.S. 301 south from Tampa. Cross the Alafia River and turn left at the light onto Balm Riverview Road. The park is three blocks up at 11020 Park Drive. 813/671-7600 or 813/643-8000.

Ruskin

PARKS, BEACHES, AND RECREATION AREAS

42 E. G. Simmons Park

🐾🐾🐾 (See Greater Tampa map on page 374)

Water dogs will love wading in Tampa Bay at this 469-acre park and preserve—as long as they go to the right place. They aren't allowed at the designated swimming beach, but there are miles of shoreline where dogs can take

DIVERSIONS

Drivin' to the drive-in: So you always wanted to find love at the drive-in theater? Forget romance and go with your best buddy. At the **Ruskin Family Drive-In Theatre,** owners Karen and Ted Freiwald hand treats to Sam, Buddy, and other canine customers, many of whom are regulars. "Some of the time, I know the dogs' names but I have no idea of the owners' names," says Karen.

Furry heads hang out of vehicle windows in search of treats and petting at the drive-up ticket booth. Karen and Ted amply oblige, saying howdy and patting the fuzzy heads.

"The dogs go crazy," Karen says.

After vehicles pull into the theater, pets watch flicks on the big outdoor screen and commonly turn their attention to their companions' popcorn and burgers. "I take mine [to the movies] to get cheeseburgers all the time," an employee said of her dog.

At Ruskin, no alcohol, drugs, or rowdiness are allowed, but well-behaved dogs are permitted, so long as they stay in the car the whole time. The theater is at 5011 U.S. 41 N., Ruskin; 813/645-1455.

---

the plunge—look for openings in the mangroves during your woodsy walks. Ironically, swimming at these spots is prohibited for the two-legged set, while dogs can't take a dip at the humans' bathing beach.

Bring a cooler for a waterfront picnic or a boat to launch into the bay. You and your dog can camp in a site with a waterfront view for $10 (no electricity) or $12 (with electricity); sites are first come, first served. This popular wilderness retreat lures outdoors enthusiasts who come for the bay-view camping and fishing, and many bring their dogs. Don't worry about alligators here; the creatures don't live in salt water.

The park is on Tampa Bay, on 19th Street Northwest, west of U.S. 41. 813/671-7655.

PLACES TO STAY

E. G. Simmons Park: See Parks, Beaches, and Recreation Areas, above, for camping information.

Ramada Inn on Tampa Bay: Actually located north of Ruskin in Apollo Beach, this 102-room bayfront hotel offers canine guests a view of the private beach and pretty sunsets from room windows, though pets aren't permitted to set paw in the sand. Instead, stretch four legs in the field across the road or head to a woodsy park down the street. A tiki bar with live entertainment, a waterfront restaurant, beach volleyball, and a heated pool number among hotel amenities. Rates range $60–150. The daily pet fee is $15. 6414 Surfside Blvd., Apollo Beach; 813/641-2700; www.ramada.com.

Sun City Center Inn: Set in the nearby retirement community of Sun City Center, this two-story motel offers tennis courts, golf, and a pool off I-75 (Exit 240). Rates range $50–80. Add $7.50 per stay for a small dog. 809 N. Pebble Beach Blvd., Sun City Center; 813/634-3331.

Wimauma

PARKS, BEACHES, AND RECREATION AREAS

4 3 Little Manatee River State Park

🐾🐾 (See Greater Tampa map on page 374)

A ranger calls this 2,400-acre park an absolutely gorgeous place for a picnic. And dogs may join you for said picnic at this favorite hangout of horseback riders, campers, and anglers. If you bring your own canoe, your dog also can enjoy an easy 4.5-mile tour on the dark waters flanked by steep banks. Considering how pleasant the ride is, it's no wonder the Little Manatee River is designated an Outstanding Florida Water.

Leashed pets may follow a nature trail in the picnic area and camp at any site in the campground. Trees, shrubs, and other greenery provide a buffer between sites, which cost $20 nightly. Reserve at ReserveAmerica.com or 800/326-3521.

Entrance is $4 per vehicle. From town, head south on U.S. 301 about five miles and turn right at Lightfoot Road. 813/671-5005.

PLACES TO STAY

Little Manatee River State Park: See Parks, Beaches, and Recreation Areas, above, for camping information.

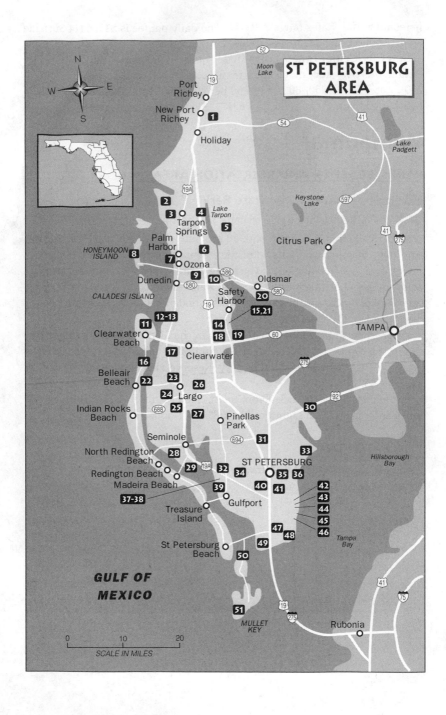

CHAPTER 14

St. Petersburg Area

Considering it's the most densely populated county in Florida (we're counting the two-legged set, not our friends with the snouts and paws), Pinellas County has done a remarkable job of preserving some green space where your pooch can romp. Some of the best places are a short drive outside St. Petersburg proper, but even in the city there are several dog parks as well as some wonderful waterfront parks on Tampa Bay, such as manicured Poynter Park.

Pinellas County was one of the first places the Spaniards visited when they explored Florida, and they called it *punta pinal* (point of pines). And even though the pine forests that once provided such ample opportunities for leg lifts have mostly been bulldozed, people and their pooches continue to visit Pinellas. One reason is the weather. You want sun? You'll find it here. St. Pete holds a spot in the *Guinness Book of World Records* for the longest consecutive sunny spell: more than two years—from February 9, 1967, to March 17, 1969. According to local lore and the visitors bureau, the publishers of the old *St. Petersburg Evening Independent* gave the paper away free of charge on days when the sun didn't shine. They had to make good on the promise only 295

PICK OF THE LITTER—ST. PETERSBURG

BEST ALL-AROUND ROMP SPOTS
John Chesnut Sr. County Park, Palm Harbor (page 410)
Fort Desoto Park, St. Petersburg (page 433)

DOG-FRIENDLIEST LODGING
Lorelei Resort Motel, Treasure Island (page 437)

BEST DOG BEACHES
Honeymoon Island State Park, Dunedin (page 412)
Fort Desoto Park, St. Petersburg (page 433)

LONGEST WALK
Pinellas Trail, Tarpon Springs and Palm Harbor
(page 409)

times in the paper's 76-year existence, an average of fewer than four times per year.

For the four-legged crowd, all that sun can be uncomfortable, or even dangerous. So be mindful of your buddy's needs for water and shade. The threat of heat exhaustion is one reason you may not be too disappointed to hear that most beaches are off-limits to dogs. For instance, don't expect to sashay with Sasha past the Don Cesar Beach Resort, the famous "pink palace" at St. Pete Beach. However, a few slices of waterfront not considered prime for sunbathing and babe- and hunk-ogling have been grudgingly set aside for our canine companions.

Don't count on ducking under the umbrella-covered tables of every sidewalk café for shade, either. Many an eatery with an outdoor area that would be considered perfectly fine for whiskered wanderers elsewhere in the state will turn away dogs here in Pinellas. Some managers cite a fear of health inspectors—who happen to follow the same state law as the pooch-friendly establishments in Miami, Fort Lauderdale, and other locales. A few with eating areas very clearly "outside" the restaurant give pooches the thumbs-up, and we've listed them here.

Despite the relative lack of canine-tolerant restaurants, pooches shouldn't sulk away from Greater St. Pete with their tails tucked between their legs. There are some real doggy gems to be dug up. The Lorelei Resort in Treasure Island is the most hound-hospitable inn we found in Florida—an 11-unit affair that caters to dogs who happen to bring their people, not the other way around. Here, dogs can dive off a dock and swim to their hearts' content. A basket of doggy treats greets them at check-in.

Getting around Pinellas County can be confusing for the first-time visitor because there are so many municipalities—we count 24. Basically, St. Petersburg dominates the southern end of the peninsula; Largo, Clearwater, and Dunedin are the main burgs in the middle portion; and Tarpon Springs and Palm Harbor (which is unincorporated) are the biggest towns in the northern section. We particularly recommend Tarpon Springs, with its dog-friendly and interesting restaurants. Most barrier islands are Nowheresville, USA when it comes to pleasing the pups.

New Port Richey

PARKS, BEACHES, AND RECREATION AREAS

◘ J. B. Starkey Wilderness Park

😁😁😁 (See St. Petersburg map on page 404)

This wilderness park, located inland from New Port Richey, is a welcome respite from the suburbs creeping north up the coast from St. Pete. Horses, not dogs, are the favored animals here, as they are allowed to camp in these 8,700 acres of oak, cypress, and pasture along the Anclote and Pithlachascottee rivers, while pooches cannot. Still, it's a heck of a place for a day hike. Lucky dogs might spot deer, turkeys, or even a bobcat. Enjoy 13 miles of hiking trails or trot along a 3.5-mile paved road. In either case, you're likely to have company: horses on hiking trails (keep your pooch leashed, and get off the trail when you see them coming) and cyclists or roller skaters on the paved road. Picnic shelters are available for a shaded lunch when your hike is done.

From U.S. 19 in New Port Richey, take Highway 54 east for 2.5 miles to Little Road, then head north to River Crossing Boulevard. Drive three miles east to the park entrance. 727/834-3247.

DOG-EAR YOUR CALENDAR

"Lord, help Sparky be a better beagle." You might pray just that at the annual **Blessing of the Animals** held each October in honor of the patron saint of critters, St. Francis. Dogs, cats, and other pets are blessed at a few local churches in honor of the occasion, including Unity Church of Port Richey, 5844 Pine Hill Rd., Port Richey; 727/848-7702. St. Peter's Episcopal Cathedral in St. Petersburg has sponsored a big blessing event some years at St. Peterburg's Williams Park. For its next date, call 727/822-4173.

PLACES TO STAY

Econo Lodge: King can request a king room at this 104-room poolside motel set at the Cottee River, seven miles from the sponge docks of Tarpon Springs. Rates range $45–90. Pet fee is $6 daily. 7631 U.S. 19, New Port Richey; 727/845-4990; www.choicehotels.com.

Tarpon Springs

Dogs have every reason to be suspicious of Tarpon Springs, the hometown of one of the largest fleets of sponge-fishing boats in the world. After all, they know what sponges are for: baths! Maggie apparently didn't make the connection, so she happily panted along as we tried to sniff out dog-friendly places.

This is an immigrant town, a few generations removed but still thick with Greekness. In Tarpon Springs, mailboxes sport such names as Katzaras and Treblas, and your pooch may even point out some signs written in old Greek. The sweet smell of Greek pastries mingles with the sights and sounds of people bustling along the sponge docks on the main drag, Dodecanese Boulevard. You might want to pass by St. Nicholas Greek Orthodox Church, an interesting yellow brick building at 36 North Pinellas Avenue. Tarpon Springs also boasts some of the best and most interesting dog-friendly restaurants in the county.

The fact that the local high school's football field is named Spongers Field gives you an idea of how central the sponging industry is to the town. The sponge docks, the epicenter of sponging activity, are the destination of most tourists.

PARKS, BEACHES, AND RECREATION AREAS

🐾 Fred Howard Park

🐾🐾🐾 (See St. Petersburg map on page 404)

Mostly locals use this park, which is well off the beaten path—a little hard to find, but worth the search. Dogs aren't allowed at the beach, but when we visited, furry swimmers were tolerated along the south side of a causeway that leads to these white sands. Here, we found a sunny spot with crystal-clear water, in which some pooches were swimming leash-free. A passing patrolman said nothing and a park employee also said it was okay. However, the causeway that borders this spot is fairly busy, so we recommend you follow the rules and keep your dog leashed.

You might see a rabbit hopping around the roadside if you drive down one of the big, looping roads that reach back into the park en route to secluded picnic sites. Munch a lunch next to Lake Avoca, if you'd like. The park also has horseshoe pits and a large waterfront softball field.

Lengthy but important sermons on the virtues of cleaning up dog waste are posted on signs throughout the park. Remember to do everyone a favor and scoop the poop.

From U.S. 19A, the main north-south road through town, take Meres Boulevard west past new and old housing developments until it dead-ends at Florida Avenue. Turn right. Following the signs directing you to Fred Howard Park, turn left at Sunset Drive and soon you'll be there. 727/464-3347.

◘ Pinellas Trail

😻 😻 (See St. Petersburg map on page 404)

This trail along an unused railroad bed is a favorite of bicyclists and in-line skaters, but it's also favored by hearty doggies. However, shade is at a premium, and you must bring water for your furry friend. Try parking at the old railroad station across the street from the old Coffee Depot, 11 South Safford Avenue. The asphalt walking, riding, and jogging path runs north along U.S. 19 from St. Petersburg, all the way to this northernmost town in Pinellas County. 727/549-6099.

◘ Paw Playground at A. L. Anderson Park

😻 😻 😻 😻 🐾 (See St. Petersburg map on page 404)

This quite hilly wildlife sanctuary on the east side of Lake Tarpon for years has served as a popular people park, and now it offers a paw park where dogs run freely. Frequented by plenty of canines, the fenced area offers dog-level water fountains, dog showers, and benches set on a sloping terrain.

Even on the hottest days, moss-draped oaks provide lots of shade for tethered dogs who exit the leash-free area and picnic in the broader park. There is a hilly, North Florida feel to this place, and scores of squirrels scurry from oak to oak. We also spied a woodpecker and other birds near the park's south end.

After padding along one of the hiking trails, take a break at one of the secluded picnic tables or join the kids at the playground. If the sprinklers are running, try not to get wet or let your dog drink from them, as they use "reclaimed" sewer water. As always, clean up after your canine companion.

For another off-leash alternative, try the city's basic dog park on Live Oak Street near the corner of Safford Avenue, east of the city parking lot. It offers benches and drinking faucets, and it looks onto the Anclote River.

The county's paw playground is in the southeast part of town at 39699 U.S. 19 North. From U.S. 19, turn east on Tookes Road. 727/464-3347.

PLACES TO EAT

Bread & Butter Gourmet Deli: Goodies from the Mediterranean and beyond will delight both you and your dog. Middle Eastern and Greek foods are supplemented by what the owner, Theo, calls "international" cuisine. This place has tabbouleh and 38 kinds of salad, though doggies would more likely go for the stuffed peppers or stuffed cabbage. For pooches with a more Middle Eastern sensibility, opt for lamb or chicken kabobs. Your hound will really hunger after the fresh-made turkey that rolls out of the oven daily between 11 A.M. and noon. Snag a small table out front of the brick building, and have your pooch wait while you walk inside to order. 1880 U.S. 19A S.; 727/934-9003.

Checkers: Okay, so it's not necessarily the most healthy stuff with which to stuff your muzzle—er, face—but doggies are happy to sit at the umbrella-shaded tables and munch fast-food burgers. Checkers is on Tarpon Avenue just west of U.S. 19, in front of the Tarpon Square Shopping Center; 727/937-3387.

Mama's Greek Cuisine: Lots of dogs show up at this 70-seat outside covered patio to watch their companions eat seafood specialties and other Grecian fare from the recipe bank of Mama Koursiotis. 735 Dodecanese Blvd.; 727/944-2888.

PLACES TO STAY

Best Western Tahitian Resort: Three miles from the sponge docks of Tarpon Springs, this 139-unit motel offers a curvy heated pool flanked by chaise lounges and clumps of palms. Rates range $50–100. Pet fee is $5 daily, and you'll sleep in rooms on the parking-lot side. 2337 U.S. 19, Holiday; 727/937-4121; www.bestwestern.com.

Palm Harbor

PARKS, BEACHES, AND RECREATION AREAS

5 Paw Playground at John Chesnut Sr. County Park

🐾🐾🐾🐾 🐕➤ (See St. Petersburg map on page 404)

Unsnap the leash! Lots of dogs show up at this popular off-leash area, favored for its woodsy setting. Big dogs run in one fenced field while small dogs run in a separate fenced grassy area. Just under two acres in size, it offers benches and cooling stations. It gets hard use, so the torn-up grass turns muddy after big rains.

A nice perk: After dogs are done playing, they can snap on a leash and take a woodsy walk down lush nature trails for a private walk through the 255-acre park with their owners. On one visit here, a butterfly danced in front of Maggie's eyes and a snowy egret glided smoothly by Brooker Creek as we enjoyed the Peggy Park Nature Trail. That trail, alternating between hard-packed sand and boardwalks, threads past pickerelweed, arrowhead, a 240-year-old cypress tree, cattails taller than Maggie's head, and primeval-looking leather ferns that resemble something out of *Jurassic Park*.

A small drawback at this county-run park is that on busy weekends you'll hear boaters and possibly those irritating Jet Skis on adjacent Lake Tarpon, a four-square-mile body of water with a beach that's off-limits to dogs. Also, watch out for poison ivy (remember: Leaves of three—let it be!), but keep in mind that the itch-inducing stuff helps feed the birds you see here. And the birds are plentiful. Look for Carolina wrens, cardinals, blue jays, mocking-birds, vireos, catbirds, sapsuckers, and warblers.

The park is at 2200 East Lake Rd., an extension of Clearwater's McMullen Booth Road. The park is two miles north of the Tampa Road overpass. From Highway 584/Tampa Road, turn north on McMullen Booth Road/County Road 611, which becomes East Lake Road. Turn west on Sandy Point Road. 727/669-1951.

6 Pinellas Trail

😺 (See St. Petersburg map on page 404)

This asphalt trail—a converted railroad bed—is a favorite of bicyclists and in-line skaters. It runs the length of the county along U.S. 19A and covers 47 miles from St. Petersburg to Tarpon Springs. The first five-mile stretch opened in 1990 and reached from Seminole City Park to Largo's John S. Taylor Park. Since then, other stretches were completed, including Largo to Dunedin and Dunedin to Tarpon Springs. Although a pooch won't complain (this is a *walk,* after all), the asphalt is largely unshaded and should be avoided in the middle of the day, especially in warmer months.

You can access the trail almost anyplace there's a parking spot along U.S. 19A. 727/549-6099.

7 H. S. "Pop" Stansell Memorial Park

😺 (See St. Petersburg map on page 404)

The best thing about this waterfront park is the opportunity to wade with your dog in St. Joseph Sound. It's also not a bad place for a picnic, with grills and shelters underneath pine trees near a boat ramp and small pier. Your pooch will wish she weren't leashed (but those are the rules) as she tries to catch fiddler crabs at low tide. From U.S. 19A, take either Nebraska or Florida avenue west. 727/785-9862.

PLACES TO EAT

D'Lites Emporium: If your dog has a taste for premium fat-free ice cream, tie him to a table out front and march inside to order a treat. Although your vet probably wouldn't approve, you can also get gourmet (read: doggy-fattening) hand-dipped ice cream cones. 36109 East Lake Rd., in the Brooker Creek Shopping Center; 727/789-1313.

Vetture's Pizzeria & Restaurant: You can order a pizza or Italian dinners to go, then carry them to the sole outdoor table to share with your dog. Or, take the eats back to a hotel room. 36137 East Lake Rd., in the Brooker Creek Shopping Center; 727/787-4858.

PLACES TO STAY

Best Western Palm Harbor: All rooms at this pleasant four-story hotel have a balcony or patio with views of Lake Tarpon. A fitness center, a spa, and a pool number among the people-pleasers. Rates start at $75. Add $10 nightly per pet (up to 40 pounds). 37611 U.S. 19 N., Palm Harbor; 727/942-0358; www. bestwestern.com.

Knights Inn: Small pets may stay at this 114-room poolside motel for $10 daily. Rates range $40–105. 34106 U.S. 19 N., Palm Harbor; 727/789-2002; www.knightsinn.com.

Red Roof Inn: This comfortable poolside inn has rooms with kitchenettes—good for storing doggy bags from the neighboring Outback Steakhouse. Rates run $50–90. 32000 U.S. 19 N., Palm Harbor; 727/786-2529; www. redroof.com.

Westin Innisbrook Golf Resort: Pet bowls and extra-comfy "Heavenly Rest" custom-designed pet beds greet canine guests at this resort, set on 1,000 acres. A welcome goodie gift box also is provided to Fido, as is a temporary ID tag with hotel contact information. People-pleasers include 72 holes of golf, a family pool and waterslide complex, miniature golf, a nature walk, and access to six pools. Nightly rates range $129–565. Pets up to 50 pounds are accepted for a flat $50 fee. 36750 U.S. 19 N., Palm Harbor; 727/942-2000; www.starwoodhotels.com/westin.

Dunedin

This city's name is frequently mispronounced by out-of-towners, so if your pup inquires, tell her to remember it this way: "If we throw a juicy steak on the grill and then give it to you, it'll be no time before you're Dunedin!" (That's "done eatin'!")

PARKS, BEACHES, AND RECREATION AREAS

8 Honeymoon Island State Park

🐾🐾🐾🐾 (See St. Petersburg map on page 404)

A ranger gave Maggie a dog biscuit when we paid to enter Honeymoon Island—a clue that this 7,000-year-old barrier island between the Gulf of Mexico and St. Joseph Sound is great for canines. The ranger directed us to turn left to South Beach, the dog beach. It's not really a "beach" in the traditional sense; the "good" beach is off-limits to dogs. But South Beach is one of those rare stretches of waterfront where dogs legally swim.

Technically, pooches must be leashed, even in water. Signs warn of a $25 fine and mandatory court appearance for violators.

Bring plenty of water. A beach umbrella is helpful, too, to protect dogs. Enterprising anglers with fishing gear can snag snook, flounder, and snapper.

Honeymoon Island is part of a chain of barrier islands that helps protect the coast against hurricanes. In fact, it was the roaring surf of a hurricane that split Honeymoon Island from Caladesi Island. Honeymoon Island got its name from a promotional gimmick by Paramount and *Life* magazine in which winning newlyweds were sent on a two-week vacation here. The island still has a remote, romantic feel.

Take the 2.5-mile-long Osprey Trail to look for ospreys and gopher tortoises in one of the few remaining stands of virgin Florida slash pine. Maggie was a happy hunter, straining at the leash. Stay on the trail to avoid prickly pears and poison ivy.

Warning: Don't attempt to avoid the entrance fee by taking your pooch to the waterfront areas along County Road 712/Causeway Boulevard, the approach to the state park. Dunedin police will stop you.

Entrance costs $5 per carload. To reach the state park from Dunedin, head west on Highway 586 and cross the Dunedin Causeway. 727/469-5942.

🖸 Happy Tails Dog Park

🐾🐾🐾🐕 (See St. Petersburg map on page 404)

Tails wag with approval at this 1.5-acre leash-free area. Opened in 2003 after a petition drive by dog owners, the park offers the amenities you might expect: water fountains for pets and people, benches, picnic tables, and fenced land for running.

Big dogs chase after balls on one acre. Small dogs run on a half acre just for them. Woods surround the park, providing a nice place to sit and contemplate while pets play canine tag. There is talk of expanding the park to include a pond so dogs may swim.

The bark park is within the 46-acre Louis A. Vanech Recreation Complex at 3051 Garrison Rd., next to Garrison-Jones Elementary School. 727/298-3278.

PLACES TO EAT

Cafe Al Fresco: Start with an appetizer of baked feta cheese, perhaps, then move on to one of several shrimp entrées or a range of other light European cuisine fare. You'll eat on the deck while your furry friend sits nearby, on the sidewalk on the other side of a small fence. Dogs are seen here only occasionally. 344 Main St.; 727/736-4299.

Sandbar Grill: Locals know this causeway-area eatery as a place for great burgers and beer. Grouper and grilled chicken sandwiches are also featured. A picket fence sets off the casual outdoor seating area where pooches and their people are welcome. "Some of our best clientele is of the canine persuasion," a staffer said. 2602 Bayshore Blvd.; 727/734-1962.

PLACES TO STAY

Dunedin RV Resort camping: The Pinellas Trail passes by this well-regarded, oak-dotted RV/mobile home park, so break out the leash—it's walk time! Campground reservations aren't always necessary, but leashes for dogs are. People with pets sleep in a designated pet area of the park. A heated pool, shuffleboard, and wintertime planned activities entertain guests. Rentals of bicycles and kayaks are offered nearby. Tents are accepted in summer only. Rates in season range $37–45, lower other times. From State Road 586, drive one-half mile north on U.S. 19A to the park. 2920 Alternate U.S. 19 N., Dunedin; 727/784-3719 or 800/345-7504; www.gocampingamerica.com /dunedinbeach.

Seaside Artisan Motel: Great Danes, cats, and even birds have slept in these nine efficiencies with kitchens, tile floors, and a sign out front that reads Pet Friendly. Proprietor Dan Clark says he accepts pets of "any size, shape, or form." Travelers uniformly bring adult, easy-going companions, not needy puppies. "They usually just lump around—the animals do. Sometimes the people do, too," says co-owner/wife Sue Clark, chuckling. Rooms in season cost $60 daily, $325 weekly. In summer, rooms go for around $45 nightly, $185 weekly. Pet fee is $5 daily, $15 weekly. A separate $200 damage deposit is refunded barring pet mishaps. At press time, credit cards were not accepted and cancellation of reservations required two weeks notice. 1064 Broadway, Dunedin; 727/736-4657; www.ij.net/SeasideArtisan.

Clearwater

PARKS, BEACHES, AND RECREATION AREAS

🔟 Countryside Recreation Center

🐾 (See St. Petersburg map on page 404)

Hounds howling for a rural romp can at least go to a park named Countryside, where many people take their four-legged friends to follow a fitness trail and sometimes stop for a break at picnic tables. Humans dominate, using ball fields, a gym, basketball courts, a playground, a volleyball court, and a recreation center.

The park is at the north end of town at 2640 Sabal Spring Drive. From the intersection of U.S. 19 North and Highway 580, go east on Highway 580. Turn

FETCHING NECESSITIES

Shop for a hog, or pay tribute to one: At the huge **Fletcher's Harley-Davidson** store in Clearwater, a jar of dog treats awaits visits by four-legged visitors. Dogs of all sizes show up, some regularly. Once a year, the store also lets dogs sit on a hog to pose for cute photos as a fundraiser for local animal-welfare organizations.

As if that's not pet-friendly enough, the Harley-Davidson shop also owns the **Green Mounds Pet Cemetery** next door. Tucked into an industrial section off U.S. 19, the cemetery is one of a handful of official resting places in the region for our dear departed animals. Your furry friend can sniff at the monuments left to dogs, cats, monkeys, cows, a kangaroo, and a duck named Scotch, whose gravestone proclaims him the only duck welcome in every bar. Founded by a veterinarian when this part of the Pinellas Peninsula was still fairly rural, the cemetery has laid 3,000 pets to rest and now has been swallowed up by the concrete blob that ate St. Petersburg and parts north. Folks at the Harley-Davidson shop now tend to it.

It's a peaceful respite from U.S. 19, a main north-south artery, and the rest of the modern rat race. Respectful conduct is appropriate at the pet cemetery, so if your pooch feels the need to leave a calling card, direct him to a section that has not been used for burial and, of course, clean up after him. Green Mounds sits behind Fletcher's Harley-Davidson at 17129 U.S. 19 N., Clearwater; 727/535-1844.

left (north) at Countryside Boulevard, then left at Sabal Spring Drive. 727/562-4800 or 727/669-1914.

11 Clearwater Beach Recreation Complex

(See St. Petersburg map on page 404)

A lot of dogs take their people here for a make-do walk along a long, green patch near the parking lot. That's about all there is for a good, leashed pooch to do at this waterfront park, unless you bring a boat to launch on the gulf. Humans dominate the rest of the park, where basketball courts, a playground, a recreation center, and tennis courts are found.

The park is at 69 Bay Esplanade. From the intersection of U.S. 19A and Gulf-to-Bay Boulevard, take the causeway over Clearwater Harbor. Continue west, passing the pier and marina. Turn right at Mandalay Avenue, then right at Bay Esplanade. 727/462-6138.

12 Sid Lickton Park

🐾 (See St. Petersburg map on page 404)

Part of a complex of ball fields, this park has little to recommend it to doggies except a small open area at the southern end. Pooches must stay leashed and out of the play areas.

The park is at 714 Saturn Ave., about 1.5 miles east of U.S. 19A. Take Drew Street/Highway 590 east to Saturn Avenue and turn left. Continue to Palmetto Street. 727/562-4800.

13 Waterfront Walk

🐾 (See St. Petersburg map on page 404)

You can stroll with your leashed dog northward along the grassy areas next to Clearwater Harbor. Not doggy nirvana, we realize, but it's a breezy alternative if you want to add some life to a tired dog-walk routine. On a cool day you may want to continue walking north into Dunedin, where you will see tiny, waterside Schiller University. The route takes you north alongside busy U.S. 19A/Edgewater Drive where there's little shade, so opt for an early or late outing on warmer days.

Take U.S. 19A north to Calumet Street and park at the Lawn Bowl and Shuffleboard Complex. Get out and head north along U.S. 19A/Edgewater Drive. 727/462-6531.

14 Cliff Stephens Park

🐾 (See St. Petersburg map on page 404)

The wide-open spaces may excite your leashed pooch at this lake-dotted park set in a residential neighborhood. Big by city-park standards, these 30 acres primarily are known by humans for their disc golf course. If your dog prefers a little shade, wander toward the back to a nature area or let her sit under one of the plentiful picnic tables.

The park is at 801 Fairwood Avenue. Take Drew Street/Highway 590 east, passing U.S. 19 North. Turn left at Fairwood Avenue. 727/562-4800.

15 Cooper's Bryan Park

🐾🐾 (See St. Petersburg map on page 404)

A lot of locals fling Frisbees to their leash-free dogs at this city park. The city ordinance requires pooches to be "under control," so think twice if your buddy is unruly off leash. Maggie is the type who'd rather go for a walk than chase a disc. For hounds like her, the jogging trail may be best; it connects to a sidewalk that leads into Safety Harbor.

The park is at 801 Bayshore Dr., north of Highway 60. Find it on the Tampa Bay side of the street. 727/562-4800.

16 Paw Playground at Sand Key Park

😺😺😺🐾 (See St. Petersburg map on page 404)

The key to happiness is parking the leash away, and this 1.5-acre broad expanse of grass lets dogs do just that. Divided into separate fenced areas for big Labs and small pets, the paw playground offers drinking fountains, dog showers, benches, and waste disposal stations.

No, dogs aren't given access to the coveted beach, but they can explore the rest of 95-acre Sand Key Park on leash and stop for a meal at the picnic tables with grills.

The paw playground is within Sand Key Park at 1060 Gulf Boulevard. 727/588-4852.

17 Doggie Days at Crest Lake Park

😺😺😺😺🐕 (See St. Petersburg map on page 404)

A five-foot-tall topiary of a St. Bernard greets visitors to this off-leash area, whose other artsy attributes include fire hydrants painted by artist Silas Beach. Dogs, of course, care little about aesthetics. They run with abandon and sniff each other inquisitively at one of the region's most popular paw parks, which is divided into three areas, one strictly for small pets.

A great plus: Lights shine until 11 P.M., allowing dog owners time to head here after work. Big oaks provide shade in various areas, a welcome relief from the broiling sun.

Benches and drinking fountains with pet bowls are offered, as are leash holders and an area to wash dirty paws before going home. The paw park is within Crest Lake Park, which offers picnic tables and a playground.

The park is at 201 Glenwood Avenue. Find parking at the northwest corner of Glenwood Avenue and Gulf-to-Bay Boulevard, which is about one-quarter mile east of Highland Avenue. 727/562-4800.

18 Eddie C. Moore Recreation Area

🐾 (See St. Petersburg map on page 404)

Ball fields make up the bulk of this park, which has a few spots around the periphery where you can walk Spot. Pine trees at the park's southwest corner make good leg-lift targets for your leashed dog.

The park is at the east end of town at 3050 Drew Street. Take Drew Street/Highway 590 east until you reach the park at McMullen Booth Road. 727/562-4800.

19 Del Oro Park

😺 (See St. Petersburg map on page 404)

If all that autumn Florida sun is ruining the sunny disposition of your hot friend in the fur coat, he should find relief in the wooded areas of this park, set in a residential neighborhood. Once you pass the basketball courts, you can start your walk in earnest—winding up as far away as Bayshore Drive. Stop at a picnic table for a meal break. Ball fields, a playground, and tennis courts are the domain of humans.

The park is at 401 McMullen Booth Road. Take Drew Street/Highway 590 east to McMullen Booth Road and turn left (north). You'll soon see the park to the right. 727/562-4800.

PLACES TO EAT

Checkers: Order burgers, chicken sandwiches, fries, and drinks, then take your bounty to the umbrella-shaded tables. 1610 N. McMullen Booth Rd.; 727/799-7715. Another location is at 1972 Gulf-to-Bay Blvd.; 727/461-1031.

PLACES TO STAY

Homestead Studio Suites Hotel: Making yourself at home is a big theme at Clearwater's better lodgings, and these 113 studios with fully equipped kitchens are no exception. Eat in your kitchen or at six nearby restaurants, including Bob Evans and Waffle House. Rates run $59–90. Pets up to 75 pounds are accepted for $25 daily, maximum $75. Two dogs are permitted per room. 2311 Ulmerton Rd., Clearwater; 727/572-4800; www.homesteadhotels.com.

Homewood Suites: If you don't want to cook in your fully equipped kitchen, then head to the lobby of this pleasant business-oriented lodging each morning to pick and choose from the nice spread of bagels, fruit, pastries, cereal, coffee, and more. Eat there or bring a breakfast tray back to your two-room suite, where your dog will be glad to scarf up scraps. In case you and your pooch can't agree on what to watch, every suite has two TVs. Rates start at $99. The pet fee is huge: a flat $150. 2233 Ulmerton Rd., Clearwater; 727/573-1500; www.homewood-suites.com.

La Quinta Inn Airport: The rules permit dogs who weigh less than 35 pounds, though bigger pets are accepted if they're well-behaved. (We recommend tying a yellow or red bandanna around your pooch's neck for the charm effect.) A wide-banked canal on the west side of this pleasant, business-oriented poolside motel offers a surprisingly good place for dog walks. Try it after your pal sneaks bites from your free continental breakfast. Rates range $80–115. 3301 Ulmerton Rd., Clearwater; 727/572-7222; www.lq.com.

Marriott ExecuStay temporary corporate housing: A kitchen, an exercise facility, a pool, and a washer and dryer are among the perks for your pack at the luxury apartments represented by this agency. Rates vary, with a minimum one-month stay. Most units accept pets no larger than 20 or 30 pounds. 5310 56th Commerce Park Blvd., Clearwater; 813/664-1125 or 800/488-1125; www.tempcorphousing.com.

Radisson Hotel Clearwater Central: After your workout in the fitness center or heated pool, your dog hopes for his own exercise at the off-leash Crest Lake Dog Park, about 3.3 miles from this comfortable three-story hotel. Rates range $70–139. Pet fee is a flat $50. 20967 U.S. 19 N., Clearwater; 727/799-1181; www.radisson.com.

Residence Inn: On chilly days, throw a log into the fireplace to warm your pup. These comfortable apartment-style suites with kitchens and VCRs and weekly manager's barbecue will make you feel right at home, particularly if you're staying for some time. Rates run $130–199. Add a flat $75 pet fee. 5050 Ulmerton Rd., Clearwater; 727/573-4444; http://marriott.com.

Super 8 St. Petersburg–Clearwater: Cats and dogs alike have slept in designated pet rooms at this three-story poolside motel. Some rooms offer fridges—good for storing doggy bags. Rates range $50–90, plus $10 daily pet fee. 13260 34th St. N., Clearwater; 727/572-8881; www.super8.com.

Clearwater Beach

Dogs aren't allowed on the beach in Clearwater Beach, so there's nothing here for a pooch to do except hang her fuzzy head out the car window and take in the sights.

PLACES TO STAY

Bel Crest Beach Resort: Most pets are permitted at this 16-unit poolside "superior small lodging," as deemed by an independent panel. It's located a block from the gulf beach and within walking distance of restaurants, and all units offer full kitchens. Rates range $95–210 in season, less other times. 706 Bayway Blvd., Clearwater Beach; 727/442-4923; www.belcrest.com.

Chart House Suites: Dogs may sleep in five designated suites at this 26-unit, four-story "superior small lodging," a label given by an independent panel. Located by Pier 60, the motel offers boat slips and an outdoor pool. Daily rates range $149–399. Pet fee is $25 for one to seven days. 850 Bayway Blvd., Clearwater Beach; 727/449-8007 or 877/242-7899; www.charthousesuites.com.

Sheraton Sand Key Resort: Dog beds and pet bowls are offered to canine guests of this resort hotel set on 10 acres of beach between the bay and the Gulf of Mexico. People-pleasers include hot-stone massages at the spa, saunas, paddleboats, tennis, and local beaches that rank among the nation's best, as judged by university researcher Stephen "Dr. Beach" Leatherman. Rates start at $140. Pets up to 40 pounds are accepted in first-floor rooms, free. 1160 Gulf Blvd., Clearwater Beach; www.sheratonsandkey.com.

Oldsmar

Still somewhat rural, this area in eastern Pinellas County has an escape-from-the-city feel that gets a doggy's juices flowing. When we drove through, Maggie paced the backseat of the car in anticipation of stretching her legs in this sleepy town.

PARKS, BEACHES, AND RECREATION AREAS

20 Dog Park at Mobbly Bayou Wilderness Preserve

(See St. Petersburg map on page 404)

Inspired by the need for a place for her one-year-old retriever to run, resident Amy Poteet presented the city a petition with 500 signatures requesting a dog park. The result is this humble, small bark park, a few thousand square feet in size. It's something—the first leash-free area in town. Poteet hoped for a bigger park, though, and complained at a July 2004 city council meeting that it's too small and, thus, a disgrace.

The thing is, people around here for at least three decades were accustomed to letting their dogs swim at a portion of private beach at the end of Shore Drive East, but that ended after the beach became part of Mobbly Bayou Wilderness Preserve in 2001 and, more recently, enforcement beefed up to turn dogs away from the beach. Dog owners hoped the city would designate part of the beach for dogs, but that didn't happen. The off-leash area is landlocked.

The park is at 423 Lafayette Blvd., in the southeastern corner of Oldsmar. 813/749-1261.

Safety Harbor

Looking for an off-leash area? Grab some plastic pooper-scooper bags from your stash and head to a legally sanctioned, no-frills dog run located beneath power lines at 1200 N. Railroad Avenue. It's simply a sun-washed rectangular fenced area where dogs can run. Expect no benches, no amenities. Considering all of the cool dog parks in the region, you may wish to head elsewhere. For information, call 727/724-1530.

PARKS, BEACHES, AND RECREATION AREAS

21 Philippe Park

(See St. Petersburg map on page 404)

People are likely to enjoy this hilly 122-acre park on Old Tampa Bay more than their pooches will, but it's not too bad for the four-legged set. Although there are no nature trails, a picturesque picnic spot awaits. Spreading oaks shade the grassy grounds. Boaters can launch here for an afternoon of fishing or tooling around Old Tampa Bay with their dogs (just bring a boat). Kids may prefer the playground and ball fields.

The county park also includes the grave of Count Odet Philippe, a French surgeon and one of the first non-American Indians to live in this part of Florida. The Count is credited with introducing grapefruit to Florida, and he considered this area "heaven on Earth." Some three centuries before the Count settled here, Spanish explorer Hernando de Soto visited the Tacobago Indian mound still found in the park today.

The park is at 2525 Philippe Parkway. From Main Street, go east to Philippe Parkway and turn left (north). The entrance is two miles ahead, not far north of Enterprise Boulevard/County Road 638. 727/724-1555 or 727/669-1947.

PLACES TO STAY

Safety Harbor Resort and Spa: A pet bed and a special treat greet Queenie at one of the fancier pooch-permissible possibilities in Greater St. Petersburg. This 22-acre, 189-room resort will keep you busy with its three pools, nine tennis courts, a golf practice range, and 50,000-square-foot spa and fitness center. Pick up Queenie to show her the pretty view of Tampa Bay from your room. Or bring her a doggy bag from the on-site bistro. Rates in season start at $129. Add $35 daily for the small pooch. 105 N. Bayshore Dr., Safety Harbor; 727/726-1161 or 888/BEST-SPA; www.safetyharborspa.com.

Belleair Beach

PARKS, BEACHES, AND RECREATION AREAS

🄝🄝 Belleair Causeway Dog Beach

🐾🐾🐾 (See St. Petersburg map on page 404)

You'll be hard-pressed to find a dog beach on the Gulf of Mexico, but locals swear by this "inside" beach found along the causeway connecting Belleair Beach and the Pinellas Peninsula. Dogs won't mind that they're not on the gulf beaches so prized by tourists. Here, in the salt water of Clearwater Harbor, they can do what all Labs love—swim! The muddy sand can be goopy and gooey, so you might want to test it before letting your pal run in it—or bring a towel to wipe all paws before your dog clambers back into the car.

From the Largo area, head west on Highway 686/West Bay Drive. Look for the dog beach along the causeway before you reach the barrier-island town of Belleair Shores. 727/595-4575.

Indian Rocks Beach

Looking for off-leash fun? If you have $50 to spare, you can buy a nonresident permit to let your dog play at the Dog Park at Indian Rocks Beach Nature Preserve. The bark park is off Gulf Boulevard between 8th and 9th avenues. That $50 seems steep to us, considering the choices of dog parks in Greater St. Petersburg and Tampa, so we'd head elsewhere. For permit information, call 727/595-2517.

PLACES TO STAY

Arbors Seaside Cottages: Innkeepers Lee and Erik Abrahamson's four cottages with full kitchens sit on a sandy Gulf of Mexico beach where dolphins occasionally pass by. Deemed a "superior small lodging" by an independent panel, this establishment offers shuffleboard, volleyball, a picnic area with grills, laundry facilities, and a library of videotapes and books. Weekly rates start at $800. Dogs under 25 pounds are accepted for a flat $75. A separate $65 departure cleaning fee is charged for all guests, with or without pets. If the cottages are booked for your desired dates, call the 800 number and ask for Deanna, who also represents other pet-permissible vacation rentals that rent for $675–3,000 weekly. 218 Gulf Blvd., Indian Rocks Beach; 727/442-3877 or 800/873-0224; www.beachesusa.com.

Sandy Shores Motel: Humans appreciate the fenced pool set right on the beach. Dogs appreciate a ride to the dog beach at Belleair Causeway (see Parks, Beaches, and Recreation Areas in Belleair Beach, above), just .25 mile from these 14 poolside apartments, most featuring terrazzo floors and full kitchens. For a regular dog walk from the pet-friendly motel, ask at the front desk about the beach trail. Rates in season range $72–110. Add $10 daily, maximum $50, for your small pet. 816 Gulf Blvd., Indian Rocks Beach; 727/595-3226 or 877/595-3226; www.sandyshoresvacation.com.

Sea Star Motel and Apartments: Molly the bassett hound serves as a greeter at this pet-friendly establishment, where small pets may sleep in designated units with full kitchens. Picnic tables, shuffleboard, and a pay phone are found in the courtyard. Guests may borrow bicycles or take a dip in the hot tub. All 13 units are cleaned by the proprietors, Betty Ann and Bruce Tripke. Rates in season range $70–110. Pet fee is $10 nightly. 1805 Gulf Blvd., Indian Rocks Beach; 727/596-2525; www.floridaseastar.com.

Indian Shores

PLACES TO STAY

Sand Glo Villas: One of precious few dog-friendly destinations awarded a "superior small lodging" designation by an independent panel, these 11 kitchen-equipped units have access to the beach and a lending library of movies and books. Yoga classes, discounted weekly gym membership, and spa packages are offered. For a dog beach, get in the car and head to the Belleair Causeway (see Parks, Beaches, and Recreation Areas in Belleair Beach). Weekly rates range $595–1,374 in winter, lower at other times. Daily stays are possible in the off-season; rates start at $97 nightly. With prior approval, pets under 25 pounds are accepted for a flat $75. 19316 Gulf Blvd., Indian Shores; 727/320-9720 or 800/816-1970; www.sandglo.com.

Sun Burst Inn: Set on the beach at the Gulf of Mexico, this two-story, nine-unit Old Florida-style motel with modern conveniences offers full or partial kitchens—good for hungry hounds. Deemed a "superior small lodging" by an independent panel, the motel features a balcony with sweeping views of the gulf. Rates in season range $90–200, lower other times. 19204 Gulf Blvd., Indian Shores; 727/596-2500 or 877/384-8067; http://sunburstinn.com.

Madeira Beach

PLACES TO STAY

Sandy Shores Condominiums: The maintenance guy keeps treats on hands for canine guests staying at these 55 gulf-area apartments. "We're real pet-oriented," says Kristal, a property manager, who notices some pets line up most days for their morning treats. Humans can take a dip in the pool. Weekly rates in season range $800–1,150. Add a $40 fee for a small dog (up to 30 pounds). 12924 Gulf Blvd., Madeira Beach; 727/392-1281.

Snug Harbor Inn: Arrive by boat or car to this small establishment on Boca Ciega Bay. Deemed a "superior small lodging" by an independent panel, it offers a heated pool by the bay, a bayside tiki hut for a picnic, a bayside deck, and a fenced grassy side yard where pets may exercise. With prior approval, well-mannered pets are accepted. Nightly rates in season range $95–299. 13655 Gulf Blvd., Madeira Beach; 727/395-9256 or 866/395-9256; www. snugharborflorida.com.

Largo

PARKS, BEACHES, AND RECREATION AREAS

23 John S. Taylor Park

(See St. Petersburg map on page 404)

Take a break at a picnic table after your leashed dog pulls you along a 1.8-mile jogging path at this county-run park. Still up for exercise? Try the popular Pinellas Trail to the west, which stretches 47 miles to link St. Petersburg to Tarpon Springs. Bring water and turn around at a safe distance for your friend in the fur coat.

DOG-EAR YOUR CALENDAR

"All I want for Christmas is my cat's two front teeth." Your naughty and nice dog can confide in Santa as part of a holiday photo fundraiser held each December at **PETsMART,** 10500 Ulmerton Rd., Largo; 727/518-2600. Busy St. Nick also takes time out of his hectic schedule to appear at other stores in the chain, including 26277 U.S. 19 N., Clearwater; 727/799-3311; and 3993 Tyrone Blvd., St. Petersburg; 727/343-7900.

Humans dominate the park's ball fields and playground, but your pooch may join you for grill-cooked franks or a boat ride (if you bring a small boat). Anglers head to the 53-acre lake, which takes up a big portion of the 156-acre park.

The park is at 1100 8th Ave. SW, which is north of East Bay Drive and west of U.S. 19A. 727/588-4847 or 727/464-3347.

24 Ridgecrest Park

😻 (See St. Petersburg map on page 404)

Eating may be the most fun doggy diversion here, considering that the ball fields and playground are for people, not pooches. Cook frankfurters at a grill or munch a packed lunch at a picnic table. A small lake provides a pleasant place to stop and gaze or even fish; measuring five acres, it takes up nearly one-quarter of the park.

For a walk, the popular 47-mile-long Pinellas Trail passes nearby. You could follow the converted railroad bed for a bit, then turn around at a safe distance so your leashed dog doesn't become overheated.

The county park is at 12000 Ulmerton Rd./State Road 688, west of U.S. 19A. 727/588-4851 or 727/464-3347.

25 Walsingham Park Paw Playground

😻😻😻😻🐕 (See St. Petersburg map on page 404)

More than 900 people signed petitions asking county officials to open this off-leash area, and their dogged determination paid off. Opened on Armed Forces Day 2003 with a salute to military dogs, this fenced broad expanse of grass is beloved. It measures a little over two acres in size and features a smattering of trees, drinking fountains for people and pets, benches, tubes for dogs to scamper through, and a separate off-leash area for Jack Russell terriers and other pets under 25 pounds.

Outside the paw park, more fun can be had within the rest of 354-acre Walsingham Park, home to white peacocks, mottled ducks, and tortoises. If you don't bring a boat for fishing or tooling around the waters of 100-acre

Walsingham Lake, then consider a walk with your leashed dog through the botanical gardens, pine flatwoods, and oak scrub. The popular, 47-mile-long Pinellas Trail passes nearby, heading northward toward Tarpon Springs and southward to its eventual terminus in St. Petersburg. Of course, you should take a far shorter walk with your leashed friend. Take a lunch break at a park picnic table, where a grill also can be found.

The park is at 12615 102nd Ave. N., which is west of U.S. 19A and south of Ulmerton Road/State Road 688. 727/549-6142 or 727/464-3347.

26 Paw Place at Northeast Park

🐾🐾🐾🐕 (See St. Petersburg map on page 404)

Ever since the Ruff Flyers Performing Dogs did tricks at the 2002 unleashing ceremony here, four-legged amateurs have been performing their versions of canine antics. Some dogs follow an obstacle course featuring an A-frame, a tunnel, and a jump. Most, though, prefer to play tag or sniff strangers' posteriors.

Measuring less than one acre, the park is divided into two areas—one for small dogs, the other for large pets. Both offer water fountains for people and pets, plus picnic tables and shade. Gravel and pine needles carpet the ground.

The bark park is at Northeast Park, 2150 Lions Club Rd., off East Bay Drive. Find the entrance just west of Lions Club Road. 727/587-6700.

Seminole

PARKS, BEACHES, AND RECREATION AREAS

27 Lake Seminole Park

🐾🐾🐾 (See St. Petersburg map on page 404)

If boaters and their alert dogs look east as they tool around three-mile-long Lake Seminole, they can see the long green banks of this popular county-run park. Although the lake is what sets this place apart, it also features lots of trees and a curvy sidewalk beside an area of pines that would make a good walk with your leashed landlubber. You'll have to look hard on some days, but you're still likely to find a private spot for a picnic at the tables and grills here. Kids may appreciate the playground and ball fields. Don't go too close to the banks of the lake, as it contains alligators.

The park is on the east bank of Lake Seminole at 10015 Park Blvd./Highway 694. Enter from 74th Avenue, between Starkey Road/89th Street and Lake Seminole, east of U.S. 19A. 727/464-3347.

28 Paw Playground at Boca Ciega Millennium Park

😊 😊 😊 🐾 (See St. Petersburg map on page 404)

Drop the leash! Dogs run joyously at this 1.5-acre green fenced area, which features dog-level water fountains, canine showers, and benches.

The off-leash area is found within a young 185-acre county park dedicated only in 2001 and worth exploring (on leash). At its entrance is a time capsule containing more than 100 items for future generations to open and ponder. Leashed pets can follow a quarter-mile nature trail and other pathways, where they might notice shore birds, wading birds, and birds of prey. The state deemed this park a stop on the "Great Florida Birding Trail." An observation tower provides a pretty view of Boca Ciega Bay and the distant skyline.

The park is at 12410 74th Ave. N./Old Oakhurst Road. 727/588-4882.

29 War Veterans' Memorial Park

😊 😊 😊 (See St. Petersburg map on page 404)

Dragonflies dart about and squirrels tempt a rambunctious pooch at this big park, where oaks, pines, and sabal palms provide bountiful shade for any whiskered wanderer whose tongue's a-hangin' low. Maggie was exceptionally excited when we visited. At the southern tip of the county park, she gazed at fancy, palm-studded homes across blue-green Boca Ciega Bay from her spot at a picnic pavilion. Here you can take advantage of the breeze coming off the bay, grill some dogs—er, wieners—and even sit in a bench swing. You could also wade into the bay with your dog at the southern end.

Dogs are supposed to be leashed and they must stay out of the adjacent wildlife sanctuary (as must their two-legged friends). Also, a sign near shelter No. 5 warns No Dogs Beyond This Point. The off-limits section is marked on the posted map you'll see as you walk around.

From downtown St. Petersburg, take U.S. 19A west until you cross Long Bayou. You'll soon see the entrance on your left at 9600 Bay Pines Boulevard. 727/464-3347.

PLACES TO EAT

Twistee Treat: As you doggedly pursue ice cream in this ultra-sunny corner of the state, look for the tan-and-white building shaped like an ice-cream cone. Sit at the picnic table or two concrete tables outside. 5994 Seminole Blvd./U.S. 19A; 727/399-1495.

St. Petersburg

PARKS, BEACHES, AND RECREATION AREAS

30 Gandy Boulevard Dog Beach

🐾🐾🐾🐕 (See St. Petersburg map on page 404)

Boy, are there dogs here! Dogs, dogs, and more dogs! And they're all wet!

So if it's time to swim, look for breaks in the mangroves that line Gandy Boulevard/U.S. 92, which connects Tampa and St. Petersburg. Unbelievably scenic? No. But we didn't hear a yelp of disapproval from the doggies frolicking in the bay. You shouldn't let your pooch wade out too far; a small channel for boats sits about 30 yards offshore.

Many a family arrives here in a van or pickup truck to stake out a little section of waterfront to call their own on major holidays. The better stretches of beach are found toward the eastern end of the causeway. Although leashes are the law on the state's causeways, dogs routinely cavort off leash in the water here. Just don't let your dog off leash if she's not well behaved—she could get run over and killed.

The park is not to be confused with the Pinellas Bayway Dog Beach on the other side of town. This free beach is located on Gandy Boulevard/U.S. 92, on the causeway linking Tampa and St. Petersburg. 727/464-7200.

31 Sawgrass Lake Park

🐾🐾 (See St. Petersburg map on page 404)

As soon as our car entered the approach road to this wildlife sanctuary, Maggie sat up in anticipation. Her demeanor and her twitching nose said it all: Wow!

Unfortunately, dogs aren't allowed along the best parts of this 400-acre wildlife-packed sanctuary: the Oak Hammock, Maple, or Sawgrass Trails. But there are plenty of places to stretch a pup's legs, and this park is popular with pooches. Along a trail by Arrow Lake, Maggie was dying to chase after the coots and moorhens skipping across the water. Don't let your pooch wander too close to the water without you, though; alligators lurk.

Leashed pets also can take in the display on butterflies, enjoy the grunts of pig frogs, or just have a relaxing picnic on the small grassy mounds.

The county park is at 7400 25th St. N. From I-275, exit at 54th Avenue. Go west to 28th Street and turn right. Turn right again at 62nd Avenue, then left at 25th Street, which leads to the park. 727/217-7256.

32 Jungle Prada & DeNavarez Park

🐾 (See St. Petersburg map on page 404)

If you live closer to this boat ramp than to Sunset Park, then this is a suitable place to watch the sun sink into Boca Ciega Bay. That's about all there is to do here with your leashed dog, unless you bring a boat. The park is in western St. Petersburg at Park Street and Elbow Lane North. 727/893-7335.

33 Crisp Park

🐾 (See St. Petersburg map on page 404)

This glorified boat ramp overlooking Smacks Bayou allows a leashed dog to partake in one of his favorite activities—eating at a picnic table. The park is at Poplar Street and 35th Avenue Northeast. 727/893-7335.

34 Northwest Park

🐾 (See St. Petersburg map on page 404)

Dominated by ball fields, this park still has some stretches where your leashed pooch can cruise. Mostly they're just in the peripheral areas, but when the weather is cool you can take the sidewalk all around this large city block. Plan something less ambitious during the crest of the summer heat wave—there's little shade. If your whiskered buddy could use a break, head beneath the large oak trees in the southwest area of the park, near the pool.

The park is at 5801 22nd Ave. N., at the intersection with 58th Street North. 727/893-7335.

35 Woodlawn Park

🐾 (See St. Petersburg map on page 404)

Stop and smell the roses if you want, but you won't find much else here for the four-legged set. Aside from a tiny rose garden, this large park is dominated by ball fields, where dogs technically aren't allowed to romp, as well as a community center and the St. Petersburg Police Pistol Club. Your only option: the few dog-friendly strips of green.

From I-275, go east on 22nd Avenue about a quarter of a mile to 16th Street. Turn right (south) and continue for half a mile to the park at 1450 16th St. N. 727/893-7335 or 727/893-7298.

36 Fountain of Youth

🐾 (See St. Petersburg map on page 404)

If you wish you were younger—in dog years or human—come make a wish at the centerpiece fountain in this mini-park. As you sit at one of the few benches and gaze at the waters, your leashed well-wisher may relax at your feet. This smidgen of a park is at First Street and Fourth Avenue South. 727/893-7335.

37 Sunset Park

 (See St. Petersburg map on page 404)

Watch the glowing orange disc of the sun lower on the watery horizon while you sit at this little park with your leashed dog. That's about all there is to do at this wee green spot overlooking Boca Ciega Bay.

The park is in western St. Petersburg at Central Avenue West and Park Street, near the entrance to the Treasure Island Causeway. 727/893-7335.

38 Walter Fuller Dog Park

 (See St. Petersburg map on page 404)

Thank goodness the city has finally put in this and four other off-leash areas. You'll find water fountains for you and your dog, a bulletin board, and a time-out area for "the occasional behavior problem," as the city puts it, in the one-acre leash-free zone.

Outside the bark park, frisky leashed pooches can run along the heart-healthy exercise course, while those with more sedate tastes will probably enjoy the small butterfly garden in the southwest corner of the park.

Dogs who like a good game of catch will be interested to know that this sprawling park in an area of quiet streets is home to the Busch Complex, the spring training home of the St. Louis Cardinals. For romping, try the large open area in the middle of this very large space, or the narrow sidewalk that rings the perimeter. If you'd like solitude, head for the northeast corner at 78th Street and 34th Avenue North. The Busch Complex is close to the southwest corner, at 80th Street and 26th Avenue North. 727/893-7335.

39 Azalea Park

(See St. Petersburg map on page 404)

A sea of Saint Augustine grass was too much for us to resist, and we let Maggie off leash here. Technically, that's against the rules, but the park is so big that there was no one for her to bother—unless, of course, you count those pigeons she scared.

One thing to keep in mind is that there are lots of red ants here—we have the bites to prove it. Keep an eye out for the sandy mounds, perhaps half a foot high. Our solution was to not stand in any one place for too long.

Aside from two lighted ball fields and a playground where kids come to shoot hoops, there are no facilities and just a smattering of trees. The park's strong point is its size.

From I-275, take 22nd Avenue west to 72nd Street. Turn left (south). The park is ahead at 1600 72nd St. N. 727/893-7335 or 727/893-7150.

40 Crescent Lake Dog Park

🐾🐾🐾🦮 (See St. Petersburg map on page 404)

When we visited last, we had to resist the temptation to let Maggie off leash because, even though this park was large and little-used after Huggins-Stengel Field here ceased to be the spring training home of the Baltimore Orioles, the rule was no dogs off leash. Now, the one-acre bark park has ended the ticketing of leash-law violators.

Curving through the middle of the half-mile-long park is Crescent Lake. There's plenty of room for a dog-tiring walk around the perimeter of the park, or you could just kick back at the oak-shaded benches next to the playground.

The park is at 1320 5th St. N., just west of U.S. 92. 727/893-7335.

41 Booker Creek Park

🐾🐾 (See St. Petersburg map on page 404)

This park is mostly a lake, leaving little room to romp. But there is one saving grace: a really large green area far from the roadway and fenced off from the nearby interstate. Technically, dogs are supposed to be leashed, however. You're likely to see ducks in the lake, but make sure your dog doesn't chase them—we also saw a large alligator cruising around.

The park is at 13th Avenue North and 22nd Street, just east of I-275. 727/893-7335.

42 North Shore Dog Park

🐾🐾🐾🦮 (See St. Petersburg map on page 404)

Liberation! Like retirees who find their true, free spirit by moving to St. Pete's warm climate, dogs feel set free by setting paw in this one-acre park, where

DOG-EAR YOUR CALENDAR

Brother, can you spare some time? More than 4,000 people and their leashed dogs—and even goats and parrots—converge on St. Petersburg's North Shore Park each October to raise money for the local SPCA by doing what dogs love most: walking. Snow White and her seven canine "dwarfs" once showed up at the costume-contest portion of the beloved event, called the **Paws on Parade Pet Walk.** Local folks love to dress up; the costume contest easily attracts 300 registrants and their devil dogs and otherwise costumed canines. It's a day for relaxing with the pack, strolling from vendor to vendor, watching flyball demonstrations, admiring demos by police dogs, and joining fellow Fidos on a mile-long walk. For the next date, call the SPCA at 727/586-3591.

leashes are taboo. Separate water fountains quench the thirsts of people and pets. A time-out area is available to calm the occasional tussle.

The paw playground is found within North Shore Park, a stretch of land worth exploring (on leash) along Coffee Pot Bayou on Tampa Bay. Not only is it a lot bigger, but it's also more open than the other waterfront parks downtown. While leashed pets must stay off the beach areas, there are ample places to walk and walk—and then walk some more. For a break, scout out a picnic table near the north end of the park, taking in fine-looking Old Spanish- and Florida Cracker-style homes with the scenery. If you go far enough north, the sidewalk curves past some docks to a rookery in the middle of Coffee Pot Bayou. The chirps of baby birds may intrigue curious canines.

The dog park is at 7th Avenue and North Shore Drive Northeast. It's within North Shore Park, at 901 North Shore Dr. NE, which spans the waterfront east of Beach Drive and north of downtown, between Fifth Avenue North and Coffee Pot Boulevard. 727/893-7335 or 727/893-7727.

43 Poynter Park

 (See St. Petersburg map on page 404)

Just a little mound of green in the central city, this pleasingly landscaped park features a few examples of those Old Florida standbys—oak and cabbage palm trees. It also gives aesthetically minded doggies a splash of bright-red impatiens to admire in winter. Lorded over by towering bayfront condos, this respite from the concrete offers a view of Tampa Bay's docks and sailing vessels. If your leashed pooch is pooped, stretch out at a bench on the sidewalk. Afterward, head over to Café Lido for lunch or dinner.

Technically, this downtown park is at 1000 Third St. S., but look for it on Bayshore Drive, north of First Avenue North. 727/893-7335.

44 Straub Park

 (See St. Petersburg map on page 404)

Part of a series of small downtown waterfront parks, this one offers your leashed pooch the possibility of eating a hot dog purchased from the vendor at Bayshore and Second Avenue Northeast. The franks are St. Pete's Best-Dressed Hot Dog, a sign brags. After your meal, strike out along a clean, pleasant walkway bordering Tampa Bay.

The downtown park (next to Poynter Park) is bordered by Beach and Bayshore drives, just south of Fifth Avenue North. 727/893-7335.

45 Coquina Key Dog Park

 (See St. Petersburg map on page 404)

Doggies worried about meeting the 20-pound weight limit at some local hotels can work off calories at the off-leash area or the .75-mile exercise trail here. The bark park features separate water fountains for dogs and people, a bulletin board, and, for the overly rowdy Rovers, a time-out area. Notice, too, the fire hydrant. Nice touch, huh?

This city park overlooks the wide waters of Big Bayou, but much of the space is devoted to people perks: a basketball court, a playground, tennis courts, and two ball fields.

The park is at 3595 Locust St. SE, on Coquina Key. 727/893-7335.

46 Bartlett Park

😺 (See St. Petersburg map on page 404)

Your pooch can enjoy a fairly shady walk by following the long sidewalk of Fourth Street South at this well-kept neighborhood park. There are ball fields, basketball hoops, and tennis courts, but no picnic facilities and not much shade overall. One lap around the park is .9 mile.

The park is at 2000 Seventh St. South, at the intersection of Lakeview Avenue/22nd Avenue South and Fourth Street South. 727/893-7335.

47 Lake Vista Dog Park

 (See St. Petersburg map on page 404)

Dogs began enjoying new vistas, attitude-wise, with the opening of this one-acre leash-free zone. Here, pets meet new friends and play, then slurp water greedily at drinking fountains. Owners sip water at their own fountains, chat, and toss Frisbees and balls to four-legged athletes.

The leash-free area is within Lake Vista Park, a sizable green spot that spans about four square blocks. Much of the rest of the lakeside park is devoted to people pursuits: ball fields, a community center, a basketball court, a playground, and tennis courts. But you can follow a mile-long exercise trail with your leashed dog and take a break afterward at a picnic table.

The park is toward the southern end of St. Petersburg at 1401 62nd Ave. South, a few blocks west of Ninth Street. 727/893-7335.

48 Bay Vista Park

😺 (See St. Petersburg map on page 404)

If your dog is an early riser, then a sunrise walk at this glorified boat ramp overlooking Tampa Bay may be a scenic break from the routine. Dogs must be leashed. A playground and community center are available for humans.

The park is at the southeastern tip of St. Petersburg at 7000 Fourth St. South. 727/893-7335.

49 Maximo Park

😺😺 (See St. Petersburg map on page 404)

The big drag for dogs who visit this park on beautiful Boca Ciega Bay is that they are not allowed on the beach or in the water. However, leashed dogs are welcome on the nature trail, on the bike trail, in the picnic areas, and at the fishing dock. You also can trot up the observation tower with your pooch and take the boardwalk to a scenic overlook, or just gaze out from a gazebo.

Hungry dogs may enjoy a picnic under a pavilion or beneath shady oaks and sabal palms. If you forgot to pick up a packed lunch, you can head to the Albertson's supermarket about a mile away at the southeast corner of 31st Street and 54th Avenue.

Take 31st Street south from 54th Avenue South, then turn right at Pinellas Point Drive. As soon as you drive under I-275, you'll be in the park. 727/893-7335.

50 Pinellas Bayway

🐾🐾🐾🐕 (See St. Petersburg map on page 404)

Water dogs will appreciate this break from the usual Pinellas prohibitions on pooches. Here, they may plunge into the wonderful salt water that helps improve their coats, skins, and dispositions. Slightly make-do as far as picnics go, this is nevertheless a great place to swim or wade with your pooch. The bayway (which is really a causeway by another name) is not an official park.

The drill here: Keep your eyes open and ears up for a firm place to pull your car onto the gray-white sand right beside the road, preferably near a break between the mangrove bushes. We've seen many a happy dog paddling without a leash here, even though leashes are supposedly required on causeways managed by the Florida Department of Transportation. Don't let your dog off leash if he's the rambunctious type and not given to minding you, though—it would be all too easy for him to bolt out into traffic. Bring cold water and, during the hotter stretches of the day, umbrellas for portable shade.

The bayway beaches are on Pinellas Bayway/County Road 679, between the mainland and Fort Desoto Park. 727/464-7200.

51 Paw Playground at Fort Desoto Park

🐾🐾🐾🐾🐾◖ 🐕 (See St. Petersburg map on page 404)

This favorite of the two-legged set used to be a ruff place for dogs, but not since officials decided to allow an off-leash area. At the popular weekend spot on anchor-shaped Mullet Key, our furry friends were previously limited to a leash no longer than six feet; today the rule still applies in all areas except the paw playground, which features a green fenced area with room to run and an off-leash beach.

Dog-level water fountains quench canines' thirsts. The park is divided into two fenced areas: one for small dogs, one for large pets. A water hose is provided to wash muddy paws.

Elsewhere in 1,136-acre Fort Desoto Park, dogs now are permitted to sleep at certain campsites. But they still must stay out of the playgrounds and any other beach.

This county park holds some special significance for historical-minded hounds. Long before the fort was built, Juan Ponce de León is said to have explored Mullet Key. So did that hero of Southern hounds, Robert E. Lee, when he was in the U.S. Army three centuries later. The fort is a bit of a historical anachronism, as it was built to protect Tampa Bay during the Spanish-American War. But it wasn't even completed by the end of the war and was obsolete by the time World War I broke out three decades later.

The park, at 3500 Pinellas Bayway South, is at the end of Pinellas Bayway/County Road 679 in the southwest part of the city. 727/866-2484.

PLACES TO EAT

Captain Al's: Set in the popular shopping/entertainment complex at the pier, this waterfront spot serves a range of eats—pasta, salads, seafood, steak, burgers, and pizzas from the wood-burning oven. Tie up your dog on the other side of the railing, then eat on the patio. Afterward, head to nearby canine-cordial Poynter and Straub parks (Parks, Beaches, and Recreation Areas, above). 800 Second Ave. NE, on the pier; 727/898-5800.

Chattaway Drive-In: Pink bathtubs transformed into massive planters for lantana, aloe, and other offbeat plants provide the first tip-off that this restaurant is funky. "An alternative to the Don Cesar," jokes the menu, in reference to the famous beach resort. Despite the name, this informal place is not really a drive-in. All seating is outdoors, though, under either a spreading royal poinciana tree or a metal roof. A 1993 *USA Today* article calls Chattaway the "40-year home of the mind-boggling burger," but a discriminating doggy can also go for sandwiches, including the namesake Chattaclub, the turkey BLT club, or the roast beef and cheese club. You also can pull a stool up to the

outdoor bar. Staffers say it's best to arrive when it's not crowded, so call first and avoid the place during the lunch rush. 358 22nd Ave. S.; 727/823-1594.

Checkers: Grab fast food at the walk-up window and sit at one of the outdoor tables shaded by the distinctive red umbrellas. 9299 Fourth St. N.; 727/576-2134.

Jo-Jo's in Citta: When Jo-Jo's advertises "Fine Southern Cooking," they're not referring to the fried chicken, mashed potatoes, and gravy that have made Robert such a "substantial" companion for Maggie and Sally. Rather, they're talking about southern Italian cuisine made with veal and seafood. And who can turn down southern Italian–style pasta? You'll sit at one of the half-dozen tables out front, shaded by a roof overhang. 200 Central Ave.; 727/894-0075.

PLACES TO STAY

Days Inn: Dog-tired travelers can retrieve food from the on-site restaurant at this two-story poolside motel west of I-275 (Exit 26). Rates run $50–90, plus $25 nightly per pet. 2595 54th Ave. N.; 727/522-3191; www.daysinn.com.

La Quinta: At this comfortable poolside motel, a fenced-in grassy area in back accommodates small doggies who need to relieve themselves. People-pleasers include a heated pool, an exercise room, and free breakfast. Rates run $60–90. 4999 34th St. N., St. Petersburg; 727/527-8421; www.lq.com.

La Veranda Bed & Breakfast: Dogs and cats of various sizes have stayed at this "superior small lodging," as deemed by an independent panel. Innkeeper Nancy Meuse welcomes pets; she says she has found that travelers with dogs and cats take better care of their little companions than some other people do of their children. Full breakfast, complimentary soft drinks, bathrobes, televisions with VCRs, and private entrances are provided at the five-unit inn. In-suite massages are available. Rates in season range $109–250. Summer rates range $99–165. 111 Fifth Ave. N., St. Petersburg; 727/824-9997 or 800/484-8423, ext. 8417; www.laverandabb.com.

St. Petersburg/Madeira Beach KOA Resort: Near dog-friendly War Veterans' Memorial Park in Seminole and the asphalt Pinellas Trail, this 50-acre resort has attracted winter campers from Canada and every state east of the Mississippi River to its 60 cabins and 460 campsites (30 of them on Long Bayou). Campers don't exactly ruff it: Three hot tubs, a pool, a game room, a bocce ball court, a rinky-dink miniature golf course, and organized social activities are among the amenities. The small cabins are packed closely together, but at least part of the campground is shaded by oaks. Air-conditioned cabins run $61–84 (bring bedrolls or linens). Campsites range $32–78. Tents are accepted. 5400 95th St. N., St. Petersburg; 727/392-2233; www.koa.com.

Sunset Bay Inn Bed & Breakfast: Amie, the resident standard poodle, loves visitors—canine or human. She acts as though all arrive just to see her, jokes Martha Bruce, innkeeper of this "superior small lodging," as designated by an independent panel. Canine guests sleep in the carriage house, which offers a king-size wrought-iron canopy bed, a two-person whirlpool tub, and a wet bar with fridge. Bottled water, beverages, and baked goods are available around the clock in the main house. A continental-plus breakfast is served weekdays; weekend offerings may include the Apple Dapple French Toast Cobbler. Martha says she and husband Bob know what it's like to try to find a nice place to stay when traveling with pets, so they're glad to open the carriage house to pets. "We've never had a bad experience," she adds. Rates range $240–280. Cleaning fee is $50. 635 Bay St. NE, St. Petersburg; 727/896-6701 or 800/794-5133; www.sunsetbayinn.com.

Vinoy House Inn: A few early developers of St. Petersburg lived in this big house, now a bed-and-breakfast inn and sometimes a setting for weddings. Located in the city's waterfront district across from Tampa Bay, the inn accepts peewee pets—under 15 pounds. People perks include made-to-order full breakfasts provided any time between 8 and 10 A.M.; guests choose their favorites from a breakfast menu. An independent panel named the establishment a "superior small lodging." Rates in season range $160–255. Off-season rates range $140–205. 532 Beach Dr., St. Petersburg; 727/432-6152; www.vinoyhouseinn.com.

St. Petersburg Beach

With all the dog-friendly motels here, Maggie can't understand why dogs aren't allowed on the beach. An arf-ful situation, she says!

PLACES TO EAT

Seaside Grill II: Kicking back and enjoying a leisurely weekend breakfast alfresco is the big draw for Nora Hawkins and her trio of dachshunds—Greta, Brisco, and Ginger—who quickly are served water whenever Hawkins makes the request. Location is key: After dining at these outdoor tables, Hawkins and her pack explore other parts of the historic, Bohemian Pass-A-Grille area. 6850 Beach Plaza; 727/367-8999.

PLACES TO STAY

Bayview Plaza Waterfront Resort: Set on Boca Ciega Bay, where dolphins and manatees occasionally swim by, these eight units received a coveted "superior small lodging" designation from an independent panel. Located 200 feet from a beach, the family-owned and -operated establishment offers access to a heated pool (across the street), a whirlpool, a fishing pier, and a human-size chess field. Rates in season range $83–115. In summer, rates start at $53. Pet fee is $10 daily. 4321 Gulf Blvd., St. Petersburg Beach; 727/367-1387 or 800/257-8998; www.thebayviewplaza.com.

Lamara Motel Apartments: One of a few precious few pet-permissible "superior small lodgings," as deemed by a local panel, this family-owned establishment offers one-bedroom and studio efficiency apartments located a short walk from the beach (where dogs aren't permitted). Rates in season range $70–80, less other times. Small pets are accepted in certain rooms for $8 daily. 520 73rd Ave., St. Petersburg Beach; 727/360-7521 or 800/211-5108; www.lamara.com.

Ritz Motel: Dolphins and manatees have been spotted off the dock of this independently owned establishment on the Intracoastal Waterway. These three motel rooms, four efficiencies, and seven condominium apartments welcome pets and provide access to both Tampa Bay and the Gulf of Mexico. A pool and marina—and your own kitchen for making homemade doggy dinners—also are offered. Off-season rates start at $55. In season, they generally don't surpass $99. Pet fee is $7 daily, maximum $50. 4237 Gulf Blvd., St. Petersburg Beach; 727/360-7642 or 800/882-5671; www.rask.com/ritz.

Treasure Island

The one thing that makes this place more than just another Florida beach town is the ultra-dog-friendly Lorelei Resort (see below).

PLACES TO STAY

Lorelei Resort Motel: A dog's life, indeed! This is one of the most dog-friendly lodgings for whiskered wanderers anywhere. Instead of chocolates on the pillow, your pal gets a bag of goodies at check-in. Then she can plunge into the bay from a dogs-only swimming platform. Or she can roam leash-free in the fenced waterfront patio and sundeck (provided she is supervised). If you're planning a day at Disney World or another destination where your pooch is unwelcome, the Lorelei will pooch-sit—free of charge. At night, your pal can snuggle with you in bed, thanks to a special sheet cover. There are no restrictions on dog size or pet type. One couple brought six birds and a monitor lizard (not to mention two teenagers). As many as 30 dogs at a time have spent a weekend here with nary a dogfight. The seven efficiencies and three apartments offer a stove, refrigerator, and ceramic tile floors. Boaters can motor to the on-site dock to check in. "It's excellent," says dog trainer Amy Gagnon of suburban Orlando. "It caters to dogs who bring their owners." Rates range $80–100 for motel rooms. A two-story house—which requires a multi-night stay—rents for $225–240 nightly; weekly rates are available. 10273 Gulf Blvd., Treasure Island; 727/360-4351 or 800/35-GO-DOG; www.loreleiresort.com.

Seahorse Cottages & Apartments: Overlooking the beach and Gulf of Mexico, these eight cottages and apartments were awarded a "superior small lodging" designation by an independent local panel. The number 20 is the magic figure here—dogs under 20 pounds and 20 inches are accepted. Rates range $65–145. Pet fee is $10 daily, $50 weekly. 10356 Gulf Blvd., Treasure Island; 727/367-2291 or 800/741-2291; www.seahorse-cottages.com.

438

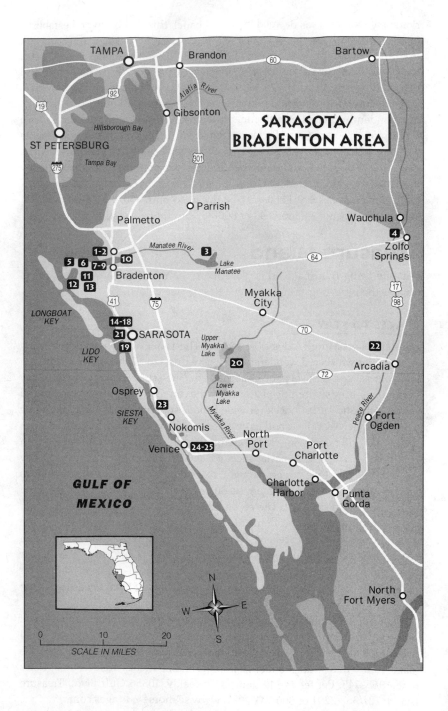

CHAPTER 15

Sarasota/ Bradenton Area

This is a great place for dogs to clown around. After all, animals from all over the world come to this part of the state to do just that. Of course, the other animals—elephants, tigers, and the like—star in the Ringling Brothers and Barnum & Bailey Circus, which winters in Venice, just down the road from Sarasota.

This little-appreciated section of Florida so often is bypassed by tourists on their way to the Keys or Disney World, yet the region contains a lot of what the Florida Park Service calls "The Real Florida": piney woods, dark forests, and scenic rivers. And let's not forget a few dog-friendly beaches, parks, and restaurants that your attention-hungry pooch will find sublime.

Maggie was particularly fond of the Peace River canoe trip (see Arcadia, below). For a more refined day of doggy fun, have a picnic at one of the parks in Sarasota, then check into one of the exquisite resorts in Siesta Key.

PICK OF THE LITTER—SARASOTA

BIGGEST DOG PARK
17th Street Paw Park, Sarasota (page 446)

WORTH-A-SNIFF THREE-ACRE DOG PARKS
Dog Leg Park at Buffalo Creek, Palmetto (page 440)
Happy Tails Off-Leash Area, Bradenton (page 444)

BEST PLACE TO SWIM
Brohard Paw Park and Beach, Venice (page 455)

BEST PLACE TO STAY
Turtle Beach Resort, Siesta Key (page 453)

BEST PLACE TO GET A DOG BISCUIT WITH DINNER
O'Leary's, Sarasota (page 450)

BEST PLACE TO CAMP
Oscar Scherer State Park, Osprey (page 455)

Palmetto

PARKS, BEACHES, AND RECREATION AREAS

1 Dog Leg Park at Buffalo Creek

🐾🐾🐾🐕 (See Sarasota/Bradenton map on page 438)

Drop the leash! At Manatee County's second off-leash area, dogs run freely on three acres. Small, young, and fragile dogs enjoy one fenced area. Rambunctious Labs run in another. Pets travel from around Manatee County to sniff each other, chase balls, then lap up water at doggy fountains. Chauffeurs chat and watch from beneath two shelters.

The park opened in May 2004, before it even had a name. A local pet columnist offered tongue-in-cheek suggestions such as BufFido Junction and Buffalo Dogs Park, paying homage to its Buffalo Creek Park location. Some called it Happy Tails Two, alluding to the county's original dog park (in Bradenton). A public contest yielded the winner: Dog Leg Park.

The park is at 7550 69th St. East. 941/742-5923.

2 Blackstone Park

😺 (See Sarasota/Bradenton map on page 438)

At first glance at the local map, this sizable chunk of green may seem like a godsend to cooped-up pups in suburban Bradenton. Alas, dogs must stay out of the 20-acre park's plentiful ball fields, leaving a nonetheless appreciated fitness trail for the four-legged crowd. Don't be misled by the No Dogs Allowed signs. The dreaded signs apply to the ball fields, not to the walking trail—so say county parks employees.

The park is at 2112 14th Ave. West. 941/742-5923.

Parrish

PARKS, BEACHES, AND RECREATION AREAS

3 Rye Wilderness

😺😺😺 (See Sarasota/Bradenton map on page 438)

A pet ostrich has hopped around this narrow, three-mile-long stretch of wilderness spanning both sides of the Manatee River—so, of course, dogs may visit. Folks occasionally bring pet lizards, snakes, and, once, a captive Florida panther. "He was on a leash," says ranger L. J. Canfield. (Your dog needs a lead, too.) Horses frequent the area, too.

The attraction is following sandy nature trails and horse trails that wind through these 147 acres of shady oaks, sun-dappled pine trees, and wide-open wetlands. Bring burgers to cook a picnic lunch at the provided grills, or a canoe to paddle down the Manatee River with your dog. A canoe launch is east of Rye Road, next to the campground.

For a water break, you can fill up a water bowl at the restrooms (or even at the showers) to replenish your pooped pooch. Horseshoes, volleyball, picnic tables, and a picnic pavilion are available. Dogs are forbidden in the playground and campground.

The county park is at 905 Rye Wilderness Trail. From I-75 (Exit 42), go east about five miles on Bradenton Arcadia Road/Highway 64 to Rye Road. (If you reach Lake Manatee, you've gone too far.) At Rye Road, turn left (north). Continue three miles to the park, crossing a narrow bridge along the way. Watch for the entrance sign at the right. 941/776-0900 or 941/742-5923.

Zolfo Springs

PARKS, BEACHES, AND RECREATION AREAS

4 Pioneer Park

🐾🐾 (See Sarasota/Bradenton map on page 438)

Your dog won't soon forget this 115-acre park—if not for its generous size, then for its makeshift zoo of penned animals who can't return to the wild. The bear? A retired professional wrestler (declawed). The cougar? Given up by its owners when the once fist-sized pet grew too big. One declawed bobcat was a house pet. All of the animals have a story, including two foxes, two squirrels, two alligators, four ostriches, and five deer (one nursed on a bottle). Signs near the pens read No Dogs, but your pal's nose is bound to pick up scents of the unusual critters.

A handful of trails to explore with your leashed dog are found by the Peace River. You may also walk the dike together. City slickers strap their bicycles to their cars and drive a couple hours so they can camp here for $7–11 for two people (and a dog). While restrooms, showers, water, electricity, and even an on-site museum are available, the place is rustic. Bring supplies.

The park is at the intersection of U.S. 17 and Highway 64. 863/735-0330 or 863/773-9430.

PLACES TO STAY

Pioneer Park: See Pioneer Park, above, for camping information.

Bradenton

People from across the state refer to the Sarasota-Bradenton area in one breath, but in fact they're two very different towns. Bradenton is the more downscale of the pair. A little ruff around the edges, you might say, but still a pleasant place to visit with a pooch.

PARKS, BEACHES, AND RECREATION AREAS

5 De Soto National Memorial

🐾🐾🐾 (See Sarasota/Bradenton map on page 438)

Swimming and following a half-mile self-guided nature trail are the doggy highlights of this park at De Soto Point, which juts into the Manatee River. Leashed canine water fans can pick their way carefully along the sharp-shelled beach and plunge (legally) into the shallow waters, more commonly known to attract anglers wearing chest waders.

Even though the park is a respectable 25 acres, it seems smaller. Much of it isn't open to hikers. There are no picnic tables, so picnickers are limited to park benches. Disposable pooper-scoopers are available for people to pick up after their dogs. The four-legged community isn't welcome in the bookstore or the museum. From December to April, smart pooches will notice that rangers are wearing costumes dating to the days of Spanish explorer Hernando de Soto; the gunfire that is part of the twice-an-hour living history demonstrations will scare many a dog, so hold tightly to your leash or leave before the gunfire begins.

The park is at the northern tip of 75th Street Northwest, a short drive north of Manatee Avenue/Highway 64. 941/792-0458.

Lewis Park

 (See Sarasota/Bradenton map on page 438)

A small canal divides this city park to create two distinct experiences for your leashed dog—on one side there's an open area suitable for running; on the other, woods where detective doggies can exercise their sniffers. But these approximately five acres are more often visited by local kids who come to use the playground equipment.

The park is at First Avenue and 31st Street West. From U.S. 41, go west on Manatee Avenue, then turn right on 31st Street West. 941/708-6200.

7 Twelfth Avenue West Park

 (See Sarasota/Bradenton map on page 438)

After sniffing around a grassy area, take a break at a picnic table at this half-square-block, family-oriented park set in a residential neighborhood. You can grill dogs—frankfurters, that is—but the playground is off-limits to your leashed pooch.

The park is at 28th Street West and 12th Avenue West. 941/708-6200.

8 Waterfront Park

 (See Sarasota/Bradenton map on page 438)

More popular with cyclists and in-line skaters than with four-legged visitors, the asphalt walkway that runs through this city park nonetheless offers leashed dogs a pleasant enough walking experience.

The park is at 101 Ninth St. West, at the Manatee River. From U.S. 41, go west on Manatee Avenue, turn right at Ninth Street West, and continue to the river. 941/708-6200.

9 Water Tower Park

 (See Sarasota/Bradenton map on page 438)

After overcoming the urge to inspect the water tower here, leashed dogs can take advantage of the somewhat limited open area to play with a companion. The city park is only a couple of acres in size, and a playground takes up some of that space.

The park is at Sixth Avenue and 30th Street West. From U.S. 41, go west on Manatee Avenue. Turn left on 30th Street West. 941/708-6200.

10 Indian Springs Park

😺 (See Sarasota/Bradenton map on page 438)

No, you won't see a spring while sitting in the gazebo with your leashed dog. The spring at this little, quarter-square-block park was covered with concrete years ago to keep kids from playing in the waters. Instead, walk around the small grassy area (subject to flooding in heavy rains). City parks employee Joe Henry considered it the best grass of any park in town. Kids appreciate the playground and basketball court.

The park is at Second Avenue East and 14th Street East. 941/708-6200.

11 Happy Tails Off-Leash Area

😺😺😺😺🐕 (See Sarasota/Bradenton map on page 438)

It used to be that the G. T. Bray Recreation Complex had this weird effect on dogs. At a comparatively huge 140 acres, it was enough to get a dog's blood going as he poked his head out the car window on arrival. But then he would find out that pets were limited to the fitness/jogging course and bicycle paths.

Thank goodness three of those 140 acres have now been set aside for the city's first off-leash park. A doggy drinking fountain and free pooper-scooper bags are available, as well as a separate area for dogs who are too small or, like Maggie, too fragile in their old age to romp with the young and the big. Underneath shady oaks, you'll find picnic tables where you can take a load off while your dog lets off some steam. Dogs are required to have a current license tag and a current rabies vaccination. Aggressive dogs are not allowed, and your pooch is expected to be obedient enough to come when you call him.

Dogs still must keep their paws off the four softball fields, five soccer fields, and the rest of the sports fields.

The dog park is at 5502 33rd Ave. Drive West. 941/742-5923.

12 Palma Sola Causeway

😺😺😺 (See Sarasota/Bradenton map on page 438)

One of the few remaining places where dogs are welcome to romp on the beach or play in the water, this doggy getaway spans about a quarter mile on both the north and south sides of the causeway over Palma Sola Bay. Cars whiz by, so a leash is a fitting precaution. But one city parks employee says he's never seen a dog on a leash in the bay.

Humane society volunteer Gina Costigan said this was a favorite of her bearded collie, Meagan, after she and Meagan moved here from Ocala. After hanging out with cows in Ocala, the 17-year-old pooch could chase seagulls here. Or at least try. "She got sick. She just did too much," Costigan reported.

Meagan has gone to the Great Doghouse in the Sky, but Costigan recommended the causeway to other dog lovers because dogs can run free and swim.

One caution: Costigan said you may sometimes find people who are a little on the rowdy side here, perhaps swilling beer and bringing along aggressive dogs. So use your judgment.

The causeway begins at the western end of Manatee Avenue and leads to Flamingo Cay and Perico Island. 941/748-4501.

13 Bishop Animal Shelter

🐾🐾 (See Sarasota/Bradenton map on page 438)

Yes, an animal shelter. Your goal is to hit the 40 acres of grassy land where canine visitors are welcome any time the gates are open (usually from 7 A.M.–4:30 P.M.). Dogs joyfully sniff around the woods. But leashes are required, and the place is closed Wednesday and Sunday. This former citrus grove was converted into a shelter to help stray and abandoned animals by the Bishop family.

The shelter is at 5718 21st Ave. West. From U.S. 41, go west on Manatee Avenue, south on 59th Street West, then east on 21st Avenue. 941/792-2863.

PLACES TO STAY

Days Inn Near the Gulf: At this 130-unit motel, which actually is closer to the Manatee River than the Gulf of Mexico, pets sleep in upstairs rooms. Rates range $60–100, plus $7 daily for pets. A separate $50 deposit is refunded, barring doggy mishaps. 3506 First St. West, Bradenton; 941/746-1141; www.daysinn.com.

Econo Lodge Airport: This economy motel isn't so economical for animal lovers due to a whopping flat $50 pet fee. Dogs sleep in designated rooms at this 78-room poolside motel. Rates run $40–99. 6727 14th St. West, Bradenton; 941/758-7199; www.choicehotels.com.

Howard Johnson Express: Jack Russell terriers and the like are accepted in certain rooms at this 50-unit poolside motel, but breeds over 25 pounds are turned away from them all. Rates range $50–100. Pet fee is $10 daily. 6511 14th St. West, Bradenton; 941/756-8399; www.hojo.com.

Inn and Suites on the Park: While humans appreciate the free evening cocktails served at this three-story hotel, your pup probably will sniff around for crumbs from your free continental breakfast. Dogs under 30 pounds are permitted for $10 daily. Rates range $69–100. 4450 47th St., Bradenton; 941/795-4633.

Motel 6: Walk your dog around the lake behind this 121-unit poolside motel. Rates range $46–66. One pet under 35 pounds is permitted per room. 660 67th St. Circle East, Bradenton; 941/747-6005; www.motel6.com.

Queen's Gate Resort: Actually located across Anna Maria Sound on nearby Bradenton Beach, this 13-unit collection of motel rooms and bungalows offers a heated pool and a picnic area where guests can cook up any fresh catch caught on one of the island's piers or a charter boat. Small pets are accepted in two-bedroom units with prior arrangement at this "superior small lodging," as named by an independent panel. Rates for two-bedroom units vary seasonally, $90–142. 1101 Gulf Dr. N., Bradenton Beach; 941/778-7153 or 800/310-7153; www.queensgateresort.com.

Sand Pebble Inn Apartments and Studios: Located on nearby Bradenton Beach, this beach-area complex of four buildings offers 14 apartments and studios with fully equipped kitchens, cable TV, VCR, and access to a heated pool. Everyone sleeps in a beachfront or poolside unit at this "superior small lodging," as deemed by a local panel. Rates in season start at $175 daily, $1,195 weekly. 2218 Gulf Dr. N., Bradenton Beach; 941/778-3053 or 800/500-7263; www.sandpebble.com.

Super 8: Sports hounds can watch ESPN at this 47-room poolside motel as long as they're peewee pets (under 20 pounds). Rates range $49–110. Add a $10 daily pet fee. 6516 14th St. West, Bradenton; 941/756-6656; www.super8.com.

Sarasota

This is the more upscale half of the Sarasota-Bradenton area, although the wealth is mostly quiet and refined. Shopping is a popular pastime with the two-legged set. But dogs, particularly those of the water-loving persuasion, will be happier at several dog-friendly beaches here. A bigger highlight for some pooches is the "bark parks"—that is, parks just for dogs.

PARKS, BEACHES, AND RECREATION AREAS

🐾 17th Street Paw Park

🐾🐾🐾🐾🐾 (See Sarasota/Bradenton map on page 438)

Freedom! Sarasota's largest and first official leash-free dog park provides six acres of romping room. That's perfect for running with abandon or—as preferred occasionally by some canine visitors—for crowding together to sniff each other inquisitively. Dogs and their people have driven from St. Petersburg and routinely travel as far as 50 miles to visit this paw-pular park, Bob Conn, county parks and recreation manager, told us after it opened.

One area is designated for small pets; another is for larger breeds. The grassy fenced-in field is dotted by a few oaks, and three picnic shelters provide a place to sit and snack. For comic (and practical) relief, models of fire hydrants are placed strategically around the park. Another nice touch: A toy box contains Frisbees, chewed balls, and other toys visitors dropped inside to share with those who may have forgotten to bring their playtime favorites.

A small fenced "time-out cage" serves as a penalty box of sorts, in the unusual case that an owner wishes to correct a four-legged pal. "That's just kind of a novelty thing," Conn says.

Open dawn to dusk, the free park formerly was used as a storage area for

DIVERSIONS

Shop with Shep! In Sarasota's beautiful outdoor shopping area of St. Armands Circle, dogs are welcomed at a store and bakery tailored to them—**Wet Noses,** 472 John Ringling Blvd.; 941/388-3647.

Celebrities number among customers, but mostly it's a huge tourist clientele that returns each year, often with pets in tow, to browse the aisles of canine necklaces, toys, crystal collar charms, bling collars, pet carriers, needlepoint pillows, treats, and oddities such as a rescue barrel to tie around a St. Bernard's neck.

"We have the most fabulous strollers for dogs," says Carol Angelotti, who runs the business with her daughter, Kim McLeod. The dog stroller comes with blinking safety lights in back and a license plate that can be customized to bear a pet's name.

Perhaps the best part for pooches is the free gourmet biscuit and fresh water they're offered as soon as they enter the canine hot spot.

Looking for more places to shop with Topper? An apricot poodle named Pumpkin has gained one pound since taking over the job as official taste tester at **Max's Dog Bakery,** 1375 Main St., in downtown Sarasota; 941/330-0330. Dogs taking a leashed stroll through the neighborhood tend to pull their owners to the front door of the bakery and "pawtique," where they're welcome to browse the toys, pet beds, and glass cases filled with trays of goodies that look like human baked goods or pretzels.

In Bradenton, Molly the store dog greets leashed customers who try out pet hammocks and shop for treats at **Bonejour,** 9122 Center Parkway, Suite 108; 941/907-0121. Ahh, it's a dog's life indeed.

dirt and fill before being turned into an off-leash area for dogs in 1998. Now, you'll find restrooms, parking, a free dog shower, a watering hole for pets, a bulletin board for posting doggy-related notices, and dispensers stocked with disposable pooper-scoopers. This off-leash area is set within 17th Street Park, a 96-acre home of softball and soccer fields. Dogs also are permitted in the rest of the park—on leash.

The county-run park is at 4570 17th Street. 941/316-1172.

15 Arlington Park

☙ (See Sarasota/Bradenton map on page 438)

Leashed dogs are limited to doing one thing at this small park—walking. No problem, Maggie says. Follow a short trail, measuring .7 mile, and skip the pool and recreation area, where Fidos are forbidden.

The park is at 2650 Waldemere Street. 941/316-1172.

16 Gillespie Park

☙ (See Sarasota/Bradenton map on page 438)

After lunch at the picnic pavilion, your leashed dog may explore the wooded areas of this 10-acre park. If that's not enough, run with Spot in the park's nice open area.

The park is at 710 N. Osprey Avenue. 941/316-1172.

17 Ken Thompson Park

☙☙☙ (See Sarasota/Bradenton map on page 438)

Next to going to the beach, Tinka and Beldar, two local Labrador retrievers belonging to Russ and Mary Nugent, always loved visiting this 84-acre park best. The sandy shoreline with shallow flats extending south are perfect for wading, swimming, or chasing balls and sticks. Shaggy, tall Australian pines provide shade near the shore, and a water fountain quenches the thirst of romping beachgoers. Dogs who prefer wide-open green areas can explore fields here instead.

Formerly known as City Island, this getaway is a large peninsula that reaches into Sarasota Bay from Lido Key. You may notice a No Dogs Allowed sign on the park's north side, but the county park office told us that dogs are permitted on the south side. Here's a rule of thumb: Leashed dogs are welcome south of Ken Thompson Parkway but are forbidden in the less-pleasant areas north of this road, which slices the park in two.

The park is at 1700 Ken Thompson Parkway. Take the John Ringling Causeway/Highway 789 to St. Armands Key and then follow the signs to Longboat Key. Just before the New Pass Bridge, you'll see Ken Thompson Parkway on the right. Follow the road about half a mile to the end. 941/316-1172.

18 Lakeview Paw Park

☙☙☙☙🐾 (See Sarasota/Bradenton map on page 438)

Run, Spot, run! That's the idea behind this two-acre fenced park, shaded by plenty of trees. Dogs run and play freely without leashes, stopping only from time to time to ask human spectators for attention or slurp water from the canine watering hole.

One area is designated for small pets; another is for biggies. Forget to bring a ball? Grab a toy from the communal toy box, in which visitors place toys they're willing to share with other dogs. Models of fire hydrants dot the grounds. Amenities also include a free dog shower, a bulletin board for posting doggy-related notices, and dispensers stocked with disposable pooper-scoopers.

The free, county-run park is at 7150 Lago Street. 941/316-1172.

19 Sarasota Bayfront/Island Park

🐾🐾🐾 (See Sarasota/Bradenton map on page 438)

A popular spot for downtown residents to walk their dogs (and for canines to check each other out), this pleasant, man-made peninsula offers lots of shoreline to explore on the south and west sides, plus plenty of grass and trees for shade. Tender paws should avoid much of the shell-covered, rock-revetment "beach" surrounding the park and head to the east side, next to the parking lot, to find sandy shoreline. Besides following a concrete waterfront sidewalk, leashed dogs can take advantage of sunny, grassy expanses and tree-covered areas. Fill up a water jug for your dog at a drinking fountain here or at a restroom at O'Leary's, a sailing school and hound-hospitable restaurant just past the park's south entrance (see Places to Eat, below). Although you may notice a dog or two running free, leashes are the law.

You'll find the bayfront, known locally as Island Park, just south of the marina. Take U.S. 41/South Tamiami Trail until you reach Ringling Boulevard. Turn toward the bay (west of the highway) and then look for a place to park. 941/954-4198.

20 Myakka River State Park

🐾🐾 (See Sarasota/Bradenton map on page 438)

Just driving along the main road through this lush, 45-square-mile park may be enough to send some woods-loving dogs into a tizzy. That may have to do, for dogs are forbidden on nature trails in this deer and alligator haven, and walks are limited to leashed hikes on the seven miles of paved roads, popular with bicyclists, and on some service roads, such as Powerline Road. Dogs are also taboo at the campground and cabins. Hungry dogs are allowed, however, to eat at the picnic areas.

With heads hanging out the window and tongues flapping in the breeze, pooches on a windshield tour can see some of what walkers get to appreciate at a leisurely pace—oaks, marshes, Upper Myakka Lake, and sloughs. It's probably a good thing that dogs are forbidden on nature trails: On one visit to the lake, without Maggie, we saw a gator who was stationary one moment suddenly race at an alarming speed toward an unsuspecting turtle.

Admission is $3 for one person in a car, $5 for two or more people. From Sarasota, head east on Highway 72 for nine miles. The park is at 13207 Highway 72. 941/361-6511.

PLACES TO EAT

Ben & Jerry's: Retrieve a scoop of vanilla ice cream for your pooch and a sundae for you, then return to benches outdoors to share with your pal. 372 St. Armands Circle; 941/388-5226.

O'Leary's: Not only are dogs allowed on the shaded, open-air deck of this very casual eatery on the Sarasota bayfront, but they also are handed a dog bone when accompanied by their owners. Among the menu items are burgers, hot dogs, shrimp baskets, grouper sandwiches, and, of course, beer. 5 Bayfront Dr.; 941/953-7505.

PLACES TO STAY

Days Inn Airport: Cooked breakfasts are free at this two-story poolside motel, so your dog might hope you'll bring back bacon. Rates range $59–110, plus $6 daily per pooch. Small pets are preferred. 4900 N. Tamiami Trail/ U.S. 41, Sarasota; 941/355-9721; www.daysinn.com.

Hibiscus Suites Inn: Every dog sleeps in a suite at this "superior small lodging," as named by an independent panel. People perks include a heated pool, a picnic pagoda, satellite TV, and feather-top mattresses. Rates in season start at $185. Add a $25 daily pet fee. 1735 Stickney Point Rd., Sarasota; 941/921-5797 or 800/822-5247; www.hibiscussuites.com.

Quality Inn Airport: There's no grassy dog walk at this 72-room poolside motel, so try walking along the street. Rates range $69–119. Add $10 for a pet under 20 pounds, $20 for a bigger dog. 4800 N. Tamiami Trail, Sarasota; 941/355-7091; www.choicehotels.com.

Ramada Limited: Free weekday newspapers keep newshounds up on current events at this 63-room, three-story hotel off I-75 (Exit 205), behind a Burger King. Rates range $79–130. Pet fee is $10 nightly. 5774 Clark Rd., Sarasota; 941/921-7812; www.ramada.com.

Ritz-Carlton Sarasota: Place the Woof sign on your doorknob to alert housekeepers to your four-legged companion at this 11-acre beach resort, called one of "the world's best places to stay" by *Conde Nast Traveler* magazine. All 266 rooms offer private balconies and a view of Sarasota Bay, the marina, or the city skyline. Three lighted tennis courts, a fitness center, a spa club, and fine dining number among the human amenities. Dogs under 30 pounds are accepted, though you must carry your pal in your arms through the hallways and take him outdoors to do his business in a designated area. Rooms in season start at $270. The pet fee is a whopping $125. 1111 Ritz-Carlton Dr., Sarasota; 941/309-2000; www.ritzcarlton.com/resorts/sarasota.

Longboat Key

At this barrier island off the coast of Sarasota, dogs are not technically allowed on the beach. But they're sometimes spotted there, particularly in the early mornings and evenings.

PLACES TO STAY

Hilton Longboat Key: At this five-story hotel with a pool, gift shop, and other amenities, small pets are accepted for a fee that might elicit howls: $100. Room rates start at $129. 4711 Gulf of Mexico Dr., Longboat Key; 941/383-2451; www.hilton.com.

Riviera Beach Resort: Many guests bring dogs to this nine-unit gulf-side motel, but pooches can't romp on the beach. Walk your buddy across the street instead. Small dogs, please. Weekly rates range $640–1,220. Pets require a $100 refundable deposit, plus $10 fee. 5451 Gulf of Mexico Dr., Longboat Key; 941/383-2552.

Lido Key

PARKS, BEACHES, AND RECREATION AREAS

🐾 Bird Key Park

🐾🐾🐾 (See Sarasota/Bradenton map on page 438)

Dogs are often seen plunging into Sarasota Bay to retrieve the balls or sticks their companions toss into the waters along this small, narrow park, also known as Causeway Park. Most of the park amounts to little more than paved parking spaces, but there is a sandy beach that water dogs will love. (Landlubbers wouldn't be so impressed.)

Leashes technically are the law, but you'll probably see some gleeful pups off leash. Your dog will need to be careful at times because the bay is popular with sailboarders and personal watercraft riders. A few palm trees provide shade between the parking area and the beach. Head to the east side of the park to find grassy patches to sniff. Bring water for your pooch.

The park is on the north side of the John Ringling Causeway/Highway 789 (which connects Sarasota to Bird Key), across from the entrance to Bird Key. 941/316-1172.

PLACES TO STAY

Coquina on the Beach Resort: Your dog can feel sand squish between his pointy toes on the private portion of this resort's beach—but he absolutely can't pass the high-water mark to cross into the public portion of the beach or swim in the Gulf of Mexico. While that's fine for water-phobes like Maggie, born-to-swim Labrador retrievers likely will be frustrated. Perhaps walk your furry swimmer in the grassy area behind the patio instead, or at nearby St. Armand's Circle. Most canine guests simply take a leashed stroll down pedestrian-friendly Ben Franklin Drive. These 34 rooms on the Gulf of Mexico feature kitchens and a heated pool. Rates are $89–379. The pet fee is $35 per stay. 1008 Ben Franklin Dr., Sarasota; 941/388-2141 or 800/833-2141; www.coquinaonthebeach.com.

Lido Vacation Rentals: A dog beach is up the street and St. Armand Circle is around the corner from these suites and guest rooms, set in a neighborhood of million-dollar homes. Well-behaved dogs under 30 pounds are permitted. Rates run $97–262. The pet fee is $30. A $150 pet deposit will be refunded, barring doggy misdeeds. 528 South Polk Dr., Sarasota; 941/388-1004 or 800/890-7991; www.lidovacationrentals.com.

Siesta Key

This is one of those funky beachside towns that has not yet been completely overrun by the crush of people who are making dog-friendly sites less and less common in this otherwise wonderful state.

For doggies who want the bare facts, Siesta Key offers an extra-special treat. Near the south end of this eight-mile-long barrier island is Turtle Beach, a secluded gulf-front strip that is favored by nudists and is not patrolled by lifeguards. Although dogs technically are not allowed to romp on the beach—not even if they're wearing a leash—locals tell us that pooches are very much tolerated there.

PLACES TO EAT

Old Salty Dog: A casual air marks this English-style pub, where laid-back quiet dogs may join their people on the patio for everything from hot dogs to surf and turf. 5023 Ocean Blvd.; 941/349-0158.

PLACES TO STAY

Tropical Breeze Resort & Spa: This 71-unit establishment on the island's north side offers several heated pools, shuffleboard, an exercise room, and massages. While locals don't always look kindly on dogs sitting on Siesta Key beaches, a staffer helpfully says that the four-legged set may tucker themselves out by walking three miles along the waterline. You'll need a very serene pooch if he is to join you at the yoga deck. Daily rates range seasonally $85–499, with additional discounts available in the fall. Weekly rates are also available. Pets are permitted in certain rooms for $50 weekly. 140 Columbus Blvd., Sarasota; 941/349-1125 or 800/300-2492; www.tropicalbreezeinn.com.

Turtle Beach Resort: A real find, this romantic hidden jewel offers 10 ground-floor cottages for you and your dog to choose from: Country French with a four-poster bed, Victorian, Southwestern, Caribbean, and so on. There's a Key West feel to the place that owner Gail Rubenfeld says is deliberate. Every room has a large private hot tub ("Oh, no!" Maggie would say. "Not a bath!"), where you can enjoy the complimentary sherry. Some guests stay for extended periods, including one woman who lingered for a month with her little pug, Dudley. Children are welcome, too.

You'll have access to loaner fishing poles and bicycles, and if you have your own boat, the inn has six docking spots. You can also grab your pooch, borrow the resort's pedalboat, rowboat, or canoe, and head out into Sarasota Bay. A top-flight restaurant serving an upscale Florida/seafood sort of cuisine is on site. As if all that were not enough, you're just a three-minute trot from dog-tolerant Turtle Beach. Nightly rates range $240–330 in the off-season. In-season rates start at $330. Many guests take advantage of weekly rates. There's a 10 percent surcharge for your pet, 15 percent if he's a big ol' honker. 9049 Midnight Pass Rd., Sarasota; 941/349-4554; www.turtlebeachresort.com.

Arcadia

Settled relatively early in Florida's history, the little town of Arcadia seems to be fraying around the edges, but open-minded visitors will see it still has a bit of authentic charm, particularly in the old downtown. Most local bank tellers will hand treats to dogs who pass by their drive-through windows.

PARKS, BEACHES, AND RECREATION AREAS

22 Morgan Park

🐾🐾🐾🐾🐕 (See Sarasota/Bradenton map on page 438)

Bruno, a chow chow, thinks he's gone to the Doggy Promised Land as he follows the wide, well-kept hiking trail along the scenic Peace River in this 240-acre park. Perhaps the best part is that he walks without a leash. His thick coat becomes a magnet for burrs as he rustles through the woodsy wildlife haven, but luckily his companion, Charlene Carroll, learned long ago to carry a brush. Dogs who obey voice commands may chuck their leashes, says Carroll, who belongs to the local chamber of commerce. Bring a water bowl to fill at the restroom or water fountain and refresh your worn-out pooch.

The park is on Highway 70, behind the food mart at 1072 W. Oak Street. From the food mart, follow the first road to the right, then turn left at the stop sign to enter the park. 863/494-4033 or 863/993-4854.

PLACES TO STAY

Best Western Arcadia Inn: Guests at this 38-unit downtown poolside motel are asked to never leave their dogs alone in the room and to walk them in the small grassy area behind the motel (not in the tiny yard in front). Rates range $59–119, plus $15 per stay for your well-behaved dog. 504 S. Brevard Ave., Arcadia; 941/494-4884; www.bestwestern.com.

DIVERSIONS

Canoe the Peace River, which is just as the name implies—peaceful. On Maggie's first camping trip, she donned a life vest and lumbered into a rental canoe in Arcadia, where she proceeded to lean from side to side as we paddled down the slow-moving river past cattle farms and walls of moss-draped oaks. Two previously hidden cows eventually came into view at river's edge, where they munched grass. They seemed oblivious to our whimpering shepherd, who pined to chase them.

Easily one of Maggie's all-time favorite trips, a canoe trip down the Peace River can be done in a day or turned into an overnight trip. The latter requires a bit of planning and patience, but we found it worthwhile. Bring dog food and a cooler packed with plenty of water, plus drinks and food for you. Campers will need such items as a tent, sleeping bags, their dog's favorite blanket, and a long rope to tie up the pooch to keep him away from approaching raccoons while you cook dinner. (They drove Maggie crazy.)

Once inside the tent, we had visions of Maggie barking at 4 A.M. and crashing through the tent to chase raccoons. Luckily, she slept through the night. Among the two local outfitters is **Canoe Safari,** which charges $37.50 for a nine-mile, half-day trip; 863/494-7865. We rented our canoe from nearby **Canoe Outpost-Peace River,** 2816 NW County Rd. 661, Arcadia. Fees run $35 per canoe for two people to enjoy a five- to 16-mile day trip. Cost is $75 for overnight rentals if you bring your own camping gear. Dogs are accepted on the shuttle ride to get to the canoe launch. Reserve at 863/494-1215 or 800/268-0083.

Osprey

PARKS, BEACHES, AND RECREATION AREAS

23 Oscar Scherer State Park

😊😊😊 (See Sarasota/Bradenton map on page 438)

Fifteen miles of hiking and bicycle trails wend through this home of rare, threatened, or endangered animals, such as the lumbering gopher tortoise and the Florida scrub jay. That's great news for wet noses with four legs. Leashed dogs may sniff to their hearts' content through this sun-dappled forest of pines and scrub. If you bring a canoe, you also may paddle along a saltwater creek. Just forget the beach—it's off-limits to pooches.

This was one of the first state parks to allow dogs to camp, and it remains one of the best places for doing so, considering its natural surroundings and proximity to urban areas. Camping at the 104-site campground costs $24.20. Reserve at ReserveAmerica.com or 800/326-3521.

Admission is $4 per car. The park is at 1843 S. Tamiami Trail/U.S. 41, two miles south of Osprey. From Sarasota, go south on U.S. 41 and look for the entrance on the left. 941/483-5956.

PLACES TO STAY

Oscar Scherer State Park: See Parks, Beaches, and Recreation Areas, above, for camping information.

Venice

PARKS, BEACHES, AND RECREATION AREAS

24 Brohard Paw Park and Beach

😊😊😊😊🐕 (See Sarasota/Bradenton map on page 438)

Howl-elujah! Dogs can head to a designated section of beach here at these times: Wednesday 7–11 A.M. and Saturday 5–9 P.M. (Hours are subject to change, so call ahead.) Any day of the week, they can head to the adjacent one-acre dog park, a fenced, sunny area with precious few trees but lots of four-legged visitors having leash-free fun. Pooches dash around and seem to race each other, burning pent-up energy before heading home dog-tired.

Models of fire hydrants dot the one-acre leash-free area. Forget to bring a toy? Grab one from the on-site toy box, in which visitors place toys they're willing to share with others. Amenities include a bulletin board for posting doggy-related notices, dispensers stocked with disposable pooper-scoopers, and a shower to wash sand off your furry beachgoer.

The dog park is set inside 84-acre Brohard Park, a popular swimming, fishing, and picnicking spot for people. The park is at 1600 Harbor Dr. South. 941/316-1172.

25 Woodmere Paw Park

🐾🐾🐾🐾🐕 (See Sarasota/Bradenton map on page 438)

Dog heaven: That's how the local newspaper described this tree-shaded, two-acre fenced area where dogs are welcome to run without dreaded leashes. Pooches periodically gather in crowds to sniff each other, then break off to race after thrown balls or just race each other for the heck of it. Afterward, some are persuaded to stand still at the on-site doggy shower to be cleaned up before jumping into the car to go home.

Dogs large and small head to this park, dotted with model fire hydrants. Leery little pooches are welcome to head straight to a Small Dog Alternative Area, a fenced area of their own. Other amenities include a bulletin board for posting doggy-related notices, dispensers stocked with disposable pooper-scoopers, and a communal toy box.

The dog park is within 38-acre Woodmere Park, featuring a jogging trail, a gym, picnic areas, restrooms, a playground, and a recreation building. The park is at 3951 Merewood Blvd. (at Alligator Creek). 941/316-1172.

PLACES TO STAY

Holiday Inn: A sand volleyball court, shuffleboard, a pool, a restaurant, a lounge, and a fitness center await guests at this comfortable 160-room lodging. Rates range $89–190. Add a flat $30 pet fee. Small pets are preferred, but well-mannered larger pets have been accepted. 455 U.S. 41 Bypass North, Venice; 941/485-5411; www.holidayinns.com.

Horse & Chaise Inn: West Highland Terriers and other small pets are permitted with prior arrangement in designated rooms of this eight-unit bed-and-breakfast inn, whose amenities include a garden, large shady deck, bicycles for guest use, a common sitting room with fireplace, and a 24-hour snack area. Rates range $115–149. Pet fee is $10 daily. 317 Ponce De Leon Ave.; 941/488-2702 or 877/803-3515; www.horseandchaiseinn.com.

Motel 6: Walk your fuzzy pal along the grassy perimeter of this U-shaped, 103-unit poolside motel. Rates run $46–71. 281 U.S. 41 Bypass North, Venice; 941/485-8255; www.motel6.com.

SOUTH FLORIDA

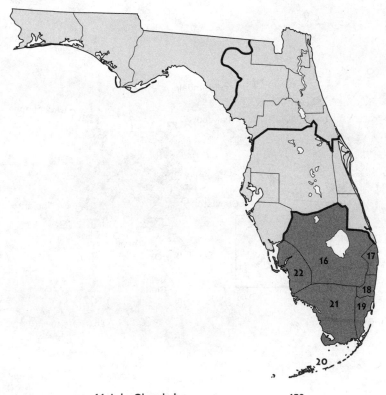

458

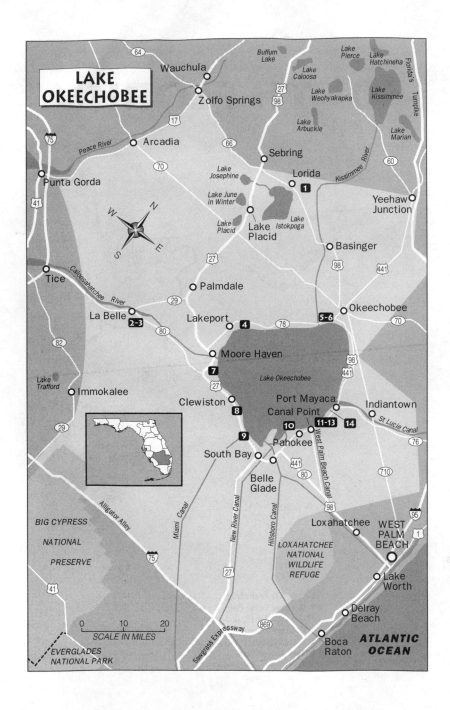

CHAPTER 16

Lake Okeechobee

You'll surely see it every night on the television weather report: that big hole in the middle of Florida. It's called Lake Okeechobee (Big Water, in the language of the Seminole Indians), and it's gotten short shrift as far as tourism goes.

This relatively little-noticed region, largely written off by tourists as a sea of green sugarcane, turns out to be a fine place for outdoorsy pooches to spend a few days hiking, boating, or camping. You won't find the finely landscaped hotels and white-glove service available a world away at coastal destinations, but how many dogs are truly impressed by that? For a bored dog, even a Sunday drive down U.S. 27 or across Highway 80 and through the sugarcane fields around Lake Okeechobee is a treat.

Even though "the Big O" is a huge lake—some 730 square miles, the second-largest freshwater lake inside the borders of the United States—getting a glimpse of it is not easy. The reason: After a hurricane drowned some 2,000 people and untold numbers of dogs in the 1920s, a dike, named after Herbert Hoover, was built to tame the lake. The 34-foot-high wall now shields the lake from the eyes of passing motorists. For a good view of these vast waters,

PICK OF THE LITTER—LAKE OKEECHOBEE

BEST LAKEVIEW HIKES
Florida National Scenic Trail, Okeechobee (page 463)
Okee-Tantie Recreation Area, Okeechobee (page 464)
Everglades Adventures RV & Sailing Resort, Pahokee
(page 468)

BEST HIKE IN THE WOODS
Hickory Hammock, Basinger (page 460)

MOST UNUSUAL PICNIC SPOT
Ortona Lock and Dam, La Belle (page 461)

we highly recommend a hike along the dike (see listings under Okeechobee, Moore Haven, Clewiston, Pahokee, and Port Mayaca).

Boating and fishing are popular here, and opportunities to rent a boat and head out onto the lake are so numerous that, with one exception, we have not bothered to list them. Any marina should be able to help you. Pontoon boats and larger craft with some shade are best for dogs. Water dogs who are tempted to jump into the drink should skip these outings because Lake Okeechobee is teeming with alligators. To them, a furry figure dog-paddling along the surface looks much like a juicy grilled steak does to your pooch!

Basinger

PARKS, BEACHES, AND RECREATION AREAS

1 Hickory Hammock Wildlife Management Area

😺 😺 😺 (See Lake Okeechobee map on page 458)

For wilderness wolfhounds tired of padding along the sun-washed levee of Lake Okeechobee, a backwoods hike in the neighborhood of the curvy Kissimmee River may be in order. A zigzag section of the Florida National Scenic Trail runs the length of this land for nearly eight miles, leading leashed hikers through open pastures and hammocks of oaks and palms. Of course, no sane dog should attempt such a long trip. Turn back at a comfortable distance for your pup. Along the way, you may see deer or a wild turkey, gopher tortoise, or wild hog.

The hammock is massive—bordered to the south by U.S. 98 and the Istokpoga

Canal, to the east by Canal 38, and to the west by Bluff Hammock Road. You're guaranteed to leave with a pooped pooch.

Rugged outdoorsy types may wish to request permission to pitch a tent with a dog at designated primitive campsites found about two miles into the trail; call 800/250-4200. Ask about other primitive campsites, too; some are located along the levee that hugs Canal 38, the new, ruler-straight incarnation of the Kissimmee River.

Bring anything you need even for a short visit, including water and food. You won't find supplies here, but you will find solace.

The hammock trailhead is on the north side of U.S. 98 in Highlands County, about half a mile west of where the road crosses Istokpoga Canal. 800/250-4200.

PLACES TO STAY

Hickory Hammock: See Parks, Beaches, and Recreation Areas, above, for information about primitive camping.

La Belle

PARKS, BEACHES, AND RECREATION AREAS

❷ Barron Park

😺 (See Lake Okeechobee map on page 458)

Somehow, huge crowds manage to squeeze onto this modest-sized piece of ground for the annual Swamp Cabbage Festival. The rest of the year, the humble park is a favorite of farmworkers and other locals who sit under moss-draped oaks to watch the Caloosahatchee River flow by. Less scenic than it sounds, the park offers a picnic pavilion, picnic tables, some benches, restrooms, and a gazebo. Dogs under voice control may ditch the leash, a staffer says.

From Fort Myers, go east on Highway 80 until you reach the town of La Belle. The park is on the south bank of the Caloosahatchee River. 863/675-2872 or 863/675-3381.

❸ Ortona Lock and Dam

😺😺😺 (See Lake Okeechobee map on page 458)

Leashed dogs get a close look at the mechanical wonders of a U.S. Army Corps of Engineers dam here, but that's only part of the allure of this getaway. Surrounded by cow pastures on two sides and set on the north bank of the Caloosahatchee River, the grassy spits of land that make up this dam's recreation area are downright pretty, and quite tranquil.

A scenic place to eat with the off chance of hearing a distant rooster crow, the park shades dogs from the sun with its six covered picnic tables and two large pavilions with grills. More picnic tables dot a strip of land closer to the glistening river. It's pretty, though Maggie was more concerned with chasing doves.

Lucky dogs might notice a manatee swim by in the Caloosahatchee River. Boaters can use a boat ramp here for $3. Fill up a pet water bowl at the restrooms.

Also called Ortona North Day Use Area, the park is located past cow pastures and the Ortona Volunteer Fire Department on Highway 78A. From Highway 80 in La Belle, go north four miles on Highway 29, crossing the Caloosahatchee River along the way. Turn right on Highway 78 to travel east nearly six miles, then turn right on Highway 78A. Travel 1.9 miles to the day-use area. 863/983-8101.

PLACES TO STAY

Ortona South Recreational Area Campground: A distant rooster may crow as you awake at this sunny, remote, tranquil campground set on the south bank of the Caloosahatchee River, where manatees sometimes swim by. The place fills up in winter with folks who make use of the fishing pier or occasionally watch boats go through the Ortona Lock (located here). The 51 sun-washed concrete-pad campsites are each outfitted with a sheltered picnic table, grill, electric hookups, and a campfire area. Hot showers are available. First-come, first-served sites are available, though reservations are advised. Sites range $10–20. From La Belle, drive seven miles east on Highway 80 to

the park, also known as Ortona Lock and Dam Campground. 863/675-8400 or 877/444-6777; www.reserveusa.com.

Lakeport

PARKS, BEACHES, AND RECREATION AREAS

4 Harney Pond Canal Access Area

🐾🐾 (See Lake Okeechobee map on page 458)

Other than fishing from the canal bank or launching a boat with your furry mate, the only activity here is exactly what dogs love—hiking. The sun-dappled nature trail is the 107-mile-long Herbert Hoover Dike, which overlooks huge Lake Okeechobee. Bring water and snacks, and turn back before you wear out your leashed pal.

The canal is on the west side of the lake on Highway 78, not far west of County Road 721. 863/983-8101.

Okeechobee

PARKS, BEACHES, AND RECREATION AREAS

5 Florida National Scenic Trail

🐾🐾🐾🐾 (See Lake Okeechobee map on page 458)

Maggie strained at her leash to sniff part of the 107-mile-long hiking trail atop the semi-grassy berm that encircles Lake Okeechobee. Your dog may think he's king of the mountain here on the Herbert Hoover Dike, rising an average of 34 feet above the lake. To one side, the levee dips toward the alternately tree-lined and exposed grayish blue lake waters in the distance. To the other, it dips toward campers, mobile homes, or other buffers from major roads. Avid hikers who belong to the Florida Trail Association circle the lake in an annual trip—taking some 570,000 steps.

The broiling sun is brutal for a dog on the flat, open trail at noon in summer, so consider a morning visit or watch the sky turn baby blue and pink at dusk. Best bet: Come in winter. The shells crunching under your dog's paws were submerged millions of years ago beneath an ocean that once reached here; Lake Okeechobee is the modern-day remnant.

Keep your dog on the raised trail and away from the lake to avoid possible encounters with alligators or water moccasins at water's edge. Technically, dogs must be leashed, but the restriction is widely ignored and seemingly not enforced. Bring plenty of water and mosquito repellent. For hiking maps and hints, call the Florida Trail Association at 877/HIKE-FLA.

The trail has various access points around the lake. In Okeechobee, you may enter next door to the Okee-Tantie Recreation Area (see below). From

DIVERSIONS

Inquiring dogs want to know: So, where exactly is **Lake Okeechobee?** It's actually not an absurd question. Yes, Lake Okeechobee is a behemoth, measuring 730 square miles, making it the second-largest freshwater lake in the continental United States. That should make it easy for an old dog with failing eyesight to see, except for one thing. Three-story-tall **Herbert Hoover Dike** surrounds the lake. The dike is so tall that motorists can circle the entire lake and never once see water.

Your mission: Show your dog the lake by hiking up to the dike from various spots mentioned in this chapter, such as the **Okee-Tantie Recreation Area,** 10430 Highway 78 West, Okeechobee; 863/763-2622. Alternatively, bring a boat or rent one from numerous area businesses scattered around the lake's perimeter. From **Everglades Adventures RV & Sailing Resort** at 190 N. Lake Ave. in Pahokee, you can access the lake by foot or rental boat. Reserve at 561/924-7832.

Hoping to make the lake region's wonders more obvious to motorists, civic leaders developed a **Big Water Heritage Trail** brochure to point out key spots along your drive. Request one from local chambers of commerce in such towns as Clewiston (863/983-7979), Okeechobee (863/763-6464), and Pahokee (561/924-5579).

Okee-Tantie, go east on Highway 78 and then turn right soon thereafter at a turnoff where you can see the levee. Follow that road to the levee. There is no official parking area. If you have trouble finding it, ask the people at Okee-Tantie. 863/983-8101.

6 Okee-Tantie Recreation Area

🐾🐾 (See Lake Okeechobee map on page 458)

A pleasant enough place to lazily grill some dogs—frankfurters, we mean—this recreation area nevertheless centers around one activity: fishing. Old dogs, though, might appreciate the smattering of benches along the Kissimmee River. And their younger leashed companions may enjoy sniffing around open grassy patches after a long drive. Folks and some dogs camp here for $31 nightly (reservations are accepted), primarily to have a convenient home base for launching a boat into the fabled fishing grounds of Lake Okeechobee.

A few picnic tables with grills are found in a grassy area. Others are outside the bait and tackle shop, which sells hot dogs, chips, and sandwiches. Dogs with bigger appetites could try takeout orders from the seafood restaurant on the premises.

The recreation area is at 10430 Highway 78 West, immediately east of the Kissimmee River. From Highway 70 and U.S. 441/Parrott Avenue in the town of Okeechobee, go south on U.S. 441 to Lake Okeechobee. Turn right (west) at Highway 78 and continue about 4.5 miles to the park at left, just before the Kissimmee River. 863/763-2622.

PLACES TO EAT

Skip's BBQ: Barbecue is so popular in these parts, a pup might conclude that a spicy barbecue sauce courses through the veins of local residents. At this joint, your dog can join you at the single outdoor table as you make a meal out of beef, chicken, or pork slathered in the savory stuff. 104 SE Sixth St.; 863/763-8313.

PLACES TO STAY

Budget Inn: If your pooch wants a midnight snack, treat him to the leftovers you've stored in your room fridge. One small dog per room, please. Rooms cost $49–120. Pet fee is $10 per stay. The size limit? "Nothing really big." 201 S. Parrott Ave., Okeechobee; 863/763-3185.

Economy Inn: No pool, no kitchens—just a basic place to sleep. Rates range $45–90. Add $5 per day for the pooch. 507 N. Parrott Ave., Okeechobee; 863/763-1148.

Okeechobee Resort KOA Kampground & Golf Course: It would be hard to claim you're ruffing it at this 750-site campground, where the palm-dotted grounds just north of Highway 78 include a nine-hole golf course, driving range, lounge, restaurant, lighted tennis courts, miniature golf, horseshoes, shuffleboard courts, and not one but two pools—one set aside for adults and equipped with a hot tub. Campsites run $33–70. Cabins and cottages range $55–155. (For cabins and cottages, bring sheets, towels, pillows, folding chairs, and other gear as if you were camping.) 4276 U.S. 441 South, Okeechobee; 863/763-0231 or 800/562-7748; www.koakampgrounds.com.

Okee-Tantie Recreation Area: See Parks, Beaches, and Recreation Areas, above, for camping information.

Pier II: Feel free to take your leashed friend fishing on the 600-foot hotel pier, which stretches into a canal that rims Lake Okeechobee. Amenities include a boat ramp, a pool, a fish-cleaning station, space for more than 100 bass boats to tie up, and a five-story viewing tower that looks onto the lake. Rooms range $55–125. Pet fee is $10 nightly. 2200 U.S. 441 SE, Okeechobee; 863/763-8003 or 800/874-3744; www.pier2resort.com.

Moore Haven

PARKS, BEACHES, AND RECREATION AREAS

7 Alvin L. Ward Sr. Memorial Park

🐾🐾🐾 (See Lake Okeechobee map on page 458)

Leashed dogs have some room to stretch their legs along the wide Caloosa-hatchee River, where manatees occasionally visit. The park isn't an ideal spot to commune with nature, but you can fish, launch a boat, or toss frankfurters onto grills next to several shady waterfront picnic pavilions with your dog. Alert canines will notice anhingas—nicknamed snakebirds—drying their wet feathers by sitting on pylons and stretching out their black wings.

Next door is the Moore Haven Lock and Dam, where dogs may hit the trailhead for the Florida National Scenic Trail. A day hike is virtually unlimited in length: You'll follow the 107-mile shell-rock path atop the Herbert Hoover Dike and look out on Lake Okeechobee. Bring water, a cap (for the sun), and any supplies.

To reach the park from the junction of Highway 78 and U.S. 27, head southeast on U.S. 27. The park is on the south side of the Caloosahatchee River. 863/983-8101.

Clewiston

PARKS, BEACHES, AND RECREATION AREAS

🐾 Park on the Levee

🐾🐾🐾 (See Lake Okeechobee map on page 458)

For the best park option in town, head to the region's focus: Lake Okeechobee. Canine couch potatoes who climb the 34-foot sides of the Herbert Hoover Dike may be winded once they reach the top—but the view is pretty. From this vantage point, you'll see cane fields stretching toward the Everglades on one side, the broad waters of the lake on the other.

If you just want a spot for a picnic, simply cross over the dike and eat at one of the picnic tables with a lake view. Barbecue grills are available at this city-maintained picnicking area, known by locals as "The Levee," Levee Park, or Boat Ramp Park.

If you're in the mood for a hike, walk as far as you want along the 107-mile-long circular levee. Morning or late afternoon jaunts on the sun-washed berm are best for your leashed dog, who will be as exposed to the hot rays as if she were crossing a bridge. Relatively few people take advantage of the shell-rock path, so you may have a private stroll. Look for wading birds, bald eagles, and possibly deer.

Fill up a doggy water bowl at the restrooms. A boat ramp and a fishing pier round out the amenities.

From U.S. 27, turn north at Francisco Street and go almost to the end. Turn left at Hoover Dike Road. 863/983-1492.

PLACES TO STAY

Best Western of Clewiston: At this pleasant 48-unit downtown motel with hot tubs, a pool, and kitchenettes, the stated policy forbids pets—but management does make exceptions on a case-by-case basis, so it doesn't hurt to ask. Rates range $79–159. When pets are accepted, owners are charged a $10 daily pet fee; a separate $50 deposit is refunded barring doggy indiscretions. 1020 W. Sugarland, Clewiston; 863/983-3400; www.bestwestern.com.

Clewiston Holiday Trav-L-Park: Pets are accepted at these cabins and campsites only in the off-season, meaning April 1 through Halloween. A convenient enough place to sleep if you want to walk with your dog along Lake Okeechobee's dike the next morning, the sunny campground has grassy pull-through sites and fewer amenities than the comparatively luxurious KOA in Okeechobee. City dogs likely will be curious about the cows next door. Cabins range $20–30. Campsites run $15–26. From U.S. 27 west of town, turn north on County Road 720 and continue a short distance. 194 County Road 720, Clewiston; 863/983-7078 or 877/983-7078.

South Bay

PARKS, BEACHES, AND RECREATION AREAS

🐾 John Stretch Park

😺 (See Lake Okeechobee map on page 458)

If your travels happen to take you to the south side of Lake Okeechobee, your furry companion may appreciate tossing some meat on a grill at this county park. Fishing is popular (of course), and you can launch your own boat into the lake. You may even catch some Little League action with your leashed pal. Basketball, a playground, and a multi-purpose field entertain people. Don't expect bicycle paths or nature trails. Fill up a water bowl at the restrooms.

The park is west of town on Lake Okeechobee. Go west on U.S. 27 as if you were going to Clewiston. The park is immediately west of the Miami Canal. 561/966-6600.

Pahokee

This town has seen better times, but the royal palms lining its entrance on U.S. 441 still project a sort of stately aura. Pahokee is a gateway city to Lake Okeechobee.

PARKS, BEACHES, AND RECREATION AREAS

🔟 Everglades Adventures RV & Sailing Resort

😺😺😺 (See Lake Okeechobee map on page 458)

A few dozen die-hard hikers converge on this marina each year for an activity that's close to many a dog's heart—a walk. The hikers begin their annual 107-mile, nine-day journey on the Herbert Hoover Dike right here, but your dog can take a shorter, saner walk. Climb to the top of the 34-foot-high earthen berm to see fields of sugarcane stretching in one direction and, on the other side, wading birds sure to attract the attention of most dogs. An early morning or late afternoon walk is a fine getaway for dogs stressed out by city life. Don't visit the unshaded levee at midday, lest your dog become overheated. And bring water. You can fill up a water bottle at the marina before striking out along the dike.

Alternatively, a dog may join you in a boat rented here (or bring your own) to explore Lake Okeechobee and to catch bass. Pontoon boats rent for $130 a half day, $185 a day. Boston Whalers go for $145 a half day, $195 a day. Fee is lower for the resort's overnight guests, and dogs may camp here or sleep in a cabin (see Places to Stay, below). Fishing from the bank is popular. Live bait, tackle, and ice are sold here. Bring water and caps for your daytime outings. The sun is merciless in summer. Best bet is to arrive in winter.

The marina is on Lake Okeechobee in the heart of town. Head west over the levee from the intersection of U.S. 441 and County Road 715. 561/924-7832.

DIVERSIONS

As you drive past seemingly endless sugarcane fields all over the **east and south sides of Lake Okeechobee** (roughly from Pahokee to Clewiston), you can peer at them and tell your canine passenger, "Robert Redford died somewhere out there."

Actually, his news-director character succumbed to a bullet in the fields—dressed up with palms to look like jungle—in the 1996 film *Up Close and Personal.* Between scenes, Redford tossed around a football amid the sugarcane.

Also noteworthy: A young Joan Collins became food for giant mutant ants out in those sugarcane fields when she portrayed a swampland-selling real-estate scammer in the cheesy 1977 sci-fi cult film, *Empire of the Ants.*

"The ants took over a sugarcane plant and processed human beings for whatever their needs were," says Chuck Elderd, Palm Beach County film commissioner. "Joan Collins and a bunch of other people became ant food."

Now, that's food for thought.

PLACES TO STAY

Everglades Adventures RV & Sailing Resort: Sleep in a fully equipped lakeside cabin with a porch or at a campsite at this marina/campground/fishing enterprise on Lake Okeechobee. It's located on the grounds of the humble former Pahokee Marina (not far from City Hall), but in recent years it began a $4 million renovation under private contract. Amenities now include cabins, airboat excursions, and rentals of boats, canoes, and kayaks. Guided fishing trips are offered, as are youth sailing classes and golf packages to off-site courses. A hurricane in 2004 hit the marina hard, prompting construction of a brand-new marina. A heated pool was expected to be built in 2005. Cabins range $75–160, plus $10 daily per pet. Campsites range $29–37. 190 N. Lake Ave., Pahokee; 561/924-7832; www.evergladesadventuresresort.com.

Canal Point

PARKS, BEACHES, AND RECREATION AREAS

🐾 Canal Point Park

😋 (See Lake Okeechobee map on page 458)

Dominated by a volleyball court, playground, athletic field, basketball court, community center, and baseball diamond, this park caters to humans more than dogs. Still, leashed pooches may cheer on Little Leaguers or partake in

SNIFF!
SNIFF!

one of their favorite pastimes—eating—at a picnic table. Romp in an open field if you have the place to yourselves.

The park is on the east side of U.S. 441, north of Highway 700 and northwest of Triangle Park. 561/966-6600.

12 Cypress Hammock School

(See Lake Okeechobee map on page 458)

For a dog who's crossing her legs to avoid a canine indiscretion in the backseat of the car, the wooded lot of this boarded-up school may do. The lot is at U.S. 441 South and U.S. 98 East.

13 Triangle Park

🐾 (See Lake Okeechobee map on page 458)

Big ficus trees will shade your dog at this county-owned roadside picnic area. If it's lunchtime, you might take advantage of the barbecue grills, then sit down at one of the eight picnic tables (three are shaded). The park is next to two busy roads, so we don't recommend letting your buddy off leash. Fill up your dog's water bowl at the restroom.

The park is at 101 Conners Hwy./U.S. 98, just east of town. 561/966-6600.

Port Mayaca

PARKS, BEACHES, AND RECREATION AREAS

14 Port Mayaca Lock and Dam

🐾🐾🐾 (See Lake Okeechobee map on page 458)

The grassy field dipping lakeward from the earthen berm seems like nirvana to stir-crazy pooches who have spent too many hours cooped up in a car during a road trip. Drive up to the levee (no hiking needed) and park. You can let your dog out to run freely far from any high-speed cars. But leash your pal if he is likely to make a beeline for alligator-infested Lake Okeechobee. Dogs need to stay away from the water's edge and its wee, shelly beach. (A Corps of Engineers staffer said, "Officially, you're supposed to have them on a leash, but as long as you're out there by yourself, ain't nobody going to say anything.")

This is just a simple stopping place with no camping, restrooms, running water, or picnic tables—just grass. During the day, you'll see boats glide along the Okeechobee Waterway. At dusk, a creamy pink lights the sky above the lake and a breeze kisses furry muzzles in winter. Maggie loves it. Don't expect a close-up view of the lock; posted signs declare it off-limits.

The lock is on U.S. 441/U.S. 98 at the Okeechobee Waterway and the intersection with State Road 76. 863/983-8101 or 561/924-2858.

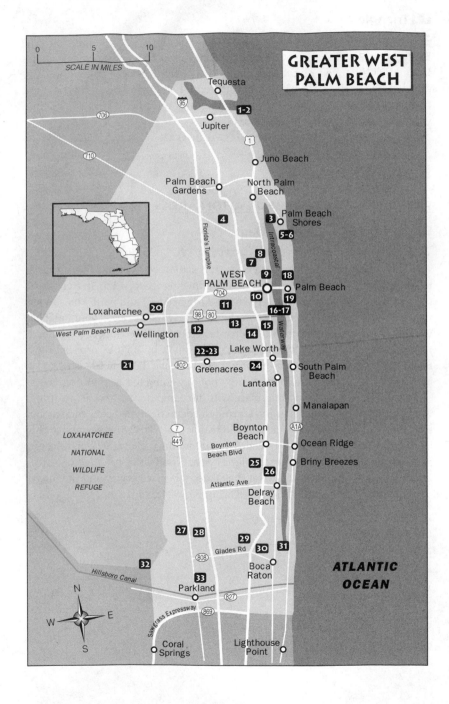

0   5   10
SCALE IN MILES

GREATER WEST
PALM BEACH

Tequesta

95

1-2

Jupiter

706

1

710

Juno Beach

Palm Beach
Gardens

North Palm
Beach

Palm Beach
Shores

4

3

5-6

8

Intracoastal

7

Florida's Turnpike

WEST
PALM BEACH

9

18

10

Palm Beach

704

19

11

16-17

Loxahatchee

20

98 80

13

15

Waterway

West Palm Beach Canal

12

14

Wellington

22-23

Lake Worth

21

802

Greenacres

24

South Palm
Beach

Lantana

Manalapan

7

A1A

Boynton
Beach

441

Boynton
Beach Blvd

Ocean Ridge

25

Briny Breezes

26

Atlantic Ave

Delray
Beach

LOXAHATCHEE

NATIONAL

WILDLIFE

REFUGE

27

28

29

30

31

Glades Rd

32

33

Boca
Raton

Hillsboro Canal

Parkland

827

ATLANTIC
OCEAN

Sawgrass Expressway

869

N

W   E

S

Coral
Springs

Lighthouse
Point

Greater West Palm Beach

True confessions time: Maggie lived in West Palm Beach for five years, and back then we were less-than-perfect dog companions. We did not realize that leaving a dog indoors all day is probably much less wearing on a pooch than tying her up outdoors. So there Maggie sat day after day, tethered outside our front door.

Of course, this freedom allowed Maggie to run after the mail carrier whenever he rounded the corner. Like one of those dogs in the cartoons, she would run headlong until—yank!—she was brought back to reality with a firm tug to the neck.

Some days, Robert would return from work to find that Maggie, always inquisitive, had crawled under the house to investigate something and gotten her chain tangled around the concrete posts that supported our tiny wood-frame home.

PICK OF THE LITTER—GREATER WEST PALM BEACH

BEST PLACE TO GET SANDY PAWS
Beach, Jupiter (page 475)

POOCH-PAMPERING PALACES
Chesterfield Hotel Deluxe, Palm Beach (page 486)
Four Seasons Resort, Palm Beach (page 487)

BEST ISLAND GETAWAY
Peanut Island, Singer Island (page 477)

WHERE KING CAN PLAY KING OF THE HILL
Pooch Pines Dog Park at Okeeheelee Park, West Palm
Beach (page 480)

Imagine Maggie's ardor, then, when she was allowed to break away from the routine and have fun, doggy-style. There's plenty to do in this area. All dogs except pit bulls are allowed in practically any inland, county-run park. They can scamper on the beach in Jupiter, walk down tony Worth Avenue in Palm Beach, watch a game of polo in Boca Raton. They can eat at sidewalk cafés and attend some festivals.

Remember, this is Palm Beach, dah-ling, and many locals just love their dahgs. Part-time resident Zsa Zsa Gabor was kicked off a plane because she insisted that her dog accompany her on the flight. Palm Beach socialite Gertrude Maxwell made the news when she spent $2,000 on surgery for a stray dog found injured on the side of the road after being struck by a hit-and-run driver. When a police officer shot a dog named Lucky, local attorney Barry Silver grabbed media attention by rushing to represent the ailing dog in a legal action.

Our friend John Grogan, a local chronicler of doggy devotion back when he was a columnist for the *Sun-Sentinel,* has attended a dog wedding: two shelties, in Boca Raton. (Wouldn't you know it?) "The groom wore a tail. So did the bride," John told his readers. John also has entertained locals with tails, er, tales of his maniacal, mango-eating, hibiscus-denuding Labrador retriever, Marley. The frenetic Marley, who is known to tear around the house like a banshee for no apparent reason and to shred baseboards in a futile attempt to escape thunderstorms, ironically was named for the late Bob Marley, the ever-mellow reggae star.

The last Palm Beach County character we feel obliged to introduce you to is Shadow, a black Labrador retriever who has learned to scuba dive. Shadow even has her own passport so she can dash to such dive destinations as the Cayman Islands or the Bahamas. (More on Shadow in the section on her hometown, Boynton Beach.)

Jupiter

PARKS, BEACHES, AND RECREATION AREAS

1 Beach

🐾🐾🐾🐾🐾 🐕 (See Greater West Palm Beach map on page 472)

Make like a Marine and hit the beach! As far as dogs are concerned, this town is appropriately named: Jupiter is out of this world. Here, without question, leashes are not required wear. Just be sure your dog is under voice control, and clean up after him. The doo-doo issue threatens to do dogs in, and civic leaders may revoke canine swimming privileges some day if people don't religiously take advantage of the posted Mutt Mitt dispensers. "It's a struggle," a parks staffer once told us. "There's always somebody complaining."

The beach that spans this growing community is dotted with Private Property signs and lifeguards. Your dog must both stay on city-owned sands and stay out of areas overseen by lifeguards. These restrictions can leave a pup scratching his head (for reasons other than fleas). Best bet: Drive down Highway A1A and park near any Mutt Mitt dispenser, which can be found at dune walkover points.

A pooch's right to the pursuit of waves is something the local government admirably wants to hang on to. A near dogfight ensued when the county bought a 300-foot stretch of beach (off-limits to dogs) and lobbied the state to build a pier. Town councilor Donald Daniels flew to the state capital in 1996 to express opposition to the pier, which would, he argued, interfere with surfing, swimming, and other "traditional activities"—including running with dogs on the beach. If you live here, please put in a good word at city hall for dogs. We hope dogs will continue to swim for some time.

From I-95, head east on Indiantown Road/Highway 706 to the ocean and park near dune walkover points—not on posted private land. The dog beaches are north of Marchinski Road and south of Carlin Park and the Jupiter Reef Club, 1600 S. Ocean Drive. 561/746-5134.

2 Burt Reynolds Park

🐾 (See Greater West Palm Beach map on page 472)

Call first to check whether an off-leash area has opened at this shady, pretty picnic spot by the Intracoastal Waterway. Plans called for allowing dogs to run freely on two acres—making it the first Palm Beach County–run dog park in the county's northern reaches.

For some pooches, the place already was notable for being named for a local boy who made good—actor Burt Reynolds, who maintains a nearby ranch. Dogs aren't allowed in the Florida History Center and Museum in this small park. But you can launch a boat together if you bring one.

The park is at 805 North U.S. 1. From I-95, go east on Indiantown Road for five miles to Highway A1A and turn left (north). The park is a mile ahead on the left. 561/966-6600.

PLACES TO STAY

Holiday Inn Express Oceanview: Your pooch can gaze at the ocean from pleasant rooms equipped with a microwave, wet bar, and refrigerator. Try the free continental breakfast bar, then head to Jupiter, the next town north, for its dog-friendly beaches. Rates range $60–260. Add a flat $25 pet fee. 13950 U.S. 1, Juno Beach; 561/622-4366; www.holidayinns.com.

Jupiter Ocean & Racquet Club: A dog may join you in these condo suites, featuring kitchens, washer/dryers, linens, and a screened balcony or court-yard. From a pooch's viewpoint, the best part is walking to the local dog-friendly beaches for a romp in the sand. Other features include three pools, 13 tennis courts, and a playground. Condominium rentals start at $1,900 monthly in season. For weekly rentals, consider Bella Vista on the Park, located within walking distance of the beach. All are offered by broker Rick Clegg, whose realty firm handles vacation rentals and will throw in free use of a hound-hospitable kayak for a week (if you mention this book listing). The pet fee for any vacation rental is a whopping $250. Contact Sherlock Home Finders, 810 Saturn St., Suite 20, Jupiter; 561/747-7368 or 800/597-7368; www.sherlockhomefinders.com.

Wellesley Inn: After a free continental breakfast buffet, take a drive to Jupiter's dog-friendly beach to feed your pet's ocean-hungry soul. Pets under 20 pounds are accepted at this 102-unit lodging. Rates range $75–130, plus $10 pet fee. 34 Fishermans Wharf, Jupiter; 561/575-7201 or 800/444-8888; www.wellesleyonline.com.

North Palm Beach

PARKS, BEACHES, AND RECREATION AREAS

3 John D. MacArthur Beach State Park

☙ (See Greater West Palm Beach map on page 472)

You can have lunch with your pooch at a shady picnic site or you may follow a quarter-mile nature trail together. That's about it. The popular beach and boardwalk are off-limits to four-legged visitors. But if you own a boat or rent one elsewhere, you could motor over to Munyon Island, where your dog may walk around as she pleases on the sometimes-mucky ground—as long as you clean up after her and watch her. A former neighbor of ours, Harry, named his tiny dog after the little-known island because Munyon loved to romp there when the two went fishing. Don't be surprised if you spot nude sunbathers at Munyon Island. Ask the rangers how to get out to the island, or consult a boating map.

Admission is $4 per vehicle. From I-95, go east on Blue Heron Boulevard all the way, crossing the bridge to Singer Island. Then curve left on Highway A1A and continue for two miles. 561/624-6950.

Palm Beach Gardens

Yay! An off-leash area finally has arrived. More good news: A bigger dog park is under consideration for City Park, 5110 117th Ct. North. For current status, call the city: 561/630-1100.

PARKS, BEACHES, AND RECREATION AREAS

4 Dog Run

🐾🐾🐾🏃 (See Greater West Palm Beach map on page 472)

Time to run! This small off-leash area gives a Border collie room to chase a ball relentlessly. Just don't expect the ample romping room enjoyed at regular dog parks. Nonetheless, this spot marks Palm Beach Gardens' first leash-free zone, to the pleasure and relief of retrievers.

The dog run is at 4425 Lilac Street. 561/630-1100.

PLACES TO STAY

Inns of America: Upon your return from your free continental breakfast, your dog has a request—how about a trip to the Dog Run for a rousing game of fetch? Rates range $65–140 at this poolside motel off I-95 (Exit 77). Add $10 nightly per pet. 4123 Northlake Blvd., Palm Beach Gardens; 561/626-4918; www.innsofamerica.com.

Singer Island

PARKS, BEACHES, AND RECREATION AREAS

5 Peanut Island

🐾🐾🐾 👣 (See Greater West Palm Beach map on page 472)

Accessible only by bringing your own boat, this county-run park in the Intracoastal Waterway is a picnic haven, with 60 picnic tables, 40 grills, and six big picnic shelters. It's a fairly cool place even in the summer because a nice breeze is usually blowing through here.

The park is in the Intracoastal Waterway between Riviera Beach and Singer Island. Look for it just west of the inlet dividing Singer Island and the town of Palm Beach. 561/966-6600.

6 Phil Foster Park

😾 (See Greater West Palm Beach map on page 472)

For those of us without boats to reach Peanut Island, this seven-acre park on the Singer Island Causeway will have to suffice. There's not a great deal for dogs to do except picnic and take a walk out to the fishing pier, but Maggie says it beats sitting at home. And, like Peanut Island, it tends to stay relatively cool even in the summer.

The park is at 900 Blue Heron Blvd., on an island in the Intracoastal Waterway east of town. 561/966-6600.

PLACES TO STAY

Best Western SeaSpray Inn: The rooftop restaurant/lounge at this 50-unit beachfront motel has a view of the Atlantic Ocean, but not all of the rooms do. A poolside bar and nightly entertainment are among the perks. Humans have a choice of swimming venues—the pool or the ocean. Furry swimmers, however, need to take a car ride to the public beach in Jupiter (see Parks, Beaches, and Recreation Areas in Jupiter, above). Rates range $70–180. Pet fee is $15 daily. 123 S. Ocean Dr., Palm Beach Shores; 561/844-0233 or 800/330-0233; www.bestwestern.com.

West Palm Beach

Looking for an off-leash area? The county seat is blessed with several, and there is talk of building one in the Villages of the Palm Beaches area. For current status, call 561/835-7042.

Originally set up by railroad magnate Henry Flagler to house the hired help employed by Palm Beach's rich and famous, West Palm Beach today has come into its own. It's also the former home of our Maggie.

PARKS, BEACHES, AND RECREATION AREAS

7 Dog Park at Sullivan Park

😾😾🐕 (See Greater West Palm Beach map on page 472)

Get the ball, Spot! This little space—about half the size of a softball field—provides room for a retriever to stretch his legs, though it is smaller than a typical paw park. Benches and water are provided.

Kids can head to the playground and basketball hoops in the remainder of 1.1-acre Sullivan Park. Leashed dogs can follow its walking trail.

The park is at Windsor Avenue and 30th Street. From Palm Beach Lakes Boulevard, go north on Australian Avenue. Turn right on 25th Street, then left at Windsor Avenue to proceed to the neighborhood park, which has streetside parking. 561/835-7042.

8 Currie Park

 (See Greater West Palm Beach map on page 472)

Plentiful room for running is the key attraction for leashed dogs, but humans tend to prefer the two fishing piers and boat ramp. Maggie lived with us across the street from this city park for years. You could say she liked the place: If we left her at home while we played tennis, we could hear her barks of disapproval from across the street.

One time Robert decided to tell off some ruffians who were hanging out in the park, so he took Maggie along for insurance. Imagine his surprise when, in the middle of his tirade, he looked down and noticed that Maggie had uncharacteristically slipped out of her collar and run away! She was off sniffing some bushes. The toughs just laughed, and the tension was diffused. Now that the park has been upgraded, these types of characters are much less of a problem.

The park is at Flagler Drive and 23rd Street, on the Intracoastal Waterway. 561/835-7042.

9 Flagler Park

(See Greater West Palm Beach map on page 472)

This green spot simply provides relief for dogs who are crossing their legs in the car. Keep your pup leashed. The park is downtown at Flagler Drive and Third Street. Park on the street. 561/835-7042.

10 City Paws at Howard Park

(See Greater West Palm Beach map on page 472)

Mayor Lois Frankel threw in the first bone at the leash-cutting ceremony of this off-leash area, opened in 2003. At least the size of a softball field, the green space is divided into one field for big dogs, and another for small pets. Amenities include water to quench thirsts and a decorative fire hydrant for, er, sniffing. Guardians watch from benches.

The park is at 1302 Parker Avenue. From I-95, go east on Okeechobee Boulevard to Parker Avenue, turn right, and continue to the park. 561/835-7042.

11 Haverhill Park

(See Greater West Palm Beach map on page 472)

Follow the exercise course with your leashed dog, then fill up a doggy water bowl at the restroom to quench her thirst. That's about all you can do in the way of exercise for your pal. This county park offers humans plenty of recreational opportunities, including picnicking, racquetball, tennis, volleyball, and playground fun.

From I-95, go west on Belvedere Road about 3.5 miles. 561/966-6600.

12 Pooch Pines Dog Park at Okeeheelee Park

🐾🐾🐾🐾🐕 (See Greater West Palm Beach map on page 472)

Freedom! Retrievers practically fly at the largest Palm Beach County-run dog park, which sits at the top of a hill. About the size of five softball fields, this five-acre hound haunt is divided into three sections: one area for small dogs (under 30 pounds) and two areas for big dogs. Only one large-dog area is open at any given time, though; that way, grass can grow on the retired well-worn section.

A favorite of local dogs Earnhardt and Roxy, this green expanse offers niceties like a paved dog-wash station, a bike rack, restrooms for people, and three human drinking fountains with attached Fido fountains. Guardians watch their pets from three gazebos and 28 shaded benches that provide relief from the sun.

The paw park is within Okeeheelee Park, which already was the park equivalent of Disney World. It offers just about anything a human would want: baseball, softball, football, volleyball, tennis, a playground, boat slips, boat ramps, waterskiing, a BMX course, and even a 27-hole golf course. Before the dog park's 2004 "leash-cutting" ceremony, about all dogs could do at this massive park was strap on the leash and follow the paved sun-washed bicycle course or the mulched exercise trail. The woodsiest, prettiest part of this massive park—a nature trail—is off-limits to dogs.

There is little shade throughout much of the park, so duck for cover at a shady picnic tables. Early-morning or late-afternoon visits are best.

The dog park, at 7715 Forest Hill Blvd., is closed Wednesday noon–3 P.M. for routine cleaning and mowing. From I-95, go west about six miles on Forest Hill Boulevard to the main Okeeheelee Park entrance at right. Follow the park road to the Pooch Pines sign; turn right, and continue to the hilltop dog park. 561/966-6600.

13 Lake Lytal Park

🐾🐾 (See Greater West Palm Beach map on page 472)

At the woefully small strip of woods next to the racquetball courts, the sounds of a ball smacking a wall startled Maggie from her sniffing ritual and prompted her to turn around. Yet these wee woods of slash pine, cabbage palms, and oak trees remain her favorite part of this county park. She sniffed the ground in earnest, as if to say, "There are animals here!"

We saw an off-leash collie nose-down in a field near the entrance, but dogs are supposed to wear leashes. This park is heavy on people pursuits—baseball, softball, football, basketball, volleyball, tennis, swimming, and picnicking. The park also features a veterans memorial.

Almost entirely devoted to sports, the park ranks low on the aesthetics scale. And it's within sight of the Palm Beach International Airport control tower. For an unusual photo, stop at the armory down the road to pose your dog in front of one of the tanks out front. The armory is on Gun Club Road, just west of Congress Avenue.

From I-95, go west on Southern Boulevard/Highway 80 one mile to Congress Avenue and turn left (south). Turn right on Gun Club Road and continue about a mile. 561/966-6600.

14 Dog Run at Mary Brandon Park

🐾🐾🐾 🐕 (See Greater West Palm Beach map on page 472)

Time to play fetch! About the size of three lots, this off-leash area is smaller than a regular dog park but provides room for retrievers and Border Collies to retrieve balls endlessly or sniff each other. There is talk of possibly dividing this space into separate areas for large and small dogs. Relax at a bench while your dog plays.

The park is at the corner of Maddock Street and Georgia Avenue. From I-95, go east on Forest Hill Boulevard to Georgia Avenue, turn right, and proceed to the park. 561/835-7042.

15 Canine Corner at Dreher Park

🐾🐾🐾🐾 🐕 (See Greater West Palm Beach map on page 472)

Liberty call! Separate areas for big and small dogs are offered at the city's largest off-leash park. An entire walkway of fire hydrants—all decorated really cool—leads up to this beloved place, which features a doggy water fountain and benches for guardians.

Outside the dog park sits the rest of 139-acre Dreher Park, whose plentiful ducks and squirrels perk up the ears of leashed visitors. The long, slightly hilly city park attracts leashed dogs and picnicking families on weekends. Prettier than nearby Lake Lytal Park (see above), this green space offers a special feature—shade. Sit under a banyan tree after following the other joggers and walkers down the semi-shady exercise trail. Or stop at any of the picnic tables scattered around the park. Forget about swimming: No one is allowed in the lake because of alligators.

From I-95, go east on Southern Boulevard to Parker Avenue, turn right (south), and travel less than a mile to Summit Boulevard. Turn right (west) and the park is on the left. 561/835-7042.

🐾🐾 Southern Boulevard Causeway

🐾🐾 (See Greater West Palm Beach map on page 472)

Water dogs may rejoice in the very small spit of whitish-tan sand found at this waterfront strip of green. You may appreciate the great view of the pastel-colored skyline of West Palm Beach, which stretches before you. To the east, you'll see the pink tower of Mar-a-Lago, Donald Trump's mansion. There are no restrooms, picnic facilities, lifeguards, or water fountains. But there also are no signs pertaining to dogs or swimming! This is simply an unfenced causeway park, found next to a busy two-lane road (so watch your dog). Most of the island is a National Audubon Society wildlife sanctuary, and you may have fun trying to name the birds flying by. It's sunny, so visit in the early morning or late afternoon to protect your pooch.

The causeway, on Southern Boulevard, links West Palm Beach and Palm Beach. Park at the few parking spaces provided.

🐾🐾 South Flagler Drive

🐾🐾 (See Greater West Palm Beach map on page 472)

With the pastel-colored skyline of downtown to the north, the resort town of Palm Beach across the sparkling waters to the east, and Spanish-style homes to the west, it's no wonder that the palm-lined bicycle trail of Flagler Drive is a favorite of joggers and in-line skaters. Dogs have a more practical take on the experience: "Hey, it's a walk!"

We saw a lapdog trotting along the seawall instead of the sidewalk here, presumably to get a better view. Later, a party of greyhounds decided to take a break in the middle of the sun-dappled trail.

For relief from the sun, sit under a fig tree at tiny wayside George S. Petty Park at Royal Palm Way. Flagler Drive's "South Way Walk" spans northward from Southern Boulevard for two miles to downtown. You will be funneled onto Washington Road for a short part of your walk. From downtown, you could continue north along Flagler Drive for about two more miles to reach Currie Park (see above), but the homes lining the street there are less impressive. We know, because we used to live in one. Simply start or end the walk wherever you'd like, with the most important goal being to keep your dog from getting too much exercise for her own good.

For the prettiest stretch, park on a side street between Southern Boulevard and Okeechobee Boulevard and begin walking. Pooper-scooper bag stations are posted along Flagler Drive, especially downtown, so don't forget to grab a bag. 561/835-7042.

PLACES TO EAT

Pizza Girls: A fine place for pooches to people-watch, this pizza joint in front of the public library serves New York-style and gourmet pizzas by the slice or by the pie. Take an outdoor table with your pooch for lunch or dinner. 114 S. Clematis St.; 561/833-4004.

Roxy's Comeau Bar and Grille: This local institution is known for its doctored burgers that remind a pooch of meat loaf, but the beer here may be even more famous. The night Roxy's original landmark location shut down about a decade ago, sentimental regulars and not-so-regulars marked the occasion with a raucous party until closing time. Sit at the few green plastic tables with your dog outside the casual, more-sedate new home. 319 Clematis St.; 561/833-1003.

Spoto's Oyster Bar: At this oddly named downtown establishment, your dog may look up at you from your sidewalk table and wonder: How can you possibly eat an oyster shooter? Oysters, clams, and seafood are the mainstays, but pasta and salads are also available at this eatery, which makes a Palm Beach Post dining critic's A-list. 125 Datura St.; 561/835-1828.

PLACES TO STAY

Comfort Inn Palm Beach Lakes: Munch a free continental breakfast at this 162-room airport-area motel, then head to the sidewalk-level dog fountain on Palm Beach's Worth Avenue less than five miles away. Small pets, please. Rates range $60–140. Pet fee is a flat $25, plus $10 daily. 1901 Palm Beach Lakes Blvd., West Palm Beach; 561/689-6100; www.choicehotels.com.

Days Inn Airport North: A putting green is featured at this 234-room motel five miles from the airport. Rates range $50–89, plus a $10 daily pet fee. 2300 45th St., West Palm Beach; 561/689-0450; www.daysinn.com.

Hibiscus House Bed & Breakfast: This former mayor's home has been called one of the state's best bed-and-breakfast inns. Instead of the main house, you'll sleep in a cottage with ceramic tile or hardwood floors—as long as you can assure the host that your quiet, well-behaved dog isn't huge and won't cause a repeat of the dreaded mastiff experience. "It was, like, 200 pounds and slobbered on everything. It was the sweetest thing in the world," said a worried host, recalling the plaintive dog. Yet the pooch was "pretty destructive." Don't give up, though; several dogs have slept here. A daily cocktail party and two-course breakfast are highlights at the 1920s house, which was home to the late Mayor Dunkle. Rates range $85–190. 501 30th St., West Palm Beach; 561/863-5633 or 800/203-4927; www.hibiscushouse.com.

Red Roof Inn: Newshounds can keep up on current events with the free weekday newspaper and many cable TV stations offered at this poolside motel off I-95 (Exit 74). Dogs under 30 pounds are accepted. Rates range $52–95. 2421 Metrocentre Blvd. East, West Palm Beach; 561/697-7710; www.redroof.com.

Residence Inn: Everyone sleeps in a suite with a full kitchen at this pleasant 78-unit hotel, which offers complimentary grocery-shopping service, a weekday evening social hour, and hot breakfasts. A dog might think he was visiting Uncle Flopsy—except he doesn't charge a big pet fee like this place does ($75). Rates range $140–230. 2461 Metrocentre Blvd., West Palm Beach; 561/687-4747; http://marriott.com.

Wellesley Inn: A pet under 20 pounds may join you at this 106-room hotel, where breakfast is free. Rates range $69–160. 1910 Palm Beach Lakes Blvd., West Palm Beach; 561/689-8540; www.wellesleyonline.com.

Palm Beach

The Duchess of Windsor was strolling down Worth Avenue with her three pugs in tow one afternoon when the dogs suddenly started running in different directions and—kerplunk!—there she lay, flat on the concrete, tangled in leashes. Watching from a few feet away was the best known of Palm Beach's society photographers, the man who has been called the world's most prolific photographer of the rich, Bert Morgan. Small, blue-eyed Morgan put down his camera and helped the duchess get up. No pictures were snapped. No words exchanged. She walked half a block, looked back at Morgan, then returned to him to thank him for his discretion. "Bert, I'll never forget that," she said, according to Morgan's son, Richard. "Thank you very much."

Palm Beachers love their dogs, and they probably will admire yours, too. The smell of old money is heavy in the air here, though, so employ at least a modicum of good manners. Also, take note that an ordinance now requires anyone walking a dog on Palm Beach to have along a baggie or other pooper-scooper, and to use it. That's right, you can be ticketed for doing nothing more than walking with your dog if you don't bring along the required equipment.

PARKS, BEACHES, AND RECREATION AREAS

18 North Lake Trail

🐾🐾 🐾👣 (See Greater West Palm Beach map on page 472)

On this island where the hired help of the wealthy shop for their employers at the Publix grocery store, a dog is likely to see manicured yards like he's never seen before. For a taste of the island, walk along this lakefront trail where cars are prohibited. The Lake View Jog, as some call it, is at least six miles round-trip and covers much of the island's lake side. Turn around at a comfortable distance to protect your dog from exhaustion.

The trail stretches northward from the Society of the Four Arts, near the bridge on palm-lined Royal Palm Way, to the Sailfish Club at 1338 North Lake Way. As you walk along the seawall and smidgens of white sand, you'll see the pastel skyline of West Palm Beach across Lake Worth. Bring water, and stop to rest at benches that dot the trail.

From I-95, take Okeechobee Boulevard/Highway 704 east to its end and follow the bridge to Palm Beach. Turn north and, at Royal Poinciana Way, turn right (east) to park at a metered space. Other meters are on Sunset Avenue,

DIVERSIONS

See Palm Beach, dah-ling: Maybe your dog hasn't visited Rodeo Drive, but he can be the first on his block to lap at the street-level doggy water fountain—labeled **"Dog Bar"**—while walking along Worth Avenue, one of the world's most exclusive shopping districts. The ground-level spigot with multicolored tiles is at 318 Worth Ave., in front of Phillips Galleries. (A shih tzu named Sushi found it more novelty than practical thirst-quencher; he held out for his companion, Marie Speed, to spike it with his favorite beverage before he'd lap the water for a photo for *Worth Avenue* magazine.)

Another water fountain for pooches sits across the street outside Trillion, 315 Worth Ave., home of a bichon frise named Gianni B Good.

As you stroll along two-mile-long **Worth Avenue** and its 200-odd stores, mosey through an archway marked Via Mizner on the street's north side. Notice the headstone honoring Johnnie Brown, the pet monkey of the late architect Addison Mizner, who lived on this street. If you have a lapdog, visit Saks Fifth Avenue, 172 Worth Ave., where shoppers often are allowed to carry pooches inside. Worth Avenue is a small-dog kind of street, but we can't say 50-pound Maggie drew bad vibes while she window-shopped. Worth Avenue is south of Royal Poinciana Way and stretches from South Ocean Boulevard/Highway A1A to the Intracoastal Waterway.

See where celebs live as you drive past the oceanfront mansions along Ocean Boulevard/Highway A1A. Jimmy Buffett's nearly 14,000-square-foot spread with tennis court and pool sits at 540 S. Ocean Boulevard. John Lennon and Yoko Ono's former home sits a couple blocks south at 720 S. Ocean Boulevard. Rod Stewart and Rachel Hunter once enjoyed the mansion at 1435 S. Ocean Boulevard. Donald Trump's 118-room Mar-A-Lago mansion is at 1100 S. Ocean Boulevard.

a block north of Royal Poinciana. Head west on foot to the manicured green lawn at Royal Poinciana Way and Bradley Place. From there, cross the lawn heading west and make your way to the seawall. The trail runs north–south along the Intracoastal Waterway. 561/838-5475.

19 Public Beach

(See Greater West Palm Beach map on page 472)

No, dogs aren't allowed on the thin ribbon of sand. But, yes, they can sit at a breezy bench along the seawall or walk along the oceanfront sidewalk to gaze onto the same broad Atlantic Ocean that residents pay a premium to see from their oceanfront windows. You can lengthen this walk by coupling it with a window-shopping stroll down two-mile-long Worth Avenue.

Park at a metered spot on Highway A1A, north of Worth Avenue. 561/838-5400.

PLACES TO EAT

Café Boulud: Just a short walk from Worth Avenue, famed New York chef Daniel Boulud opened this breakfast/lunch/dinner eatery at the historic Brazilian Court hotel. Its tropical courtyard is a lovely place to dine outdoors. Dogs may join their people, whether they're guests of the hotel or not, to watch them sample such seasonally changing dishes as duck leg confit, roasted chicken cobb salad, or a tuna steak tartare with sunny-side-up quail's egg. Star chef Boulud proves popular; reservations are recommended and are taken up to one month ahead. 301 Australian Ave.; 561/655-7740 or 800/552-0335.

PLACES TO STAY

Bradley House Suites Hotel: All rooms come with fully equipped kitchens with granite countertops at this 31-unit apartment hotel located two blocks from the beach. If you don't feel like cooking and have a hankering for a fancy snack, the Publix grocery store next door sells caviar, pâté, champagne, and other fancy wines. There, you might rub elbows with white-uniformed maids from local mansions. Deemed a "superior small lodging" by an independent local panel, the hotel's suites have wood floors and come with niceties such as DVD and CD players. Deluxe studios range $155–295 in season, less other times. 280 Sunset Ave., Palm Beach; 561/832-7050 or 800/822-4116; www. bradleyhousehotel.com.

Brazilian Court: This local landmark has served as an elegant, low-key, secluded retreat for the likes of Cary Grant, Gary Cooper, and Richard Nixon. The fountain courtyard has hosted hundreds of weddings since opening in 1926, and your pet is welcome to dine at the outdoor tables of the on-site Café Boulud. The two-story Spanish condominium hotel offers people-pleasers like twice-daily maid service, concierge services, 24-hour valet parking, and robes and umbrellas in all rooms, as well as a fitness center, library, spa services, and beauty salon. Rates vary seasonally. A studio starts at $500 nightly in winter, $155 nightly in the off-season. 301 Australian Ave., Palm Beach; 561/655-7740 or 800/552-0335 (reservations only).

Chesterfield Hotel Deluxe: Courtyard dining with your pet is just one perk offered at this 53-room landmark, where Margaret Thatcher and Winston Churchill III have stayed. Other amenities include pet beds, chew toys and treats upon arrival, and a VIP bowl of water. A concierge can round up a veterinarian, pet sitter, or dog-walking service. Meals can be made just for your dog. Ask about the Privileged Pooch two-day, one-night package (begun in 2003), which includes an in-room dinner for two including martinis and a special doggie bag, pet bedtime stories, a Bow Wow pillow, a pet-themed movie such as *Beethoven,* and more. The circa-1926 Mediterranean-revival hotel near Worth Avenue features guest rooms with marble bathrooms and a fireside library. In-season rates range $375–1,600 nightly; off-season, $139–600. Add $50 for your small or medium pet. A separate pet deposit is refundable. 363 Cocoanut Row, Palm Beach; 561/659-5800 or 800/243-7871.

Four Seasons Resort: One of the nation's top-echelon hotels, this 210-room luxury beachfront resort makes tails wag. At check-in, your pet's name is included in the guest register. Bellhops are at the ready to walk your buddy, and pet beds are available. The best part: A dog dish is delivered on a silver platter, along with chilled Evian water and a dog bone emblazoned with the pet's name. The pets-only room service fare sounded good enough for us to eat: sirloin burger with steamed rice or chicken breast with noodles. Pooches aren't allowed in the pool area or the two hotel restaurants, but you and your buddy may follow a variety of jogging trails. Daily rates start at $420. Dogs under 15 pounds, please. 2800 S. Ocean Blvd., Palm Beach; 561/582-2800; www.fourseasons.com.

Heart of Palm Beach Hotel: When this 88-room hotel opened within a block of 182 businesses and professional offices in 1961, it lured guests by stating in a brochure: "There's no need to dress for dinner—shorts will do.... Good taste alone dictates the limits of informality among our relaxed and fun-loving guests!" The hotel's slogan became "A Palm Beach address... for less," and some guests would spend the entire winter in the spacious rooms with refrigerators and big picture windows (some have balconies). Your dog may be impressed by the double row of towering royal palm trees that line the picturesque street out front. You'll pass them on a walk to the beach area. Rooms range $110–360. Pets under 25 pounds are preferred; you'll stay in one of the designated pet rooms. 160 Royal Palm Way, Palm Beach; 561/655-5600 or 800/521-4278; www.heartofpalmbeach.com.

Plaza Inn: "I just had Loretta Swit here with her cat," says a staffer at this Art Deco boutique hotel. Your small dog is welcome, too, if you sign a waiver accepting responsibility for any damages. At the 50-room European-style inn, the heated pool and hot tub feature tropical waterfalls. Deluxe rooms offer a choice of Italian, French, traditional four-poster, or rice beds. Hand-blown Murano chandeliers light some rooms. The inn is in the heart of Palm Beach, only a block from the beach. Rates range $135–375. 215 Brazilian Ave., Palm Beach; 561/832-8666 or 800/233-2632; www.plazainnpalmbeach.com.

Manalapan

PLACES TO EAT

Cafe Del Mar: Two ficus trees help shade courtyard diners who sip cappuccino and sample sandwiches, salads, and omelettes in tasteful Plaza Del Mar. Wine and beer are available until the place closes daily at 5 P.M. 244 S. Ocean Blvd.; 561/547-2233.

Ice Cream & Yogurt Club: Heart-smart dogs needn't settle for second best when they can sample the nonfat, sugar-free frozen treats sold at this shop, part of a popular regional chain. Some of the sidewalk tables where you must sit are under an overhang, and others are exposed to the elements. Afterward, go window-shopping in this sophisticated open-air mall (though lapdogs may feel much more at ease than larger mutts). 278 S. Ocean Blvd.; 561/582-0778.

Loxahatchee

PARKS, BEACHES, AND RECREATION AREAS

20 Loxahatchee Groves Park

(See Greater West Palm Beach map on page 472)

If you're making the trek to the west coast of Florida on Highway 80, a break at a picnic table or pavilion here may be in order. You can fill up a water flask for your dog at a restroom while the kids blow off steam at the playground.

From I-95, go west on Southern Boulevard about 11.5 miles to the park, at right. 561/966-6600.

PLACES TO STAY

Lion Country Safari KOA Kampground: Wake up to the roar of lions—a sound that's sure to surprise any pooch. Around the 6:30 A.M. feeding time at the Lion Country Safari wildlife park next door, the great, noble cats tend to express their opinions. It's so unexpected that "a lot of people think it's a recording," a campground staffer says. In the afternoon, monkeys get into the verbal act. Since dogs aren't allowed inside the safari (they're ushered into kennels), sleeping at a tent site or the 200 full-hookup sites here may be the next best thing. A pool, shuffleboard, and volleyball are available. Dogs must not walk through the campground, but instead use a special pet walk. Campsites range $30–60. The KOA is on Southern Boulevard/Highway 80, west of Florida's Turnpike. 2000 Lion Country Safari Rd., Loxahatchee; 561/793-9797 or 800/562-9115; www.koakampgrounds.com.

Sunsport Gardens Nudist Retreat: Dogs already wear nothing but their birthday suits (and sometimes those darned leashes), so their two-legged companions are the ones who will need an open mind if they decide to stay in a cabin or at a campsite here. On these 40 woodsy acres, tenters and self-sufficient RVs may set up primitive campsites for $18 nightly. RVers who require hookups head to assigned sites for $33. Pooches and their pals may sleep in a cabin for $75 or a rental trailer for $40–60. Grounds fees of $25 daily are charged for use of facilities. Everyone is expected to be in their altogether—even while swimming, playing volleyball, pitching horseshoes, following a nature trail, playing tennis, accompanying dogs in the fenced-in dog area, or resting in the hot tub or sauna. Reservations are strongly recommended, particularly in winter. 14125 North Rd., Loxahatchee; 561/793-0423 or 800/551-7217; www.sunsportgarden.com.

Wellington

PARKS, BEACHES, AND RECREATION AREAS

2.1 The Dog Park at Greenbriar Park

🐾🐾🐾🐾 🐕 (See Greater West Palm Beach map on page 472)

This three-acre slice of hound heaven serves as a community gathering spot for the canine set. Here on Independence Day, pups are known to show up festooned in red-white-and-blue clothing or ribbons for a patriotic pooch parade. Most days, retrievers joyously chase each other or romp after balls, then slurp generous gulps from the water bowls. Small dogs play in a separate area. Guardians watch from benches and tables.

Kids can play at the adjacent tot lot. The dog park is within Greenbriar Park, which also features four sand volleyball courts and two shuffleboard courts.

Find the park at 2975 Greenbriar Boulevard. From State Road 7, go west 3.2 miles on Forest Hill Boulevard and turn right onto Wellington Trace. Travel nearly one mile to Greenbriar Boulevard, turn right, and proceed to the park, which is past New Horizons Elementary School. 561/791-4005.

Greenacres

PARKS, BEACHES, AND RECREATION AREAS

2.2 Community Park

🐾 (See Greater West Palm Beach map on page 472)

This park has been used for a K-9 Frisbee tournament, and a city staffer told us there is lots of green space where it's possible to "run and romp and throw the Frisbee" (though leashes are the law). The park is at 2905 Jog Rd., one block north of 10th Avenue. Leashed dogs also are permitted at these city parks: Veterans Park, 6250 Purdy Ln.; Friendship Park, 3140 Martin Ave.; Burrowing Owl Park, 2665 Sherwood Forest Blvd.; and Rambo Park, 3626 S. 57th Avenue. 561/642-2181.

23 Ira van Bolluck Park

🐾 (See Greater West Palm Beach map on page 472)

We saw a bicyclist taking a break with his leashed chow chow at his side here, but this small park near the former city hall amounts to little more than two ball fields. If a ball game is in progress when you arrive, your leashed pup may howl his encouragement to the amateurs. A small pavilion and restrooms separate the two fields.

From I-95, go west on 10th Avenue North for about 3.5 miles, then turn left at Perry Avenue. The park is at left. 561/642-2181.

Lake Worth

Local dog Dixie, rescued from life (and possibly death) on a bad section of Dixie Highway, is an urban girl. So she loves a brisk walk from her house to make a pit stop at Bryant Park, located at Lakeview and Golf avenues on the Intracoastal Waterway.

"I'm not so sure she really prefers the park as much as she does the walk to the park, past an assortment of houses in our gentrifying neighborhood, with dogs yapping out their windows as Dixie trots by," yet the park is "always cooler and breezy, and all that grassy area is full of smells, including picnic aromas," reports her human companion, Lisa Ocker. Plus, "there are a million squirrels in the cabbage palms and live oaks at the park, although Dixie's not terribly impressed with them anymore. Also, there are lots of dogs here, including some that go leashless—although I think that's not allowed—and chase around in a big expanse of open space."

PARKS, BEACHES, AND RECREATION AREAS

24 John Prince Park

🐾🐾🐾 (See Greater West Palm Beach map on page 472)

At 726 acres, this favorite local destination is so big that it has at least three entrances. In the northeastern portion of the county park (enter at 2520 N. Lake Worth Rd.), your dog will be tempted to chase a few ducks at mirror-smooth Lake Osborne. There's one golden retriever, also named Maggie, who loves to follow the shady walking trail along the lake. Banyan trees and Australian pines shade scattered picnic tables near the tennis courts and two volleyball nets. Families, some including dogs, hang out at picnic tables here on weekends.

The more popular portion of the park is entered from Congress Avenue, south of Lake Worth Road. There, pretty tree-shaded scenery and water views make an exercise path a highlight for dogs and joggers. Folks tend to make a day out of relaxing at picnic tables and pavilions on weekends. Golfers will find a driving range; other visitors prefer freshwater fishing, boating, and waterskiing (just bring the gear). Kids will appreciate the playground.

If you're having such a good time that you don't want to leave, you can camp in a tent or RV with a well-mannered, leashed dog. Some water-view sites are shady, while inland sites tend to have little or no brush separating neighbors. Campfires are permitted in three fire pit areas at the 265-site campground. Sites cost $16.50 to $20. For camping reservations, call 561/582-7992.

The main entrance is on the east side of Congress Avenue, south of Lake Worth Road. 561/966-6600.

PLACES TO EAT

Kaminsky's Cafe: Lasagna, fettuccine Alfredo, individual-sized pizzas, and other eats are served at this lunch/dinner destination, along with a wide range of coffees. Sit at the outdoor tables. 517 Lake Ave.; 561/585-5911.

PLACES TO STAY

John Prince Park: See Parks, Beaches, and Recreation Areas, above, for camping information.

Lago Motor Inn: The guest laundry room makes it possible for doggies to wash their bandannas before heading out for dinner at pooch-friendly eateries. Rates start at $60. Add $10 daily for the dog. 714 S. Dixie Highway, Lake Worth; 561/585-5246.

Martinique Motor Lodge: Small pets may sleep in certain rooms at this 26-unit poolside motel. Rates start at $55, plus $10 per pet. 801 S. Dixie Highway, Lake Worth; 561/585-2502.

Motel 6: A guest laundry room is at your disposal, so you can wash your dog's favorite blanket at this 154-room poolside motel off I-95 (Exit 61), just south of Lake Worth. Rates range $46–62. 1310 W. Lantana Rd., Lantana; 561/585-5833; www.motel6.com.

The Parador of the Palm Beaches: Two black Labrador retrievers named Jessie and Razor serve as official greeters at Ed Menzer's bed-and-breakfast establishment, which offers a collection of several buildings built between 1930 and 1953. The best pooch-permissible option in Lake Worth, these tropically decorated suites measure 250 to 480 square feet, and each has cable TV, individual air conditioners, and a refrigerator. A jungly fern garden and courtyard offer places to sit and contemplate. Guests may borrow bicycles, beach chairs, and snorkeling equipment. The beach (where dogs are forbidden) is a few minutes' drive away. At reservation time, you may be asked about your pets' breeds; if the dogs sound too scary, you may not be permitted to stay. Rates range $75–150. 1000 S. Federal Highway, Lake Worth; 561/876-6000; www.theparadorinn.com.

Boynton Beach

This is the hometown of Shadow the scuba dog, a rescued Labrador retriever mix who has made dozens of television appearances and gone on at least 125 magazine shoots, thanks to her owner and trainer, Dwane Folsom.

"She has made 171 dives to date," Folsom told us a few years back. "She's even recognized by the Jacques Cousteau Society."

How did the rescued pound dog get started in diving? Whenever Folsom dove, his Labrador retriever mix tried to follow him into the water. That gave him the idea of fashioning dog-friendly scuba gear. He suited her up and hooked her up to his air regulator. At first, he used hand signals to give her commands. Later, he spoke through an intercom.

Alas, Shadow is not a certified diver. "Taking the written test would be awful hard for her," Folsom explains. And to think that Ogden Nash said, "A dog's best friend is his illiteracy." Guess he hadn't met Shadow.

Given the "pawcity" of parks where dogs can romp in Boynton Beach, we can't blame Shadow for running off to the Cayman Islands and the Bahamas on a regular basis.

PARKS, BEACHES, AND RECREATION AREAS

25 Caloosa Park

🐾🐾 (See Greater West Palm Beach map on page 472)

The open fields of this 64-acre county park beckon dogs who pine to snag Frisbees, while the picnic pavilion opening onto a little lake is just the right speed for Grandpa King. Follow a 1.25-mile exercise trail with your leashed dog. Or, on the next visit, vary your routine by hitting the bicycle paths.

This park crams in a lot of people-pleasing activities: racquetball, basketball, tennis, volleyball, playground frolicking, baseball or softball, and freshwater fishing. You can fill the doggy water bowl at the restrooms.

The park is at 1300 SW 35th Avenue. From I-95, go west on Woolbright Road, then turn left (south) on Congress Avenue. The park is 1.5 miles ahead on the left. 561/966-6600.

PLACES TO EAT

Ice Cream & Yogurt Club: Locals consider this chain's nonfat, sugar-free treats the best in the region. Sit at an outside plastic table with your pooch. 220 N. Congress Ave.; 561/737-1597.

Delray Beach

PARKS, BEACHES, AND RECREATION AREAS

26 Lake Ida Park

🐾🐾🐾🐾🐕 (See Greater West Palm Beach map on page 472)

"Boat ramps: 2. Boat/trailer parking spaces: 42. Children's play area: 1. Dog park: 1." So reads a county parks description of this park. It's tossed in matter-of-factly, but the dog park is a big deal: For years, it served as the first and only place where dogs officially were allowed to run off leash in southern Palm Beach County.

These 2.5 acres feature two separate off-leash areas, one for large dogs and one for small pooches, like a puffball named Sophie, who loves the feel of the grass in her paws, reports her chauffeur/companion, Marie Speed. Big and small pets share a dog-washing area, and eight shaded seating areas keep humans cool. Be sure to use the dispensers and receptacle provided for the infamous poop.

Delray Beach philanthropist and dog-lover George D. Cornell chipped in a lot of the money for this park. Other supporters include Imperial Point Animal Hospital of Delray Beach, the Fins, Furs 'n' Feathers pet supply store in Boca Raton, and Gold Coast Critter Sitter Inc./Daily Dogs in Boca Raton.

Elsewhere in this park overlooking Lake Ida, dogs can be seen lounging around with their families during laid-back meals at the concrete picnic tables.

From I-95, go east on Atlantic Avenue, then turn left (north) on Swinton Avenue. Turn left (west) at Ninth Street, then veer left at Lakeshore Drive and continue to the park. 561/964-4111 or 561/966-6664.

PLACES TO EAT

Blue Anchor British Pub: If your English bulldog recognizes this lunch/dinner/bar hangout as a British pub, there's a reason—its exterior was transported here from Chancery Lane in England. A young Winston Churchill was said to have passed through these doors (as did two of Jack the Ripper's victims on their last nights alive). But don't you step inside, puppy. Unlike in the U.K., local rules require that four-legged patrons stay outside to eat steak-and-stilton pie, Cornish pasties, shepherd's pie, sandwiches, and salads at the umbrella-covered tables facing a side street. For that reason, dog-toting customers unfortunately lose out on the pub experience indoors. 804 E. Atlantic Ave.; 561/272-7272.

Boston's on the Beach: Tanned patrons saunter over from the beach across the street to join out-of-towners and locals at this area institution, where the music, the beer, and the opportunity to sit outdoors arguably rate higher than the cuisine. Tie your dog to the sidewalk-side railing, then take a patio table immediately on the other side to try mahimahi, chicken, appetizers, and other eats. 40 S. Ocean Blvd.; 561/278-3364.

Boheme Bistro: Tasteful music fills the small, palm-shaded courtyard on weekends, providing a pleasant respite from the beach-area hubbub on Atlantic Avenue. Tie your dog to an umbrella-covered table, walk inside to order, then return to your hungry pooch with sandwiches or a breakfast jolt of espresso. At dinner, individual-sized pizzas, filet mignon, pasta, salads, and 14 draft beers are among the consumables. Dogs take note: A block east is Purrfecto, a feline-fancier store selling T-shirts that state, "In Egypt, cats are revered as gods." 1118 E. Atlantic Ave.; 561/278-4899.

Ciao Sidewalk Cafe: Dogs practically are fixtures at the black mesh tables of this tasteful courtyard café, which provides relief from the beach-area throng. "We give a complimentary bowl of water," says an enthusiastic staffer. Daily specials may include blackened chicken sandwiches, veggie melts, or quiche, while the regular lineup includes pizza, salads, and sandwiches. Baked goods are made here daily. 1208 E. Atlantic Ave.; 561/278-4520.

Dakotah 624: Ostrich steak makes the menu at this expensive New American–style bistro, where dogs may plop down beneath the linen-covered outdoor tables. An extensive wine list sets this place apart. 270 E. Atlantic Ave.; 561/274-6244.

Doc's All-American: Some restaurants try to look like throwbacks to the 1950s, but Doc's, in business since 1951, is the genuine article. The landmark at busy Atlantic Avenue has been spruced up with a small wall and landscaping since the avenue's renaissance, but your pup is still welcome to watch you eat hot dogs, ice cream, burgers, and other fare. Just take a table in a corner of the outdoor eating area (out of respect for potentially leery diners). 10 N. Swinton Ave.; 561/278-3627.

Elwood's Dixie Barbecue: At this old gas station that's been converted into a funky barbecue joint, you can sit with your dog where the gas pumps used to be and watch the world go by from your seat on the patio. The barbecue sandwiches are worth trying, but the attraction is the experience. "What I like about it is you can sit there and have a couple of beers with your dog," says Neil Santaniello, who heads to this bar and grill with his wife, Tari, and their nine-pound Maltese, Zu-Zu. Small dogs are preferred, but 50-pound Maggie has nibbled scraps here and advises that the sidewalk tables with white lawn chairs provide bigger dogs more turning-around room than patio booths. Pooches may be turned away altogether if the eatery is too busy. 301 E. Atlantic Ave.; 561/272-7427.

Ice Cream & Yogurt Club: Dieting doggies will appreciate a few licks of one of the region's best nonfat, sugar-free frozen treats. Sit at one of two outdoor tables after window-shopping down the street. 1229 E. Atlantic Ave.; 561/265-1036.

Jimmy's Stone Crabs: With the likes of lobster and stone crabs on the menu, this place isn't for budgeting Bowsers. Most pooch-permissible tables are small cocktail tables (we saw one regular-sized table). It's best to be flexible; if the eatery can't accommodate you, try others a short walk away. 411 E. Atlantic Ave.; 561/278-0036.

Rocky's Italian Bistro: Every time a patron opens the glass front door, your dog will enjoy an aromatic snoutful of Italian scents: tortellini, roasted peppers and mushrooms, veal chops, and chicken dishes. Sit at one of the few tables overlooking very busy Federal Highway. 20 S. Federal Highway; 561/276-9703.

PLACES TO STAY

Colony Hotel & Cabana Club: This 69-room historic hotel now is open year-round, not just in winter. Canine guests will appreciate getting some exercise during the half-mile walk to the beach, punctuated by stops to window-shop or sit at a sidewalk café. Rates generally range $179–250. In summer, prices dip to $105–155. Add a $20 daily pet fee. 525 E. Atlantic Ave., Delray Beach; 561/276-4123.

Residence Inn: The beach is within easy walking distance of this 95-unit, 11-story tower, whose amenities include a pool, heated spa, fitness center, and grocery shopping services. While your pal can't romp on the beach, he can join you at nearby pet-permissible eatery Boston's on the Beach. Rates range $109–399. Pet fee is a flat $75. 1111 E. Atlantic Ave., Delray Beach; 561/276-7441 or 800/331-3131; http://marriott.com.

Boca Raton

Animals are taboo at beaches and all city-run parks except for one: the city's first permanent dog park. It's a laudable Labrador retriever–style leap in the right direction, a grand opening worthy of howls. The city's near-deified original developer, Addison Mizner, would approve. The 300-pound bachelor with a Klondike vocabulary was responsible for the pink color scheme that dominates much of Boca Raton today. He was also known to walk around in public with a pet monkey or two. If Mizner were alive today, he would find one city-run park where his monkeys would be welcome.

PARKS, BEACHES, AND RECREATION AREAS

27 Pinewood Park

(See Greater West Palm Beach map on page 472)

This is just a make-do spot for any Spot itching to stretch his legs in west Boca. The 22 acres offer a chance to walk on leashes. Forget the ball fields; dogs aren't even allowed to root for the home team here. The regional headquarters

DIVERSIONS

Polo, anyone? For polo's richest purse, head to the **Royal Palm Polo Club,** home of the $100,000 International Gold Cup Tournament, held in March. The club is a fun place to tailgate—folks break out their portable tables and are judged on decorations for the fundraising events. Bring the kids, dog, cat, bird (really). Just stick to tailgating with your tail-wagger: Dogs aren't allowed in the stadium itself, says a staffer. This diversion is best left to laid-back, well-mannered dogs. You'll find the grounds at 6300 Clint Moore Rd., Boca Raton. For tournament dates, call 561/994-1876.

of the sheriff's office is here, so no letting dogs off leash! And don't get too close to the lake—you never know about gators.

The park is at 18069 U.S. 441. 561/964-4420.

28 American Homes Park

(See Greater West Palm Beach map on page 472)

Follow the exercise course with your leashed pooch at this 16-acre neighborhood park, named for the residential development here. Bring water. There are no restrooms—or anything else, for that matter, except a playground.

From I-95, go west on Yamato Road, past Florida's Turnpike and Lyons Road. The park is on the left. 561/966-6600.

29 Dog Park

(See Greater West Palm Beach map on page 472)

Your dog will think you're a hero for bringing him to this new and badly needed off-leash park. Dogs chase each other and pursue balls at this four-acre park featuring an agility course, comfort stations with showers, a separate area for small dogs (under 30 pounds), and ground-level water fountains to quench the thirsts of canines. Newly planted trees lend some shade. Human companions watch the action from benches and a pavilion.

Opened in 2005, the city's first permanent dog park didn't yet have a name. Officials knew they wanted to name it in honor of a retired city police or fire dog. But, by press time, they hadn't decided which loyal worker to honor—Juke, Rambo, Christmas Holly the fire dog, or a former nominee for police officer of the year named Branko.

One of the park's four acres is set aside for events such as dog fairs. An agility section fills its own separate area. So, the running room isn't quite as big as you might expect from a four-acre park—not that dogs are complaining, of course.

The park is at 751 Banyan Trail, just east of Military Trail. Find it between Spanish River Boulevard and Palmetto Park Road. 561/393-7810.

30 Florida Atlantic University

🐾🐾 (See Greater West Palm Beach map on page 472)

Ample room to run can be found in the sunny, broad, slightly uneven grassy areas on the southeastern end of these former World War II blimp fields, now home to a state university. Tiny living versions of the school mascot—the burrowing owl—sometimes sit on the ground next to their burrowed holes. Watch your step so you won't step on the homes of these protected critters, and don't let your dog bother them.

A few cabbage palms provide a little shade in the 20 or so acres of open fields. A short visit is best to protect your dog from the heat. Voice-controlled pooches should be able to drop the leash, although technically they are supposed to stay tethered. Bring water and be aware of sandburs; Maggie sat down and tried to eat a prickly spur stuck between her paws. Other fields are on the north side of campus.

From I-95, go east on Glades Road; the campus is on the left. The easiest way to reach the southeastern fields is to turn left from Glades Road into the second FAU entrance, located east of the main entrance. 561/297-3000 or 561/297-3500.

31 Highway A1A Bike Trail

🐾🐾 (See Greater West Palm Beach map on page 472)

Just because dogs aren't allowed to visit the beach or set paw inside popular Spanish River Park doesn't mean a pooch has to leave the neighborhood with his tail tucked between his legs. Instead, follow the bike trail that spans two-lane Highway A1A. Some spots along the path are shaded by red-barked gumbo-limbo trees, towering Australian pines, or round-leafed sea grapes. But much of the trail is pretty doggone sunny. So head here with your leashed pal in early morning or late afternoon and bring water.

Park on Spanish River Boulevard, just west of Highway A1A, and head either north or south on foot.

32 South County Regional Park

🐾🐾 (See Greater West Palm Beach map on page 472)

For all the pups who have prayed to the great dog gods for relief from the No Dogs signs posted at city parks, a visit to this expanse of open space is akin to having Milk Bones rain from the skies. This 836-acre, hound-hospitable park run by Palm Beach County is bigger than all Boca Raton city parks combined.

Walk your leashed dog along an exercise course on one visit, then try a bicycle path the next time. A short nature trail is available, too. This mammoth

DIVERSIONS

Pray to the patron saint of dogs: Bruiser, a local American bulldog, has been known to scare Great Danes on sight and accidentally broke a glass door pane upon greeting a returning loved one. But the big lug has good intentions, and he does like to visit the outdoor statue of **St. Francis of Assisi.** The saint, known for his affinity for animals, is posed with that great canine ancestor, the wolf. Bruiser, for one, is repentant after his mishaps—like when the broken pane of glass cut owner John Moran's fiancée. "He wanted to lick the wound," says Moran. "He was so upset." Kindly clean up after your dog if he leaves an offering to the saint. The statue is at St. Joan of Arc Catholic Church, 370 SW Third St., Boca Raton.

Want to bless your Bess? Horses and pigs, as well as dogs and cats, have tromped into the patio of **St. Gregory's Episcopal Church** in Boca Raton for the annual blessing of the animals, held in honor of that holy dog lover, St. Francis. The blessing takes place on the Sunday closest to the feast day of St. Francis, October 4, at 100 NE Mizner Blvd., Boca Raton; 561/395-8285.

Naughty dogs around the region are certain to find a church nearby that offers a similar annual blessing, such as St. Joseph Episcopal Church, 3300A S. Seacrest Blvd., Boynton Beach, 561/732-3060; and St. Andrew's Episcopal Church, 100 N. Palmway, Lake Worth; 561/582-6609. Pets and people gather annually by the St. Francis statue at St. Patrick Catholic Church, 13591 Prosperity Farms Rd., Palm Beach Gardens; 561/626-8626.

park offers something for most humans—a playground, picnic pavilions, picnic tables, and courts or fields for basketball, racquetball, tennis, baseball, football, and soccer. Unfortunately, dogs are forbidden at ball fields, even to cheer on a team.

From U.S. 441, head west on Yamato Road to the entrance at road's end. Another entrance is off Cane Boulevard, west of Boca Raton. 561/966-6600.

🐾 Veterans Park

🐾 (See Greater West Palm Beach map on page 472)

A veterans memorial helps set this county park apart, but the place is better known for its two lighted basketball courts, four lighted tennis courts, and an athletic field that will tempt leashed dogs to run (though dogs are forbidden there). While it's nothing to write Grandma Queenie about, you can share a lunch in the picnic area and fill up a doggy bowl at the restrooms.

The park is at 9400 W. Palmetto Park Rd., west of Lyons Road. 561/482-0269 or 561/966-6600.

PLACES TO EAT

Mark's at the Park: This bistro catering to an upscale crowd is one of celebrated chef Mark Militello's four South Florida eateries. Salads, pasta, and gourmet pizzas are served, as well as specialties such as peppercorn-crusted and seared rare yellowfin tuna with celeriac mash or Russet potato goat cheese tartlet with bitter greens and spiced walnuts. Declare your dining companion at reservation time or while approaching a host at lunch or dinner; you may be declined if it's busy. Lucky dogs will join companions at the outer-perimeter tables of the pleasant patio. Realistically, lap dogs fit in best. 344 Plaza Real, in Mizner Park; 561/395-0770.

Starbucks Coffee: Retrieve java, tea, juice, water, brownies, or other treats, then return to your adoring dog tied to an outdoor table. 7777 Glades Rd.; 561/470-4882. Find another location at 9961 Glades Rd.; 561/883-8984.

PLACES TO STAY

Doubletree Guest Suites: Two chocolate chip cookies are handed to guests as they check into this pleasant 180-suite hotel. Maggie hopes someday they'll fork over Milk Bones, too. Suites feature wet bars, refrigerators, and microwaves, and you get a continental breakfast. Rates run $90–199. The nonrefundable pet fee is $50–75, plus $10 nightly per pet. 701 NW 53rd St., Boca Raton; 561/997-9500.

Residence Inn: A pup might think he's visiting a long-lost relative upon crossing the thresholds of these 120 apartment-style suites—except relatives, as a rule, don't charge a big pet fee (the Residence Inn's is $75–100). These one-bedroom suites and studios come equipped with kitchens, fireplaces, cable TV, and other trappings of home. Rates range $94–209. 525 NW 77th St., Boca Raton; 561/994-3222; http://marriott.com.

Towneplace Suites by Marriott: The townhouse exterior and the barbecue grill by the pool aim to make guests feel at home. So do the full kitchens and the lending library, which lends out niceties like feather pillows, cordless phones, allergen-protective bedding, and board games. A fitness facility is available at the 91-unit lodging set in an office-park neighborhood. Rates range $80–230. Pet fee is a flat $75. 5110 NW 8th Ave., Boca Raton; 561/994-7232; www.towneplacebocaraton.com.

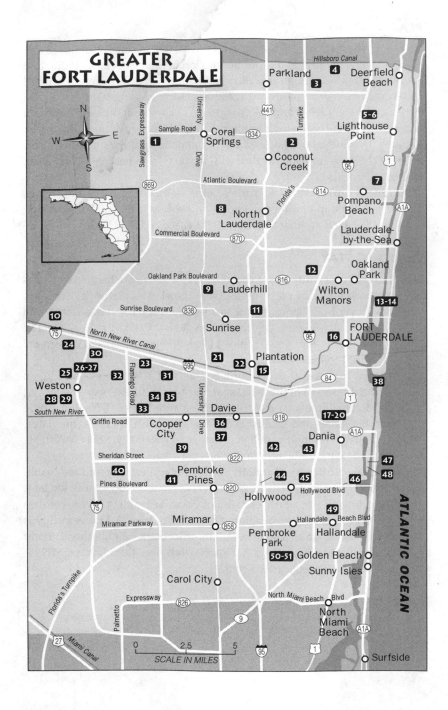

GREATER FORT LAUDERDALE

N W E S

Hillsboro Canal

Parkland **4** Deerfield Beach **3**

5-6 Lighthouse Point

Sawgrass Expressway

University Drive

Sample Road **1** Coral Springs 834 441

Turnpike

2 Coconut Creek

95 U.S. 1

A1A

869

Atlantic Boulevard

814 **7** Pompano Beach

8 North Lauderdale

Commercial Boulevard 870

Lauderdale-by-the-Sea

Oakland Park Boulevard

12 Oakland Park

816 **9** Lauderhill Wilton Manors **13-14**

Sunrise Boulevard 838 **11**

10 Sunrise

75 95 **16** FORT LAUDERDALE

North New River Canal

24

30 **23** 595 **21** **22** Plantation **15**

25 **26-27** **32** **31** 84 **38**

Weston **28 29** **34 35**

South New River **33**

Griffin Road Davie 818

Cooper City **36** **37** **17-20**

Dania A1A

39 Dania **43** **42**

Sheridan Street 822 **47**

40 Pembroke **41** Pines 820 **44** **45** **46** **48**

Pines Boulevard Hollywood Hollywood Blvd

75 **49**

Miramar Parkway Miramar 858 Hallandale Beach Blvd

Pembroke Park Hallandale

50-51 Golden Beach

Sunny Isles

Carol City

Florida's Turnpike

Expressway 826

Palmetto

North Miami Beach Blvd

9 North Miami Beach A1A

27 Miami Canal

0 2.5 5 95 1 Surfside

SCALE IN MILES

ATLANTIC OCEAN

CHAPTER 18

Greater Fort Lauderdale

Years ago, it used to be "Where the Boys Are." But a stretch of Fort Lauderdale's beachfront has become "Where the Dogs Are," thanks to a dog named Snorkel.

Pooches couldn't set paw on any grain of Fort Lauderdale sand until the water-loving Snorkel came around. The golden retriever/German shepherd loved to plunge into the New River as well as the pool. So in 1985 his owner, city commissioner Jim Naugle, tried to persuade fellow commissioners to let dogs run on the beach. The response was familiar: No!

"The line back then was I couldn't collar three votes and I had to 'flea' the issue," recalls Naugle, now mayor. He doggedly persisted, though, and a decade later scratched out a victory.

Sadly, 10 days before the new rules took effect, Snorkel died. "It was awful," Naugle says. When he signed the 1995 law, he jotted these words along with his signature: "For Snorkel."

PICK OF THE LITTER—FORT LAUDERDALE

BEST BEACH
Dog Beach, Fort Lauderdale (page 513)

BEST DOG PARKS
Dr. Paul's Pet Care Center Dog Park, Coral Springs
(page 503)
Bark Park at Snyder Park, Fort Lauderdale (page 517)

WHERE TO SNIFF OUT OLD FLORIDA
Easterlin Park, Oakland Park (page 511)
Hugh Taylor Birch State Park, Fort Lauderdale (page 513)

BEST PLACE TO DIG INTO NATIVE HISTORY
Peace Mound Park, Weston (page 525)

Today, Dog Beach in Fort Lauderdale, open to pooches three nights a week, is a highlight of the pooch-friendly destinations in this county. In all, more than eight square miles of parks are open to whiskered wanderers. Our best friends can climb an observation tower, sniff around for french fries under sandlot bleachers, or follow a boardwalk through marshland.

Pooches can also pad through the woods or shrink back at the sight of galloping horses. And there are enough jogging trails to follow that it would take a determined dalmatian weeks to explore them all. Most hound-hospitable parks are tended by the Broward County park system, which has won national awards from agencies such as the U.S. Department of the Interior.

All is not perfect, though. Dogs must be leashed in almost every park in Greater Fort Lauderdale.

Thankfully, several off-leash parks have emerged in recent years: Doctor Paul's Pet Care Center Dog Park in Coral Springs, Bark Park in Fort Lauderdale, Hollywood's Poinciana Park, and South Broward's Markham Park among them. Since more than 700,000 pets have been registered in Broward County since 1994, we won't be surprised to see more "paw parks" opening.

Coral Springs

Dogs may be glad to know that in this family-oriented suburb, about eight miles of bike paths rim major roads such as Atlantic Boulevard, west of Coral Drive. Walking along the sun-splashed paths is nothing to howl about. But Doctor Paul's park is.

PARKS, BEACHES, AND RECREATION AREAS

1 Doctor Paul's Pet Care Center Dog Park

🐾🐾🐾🐾🐕 (See Greater Fort Lauderdale map on page 500)

Everyone knew that this two-acre grassy park would go to the dogs. South Florida's granddaddy off-leash area features a sun-washed oval walking trail, an obstacle course, fenced land for leash-free romping, and a nice extra touch: lights that shine until 9:30 P.M. so pets can play after dark.

Dogs can climb makeshift wooden ramps and walk through giant concrete tubes. A few hurdles have changeable heights. As pets play, their chauffeurs watch from a gazebo, benches, or two shady canopies. Some sip sodas available for purchase here or drink from a water fountain. Plentiful water bowls serve canines.

Trees are filling out and more trees have been planted since the park's 1997 opening. Inspired by seeing dogs running around Boston Commons during a business trip, local veterinarian Steven Paul gathered 500 signatures to petition Coral Springs' mayor to open a dog park here. The city agreed to set aside land if Paul raised money for a fence.

Paul howled his pitch online: "Want a park where you and your dog can run and play together? So do we and a lot of other folks in Coral Springs!" Paul chipped in $1,000. His clients, area vets, and animal lovers gave $4,000. InnoPet Brands Corp. gave $5,500. Nearly four years after he broached the idea, the veterinarian erected several dog statues and witnessed the park's opening.

There is talk of expanding the park to 3.5 acres by 2007, perhaps to accommodate obedience training.

The park is within Sawgrass Regional Park, which is bounded by the Sawgrass Expressway, Royal Palm Boulevard, Sample Road, and Northwest 123rd Avenue. From the Sawgrass Expressway, exit at Sample Road. Head east, then almost immediately turn right (south) on Sportsplex Drive to enter the park. Follow the curves and the dog park is at left. 954/344-1840.

PLACES TO STAY

Coral Springs Marriott Hotel, Golf Club, and Convention Center: A tropical seven-story atrium lobby sets the tone of this 224-unit hotel located on the PGA Tour's Tournament Players Club on Heron Bay golf course. A golf-course-view restaurant, a lounge, a fitness center, a sauna, and an outdoor heated pool entertain human guests. Dogs can hope for a ride to the city's off-leash area at Dr. Paul's Pet Care Center Dog Park. Rates range $90–175. A $50 pet deposit is refundable barring doggy indiscretions. 11775 Heron Bay Blvd., Coral Springs; 954/753-5598; http://marriott.com/fllmc.

La Quinta: After you swim laps in the heated pool of this pleasant five-story hotel, you could drive your dog to the city's off-leash area at Dr. Paul's Pet Care Center Dog Park. Rates range $70–125. 3701 N. University Dr., Coral Springs; 954/753-9000; www.lq.com.

Wellesley Inn: This nicely landscaped four-story hotel permits pooches under 20 pounds. Rates run $79–150. Pet fee is $10–20 daily. 3100 N. University Dr., Coral Springs; 954/344-2200; www.wellesleyonline.com.

Coconut Creek

PARKS, BEACHES, AND RECREATION AREAS

◙ Tradewinds Park

🐾🐾🐾 (See Greater Fort Lauderdale map on page 500)

A Labrador retriever mix named DeAnna knows this nearly square-mile park as the place where she sniffs other dogs when she is supposed to be cheering on softball player Steve D'Oliveira. Some teammates even bring pets into the dugouts: Everyone knows when Cassie Armstrong is at the plate because "her dog barks when she's batting," says teammate Steve. Zoey, a dalmatian, rears up on her hind legs like a horse as if to say, "I see you, Mom!"

But there is more for dogs to do at this park than sniff under bleachers for food dropped by spectators—a favorite pastime of Brandi, the shepherd/collie mascot of the Humane Society of Broward County.

Leashed dogs may follow the woodsy, nearly mile-long Cypress Trail and later rest at picnic tables. A longer bicycle/jogging path forms a figure eight around a Frisbee golf course, a horseshoe pit, a playground, restrooms, and a concession stand.

Best known for its Butterfly World tourist attraction, where visitors walk amid thousands of butterflies, Tradewinds Park is divided in two by Sample Road. Dogs are forbidden in the area north of Sample Road, home to horse stables, farm animals, and an equestrian trail. Yet the more popular southern portion is open to pooches—as long as they stay out of Butterfly World, rental boats and canoes, and the tempting grassy interiors of ample athletic fields.

The park is a favorite of many dogs, including Jasmine Rose, a golden retriever/cocker spaniel mix. "All I have to say is, 'Bye-bye in car,' " says Andrea, a humane society employee, and Jasmine "goes crazy."

Admission is $1 per person on weekends and holidays. From I-95, turn west on Sample Road. You will immediately enter the park at 3600 W. Sample Road. 954/968-3880.

Deerfield Beach

PARKS, BEACHES, AND RECREATION AREAS

3 Quiet Waters Park

😺😺😺 (See Greater Fort Lauderdale map on page 500)

A small army of feral cats and some raccoons stand near the road on the north side of this popular 427-acre park, begging for food from compliant visitors who don't know any better. Of course, this means more dogs should visit.

The highlight for pooches is following the long jogging path, which rims the lakeshore. Stop for breaks at the lakeside picnic tables or shelters. Bring water or fill up a flask at restrooms to quench your leashed pal's thirst.

Better yet, camp with your dog at the pleasant waterside campsites. Not owning a tent isn't a good excuse; most spots are "Rent-a-Camp" sites, which include tents. Camping is $25, plus a $25 security deposit.

The smile on the 20-foot-tall fiberglass clown statue near the playground and picnic area probably turns to a frown whenever a male dog approaches. Luckily, the circular bench surrounding the statue should provide a diversion and save you the embarrassment of leg lifts. The clown was a landmark at a Fort Lauderdale Car Circus dealership until a new sign ordinance sent the colorful bozo packing in 1984.

Dogs are off-limits in the most popular areas of the water-oriented park: the Ski Rixen cable-waterskiing concession, swimming beach, and rental boats.

The park is at 6601 N. Powerline Rd., south of Hillsboro Boulevard and just east of Florida's Turnpike. 954/360-1315.

4 Villages of Hillsboro Park

😺😺 (See Greater Fort Lauderdale map on page 500)

This park beside the Hillsboro Canal features large swaths of nicely maintained St. Augustine grass, the lush green stuff Maggie loves to roll around in. "Everybody from all over the place takes their dogs there," says local pet-sitter Shirley Mitchell, who brings her pals, George and Frisky. "The dogs are really well accepted."

Oaks and palms dot the fields. Signs warn against letting your dog off leash, though locals apparently are tempted by the open field in the southwest corner. A half-mile walking trail is shared by pedestrians and skaters. Expand your walk by strolling along the park's adjoining canal. The right-of-way there, a strip about 100 feet wide and a mile long, is owned and maintained by the South Florida Water Management District. Be courteous: The right-of-way, located behind yellow gates that bar vehicular access, is at the edge of some private backyards. Notice birds typical of the Everglades, such as anhingas and moorhens, along the waterway. Don't let your water dog take a dip—alligators are present.

At the 10-acre park, courts for tennis, basketball, volleyball, and skating occupy much of the ground, but there are also two picnic pavilions and several individual picnic tables, a few of them shaded. For a pleasant break, sit at a bench by the canal, which receives morning shade from a tall Australian pine and strangler fig tree.

Be sure to toss the poop-filled baggie into the metal boxes designed especially for those little lovelies, and not the regular garbage cans, which are cleaned out less often.

The park is at 4111 NW 6th Street. From Powerline Road and Hillsboro Boulevard, head west on Hillsboro. Turn right at 41st Way and go six blocks. Turn right onto Northwest Sixth Street. After .2 mile, turn left into the park. 954/480-4495.

PLACES TO STAY

Comfort Suites: Every dog sleeps in a suite at this 101-unit, four-story lodging off I-95, just a few exits south of Boca Raton and its off-leash dog park. A heated outdoor pool, a whirlpool, and continental breakfast are offered. Rates range $85–150. 1040 E. Newport Center Dr., Deerfield Beach; 954/570-8888; www.choicehotels.com.

La Quinta: After running hard at off-leash areas in Boca Raton or Coral Springs, your dog may wish for a quiet night at this pleasant, 130-room poolside motel. By flipping through the cable TV lineup, he may find *Dog Day Afternoon*. Rates range $59–115. 351 W. Hillsboro Blvd., Deerfield Beach; 954/421-1004; www.lq.com.

Quiet Waters Park: See Parks, Beaches, and Recreation Areas, above, for camping information.

Ramada Inn: Located just a few highway exits south from off-leash fun at Boca Raton's dog park, this 157-room motel bordering Boca Raton offers a heated pool and exercise room. The on-premises Denny's makes it possible to satisfy canine cravings for bacon around the clock. Rates range $40–130, plus $10 daily for the dog. 1250 W. Hillsboro Blvd., Deerfield Beach; 954/427-2200; www.ramada.com.

PLACES TO EAT

Starbucks: Free "canine lattes"—a concoction of whipped heavy cream—are treated to furry customers at the drive-through window of this coffee/tea/baked-goods chain, a convenient pit stop for shoppers at the dog-friendly Pet Supermarket across the street. A local Chihuahua named Gigi is a Starbucks regular; she happily laps up her latte, then prompts chuckles from onlookers as she lifts her tiny chin to reveal a foamy beard. 130 S. Federal Highway, Deerfield Beach; 954/596-8450.

Pompano Beach

At long last, Pompano Beach has dropped its "absolutely not" policy about walking dogs on Pompano Beach Boulevard, where you're close enough to smell the salt spray of the Atlantic Ocean. Just make sure your little buddy stays on the west side of the street, the side across the road from the beach, between Atlantic Boulevard and Fifth Street.

PARKS, BEACHES, AND RECREATION AREAS

5 North Broward Park

🐾 (See Greater Fort Lauderdale map on page 500)

If you happen to be near this well-used neighborhood park maintained by the county government, stop to see if your leashed dog can stake out a parcel to stretch his legs. Many activities are possible on these 20.4 acres: baseball, basketball, football, picnicking, soccer, softball, and volleyball.

From Federal Highway/U.S. 1, go west on Sample Road/Highway 834. Head north on Northeast 18th Avenue to the park. 954/786-2195.

6 Pompano Beach Highlands Park

🐾 (See Greater Fort Lauderdale map on page 500)

A leashed dog who happens to be in the area might appreciate a brief stop at this 3.3-acre county park, featuring a small green spot, a playground, and basketball courts. Skip it if it's out of your way.

The park is at 1650 NE 50th Court. From Federal Highway/U.S. 1, head west on Northeast 51st Street. Veer left (southeast) onto 50th Court and continue to the park. 954/360-1325.

7 Community Park

😾 (See Greater Fort Lauderdale map on page 500)

Besides hanging out at the ball field here, your leashed buddy can get dog-tired following the sunny bike path just outside the park on U.S. 1. The path goes on to encircle Pompano Beach Airport to the north. It's not a picturesque walk, but dogs and in-line skaters don't mind. Arrive early or late in the day to protect your dog from the sun, and don't forget to bring water.

Inside the park, pups are allowed only on the west side of the road that bisects the park. They must avoid the east side's playground and jogging path.

The park is south of the city's airport and golf course on Federal Highway/U.S. 1, north of Atlantic Boulevard. 954/786-4106.

PLACES TO STAY

Cottages by the Ocean: A dog under 20 pounds may join you at this collection of six studio cottages, deemed a "superior small lodging" by an independent panel. Located two blocks from the beach (where pets are forbidden), the cottages have a central barbecue area and are rented by the week. Guests may borrow beach chairs, beach towels, and coolers. Weekly rate is $750 in season, $550 in summer and fall. For rental information, contact a central office at 3309 SE 3rd St., Pompano Beach; 954/956-8999; www.4rentbythebeach.com.

Motel 6: At this 127-unit poolside motel off Florida's Turnpike (Exit 67), one small pet is permitted per room. Rates range $46–62. 1201 NW 31st Ave., Pompano Beach; 954/977-8011; www.motel6.com.

Sea Castle Resort: This 40-unit beachfront motel has been known to take the rare, bold step of advertising its two pet rooms in the Yellow Pages—proof that the owners are not shy about accepting dogs. Rates range $114–130 in winter, and fall to about half that at other times. Pet fee is $10. 730 N. Ocean Blvd., Pompano Beach; 954/941-2570.

North Lauderdale

PARKS, BEACHES, AND RECREATION AREAS

8 Woodville Dog Park

😾 😾 🐕 (See Greater Fort Lauderdale map on page 500)

When dog lovers suggested to Ken O'Farrell that he turn a dormant acre of little Woodville Park into an off-leash area, he had no idea what would come next. "It's just gone over so huge. It's being torn up with use. It's a nice problem," says O'Farrell, who oversees city parks.

Basically an open grassy field featuring a few trees, benches, water bowls, and plastic kiddy pools for cooling off, this park is divided in two. One side is for big dogs; the other is for small pets.

New grass was laid twice in a year to help repair the worn ground in the big-dog section. In early 2005, O'Farrell was brainstorming options for cutting down wear-and-tear. One possibility was fencing a new area of the broader park and rotating big Bowsers there from time to time.

The dog park is at 1500 SW 83 Ave., at West McNab Road. Find it between University Drive and Rock Island Road. 954/726-0274.

Sunrise

PARKS, BEACHES, AND RECREATION AREAS

🐾 C-13 Canal Right-of-Way

🐾 (See Greater Fort Lauderdale map on page 500)

If you're looking for scenic beauty, this is not the answer. It's a canal bank in a busy suburban setting. But if your furry friend is looking for a place to stretch her legs leash-free, consider it. It's just a strip of grass about 50 feet wide that runs along the south side of the C-13 Canal, which is maintained by the South Florida Water Management District. The water district doesn't encourage use of this land for recreation, but it also doesn't actively patrol the area. You'll usually be alone with your pooch. If you walk far enough you might end up at the edge of someone's backyard, so be on your best behavior.

The right-of-way is located on both sides of University Drive where it crosses the C-13 Canal, just south of Oakland Park Boulevard. 561/686-8800.

🔟 Markham Park

🐾🐾🐾 🐕 (See Greater Fort Lauderdale map on page 500)

Here by the Everglades, where you might see long-legged wading birds, dogs now can stretch their legs, too. The three-acre off-leash area offers separate parks for big and small dogs and marks the first bark park run by the Broward County Parks and Recreation Department.

Weston veterinarian Jan Bellows campaigned for the long-awaited bark park, which opened in 2005 over some objections from officials in Davie, Sunrise, and Southwest Ranches. Hounds everywhere howled with approval when Sunrise finally agreed to add an off-leash area to the county's 665-acre Markham Park.

One of the biggest stretches of green this side of the Everglades, Markham Park already was a pleasant destination. An Australian shepherd named Holmes thinks of it as a place to chase birds, but humans flock here for the target range, observatory, model airplane field, boat ramp, swimming, and playing sports.

Leashed dogs may follow a nature trail that heads out toward the Everglades, wending past saw grass and leather ferns. "Watch out for the red ants and ticks," advises Carolyn Contois, a sitter with New River Pet Sitting Service. Her late dog, Coda, loved the park.

You can camp here with your dog for $18–19. You'll also fork out $1 for a special collar to help you locate your dog should she get separated from you. The 86 campsites provide a compromise between total wilderness and a citified park experience.

A final note: Some people take their dogs swimming in the canal and lake at the edge of this park, but we recommend strongly against it. This is smack dab next to the Everglades, and you know what that means—hungry gators!

The park is at 16001 W. Highway 84. Take I-595 west until it becomes Highway 84, then continue to the entrance. 954/389-2000.

PLACES TO STAY

Baymont Inn and Suites: One pooch under 50 pounds or two dogs under 15 pounds may join you at this lodging near Sawgrass Mills Outlet Mall and off I-595. The poundage limit may not be strictly enforced, but a staffer says dogs must definitely be "not huge." Rates range $70–95. Pet fee is $50 per stay. 13651 NW Second St., Sunrise; 954/846-1200; www.baymontinns.com.

Markham Park: See Parks, Beaches, and Recreation Areas, above, for camping information.

Wellesley Inn: The impressive porte cochere and tended landscaping may impress penny-pinching canines accustomed to more modest digs. Dogs under 15 pounds, please. Rates at the motel, located off I-595, are $70–130, plus $10 daily for the pooch. They will take a credit card imprint and make you sign away your life savings in case your dog does damage. 13600 NW Second St., Sunrise; 954/845-9929; www.wellesleyinnsandsuites.com.

Lauderhill

PARKS, BEACHES, AND RECREATION AREAS

11 Wolk Park

(See Greater Fort Lauderdale map on page 500)

As small as it is, there are a surprising number of things you can do in this city park—play baseball, tennis, or volleyball, swim in a pool, or picnic at a pavilion. The highlight for dogs is walking on the grassy slopes that encircle a pond and eyeing any wading birds that happen to lurk there. The walk is pleasant enough, but it's short and there is no pathway.

Eat a private lunch at a pavilion on the peninsula that looks like an island in the center of the pond. Or take a break at benches overlooking the pond. On a windy day, you might smell the aromas of Caribbean foods being cooked in homes near the park. Kids will like the nifty playground, with a jungle gym that incorporates a galvanized tube.

From U.S. 441, head west on Northwest 12th Street/Sam Sutton Road to Northwest 44th Way. 954/321-2466 or 954/730-3080.

FETCHING NECESSITIES

Well-behaved dogs rarely make history... but they are welcome at **Tate's Comics & More,** as the sign on the front window reads. These books are more reliably comic than a Lab who sweeps a coffee table clean with a flip of its lively tail. Peruse the treasure chest of comics, toys, videos, and seemingly all things pop culture. Staffers bring their dogs to work, where they mingle with canine regulars. 4566 N. University Dr., Lauderhill; 954/748-0181.

PLACES TO EAT

Sonny's Real Pit Bar-B-Q: For doggies on the go, the drive-through window of this chain location serves ribs, chicken, pork, and beef. 2100 S. State Rd. 7; 954/987-2336.

Oakland Park

PARKS, BEACHES, AND RECREATION AREAS

⓬ Easterlin Park

🐾🐾🐾 (See Greater Fort Lauderdale map on page 500)

Our friend Larry Keller loved to take his dogs to this "very relaxed," tree-shaded park, where the 100-foot cypress trees are older than the United States. His black Labrador retriever, Stella, was particularly taken with the curvy, .75-mile Woodland Nature Trail, which winds around the park through an oak, cypress, and maple forest. "You can't see what's around the corner," Larry reports. "There's always an element of mystery ahead." It's rare to see another party, and Larry adds that they usually feel like they're all alone.

Larry discovered that this 47-acre county park offers the solitude and element of surprise that mighty hunter dogs and other leashed pooches crave. The mulched trail can turn into a quagmire in the rainy season, so be prepared to turn back if need be. You're likely to hear passing cars, but the fresh scent of cypress and the sight of waist-high ferns and coffee plants towering overhead is rewarding. Some twisted oak limbs in this designated Urban Wilderness Area look like they belong in the front yard of a haunted house.

Urbanites will appreciate the playgrounds, horseshoe pit, shuffleboard courts, and scattered picnic tables with grills. But what sets the place apart is its lush feel and the amoeba-shaped pond visited by Muscovy ducks. Easterlin Park is a slice of Old Florida plopped down in the middle of urban Broward County.

At the park's 55-site campground, two leashed dogs are allowed per campsite, for $1 each per night. Rates are $18 for a site with electricity, $17 without.

There is a $1 entrance fee on weekends and holidays. The park is at 1000 NW 38th St., about a mile southwest of the intersection of Powerline and Prospect roads. Take Powerline Road north from Oakland Park Boulevard, then turn west at Northwest 38th Street. 954/938-0610.

PLACES TO EAT

Dixie Pig Bar-B-Q: Some locals consider this humble breakfast/lunch/early dinner spot the best barbecue joint around, and Maggie appreciates the breeze that unexpectedly blows past the half-dozen concrete tables even on many hot days. Everyone eats under a canopy or orders food to go. The vinegar-based shredded pork sandwiches are justifiably popular, and the house barbecue sauce is sold by the bottle or half gallon, attesting to its appeal. Crispy fried chicken, pork chops, hoagies, catfish, burgers, rotisserie chicken, wings, ribs, and sweet tea help round out the menu. Hungry dogs can buy barbecue by the pound. 4495 N. Dixie Highway; 954/772-5977.

PLACES TO STAY

Easterlin Park: See Parks, Beaches, and Recreation Areas, above, for camping information.

Fort Lauderdale

In a county where a Persian cat named Cherry Pop was featured on *Lifestyles of the Rich and Famous,* the most celebrated dog may be Brandi, a shepherd/collie mix whose mascot position for the Fort Lauderdale–based humane society began after someone gave her up as a five-year-old new mama. Depressed and unwilling to eat, Brandi sulked in a humane society cage until the agency's education director just happened to need a dog for a television interview—and chose Brandi. A star was born.

"I've gone into restaurants and had people call me Brandi," says her current companion, Caroline Crane. She and Brandi go on speaking engagements to teach 40,000 schoolchildren and adults each year how to care for dogs. "She has a doghouse full of fan mail," says Cherie Wachter, spokesperson for the Humane Society of Broward County.

When it's time for an outing with Brandi, Caroline lays out a dozen bandannas and lets Brandi pick one. Then the lucky dog goes nuts, knowing she's outdoor-bound. Brandi knows that if she doesn't go through the bandanna ritual, Caroline is about to leave without her. Then it's time for the guilt trip: "When she has to stay home, she mopes," Caroline says. "She hangs her head low, drags her feet, and goes back to bed. She has that pathetic look like, 'How could you?'" Sound familiar?

PARKS, BEACHES, AND RECREATION AREAS

13 Dog Beach

🐾🐾🐾 (See Greater Fort Lauderdale map on page 500)

Connie Francis made Fort Lauderdale beaches famous when she wailed "Where the Boys Are" back in 1960. Now, this 100-yard portion is where the dogs are—at least from 5–9 P.M. Friday, Saturday, and Sunday during daylight saving time, or 3–7 P.M. Friday, Saturday, and Sunday during Eastern Standard Time. That's when leashed pooches may swim here, so long as their owners buy a $5.30 one-day pass from a park ranger at the beach.

Alternatively, they can buy an annual permit weekdays before 5 P.M. at the Parks and Recreation Department, 1350 W. Broward Boulevard. An annual pass costs $21.20 per resident dog, $37.10 per nonresident dog. You must have the Dog Beach permit with you while you're watching your buddy plunge into the waves. (Saying your dog ate it is no excuse.)

Considering the rest of the county's 22 miles of beaches ban dogs, Dog Beach is popular. The little matter of canine calling cards has threatened at times to close this strip to the pitter-patter of paws. So scoop the poop.

Sadly, Mayor Jim Naugle doesn't use this beach, even though it was inspired by his old dog Snorkel. Just a week and a half before Dog Beach was liberated, Snorkel passed on to the Great Doghouse in the Sky.

Important: Stay on the west side of the street when you're using the State Road A1A sidewalk during the permissible dog-walking hours of 6–9 A.M. daily. You even need to carry a Dog Beach permit to do that.

Dog Beach is immediately north of Sunrise Boulevard/Highway 838 on Highway A1A. Posted signs mark the beach. For permit information, call 954/761-5346.

14 Hugh Taylor Birch State Park

🐾🐾🐾 (See Greater Fort Lauderdale map on page 500)

Chicago attorney Hugh Taylor Birch wanted to escape a house full of relatives during the 1893 Chicago Exposition, so he took off on a summer trip that ended with a shipwreck near these woods. Birch loved what he saw and bought land here for as little as 75 cents an acre. Dogs today now have a shady place to walk amid the concrete sea of Fort Lauderdale.

Maggie's favorite destination in the 180-acre park is the little-used interpretive nature trail. A 1.7-mile exercise course also rims the park, but it's hard to beat the nature trail for privacy. Maggie tugged at her leash to follow the curvy, tree-shaded dirt path past wild coffee bushes and Spanish stopper bushes (used long ago to stop diarrhea, hence the name). It's a short walk, about 20 minutes. You'd have to look hard to find another oak hammock located across the street from the Atlantic Ocean. The hardwood hammock and freshwater lagoons help make the park unique.

DOG-EAR YOUR CALENDAR

Bark at the ball park: One game every year, leashed pets pad through the stadium gates to watch the World Champion Florida Marlins play the human version of fetch. Going to a pro baseball game is a treat for a four-legged fan, what with the commotion, the sticky substances on the ground to lick, and all the smells. Humans can just enjoy the game. Dogs and their owners sit in a particular section and howl with approval.

A talent scout for David Letterman's Stupid Pet Tricks segment videotaped potential contestants at the 2004 game, so you never know who'll show up. Tickets cost around $12; kids and dogs pay half-price.

Bark in the Park Night benefits two local humane societies, one being the Humane Society of Broward County, which throughout the year entertains local dogs in other ways—most famously with its 1.5-mile Walk for the Animals held each February in downtown Fort Lauderdale.

Leashed pets any day may browse the shelter's pet boutique to find such novelty items as Timmy Holdigger dog cologne, pet totes for jet-setters, and faux leather collars with rhinestone letters that slide on so you can spell out your lap dog's name. The shop's few short aisles are found in the shelter lobby at 2070 Griffin Rd., Fort Lauderdale; 954/989-3977.

On the west side, picnic tables look onto the boats speeding along the Intracoastal Waterway. Other tables are shaded by tall, shaggy Australian pines. Once the most-visited park in Florida, this place has fallen enough in popularity that its now-quiet paved circular road (with a 15 mph speed limit) is popular with in-line skaters. Still, you can expect crowds on holidays.

All the mainstays of fun—fishing, swimming, horseshoes, and volleyball—are available. On a hot day, a dog can get a little relief by walking into the tunnel that leads to the beach. But forget about reaching the sandy shore on the other side. Dogs are turned away from the park's beach and rental canoes.

The entrance fee is $4 per vehicle. The park is at 3109 E. Sunrise Blvd./Highway 838, just west of Highway A1A. 954/564-4521.

15 Sunview Park

(See Greater Fort Lauderdale map on page 500)

At this pleasant enough 21.5-acre neighborhood park, Maggie liked to head to the fenced perimeter of the well-kept ball fields to run or sniff the grass. Tall trees shade the eastern and southern perimeters of the ball fields, so try a pit stop there when it's sunny.

You're likely to have the fenced area at the park's north side to yourself on weekdays. Visitors tend to stay clear across the park at the swings, basketball courts, football field, and tree-shaded picnic tables south of the ball fields. Dogs are supposed to be leashed.

From U.S. 441 and Davie Boulevard/Highway 736, head west on Peters Road. Turn south on Southwest 42nd Avenue and continue to the park entrance at 1500 SW 42nd Avenue. 954/791-1040.

16 Riverwalk

🐾🐾🐾 (See Greater Fort Lauderdale map on page 500)

Walking along the New River to see the yachts and water taxis glide past the city's Arts and Sciences District is a treat—for both people and dogs. A shih tzu named Rosebud loves Riverwalk: "We call it Rosie Walk," says Elaine Davis, who also takes Rosebud to work at a Hollywood wholesale furniture shop.

For people, a highlight is seeing the New River and walking around a plaza between the New River and the child-oriented Museum of Discovery and Science, 401 Southwest Second Street. This plaza is fun: Near Southwest Second Street, stand with your pooch at a white-and-yellow circular dish that looks like a satellite dish. Have a friend whisper into the central ring of another dish located about 20 yards away. Your dog may wonder why he is hearing whispers when no one is around.

Leashed dogs could walk a mile easily if they hug the river from behind the Broward Center for the Performing Arts, 201 SW Fifth Ave., and head east beyond downtown's high-rises to end up at Stranahan House, 335 SE 6th Street. Of course, for all intents and purposes, Riverwalk is considered to end at about Southwest Second Avenue. In this stretch, people stroll to take in the city's skyline, particularly on weekends, and festivals are sometimes held here.

This is the only city-run "park" open to dogs besides Dog Beach.

Riverwalk stretches eastward from the Broward Center for the Performing Arts at 201 SW Fifth Avenue. Park across the street at the city garage on Southwest Second Street. 954/761-5784.

17 Airport East

🐾🐾 (See Greater Fort Lauderdale map on page 500)

Since the powers that be decided to close downtown-area Smoker Park for—what else do we need?—more development, doggies who used to roam free by the banks of the New River have had to sniff out new running areas. This airport option is a pretty good one, although it pales in comparison to the nearby Bark Park at Snyder Park (see below). This spot is little more than a few picnic tables under some shady strangler figs, but the adjacent water-retention area is usually dry. Maggie frequently runs there and occasionally chases long-legged cattle egrets. The only drawback might be that occasionally a plane

DIVERSIONS

"Lord, please make my neighbor's cat easier to catch."
Naughty and nice dogs are welcome to send prayers, whatever they may be, as they join their people at the weekly Saturday 6 P.M. services at **All Saints Episcopal Church,** 333 Tarpon Dr., Fort Lauderdale; 954/467-6496.

Pets get special treatment at the service held the second Saturday of each month. They get treats, and they're also blessed afterward.

If dogs bark, the Rev. Roger Allee takes it in stride. His attitude: They're praising God with their barks. The church got the idea of welcoming pets when they noticed so many dog owners exercising pets on All Saints' grassy grounds (which is permitted). "We lovingly call that community 'the dog people,'" says the Rev. Allee, who posted fliers in the park inviting dog lovers to church services and initially drew a big response, though it's since tapered off.

Iguanas, snakes, and birds, as well as dogs, show up at the church's annual Blessing of the Animals held each October in honor of the patron saint of pets, St. Francis of Assisi.

Some T-shirts ask, "Dog worship. Is it wrong?" Here, you can be sure it's not.

taking off from the nearby runways at Fort Lauderdale-Hollywood International Airport would startle your pooch. Note that the field is not fenced, and it's next to a two-lane road. However, it's recessed into the ground and even an only moderately obedient dog, like Maggie, seems safe off leash here.

Finding this strip of green is a little tricky. It's on Perimeter Road at the southeast corner of the airport (south of the terminal entrance). From I-95, go east on Griffin Road. In a few blocks, turn left onto Perimeter Road (just west of U.S. 1). Follow Perimeter Road as it veers right. Look for the left-hand turn into the small park's parking lot just after the road curves to the left. 954/359-1200.

18 Airport Greenbelt

🐾🐾 (See Greater Fort Lauderdale map on page 500)

A wide asphalt trail winds through manicured grounds of coconut palms, trimmed bushes, stately royal palms, and other greenery at this mile-long swath on the southern perimeter of Fort Lauderdale-Hollywood International Airport. Maggie likes to roll around on the thick carpet of St. Augustine grass.

At one time, you could get away with letting dogs off leash here, but now those onerous Leash-Them-or-Else signs are up. To jog with your leashed pooch, head east from the parking area to trot along the asphalt path that runs along the top of a small ridge that runs parallel to Griffin Road. Bring water for your pal; the park has no facilities.

The unattended park is on the north side of Griffin Road about a half mile east of I-95. From I-95, go east on Griffin Road. In a few blocks, turn left onto Northwest 10th Street, which serves as the park's entrance. 954/359-1200.

🐾 Airport West

🐾🐾 (See Greater Fort Lauderdale map on page 500)

This humble destination is really just a few open fields on the west side of the airport, not far from the place where people and pooches are allowed to park and watch jets glide in. About five acres of grassy fields sit across from a some-times-used parking lot for rental cars. During the busy Christmas season, you may not be able to run Rover here; sometimes the rental cars overflow onto the fields. A few trees provide nominal shade, including one very large oak for dogs to sniff around. Maggie preferred now-closed Smoker Park in downtown Fort Lauderdale, but she doesn't complain when we come here. The place is not fenced, but there is never much traffic. Like the Airport East location, this one takes a little sniffing out to find. A better choice, particularly for compan-ionship-hungry hounds, is nearby Bark Park at Snyder Park (see below).

From I-95, go east on Griffin Road. In a few blocks, turn left onto Perimeter Road (just west of U.S. 1). Once on Perimeter, head west, passing tall chain-link fences. The road will curve right, and eventually you'll come to a stop sign. Proceed through and make the next left, onto 40th Street. The fields are about half a block ahead on your left. Park in the small parking area on the north side of the street. 954/359-1200.

🐾 Bark Park at Snyder Park

🐾🐾🐾🐾🐕 (See Greater Fort Lauderdale map on page 500)

It's the biggest thing that's happened to dogs in Fort Lauderdale—ever. So contends Faye, a small Lab/shepherd mix, who for months visited the park practically every weekend after it opened in September 2000, trying to get one of her canine brethren to chase her around the two-acre, double-gated park. Here, dogs have a place to run free! They also can practice agility training and socialize with the in-the-know dogs in town.

The fenced park sports two water fountains—with bowls at human and doggie level. It also features tubs for soaking and a short wooded trail. Also in the works are shelters, picnic tables, benches, a community bulletin board, and a separate fenced area just for small dogs. Bark Park is supervised by an attendant and has a few rules: a maximum of three dogs are permit-ted per human; all dogs must have and display a rabies tag; and owners are required to clean up after their pooches. Dogs also are expected to stay within the off-leash area instead of venturing into the rest of the city park, prompting this wish from a flatcoat retriever named Maya: "She wishes they would open up the entire park to dogs and restrict the humans," quips her human companion, Pat.

Admission is $1.50 weekdays, $2 on weekends. Yearly passes cost $60. Bark Park is inside Snyder Park at 3299 SW 4th Ave., which is near Fort Lauderdale-Hollywood International Airport. From I-95, take the State Road 84 exit and go east to Southwest 4th Avenue, where you'll turn south (right). The park is a half-mile ahead, at right. 954/828-3647.

PLACES TO EAT

Atlanta Bread Company: It sounds so unappealing—all they serve is bread? But don't let Fido mistake this for your average bakery. Sure, you can get your soup served in a sourdough bowl, and all the bread is baked fresh daily. But you can also get great sandwiches, salads, mini pizzas, scrumptious cookies, and so forth. Breakfast is also available. Maggie sat at the sidewalk tables here back when Robert worked across the street at the *Sun-Sentinel*. 301 E. Las Olas Blvd.; 954/522-0888.

Big Louie's Pizzeria: Walk up to the order window at this local favorite to pick up pizza and Italian dinners to eat at an outdoor table with your dog. The view is busy Andrews Avenue, which may intrigue pooches stuck indoors all week. 3064 Andrews Ave.; 954/564-6276.

Cheeburger, Cheeburger: Mayor Jim Naugle's dogs have all made trips to this home of some of the best thick burgers in Fort Lauderdale. The most informal pooch-permissible eatery on trendy Las Olas Boulevard, this burger joint has a roll of paper towels on each of its half dozen or more sidewalk tables, so you can wipe the juicy drippings off your dog's whiskers. Try bacon on your burger, Maggie says. 708 E. Las Olas Blvd.; 954/524-8824.

Dairy Queen of Wilton Manors: Every Monday, dogs get a free cup or cone of vanilla ice cream here, thanks to manager Lynn Lawrence, who instituted the freebie policy. What used to be the slowest day of the week now ranks up there with busy weekends now that the shop has gone to the dogs. As many as 100 four-legged customers show up on Mondays in the hot summer. 1950 Wilton Drive, Fort Lauderdale; 954/566-5735.

Downtowner Saloon & Steak House: Staffers automatically brought Maggie a bowl of water along with our menus at our favorite hound-hospitable Sunday brunch spot, tucked away from the tourist hubbub. Try eggs, dolphinfish sandwiches, omelettes, steaks, burgers, or brunch fare. Rarely busy on Sundays, it's a great place to sit back at a sidewalk table, enjoy the weather, and gaze at the boats gliding by on the New River. Dogs are protected from the scant road traffic (and river view) by a hedge. The place can be tricky to find, so take Andrews Avenue south from Las Olas Boulevard to cross the New River. At Southwest Seventh Street, turn left and go one block. Turn left at Southeast First Avenue and proceed to the end. Park at the lot on your left and walk to the riverfront. 10 S. New River Drive East; 954/463-9800.

DIVERSIONS

Itching to satisfy your dog's hunger? Do it at **Bone Appetit Bakery,** where dogs can view crunchy biscuits, cookies and other yummy treats through the glass case at this petite canine café. Among the offerings are Down Boy Bagels, Bark-B-Q Ribs, Puppa's Pizza, and Russel Rover Bon Bons. Faye, a Lab-shepherd-terrier mix, likes to take her companion, Tracy Ahringer, to this dog bakery to sample, er, gobble a Beefy Boy with carob, after which Faye looks lovingly through the glass for another treat. Dogs and their humans can also sit outside under a striped awning. Hank, a friendly Pomeranian, keeps watch at this hound hangout, which also offers doggy and kitty shampoos, toys, leashes, and other canine accoutrements.

More unusual offerings include pet fragrances, pet placemats, and the Beastly Furnishings line of pet sofas and chaise lounges. A favorite among locals, the place has hosted birthday parties, a fashion show, and blessings of animals. Next door is **Posh Paws Salon,** where Sheila Weise and Paulo Rodrigues offer professional grooming services and holiday makeovers for all dog breeds (it's where Hank gets his regular 'do). To reserve a grooming time, call 954/565-3395. To stick with the treats, head to the bakery at 3045 N. Federal Highway in Coral Center; 954/565-3343.

Barkers elsewhere in the county can find baked treats at **Three Dog Bakery,** a franchise of the nation's first dog bakery. Cleverly named treats include the Scottie biscotti and SnickerPoodles, yet howlers with an eye for volume may prefer a five-pound box of Bark 'N' Fetch biscuits. 236 S. University Dr., Plantation; 954/424-3223.

Einstein Brothers Bagels: Strong coffee and bagel sandwiches smeared with chicken salad or other goodies are the highlight here. Furry customers are a common sight at the outdoor tables at 6256 N. Federal Highway, 954/771-3993, says humane society volunteer Lynn Schulke, whose four-legged companion, Cleo, likes to join them. Pooches are uncommon but permitted at the downtown-area branch at 19 N. Federal Highway, 954/462-1132. Also try 3200 N. Federal Highway, 954/565-2155.

Giorgio's: "Luscious" is how Maggie described many soups, sandwiches, pastas, and dinner offerings at this trendy eatery in the Publix shopping center on Southeast 17th Street. Check out the pizzas cooked in a wood-burning oven, and ask about daily specials. The desserts are quite good, and vegetarian doggies won't have any trouble getting filled up. Dogs are often welcomed with water at the seven overhang-shaded tables out front. 1499 SE 17th St.; 954/767-8300.

Hot Dog Heaven: Maggie imagined she'd gone to the Great Doghouse in the Sky when she scarfed down little slices of the all-beef, Chicago-style hot dogs served at this busy, historic little hot dog shop, considered the best in southern Florida. Order slaw dogs, chili cheese dogs, Italian sausage, Polish sausage, burgers, or other sandwiches at the tiny counter while your pooch stays outside on a patio by busy Sunrise Boulevard (tie her up!). We order our dogs with the works, including those little hot peppers, then shave off little bits of the meat for Maggie. It's heavenly, Maggie agrees. Try the delicious lemonade, and ask for an extra glass of water for the pooch. The only down side: Heaven closes at 4:30 P.M. 101 E. Sunrise Blvd.; 954/523-7100.

Indigo Restaurant: Set on the ground floor and sidewalk of the venerable Riverside Hotel, this casual restaurant is a favorite of a standard poodle named Chuckie, who often is immediately given water by servers and happily overlooked by nearby diners because she lays flat at the feet of her human interpreter, Susan Smith. The two like to take a corner patio table at this home of Indonesian and other Asian-inspired fare. If you prefer steaks, chops, lamb, or lobster, The Grill Room on Las Olas also has outdoor seating at this address. Reservations are suggested for The Grill Room. It's best to call first, in case the place is too crowded to accept dogs. 620 E. Las Olas Blvd.; 954/467-2555 (Grill Room), 954/467-0045 (Indigo Restaurant).

Louie, Louie: The managers of this Italian-oriented eatery with red, green, and white trimmings are happy to accommodate pooches at outdoor tables. 1103 E. Las Olas Blvd.; 954/524-5200.

Mark's Las Olas: A few regular customers bring their dogs to the stylish outdoor tables of this renowned restaurant, where the kitchen is overseen by demidog, we mean, demigod chef Mark Militello. Fancy cuisine with a Florida flair is the common thread through the daily changing menu. Reservations are suggested. 1032 E. Las Olas Blvd.; 954/463-1000.

Mister Nick's Sub Shoppe: For more than 20 years, the city's best bargain submarine sandwiches have been served at this decidedly casual establishment, where we once saw a parrot sitting on a patron's shoulder. Try the homemade clam chowder, sweetened ice tea, and the Old World Special—a sub with Genoa salami, provolone, hot ham, and imported ham. Maggie loves the Chizzer—a steak sandwich with two types of cheese, grilled onions, lettuce, and tomatoes. But the chicken and original hoagies are more popular. Eat at the long picnic tables or the few plastic tables protected by a roof overhang and trellis walls. (We try to stake out seats far from the well-used door to avoid any anti-dog patrons.) 901 S. Andrews Ave.; 954/462-1913.

Premo's Subs: Staffers carve deli meats for your sandwich as you watch from the order line, making this pricey downtown lunch shop one of the best. Sub sandwiches come in three dog-pleasing sizes and include fillers such as turkey, ham, or cheese. The house special is filled with all three and purple coleslaw. An overhang shades the white plastic outdoor tables that face a parking lot. 195 N. Federal Highway; 954/463-4363.

Skyline Chili: From Greek immigrant Nicholas Lambrinides's first restaurant outside Cincinnati, diners could see the skyline of the city's downtown. The Skyline name stuck, and so did the family's popular chili recipe. Now you can sample chili spaghetti or smothered four-inch hot dogs at the two big picnic tables on the concrete patio in front of this chain location. Almost no one uses the tables (perhaps because they overlook a noisy intersection), but Maggie gladly plopped onto the concrete in hopes of snarfing up wayward hot dog pieces. Besides, a short hedge shielded her view of the traffic. 2590 N. Federal Highway; 954/566-1541.

Solo Trattoria: Pizza is a main draw, but salads and small à la carte portions of fairly pricey yet tasty pasta take up more of the menu. Sit outside at tasteful metal mesh tables. Reservations are suggested for dinner. 208 SW Second St.; 954/525-7656.

Sushi One: At about $6 per meal, this little downtown-area eatery is Fort Lauderdale's best bargain spot for made-to-order sushi prepared by polite staffers. Regulars swear by the place. Tie your dog to one of the few outdoor tables, step inside to order, then return with the goodies (or get your order to go). 23 N. Federal Highway; 954/761-9009.

Waxy O'Connor's: Irish wolfhounds will feel right at home at this Irish food joint in the tourist-friendly area of southeast Fort Lauderdale. On some nights and weekend afternoons, you may be treated to Irish music flowing out from inside the pub to the four outdoor tables, each shaded by an umbrella advertising a European beer. The outdoor scenery is not great, as you'll look onto busy 17th Street. But it's a nice change of pace for a meal, most pooches will agree. 1095 SE 17th St.; 954/525-9299.

PLACES TO STAY

AmeriSuites: Small dogs can stretch their legs in these 128 suites located in the heart of tourist country—and near pooch-permissible eateries such as Giorgio's (see Places to Eat, above). Rates are $109–209. 1851 SE 10th Ave.; 954/763-7670; www.amerisuites.com.

Aqua Mar Resort and Marina: Arrive by boat or car to sleep at these 10 poolside hotel rooms, suites, and efficiencies, located on a waterway near the beach and within walking distance of some pooch-permissible eateries. The hosts can say "Good dog" in French, German, and English. Rates vary seasonally $59–190; weekly rates are also available. 90 Isle of Venice, Fort Lauderdale; 954/763-5501; www.aqua-mar.com.

Birch Patio Motel: These 14 efficiencies and motel rooms near the beach and Birch State Park permit two dogs per room. Rates are $40–105, plus a dog fee of $10 for the first night, $5 per subsequent night. 617 North Birch Rd., Fort Lauderdale; 954/563-9540.

Doubletree Guest Suites: Your dog can step onto a private balcony or beg for treats in your private kitchen at this 230-room hotel, which features an exercise room, hot tub, gift shop, restaurant, and bar. But the real highlight for canine guests? Dog Beach is about three blocks east. Rates are $119–309, plus a $15 daily pet fee. 2670 E. Sunrise Blvd., Fort Lauderdale; 954/565-3800; www.doubletree.com.

La Quinta: At this pleasant, 145-room motel set far from the tourist hub-bub, a coin laundry machine makes it easy to keep bandannas clean for traveling terriers. Dogs under 30 pounds are allowed if they can stand staying in a smoking room. Rates are $59–125. 999 W. Cypress Creek Rd., Fort Lauderdale; 954/491-7666; www.lq.com.

Red Roof Inn: Dogs up to 80 pounds may set paw beyond the impressive entrance and sleep in one of the 108 rooms at this poolside hotel. Rates are $50–90. 4800 NW Ninth Ave., Fort Lauderdale; 954/776-6333; www.redroof.com.

Venice Bay Guest Quarters: This 14-unit poolside motel, formerly the family-operated The Trevers at the Beach, now targets a gay clientele and still permits dogs. It's one of the nearest pooch-permissible lodgings to Dog Beach. Rates are $95–165 in winter, $75–145 at other times. 552 N. Birch Rd., Fort Lauderdale; 954/564-9601 or 800/533-4744.

Westin Hotel Fort Lauderdale: This 293-unit lakeside hotel, which features room service, a restaurant, gift shop, spa, and lounge near Fort Lauderdale Executive Airport, welcomes dogs who weigh under 40 pounds. Westin's corporate policy is to offer dog beds and pet bowls to those who ask. Rates are $99–270. 400 Corporate Dr., Fort Lauderdale; 954/772-1331; www.starwoodhotels.com/westin.

Plantation

PARKS, BEACHES, AND RECREATION AREAS

21 Happy Tails Dog Park at Seminole Park

🐾🐾🐾🐾🐾 🐕 (See Greater Fort Lauderdale map on page 500)

Tongues were wagging among dog lovers as soon as they found out this large park was under construction. A whopping five acres in size, the park basically is a grassy field and is divided into one section for big dogs, another for small pets. Pavilions, benches, drinking water, and plenty of good times round out the scene.

The park is at 6600 SW 16th Street. 954/452-2502.

22 Plantation Heritage Park

🐾🐾 (See Greater Fort Lauderdale map on page 500)

Maggie considers this sea of manicured sod pretty boring, except for the short Anne Kolb Memorial Nature Trail, which winds through a hardwood hammock, pine flatwoods, and a coastal strand forest. Leashed dogs may also follow a 1.25-mile, sun-washed fitness trail that loosely circles the centerpiece lake. Your dog might stop you along the way to sniff at leg-lift targets—for instance, the tropical flowering trees and palms scattered around this former University of Florida agricultural experimentation farm. Dogs aren't allowed on rental boats, in the lake, or in the playgrounds.

If your pup wonders what in the heck that blue sculpture is just within the park entrance, you can tell him it's not a giant's version of a game of Pick Up Sticks. Artist John Henry calls the metalwork piece *Baldwin's Mountain*.

There is a $1 entrance fee on weekends. The park is at 1100 S. Fig Tree Lane. From U.S. 441/Highway 7, drive west on Peters Road, then head north on South Fig Tree Lane. 954/791-1025.

23 North New River Canal Trail

😽 (See Greater Fort Lauderdale map on page 500)

Maggie adores the mornings she is allowed to trot along the right-of-way next to this South Florida Water Management District canal. The right-of-way is kept clear so that big Water Management District trucks can have access to the canal, which is important should a hurricane strike and debris need to be removed from the canal to drain flooded surrounding neighborhoods. But any other time, which is virtually all the time, it's a nice mile-long stretch of nothingness.

You're not exactly out in the country—your view to one side is I-595, while on the other side, you'll see houses. Be respectful: While you're on public land, it will seem like you're basically in someone's backyard, and these folks weren't crazy about the right-of-way being cleared in the first place. Still, it is public property, part of what could someday become a huge interconnected system of walking and biking trails running along canals across Broward County. What better way to use otherwise-wasted public space? Maggie asks. Unfortunately, there is next to no shade. After you're finished walking, be prepared to pick the brambly stickers from between your dog's toes. Also, keep your dog leashed and guide her away from broken glass you may find near the beginning of the trail.

To reach the tucked-away spot from I-595, exit northbound on Flamingo Road, by the Mobil station. After .3 mile, turn right and head east on Broward Boulevard. After about one mile, turn right and head south on Hiatus Road. It will dead-end a half mile later at the canal. Park there and walk around or duck under the yellow gate. Don't worry, the gate isn't meant to keep pedestrians and pooches out—only unauthorized cars. 561/686-8800.

PLACES TO STAY

AmeriSuites: Your small- to medium-sized dog can stretch his legs in a suite at this 128-unit hotel, and you can stretch out in an exercise room. Rates are $89–150, plus $10 a night for the pooch. 8530 W. Broward Blvd., Plantation; 954/370-2220; www.amerisuites.com.

Holiday Inn: Dogs under 25 pounds may sleep at this 335-room motel located about 12 miles southwest of Fort Lauderdale's Dog Beach. Rates are $89–129, plus a $25 non-refundable, per-stay fee for the furry vacationer. 1711 N. University Dr., Plantation; 954/472-5600; www.holidayinns.com.

Residence Inn: Whip up dinner for your best friend in the kitchen, then settle down for an in-room movie. These comfortable apartment-style suites are less than two miles from manicured Plantation Heritage Park. Rates are $109–220. The pet fee is $30 nightly, $200 maximum. 130 N. University Dr., Plantation; 954/723-0300; http://marriott.com.

Weston

If there were any doubt that dogs are bone-ified family members, Broward County's newest city—known as family-oriented—allows pooches to sniff around at least some portions of its parks. Look for areas posted with clearly marked signs permitting domestic animals.

PARKS, BEACHES, AND RECREATION AREAS

24 Eagle Point Park

😋 (See Greater Fort Lauderdale map on page 500)

The lakefront passive area on the northern end of this seven-acre neighborhood park may be the best bet for leashed pooches looking for a change of

scenery after spending the week in the doghouse back home. Four basketball courts and two baseball fields entertain humans.

The park is at 18691 North Lake Blvd., next to Eagle Point Elementary School. From I-75, go south on Indian Trace. Turn left onto North Lake Boulevard. Continue to the park, at left. 954/389-4321.

25 Heron Park

🔥 (See Greater Fort Lauderdale map on page 500)

At this five-acre neighborhood park, human pursuits dominate: a playground, two baseball fields, a basketball court, and football field. But pent-up pooches may make do.

The park is at 2300 Country Isles Rd., next to Country Isles Elementary School. From I-75, go west on Arvida Parkway, passing Weston Road. Turn right at Country Isles Road. The school and park are ahead at the right. 954/389-4321.

26 Country Isles Park

🐾 (See Greater Fort Lauderdale map on page 500)

Go for a W-A-L-K. Following the exercise path is about all that leashed dogs can do at this four-acre neighborhood park. Humans enjoy the playground, volleyball court, multipurpose field, and gazebo.

The park is at 2260 Country Isles Road. From I-75, go west on Arvida Parkway. Turn right at Weston Road, then left at Indian Trace. The park is at left, across from Peace Mound Park. 954/389-4321.

27 Peace Mound Park

🐾🐾 ◀🐾 (See Greater Fort Lauderdale map on page 500)

Known as Florida's only public archaeological park, this unexpected pleasure is built around a 5,000-year-old Tequesta Indian burial mound. Leashed dogs can look down from a boardwalk and peer through a transparent cover to see an excavation site dug by people who are paid to dig holes—a job some pooches would like to apply for.

Alternatively, set your sights on the exercise trail of this county-owned, eight-acre park. Kids may appreciate the playground.

The park is at 300 Three Village Road. From I-75, follow Arvida Parkway west. Turn right on Weston Road and left at Indian Trace, then follow the signs. 954/389-4321.

28 Tequesta Trace Park

🐾🐾 (See Greater Fort Lauderdale map on page 500)

When Jasmine, a shepherd/terrier mix who is scared of other dogs, visits Weston's largest park, she likes to bark at—but not fight, of course—any dog who dares approach. These 47 acres are devoted mostly to sports, with roller-hockey rinks and baseball, football, and soccer fields. Nevertheless, the community park isn't a disappointment for Jasmine, who was rescued from the pound one Christmas Eve by Trish Rector. Instead, Jasmine is disappointed when it's time to leave.

The park is at 600 Indian Trace. From I-75, follow Arvida Parkway west. Turn right on Weston Road, and left at Indian Trace. The park is ahead at left, two blocks past pooch-permissible (but boring for Bowser) city-run Indian Trace Park. 954/389-4321.

29 Emerald Estates Park

🐾 (See Greater Fort Lauderdale map on page 500)

Follow an exercise path with your leashed pooch at this waterfront park on the southeastern end of town. Afterward, you could retrieve water for your pooped pooch; just head to the restroom. The five-acre neighborhood park is favored by humans for its playground, tennis courts, basketball court, and two picnic shelters.

The park is at 16400 Emerald Park Circle. From I-75, go west on Griffin Road. Soon turn north on Weston Road, then west soon after onto Emerald Park Circle. Continue to the park, at left. 954/389-4321.

PLACES TO EAT

Einstein Brothers Bagels: Even sandwiches are served on bagels at this breakfast and lunch spot. Sit at an outdoor table with Spot. 1356 Weston Rd.; 954/384-6479.

Davie

Four-legged animals are star citizens here—but we're talking about horses, not dogs. Locals ride horses to McDonald's, Grifs Western Feed and Ranch Supply, and other establishments, using an extensive system of horse trails and bike paths. That's good news for dogs, who can take advantage of the trails and horse-oriented parks. The town's pooch-friendly parks are pleasant—especially when you consider that this is a small town (at least the civic leaders try to hold on to that image as the community grows). Maggie thinks Davie's park system should serve as a model for bigger cities.

PARKS, BEACHES, AND RECREATION AREAS

30 Shenandoah Park

🐾 (See Greater Fort Lauderdale map on page 500)

If you're in the area, introduce your dog to this neighborhood park's big grassy field facing 14th Street. It is virtually ignored by visitors, who prefer the lighted ball field to the north or the playground. For a dog walk with your leashed pal, follow a straight, tree-shaded path at the western edge near the park's entrance or choose the largely sunny path on the east side. For a longer walk, exit the park on foot and follow the curvy, rolling bike path down pleasant Shenandoah Parkway.

The sun-washed picnic area at the park's northeastern corner is dotted by young native pine trees that look like taller versions of Charlie Brown Christmas trees. Skip a picnic on warm days, or at least fill up a doggy water bottle at the restrooms.

From I-595, exit at Southwest 136th Avenue and go south. Turn right (west) at Appalachian Trail, then south at Shenandoah Parkway. Follow the parkway around a curve and the park is on the south side. 954/797-1145 or 954/423-5102.

31 Bergeron Park

🐾 (See Greater Fort Lauderdale map on page 500)

For dogs, the highlight is following an asphalt trail through this small park. Named for Percy and Dorothy Bergeron—the couple who opened one of the town's first grocery stores back when fewer than 400 people lived here—the park has too few trees for most dogs' tastes. Arrive early or late in the day to avoid too much sun exposure.

If the trail is too short for your leashed dog, consider exiting the park on foot and following the bike trail along Nob Hill Road. The trail curves away from the road to a hilly area. Truth be told, this walk is little better than walking around a neighborhood at home.

From I-595, take Nob Hill Road south. Look for the park at 1900 S. Nob Hill Road. 954/797-1145.

32 Oak Hill Equestrian Park

🐾🐾 (See Greater Fort Lauderdale map on page 500)

We saw a family playing baseball on the asphalt road and another party smacking a tennis ball in the parking lot, so we quickly assumed this park would be too small for canine fun. We were wrong.

Head to the east side of this quiet neighborhood spot to let your leashed buddy roam a tree-dotted field and smell the water trough outside the fenced horseback riding area. Go inside the riding area if no horses are around. Maggie sniffed with interest at the grass inside this small field.

You'll feel like you're out in the country, and it still may be possible to walk through a gap in the eastern fence to emerge onto vacant land that is bigger than this park. (The vacant land was being prepared for development the last time we visited.) Fill up a doggy water bowl at the restrooms and stop for a break at a picnic table. A pavilion is available by permit only.

The park is at 3100 SW 130th Ave., just west of Flamingo Road/Highway 823. 954/797-1145.

33 Linear Park

🐾🐾 (See Greater Fort Lauderdale map on page 500)

Even the hardiest dog will tire at this favorite haunt of local hounds. Spanning a few miles, the grassy strip features an asphalt trail overlooking the C-11 Canal. City dogs may become excited, as they are sure to encounter horse dung—or maybe even a horse—somewhere along the trail. For a rest break, stop at a shelter at Hiatus Road or other spots. With precious few trees, this trail is best visited early or late in the day to protect your pooch from the sun. Dogs must be leashed.

The park is on Orange Drive and stretches eastward from Flamingo Road/Highway 823. Some people pull their cars off the road and park on "the park's" grass, particularly at the bridge near Southwest 105th Avenue, where anglers sometimes fish. 954/797-1145.

34 Robbins Lodge

🐾🐾 (See Greater Fort Lauderdale map on page 500)

This pleasant site of the town's Easter egg hunt is sure to convince an urban dog that he is in Smalltown, U.S.A. A massive sea of grass surrounded by a horse fence is the first thing a dog will notice here. A half-dozen scattered picnic tables—each with its own shelter—are found in a tree-shaded area just west of the parking lot. You and your dog may have the entire park to yourselves on a weekday.

To see most of the park, you must do what pooches love to do—walk. As you follow a wide path westward, you're likely to notice horseshoe prints in the dirt. Eventually, you'll pass a brick lodge and see another massive green field with picnic tables at a shelter. Leashed dogs may run with you; however, note that a sign at the park's entrance warns: "Open space areas are natural areas which may contain fire ants, bees, snakes, and plants that may cause allergic reactions." If you want to follow a nature trail, you must obtain a permit.

The park is at 4005 Hiatus Rd., north of Griffin Road/Highway 818. 954/797-1145.

35 Tree Tops Park

🐾🐾🐾 (See Greater Fort Lauderdale map on page 500)

At what may be Maggie's favorite park in Broward, we can count on her to bark at horses thundering by and sniff doggedly along the 1,000-foot board-walk in a man-made wetland that looks like the Everglades. Yes, these 358 woodsy acres are sure to excite any pooch.

Leashed dogs can revel in three nature trails, a 1,000-foot paved Sensory Awareness Trail, and more than seven miles of equestrian trails (weekdays are best if you want to avoid horses). For the longest nature walk, follow the nearly mile-long paved path and the quarter-mile mulched trail of the Pine Island Ridge Trail, which basically rims the park. At the sunny boardwalk trail overlooking 23 acres of marsh near the park entrance, Maggie sticks her head through openings in the wooden fence and strains to sniff at the watery homes of elusive critters. Farther south at the half-mile mulched Live Oak Trail, dogs climb 28 feet to the top of an observation tower.

Don't let dogs go swimming—not only is it not allowed, but one dog that did got sick. There are scattered picnic tables.

Your dog can also brag that he padded around the highest natural elevation in the county if you visit an area highlight—Pine Island Ridge. So what if it's only 29 feet tall? It's a pleasant place to sit under a tree and let the breeze waft over you. Indians and federal troops tangled at this ridge in a Second Seminole War battle in 1838. Humans have lived at or visited the ridge for at least 5,000 years, and one of the county's best preserved Tequesta Indian habitation sites is said to be on the western side.

There is a $1 entrance fee on weekends and holidays. The park is at 3900 SW 100th Ave., north of Griffin Road/Highway 818. 954/370-3750.

36 Lange Park

🐾 (See Greater Fort Lauderdale map on page 500)

One of the region's tallest leg-lift targets stands in this 4.5-acre park, said to be the first melaleuca tree planted in southern Florida. Nowadays, this tree with the papery white bark is considered by Everglades fans to be akin to a monster in a horror flick. First planted in the days when locals wanted to soak up swampland, the melaleuca trees are doing such a good job that they're taking over the now-beloved 'Glades. Still, this early invader is enshrined for posterity. After viewing it, stop to rest with your leashed dog at a picnic table. Kids might enjoy the playground.

The park is at 6550 SW 47th St., just south of Griffin Road/Highway 818. 954/797-1145.

37 Wolf Lake Park

🐾🐾 (See Greater Fort Lauderdale map on page 500)

Ducks look like tiny airplanes as they take off, wings flapping wildly, from the surface of the centerpiece lake at this town park. Picnic tables circle the lake, and at the south side, they are nestled in a forest of tall Australian pines. No one is allowed to swim here—so keep water dogs at bay. What makes the peaceful place special for leashed dogs is a trot on the horse trail, which you can access by walking around the lake to the northeast side.

From University Drive/Highway 817, turn east on Stirling Road. After a short distance, turn north on Southwest 76th Avenue to reach the park. 954/797-1145.

PLACES TO STAY

Homestead Studio Suites Hotel: "A room. A kitchen. A reasonable price." That's what this chain promises. And the $65–100 rates are not so bad, considering they take large dogs. Weekly rates are available. You also must pay a $75 per stay pet fee. 7550 State Road 84, Davie; 954/476-1211; www.homesteadhotels.com.

Dania Beach

PARKS, BEACHES, AND RECREATION AREAS

🐾🐾 John U. Lloyd Beach State Park

🐾 (See Greater Fort Lauderdale map on page 500)

Eating at a picnic table is the only thing dogs may do at this popular 244-acre beach park—unless you bring a canoe for a short trip down Whiskey Creek (which we recommend). While this park is known for its long beach, dogs can't set paw on it. Keep your pup leashed.

Admission is $3–5 per vehicle. The park is at 6503 N. Ocean Dr., just north of Dania Beach Boulevard. 954/923-2833.

PLACES TO EAT

Checkers: Eat burgers at the half-dozen umbrella-shaded tables to the side of this restaurant on five-lane U.S. 1. 645 South Federal Highway; 954/925-4729.

PLACES TO STAY

Motel 6: At this 163-unit poolside motel near John U. Lloyd Beach State Park, one small pet is permitted per room. Rates are $57–63. 825 E. Dania Beach Blvd., Dania; 954/921-5505; www.motel6.com.

Sheraton Fort Lauderdale Airport: This 250-room hotel across the street from the Design Center of the Americas is often used for business meetings, but the hoteliers are happy to have your dog's business as well. They even offer fancy dog beds and pet bowls. Pets are accepted for a $50 per stay fee. Rates are $89–329. 1825 Griffin Rd., Dania Beach; 954/920-3500; www.starwoodhotels.com/sheraton.

Cooper City

PARKS, BEACHES, AND RECREATION AREAS

39 Brian Piccolo Park

🐾🐾 (See Greater Fort Lauderdale map on page 500)

Dogs tend to walk around the perimeters of the open fields at this 180-acre park, named for the local high school football star who went on to play for the Chicago Bears before dying at age 26. Fittingly, the park is sports-oriented. But that means the four-legged set is shunned from the athletic fields, which breaks the hearts of those who long to scamper in open spaces.

Leashed dogs may run, however, on the sunny jogging path that circles the quadplex of lighted softball fields before making an oval around picnic tables, a playground, and a cricket field. The path then straightens and heads westward past a tennis and racquetball center on the way to Palm Avenue.

To vary your dog-walk routine, head to the east side of the park. There, a bicycle/jogging path makes a lopsided figure eight around four football/soccer fields and two lighted basketball courts. Then the path curves around the west side of the popular Velodrome—home to a 333.3-meter cycling track and a 200-meter banked in-line skating track—before leading to a long, narrow fishing lake.

Bring water or fill up a flask at the restrooms to quench your pooch's thirst. Snack bars are at the center of each of the park's three athletic field quadplexes.

Admission is $1 per person on weekends and holidays. From University Drive/Highway 817, turn west on Sheridan Street and continue several blocks to 9501 Sheridan Street. 954/437-2600.

Pembroke Pines

PARKS, BEACHES, AND RECREATION AREAS

40 C. B. Smith Park

🐾🐾 (See Greater Fort Lauderdale map on page 500)

A poodle/Pekingese mix named Teddy loves to take his person, Jennifer, for walks at this popular 320-acre park. Leashed dogs may follow the long biking/jogging path that hugs much of the shoreline of the 80-acre lake. The wiggly, winding path is like something out of a "Family Circus" cartoon, veering crazily past picnic shelters, playgrounds, picnic tables, restrooms, basketball courts, tennis courts, an 18-hole miniature golf course, and more before it ends. Of course, turn back long before your pooped pooch collapses and fill up a water flask at restrooms to quench your dog's thirst. A lakeside snack bar is southwest of the park entrance. Take rest breaks at picnic tables along the way.

Dogs can't take part in the most popular activities at this water-oriented county park. They aren't allowed in the water, on the beach, on the 700-foot water slide, in rental canoes, or at concerts in the 8,000-capacity amphitheater.

Leashed dogs can, however, sleep at one of the park's 60 RV campsites or 12 tent sites. Rates are $19 for RVs, $17 for tents.

The park is at 900 N. Flamingo Rd./Highway 823, north of Pines Boulevard/ State Road 820. 954/437-2650.

41 City of Pembroke Pines Dog Park

🐾🐾🐾🦴 (See Greater Fort Lauderdale map on page 500)

Finally, dogs from the city of the twin Ps don't have to hightail it all the way to Hollywood to run unencumbered. This fairly large, wide open leash-free area comes with separate areas for small dogs and large dogs. Also called John S. Fahey Park, this stop comes with a playground next door.

The park is at 9751 Johnson St., Pembroke Pines, a couple blocks east of Palm Avenue on the north side of Johnson Street; 954/435-6520.

PLACES TO STAY

C. B. Smith Park: See Parks, Beaches, and Recreation Areas, above, for camping information.

Hollywood

PARKS, BEACHES, AND RECREATION AREAS

42 Oak Lake Park

🐾 (See Greater Fort Lauderdale map on page 500)

Almost all of this 11-acre park is taken up by a lake and a small fire station. There are plenty of ducks to chase, but the only real green stretches for romping are right by the road. Although the park's name refers to oaks, the most common trees here are ficus, black olive, and cypress—and there aren't enough of them to shade the park. An off-leash area is being considered here.

The park is at 3200 N. 56th Ave., a few blocks north of Sheridan Street/ Highway 822. 954/921-3460.

43 Topeekeegee Yugnee (T.Y.) Park

🐾🐾🐾 (See Greater Fort Lauderdale map on page 500)

Judging by the weekend crowds in this county-run park, its Indian name— meaning Gathering Place—is taken to heart. For a more private picnic with

Maggie, we lug a cooler along a path that rims the south side of the 40-acre centerpiece lake and leads to tree-shaded picnic tables. It's amazing how many picnickers stick near their cars on the park's west side and avoid the parking lot-deprived southeast side.

Determined leashed dogs will get winded by following a biking/jogging path around the perimeter of this 150-acre park, taking in views of the lake, volleyball court, swimming lagoon, tennis courts, playgrounds, basketball courts, and more. Of course, turn back before your pooch becomes dog-tired, and stop first to fill up a water flask for her at a restroom. A snack bar is on the northeast side of the lake.

If your dog doesn't want to leave, you may camp here together for $17–18 on the southeast side of the park. Dogs aren't allowed in rental boats or on the swimming beach.

Weekend and holiday gate entrance fee is $1 per person, but children under age five are free. The park is at 3300 N. Park Rd., north of Sheridan Street/ Highway 822 and west of I-95. 954/985-1980.

44 Carlton Montayne Park

😺 (See Greater Fort Lauderdale map on page 500)

This remnant of an ancient oak hammock, right next to Florida's Turnpike, has some playground equipment and a reasonable amount of shade. It's also off the beaten track. You probably could let your dog off leash as long as there are no kids around. The park is at Garfield Street and North 62nd Avenue. 954/921-3460.

45 Stan Goldman Park

😺😺 (See Greater Fort Lauderdale map on page 500)

It's the invasion of the aliens—trees, that is—at this 12-acre park. An asphalt path leads you and your pooch through a grove of melaleucas and pines native to Australia. Alongside them are the hated Brazilian pepper shrubs.

Eventually, though, you'll pass under a huge strangler fig and cypress trees—native trees that will give you an opportunity to remind your dog that you are standing on what once was the eastern edge of the Everglades. Maggie couldn't have cared less about where these trees came from because they provided a dark, cool respite from the Florida sun. At the far end of the park is a pavilion with a few picnic tables and grills. There, Maggie made friends with some homeless men who were hanging out the day we visited. A fisherman said he catches sheepshead, sand perch, and snook in the brackish C-10 Canal, which you can cross by bridge to enter tiny Lions Park.

The park is at the northwest corner of I-95 and Hollywood Boulevard. 954/921-3460.

FETCHING NECESSITIES

Head to where designing dogs go: Your interior designer may usher you and your four-legged discriminating pal inside **Jessica Sidney & Company,** a wholesale furniture store where a shih tzu named Rosebud shares the job of receptionist with her German Shepherd sidekick, Maxwell Sidney. One steadfast rule, doggies: No sitting on the furniture. Oh, and you must arrive with a designer. 2862 Pershing St., Hollywood; 954/922-0299.

46 Young Circle

😼 (See Greater Fort Lauderdale map on page 500)

This pleasant spot of green, in the middle of the downtown Hollywood renaissance, is a happenin' place, with concerts and festivals held here frequently. Even when nothing is scheduled, it's a great place for dog- and people-watching. The park is named for the city's founder, but it keeps dogs feeling young, too. Maggie remembers coming here for the Tropic Hunt, the wacky citywide scavenger hunt once sponsored annually by *Tropic,* the once-great but now-defunct Sunday magazine of *The Miami Herald.*

Young Circle is at the convergence of Hollywood Boulevard and U.S. 1. 954/921-3640.

47 West Lake Park

😼 (See Greater Fort Lauderdale map on page 500)

Forget about the fact that these 1,500 acres are a great place to canoe through a wetland preserve—dogs aren't allowed in the entire watery north side of the county-run park, let alone in rental canoes. Still, a young Lab mix from the pound named Lally loves coming here, because leashed dogs may follow a biking/jogging path that passes a playground, picnic areas, and a garden called the Cause of Freedom War Memorial on the south side of the park. The path straightens out to hug a road leading to the park's entrance on Sheridan Street. Afterward, you can grill hot dogs with your hot dog in the picnic area.

The park is at 1200 Sheridan St./Highway 822, east of U.S. 1/Federal Highway. The dog portion is on the south side of Sheridan Street. 954/926-2410.

48 Holland Park

😼 (See Greater Fort Lauderdale map on page 500)

To dogs, this 23-acre waterfront park sounds better than it is. Sure, boating, picnicking, bicycling, walking on a nature trail, and taking in the view from the waterfront tower certainly are featured activities. But much of the action centers on North Lake in the eastern portion of the park, so privacy is unlikely amid all the anglers, picnickers, and others. Trails head westward to a humble, woodsy area, but with so little real space for stretching one's legs, it's no wonder that Maggie was the only dog around during our visit.

The park is at Sixth Avenue and Johnson Street, 1.5 miles east of Federal Highway. 954/921-3460.

49 Poinciana Park

🐾🐾🐾🐾 (See Greater Fort Lauderdale map on page 500)

People have been bringing their pooches here to run off-leash for years, so we sure were glad to see the city of Hollywood decide to accommodate the needs of dogs and their owners here. This four-acre park with poinciana and jacaranda trees was split in half, with the southern half set aside for a leash-free area with a water station especially for dogs. "It always was a doggy park, but now it will be official," said Sergio Cortella, who runs the Hollydogs pet hotel, grooming service, and greyhound rescue effort, which is located near the park. Cortella and his wife Silvana, who helped the city set up the park, have 10 dogs of their own, mostly greyhounds.

Hollywood officials caution that one big reason the off-leash area was set up was to keep dogs from running in the northern half of the park, where there is a playground used by children.

The park is located on Dixie Highway, just north of Pembroke Road. 954/921-3460. Hollydogs and the Cortellas can be reached at 954/925-7758 or www.hollydogs.org.

PLACES TO EAT

Chocolada Bakery: Anyone with a sweet tooth can rationalize that a trip here has a noble purpose—entertaining the family dog. People-watch with your well-mannered pooch at a sidewalk table. Although it's famous for desserts, Chocolada also offers salads, soups, sandwiches, and a few entrées, such as chicken Kiev and salmon steaks. Live music is featured outside at night sometimes. 1923 Hollywood Blvd.; 954/920-6400.

Dog Spot: This daytime coffee bar has, by design, gone to the dogs. Actually a doggy daycare center/grooming business/human coffee bar, this unusual spot for Spot sells coffees, frozen cappuccino, and sodas to humans and a wide range of typically organic treats to visiting pooches. Read the newspaper or just hang out with your dog. Afterward, visit the 6,000-square-foot backyard—a pseudo park. Dogs don't have to leave: Owner Amy Seltzer tries to make four-legged sleepover guests feel at home in the kennel portion of the business by allowing boarders to sleep on big pillows instead of in cages. 2112 Washington St.; 954/923-SPOT.

Mama Mia: At this home of pasta, salads, and Italian dishes, a poodle/Maltese mix named Vanna White always loved the plain meatball. That's

what she got when she sat on her own chair alongside her loving chauffeur/ companion, Cherie Wachter, who adopted Vanna as a 10-year-old homeless dog at the Broward County Humane Society. You can sit at an outdoor table, too, at this eatery in the walkable Young Circle neighborhood. 1818 S. Young Circle; 954/923-0555.

Papa John's Pizza: Better known as a place to call when you want a pizza delivered to your home, this chain location nonetheless has four red tables outside. There, your dog is welcome to watch you eat pizza, bread sticks, cheese sticks, and other offerings. 207 N. Federal Highway; 954/929-3100.

PLACES TO STAY

Comfort Inn: While humans may appreciate the free continental breakfast at this 191-room airport-area motel, dogs are glad it is located just a couple highway exits south of one of Maggie's favorite parks, Stan Goldman (see Parks, Beaches, and Recreation Areas, above). Rates are $77–140, plus $25 for the pooch under 25 pounds. 2520 Stirling Rd., Hollywood; 954/922-1600; www.choicehotels.com.

Days Inn Airport South: This 114-unit high-rise is considered by the Days Inn chain to be one of its best. A pool, bar, hot tub, and exercise room are featured. Rates are $69–199, plus $10 nightly per dog. 2601 N. 29th Ave., Hollywood; 954/923-7300; www.daysinn.com.

Howard Johnson Express: Rates at this 72-room, two-story poolside motel are $55–119, plus $26.50 per dog. Specific rooms are set aside for doggy travelers; only one dog per room, please. Doberman pinschers, German shepherds, rottweilers, and pit bulls are not allowed. 2900 Polk St., Hollywood; 954/923-1516.

Topeekeegee Yugnee (T.Y.) Park: See Parks, Beaches, and Recreation Areas, above, for camping information.

Pembroke Park

PARKS, BEACHES, AND RECREATION AREAS

50 McTyre Park

😺 (See Greater Fort Lauderdale map on page 500)

This 19-acre neighborhood park tries to offer something for everyone: picnicking, baseball, basketball, softball, tennis, volleyball, and a playground. Watch a sandlot game with your leashed buddy after a picnic or just make a pit stop. The focus is on sports, as made clear by artist Bob Jenny's colorful mural—depicting athletes in action—on the outside wall of the recreation center. But a tree-shaded grassy area toward the park's south side is a pleasant, albeit confined, place to walk. A staffer told us that if you're way in back and no one's around, it's okay to let your dog off leash.

The county park is at 3500 SW 56th Avenue. From U.S. 441, head east on Hallandale Beach Boulevard, then south on Southwest 56th Avenue. 954/964-0283.

51 Patrick Behan Park

😺 (See Greater Fort Lauderdale map on page 500)

You have to hand it to this 1.6-square-mile town. It may be small. It may have had its share of problems—such as when, some time ago, residents showed up at municipal government meetings in clown suits to heckle commissioners. But unlike in some bigger cities, leashed dogs may visit the waterside town park. If you happen to be in the area, stop at this well-kept park to follow a fairly short walking path or gaze at the water, as some locals do.

The park is on 25th Street. From Hallandale Beach Boulevard/Highway 858, turn north on Park Road and continue to the park. 954/435-6520.

538

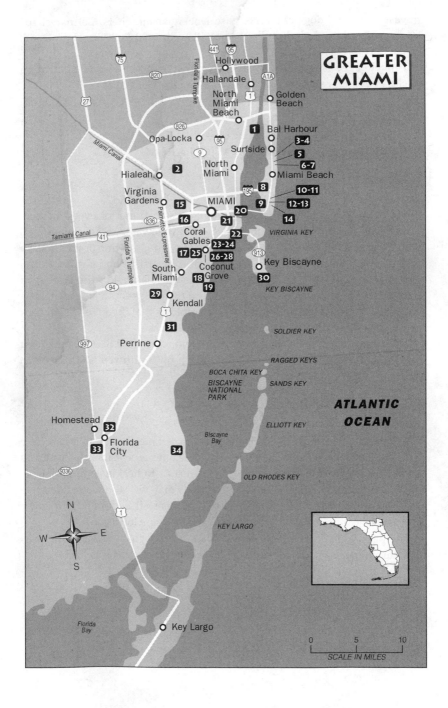

GREATER MIAMI

ATLANTIC OCEAN

0   5   10
SCALE IN MILES

CHAPTER 19

Greater Miami

This county where Maggie was rescued from the streets as a pup has gotten a lot more dog-friendly in the last few years. It started with Miami Beach, where the Lincoln Road pedestrian mall went to the dogs some years ago, with almost every eatery there from simple Cuban-food walkups to fancy restaurants fairly boasting, "Bring along the pooch!"

There's still something of a "paw-city" of dog-friendly parks in Miami-Dade County, although off-leash areas have sprung up in Miami Beach, Hialeah, Miami, and South Dade in recent years. And more are in the works, as we detail in area introductions below.

Miami is rife with dog lore. When Cuban refugees braved sharks and dehydration on the 90-mile journey to reach Miami shores by raft some years ago, a few brought along tiny dogs. They didn't want to leave their pals behind. Actor Mickey Rourke, who sometimes hangs out in Miami Beach, has appeared on national television with his dog. Latin America's Oprah—Miami star Cristina Saralegui—was looking forward to getting a small dog for years. Part of the holdup? Her boy was holding out for a big dog. (They eventually settled on

PICK OF THE LITTER—GREATER MIAMI

MOST DOG-FRIENDLY DINING DISTRICTS
Lincoln Road, Miami Beach (page 548-550)
Sunset Drive/town center, South Miami (page 556-557)
Main Highway and Grand Avenue, Coconut Grove (pages 564-565)

DOG-FRIENDLIEST BOOKSTORES
Books & Books, Coral Gables, Miami Beach (page 545)

BEST WILDERNESS EXPERIENCE IN THE CITY
Oleta River State Park, North Miami (page 540)

BEST (AND ONLY) DOG BEACH
Rickenbacker Causeway, Miami (page 558)

four beloved dachshunds.) In the oddest story of all, folks in suburban Sweetwater knew who to blame when 31 chickens and two goats were found dead with puncture wounds in their necks in a yard. No, not dogs, as authorities surmised. It had to be the Chupacabras—a two-legged creature in Puerto Rican legend that's part alien, part porcupine, part kangaroo.

Your dog's a lot nicer than any Chupacabra! So tie a bandanna around his neck and head to some of the places we've included below.

North Miami

Miami-Dade County is planning to build a "dog run" at the Country Club of Miami, 6801 Miami Gardens Drive. For more information, call the parks department at 305/755-7899.

PARKS, BEACHES, AND RECREATION AREAS

1 Oleta River State Park

🐾🐾🐾 (See Greater Miami map on page 538)

Luckily, Maggie didn't notice the plump raccoon eyeing us as he stood on his hind legs in broad daylight near a stand of Australian pine trees at this 854-acre park. Signs warn visitors to avoid the masked panhandlers, as rabid raccoons have posed a bit of a problem down the Florida coast. Oblivious, Maggie practically galloped to a trailhead to follow a long, sun-washed asphalt bicycle path. It spans the length of the park's eastern edge, running 1.5 miles to the park entrance at Northeast 163rd Street. Without much shade, it's an impractical trail for dogs on hot days. When the mercury rises, consider using the shady, gravelly, seven-mile-long mountain bike path instead. Of course, look out for bicyclists, who will be busy trying to maneuver the rugged, rock-ridden course, which in some spots features 45-degree climbs and tight turns.

Check with the latest concessionaire—they've changed quite a few times over the years—on whether dogs are allowed in the rental boats. Last we checked they only had kayaks, which aren't very dog-friendly, but like we said, the concessionaires come and go. Remember that your dog is not allowed on the swimming beaches here.

This nesting site of bald eagles and hawks is a fine place for a breezy picnic—if you eat at one of the seven pavilions, named Osprey, Manatee, and the like. Reservations are requested but may not be necessary for a small party. At least one open field will tempt dogs to run, but they must stay leashed.

Admission is $5 per vehicle. The park is at 3400 NE 163rd St., a mile east of Biscayne Blvd./U.S. 1. For concession information, call 305/947-6707 or 305/947-0302. For rangers, call 305/919-1846.

North Miami Beach

PLACES TO EAT

Miami Juice: Before heading for nearby Oleta River State Park, you can stoke up energy with a falafel lunch, or try other sandwiches, fruit salads, fresh juices, or tropical smoothies at the single table outside this nondescript, mostly-vegetarian shopping-center health food business. It has recently added fish, rice, soups, and similarly substantial fare. They love dogs here. 16218 Collins Ave.; 305/945-0444.

Bal Harbour

PLACES TO EAT

Bal Harbour Bistro: In the pretty garden setting of this Bal Harbour Shops eatery, slip your pooch a few bites from a customer favorite: Caesar salad with grilled chicken. Rigatoni caprese or with meat sauce and homemade cakes are also popular. The continental menu features everything from light bites to filet mignon, with vegetarian and seafood offerings to boot. 9700 Collins Ave.; 305/861-4544.

FETCHING NECESSITIES

Window-shop with the elite: Occasionally, the furry head of a pampered pooch may be seen peering out of a visitor's Louis Vuitton bag at Greater Miami's tony **Bal Harbour Shops.** At this open-air mall and magnet for international tourists, "we have seen everything from 'small ponies' to little Maltese with diamond collars and diamond bows in their hair," says former spokeswoman Enid Rosenthal. Stroll along the sidewalks to gaze into the windows of such stores as Neiman-Marcus, Saks Fifth Avenue, Gianni Versace, Gucci, and Louis Vuitton. 9700 Collins Ave., Bal Harbour; 305/866-0311.

Sunny Isles

PLACES TO STAY

Newport Beachside-Westgate: Rates are $119–299. Dogs under 35 pounds, please. 16701 Collins Ave., Sunny Isles; 305/949-1300.

Hialeah

Fresh on the heels of the super-duper leash-free area at Amelia Earhart Park in Hialeah, the city council next door in the town of Miami Springs is considering building one, too. Check with organizers at 305/887-1764 to find out about progress.

PARKS, BEACHES, AND RECREATION AREAS

🂡 Amelia Earhart Park

🐾🐾🐾🐾🐕 (See Greater Miami map on page 538)

Just as the famed aviatrix for whom this park is named relished the freedom of flying, so too can your little rebel leave behind the constraints of the "civilized" world of leashes. Reviews are good for the off-leash park here. It comes with a small-dog area that includes some agility- and show-training equipment such as ramps, as well as a large-dog area. We were glad to see the large grassy fields do offer some shade from black olives and other trees. And there's running water for your furry pal. You and your pooch can cool off in outdoor showers together, or your pooch can take a dip in the small wading pools set aside for those of the four-legged persuasion. And the little fire hydrants are a cute addition.

This is one of the cooler dog parks we've seen, but you may have to pay. On weekends, admission to Amelia Earhart Park, which also includes a pioneer farm village and country store, barbecue grills, a skate park and other amenities, is $4 per carload. It's also the first Metro-Dade County park to include a bark park. We're looking forward to others being built in Kendall. (see below.)

The park is at 401 E. 65th St., Hialeah.

Miami Beach

A Labrador mix named Magica made the news some years back when she jumped onto her own surfboard and rode the waves here. Yes, the dog, owned by a Hawaiian surfer, loved to hang 20. Word is that dogs are tolerated on the beach after 6 P.M., but posted signs say dogs aren't allowed on the broad, sandy expanse at any hour. Still, South Beach is the place for dogs—and, unfortunately, cats. Wild cats have become such a nuisance that city leaders pondered extreme ways to drum them out of town, leaving cat fans outraged. No one thought to enlist pooches to do the job. But word must have spread through the canine ranks because some say the Beach's Lincoln Road, at least, is going to the dogs.

Miami Beach is much like a piece of New York City plopped onto a sandbar in front of Miami, along with similar parking problems. The southern part—the late-night partying hot spot of South Beach—is your prime destination. Head to the generally relaxed and sometimes funky sidewalk cafés of the Lincoln Road pedestrian mall.

Just like Carl Fisher, the unstoppable Indiana Hoosier who transformed Miami Beach from a little more than a strip of jungle on a sand bar into a vacation destination, dog owners here leaned on the city to transform lesser-used open spaces at Flamingo Park and Pine Tree Park into popular off-leash areas. They're "small, but not too small," says city employee Boris Rodriguez. "We've gotten complaints—it has fleas, or they don't want their little baby with such aggressive dogs," he explains. But the biggest threat to keeping the bark parks open: "Problems with people not picking up the poop."

Aside from those two parks, Lincoln Road is probably the most welcoming dog destination in town. But you also can follow tourists and fashion models to the sidewalk cafés packed side by side along Ocean Drive. The oceanfront road is so trendy that a local magazine took its name. The late fashion designer Gianni Versace spent $8 million turning an abandoned Ocean Drive apartment building into a villa with a mini-planetarium. Restaurants and bars tend to open and close faster than a dog can celebrate seven birthdays in a year, so we've listed several pooch-permissible options amid the colorful buildings of the ever-changing Art Deco District.

PARKS, BEACHES, AND RECREATION AREAS

🄱 Cronish Plaza Park

🔥 (See Greater Miami map on page 538)

This half acre of grass is little more than a pit stop for pent-up pooches. If you happen to live within a half mile or so, however, this would be a nice turning-around spot for a walk from home. A tennis court and two fenced basketball courts are offered.

From Miami, take the Julia Tuttle Causeway to Miami Beach. Turn left at Chase Avenue. The park, also known as Muss Park, is at right, just south of West 44th Street. 305/673-7730.

🄳 Fisher Park

🐾 (See Greater Miami map on page 538)

A fenced playground is the human highlight of this triangular strip of land, but a big, unfenced, mostly unshaded grassy field beckons leashed dogs on the southern half. The park is set in a nice residential area of single-family homes. A bust memorializes entrepreneur and developer Carl Graham Fisher, who "carved a great city from a jungle." (Watch those leg lifts, pooches.) For a picnic, try the shady table beneath the black olive tree.

The park is on busy Alton Road at about 50th Street. 305/673-7730.

🄴 Indian Beach Park

🐾 (See Greater Miami map on page 538)

On a breezy day at dusk, this oceanfront spot is a nice stop if you're in the neighborhood or staying at the nearby pooch-permissible Alexander All-Suite Luxury Hotel (see Places to Stay, below). Leashed dogs are supposed to stay on the token grassy areas and on the landward side of the dunes. The scattered coconut palms are pretty, but expect no shade.

The park is on Collins Avenue at about 52nd Street, behind fire station number 3. Park at a metered space. 305/673-7730.

🄵 Pine Tree Park

🐾🐾🐾🐕 (See Greater Miami map on page 538)

Before the opening of the off-leash area here, this was simply a large, little-used, off-the-beaten-path park, a nice place to stroll across the grassy and somewhat uneven expanses or follow the asphalt walking path.

Back then, it was not unusual even on a breezy Sunday afternoon to have the roughly 10 acres to yourself as you sat on a bench overlooking a waterway.

Now, though, this is quite the place to be if you're a dog longing to run free. The two fenced areas offer a fair amount of room to run and according to the *Miami Sun Post,* a small local paper, it's "Still the king of Fido parks."

FETCHING NECESSITIES

Buy books with Bowser: A jar of dog biscuits sits on the counter of Miami's best independent bookstore, where pooches are welcome despite the relative lack of space in the book-crammed aisles. On a drizzly day, we saw a dog lounging lazily beneath his person's feet at a café table in the bay window of **Books & Books.** Yes, dogs are allowed inside the small independent bookstore where sandwiches, espresso, cakes, and cookies are sold along with poetry, journals, fiction, best-sellers, and rare and used books. Sidewalk tables also await outside the local favorite. 933 Lincoln Rd., Miami Beach; 305/532-3222.

A second, far bigger, more famous location—in Coral Gables—not only welcomes leashed pets to browse bookshelves with their people, but dogs also may lounge at the on-site café to watch their companions sample desserts, light foods, and beverages. It's a quiet, pleasant, tasteful place to spend a few hours reading books and sipping coffee. 265 Aragon Ave., Coral Gables; 305/442-4408.

Gumbo-limbo trees and shaggy Australian pines shade about one-third of the park, set in a pleasant residential neighborhood. A drawback: The parking lot fits only four or five cars.

The park is at 4300 Pinetree Drive. From Ocean Drive, go west on 8th Street, then north (right) onto Collins Avenue/Highway A1A. Turn left onto Arthur Godfrey Road, right onto Pinetree Drive, left onto West 45th Street, then left again onto Pinetree Drive to the park. 305/673-7730.

7 Polo Park

 (See Greater Miami map on page 538)

Set behind a school, these roughly eight acres of open, unfenced, mostly unshaded grassy fields get their name from the polo statue located by the tennis courts. Hot dogs can find some shade under the strangler figs that reach skyward from the park's borders. But this park is mostly devoted to human pursuits—basketball, racquetball, and a ball field.

Park any time on West 42nd Street by Jefferson Avenue. During school hours, parking is forbidden in the lot on the western park boundary on Michigan Avenue. 4301 N. Michigan Avenue. 305/673-7730.

8 Belle Isle Park

 (See Greater Miami map on page 538)

Nothing like the well-known park by the same name in Detroit, this little bit of a green spot is set in the shadows of several condominiums and is no great

DIVERSIONS

Go to the dogs—on foot or on skates: If you do nothing else with your urban dog in Greater Miami, you must visit **Lincoln Road.** Perfect for dogs who love the feel of concrete under their paws, the sights and smells of plentiful sidewalk cafés and strangers passing by will keep sniffers twitching. Some say people actually come to this relaxed pedestrian mall to show off their dogs. The big activity is lounging at a sidewalk café (see Places to Eat), but if your dog pines to walk, he'll enjoy padding along the wide concrete pedestrian mall to window-shop. There is precious little grass, so when your pup needs relief, head to a narrow, half-block stretch of green on Washington Avenue, just north of Lincoln Road.

At least a couple of shops allow pets inside, including Fritz's Skate Shop, 726 Lincoln Rd.; 305/532-1954. Humans can rent in-line skates ($24 daily, $8 hourly), then glide off to skate down the Lincoln Road mall as a leashed pooch runs alongside. It's a new take on walking the dog.

Your little doggy can try on cowboy hats and denim jackets at The Dog Bar, a pet boutique offering unusual gear (including dog strollers) at 723 N. Lincoln Lane, just around the corner from Lincoln Road mall; 305/532-5654.

Lincoln Road is a fun place to spend an afternoon. We saw a fellow with two golden retrievers inch his way down the pedestrian mall in a curious way. He tossed two tennis balls down the sidewalk for his retrievers to fetch while he peered into shop windows. They had the routine down: Toss, retrieve, move a few feet down the mall, toss, retrieve, move down the mall again.

---

paw shakes. It would be a pleasant enough turning-around point if you happen to be walking from home. But finding a parking spot to make a quick stop may be a problem. During our Sunday visit, absolutely no one was in the fairly shady park—but every parking space was taken (probably by condo residents). A sign threatens a $500 fine for not leashing or cleaning up after Fido.

The park is immediately south of Dade Boulevard (which leads to the Venetian Causeway) on Belle Isle, the little island just west of the Miami Beach "mainland" as you head west toward Miami. 305/673-7730.

◙ Island View Park

 (See Greater Miami map on page 538)

Seagulls on the lookout for handouts fly overhead at this strip of land overlooking Biscayne Bay. Sometimes, they get them. Some of the half-dozen picnic tables here are shaded, and it's a nice spot to sit at a bench and gaze at the water and the sailboats anchored in northern Biscayne Bay. Anglers can launch a boat here or fish from a boardwalk. Kids may like the playground.

The park is basically on the western edge of Miami Beach, at the Venetian Causeway. It's at Sunset Harbor Drive and Dade Boulevard (which leads to the Venetian Causeway). 305/673-7730.

10 Flamingo Park

🐾🐾🐾 (See Greater Miami map on page 538)

One of the largest stretches of greenery in Miami Beach, this park has changed a lot since the days when hippies camped out here in 1972 to protest the Vietnam War at the Republican National Convention in Miami Beach.

Today, Flamingo Park is a heaven-sent break for dogs longing to run free. After many requests from the public, the city installed a leash-free area. Actually, there are two of them, right next to each other, each about 170 feet by 110 feet, and separated in the middle by ficus trees. A doggie water fountain is provided.

Leashed dogs can also head to the grassy path down the middle of this 36-acre park. Many tall melaleuca and ficus trees provide shade by the basketball courts, and a small patch of green is found next to the baseball stadium. Generally, though, it's best to stay away from the stadium areas, which are off-limits to dogs. But it is comical to see signs declaring No Dogs and Leash and Clean Up After Your Pet sharing the same panels of chain-link fence surrounding the stadium. Apparently some irresponsible dog owners are endangering dogs' opportunities here by failing to keep their buddies leashed and not cleaning up properly. Don't compound the problem.

The park stretches from 11th Street to 15th Street, between Meridian and Michigan avenues. 305/673-7766 or 305/673-7730.

11 Holocaust Memorial

🕯🐾 (See Greater Miami map on page 538)

It's an impressive sight: A sculpture of a giant hand—about 40 feet tall—rising from the ground, bearing a tattooed identification number. Farther down the arm, scores of tiny sculptured people are climbing up the arm as if trying to escape. Your leashed dog may walk along the lime rock walkway that surrounds the sculpture and its circular pond, but she is not supposed to set paw inside the museum. For a make-do walk, cross the street to the triangular field at the northeast corner of busy Meridian Avenue and Dade Boulevard; keep your dog leashed. Street parking is available there. The memorial is at 1933 Meridian Ave., near City Hall. 305/538-1663.

12 Lummus Park

🐾🐾 (See Greater Miami map on page 538)

This long, linear oceanfront park in the Art Deco District features plenty of pigeons your dog will be tempted to chase and a wide, curvy sidewalk to follow. It's a natural destination for those who want to walk off the pounds gained at the sidewalk cafés crammed side by side across the street. Take a break at the Adirondack chairs or benches and notice how the curvy coconut palms lean like armless outfielders trying to stop a fly ball.

A fine of up to $200 can be levied on dogs who are caught running leash-free through this largely unshaded park. And dogs are forbidden on the beach. They are technically allowed to attend events at the makeshift grandstand, but a parks department staffer advised against it because of crowds. Kids will appreciate the swings and jungle gym.

The park is at Ocean Drive and 13th Street, on the east side of town, and stretches for several blocks. 305/673-7730 or 305/672-1270.

13 Marjory Stoneman Douglas Park

😃 (See Greater Miami map on page 538)

Maggie wasn't too impressed when we visited, back when this place was called Ocean Beach Park (no ocean or beach for dogs, she harrumphed). But we have a soft spot in our hearts for it now that it's been named for the grande dame of Everglades restoration. Douglas wrote the classic *The Everglades: River of Grass* after rejecting an editor's suggestion to write about the comparatively puny Miami River.

The playground looks like a giant plastic toy at this small green spot dotted by coconut palms and sea grapes. Keep your dog leashed. The park is located on Ocean Drive, between Second and Third streets. 305/673-7730 or 305/672-1270.

14 South Pointe Park

😃 (See Greater Miami map on page 538)

If your dog wants to finally see water in Miami Beach without fearing the long arm of the law, head to this park. He can see—but not splash in—the ocean from this big grassy field and a short fishing pier. The park is at 1 Washington Ave. and runs from Biscayne Street to Government Cut. 305/673-7224.

PLACES TO EAT

Balans: Immediately, we were asked whether Maggie needed water, and soon a server reappeared with an actual dog bowl filled with the wet stuff. It was an impressive start to a pleasant meal at this South Beach outpost, a sister to two London locations. The eclectic continental menu changes twice a year or so. Past offerings have ranged from rack of lamb and lobster club sandwiches to chicken breast and Mediterranean pork sausages. Fancy daily specials are also available, such as the pork tenderloin in tamarind sauce. Pastas and salads are popular. All this can be washed down with champagne, wine, or pitchers of tropical drinks—sangria, planter's punch, margaritas. While we were people-watching from one of the two dozen tables (some under overhangs), a man on an adult tricycle pedaled by with his boxer in a basket in back. 1022 Lincoln Rd.; 305/534-9191.

Cafe Papillon: While entrées such as chicken cordon bleu, fish, and penne pastas may cater to heartier appetites, light eaters can try sandwiches, salads, muffins, and fruits at the dozen outdoor tables. 530 Lincoln Rd.; 305/673-1139.

Da Leo Trattoria: If the gorgonzola rigatoni or the recommended veal marsala don't fill you up at this popular budget trattoria, then try crème brûlée for dessert. The menu includes veal, chicken, steak, lamb chops, and several pasta dishes, plus refreshing appetizers such as prosciutto with melon. Sit at one of the many pooch-permissible sidewalk tables. Reservations are suggested. 819 Lincoln Rd.; 305/674-0350.

David's Cafe II: Head to the walk-up window to ask for sugarcane juice, papaya juice, a stuffed potato, stuffed yucca, or what everyone else will likely be ordering—*café con leche.* It's a cup of atomic-powered Cuban espresso mixed with lots of hot milk, making it sort of a strong version of French café au lait. If you'd like a dinner of paella, palomilla steak or other offerings, ask to sit at the outdoor tables packed in the authentic Cuban eatery's doorway. 1654 Meridian Ave.; 305/672-8707.

Les Deux Fontaines: The maître d' suggests taking a sidewalk table with your pooch at this casual yet elegant seafood-oriented eatery. Maine lobster is served year-round. 1230-38 Ocean Dr; 305/672-7878.

Lincoln Road Cafe: What used to be a place for simple Cuban fare and sandwiches has branched out a bit into things American, including lots of beef and pork dishes. But you can still go Cuban. Ten outdoor tables are protected from the rain by a canopy. You can try a *cafe cubano* for a jolt of caffeine. 941 Lincoln Rd; 305/538-8066.

Mango's Tropical Cafe: On a hot day, settle your pooch down under the gargantuan white cloth umbrellas here and—your dog may be good at this—dig in! Finger food, steaks, seafood, pasta, Mexican dishes, and sandwiches are available, and the daiquiris must be delicious considering how many people order them. 900 Ocean Dr; 305/673-4422.

News Cafe: Not only can you eat at this 24-hour café, but you can sit at a sidewalk table and read to your newshound from a magazine purchased here. Also for sale are hand-rolled cigars, which dogs may sneeze at. 800 Ocean Dr.; 305/538-6397.

Pacific Time: Your dog won't find a plain burger on the menu at Chef Jonathan Eismann's pricey dinner-only restaurant, but she can try a vegetarian portobello steak. No dish served at the half-dozen linen-topped outdoor tables is routine: Witness the sweet sake-roasted sea bass, the herb-and-truffle-roasted chicken, and the barbecue duck breast with fresh plums, port wine, huckleberries, and mandarin duck sauce. Reservations are recommended, and the place gets crowded. The earlier the better if you're coming with a pooch, staffers advise. 915 Lincoln Rd.; 305/534-5979.

Paninoteca: European sandwiches are the craze here, running the gamut from vegetarian sandwiches to hearty veal alternatives. Quiche, orzo salads, and couscous number among other ever-changing eats. We saw a yellow Lab sit with his snout resting in the lap of his master in hopes of getting handouts. (And Maggie took a mental note of that untried tactic.) Find a seat at the outdoor wooden tables. 809 Lincoln Rd.; 305/538-0058.

Pelican Cafe: Dogs tired of trendy foods might hope their dining companions order a burger or the daily pizza at a sidewalk table here. Of course, this *is* Ocean Drive, so more sophisticated canine palates can beg for bites of the daily fish specials, such as blackened dolphinfish with roasted onions and fries. 826 Ocean Dr.; 305/673-1000.

Pizza Rustica: Pooches and pizza—what could be finer? Your little ball of furry fun will have her choice of 20 kinds of pizza here. But be forewarned: Pizza is about it as far as the menu goes. This is in South Beach, but an excitable dog might feel more comfortable here because it's away from the crazy scene on Ocean Drive. 836 Washington Ave.; 305/674-8244.

Restaurant Tiramesu: Canine early-birds make out at this decade-old eatery since the "beat the clock" price you pay matches the time you arrive: $5.30 if you show up at 5:30 P.M., $7.30 if you arrive at 7:30 P.M. The savings end at 7:30 P.M., though. Spaghetti pomodoro and linguine alla carbonara number among the special pasta offerings in this special offer. 721 Lincoln Rd.; 305/532-4538.

Sushi Rock Cafe: Besides sushi—of course—you can try tempura and teriyaki at this popular spot where dogs are welcome at outdoor tables. It's removed just a bit from the frenetic Ocean Drive scene, but still in South Beach. 1351 Collins Ave.; 305/532-2133.

Van Dyke Cafe: Two lion statues guard a door of this tasteful café, bordered by Lincoln Road. Dogs far and wide know they may plop down with their people at the 20-plus outdoor tables to people-watch and listen to the pleasant strains of jazz at night. On a drizzly Sunday, we counted two dogs and only one human beneath the deep-red canopy. Watch out for one potential leg-lift target: the British-style phone booth outside. 1641 Jefferson Ave.; 305/534-3600.

Yuca: Innovative Cuban cuisine is the catch phrase at this lunch/ brunch/ dinner eatery, where daily specials may include ribs with spicy guava sauce or cured Chilean salmon with fresh dill hollandaise. Sit at one of a dozen linen-covered sidewalk tables. 501 Lincoln Rd.; 305/532-YUCA.

PLACES TO STAY

Alexander All-Suite Luxury Hotel: Before turning your car over to the valet at this 152-room hotel, you could forget room service and instead dine at a pooch-permissible eatery farther south. Rates at this home of two pools and an exercise room are $225–1,250. Of the $500 pet deposit, $250 is not refundable. 5225 Collins Ave., Miami Beach; 305/865-6500; www.alexanderhotel.com.

Fontainebleau Hilton Resort and Towers: Elvis, Bob Hope, Jackie Gleason, and Lucille Ball are among the celebrities who have visited this 1950s jewel in Miami Beach. Informality is the rule: No need to wear proper attire in the lobby—just throw something over your swimsuit. For a stuffier feel, walk into the Dining Galleries, a locally noted candlelit restaurant with secluded tables (no dogs allowed). The 18-acre, 1,206-room resort overlooking the Atlantic Ocean has had at least $120 million in renovations since 1978. If you don't want to swim beneath the cascading waterfalls of the rock grotto lagoons, then the boat rentals, sauna, tennis courts, 20 on-site shops and businesses, 12 restaurants, lounges, nightclubs, and other amenities can entertain you instead. Each guest room has two phone lines, so your dog can arf at Aunt Gertrude while you call the boss. One dog under 20 pounds is permitted per room. Rates are $215–370. 4441 Collins Ave., Miami Beach; 305/538-2000; www.Fontainebleau.Hilton.com.

Franklin Hotel: Pooch-permissible Lummus Park is across the street from this circa-1934 restored art deco/Mediterranean-style hotel. Beyond the small lobby bar, the 48 air-conditioned rooms feature cable TV and a small fridge for storing doggy bags. Several dogs are repeat canine customers, but you must ask for co-owner Howard Cohen when reserving a room. Dogs must be under 30 pounds. No puppies, please. Rates are $90–125 in season, $50–65 at other times. The $150 pet deposit is refundable barring canine calamities. 860 Collins Ave., Miami Beach; 305/531-5541.

Hotel Ocean: Not only may dogs sleep at this Mediterranean-style hotel built in the 1930s, but they may eat at its sidewalk café, Les Deux Fontaines (see Places to Eat, above). All 27 air-conditioned rooms have safes, VCRs, wet bars—and period furniture. Rates are $190–515, plus $15 daily for pets. 1230-38 Ocean Dr., Miami Beach; 305/672-2579; www.hotelocean.com.

Loews Miami Beach Hotel: This upscale 800-room hotel about four blocks from the convention center provides a perfect weekend getaway for Zeus, the mutt owned by local humane society spokeswoman Kelly Grimm. "There is a special pet menu that Zeus always likes to order room service from," Grimm says. Rates are $210–460 a night, but weekend packages may cut the cost at times. 1601 Collins Ave., Miami Beach; 305/604-1601; www.loewshotels. com/hotels/miamibeach/default.asp.

Raleigh Hotel: With the 24-hour room service at this 111-room, full-service art deco hotel, dogs can hold out hope that they'll feast on scraps around the clock. Rates run $195–750 in the off-season and $295–1,500 in the winter (not including the penthouse, which was $5,000 a night last we checked.) *Conde Nast* named the hotel's pool "one of the sexiest hotel pools in America"; dogs aren't allowed there, of course. 1775 Collins Ave., Miami Beach; 305/534-6300; www.raleighhotel.com

Villa Paradiso: All 17 apartments overlook a tropical courtyard and include kitchens, bathrooms, and free local calls. Rates are $99–150. The $100 doggy deposit is refunded barring any misdeeds. Small pets only, please. And, unfortunately, dogs are only permitted in the off-season. 1415 Collins Ave., Miami Beach; 305/532-0616; www.villaparadisohotel.com.

Virginia Gardens

PARKS, BEACHES, AND RECREATION AREAS

15 Virginia Gardens Park

🐾 (See Greater Miami map on page 538)

Dogs aren't allowed in the ball fields, but they can walk around a little patch of grass at the city's sole park. So stop only if you happen to be in the area. The park is at 6498 NW 38th Terrace. 305/871-6104.

Coral Gables

The lack of No Dogs signs is enough to make a pooch rejoice—but don't. Sure, the dreaded placards aren't seen at each and every city park, but you're supposed to know that Code 5-12 prohibits dogs in this appearance-conscious city's parks. Why aren't signs always posted? "That in itself is unattractive," sniffs a staff member of the city attorney's office. If the watchdogs notice a problem with canine scofflaws in a particular place, they erect a sign. Dogs are allowed only on thoroughfares and waysides.

PARKS, BEACHES, AND RECREATION AREAS

16 Country Club Prado

🐾🐾 (See Greater Miami map on page 538)

Not an actual park, this large grassy median in a neighborhood of fine homes is nonetheless bigger than some designated parks. Leave your car beside the courtyard of the Spanish-style gated entrance to Coral Gables, found at the north end of Country Club Prado. During our visit, a couple was admiring the trellis and fountain in the courtyard, but otherwise the street was devoid of people. The courtyard is a good place for a brief doggy break, although there isn't much shade.

Walk south as far as you'd like along the wide, unshaded median of this little-traversed street. It's just plain grass, so a short walk will probably suffice for leashed dogs who prefer woods and beaches. Only the strongest dogs, and only on cool afternoons, should attempt to walk the entire length of the median (about a mile one-way) before turning the corner to find two large grassy triangles near the city's western entrance on Coral Way. Big old oaks, some sport-

DIVERSIONS

Ride in a Rolls fit for a Queenie: Queen Elizabeth has ridden in a limousine hired from **Vintage Rolls-Royce Limousines of Coral Gables,** and your little Queenie can, too. It isn't easy finding a Rolls company that welcomes pooches, but a small, well-mannered dog may step into the vintage limos used in a Grey Poupon commercial—as well as classic cars such as a 1947 Baby Phantom and a 1957 Bentley—"as long as he goes to the bathroom before," says a staffer.

As for the size of potential canine customers, one staffer made it clear that small dogs are preferred when she said, "I hope it isn't a Great Dane." Just think of what the neighbor dogs will say when your limo driver—wearing a Nehru jacket, hat, and riding pants—shuts the limo door behind your pup. Most customers head to weddings or the airport. Prices start at $110. Call 305/662-5763.

Prefer to drive your own vehicle to take a windshield tour of **Coral Gables?** Pick up a free map at Coral Gables City Hall, 405 Biltmore Way (at the west end of Miracle Mile), to take a self-guided driving tour that gives your pooch a peek into developer George Merrick's past. Merrick envisioned a total Mediterranean scene for swanky Coral Gables, planning boulevards, plazas, and intriguing entryways—until a land boom went bust in the 1920s. His company went bankrupt, and Merrick ended up operating a fishing camp on Matecumbe Key. His final job: Miami postmaster. "It's really kind of a sad story," says Ellen Uguccioni, former Coral Gables Historic Preservation administrator. See some of Merrick's work on the driving tour of Coral Gables, which includes Merrick's house at 907 Coral Way. Call 305/446-1657.

ing the tiny curled fingers of resurrection ferns on their bark, shade some of this western entrance. A sidewalk rims one of the grassy, mostly open triangles.

Parking is a problem. Try to find a spot beside the courtyard at the Coral Gables entrance on Country Club Prado, just south of Southwest Eighth Street. If that's impossible, consider parking along Southwest Eighth Street. Parking is forbidden along the Country Club Prado median itself. 305/446-1657.

17 University of Miami

🐾🐾🐾 🐕 (See Greater Miami map on page 538)

A grassy field where helicopters land on rare occasion attracts many a dog early in the morning. Best of all, dogs may scamper leash-free, as long as they're under voice control. When Pat Hayden served as a University of Miami crime prevention officer, she sometimes took her pooch to the field on the southeastern side of campus, along busy four-lane Ponce de Leon Boulevard.

Leashed dogs may follow the walkways through the pretty campus if they don't get in the way of students; use your judgment. A lion statue stands guard outside the Sigma Alpha Epsilon fraternity house on San Amaro Drive.

At Suarez Street and Ponce de Leon Boulevard, you'll find a square block of nothingness—simply a field with a few pines, oaks, and ficus trees. Metered parking spots are nearby. For some running room, go to the corner of Granada and Ponce de Leon boulevards, which has a quite large unfenced lot with no trees at its center. A long open area dotted by royal palms is found at the eastern end of Miller Drive. Clean up after your pooch. 305/284-2211 or 305/284-6666.

18 Pinewood Cemetery Historic Site

🐾🐾🐾 🐕 (See Greater Miami map on page 538)

You wouldn't know that this slice of lush subtropical woods was a cemetery if it weren't for the small sign outside and the occasional grave marker that you'll encounter when you follow the winding mulched paths. The sporadic soft chirps of cardinals and the warbles of other winged creatures may help you forget where you are until you stumble upon the gravestone of, for instance, Richard Steele, 1848-1920, journalist and humorist. Continue to follow the network of trails through the pines and oaks, and you may find the marker of Lemuel O. Anderson, 1876-1934, private in First Tennessee Infantry in Spanish-American War. What's remarkable is that the cemetery, here since 1855, is less than a mile from busy U.S. 1, but it feels a world away. Clean up after your leashed pooch.

The historic site is at Sunset Drive and Erwin Road/Southwest 47th Avenue. A low-rise coral rock wall surrounds the cemetery, whose walk-in entrance is south of Sunset Drive. 305/446-6800 (ask for historic preservation).

19 Old Cutler Road

🐾🐾 (See Greater Miami map on page 538)

Joggers and bicyclists love passing the fine homes of tree-canopied Old Cutler Road, where big, wide leaves shade the thankful pooches who follow the bike path and the sidewalk. You'll see odd ficus trees that drop down roots from their branches to form alternate trunks—potential leg-lift targets for dogs. Walk as far as you'd like, but turn around at a comfortable distance for your pooch. Bring water, leash your dog, and clean up after him.

Parking is difficult, so head to the few parking spaces east of the landscaped traffic circle called Cartagena Plaza, at Sunset Drive and Old Cutler Road. It's at the eastern terminus of Sunset Drive. Don't sit at a bench to gaze onto the Coral Gables Waterway from nearby Ingraham Park (a quick walk across the waterway): The city insists dogs aren't permitted there. 305/539-3000 or 305/446-1657.

PLACES TO EAT

Atlanta Bread Co.: We remember what we thought when this chain first showed up near our house in Fort Lauderdale: Bread? They serve bread? But really, you can enjoy soups, sandwiches, salads, even breakfast. 137 Miracle Mile; 305/444-5320.

Baja Fresh: The folks at this chain say their Mexican food is fresh and healthy, and we believe them. They say dogs are fine at the sidewalk tables, and we believe them. 230 Miracle Mile; 305/442-9596.

Café at Books and Books: Dogged pursuit of the charms of books is the name of the game here at this venerable independent bookstore. Grab a tome (well-behaved dogs can go in the store) and then wolf down regular sandwiches or panini (popular ones include turkey; avocado and cheddar; and prosciutto and mozzarella). Or check the two daily soup offerings. 265 Aragon Ave. (1 block north of Miracle Mile); 305/448-9599.

Chispa: This contemporary Latin fusion spot counts ceviche, empanadas, flatbread gourmet pizzas, and more among patrons' favorites. Chispa means "spark" in Spanish. It's at the Villages of Merrick Park, 225 Altara Ave.; 305/648-2600.

Le Provencal: Casual French is the way the proprietors describe this eatery, but the offerings are fancy: rack of lamb, filet mignon, duck, shrimp, sea bass, and so forth. You'll sit on a covered patio by the railing, while your dog sits on the other side in easy range for flying treats. 382 Miracle Mile; 305/448-8984.

Panini Café Bar: Yep, they got them there panini—you know, the grilled sandwiches—plus regular sandwiches, salads, pastries, and coffee. 169 Miracle Mile; 305/442-0801.

Tarpon Bend: "The Restaurant People" is the unassuming name taken on by the proprietors here, who also run the divine River House restaurant in Fort Lauderdale, as well as versions of Tarpon Bend in Fort Lauderdale and Weston. The emphasis is on seafood—lobster, ceviche, oysters, and stone crabs are popular—but steaks, burgers, and more are available. 65 Miracle Mile; 305/444-3210.

Westchester

This neighborhood tucked between Coral Gables and Kendall is pretty much covered in concrete, although there are a few spots for Spot to get a bite.

PLACES TO EAT

Arbetter Hot Dogs: "Hot dogs, fries, and corndogs"—that pretty much completes the menu. 8747 SW 40th St./Bird Rd.; 305/207-0555.

Latin American: This is one of a gazillion Latin American chain restaurants in Miami but the only one we know where it's possible to plop down outside with the pooch. You order "to go" (or "para llevar") and sit at a table outside. They offer all manner of Cuban food. Robert's favorite is *masas de puerco*—fried pork chunks; Maggie thinks they're great! 6820 SW 40th St./ Bird Rd.; 305/207-0555.

Miami Subs: The menu here has a staggering number of choices. Gyros are a good bet, but, gee, there's so much to choose from. The street here used to be known by locals as Galloway Road, although it's since been re-nicknamed "Brothers the Rescue Martyrs Boulevard" in honor of those who lost their lives trying to save Cuban refugees in the Florida Straits. 2501 SW 87th Ave.; 305/559-8616.

South Miami

A number of dog-friendly restaurants are springing up in South Miami. This is a good spot to grab a bite if you're visiting the Pinewood Cemetery or the University of Miami (see Coral Gables). You could walk to these eateries from the cemetery.

PLACES TO EAT

Beverly Hills Café: How anyone confused this laid-back and fun corner of the county with that overwrought, star-studded suburb on the West Coast, we don't know. But, wow! This wonderful eatery advertises, "The endless search is over... food, friends, music, doggies." Tucked into a patio near Sunset Drive and Red Road, close to where South Miami and Coral Gables come together, this restaurant offers a "Fresh Express" market where you might get coffee, bagels, and other baked goods. Or, later in the day, choose from offerings such as cheeseburgers, chicken, salads, pasta, skirt steak, or the popular teriyaki salmon. Kids are also welcome, and you get one hour's free parking. The menu offerings go on and on. 1549 Sunset Dr.; 305/666-6618.

Blu la Pizzeria Del Sol: We can't quite translate that, but suffice it to say it means tasty and mostly light Italian dishes, including—of course!—pizza, but also antipasti and panini. A variation on the pizza, though also from the wood-fired oven, is the foccacia. It's sidewalk dining, so your pooch will have to be fairly well behaved to fit in here. 7201 SW 59th Ave.; 305/666-9285.

Deli Lane Café: It's known for breakfasts, but you can get pasta, pizza, or sandwiches in the afternoon and evening. The outdoor seating area is popular even among folks who aren't with dogs. 1407 Sunset Dr.; 305/665-0606.

Sunset Tavern: Pizzas—whole-wheat crust or regular—are one of the more popular items here, along with the pressed-duck sandwiches and fresh fish. It features about 50 rotating daily specials, which have included shrimp fra diavolo, teriyaki tuna, and maple-glazed meatloaf. 5818 Sunset Dr.; 305/665-9996.

Trattoria Sole: Pasta and seafood are the favored dishes of diners who patronize this Northern Italian restaurant. They are perhaps proudest of their homemade ravioli. Try the crabmeat version for a treat. The menu offers a mushroom and asparagus risotto, but truth be told, you can get risotto made with seafood or whatever you like. "Tonight we had a foie gras risotto," we were told on the evening we inquired. 5894 Sunset Dr.; 305/666-6392.

Whip 'n' Dip Ice Cream Shoppe: Eat ice cream while sitting at a bench out front or while taking a quick walk to the nearby limestone walls that make up the old city gates of next-door Coral Gables. 1407 Sunset Dr.; 305/665-2565.

Miami

Miami is an international city, but don't envision dogs sitting at the feet of bar patrons or taking the escalator to a commuter train as they do in London. Yes, Miami's new slogan is "the world meets here." But this world doesn't necessarily include canines. (To be fair, Coconut Grove is technically part of Miami, and two leash-free parks are available there. See Coconut Grove, this chapter.)

Here, only a few hundred miles from the coast of Cuba, you'll see billboards that talk about something dogs care about—*sabor* (flavor)—and plenty of signs beckoning customers in Spanish. If your dog already knows how to shake hands, teach him the command in Spanish to get into the local rhythm. Make your pup sit. Say, *"Da me el mano"* (DAH may el MAH-no). Maggie also knows *¡sienta se!* (see-YENT-ah-say), meaning "sit!"

PARKS, BEACHES, AND RECREATION AREAS

20 Bayfront Park

🐾🐾 (See Greater Miami map on page 538)

Plenty of vagrants once hung out at this downtown waterfront park, but they are pretty much gone now and the green expanse usually sits empty—just perfect for pooches. You can expect to be the only person with a dog in the sometimes-bustling downtown area, where you would think canines were akin to space aliens, judging by some of the surprised looks and smiles you'll get at nearby Bayside Marketplace (dogs aren't officially permitted there).

At Bayfront Park, the attraction is gazing at the calm green waters of Biscayne Bay. Dogs, however, may prefer to sniff every inch of the park's broadest grassy area at Northeast Third Street and U.S. 1. Another grassy field—found farther south and closer to the water—is partially fenced and big enough that dogs will be tempted to run leash-free. Considering that the lack of No Dogs signs here is a refreshing break from the discouraging city routine, it's best not to push your luck. Keep dogs under control. (The sole sign barring dogs is at the gated entrance to the often-locked amphitheater.)

Potentially embarrassing leg-lift targets include a statue of Christopher

Columbus and the Dade County War Memorial. Luckily, a green mound surrounding a giant, DNA-like monument to the space shuttle *Challenger* will prevent all but the most determined sniffer from making his mark there. For a rest, sit at a bench on the bayfront's little dock.

The city park, also known as Mildred & Claude Pepper Bayfront Park, is on Biscayne Blvd./U.S. 1 at Northeast Third Street. 305/358-7550.

2️⃣1️⃣ Cuban Memorial Boulevard

🔥 🐾 (See Greater Miami map on page 538)

An eternal flame burns orange in the heart of Little Havana as a monument to John F. Kennedy's failed Bay of Pigs invasion, which was supposed to liberate Cuba from communism. Starting at the flaming torch at Southwest Eighth Street/Calle Ocho, a dog can sniff out a bit of Cuban history by walking south down Southwest 13th Avenue/Cuban Memorial Boulevard. Really just a long, glorified median strip, this patch of green is home to several monuments: a map of Cuba, a statue of Mother Mary and Baby Jesus, a monument to Cuban revolutionary José Martí, and a few other remembrances. The walk spans about seven blocks, ending at about Southwest 15th Street. For a break, sit at benches under a big spreading tree at Southwest 10th Street.

The torch is at Southwest Eighth Street/Calle Ocho and Southwest 13th Avenue/Cuban Memorial Boulevard. Park on either road. 305/324-8127 or 305/539-3000.

2️⃣2️⃣ Rickenbacker Causeway and Beach

🐾🐾🐾 (See Greater Miami map on page 538)

Time to dog-paddle at Miami's only official (or at least semiofficial) dog beach! Some dog people rave about this long stretch of man-made beach, which tends to be gravelly underfoot unless you stake out a less-rocky spot on the sunnier southeast side of the bridge. Maggie preferred to chase pigeons and sniff around here. She ignored the pretty bay with its Key Biscayne skyline, except when pelicans dive-bombed for fish. Other dogs joyously plunge into the water to fetch sticks and then hang out afterward for a picnic. Technically, leashes are required.

The best beach, known locally as Hobie Beach, is on the south side of the causeway. Or you can try the less-crowded north side. Together, they form more than a mile of beachfront. Expect crowds on popular picnicking holidays.

Once the leading contender for the most littered dog beach in Florida, the causeway park is well maintained these days, and garbage cans are provided throughout. You may fish from a pier here, but Jet Skis are prohibited, helping to keep things calm for skittish Chihuahuas. This area is maintained by the Dade County Public Works Department.

From I-95, take the Key Biscayne exit (Exit 1). Go east, following signs to Key Biscayne and the Rickenbacker Causeway. The causeway is a toll road

DIVERSIONS

¡Da un paseo (Go for a walk)! Stroll the brick sidewalks of Little Havana's **Calle Ocho** and introduce your dog to a dizzying array of Spanish-language signs: *la barrata* (the bargain), *mejores precios* (best prices), and *comidas para llevar* (food to go), to name a few. It's a stimulating trip, if only because of the atomic-level caffeine delivered in demitasse cups at walk-up cafeteria windows. Start at Cuban Memorial Boulevard (see Parks, Beaches, and Recreation Areas), then walk west on Southwest Eighth Street/Calle Ocho.

At tiny Maximo Gomez Park at Southwest 15th Avenue, you're likely to see grandfatherly Cubans playing dominoes. Two blocks west on Eighth Street, the sign for Southwest 17th Avenue also reads "Teddy Roosevelt Avenue." The mustachioed leader helped free Cuba from Spain by leading the Rough Riders up San Juan Hill. Calle Ocho is frayed around the edges and some landmarks, such as El Pub restaurant, have closed down. You're more likely to bump into recent immigrants from Nicaragua or elsewhere than the Cubans who first injected Latin flair into Miami four decades ago, after Fidel Castro took over Cuba. Head to the walk-up window at El Coladito Cafeteria, 1837 SW Eighth St., to order Cuban coffee with your pooch. Or choose from other walk-up cafés. The *cafe cubano* will deliver more than enough pep to get you back to your car.

named for World War I flying ace Eddie Rickenbacker; it connects Miami and Key Biscayne. 305/854-2468 or 305/375-2694.

PLACES TO EAT

Baja Fresh: The ingredients here are fresh and the food is always prepared to order, even though it's a chain. Be sure to try all the serve-yourself salsas. 1010 S. Miami Ave.; 305/523-2393.

El Coladito Cafeteria: Approach the walk-up window with your pooch to order a jolt—er, cup—of Cuban coffee to go. 1837 Southwest Eighth Street; 305/649-6052.

Football Sandwich Shop: Go inside to order from the wide-ranging menu of sandwiches, including turkey and the Superstrami (pastrami and turkey). Then take the food outside to share with your pooch at a table. 8484 Northeast Second Ave.; 305/756-7996.

River Oyster Bar: You may have to talk your way onto the few little bar stools at tiny tables outside this tasteful oyster and seafood bar, but it's been done before. The ceviche is said to be good, and there are always fresh fish specials on the blackboard. 650 S. Miami Ave.; 305/530-1915.

Rosinella: This traditional Italian place has some outdoor seating, and it's tucked into a little-known, quiet section of Miami south of downtown, across the Miami River. Pizza, pasta, and seafood are all on offer, or try the gnocchi. 1040 S. Miami Ave.; 305/372-5786.

PLACES TO STAY

AmeriSuites: This business-oriented, all-suite high-rise charges a one-time $10 pet fee no matter how many nights you stay. Rates are $90–129. 3655 Northwest 82nd Ave., Miami; 305/718-8292; www.amerisuites.com.

Baymont Inn and Suites: Small dogs may sleep in rooms set aside for guests with pets. How small? "Not big." (A few years ago they were saying 80 pounds.) And only one per room. Rates are $70–145 and the $25 pet deposit is refundable. 3501 Northwest LeJeune Rd., Miami; 305/871-1777; www.baymontinns.com/lq.

Hampton Inn: Miami's dog beach, Rickenbacker Causeway, is two miles from this downtown-area motel with a pool. Rates are $89–125. 2500 Brickell Ave., Miami; 305/854-2070; www.hamptoninn.com.

Holiday Inn Downtown: This 14-story, 256-room hotel adjoining Miami's convention center is four miles from the dog-friendly cafés in Coconut Grove and three miles from South Beach. Rates are $109–160. The pet fee is $35 per stay. 200 Southeast Second Ave., Miami; 305/374-3000; www.holiday-inn.com.

Homestead Village: Budget-minded corporate canines may sleep at this 105-unit extended-stay lodging, where every room has a kitchenette (good for storing doggy bags). Expect to pay about $80–90 a night; weekly rates also are available. A refundable $75 pet deposit is required. 8720 Northwest 33rd St., Miami; 305/436-1811;.www.homesteadhotels.com.

Hotel Sofitel: This 285-room, airport-area hotel overlooking a lagoon is part of a chain with locations in Budapest, Montreal, San Francisco, and other big cities. A French bistro, bakery, restaurant, and a shop featuring items from France explain the hotel's slogan: classic comfort with a French accent. Rates are $125–219. 5800 Blue Lagoon Dr., Miami; 305/264-4888; www.sofitel.com.

La Quinta: Free local calls and breakfast pastries are featured at this business-oriented motel that offers some suites. Rates are $88–138. 7401 Northwest 36th St., Miami; 305/599-9902; www.lq.com.

Red Roof Inn: At this poolside motel, rates are $67–127. 3401 Northwest LeJeune Rd., Miami; 305/871-4221; www.redroof.com

Coconut Grove

Miami police officer Audrey Eckert got tired of the same old routine: She would pull up to local parks in her police cruiser and people with dogs would head for the hills. Reason: The dogs were off leash—a definite no-no.

"Everybody would run, when all I wanted to do was talk to them," Eckert recalls. She wasn't planning to bust them, just "see where their heads were at," she says.

"We had massive problems—the two-leggers arguing with the four-leggers every day," Eckert said. Inspired by San Francisco's Fort Funston and other dog parks she had seen in California, the resourceful officer hatched a plan for dog parks in the Grove. After checking with the city attorney and parks department, Eckert started scratching around for money to make her plan a reality.

Ralston Purina generously came through with $30,000 for fencing, lighting, water supplies, and more. Ace Hardware/Shell Lumber came up with some benches. Today, Eckert has created leash-free zones at two parks, though both will require continued work to become fully developed over the next few years.

And you know what? These dog parks actually worked to help the police department with its basic crime-fighting mission. Neighbors are meeting each other at the dog park and—get this—talking to each other! "This has brought the whole community together," Eckert says. "People who hadn't spoken to each other for 10 years, now they're housesitting each others' houses."

Although the dog parks are the biggest draw for pups in the Grove, they're not the end of the fun. This is a place to which hippies "followed the sun" in the 1960s and 1970s, when Robert was growing up in Miami. Today, instead of Birkenstocks, you'll see neon signs and other advertisements for the sidewalk cafés of the now-yuppified Grove—many of which are fine places for dogs to lounge with their people.

PARKS, BEACHES, AND RECREATION AREAS

23 Alice Wainwright Park

😻 (See Greater Miami map on page 538)

Tucked around the corner from Madonna's old digs, this quiet, off-the-beaten-path park features a spectacular view of Biscayne Bay and Key Biscayne. Big, old live oaks are covered in resurrection ferns, and the waterfront is dotted by coconut palms. This is a great place to see the bluffs that characterize this part of Coconut Grove, the ancient shorelines from when the seas were much higher. Dogs might enjoy a short walk or a barbecue here. Humans might enjoy the basketball courts.

The park is at 2845 Brickell Ave., not far north of Vizcaya and the Museum of Science; 305/416-1320.

24 Kennedy Park

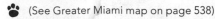 (See Greater Miami map on page 538)

This large park with a stunning view of beautiful Biscayne Bay has long attracted furry-faced creatures seeking leg room, and it was acknowledged as an informal off-leash area when Robert lived nearby. But in recent years, thanks to Miami police officer Audrey Eckert, the Ralston Purina Company, and others, an officially sanctioned off-leash area has been established here. Hooray!

After a Valentine's Day ribbon cutting in 2001, the teardrop-shaped grassy knoll in the rear of the park was halved, with half fenced off for the off-leash area. Inside 725 linear feet of fence is "enough room for you to throw your Frisbee and have Fido run around to catch it," Eckert said.

Running water is provided, and we saw one dog very happy to cool off in it by taking a little mini-bath. The park is at 2200 S. Bayshore Dr., less than a mile northeast of the Coconut Grove shopping district; 305/416-1320 or 305/579-6018.

25 Metrorail

(See Greater Miami map on page 538)

If your dog is desperate for a shady walk, consider following a bike path that runs along the west side of Dixie Highway. Much of the curvy path gets some kind of sun protection from trees or overhead Metrorail tracks. Park at the Metrorail station across from the Museum of Science, 3280 S. Miami Avenue.

26 Barnacle Historic State Park

(See Greater Miami map on page 538)

It's easy to miss this shady retreat hidden in the bustling maw of Coconut Grove. But you may be sorry if you do. Pleasant enough to be rented for a casual wedding reception (dogs are allowed on the grounds, but not in the house), this park is the former homestead of Coconut Grove pioneer Ralph Munroe, who didn't much like crowds. Those lucky enough to show up during the limited park hours to wander beneath the shade trees and approach Munroe's peculiar house will marvel that such tranquility exists in this touristy neighborhood. The long park opens into a broad grassy expanse that slopes to the shore of picturesque Biscayne Bay.

Leashed dogs may sniff around the grounds, but they can't enter the intriguingly engineered century-old house, which stays cool without air-conditioning. The park is open 9 A.M.–4 P.M. Friday through Monday. The entrance tends to be locked except at the start of tours—10 A.M., 11:30 A.M., 1 P.M., and 2:30 P.M.—when a ranger arrives to open the gate. You must arrange for someone in your party to stay with your dog if you take the tour.

Admission is $1 per person. The site is at 3485 Main Highway. From U.S. 1,

take Grand Avenue east. When you pass Main Highway, the park will come up on your right. 305/442-6866.

27 Blanche Park

🐾🐾🐾🐕 (See Greater Miami map on page 538)

This postage stamp of a park not far from Cocowalk might not look too impressive, but it has a singular attribute that should cheer every dog's heart: It's the first official, sanctioned off-leash area in Miami. This formerly under-used spot of green under coconut palms and spreading ficus trees has become a place of magic in the Magic City, at least for the four-legged set. In a few places the green has worn thin from overuse.

In addition to a place for your pal to run, you'll find benches, a dual-service water fountain for doggies and people, and poop-scooping mitts. It's lighted at night until 9 or 10 P.M. A sprinkler system is planned, so don't be surprised to see the place torn up at some point. If that happens, trot on over to Kennedy Park, not far away (see above), which, like Blanche Park, was financed by the Ralston Purina dog food company.

The park has only a short fence around it—waist-high in places—so don't go here with an escape-artist dog, particularly if she can jump high. The park is located at the corner of Virginia Street and Shipping Avenue. 305/416-1320 or 305/579-6018 or 954/862-3440. Email Purina@ccmiami.com for more information on the park.

28 Peacock Park

🐾 (See Greater Miami map on page 538)

The two well-mannered huskies we saw running freely in the ball field seemed to consider this waterfront park a sight for sore canine eyes. Considering the county's obsession with No Domestic Animals signs, it's a wonder that this green home of tennis courts, a playground, and a basketball court has managed to hold on to its reputation as a place for dogs for so long. It's not a huge park, but the sometime festival site abuts the small Kenneth M. Myers Bayside Park to form an L-shaped green zone that permits dogs. It's a fine place to escape the nearby tourist throng. Just sit at a bench beneath big oaks.

Cars tend to zoom by on McFarlane Road, so keep your dog leashed. For an unusual snapshot, sit with your pooch at a metal bench beneath an artsy metal palm tree at Myers Park.

Peacock Park is at 2820 McFarlane Road. From U.S. 1, take Grand Avenue east. Turn right at Main Highway. The park is a few blocks down on your left. 305/444-7270.

PLACES TO EAT

There are way too many restaurants with outdoor seating in Coconut Grove for us to mention them all in these pages, but here's a representative sampling. Suffice it to say you won't have a problem getting your dog served in the Grove.

Cäafe Häagen-Dazs: Besides the famous ice cream, this café serves muffins and coffee. Order at the indoor counter and take the treats outside to a table (or sturdy fire hydrant) where your dog is waiting. 292 Grand Ave.; 305/446-8797.

Don Quixote: You can sit on gliders outside this place, as long as your dog will stay put to the side. It's Spanish food, they say, and while it's all said to be very good, the star of the show here is paella, the heady rice dish that includes seafood, chicken, and sausage. 3148 Commodore Plaza; 305/443-2774.

Greenstreet Cafe: Many dogs have plopped beneath these sidewalk tables, shaded from the sun by tasteful kelly green umbrellas. Pooches will hope for scraps from the grilled Cajun dolphinfish, Jamaican chicken wings, duck in orange sauce, or skirt steak with a green peppercorn sauce. (If you cave in on the Cajun dolphinfish, scrape off the hot spices before Fido feasts.) Live music and people-watching are part of the allure of this café, which offers pastas, salads, pizza, and more. Breakfast is served until 3 P.M., and if you're lucky you'll get to sit at one of the outdoor couches. 3110 Commodore Plaza; 305/444-0244.

Joffrey's Coffee & Tea Co.: Coffee is the main attraction, but the baked goods and desserts are nothing to turn your nose up at. Tie your dog to a table, go inside to order, then rejoin your buddy with the goodies. 3434 Main Highway; 305/448-0848.

Johnny Rockets: The waiters in bow ties and white outfits will make you wish it were 1950, if only because back then people could consume malts, burgers, fountain drinks, chili, and pies free of guilt. (Live a little; your dog doesn't mind.) Plenty of sidewalk tables await your pooch at this 1950s-style joint, found at a busy traffic triangle. 3036 Grand Ave.; 305/444-1000.

Mambo Café: They're pretty enthusiastic about dogs here, where we saw an Australian shepherd quickly served water on the day we visited. It's authentic Cuban food, although they curiously boast here about churrasco, the Argentinian steak dish. 3105 Commodore Plaza; 305/448-2768.

Scotty's Landing: This eatery near the Blanche Park off-leash area is a favorite of Zeus, who is described by his owner, Kelly Grimm, as "Humane Educator, Pet Therapist, Super Mutt, and Dog Extraordinaire." The restaurant has a huge menu that includes seafood, steaks and burgers. The waterfront restaurant near Miami City Hall is accessible by boat from the Dinner Key Marina. 3381 Pan American Dr.; 305/854-2626.

Wet Willie's: "A bar. A party. An institution." That doesn't quite sum up Wet Willie's, because it does serve some innovative twists on the food we're used to. Try the Aztec corn chowder, the salmon BLT, fried grouper, or the nachos. Daiquiris are the big hit here. Sit on a covered patio or at tables with blue umbrellas that say "Support global cooling." If you come on Sunday night, watch out—it's karaoke time! 2911 Grand Ave.; 305/443-5060.

PLACES TO STAY

Grove Isle Hotel: The elegant, all-suite hotel with airy guest rooms is located on a private island on Biscayne Bay. Lucky dogs also can hope for a doggy bag from the on-site restaurant. Dogs under 30 pounds will fork out $35 per day to stay here. Rates run $326–639 nightly. 4 Grove Isle Drive, Miami; 305/858-8300 or 800/88-GROVE (4768). www.groveisle.com.

Mayfair House: When the man known for Stupid Pet Tricks brought his show to Miami, he chose to stay at this very upscale hotel, right in the middle of the Grove's shopping and entertainment district. We're not sure if it was David Letterman's idea to book his entourage here, or perhaps that of his dog-loving ex-girlfriend, but it sure was a gas to see him at the Mayfair's rooftop pool. Pooches under 40 pounds can live in the lap of luxury at this opulent hotel with an Old World feel, located right next to the restaurants, shops, and movie theater of the Cocowalk mall. Many dog-friendly restaurants and the leash-free section of Blanche Park are an easy walk from here. Each room at Mayfair House is a little different, but they all feature hand-carved mahogany furniture and most include a Roman tub or whirlpool. Rates are $169–800, plus $20 a night for your furry friend. 3000 Florida Ave., Coconut Grove; 305/441-0000 or 800/433-4555; www.mayfairhousehotel.com

Kendall

About time! That's what Maggie says about Miami-Dade County's plans to finally build some off-leash parks here in her old haunts. The county parks department is planning bark parks at Tropical Park, 7900 SW 40th St., and at West Kendall District Park, at the corner of Southwest 120th Street and 157th Avenue. For more information and updates call the parks department at 305/755-7899.

PARKS, BEACHES, AND RECREATION AREAS

29 Power Lines

 (See Greater Miami map on page 538)

The fact that we're even suggesting a romp under a series of high-tension wires tells you something about the state of pooch-friendly parks in this popular suburb. Actually, these 10 or so acres aren't bad for running like the wind or fetching a ball for 20 minutes. The power lines cut a long Z shape into a residential neighborhood. To one side of the grassy field is a two-lane residential road, which will pose a traffic hazard if your dog doesn't obey voice commands. There are no shade trees, so a short visit is best.

The power lines are on the west side of Southwest 102nd Place, south of Kendall Drive/Southwest 88th Street. This is an unofficial park, so pull onto the grass to park parallel to the road.

PLACES TO EAT

Roberto's Taco Shop: Just a little storefront tucked back into the Kendall Mall, this place has three small tables out front, protected from the rain, where you can sit in a red rattan chair. Although folks with roots in the Caribbean and South America tend to dominate Miami, this is a traditional Mexican taquería, with tacos, nachos, and much more. It's open until the wee hours of the morning—a reason it's a favorite of students from nearby Miami-Dade Community College, whether they've been up late studying or partying. 8845 SW 107th Ave.; 305/412-7250.

PLACES TO STAY

AmeriSuites: Dogs 25 pounds or less are permitted. Rates are $99–189. 11520 Kendall Dr., Miami; 305/279-8688; www.amerisuites.com.

Quality Inn South: This 100-room poolside motel near Miami's Metrozoo supposedly accepts only small dogs, but a staffer told us, "We can't fight with everybody who has a big dog." Rates are $69–129. 14501 South Dixie Highway/U.S. 1, Miami; 305/251-2000; www.qualityinn.com.

Key Biscayne

President Richard Nixon had a winter vacation home on this northernmost island in the sun-kissed archipelago that stretches to Key West and beyond. Incidentally, well before he was president, Nixon invoked the cuddly image of his dog, Checkers, to help him fend off charges of financial improprieties when he was in the United States Senate.

PARKS, BEACHES, AND RECREATION AREAS

30 Bill Baggs Cape Florida State Park

🐾🐾🐾 (See Greater Miami map on page 538)

A dog might think he's the richest pup in the world when he surveys the calm green waters of Biscayne Bay at this historic 415-acre park on the southern tip of Key Biscayne. A welcome breeze often caresses the faces of lazy pooches who plop down comfortably at the southwestern picnic pavilion in winter. From there, your dog may gaze curiously at seven houses perched above the bay on stilts—the landless community known as Stiltsville.

You can walk your leashed dog along a sunny bike trail that hugs the aqua waters of the park's west side before curving to meet the park's main road. Go early or late in the day to protect your dog from the sun, and skip the walk in summer. This once-shady respite changed when Hurricane Andrew knocked over most of the park's towering Australian pines in 1992. Rangers have replaced the dead nonnative trees with 313 native species. While the place had a desert-like feel after Andrew, the gumbo limbo, seagrape, and other native trees growing in are starting to offer a little shade.

At the park's southeastern edge, the circa-1825 lighthouse on the Atlantic Ocean is South Florida's oldest building. It survived a Seminole siege in 1836 and had its light extinguished by Confederate sympathizers during the Civil War.

At the Boaters Grill, on No Name Harbor on the park's west side, you can get a takeout order to eat at a picnic table with your dog. Most tables are on the park's east side. The restaurant's number is 305/361-0080.

Admission is $3 per carload. The park is at 1200 S. Crandon Boulevard. From Miami, take the Rickenbacker Causeway east, which becomes Crandon Boulevard. Follow it to the end. 305/361-5811.

PLACES TO EAT

Ad Gustum Market, Deli & Grill: The name means "to one's taste" in Latin. This is great place to pick up a lunch if you're on your way to Bill Baggs Cape Florida State Park. It's first-class deli food, but there's lots more to choose from, including smoothies and even the hearts of palm salad, which is made out of the state tree, the cabbage palm. The place includes a little grocery store to round out your meal if they don't have everything you want behind the counter. Breakfast is also served; check out the omelettes. If you're eating here, get the food inside and sit at tables under blue umbrellas by Crandon Boulevard. 180 Crandon Blvd.; 305/365-9333.

Sundays on the Bay: Pull up to this popular hangout in your boat or car, and your dog may join you for food on the lower dock, by the water. Seafood and Italian dishes are the most popular. Try the Gabriel salad, featuring calamari, crab, shrimp, scallops, and avocado. Lobster is also popular. 5420 Crandon Blvd.; 305/361-6777.

Palmetto Bay

Ah, the joys of incorporation. This newly incorporated village got around to the important stuff early on and established a leash-free area.

PARKS, BEACHES, AND RECREATION AREAS

31 Perrine Wayside Bark Park

(See Greater Miami map on page 538)

Surrounded by businesses, frequented by junkies, and centered on a rock pit left over from gravel excavation when U.S. 1 was built, this was a neglected and sad place when Palmetto Bay incorporated.

Initially dog-park supporters were arguing for an off-leash park at another park, but neighbors complained. The early efforts were spearheaded by village resident Amy Boyers, who was inspired by her hyper yellow Lab.

We're not rating this park because it was just recently approved by the village council after more than a year of arguments. It's scheduled to come on line in 2006. The property sits across a canal from the Deering Estate, at U.S. 1 and Southwest 160th Street. For more information call 305/259-1234 or go to www.dogparkmiami.com.

Cutler Ridge

PLACES TO STAY

Baymont Inn and Suites: Maybe *Air Bud* will be offered as an in-room movie during your stay at this 107-unit motel in southern Miami-Dade County. Two dogs of 15 pounds or less each or one dog 15 to 50 pounds is permitted. Rates are $69–199. 10821 Caribbean Blvd., Cutler Ridge; 305/278-0001; www.baymontinns.com.

Florida City

PARKS, BEACHES, AND RECREATION AREAS

32 Everglades International Hostel

 (See Greater Miami map on page 538)

Yes, it's a boarding house and not a traditional park. But older folks from area trailer parks head to this dog-friendly spot to let their pooches run in the fenced, suburban-style yard located next to the popular eatery Rosita's. You may visit, too. The lot is 175 by 145 feet, so Owhnn, the woman who runs the place, decided it would be criminal not to let dogs take advantage of the romping room. She kindly asks that visitors leave a small donation. The hostel is at 20 SW Second Avenue. 305/248-1122.

PLACES TO STAY

Coral Roc Motel: Small dogs may stay at this small motel. Rates are $40–65, plus a $5 pet charge. What's a small dog? "I'd have to look at him," says the proprietor. 1100 North Krome Ave., Florida City; 305/247-4010.

Everglades International Hostel: For budget-minded hounds, it would be hard to beat the prices at this International Youth Hostel located about eight miles from Everglades National Park, at the gateway to the pricey Florida Keys. Of course, these are very basic boardinghouse digs. Everyone sleeps in bunk beds: men share a room with male strangers, while women share a room with other women from around the world. Your dog should be able to sleep on the floor by your bed (he also may sleep outdoors).

A woman named Owhnn runs the place and says your pooch may stay in the hostel's big yard during the day while you canoe or visit Everglades National Park. For a minimum $3 or $4 donation, you can join other travelers for communal dinners such as homemade linguine. (Dinners aren't usually offered in the warmer months, though.) As at most hostels, guests are expected to perform a small chore in the morning, such as sweeping the floor. Rates are $13–16 per person for dormitory-style accommodation, plus $2 a night for sheets (or you can bring your own sheets, but sleeping bags are not allowed). You'll pay $26–35 per night for semiprivate and private rooms. You'll also put down a refundable $20 doggy deposit, and the room has to look like no dog ever stayed there when you leave. Camping is also possible at $10 per person. 20 Southwest Second Ave., Florida City; 305/248-1122; www.evergladeshostel.com.

Hampton Inn: This pleasant motel can be an inexpensive launching pad for a southern trek through the usually costly Florida Keys. Everglades National Park is also nearby. Rates are $69–129. 124 East Palm Dr., Florida City; 305/247-8833; http://hamptoninn.hilton.com.

Homestead

When Freeway, a mutt picked up along a highway, lived here, she loved to bum Cuban coffee and ice cream from a neighbor, says the late dog's companion, Brook Green. Skip the caffeine for your dog, and instead let him be jolted by the sight of the standout parks available in this often-overlooked South County area.

PARKS, BEACHES, AND RECREATION AREAS

33 Pinelands/Florida Keys Aqueduct Authority Wellfield

🐾🐾 (See Greater Miami map on page 538)

If you happen to see a tribe of three or four wild monkeys hanging out in the Florida holly trees, you're not hallucinating. They're real. But you're unlikely to spot the shy critters as you walk down the firebreak roads that cut through these 400 little-known acres of Old Florida pinelands. It's a sunny walk, so avoid this stop in summer. Also be aware that there are no facilities, and you must bring water for you and your pooch.

The widely spaced trees here somewhat resemble tall, spindly Christmas trees to the uninitiated, and they simply provide a place to breathe fresh air far from urban worries. Many of the remaining patches of this now-rare habitat died after 1992's Hurricane Andrew, but the damage wasn't caused by high winds. The U.S. Army Corps of Engineers needed a place to dump hurricane debris, so they looked at these woods and—bingo!—piled garbage on many stretches of this type of forest, found only in southern Dade County.

Take Florida's Turnpike to its southern terminus, then go west on Highway 9336 and follow signs to Everglades National Park. Short of the national park, you will reach an intersection marked by the Robert Is Here fruit stand at 19200 Southwest 344th Street. Turn south. About a half mile down, you will reach a sign that marks the Florida Keys Aqueduct Authority Wellfield. Pull off to the right to park and head on foot into the pinelands.

34 Biscayne National Park

🐾🐾 (See Greater Miami map on page 538)

Ponce de Leon sailed across this bay in his search for the Fountain of Youth in 1513. Since then, pirates and presidents—and pooches—have spent time on the keys of Biscayne. The big sky and clear blue waters dominate. Leashed dogs can get a taste of what it's like to be a flatlander while gazing onto Biscayne Bay from the small, sea-level picnic area or the short boardwalk outside the mainland Convoy Point Visitors Center. You can throw burgers onto grills and enjoy a view comparable to that found at nearby Homestead Bayfront Park, where dogs are forbidden.

Much of this sunny, 181,500-acre park is under water. More than 4,000 acres of the park are on dry land—but mostly on islands reachable only by boat.

One such place is Elliott Key, where the hiking trails are a park highlight. This thin strip of land can give a leashed pup the feeling that she is on television's *Gilligan's Island*. It's possible to walk from one side of the island to the other in a few minutes—though it can be difficult to find a trail to get there. Winter is best for visits. Bring mosquito repellent and a water bottle at minimum.

To reach Elliott Key, you can rent a boat from Coconut Grove's Club Nautico, 2560 Bayshore Drive. Call 305/858-6258 for reservations. Dogs aren't allowed on the park's own boat, which departs regularly and is more economical. Dogs can also hop into canoes, but it's impossible to access Elliott Key by canoe. Canoe rentals are $8 hourly. Call 305/230-1100.

The Dante Fascell Visitors Center, open 9 A.M. to 5 P.M., is at 9700 SW 328th St., about nine miles east of Homestead. Take Florida's Turnpike to the Speedway Boulevard exit. Turn left from the exit ramp; continue south to Southwest 328th Street/North Canal Drive. Turn left. Continue about five miles to the park, at road's end. 305/230-7275.

PLACES TO STAY

Everglades/Homestead KOA Kampground: These large campsites are in a rural setting, but they feature such creature comforts as shuffleboard, a playground, hot tub, pool, and game room. Campsites are $24–34 for two adults, and reservations are accepted. From Florida's Turnpike, go five miles west on Quail Roost Drive to Southwest 162nd Avenue. Turn left (south) and the campground is on the left. 20675 Southwest 162nd Ave., Homestead; 305/233-5300; www.koakampgrounds.com.

Everglades Motel: Small pets are allowed at this basic motel, where rates are $43–68. 605 South Krome Ave., Homestead; 305/247-4117.

Homestead Days Inn: Live entertainment and a playground are featured at this 100-unit motel, located 10 miles from Everglades National Park. Rates are $45–99, plus $7 a night for your furry pal. 51 South Homestead Blvd./U.S. 1, Homestead; 305/245-1260; www.daysinn.com.

Ramada Limited: Dogs under 20 pounds are allowed. Rates are $50–135, plus $15 per night for the pooch. 990 North Homestead Blvd./U.S. 1, Homestead; 305/247-7020; www.ramada.com.

Villager Lodge: At this 50-room poolside motel, formerly a Howard Johnson's, refrigerators and microwaves make the rooms homey. Sometimes the clerks say they take only small dogs and want a $50 deposit; sometimes they don't. Rates are $48–70, plus a $10 per night pet fee. 1020 North Homestead Blvd./U.S. 1, Homestead; 305/248-2121; www.villager.com.

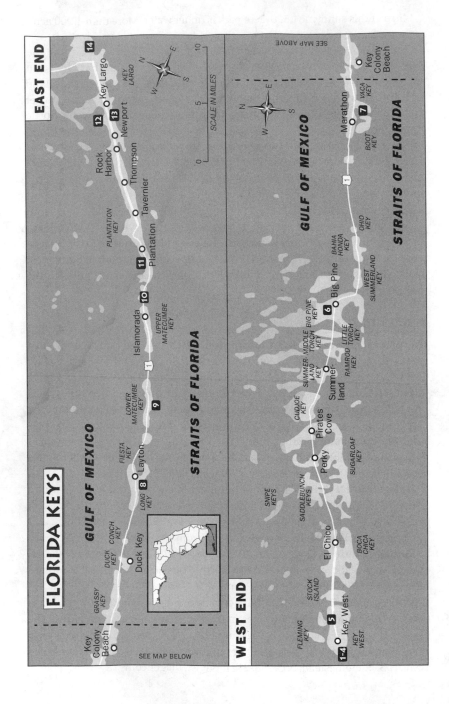

FLORIDA KEYS

EAST END

GULF OF MEXICO

Key
Colony
Beach

GRASSY
KEY

DUCK
KEY

CONCH
KEY

Duck Key

LONG
KEY

8 Layton

FIESTA
KEY

LOWER
MATECUMBE
KEY

9

11

Islamorada

10

UPPER
MATECUMBE
KEY

PLANTATION
KEY

11 Plantation

Tavernier

Thompson

Rock
Harbor

Newport

12

13

Key Largo

14

KEY
LARGO

STRAITS OF FLORIDA

SEE MAP BELOW

SCALE IN MILES
0   5   10

WEST END

SEE MAP ABOVE

GULF OF MEXICO

Marathon

7

VACA
KEY

Key
Colony
Beach

BOOT
KEY

1

OHIO
KEY

BAHIA
HONDA
KEY

Big Pine

6

BIG PINE
KEY

WEST
SUMMERLAND
KEY

SUMMER-
LAND
KEY

MIDDLE
TORCH
KEY

LITTLE
TORCH
KEY

RAMROD
KEY

CUDJOE
KEY

Summer-
land

Pirates
Cove

Perky

SUGARLOAF
KEY

SNIPE
KEYS

SADDLEBUNCH
KEYS

El Chico

BOCA
CHICA
KEY

STOCK
ISLAND

FLEMING
KEY

5 Key West

1-4

KEY
WEST

STRAITS OF FLORIDA

CHAPTER 20

Florida Keys

Freedom.

That's what the Florida Keys are all about. What they've always been about. Drug smugglers, pirates, writers, gays, even the first settlers from the Bahamas: They have all come to this string of islands in a shimmering subtropical sea to escape the long arm of the law—or the strictures that people seemingly must impose on others. Even in the modern era, the Keys "seceded" from the United States, becoming the mythical "Conch Republic" in the early 1980s, when folks here got sick of the U.S. government's endless requirements.

But dogs? Freedom? Let's just say that around here, things seem to be getting a little less free all the time. It's true that the first edition of the *Dog Lover's Companion* described the Keys as one of Florida's most dog-friendly destinations. But since then, events have intervened to dampen our enthusiasm.

It once was that dogs could swim to their heart's content at county-maintained beaches, and they had the run of county-operated parks. This was courtesy of a county commissioner named Keith Douglass. One day, pawing

PICK OF THE LITTER—FLORIDA KEYS

BEST BEACHES
Sombrero Beach, Middle Keys (page 586)
Beach, Upper Keys (page 589)

BEACH WITH MOST CHARACTER(S)
Dog Beach, Key West (page 577)

DIG A REEF
Windley Key Fossil Reef Geologic State Park, Upper Keys
(page 589)

WHERE "DOG-SIZED" WILDLIFE ROAM
Key Deer National Wildlife Refuge, Lower Keys
(page 585)

through a stack of agenda papers taller than a Milk Bone box, Douglass came across a proposed ordinance to ban "domestic animals" at beaches. Seems dogs had been running loose there. Douglass thought of his daughter's iguana, Forest. A "domestic animal" all right. Douglass pondered: "You mean to tell me that my daughter can't take her little iguana on its little harness?"

Douglass doggedly sniffed out reasons to defeat the proposed change and to open the beaches to dogs instead. Laws requiring people to clean up after their pets were already on the books, he reasoned. And many beaches had gone to the dogs anyway, according to the public works director. Doggone it, Douglass thought, while we're at it, let's open county parks to pets, too. Commissioners agreed after an exchange that was far more congenial than a dogfight. That was in 1995.

But, like the people who are crowding the Keys and making the islands a little less like paradise all the time, the dog thing got out of hand. "We continued to have complaints from the general public concerning dogs that were allowed to run," says Carlos Zarate, senior director of facilities at the county maintenance department. "What was happening was the leash law was being overlooked." Just as people have abused the Keys, dog lovers abused their newfound privileges. Then, at Key Largo Park, a rottweiler left tied to a bench somehow got loose and mauled a child.

Enter Nora Williams, the county commissioner who took Douglass's seat. Now, we don't think Williams is all bad. In fact, she has been at the forefront of efforts to clean up the horrible situation the Keys faces with uncontrolled sewage leaking into local waters.

But a citizens' committee organized by Williams recommended that Bowser be banned from all but two county parks. Exceptions were made only for Key Largo Park in the Upper Keys and Sombrero Beach in Marathon. The overall take-home message: Keep your dog under control, be nice, and clean up the poop!

To be fair, the Keys are still a decent dog destination, especially for pooches who "go all the way"—to Key West. Where else can dogs get a close-up view of sharks at an aquarium? Like any two-legged tourist, a dog can take in a sunset and get his picture taken by the buoy that marks the nation's southernmost spot (watch the leg lifts, though). Small dogs may sleep in a mansion built by Florida's first millionaire, while others are welcome at quaint bed-and-breakfasts. For every Florida town where residents complain about dogs, the Keys can serve as a poster place for the other side of the argument. Dogs haven't hurt the tourism industry here: Five million people visit annually.

There are still a few parts of Key West where dogs run freely in the streets, chasing chickens that wander around scratching for food. Dogs who become well known in neighborhoods such as Bahama Village can rely on certain friendly locals and restaurant workers for handouts.

And there are signs that at least some in the Keys are ready to do right by Rover. In Islamorada, where residents organized themselves into a village government after bowing to Monroe County rules for too long, one of their first actions was to buy out a local marina with a lot of green space out front and transform some of it into a dog park (see the Upper Keys, below). Key West canines in 2005 celebrated the leash-cutting of their first dog park.

A note about visiting the Keys: Even more than elsewhere in Florida, it can get downright hot down here in the broiling sun. Try to arrange your visit for the cooler months and, if you arrive in summer, think about laying low with the pooch in a cool, dark motel room in the middle of the day.

Key West

Key West is the end of the line. The nation's southernmost point is as far south as you can go on U.S. 1. For most of Key West's history, dogs slept in the streets and cars drove around them. Now, as tourist numbers grow, the tropical town is becoming a tidier, busier place, especially over the last decade. Still, dogs are often seen running alongside locals as they lazily ride their bikes, the favorite mode of transportation for residents. Overall, the town is very welcoming to animals.

One local dog was apparently so popular that he decided to run for mayor. During a fairly recent mayoral election, posters the size of notebook paper started popping up with the face of an old, smelly mutt on them. "Jeremiah

DIVERSIONS

When your dog brags that he's visited the southernmost point in the nation, give him something to prove it. Snap a picture of him standing next to an oversized red-striped buoy at the southern end of Whitehead Street in **Key West.** The buoy reads, "The Southern-most Point, Continental U.S.A., Key West, FL." A nearby sign reads 90 Miles to Cuba. That's all you'll see, so continue on to the **Key West Aquarium.**

Dogs may watch handlers feed sharks, rays, and turtles and may peer at fish swimming in a 50,000-gallon tank at the Key West Aquarium, 1 Whitehead St.; 305/296-2051. They must, however, obey one rule—stay leashed.

"We have had dogs jump into some of our pools," a staffer says. Says another: "They like to lick the water, and they try to swim."

Pooches may view indoor and outdoor exhibits at the Keys' first tourist attraction, opened in 1932. Tickets cost $10 for adults, $5 for ages 4 to 12, free for younger kids (and dogs).

End the day as every tourist does—by joining the sunset pack at **Mallory Square.** A dog who doesn't mind crowds might enjoy the daily ritual of flocking to the square to watch the sun's fiery orange ball drop to the horizon.

The crowd is the real spectacle: Your pooch might see jugglers tossing flaming sticks, a unicyclist wriggling out of a straitjacket, perhaps a weightlifter tossing around an electric range. Cats actually have performed here. (Yes, some apparently are able to obey commands.) The pier is in Old Town by the Pier House Resort, west of Duval Street, off Wall Street. Crowds can be elbow-to-elbow, particularly in winter and spring, so consider people-watching from a greater distance. For information, call 305/294-5988.

for Mayor. Integrity," the signs said. There were half a dozen humans on the ballot, but, said Jeremiah's owner, Eric Bissell, "I thought he would do just as good as a lot of the people who were running." Jeremiah didn't win the election; now he can often be found hanging out at the Green Parrot, where Bissell tends bar sometimes.

Perhaps dogs have a natural affinity for Key West because of its nickname—Bone Island. When Spanish explorers discovered the two- by five-mile island, it was littered with the bleached bones of American Indian warriors, leading them to christen it Cayo Hueso (Island of Bones). The British saw Cayo Hueso on maps and mispronounced the name, calling it Key West. Until it became defunct, newshounds could read the *Bone Island Sun,* a local publication.

PARKS, BEACHES, AND RECREATION AREAS

🔳 Key West Historic Memorial Sculpture Garden

🐾🐾 ◄🐾 (See Florida Keys map on page 572)

More of a park for humans than dogs who pine to sniff dirt, grass, and sand, this manicured brick patio at Mallory Square honors famous Key West residents such as Harry Truman and Ernest Hemingway. Their likenesses are seen here on the 36 bronze busts sitting atop pedestals. (Watch those leg lifts, pooches.)

Here, visitors bend over to read bricks such as: "Orion/Golden Retriever/1987-1995" or "Jack Appel/He could have sold seawater to Columbus."

The garden is in front of the Waterfront Playhouse and next to the Key West Chamber of Commerce in Mallory Square, 1 Whitehead Street. 305/294-2587.

🔳 Dog Park at Higgs Beach

🐾🐾🐾 (See Florida Keys map on page 572)

Freedom, at last! In this fenced grassy area, dogs unquestionably may run at full speed and enjoy the first official leash-free park within Key West. Playing fetch and chasing other retrievers serve as the main activities; unfortunately, there's no swimming. In April 2005, the park opened after a government dogfight.

Despite being a city known for freedom, city officials howled at the idea of placing a paw park at county-run Higgs Beach. The sticking point: dog doo.

The health department already periodically issued advisories against humans swimming at Higgs Beach due to fecal matter offshore, 15 percent of which came from dogs, complained Assistant City Manager John Jones. A dog park only would make things worse, he reasoned, if people didn't clean up after their pets. The county commission collared more than enough votes to okay the park anyway, pleasing 835 pet owners who signed petitions and raised $25,000 on their own to pay for the dog park's fencing. Peeved, the city instituted demands, including having a say in the style of fencing.

So consider this a reminder: Pick up your pet's calling cards. Jones threatened to cite the county and force it to shut down the bark park if he could prove dog waste dominated the fecal matter contaminating Higgs Beach.

Considering all of the government wrangling in this land of freedom, call before you head to the dog park to make sure it's open. Higgs Beach is at Atlantic Boulevard and White Street, at the southernmost end of Key West on the Atlantic Ocean. 305/294-2587 or 305/295-4385.

🔳 Dog Beach

🐾🐾🐾 (See Florida Keys map on page 572)

This tiny, scruffy municipal beach is loaded with eccentric dogs and equally eccentric dog owners, who might say something like: "A good man in Key West is a man who has a job, isn't living in his car, and has his own teeth." Here, pretty women sit on folding chairs near neo-hippies who lounge on sleeping bags. Dogs play together here, so don't bring a pet who tends to fight.

Only 50 feet wide and 100 feet deep, the beach is sandwiched between a large private home and Louie's Backyard, an exceptional local restaurant (where dry dogs are allowed at the deck bar, called Louie's Afterdeck). But for tiny Key West, the beach actually seems spacious. Canine swimmers have fun fetching coconuts that have fallen from one of the beach's five hardy coconut palm trees. After a swim, some friskier pooches go wild and tear the stringy, fibrous shells off the coconuts. Technically, leashes are the law.

The beach is at Waddell and Vernon avenues, just south of South Street. 305/292-8296.

4 Fort Zachary Taylor Historic State Park

🐾 🐾 🐾 (See Florida Keys map on page 572)

This national landmark is one of the few places to get away from it all in crowded Key West. The wooded area—consisting primarily of tall, shaggy Australian pines along the beach—calls out to every dog's explorer soul. What's more, dogs can sniff around the outer perimeter of a two-story brick fort that is believed to hold the largest number of Civil War artifacts in the nation. Until a local man named Howard England spent his spare time in the 1960s shoveling the tons of sand that buried Fort Forgotten, as it was nicknamed, the fort had such a low profile that even fairly recently it was considered a potential site for a sewage treatment plant. Thousands of cannonballs have since been uncovered, and the place was designated a park in 1985.

If you forget to bring burgers to toss onto the grill, head to the concession stand for food to share with your pooch. Don't forget to pose your dog next to a cannon for a photo.

This park isn't perfect. Pooches must be leashed, and they can't go inside the fort or to another visitor highlight—the beach. That's a shame, considering most of the park's approximately 300 acres are underwater.

Admission is $1.50 for those who walk in. If you arrive by car, the fee is $3.50 for one person, $6 for two. The fort is at the end of Southard Street. Take Southard Street as far west as you can through Old Town. Drive into the Truman Annex housing development and follow signs to the park. 305/292-6713.

5 Bayview Park

🐾 🐾 (See Florida Keys map on page 572)

This roomy park spans several city blocks and is fine for walking your leashed dog along large, open grassy areas. There's an adequate supply of trees, and your dog may want to sniff the bases of every one of them. The downside:

DIVERSIONS

Go on a walk befitting the literati of the litter: Locals hold a festival each July in honor of the late Key West resident **Ernest Hemingway,** but many other authors have called this town home. See some of their homes on a self-guided walking tour with your dog, starting from Hemingway's house at 907 Whitehead Street. From there, you can either pass the homes where the young authors struggled to make it, or you can head to where they lived after they made it big (or bigger).

To take the **"Made It"** tour, go south on Whitehead Street, turn east on South Street, south on Alberta Street, then east on Seminole Avenue, where you'll find poet Robert Frost's rental home at 707 Seminole. Turn south at nearby Reynolds Street, then east on Casa Marina Court to see the street where Frost later lived. Author Philip Caputo has lived at 1101 Casa Marina Court. Go east to see the late poet Elizabeth Bishop's home at 624 White Street.

A fair amount of the park is devoted to a baseball field, tennis courts, and a recreation center. Plus, it's bounded by fairly busy city streets.

From the Mallory Square area, go south on Duval Street to Truman Avenue. Turn left (east). The park is less than two miles ahead at José Martí Drive. 305/292-8296.

PLACES TO EAT

Blue Heaven: It's not every day that a pooch can eat in a compound of buildings that once housed a brothel and a tiny casino. Now a delightful, funky outdoor restaurant where chickens run free and the food is excellent, this place is attracting a more upscale tourist crowd. But dogs are welcome, "as long as your dog won't chase the chickens or the cats," says a waitress. Cultured pooches can hear live entertainment nightly. Local artists have shops in back of this compound of buildings in Bahama Village. 729 Thomas St.; 305/296-8666.

B.O.'s Fish Wagon & Cafe: Catty-corner from landmark Pepe's (see below), you'll find the home of a great fish sandwich called the square grouper. The square grouper is twice the price of a regular sandwich and isn't on the menu anymore because, as one staffer put it, "people freak out about the price" and it's a sandwich "bigger than your head." You can still order it, though. You can grab a beer, too. TV's *Food Network* chef Bobby Flay sampled seafood here for a 2003 segment. Bands play on some evenings. Dogs can hang out, but patio space is limited. 801 Caroline St.; 305/294-9272.

Louie's Afterdeck Bar: Next to Dog Beach (see Parks, Beaches, and Recreation Areas, above), this casual yet upscale waterfront bar serves great drinks and a wide range of lunches. Stop here before heading to Dog Beach because of the house rules: no wet dogs, please. Kindly keep your dog leashed so he won't plunge into the water then rush back to shake off, sending spray onto everyone's plates. Dogs are not allowed after sunset. (Patrons tend to trip over them when it's dark and packed.) 700 Waddell Ave.; 305/294-1061.

Mangoes: "Feel free." That could be the island's motto, but it's also what a staffer said to us when we asked about bringing our dog to this award-winning restaurant set in an old house. Take a seat on the outdoor brick patio and dig into fare that is described as "Floribbean," meaning a combination of Floridian and Caribbean dishes. The eatery's namesake fruit appears in some dishes, such as the conch fritters served with mango habanero dipping sauce and the Island Chopped Salad featuring chopped romaine hearts, pink shrimp, bacon, and hearts of palm. The use of mangoes is understandable considering the restaurant's motto: "It's not just a fruit, it's a lifestyle." 700 Duval St.; 305/292-4606.

Papa's Restaurant: A well-behaved dog is welcome to help you scarf down local seafood (the specialty), as well as pasta, personal pizzas, sandwiches, salads, or steak. You'll sit at white outdoor tables under green umbrellas. Staffers bring water to thirsty pooches. 217 Duval St.; 305/293-7880.

Pepe's Bar and Restaurant: This busy restaurant, located a block from the docks of the Key West Seaport, was founded in 1909 (making it the one of the oldest restaurants in the Keys) and is very dog-friendly. In fact, one day a year at 5 A.M. and 5 P.M., stray animals follow Friends of Animals folks down the street and converge at an open area beside Pepe's to devour the cat and dog food put out for them. "We feed every animal who comes to our back door," says a waitress. Your dog—as well as cats and birds—may join you in the cool outdoor fenced-in patio, where a dog bowl is filled with water. Pets are considered a charming addition to the colorful surroundings. "I know more dogs' names than customers' names," a staffer says. Try the seafood or a steak. 806 Caroline St.; 305/294-7192.

Schooner Wharf Bar: A big outdoor bar right on the waterfront with a view of a marina and the activity on the water, the Schooner Wharf is great for dogs. It's a scruffy local favorite that sponsors such events as the annual Wrecker's Race, in which boaters re-create the old custom of racing out to the reef after a shipwreck to lay claim to the wrecked boat's cargo. Munchies, sandwiches, and some entrées are available, and dogs can enjoy live music nightly. Employees gladly bring water to thirsty pets. 202 William St.; 305/292-9520.

Turtle Kraals: What a place! This restaurant—built where the old shrimpers and turtlers used to haul in their catches—is all open-air and all dog-friendly. Maggie sat patiently at our feet while her canine pal, Lisha Von Staden, hoped for treats from her human pals, Sandy and Alexa. The pooches had a blast sniffing the local dogs who wandered through the casual restaurant. The food is excellent and so is the beer selection. Fresh seafood is the highlight—stone crab claws, stuffed fish, Florida lobster, steamed shrimp, "secret recipe" Conch chowder, and clams and oysters on the half shell (shucked to order). The menu also includes chicken, prime rib, and bar fare, including deep-dish nachos and burgers. Incidentally, the name stems from the old practice of catching sea turtles live and keeping them penned up. 1 Lands End Village, at the west end of town by the historic seaport; 305/294-2640.

PLACES TO STAY

Ambrosia House: Airy suites, town homes, and cottages with a tropical touch in Old Town are designed for honeymooners and others feeling really romantic, but, hey, you can shower your little furry buddy with love here, too. Enjoy a free breakfast and in-room refrigerators. Rates run $149–425 in season, $120–375 other times. Pet fee is $25 per stay. 615 Fleming St., Key West; 305/296-9838 or 800/535-9838; www.ambrosiakeywest.com.

Atlantic Shores Resort: If you're looking for a resort that describes itself as "tropical, art deco, adult, alternative," where "you can find hot bodies and cool cocktails," then, yes, you are allowed to bring your dog along to this 72-room resort. The clothing-optional pool and bar are right on the ocean. Your pet may join you on the porch of the hotel's diner, The Diner Shores. After the grill closes at around 4 P.M., your pooch is permitted to hang out with you in the clothing-optional pool area. "We like our furry little friends," a friendly desk man said. Rates run $135–275 in season, $90–150 when things are slow. Add a flat $10 fee per dog. 510 South St., Key West; 305/296-2491 or 888/324-2996; www.atlanticshoresresort.com.

Boyd's Key West Campground: The nation's southernmost campground features a pool, a game room, and sunny campsites—some facing the Atlantic Ocean. Despite the park's name, you'll actually sleep just outside city limits on Stock Island. Dogs may stay in hard-shell, air-conditioned campers. They're discouraged from sleeping in tents, though not barred. Certain breeds are forbidden at the park, apparently because insurance won't allow them: Doberman pinschers, pit bulls, rottweilers, chow chows, wolf hybrids, and German shepherd dogs. Smart doggies make reservations in winter; in summer, space is almost always available for drop-ins. Tent sites range $45–65. RV sites run $60–95. 6401 Maloney Ave., Key West; 305/294-1465; www.boydscampground.com.

Center Court Historic Inn & Cottages: The resident Jack Russell terrier, Daphne, dives into the pool to "surf" on floating pool toys, and she pulls so hard during tug-of-war games with the resident cocker spaniel, Sasha, that her furry opponent falls into the pool. Guests get a kick out of Daphne's antics. "I'm a real animal lover," says owner Naomi Van Steelandt. Birds, cats, and a capuchin monkey have stayed here, so of course your dog may join you in suites and cottages that sleep two to six people. They're on a quiet lane with gardens and sundecks. Guests have access to a sundeck, a whirlpool, and parking, while canine visitors may play with the resident dogs' toys. Cottage rates range $158–368 in season, $98–298 in summer and fall. Larger private homes are available. Pet fee is $10 nightly. 916 Center St., Key West; 305/296-9292 or 800/797-8787; www.centercourtkw.com.

Chelsea House: Dogs may sleep in several rooms that have direct access to the outdoors and overlook the lushly landscaped pool of this Victorian bed-and-breakfast inn, built in 1870. The pretty spot features a clothing-optional sundeck, full concierge services, parking, and rooms with private bathrooms, safes, refrigerators, and other amenities. Pets are forbidden inside the Victorian business, so stick to proscribed areas. Humans must be 16 or older to stay here. Rates range $159–275 in season, $85–155 in summer. Pet fee is $15 nightly. Bigger dogs require approval by the owners. 707 Truman Ave., Key West; 305/296-2211 or 800/845-8859; www.chelseahousekw.com.

Courtney's Place Historic Guest Cottages and Inn: A jar of dog biscuits sits alongside a candy jar in the dining room, and pet blankets are provided upon request. Well-behaved pooches have been known to eat breakfast with their people in the dining room. Birds, cats, and even monkeys have stayed at these Old Town cottages. The innkeepers brag that the place offers the amenities of home, including free breakfast treats. At the special pet check-in, a few rules are recited, including no chewing or sleeping on furniture. Bottom line: You're responsible in the event of any damage. Problems are rare, says a staffer, though "an occasional Venetian blind is eaten." A Fort Lauderdale Humane Society volunteer heads here with his dogs when traveling to Key West because "they love pets." Rates run $139–259 in winter, $79–199 in summer. Pet fee is $25 per stay. 720 Whitmarsh Lane, Key West; 305/294-3480 or 800/869-4639; www.courtneysplacekeywest.com.

Cuban Club Suites: Once upon a time, Key West doggies would go "ah-choo" here because Key West was a thriving cigar-making town and this was a club where the cigar-makers would retire to enjoy their wares. Today the place has been converted into modern, condominium-like one- and two-bedroom suites with kitchens. Expect to pay $189–329 in season, $99–259 the rest of the time. Add $10 nightly per pet. 1108 Duval St., Key West; 305/296-0465 or 800/883-0372; www.cubanclubsuites.com.

Curry Mansion Inn: Dogs under 20 pounds may enter the Tiffany sliding glass doors to admire the maple fireplace, the chandelier from Prague, and other details in this impressive mansion built by the man reported to be Florida's first millionaire. It's not every day that a dog can sleep in a museum (which this place is by day). The 22-room, antiques-filled inn is listed on the National Register of Historic Places. Built by William Curry, a shipper and salvager, and now owned by innkeepers Al and Edith Amsterdam, this poolside honeymoon destination and wedding ceremony site features European breakfasts, live piano music, and cocktail parties 5–7 P.M. But once dogs bark or cause trouble, they're tossed out—along with their owners. Dogs are tolerated here, not encouraged. Rates range $180–325 in season, $145–250 otherwise. 511 Caroline St., Key West; 305/294-5349 or 800/253-3466; www.currymansion.com.

Douglas House Guest Rooms: At this 15-room guesthouse, rates are $169–359 in season and $99–259 in summer, including breakfast. Look for two pools and a Jacuzzi on the grounds. 419 Amelia St., Key West; 305/294-5269 or 800/883-0372; www.douglashouse.com.

Frances Street Bottle Inn: At this gracious, veranda-wrapped, Conch-style home shaded by poinciana trees, dogs are accepted for $25 per stay per pet. Humans enjoy continental breakfast and an evening social hour, both complimentary. Rates run $169–189 in season, $119–149 in the slow months. 535 Frances St., Key West; 305/294-8530 or 800/294-8530; www.bottleinn.com.

La Casa de Luces: A single suite is open to dogs at this small establishment located off Duval Street. The pet-friendly suite has tile floors, a queen bed, a kitchen, and a shared wraparound veranda. Two pools, daily breakfast, and a hot tub are primary amenities. Concierge services are available. The suite ranges $129–229. Add $10 nightly per pet. 422 Amelia St., Key West; 305/296-3993 or 800/833-0372; www.douglashouse.com.

Old Customs House Inn: This bed-and-breakfast inn's five suites and rooms feature pedestal sinks, wood floors, wicker furniture, handcrafted beds, and tiled baths on busy Duval Street. Well-mannered dogs weighing 25 pounds or less may sleep here. (Rooms won't accommodate larger pets, we're told.) Rates range $150–229 in season, $99–129 other times. Add $10 nightly for your furry pal. 124 Duval St., Key West; 305/294-8507 or 800/958-7101; www.oldcustomshouse.com.

Olivia by Duval: This small compound with a pool is located near the Duval Street scene that everyone seems so crazy for in Key West, yet is modestly priced in comparison to most places. A two-bedroom unit here is said to accommodate six guests. You'll have to put down a $100 deposit for the dog, $20 of which will stay on premises to remunerate the housekeepers. Rates range $79–250 in season, $49–199 the rest of the time. The proprietors also offer other dog-friendly lodgings, including a single Conch cottage located nearby called Kay's Cottage ($129–199) and an all-suite inn located three blocks from the beach called Suite Dreams ($110–500 nightly). So, if any is booked up, you can inquire about the others. 511 Olivia St., Key West; 305/296-5169 or 800/413-1978; www.oldtownsuites.com.

Palms Hotel: A tiki bar sets this 19-unit poolside bed-and-breakfast apart. Here, all well-mannered canines get the green light, no matter the size. "We don't care what size. We've had Great Danes," says a friendly front desk woman. Owners "just have to pack a shovel to clean up after them!" Rates range $185–205 in season, $120–130 at other times. 820 White St., Key West; 305/294-3146 or 800/558-9374; www.palmshotelkeywest.com.

Seaport Inn: The dog-friendly folks of Courtney's Place Historic Guest

Cottages and Inn have expanded their offerings to include this hound-hospitable 19th-century Victorian inn featuring six suites and efficiencies. Amenities include a pool surrounded by tropical foliage, an extended continental breakfast, and bike rentals. Rates range $159–209 in season, $109–149 other times. 329 William St., Key West; 305/294-3480 or 800/869-4639; www.seaportinnkeywest.com.

Sheraton Suites: Luxurious doggy beds add to the attraction of what may be Key West's only all-suite deluxe hotel. Pet bowls, too, are provided, as are plastic bags for picking up canine calling cards. Called the "Starwood Love That Dog" program, the pooch pampering is a company-wide trend. "We intend to become the most dog-friendly hotel company in the land, and not just allow dogs to stay, but actually pamper and spoil them," Barry Sternlicht, CEO of parent company Starwood said upon the program's 2003 launch. One dog weighing 80 pounds is accepted in any suite, as a result. People-pleasers here include a free-form pool with waterfall, fitness facility, concierge desk, and room service. Rates range $130–360. 2001 S. Roosevelt Blvd., Key West; 305/292-9800; www.sheratonkeywest.com.

Southernmost Point Guest House: Rabbits hop around the yard, so keep the leash taut at this six-unit bed-and-breakfast establishment, located across the street from the beach in Old Town. Forget beach chairs? Ask to borrow them here. Beach towels are provided free, too. Rates range $115–265 in season, $75–165 in summer. 1327 Duval St., Key West; 305/294-0715; www.southernmostpoint.com.

Travelers Palm Inn and Guesthouses: Lounge in a hammock while your pooch lies beneath you at this enclosed compound of five cottages and apartments that encompass a big part of a city block. A Great Dane, cats, and even a monkey have stayed here. A heated pool entertains guests, though dogs love taking a short walk to Dog Beach. Rates run $208–708 nightly in season, $158–548 nightly at other times. Add $10 nightly per pet. 815 Catherine St., Key West; 305/294-9560 or 800/294-9560; www.travelerspalm.com.

Vacation rentals: A few local real estate offices handle rentals of hound-hospitable condos, cottages, single-family houses, and duplexes. Weekly rates range $650–5,800. Try Coldwell Banker Schmitt Real Estate, 2720-A N. Roosevelt Blvd., Key West; 305/296-7727 or 800/598-7727; www.realestateflorida-keys.com. Alternatively, try Century 21 Keysearch Realty, 701 Caroline St., Key West; 305/294-6637 or 800/654-2781; www.c21rents.com.

Whispers Bed & Breakfast Inn: It's not every day that a pooch can set paw inside a 150-plus-year-old Victorian house listed on the National Register of Historic Places, but well-mannered dogs under 60 pounds may sleep here in two rooms on the first floor. Save your pooch a few scraps from your full gourmet breakfast, which might include French toast à l'orange, eggs Florentine, and eggs benedict, served in the tropical garden. A 16-year-old dog once showed up to celebrate his birthday at this home built by Gideon Lowe, the youngest son of one of Key West's earliest Bahamian settlers. Guests have free access to Fort Zachary Taylor State Park, as well as the inn's pool. A rarity: You may leave your dog alone in your room if you tell management and provide a cell phone number to reach you. Rates range $159–250 in season, $79–140 in summer. Pet fee is $25 per room. 409 William St., Key West; 305/294-5969 or 800/856-7444; www.whispersbb.com.

Lower Keys

PARKS, BEACHES, AND RECREATION AREAS

6 Key Deer National Wildlife Refuge

🐾 🐾 🐾 ◀● (See Florida Keys map on page 572)

"Dog-sized" is how countless writers have described the diminutive white-tailed Key deer that live on Big Pine Key and some other local islands. To which Maggie always retorted, "As big as which dog?" Actually, they're bigger than a typical golden retriever.

Important: These deer are just barely dodging extinction, so drive very slowly through Big Pine Key. Follow speed limits that pace you at 30 mph or less. Yes, we know it takes a long time to get around, but these deer can dart out of the pine woods quickly. Second, do not under any circumstances feed deer. Some will solicit you, but don't fall for it. They lose their wild instincts and can become ill. Third, under no circumstances let your dog harass deer. (That's common sense, but if your pooch needs any more discouragement, consider that it's a federal crime under the Endangered Species Act.)

Your reward is viewing interesting, beautiful backcountry. A nature trail winds through rare silver and thatch palms as well as common saw palmetto. Interpretive signs explain the Lower Keys' unique nature. If you drive a little farther north on Key Deer Boulevard, still looking to the left, you'll find Blue Hole, an old rock quarry that today is filled with fresh water—a rarity here-abouts. Keep your dog by your side at Blue Hole, as alligators are pretty thick here. The best time to see deer is in early morning or at dusk—when mosquitoes are worst, unfortunately.

From the intersection of U.S. 1 and Key Deer Boulevard in Big Pine Key, head north on Key Deer Boulevard. After passing a church on your left, start looking for a trailhead at left. You can also drive to the end of Key Deer Boulevard, where deer frequently visit a field. 305/872-2239 or 305/872-0774.

PLACES TO EAT

Geiger Key Marina: Sample burgers, chicken sandwiches, and other eats at the marina's outdoor bar and grill. Sunday is barbecue day: chicken and ribs. Breakfast and lunch are served, too. Please leash your dog. From Key West, take U.S. 1 to Mile Marker 10.5, turn right at the Circle K convenience store, drive 1.25 miles, and turn left at Geiger Road. 5 Geiger Road; 305/294-1230 or 305/296-3553.

PLACES TO STAY

Lazy Lakes Campground: Canine guests may use the free kayaks to get a closer look at the six-acre saltwater lake that was once a rock quarry but now serves as a place for people to snorkel, dive, fish, and swim. "A lot of dogs swim here," a staffer adds. This big campground at Mile Marker 19.8 features a pool, a store, and a laundry. Campsites range $35–62. From U.S. 1, turn south on Johnson Road; the park is one-half mile ahead at 3000 Johnson Road. P.O. Box 440179, Sugarloaf Key; 305/745-1079 or 800/354-5524; www.rvonthego.com.

Sugarloaf KOA Kampground Resort: You won't ruff it here—the campground at Mile Marker 20 offers snorkeling, diving, a waterfront grill, and a pool. Dogs may see the sea in a rental boat; rates start at $130 a half day for a 16-footer, $180 a half day for a pontoon boat. Elsewhere, leashed pets are relegated to a dog walk and are forbidden at the beach. Campsites range $45–112 nightly. P.O. Box 420469, Summerland Key; 305/745-3549; www.koa.com.

Sugarloaf Lodge: An airstrip and tennis courts set this 55-unit bayside resort apart. Rates run $140–150 in season, $100–110 in summer. Pets are $10 extra nightly. At Mile Marker 17, P.O. Box 148, Sugarloaf Key; 305/745-3211 or 800/553-6097; www.sugarloaflodge.com.

Sunshine Key Camping Resort: At this 35-acre private campground, sites range $65–95 nightly. Located at Mile Marker 39. 38801 Overseas Highway, Big Pine Key; 305/872-2217; www.rvonthego.com.

Vacation rentals: A few real estate offices handle rentals of pooch-permissible private homes. Weekly rates tend to fall between $550 and $3,500. Try Century 21 Keysearch, 30515 Overseas Highway, Big Pine Key; 305/872-4148 or 800/475-2296; www.c21rents.com. Nearby is ERA Lower Keys Realty, 29960 Overseas Highway, Big Pine Key; 305/872-2258; www.erarealty.com. Farther south at Mile Marker 21.5 is Florida Keys Realty, P.O. Box 421177, Summerland Key; 305/745-3717 or 800/277-7756; www.floridakeysrealty.com.

Middle Keys

PARKS, BEACHES, AND RECREATION AREAS

7 Sombrero Beach

😺😺😺 (See Florida Keys map on page 572)

Dogs had been legally banned from this beach until 1995, so rejoice and toss a stick into the expansive Atlantic Ocean for your furry swimmer to retrieve. You and your leashed pal can also celebrate the canine world's independence from the beach ban with a picnic at the tables here. Dogs must be leashed, except when they are swimming. (And—need we say it again?—pick up after your pooch or risk losing this little gem.)

From U.S. 1/Overseas Highway and Mile Marker 50, go south on Sombrero Beach Road, veer west at the fork in the road, and follow it to the end. 305/295-4385.

8 Long Key State Park

🐾🐾 (See Florida Keys map on page 572)

Imaginative doggies can pretend they're on a Caribbean island as they pass tropical trees—mahogany, poisonwood, red-barked gumbo-limbo, and others—along 1.25 miles of nature trails. Maggie, wanting to go around every corner, strained at her leash and overexhausted herself on a hot, late-spring day. The key is to take lots of breaks, bring plenty of water, and stop for a make-do picnic at any shaded spot you can find along the sunny paths. After a lengthy enforced rest in the shade with plenty of water, Maggie was okay.

Dogs aren't allowed to camp, swim, hop into a rental canoe, or step onto the beach. But they may eat at picnic tables. Much of this 960-acre park is inaccessible because of the off-limits mangroves.

Admission is $3.50 for one person, $6 for two people. Add $.50 per extra person. The park is on U.S. 1/Overseas Highway at Mile Marker 67.5. 305/664-4815.

PLACES TO STAY

Bonefish Bay Motel: After whipping up a treat for your dog in the kitchen, pedal a rental bicycle or maybe rent a boat down the road. You also can enjoy a

DIVERSIONS

Peer at the world's longest pier: Did you squeeze your dog for comfort while watching Arnold Schwarzenegger's vehicle try to jump a huge gap in a bridge in the film *True Lies?* Well, you can see the actual bridge right here. Locals think of the **Old Seven Mile Bridge** as "the world's longest fishing pier," not a movie backdrop.

At Mile Marker 47 in Marathon, you can walk along the sun-washed span of concrete with your dog (just turn back before he gets too hot). Filmmakers didn't actually blow up the span; there already was a gap in the bridge. The gap, at Moser Channel, is where a swing span once allowed boats to pass. So the gap found on the opposite side of the pier—toward Pigeon Key—was bridged with wood for the movie. To give the illusion of an explosion, filmmakers destroyed a model. For information, call 305/743-5417.

dip in the pool and then take advantage of the barbecue grills. Rates at the 19-unit motel are $89–149 in season, $59–109 in summer. Add $10 nightly per dog. 12565 U.S. 1 at Mile Marker 53.5, Marathon; 305/289-0565 or 800/336-0565; www.bonefishbay.com.

Bonefish Resort: If your pooch isn't a landlubber, perhaps you'll like checking out a complimentary rowboat, canoe, or pedalboat at this small, family-owned stopover. Some units have kitchens and all have refrigerators and access to barbecue grills. A hammock and swing are outside, with a pool nearby. Rates run $89–179, plus $10 for the dog. 58070 Overseas Highway, Marathon; 305/743-7107; www.bonefishresort.com.

Jolly Roger Travel Park: Dogs are permitted in RVs (not tents) at this sun-washed Grassy Key campground whose little peninsula sticks out into Florida Bay. Hungry hounds can walk to a nearby convenience store for... bacon! The drawback here is there isn't much shade, so your best bet is to come in the cooler months or crank up the RV's air conditioner. Sites range $33–52. Located at Mile Marker 59.5, 59275 Overseas Highway, Marathon; 305/289-0404 or 800/995-1525; www.jrtp.com.

Key Colony Bay Hotel: Perhaps the best choice in the Middle Keys for dogs with big-city sensibilities, this 80-unit motel features a pool and rentals of boats and wave runners. Pets are permitted in smoking rooms for $20 nightly per dog. Rates range $135–269 in season, $89–169 other times. 13351 U.S. 1 at Mile Marker 54, Marathon; 305/743-8550 or 800/791-5397; www. keycolonybay.com.

Knight's Key Campground & Marina: Dogs who arrive in air-conditioned RVs or trailers may sleep at this Mile Marker 47 campground, where some of the 192 sites are on the shoreline. Tenting doggies are out. Furry campers can't set paw on the beach and they'll find no official dog walk. Go just outside this big park's boundaries for a relieving stroll with your dog—perhaps to the Seven Mile Bridge nearby. Campsites range $25–72. P.O. Box 525, Marathon; 305/743-4343; www.keysdirectory.com/knightskeycampground.

Vacation rentals: A few local real estate offices handle rentals of hound-hospitable condos, houses, and duplexes. Rates generally range $600–4,000 weekly. Try Coldwell Banker/Schmitt Real Estate Marathon, 11100 U.S. 1, Marathon, 305/743-5181; www.rentalsfloridakeys.com. Alternatively, try Conch Realty Sales, 12222 Overseas Hwy., Marathon, 305/743-8877; www. keyrentals.com. Another is Key Colony Beach Realty, 1 Seventh St., Key Colony Beach, 305/743-6226; www.keysproperties.com.

Yellowtail Inn: Set on Grassy Key at Mile Marker 58.3, this oceanfront collection of cottages, efficiencies, and vacation homes has a private beach. Guests can whip up dinner in fully equipped kitchens after swimming in the small pool or renting kayaks, fishing gear, snorkeling gear, bicycles, or pedal boats. Rates range $109–330 in season or during holidays. Rates start at $89 other times. Pet fee is $10 daily. 58162 Overseas Hwy., Grassy Key; 305/743-8400 or 800/605-7475; www.yellowtailinn.com.

Upper Keys

PARKS, BEACHES, AND RECREATION AREAS

9 Beach

🐾🐾🐾 (See Florida Keys map on page 572)

A favorite of furry swimmers, this unmarked and informal strip of long sandy beach is considered just perfect by local dog fans. A big mound helps hide the beach from the highway, and before you, the wide-open Atlantic Ocean spans all the way to the horizon. Just pull over to the side of the road and park. It's one of the few places you can still get away with romping in the surf with your pooch, now that the county has cracked down on official beaches.

The beach is on U.S. 1/Overseas Highway at Mile Marker 76, across the street from the Port Antigua subdivision in Lower Matecumbe. 305/664-2345.

10 Windley Key Fossil Reef Geologic State Park

🐾🐾 ◀▩ (See Florida Keys map on page 572)

No dog or person should miss visiting the highest point in the Keys. Okay, it's only 18 feet above sea level. But what a difference those few feet make. Many, many thousands of dogs' lifetimes ago, all of the Florida Keys were underwater. In that ancient time, this island was a coral reef buried under the sea, much like the colorful offshore reefs that draw so many visitors today. When the Earth cooled somewhat and the seas receded, this reef was left high and dry.

Then, just, oh, maybe six or seven doggies' lifetimes ago, people around here began digging out the rock left behind in the old exposed reef for construction uses, particularly building houses and other buildings. That came to a halt in the 1960s when other building materials came into use. In the 1980s plans called for this place to—what else?—be developed into condos.

No way, said a determined little lady named Alison Fahrer. She beat out the political establishment and got elected county commissioner, spearheading a drive to preserve the site and turn it into a park. Today, your leashed pooch can take several trails leading through the 32-acre site, passing through several different habitats and then—this is the coolest part—walking right down into the 125,000-year-old coral reef. Courtesy of the people who dug out the rock, people and pooches entering the quarry today can see how the tiny living coral animals accreted layer after layer to create this high point in the island chain. After your enlightening walk, take advantage of the picnic facilities.

The geologic site is located at Mile Marker 84.5 in Windley Key. Admission

DIVERSIONS

Feed tarpon with your terrier: It's an amazing sight—long, sleek tarpon line up in the water like cars on a freeway, looking for fishy handouts. For $1 per person, you and your leashed pal can walk down a dock and admire the dozens of tarpon. For $2 per bucket of chopped fish, you can hand-feed the 100-pound treasures while someone in your party holds your dog's leash. Tarpon choose to live around the no-fishing zone near **Robbie's Boat Rentals and Charter** at Mile Marker 77.5 on Islamorada. If your dog is likely to raise a stink with the resident pooches, skip the dock walk. Instead, you can rent a 15-foot boat from Robbie's for $70 per half day to see the sea with your pooch. Rental fees range up to $225 for a full day on a 23-footer. Call 305/664-9814.

is $1.50. The site is closed early in the week, usually Tuesday and Wednesday. 305/664-2540.

11 Islamorada Founder's Park

😊😊😊🐾 (See Florida Keys map on page 572)

For years, Maggie would drive past this big open space out in front of the Plantation Yacht Harbor and, no doubt, wonder why we couldn't pull over and let her stretch her legs. Now doggies can in fact do their thing here, thanks to the incorporation of Islamorada into a village after years of living under the yoke of what locals considered the inappropriate policies of the Monroe County government. They took things into their own hands and, once incorporated, plunked down $9.5 million for the marina. To doggies, though, the best part is the big green space out front, part of which has been converted into a 1.4-acre dog park.

Water, benches, poop bags, and some landscaping are enclosed by a fence between groves of mahogany trees. You can wax poetic to your pooch about how South Florida is the only place in the country where you can find these tropical trees, but we'll bet he'll be too busy frolicking with his own kind to care.

The catch here is the admission. This is a "resident's park," meaning that unless you can show a lease or hotel pass proving you're staying overnight in Islamorada, they'll get you where it hurts: your wallet. Admission is $6 on weekends or holidays, $4 weekdays for those who can prove they're staying somewhere else in the Florida Keys. Admission is $12 on weekends and holidays and $8 weekdays for those who can't show any hotel pass or lease for Monroe County properties. The park is on the west side of U.S. 1/Overseas Highway at Mile Marker 87, on Plantation Key. 305/664-2345.

12 Key Largo Community Park

😺 (See Florida Keys map on page 572)

There's not a whole lot to recommend this park. It was intended mostly for kids, with a baseball field, playground... you get the idea. But it's about the only Monroe County-run park left where dogs are still tolerated. They have to be leashed, though. And there is not much shade here, so you won't want to plan a long visit.

The park is just off Overseas Highway at Mile Marker 100, behind the Key Largo Shopper. 305/292-4431.

13 John Pennekamp Coral Reef State Park

😺😺😺 (See Florida Keys map on page 572)

Locals think of snorkeling amid brain coral whenever the nation's first underwater state park is mentioned, but your mission as a dog lover is to follow a few nature trails through a mangrove swamp and a tropical hardwood hammock. Afterward, picnic with your leashed pal at the picnic areas with barbecue grills.

Don't be surprised if a line of cars stretching 200 yards is waiting to get in when you arrive at this popular hangout of snorkelers and divers. Best bet: Arrive early and be patient. In summer, you'll avoid the crowds—but not mosquitoes. Nearly four square miles of the park are on land, yet the park is best known for its 70 nautical square miles of watery wonders, including the only living coral reef in the continental United States. Dogs are forbidden in the campground, the glass-bottomed boats, and swimming areas.

Admission is $3.50 for one person, $6 for two, plus $.50 per extra person. The park is on the south side of U.S. 1/Overseas Highway at Mile Marker 102.5, on Key Largo. 305/451-1202.

14 Key Largo Hammocks State Botanical Site

😺😺😺 🐾 (See Florida Keys map on page 572)

Time for a W-A-L-K, doggies! This often-overlooked free nature trail winds through a tropical hardwood hammock, making it a cool retreat for leashed dogs tired of the sun in the Florida Keys (where the average year-round high temperature is 81.9°F).

Pick up a pamphlet to follow a 29-stop interpretive trail, where highlights include the "tourist tree" (gumbo-limbo), so nicknamed because of its sunburn-resembling peeling red bark. Maggie was more interested in sniffing the ground than peering up at the black ironwood, strangler fig, wild sage, and other greenery.

Warning: The state barely managed to rescue this rare botanical gem from developers, whose handiwork remains in the form of half-built condos. (Not satisfied with the incredible biological diversity of the Florida Keys, they set

FETCHING NECESSITIES

Take your dog to buy beach togs: Kathy Rayfield, owner of **Expressions Swim N' Sun Wear,** invites patrons to bring their dogs with them while they shop for swimsuits and other sportswear. Rayfield's pooch, Pounder, normally accompanies her to work—maybe to help four-footed shoppers choose from the leashes, "I Love My Dog" luggage tags, and pet collars sold here. Thirsty pooches will often find a welcome bowl of water at the store. 86713 U.S. 1/Overseas Highway at Mile Marker 86.7, Islamorada; 305/852-1155.

Down in Key West, leashed art connoisseurs may shop at the **Guild Hall Gallery,** 614 Duval St., where a sign out front reads Kids & Dogs Welcome. The big co-op gallery houses works by two dozen artists, many of whom paint dogs and cats at least occasionally. Call 305/296-6076.

---

out to remake it in the form of a Mediterranean resort. It's a long and sordid tale.) This case of developmentus interruptus looks like a battle scene, with the jungle encroaching on windowless, partially roofed buildings with construction materials strewn all over the place. It's illegal and dangerous to go around the fences marked with No Trespassing signs and enter the half-finished development. If you're dying to do so, just show up at 10 A.M. on a Thursday or a Sunday, when you can get a guided walk. The guide will know how to avoid the dangerous spots. You'll also get a thorough introduction to the biology of a tropical hardwood hammock. Leashed dogs are welcome, the state says.

If you show up on another day, bring a picnic lunch and walk to the end of the paved road. You'll find a little picnic area—likely to be all yours—out in the middle of a hardwood hammock. Bring mosquito repellent!

From the Florida mainland, go south on U.S. 1. At Mile Marker 106.5, turn left at the Circle K. The pink archways marking the entrance of the state-owned botanical site are less than one mile ahead on the right. 305/451-1202.

PLACES TO EAT

Fish House: The soft-shell crab sandwich, the pan-fried yellowtail snapper, and other fresh seafood delights at this packed restaurant are worth a stop. Dogs must get their owners to order the food to go and head to the sole picnic table by the phone booth or the two umbrella-shaded tables. Mile Marker 102.4, Key Largo; 305/451-4665.

Flamingo Seafood Bar & Grill: Tie your pal to a canalside table and return with a takeout order of rack of lamb, mussels marinara, peel-and-eat shrimp, seafood, or sandwiches from this casual eatery. If absolutely no one is at the outdoor tiki bar, your dog may be allowed to join you there. 45 Garden Cove Dr. at Mile Marker 106.5, Key Largo; 305/451-8022.

Hog Heaven Sports Bar & Food Emporium: A potbellied pig used to roam the grounds of this ocean-view eatery whose odd slogans include "Where insanity reigns supreme" and "Try our 'almost' delicious food!" Many dogs have plopped down at the plentiful outdoor tables to watch their companions sample burgers, wings, pastas, steaks, and finger foods. Sports fans come for the two dozen televisions tuned to games. Trot around the side to reach the back area; don't go through the front door. Mile Marker 85.3, Islamorada; 305/664-9669.

Papa Joe's Landmark Restaurant: Seat yourself at the tiki bar and order seafood, steaks, burgers, chicken, or other eats from the bartender, who may also serve your pal a bowl of water. Sunsets are excellent, but dogs may want to stay away then: A waitress tells us that things turn crazy, with crowds crammed into the tiny outdoor space. Her even-tempered collie has seen the scene, but "people could step on him, and he couldn't care less," so he's not a good benchmark for most pooches. Laid-back lunchtime is best for most dogs. Mile Marker 79.7, Islamorada; 305/664-8109.

PLACES TO STAY

America Outdoors Campground: Sandy, shady, but small campsites are featured in this family-oriented campground. Here, dogs are allowed to jump into Florida Bay—but only at the boat launch and not at the beach. Because it was built in a native hardwood hammock, the park at Mile Marker 97 is lush and jungle-like. Rates range $55–150 in season, $35–100 other times. 97450 South Overseas Hwy., Key Largo; 305/852-8054 or 866/313-2267; www.aokl.com.

Bed & Breakfast Islamorada: Well-behaved dogs under 50 pounds are welcome at this two-unit bed-and-breakfast at Mile Marker 81.1, a favorite of two Fort Lauderdale Scotties named Fergie and Skya. Star fruit and mangoes grow on trees here. One thing: No washing down the dog and heading straight into the room! Dry, dry, dry. Rates range $72–125. Pet fee is $15 daily. 81175 Old Hwy., Islamorada; 305/664-9321.

Coconut Cove Resort & Marina: Some suites have an ocean view, while cottages are 300 yards from the shore at this 10-unit getaway at Mile Marker 85, near the Windley Key Fossil Reef State Geologic Site. It's a sunning beach—not a swimming beach—because of the muddy ocean floor. If your dog plunges his four paws into the muck anyway, "you'll end up washing a stinking dog," a staffer says, chuckling. Half of the seven-acre spread is a nature preserve. A pet-sitter is available, as are boat rentals. Kayaks are free. The dog rules: Keep her leashed, clean up after her, and keep barking to a minimum. Disruptive dogs are shown the door. Rates range $130–170 in season, $60–95 in summer. Add $25 nightly per pet, though the fee will drop if you stay several few days or bring a tiny dog. 84801 Old Hwy., Islamorada; 305/664-0123; www.coconutcove.net.

Fiesta Key Resort KOA Kampground: This 28-acre gulfside resort entertains humans with a pool, hot tubs, a waterfront pub, a restaurant, and a marina. As for your dog, ask about taking him on a rental boat. Clean up after your leashed, attended, quiet pal, and walk him only in the designated campground pet walk. Campsites range $74–94 in season, $66–86 other times. Reservations are advised, though usually unnecessary in summer. Mile Marker 70, Long Key; 305/664-4922 or 800/562-7730; www.koa.com.

Howard Johnson Resort: At this 100-room bayside motel, dogs may sleep in certain smoking rooms for an extra $10 daily. Sorry, they are forbidden on the beach. Rates range $119–279 in season, $99–129 at other times. Route 1, Mile Marker 102.3, P.O. Box 1024, Key Largo; 305/451-1400; www.hojokeylargo.com.

Key Largo Kampground and Marina: At one of the nicest campgrounds in the Florida Keys, tenters and RVers alike will enjoy the feeling of sleeping in a rustic, jungle-like setting even though, at Mile Marker 101.5, you're close to shopping, Pennekamp Park, and the Key Largo Hammocks State Botanical Site (see Parks, Beaches, and Recreation Areas, above). Pets weighing 40 pounds or less are accepted. Rates range $30–63. 101551 Overseas Hwy., Key Largo; 305/451-1431 or 800/KAMPOUT.

Lookout Lodge: Your dog can admire sunsets on Florida Bay by looking through the sliding glass doors of the one pet efficiency (or two suites) at this 10-unit lodge. Attended dogs may hit the small beach. They're simply asked to not approach sunbathers. Ask for Room 105 to enjoy a screened-in porch and full kitchen. "It is fabulous, and the room faces the bay," says Helene Jones, who, with sister Sharon, co-owns Sisters Sitting Service in Broward County. The duo vacations here, treading along a 1.5-mile-long shaded path with their dogs. Nice touches: Free phone calls throughout the U.S. and Canada, plus Wi-fi on the beach. Rates range $135–325 in season, $115–275 other times. Two dogs may join you, though only three dogs are allowed on the property at any given time. Reservations are not taken for single-night stays. 87770 U.S. 1/Overseas Hwy. at Mile Marker 88, Islamorada; 305/852-9915 or 800/870-1772; www.lookoutlodge.com.

Ocean Dawn Lodge: A clay tennis court sets this basic eight-unit motel apart from others. A pool, tiki hut with barbecue pit, floating dock, and lots of lounge chairs are offered. The official dog-walk area is limited. And remember: "No mean dogs." Rates normally range $129–159, though they can be "very negotiable" Sunday through Thursday, a staffer says. Add $10 nightly per pooch. 82885 Old Hwy. at Mile Marker 82.8, Islamorada; 305/664-4844; www.oceandawnlodge.com.

Port of Call Townhouses: You and your pooch can feel like a million renting one of these 10 units on "Millionaire's Row" in Plantation Key. The two-bedroom, two-bath townhouses have everything to make you feel pretty much like you're staying in someone's house for a week. Weekly rates run $1,600–1,950 in season, $1,000–1,600 at other times. Pet fee is $85 weekly. 136 Aregood Ln., Islamorada; 305/232-3569 or 888/587-0508; www.4vacationrentals.com.

Sands of Islamorada: Larry the six-toed cat is gone, but Dolly, Tella, and Scooty the parrots still live here, and pooches are still welcome, says Cindy, the manager. "We've had as many as eight dogs on one day," a reservationist says. The motel features a pool, hot tub, boat ramp, dock, and barbecue grills. Two rooms front the ocean. Rates range $135–275 most of the time but drop as low as $99 in the fall. Each pet is charged $15 nightly. 80051 U.S. 1/Overseas Hwy. at Mile Marker 80, Islamorada; 305/664-2791 or 888/741-4518; www.sandsofislamorada.com.

Vacation rentals: A few real estate offices handle rentals of hound-hospitable homes. Weekly rates generally range $600–6,400. Try Florida Keys Rental Store, P.O. Box 600, Key Largo; 305/451-4078 or 800/585-0584; www.floridakeysrentalstore.com. Farther south, consider American Caribbean Real Estate, 81800 U.S. 1, P.O. Box 358, Islamorada; 305/664-5152; www.americancaribbean.com.

White Gate Court: "Many people leave their pets behind.... You wouldn't do that. You want your pet around, running, swimming, having fun with you." You gotta love this attitude, expressed in ads for this bayside getaway on Lower Matecumbe Key in Islamorada. The beach here is about as good as it gets in the Keys (although that's a lot less impressive than, say, the sugar sand of the Panhandle). And you can cook for Spot inside the seven suites and villa units or use the gas barbecue outside. "No luxury, but a lot of class," is how the proprietors describe the place. Rates range $165–298 in season, $149 and up other times. Pet fee is $5 or $10 nightly, depending on size. 76010 Overseas Hwy., Islamorada; 305/664-4136 or 800/645-4283; www.whitegatecourt.com.

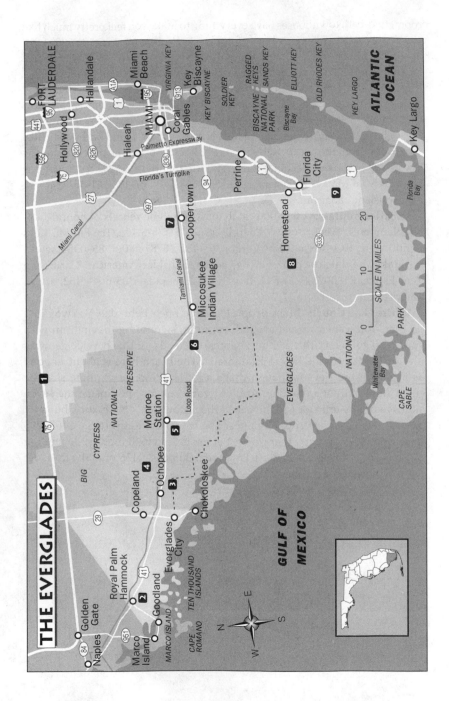

THE EVERGLADES

ATLANTIC OCEAN

GULF OF MEXICO

SCALE IN MILES

N
W E
S

GRRRRRR

CHAPTER 21

The Everglades

We're on Alligator Alley, and Maggie looks like a different dog with her head swinging outside the window, the wind whipping her fur back so that her big, chocolate-colored eyes stick out comically. The wind makes a sail of her lips, and we can see her gums in all their pink-and-black glory.

Without fail, whenever we leave the suburbs or sugar fields and cross into the so-called River of Grass, our sleeping Maggie sits upright in the backseat and sticks out the old sniffer. Her expression practically screams, "Animals! Animals!" Her nose is a-quiver. Hidden creatures, furry and otherwise, are lurking nearby, and she knows it.

While motorists might be bored with the ribbon of asphalt that stretches ahead, Maggie acts like it's Christmas morning as she keeps turning around in her seat to get a better look at the prairie-like expanse to either side. Your dog probably will, too.

The subtly beautiful wet prairie can be a lot of fun for people as well as their pooches. More than any other section of Florida, the Everglades epitomizes the Sunshine State. It's here that you'll most likely notice Florida's "mountains,"

PICK OF THE LITTER—THE EVERGLADES

BEST DRIVE
Loop Road, Everglades National Park (page 602)

BEST WIDE SPOT IN THE ROAD
Coopertown, Everglades (page 602)

NATION'S SMALLEST POST OFFICE
Ochopee Post Office, Ochopee (page 600)

BEST PLACE TO STAY
Rod & Gun Club, Everglades City (page 607)

the billowing white cumulus clouds that burst ever higher against a background of blue and indigo sky.

For dogs, this mysterious wilderness unique among the world's marshes can be truly fascinating, but you need to know where to go. Most people think of Everglades National Park, but because dogs are limited to the campgrounds and parking lots there, that's actually one of the most pooch-restrictive places in the 'Glades. The swampy grassland actually extends from the Disney World area in Central Florida to the southern tip of the state, an area that can be covered in a five- or six-hour drive. In this chapter, we deal only with the fabled portion south of Lake Okeechobee, a marshy ecosystem that has been reduced to half its size over time by farming and development.

Consider taking an airboat ride with your pooch to get out and really see the 'Glades, which the United Nations considers as important as the Egyptian pyramids and the Grand Canyon, judging from its equal status as a World Heritage Site. If you can't spare the time, take the east-west drive across this watery wonder on Alligator Alley (I-75) from either Fort Lauderdale or Naples.

A note of caution: Alligator Alley isn't called that for nothing. Across the Everglades, the gator is king. They are important players in the cycle of life here, as their habits make it possible for smaller critters to live in this troubled paradise. Don't let your furry traveling companion wander far from you. Small dogs have been eaten by gators in South Florida, although such incidents have generally occurred in suburban settings.

Gators are generally quite scared of people, but to be on the safe side, you shouldn't approach too close when trying to snap a photo. In any case, DO

NOT crouch down in front of a gator. He will think you're smaller than you actually are and might consider you fair game for dinner. Generally, if you and your dog keep your feet dry, you won't get near enough to give an alligator second thoughts.

Try to visit in winter for the best weather and the fewest mosquitoes. That's also when you and your pooch are most likely to see the Everglades' increasingly rare wading birds. Do not allow your little buddy to frighten these poor creatures; they have enough to worry about already. The second-best times to visit are late fall and early spring. As for summer, just take Maggie's advice and stay away.

You can enjoy anything from an afternoon jaunt on the Tamiami Trail to an extended camping trip in the Everglades. Some people have been known to hurry into the Everglades while on layovers at Miami International Airport just to catch a glimpse of the unusual birds that stop here for dinner in winter. Don't forget to bring your binoculars if you're at all interested in birding. The same goes for the mosquito repellent—the national park is home to nearly 50 types of mosquitoes.

PARKS, BEACHES, AND RECREATION AREAS

(Also see Florida City and Homestead in the Greater Miami chapter for more nearby places to play.)

1 Alligator Alley

🐾🐾 (See The Everglades map on page 596)

It's not the most scenic spot in the Everglades, but, boy, if you're in Naples or Fort Lauderdale, the access sure is easy. And it's sure to please the black-nosed, whisker-faced crowd. A series of small pull-offs along I-75 between Naples and Fort Lauderdale offers fun for pooches of most any activity level.

Probably the best place for a hike is a trail leading back into deep woods that heads north from a rest stop at Mile Marker 71, about an hour west of Fort Lauderdale and a half-hour east of Naples. Go to the parking area on the north side of the road (you may have to double back if you came from Naples). Look for the break in the chain-link fence and a sign labeled Big Cypress National Preserve Recreational Access Point.

Another rest stop is at about Mile Marker 63, where you can pick up the Florida National Scenic Trail. Unlike the trailhead at Mile Marker 71, this one has a restroom and phones. The disadvantages: The trailhead, just east of the rest stop, is not clearly marked, and parking can be difficult.

These woods serve as home for the endangered Florida panther. If you tromp off into the wilderness, don't penetrate too far. Keep your dog leashed. Dogs scare cats, and, frankly, these cats need all the loving they can get. It's important to scoop poop. The scent can scare away panthers. Only 70 to 100 panthers remain in the wild.

Be prepared to slog through mud if it's been raining enough. Supplies are nonexistent except at the Miccosukee Indian Reservation truck stop at Mile Marker 51, by the Broward-Collier county line.

Cross-state Alligator Alley, a $1.50 toll road, is also known as I-75. Head west from Fort Lauderdale or east from Naples. 954/389-0016.

2 Collier-Seminole State Park

🐾🐾🐾 (See The Everglades map on page 596)

Hop aboard the *Seminole Princess* pontoon boat for an hour-long sightseeing tour at this popular state park. Lots of dogs and cats have made the trip, which costs $10 for adults, $7.50 for kids ages 6–11. Furry seafarers ride free.

Otherwise, dogs are relegated to picnic tables, parking lots, and the campground at this memorable canoeing haven for humans. Eat a packed lunch with your leashed companion near palm trees, then take a windshield tour of this wilderness home of the rarely seen Florida black bear and Florida panther. World-traveling canines may do a double take at the tropical hardwood trees, which are like those found on Mexico's far-off Yucatán Peninsula. Yet the threatened or endangered manatees, bald eagles, and crocodiles seen sporadically at this 6,423-acre park have kin in nearby Everglades National Park.

If you want to avoid the nominal entrance fee, you could barbecue at the small, less-picturesque picnic area on noisy U.S. 41/Tamiami Trail. Not far from the park's main entrance, this spit of land is more like a mowed indentation cut into woods of swamp cabbage trees and pines. Bring mosquito repellent.

Admission is $4 per vehicle. The park is 17 miles south of Naples at 20200 E. Tamiami Trail. Going west from Fort Lauderdale, take I-75 to Exit 80 and travel south on State Road 29. At U.S. 41, turn right and go about 15 miles to the park at left. 239/394-3397.

3 Ochopee Post Office

🐾 (See The Everglades map on page 596)

The nation's smallest post office is more the size of a phone booth than a typical post office. You may be fascinated by this suggested photo-op spot, but for dogs, the tiny field here is simply a place to stop in a pinch. Keep your leashed pooch outside (as if the two of you could squeeze in there anyway). It's hard to believe this is where a postmaster and clerk work, and a mail carrier is based.

The post office is on U.S. 41/Tamiami Trail in the tiny town of Ochopee, three miles east of Highway 29 and 40 miles east of Naples. 239/695-3941.

DIVERSIONS

Ride on air: When people first explored the mysterious Everglades, they poled through the marshy grasses in dugout canoes. But in the early 1900s, a Miami developer named Glenn Curtiss put together a kind of combination airplane propeller/johnboat/auto engine—and, presto, he invented the airboat. Today people use the craft to traverse shallow marshy areas everywhere from the Congo to Alaska. Your whiskered explorer can try an airboat ride, too.

A half-dozen airboat outfits are strung along U.S. 41/Tamiami Trail, west of Miami. Whether dogs are allowed at any given one seems to depend on the airboat driver, but you'll be sure to find someone who will accept you and your pooch. Competition is stiff. Perhaps the best bet is **Coopertown** on U.S. 41, west of Krome Avenue, which charges $16 per adult, $9 for children (ages 7–11), free for younger kids; 305/226-6048.

During Maggie's inaugural airboat ride from the Miccosukee Indians, she ignored the bug-splattered windshield and instead wagged her tail and craned her neck over the side to watch the greenish-golden saw grass fly by. It's a noisy affair, too deafening to attempt conversation. Passengers are handed cotton to stuff into their ears to deaden the noise, but Maggie repeatedly shook her head and sent her cotton balls flying onto the wooden-plank floor. An amused stranger in the next row reached over to pet her.

You're likely to see alligators, wading birds, and the simple, unvarnished beauty of the River of Grass. Bring water for your dog, and skip this diversion if she's hyperactive. One airboat service that doesn't permit dogs warned us that some boats emit a high-pitched screech that can send pets jumping off the boat. Maggie didn't jump, but consider this carefully if your dog is unpredictable; alligators live in that water.

H. P. Williams Roadside Park

😊 (See The Everglades map on page 596)

A dog may find himself drooling at the sight of birds while making a wintertime pit stop at this tiny no-frills roadside park. A picnic is possible at the few concrete tables here, but you can expect to hear the sound of cars rushing past on U.S. 41/Tamiami Trail while you dine.

The small park, located within Big Cypress National Preserve, is at U.S. 41/Tamiami Trail and Turner River Road/Highway 839, about 12 miles west of the Oasis Visitors Center. 239/695-1201.

5 Kirby S. Storter Park

😼 (See The Everglades map on page 596)

Not really a place to brag about to Granddog Spot, this small roadside park within Big Cypress National Preserve nonetheless offers a road-weary pooch the chance to enjoy a picnic with her travel companion. Bring mosquito repellent.

Dogs unfortunately are forbidden on the short boardwalk. Indeed, while we recommended hikes in Big Cypress National Preserve in past editions, pets now are forbidden to hike anywhere in the massive park. After feral dogs became a problem—apparently from people dropping off pets, in some cases—officials in 2001 adopted rules now spelled out in the Code of Federal Regulations, Title 36, Chapter 1.

To the chagrin of many a four-legged traveler, dogs now "are permitted only within 50 feet of established front country roads and parking areas. Dogs and cats are prohibited on established trails, boardwalks, and in the backcountry." The only exceptions are bird dogs and retrievers physically taking part in seasonal hunts.

The park, located within Big Cypress National Preserve, is on U.S. 41/ Tamiami Trail, approximately seven miles west of the Oasis visitors center. 239/695-1201.

6 Loop Road

😼😼 (See The Everglades map on page 596)

A frogger tells us that he has seen a Florida panther traipse across this road at night. When we told Maggie about this big cat she perked up immediately. She never saw one, though, and you likely won't either. Only about 50 remain in the wild. Yet this 28-mile-long road is a popular scenic drive for humans because of the very large cypress trees along the way and the pregnant promise of seeing critters.

Oddly, an interpretive center located about eight miles west of Forty Mile Bend is off-limits to the public. No off-road vehicles are allowed within the many woodsy acres bordered by Loop Road and U.S. 41/Tamiami Trail. We recommend a windshield tour. Drive slowly lest you whiz past the wildlife.

To reach Loop Road from Highway 29, drive east on U.S. 41/Tamiami Trail for about 16 miles and turn south when you reach the road. 239/695-1201.

7 Coopertown

😼😼 (See The Everglades map on page 596)

At this wide spot in the road, dogs can do two favorite things—eat and go for a ride. Only the rides here (on airboats) are like nothing most furry passengers have tried. Maggie smiled as the wind breezed through her fur on a noisy ride through the wispy saw grass. Afterward, perhaps try frog legs and "Everglades coffee" (Budweiser) at the Coopertown family restaurant.

Coopertown was an Indian camp when John Cooper and his family arrived in 1945 to live in tents until the "town" was built two years later. A billboard states the current population: eight. But, hey, this never was a boomtown. Cross the short bridge spanning a canal, and your leashed dog can pad along the canal. On one visit, we saw a leashless cocker spaniel sitting on the bridge as her companion fished. This wee bridge has some historic importance: In the 1970s, a woman named Ellen Curtis sat on it for 10 days so the U.S. Army Corps of Engineers wouldn't tear it down.

You must patronize Coopertown's family restaurant or airboat concession, otherwise you risk getting "toad" from its parking lot, a sign warns. You may get fried frog legs to go and head to the picnic tables found west of Krome Avenue, along the north side of U.S. 41/Tamiami Trail. Look for bridges to cross the canal, such as at the bureaucratically named Gate S-333. Drive along a flat area and pull up at a picnic table; the Everglades will be behind you, but a tall levee prevents you from seeing them. Your dog will love climbing atop the levee for a walk with a panoramic view.

These no-frills picnic spots offer the most convenient access to the 'Glades from Miami, but you may see litter around often-overflowing garbage cans. Still, it's a favorite place for some locals.

From Miami, drive about five miles west on U.S. 41/Tamiami Trail to just past the intersection with Krome Avenue. 305/226-6048.

🐾 Everglades National Park

🐾🐾 ◄● (See The Everglades map on page 596)

It's the rare day that a dog can take a windshield tour of a park considered as important as the Great Pyramids of Egypt and the Grand Canyon, as declared by the United Nations. But a windshield tour and a leashed walk around the asphalt parking lots or alongside the paved roads are all a pooch can get, unless you camp here and barbecue with your dog at a campground picnic table or sleep at the park's Flamingo Lodge (see Places to Stay, below). Dogs are banned from the best parts of the park, including the hiking and canoe trails and the day-use picnic spots.

Still, most Americans see national parks by car, so here's your chance to take your pooch to the third-largest national park in the continental United States. Her sniffer may twitch with excitement during a pretty 38-mile ride from the main visitors center to the shouldn't-be-missed Flamingo area at road's end. You'll pass stands of skinny pine trees (some snapped in two by 1992's Hurricane Andrew), shaggy-limbed cypress trees, jungly tropical trees, and the trademark fields of saw grass.

Look for turkey vultures and ospreys circling overhead. Bird enthusiasts who have a layover at Miami International Airport have zipped here between flights to see unusual wintering birds. But you must leave your car if you want to see a pink flamingo (or alligator).

Admission is $10 per car. To reach the main entrance from Miami, take Florida's Turnpike south to the Florida City exit, make the first right on Palm Drive, and follow the signs. At the less-visited, water-dominated Everglades City entrance on the west coast of Florida, leashed dogs are restricted to the grassy field by the parking lot. 305/242-7700.

9 Canals to Nowhere

🐾🐾🐾 🐾 (See The Everglades map on page 596)

If you *really* want to get away from it all on a winter afternoon in a peaceful part of the Everglades, set your sights on this place. This is where the ditching and the diking of the Everglades finally ground to a halt in the early 1970s. Canals 109 and 110 were supposed to drain a 227-square-mile area of southern Miami-Dade County but were never punched all the way through the sensitive marsh that is now set aside permanently as a wilderness area owned by the South Florida Water Management District.

Your leashed doggy and you can hike west along a dike where you might be able to look out into the marsh on either side and see any number of wading birds, including, if you're lucky, the coral-colored roseate spoonbill. The birds usually make an appearance in winter or spring (it varies each year). As long as there's a breeze or you're here in winter, you can have a fine little hike while your dog trots along, enraptured by the surrounding marsh.

The canals are on the west side of U.S. 1 south of Florida City. To reach the levee most suited for hiking, head south along U.S. 1 from Miami (or

take Florida's Turnpike to where it empties out into Homestead). You'll reach a "last chance" beer place, where you can either continue south on U.S. 1 or cut off onto Card Sound Road. Take U.S. 1. Pass the turnoff to the South Dade Correction Center and keep going. After a few miles you'll see a small road cutting off to the right, with a yellow gate blocking your way. Park so you are not blocking the gate, then hop out and go west, young doggy! 561/686-8800.

PLACES TO EAT

Cheryl's Deli at Glades Haven: If you squint hard and ignore the parking-lot view immediately in front of you, you can see Chokoloskee Bay way across the street while eating made-to-order subs, a light breakfast, or a barbecue beef platter with your pooch at the single table out front. While you're at this combination store/deli, you can stock up on mosquito repellent. Glades Haven is across from Everglades National Park's Gulf Coast Ranger Station on Highway 29, south of U.S. 41/Tamiami Trail. 800 Southeast Copeland Ave., Everglades City; 239/695-2746.

Coopertown Restaurant: People from as far away as Paris and London have signed the guest book at this informal family-run restaurant. Now your pooch can follow in their footsteps. While most people eat indoors, you'll snack on alligator tail, burgers, frog legs, hot dogs, steak sandwiches, or other fare on picnic tables covered by Indian-style chickees (a thatched-roof gazebo) out front. 22700 U.S. 41/Tamiami Trail, west of Miami; 305/226-6048.

Pit Bar-B-Q: Doggies and their companions often plop down at the picnic tables outside this rib joint for pork sandwiches or tender pork ribs. 16400 U.S. 41/Tamiami Trail, west of Miami and about two miles east of Krome Avenue; 305/226-2272.

PLACES TO STAY

(Also see Florida City and Homestead in the Greater Miami chapter.)

Big Cypress RV Resort: Seminole Indians manage this full-service campground where tents and RVs can be set up on their remote reservation, located far west of Fort Lauderdale. With a hot tub, heated pool, shuffleboard, bocci court, aerobic trail, and weight room, it may be stretching it to say you're ruffing it. If your pooch is scared of the local cats—the Florida panthers that roam this part of the world—you can always stay in camp and pass the time with basketball, horseshoes, putt-putt golf, or even backgammon. Rates range $17–24. From Fort Lauderdale or Naples, take I-75 to Exit 49, then head north 19 miles to the park at right. 863/983-1330 or 800/437-4102; www.seminoletribe.com/bcrvresort.

Big Cypress National Preserve primitive camping: Maggie once tromped through the muck at the primitive Burns Lake Campground and looked afterwards as if she were wearing black boots. She had a ball. Campers actually have a number of places to choose from here. Perhaps the best for primitive tent campers is the peaceful, remote Pinecrest Campground on Loop Road. The open and sunny clearing is too small for big rigs, and it's near where Florida panthers are sometimes spotted—if only very rarely. Also off Loop Road is Mitchell's Landing Campground, which also offers free camping and no facilities except chemical toilets. Up on Tamiami Trail/U.S. 41, it's free to camp primitively at Burns Lake; however, it's open only Nov. 15–Jan. 4. Mosquitoes make camping unbearable except in winter, so show up then. All campgrounds are reached via U.S. 41. For directions, call the Oasis visitors center at 239/695-1201.

Big Cypress National Preserve campgrounds: To camp in relative style for a National Park Service campground, you have two choices at Big Cypress National Preserve. At Monument Lake Campground on Tamiami Trail/U.S. 41, amenities amount to flush toilets, sinks with running water, a big lake, and an outdoor cold shower to use while wearing a bathing suit. Also on Tamiami Trail, Midway Campground near Monroe Station is undergoing renovations to provide similar facilities. Campsites cost $16 nightly. Warning: Mosquitoes make Big Cypress intolerable except in winter. For campground directions, call the Oasis visitors center at 239/695-1201.

Collier-Seminole State Park: At this worthwhile state park, visitors may sleep in a woodsy area with 19 campsites favored by people with tents, vans, or pop-ups. Or they may sleep in a separate camping area offering 118 sites for RVs or tents. All sites have a picnic table, a grill, and access to hot showers, a washer and dryer, and an activity room. Forget tent camping in summer, when afternoon rains and plentiful mosquitoes are the norm. Winter is best to avoid mosquitoes. Reservations may be made up to 11 months ahead. 20200 E. Tamiami Trail, Naples; 239/394-3397 or 800/326-3521 (reservations); www.reserveamerica.com.

Everglades Holiday Park camping: Lots of doggies have spent many a happy night here on the edge of the Everglades west of Fort Lauderdale. In fact, the doors on the restrooms by the camp store are labeled "Setters" and "Pointers." Airboat rides, boat rentals, and fishing help attract visitors to these 100 RV campsites and 36 tent sites. There's one ironclad rule: Your dog must stay inside your tent or RV with you; no chaining him up outside at night. Camping ranges $17–22. The privately run park is at the end of Griffin Road, past U.S. 27 and the South Florida Water Management District's S-9 pump station. From Fort Lauderdale, head west on Griffin Road. 21940 Griffin Rd., Fort Lauderdale; 954/434-8111 or 800/226-2244; www.evergladesholidaypark.com.

Everglades National Park: It's hard to beat a campsite overlooking mirror-smooth Florida Bay and its far-off mangrove islands, home to ospreys and other creatures. That's the view from Flamingo Campground, located at the end of the main park road. Of the 234 drive-in sites, 55 offer water views. Forty other sites require walking across a lawn from the car; nine sites are at water's edge. Showers are cold, and there are no RV hookups. Limited groceries are sold and an observation platform is nearby at Eco Pond, though dogs are forbidden to stray from the campground or park roads. Alternatively, the Long Pine Key Campground, located seven miles from the main park entrance, offers 108 campsites, restrooms, a dump station, and a nearby picnic area, but no showers or hookups. Sites cost $14. 40001 State Road 9336, Homestead; 305/242-7700 or 800/365-CAMP; www.nps.gov/ever/.

Flamingo Lodge & Marina at Everglades National Park: This motel-style 74-unit lodge is the only place in the park where anyone can stay without needing a sleeping bag or an RV. From your window, your dog can get his only permitted view of glass-smooth Florida Bay without camping (dogs are prohibited on park trails). Unlike at some national parks, rooms here have televisions. The screened pool affords a pleasant view of Florida Bay. The local fare served here is good, and the bar's tropical rumrunners are a favorite of some visitors. Be prepared for wayward mosquitoes to show up in your room in summer. If you forget mosquito repellent, pick it up at the nearby store. Dogs under 40 pounds, please. Lodge rooms range $68–98. Cottages go for $138 in winter, $92 in summer. 1 Flamingo Lodge Hwy., Flamingo (within Everglades National Park); 239/695-3101 or 800/600-3813; www.flamingolodge.com.

Rod & Gun Club: Five presidents and luminaries such as Mick Jagger and Ernest Hemingway have visited this private-club-turned-lodge featuring an impressive lobby fireplace and a small black bear perched atop the lobby phone booth. The comfortable place calls to mind images of rich men smoking fat cigars while playing billiards in the lobby. Settle in at a table on the broad, screened porch for a tasty dinner of stone-crab claws or other seafood. (Sorry, no pooches in the restaurant.) Don't expect grandeur from the pooch-permissible plain rooms, which are air-conditioned and have private bathrooms. Rooms run $120 in winter, lower other times. Closed July and August. 200 Riverside Dr., Everglades City; 239/695-2101; www.evergladeschamber.com/rodandgunclub.htm.

FORT MYERS/
NAPLES AREA

CHAPTER 22

Fort Myers/ Naples Area

This region is famous not for dogs but for Florida's biggest cats. A few dozen endangered Florida panthers still manage to eke out a living in the cypress swamps and pinelands of southwest Florida. But don't get excited, pooches. The chairperson of a state commission remarked a few years ago that this corner of the state, one of southern Florida's greenest swaths, is as ripe for urbanization as concrete-covered Broward County was 15 or 20 years ago. Come before it's completely paved over into another endless sea of subdivisions and shopping malls.

Even with the remaining green space, it's not easy to find a place to play with your dog, particularly if you want to let him run free. That's especially true in the two biggest towns—Fort Myers and Naples—so you may well want to head to the more hound-hospitable destinations of Sanibel Island, Pine Island, and Bonita Springs.

PICK OF THE LITTER—FORT MYERS

BEST BEACH
Dog Beach, Bonita Springs/Bonita Beach (page 626)

BEST VACATION DESTINATION
Sanibel/Captiva Islands, (pages 622-625)

PARKS PARTICULAR TO POOCHES
Wagging Tails Dog Park at Rotary Park, Cape Coral
(page 612)
Barkingham Dog Park at Buckingham Community Park,
Fort Myers (page 616)
Rover Run at Veterans Park, North Naples (page 628)

RITZIEST DIGS
Ritz-Carlton Golf Resort, Naples (page 633)

Still, the area holds promise. You and your canine companion can enjoy everything from fishing and boating to sleeping in ritzy digs at the Ritz-Carlton Golf Resort. And in recent years a few dog parks have been added to the mix, even though you may have to drive a little way to reach them.

A water-loving dog will enjoy Sanibel Island, an enlightened spot that allows pooches to cavort on coveted beachfront (smart people, these Sanibellian tourism promoters). But don't forget Pine Island, particularly if your pooch is the type who likes to get away from the well-trod tourist paths. Maggie's favorite place was the usually deserted Rookery Bay National Estuarine Research Reserve (see Parks, Beaches, and Recreation Areas, in Naples, below). Stay in salt water—or at least the brackish stuff—and you're unlikely to encounter alligators.

Pine Island

The economy of this barrier island is based on fishing and tourism, yet this is a relaxing, untouristy kind of place. You won't find any drive-through restaurants, just the occasional pileated woodpecker or osprey.

The island rose from the sea more than 24 million years ago and today is home to 8,100 year-round residents (plus half that number in visitors during the winter). Several communities are sprinkled along the 17-mile island: Matlacha (mat-luh-SHAY), Pine Island Center, Bokeelia, and St. James City.

People here are proud of the fact that they're still friendly—"Mayberry-like" is the way the local chamber of commerce puts it—and Maggie found them quite tolerant of her kind, too.

PARKS, BEACHES, AND RECREATION AREAS

1 Wayside Pull-Off

🐾 (See Fort Myers/Naples map on page 608)

This is just a small waterside pull-off and parking area where you could wade out into Pine Island Sound with your pooch. It's a great way to cool off on a hot day if you can overlook the fact that it's so small. We met a sandy-haired boy named Jason, about seven years old, who hurried home to get his mutt, Buddy. Jason and Buddy swim here all the time. Unfortunately, Buddy's leash got tangled in Jason's bicycle tire upon their return, and the adolescent puppy and Maggie decided to play a game of "Who's Boss?" while Robert untangled the mess. You could say Maggie's impressions of this place were fine, while the humans in the crew could have had a more relaxing visit. Things probably will go smoother for you, and with dog-friendly beaches in short supply around here, this is worth a stop.

Across the street from the waterfront pull-off is a group of mounds built by the Calusa Indians, some of the earliest inhabitants of Pine Island. Unfortunately, dogs are forbidden there, we've been told.

Take Highway 78/Pine Island Road west from Cape Coral, passing through Matlacha. Turn right at Highway 767/Stringfellow Road. After three miles, turn left at Pineland Road, which will curve to the right to become Waterfront Drive. Look for the small pull-off area on your left. 239/283-0888.

PLACES TO STAY

Fort Myers/Pine Island KOA Kampground: Sleep in a cabin or at a campsite at this quiet, remote campground. The lanes are named after birds such as wood storks and seagulls, but dogs are welcome, too. Some folks have set up semi-permanent residences in their RVs, whereas others are more transient. A cattail-fringed, man-made lake near some sabal palms offers a place for tenters away from the RVs. Ask for a site with shade, which is scarce here. It is very important to clean up after your pet; other campers get upset about dog doo, so you need to do your part to preserve this as a dog-friendly sleeping spot. When we visited, we noted a big white shepherd walking around on a leash and an Irish setter hanging out under a picnic table beneath an RV overhang, his human friend peacefully reading at his side. Campsite reservations are a must in winter; cabin reservations are recommended year-round. Cabins range $40–68. Campsites range $20–60. 5120 Stringfellow Rd., St. James City; 239/283-2415 or 800/562-8505; www.koakampgrounds.com.

Two Fish Inn: Deemed a "superior small lodging" by an independent panel, these pet-friendly apartments with full kitchens have direct access to the Gulf, where people like to fish. Rooms cost $79 nightly, plus $5 nightly per pet. 2960 Oleander St., St. James City; 239/283-4519; www.twofishinn.com.

Cape Coral

Cape Coral used to be Cape Fear, as far as dogs were concerned. Pooches were forbidden at most city parks and at county parks. Today, hounds finally enjoy a park of their own.

PARKS, BEACHES, AND RECREATION AREAS

2 Vacant Lots

(See Fort Myers/Naples map on page 608)

Maggie enjoyed pouncing every few feet in pursuit of the elusive crickets that jumped around a vacant lot at the northeast corner of Southwest Pine Island Road and Chiquita Boulevard. It was virtually a never-ending game. Once she lost sight of one cricket, she sprang after another, and so on, sort of like someone trying to catch far-flung corn kernels popping late in the cycle of a giant popcorn machine.

A chamber of commerce employee once suggested we walk Maggie in the grassy vacant lots that pepper this largely tree-free bedroom community. Yellow wildflowers cover many of the large open areas in spring, especially on the northern end of town. There's only an occasional shade tree, as most lots have been practically scraped clean of the cypress, pine, oak, and sabal palm trees that once graced the neighborhood. The result is that it's too hot to spend much time here in summer. We don't advise dawdling, anyway. We were told that landowners generally don't mind visitors—at least most of the time.

A good vacant lot is at Southwest Pine Island Road and Chiquita Boulevard, but plenty of others are scattered north of Cape Coral.

3 Wagging Tails Dog Park at Rotary Park

(See Fort Myers/Naples map on page 608)

This place lives up to its Wagging Tails name. Retrievers bound excitedly through Cape Coral's first leash-free park. Jack Russells and other small dogs scamper around their own separate fenced area. Companions watch and chat beneath pavilions that provide welcomed shade from a sometimes-relentless sun.

The paw park—which also offers Fido fountains and waste-bag dispensers—is an occasional site of events like dog washes and the February Woofie Walk (where awards are given for biggest dog, littlest dog, and best costume).

The park's birth required a yeoman's and yeodog's effort. Jumpstarted by an anonymous donor, the off-leash area also was financed by the Cape Coral Rotary clubs and by sponsorships from local businesses and dog owners. Now it's a production of the city and the rotary clubs. A donation box at the park collects money for upkeep, amenities, and pooper-scooper bags.

The park is at 5505 Rose Garden Rd., on the west side of the Rotary Park Environmental Center. 239/549-4606.

4 Camelot Park

☙ (See Fort Myers/Naples map on page 608)

Cape Coral was scraped clean of native vegetation by its original developers, leading to sunny parks with little shade like this one. There are a few older trees and a few younger ones, but Maggie says it's a loooong stretch to call this Camelot. (It's reflective of the town, though; the original developers were chronicled in a number of books, one entitled *Lies That Came True*.) You can stroll on the walking trail, which a town employee told us is a good place to run your dog on leash, but you must stay away from the playground.

The park is at 1718 Southwest 52nd Terrace. Head south on Chiquita Boulevard from Cape Coral Parkway, then turn right at Southwest 49th Terrace. Turn left at Southwest 16th Place, right on Southwest 52nd Terrace, then left at Southwest 17th Avenue to reach the parking lot. 239/573-3128.

5 Lake Kennedy Park

☙☙ (See Fort Myers/Naples map on page 608)

This 46-acre park is one of the few in town where pooches are permitted. (All parks with athletic fields are off-limits, even for an athletic dog. Go figure.) It's a nice option, with a fitness trail, lake, and picnic shelters. However, whiskered visitors like your little buddy are verboten at the playground.

The park is at 400 Santa Barbara Boulevard. Head south from the intersection of Pine Island Road and Santa Barbara, and you'll see it on your right. 239/573-3128.

6 Jaycee Park

☙☙ (See Fort Myers/Naples map on page 608)

This waterfront stretch of green on the Caloosahatchee River is a breezy place for a picnic. You also can get Rover in shape by following the fitness trail. Dogs must stay leashed, but at least there is somewhere in this town where a pooch can laze away a summer afternoon at a family picnic.

From the Cape Coral-Fort Myers Bridge, proceed west on Cape Coral Parkway a few blocks and make a right onto Del Prado Boulevard South. After about 10 blocks, turn right onto Beach Parkway/42nd Street, which will lead to the park. 239/573-3128.

PLACES TO STAY

Del Prado Inn: Dogs under 30 pounds are allowed at this self-described home of Lee County's largest poolside tiki bar. Located downtown, the dog-walking options include padding along sidewalks or the field across the street from this 100-unit lodging. Rates run $40–70. Pet deposit ranges $50–300, depending on length of stay; three-quarters of that will be returned barring doggy indiscretions. 1502 Miramar St., Cape Coral; 239/542-3151; www.delpradoinnrentals.com.

Dockside Inn: Dockside Inn… Efficiencies, Dockage, Pets Welcome, reads the sign in front of Yolanda Migone's two-story motel, whose official greeters are Bubba the mastiff, Nova the dalmatian mix, and two cats, Deydey and Mack-Doodle. "We've seen such a strong impact just by welcoming pets," says Migone. Pets stretch their legs in an ample grassy area out back; plans called for fencing it in 2006 so canine guests can run freely (as owners watch). People-pleasers include a tiki deck overlooking the Rainbow Canal, a rectangular pool heated to 86 degrees, and a boat dock. Simple guest rooms offer two double beds, a sofa bed, and kitchens with a range, fridge, and microwave to whip up meals for the family, including pets. Off-season rates range $75–95. In-season rates run $105–125. Add a $20 cleaning fee. Up to three pets are permitted per room. 3817 Del Prado Blvd., Cape Coral; 239/542-0061; www.docksideinncapecoral.com.

Quality Inn Nautilus: After sleeping in a first-floor pet room of this pleasant 146-room, five-story lodging, you can order a takeout side of bacon for your furry companion at the on-site Perkins restaurant. Then he can work it off at Wagging Tails Dog Park, located 3.25 miles away. Home to a poolside tiki bar, the hotel also features amenities like an exercise room and shuffleboard. Rates range $66–130. Pet fee is $8 daily. 1538 Cape Coral Parkway, Cape Coral; 239/542-2121; www.choicehotels.com.

Fort Myers

When this town's most famous resident still lived here, the family dog was a fixture. That was the famous inventor, Thomas Edison, who rubbed ankles with a number of dogs, including Cinnamon, a cocker spaniel. Cinnamon is no more than an image on the wall of Edison's estate here now, and it's probably a good thing: There's very little for pooches to do in Fort Myers proper.

So little, in fact, that when Jim Barney, the city's (now former) parks director, arrived, he was taken aback by the way dogs had been excluded from his domain. By the time he showed up, even the old "dog beach" out at the end of John Morris Road near the Sanibel Island causeway had been pronounced canine-free.

"It was one of the biggest culture shocks we had," Barney said. This, he saw, was nothing like the Ohio parks where Barney was used to walking his furry buddies: a purebred collie named Cassie, and Murphy, an older dog who was half golden retriever and half "midnight visitor."

Despite being a dog lover, Barney has been cautious about opening Fort Myers parks to pooches. Nevertheless, at least two city parks now at least tolerate the four-legged set and two county parks welcome them. "Before, we actively discouraged them," Barney said. "Now we're encouraging people to use the pooper-scooper." (Hmmm… how long since we've launched into our pick-up-the-poop lecture? We'll assume you know the drill by now.)

PARKS, BEACHES, AND RECREATION AREAS

7 Riverside Park

🐾 🐾 (See Fort Myers/Naples map on page 608)

Lucky pooches may get to hear the strains of the Southwest Florida Symphony rehearsing here, but all dogs can take advantage of the open space by the old railroad station. This park, built in 2000, was opened to leashed dogs on an experimental basis. So step lightly here.

From the foot of the Edison Bridge, head northeast on Palm Beach Boulevard/State Road 80 about three-quarters of a mile to East Riverside Drive. Turn left and the park is ahead at 3061 E. Riverside Dr.; 239/461-7155.

8 Shady Oaks Park

🐾 (See Fort Myers/Naples map on page 608)

By far the city's biggest park, here your little buddy can while away the hours watching football, baseball, soccer, and more at the big open area that backs up onto Billie's Creek. Again, tread carefully, for the way your dog comports herself here might influence how those of the black-nosed persuasion are accepted at Fort Myers parks in the future.

From the foot of the Edison Bridge, head northeast on Palm Beach Boulevard/State Road 80 about a mile to Marion Street. Turn right. The park is ahead about two blocks on your right. 239/338-2287.

9 City of Palms Park—Stadium Area

🐾 🐾 (See Fort Myers/Naples map on page 608)

The great thing about this open area is its size: It's about a city block, with plenty of room for a pooch to stretch his legs. Its biggest drawback is that it is, in reality, a parking lot for the Red Sox Stadium across the street. That's where the Boston Red Sox can be found every spring. So your pooch won't be welcome at this sunny field on game days during that month or so. But the rest of the year, and even much of the time during spring training, there are no ball games and dogs are tolerated.

The field is southwest of downtown, a block east of Cleveland Avenue/U.S. 41, between Grand Avenue and Broadway at Crawford Street. 239/461-7400.

DIVERSIONS

Go drivin' to the drive-in: At the **Northside Drive-In** in North Fort Myers, you can share burgers, hot dogs, and smoked sausages with your pooch while gasping as Bruce Willis leaps out of the path of danger on the big screen.

Former manager Rafael Romero noticed that his pit bull, Trixie, sometimes gazed at the television set at home, but he never tallied how many flicks she caught on the silver screen. Who knows, Trixie may be the Roger Ebert of the canine world, considering she used to live at this 400-car-capacity drive-in theater at 2521 N. Tamiami Trail in North Fort Myers. For show times, call 239/995-2254.

🔟 Open Fields—I-75 Area

😺 (See Fort Myers/Naples map on page 608)

These fields are perfect for bored doggies passing by on the I-75 who would like to get off the leash and GO! Only well-behaved dogs should be let free, of course. These are just large, grassy areas along busy Highway 82/Martin Luther King Boulevard, in a commercial/industrial area not far from a public housing project.

To reach the fields, take Exit 138 off I-75. Head west about two miles on Highway 82/Immokalee Boulevard, which will become Martin Luther King Boulevard. You'll see several fields along the road. Probably the best one is by Michigan Avenue, near the Public Works Department complex. It's not fenced, but a canal between the field and the main road should keep a leash-free dog safe.

1️⃣1️⃣ Barkingham Dog Park at Buckingham Community Park

😺😺😺😺🐕 (See Fort Myers/Naples map on page 608)

Go, dog, go! This county-run park near the incinerator is the answer to long-suffering Fort Myers residents who until 2001 had few real options for running their dogs, save the City of Palms Park by Red Sox Stadium.

The fenced off-lead area features running water and about 1.25 acres for Rover to romp in. A separate fenced area is for young, shy, and small dogs. Watering holes, a cool-off doggy shower, and benches are offered.

If he's still not tuckered out, consider leashing your dog and scooting down the hiking trails that run through the melaleuca and pine flatwoods forests here. The leash-required trails are the other primary feature of Barkingham Dog Park. You'll walk around a mitigation lake that will tempt canine swimmers, but swimming in any ponds is forbidden.

A maximum of three pets may accompany each owner at the dog park. No children under age 5 are permitted. Kids under age 12 must be accompanied by an adult.

The park is at 9800 Buckingham Road. Head east from town on State Road 80/Palm Beach Boulevard about three miles and turn right on Buckingham Road. Proceed to the park. 239/338-3288.

12 Summerlin Road Bike Path

🐾 (See Fort Myers/Naples map on page 608)

A bike path runs for miles along busy Summerlin Road between Pine Ridge Road and Gladiolus Drive, south of town in the unincorporated area. There's no shade, so you'll want to keep the walk short, particularly on a hot day. The trail runs past lots of woods, mostly dominated by exotic trees considered invasive pests: melaleucas and Brazilian pepper plants. For parking, try the south side of Summerlin Road, about a half-mile west of Bass Road.

PLACES TO EAT

French Connection: At this downtown-area lunch and late-night dinner spot, try quiches, crepes, sandwiches, salads, and muffins with your Muffin at outdoor tables. 2288 First St.; 239/332-4443.

Ida's Bone Appiteatery: Maggie's always been a beefeater, so we were sure she'd enjoy the recommended roast beef or Philly cheese steak sandwiches. Sit at a few small tables under an overhang outside this downtown-area eatery, open for breakfast and lunch. 2208 First St.; 239/332-8151.

Ike's Pizza and Subs: You'll have to take leave of your furry buddy to run inside and order an Italian dinner, soup, sub, or pizza at this concrete-block building painted red, green, and white. Then return to your dog to eat at several unshaded picnic tables out front. Closed Mondays. 13302 Palm Beach Blvd./Highway 80, east of town; 239/694-2827.

Juicy Lucy's: Locals have voted these fast-food burgers the best in town, but your dog might want to do some first-hand research. The familiar red outdoor tables can be found at various branches of this fast-food chain. One location is at 16343 S. Tamiami Trail; 239/481-9944.

Love Boat Ice Cream: Grab extra napkins to wipe your pup's whiskers after sharing a scoop of homemade sugar-free or fat-free ice cream. Tie your dog to one of the three picnic tables out front, then go inside to order. 16229 San Carlos Blvd.; 239/466-7707.

Old Thyme Subs & Pizza: The Old Thyme sub is the house specialty, but all Italian dinners are under $5 here, so you'll have enough food to share with your big-eyed buddy, who'll be staring from beneath one of the four outdoor tables. 17105 San Carlos Blvd., in the Summerlin Square Shopping Center; 239/466-3733.

Sweet Things: When the sun is blazing, sit at one of two benches outside this shopping center ice-cream shop and see who can wolf down a scoop of nonfat vanilla frozen yogurt faster—you or your dog. 17284 San Carlos Blvd.; 239/466-1171.

Tropical Beach Grill: This former home of a Juicy Lucy's still serves hamburgers and similar fast food. 17260 San Carlos Blvd.; 239/454-0319.

PLACES TO STAY

Best Western Island Gateway: Sanibel Island—home to pet-friendly beaches—is a short 1.5-mile drive from this full-service former Radisson Inn, whose Olympic-size pool offers swim lanes and a hot tub. A mangrove forest next door to this well-landscaped 157-room inn will intrigue inquiring canine minds. Rates range $70–199. Pet fee is $25 per stay. 20091 Summerlin Rd./County Road 869, Fort Myers; 239/466-1200; www.bestwestern.com.

Best Western Springs Resort: Two mineral water spas and a poolside tiki bar are offered at this 49-unit, two-story motel, where dog owners walk pets in a large garden in back. For canine swimming, Dog Beach in Bonita Beach is within a half hour's drive of this "superior small lodging," as deemed by an independent local panel. Rates range $69–140. Pet fee is $15 daily. 18051 S. Tamiami Trail, Fort Myers; 239/267-7900; www.bestwestern.com.

Comfort Inn: "We love pets here," says a staffer of this pleasant 61-room, three-story hotel, which offers an outdoor heated pool and spa. Canine guests stretch their legs by sniffing around empty fields in the area. Rates range $79–149. Add a flat $10 pet fee. 4171 Boatways Rd., Fort Myers; 239/694-9200; www.choicehotels.com.

Comfort Suites Airport: Provided you take your buddy with you every time you leave the room, your pooch may join you in a suite featuring a wet bar, in-room VCR, and handy refrigerator to store doggy bag scraps. Rates range $75–170, plus a $10 per night pet fee. 13651A Indian Paint Ln., Fort Myers; 239/768-0005; www.choicehotels.com.

Country Inn & Suites by Carlson-Sanibel Gateway: The pet-friendly beaches of Sanibel Island are a short drive down the road from this pleasant 112-unit lodging, located just shy of the Sanibel Causeway. Guests tend to give pets potty breaks at an open field next door. A free breakfast, a pool, an adjacent golf course, and an exercise room are available. Rates range $80–210. Add a $10 daily pet fee. 13901 Shell Point Plaza, Fort Myers; 239/454-9292 or 800/456-4000; www.countryinns.com.

Homewood Suites by Hilton: Every dogs sleeps in a pleasant suite at this 130-unit, three-story lodging offering a heated pool, whirlpool, and fitness center next to Bell Tower Shops. Rates range $109–260. Add a nonrefundable $75 pet fee. 5255 Big Pine Way, Fort Myers; 239/275-6000; www.homewood-suites.com.

Howard Johnson Inn: A dog may join you in one of the designated pet rooms of this 116-unit poolside motel near downtown. Rates range $70–120. Pet fee is $25. 4811 Cleveland Ave./US 41, Fort Myers; 239/936-3229; www.hojo.com.

La Quinta: Your dog will happily lick crumbs from your face after your

DOG-EAR YOUR CALENDAR

Go wild about nature: On **Dog Day Sundays**—held the first Sunday of every month—leashed pets get a break from the usual neighborhood dog-walking routine. For two precious hours, they may follow three trails at the normally off-limits Calusa Nature Center and Planetarium, 3450 Ortiz Ave., Fort Myers. Small dogs favor the half-mile Cypress Boardwalk Trail or similar-length Pine Loop Trail. Young 'uns with energy to burn prefer the 1.5-mile Wildlands Trail.

It's a novel idea that Maggie Dog hopes will spread like wildfire among nature centers everywhere. Instead of banning dogs outright, go ahead and open doors—if only during very limited periods. At Calusa, dogs' green-light period is the first Sunday of the month, 4–6 P.M. Admission costs $5 per dog. Humans enter free, so long as they're with a pooch. Call 239/275-3435.

free expanded continental breakfast at this pleasant poolside motel targeted to business travelers. Rates run $75–150. 4850 Cleveland Ave./U.S. 41, Fort Myers; 239/275-3300; www.lq.com.

Motel 6: Actually located in the suburb of North Fort Myers, this budget motel accommodates pets looking to save money on lodging costs so they can buy more treats. Rooms at this 110-unit poolside motel are larger than at typical Motel 6s. Corporate policy permits one well-behaved pet per room. Rates range $46–71. 3350 Marinatown Lane, North Fort Myers; 239/656-5544; www. motel6.com.

Residence Inn: A hound may think he has arrived at Uncle Boxer's house, not a motel. Fix dinner in the kitchen of a homey apartment-style unit, or relax in the pleasant living room or bedroom. Two-bedroom suites feature fireplaces. Rates start at $99. The nonrefundable pet fee will produce a howl—$125. 2960 Colonial Blvd., Fort Myers; 239/936-0110; www.residenceinn.com.

Ta Ki-Ki Motel: Sure, dogs are permitted, just not "elephants, snakes, or rabbits," said a staffer, who recalled the time a pet rabbit chewed the coating off an electrical cord and nearly shocked a maid. Deemed a "superior small lodging" by an independent local panel, this 23-unit riverside motel offers a pool, boat dock, and rooms with kitchens. Rates range $46–105. 2631 First St., Fort Myers; 239/334-2135 or 866/453-0016 (reservations).

Woodsmoke Camping Resort: Curious pups will delight in the short, lake-area nature trail at this shady 31-acre campground. Dogs also are welcome at the shuffleboard court, as long as their companions clean up after them. Official dog walks are found in various sections of this park, where reservations are required in winter. Rates range $26–46. Limit one dog per party; breeds considered "vicious" by management are barred. 19551 S. Tamiami Trail, Fort Myers; 239/267-3456 or 800/231-5053; www. woodsmokecampingresort.com.

W. P. Franklin Lock and Dam (North): If only this 33-site campground welcomed daytime visitors, it would rate as the best dog-friendly park around Fort Myers. Campers are more likely to see manatees lolling here than at another U.S. Army Corps of Engineers campground farther up the Caloosahatchee River near LaBelle. But visitors tend to fall into one of two groups: Either they like the fairly lush island digs of Franklin Dam, which is a short drive from Fort Myers and surrounded by development, or they prefer the remote, sunny Ortona Lock and Dam (see the Lake Okeechobee chapter)—rarely both. At Franklin, boaters can motor their craft straight to the campground, which has a boat ramp, fishing pier, showers, a dump station, restrooms, and campsites with electricity. The first-come, first-served campsites cost $16 daily. The lock is on Highway 78, about eight miles west of I-75 (Exit 143). 239/694-8770.

Fort Myers Beach

A pirate named Black Augustus is rumored to have left buried treasures along the shores here, but dogs on the lookout for loot will have to dig elsewhere. That's right, they aren't allowed on the beach. And that's what this town is all about—the beach. Still, if you're coming south after a hot time at Sanibel Island's beaches, you'll find some laid-back restaurants and good places for a pooped pooch to rest for the night. This town of 14,000 swells to 42,000 between November and April.

PLACES TO EAT

Bridge: Dock your boat here under the Matanzas Bridge or drive up to take a seat outdoors and sample steak, lobster, shrimp, clams, sandwiches, oysters, or seafood pasta with your pooch. The motto of this waterfront home of live entertainment and a Sunday dock party is "Casual dress, serious food." You sit on a deck outside; your dog is on the ground just below. Outdoor service isn't always available, so call first. 708 Fisherman's Wharf; 239/765-0050.

McDonald's: Most Mickie D's in Florida have an outside seating area, but to get to it you have to walk through the restaurant, which is of course verboten. Not here. Fast-food fans can gulp down Big Macs and fries as their dogs gaze up at them longingly from the floor of an outdoor patio that's accessible from the outside. It's across from the Ramada Inn. 1133 Estero Blvd.; 239/765-6555.

Pete's Time Out: One patron called out "Fido!" as we took a seat at a picnic table in the back of this busy open-air beach joint, where folks in swimsuits down beer and seafood as loud music blares in the background. When asked

DIVERSIONS

See the sea or go fishin': Just because dogs aren't allowed on the beach doesn't mean they can't see the sea. The family dog may join the family on a 16-foot Scout rented from **Fish Tale Marina,** 7225 Estero Blvd., Fort Myers Beach. To lounge around in the sun with a large party, consider an 18-foot pontoon boat. Rentals start at $115 for four hours. Reserve at 239/463-4448.

Elsewhere in the region, you could check out the sound—**Pine Island Sound,** that is. One of the most picturesque places in Florida for inland boating, it's also one of the best fishing grounds in Florida. Even if your pooch isn't too excited about sharing his boat with scaly, slimy creatures, he'll enjoy the feeling of the breeze rippling through his coat as you glide across the water. Boating isn't for misbehavin' dogs or landlubber humans, nor is it the best choice of activities on Florida's hottest days. But if tooling around on the sound is your kind of thing and the weather is right, you'll find plenty of places to rent a vessel on Pine Island. Try the Pineland Marina at 239/283-3593.

whether Maggie was permitted, a waitress giggled and said, "Of course!" It's a good place to spend a lazy-day afternoon munching tender clam strips, small broiled burgers, wings, conch fritters, hot dogs, or other fare under a roof overhang that cools down hot canines. A fellow patron who sampled perhaps a bit too much brew took a look at tired Maggie and Sally in her dark sunglasses, then approached to mumble that he admired Sally for getting out into the world. He had assumed she was blind! 1005 Estero Blvd.; 239/463-5900.

Shamrock Irish Pub & Eatery: Sit with your dog at a picnic table out front and sample burgers, fish sandwiches, chicken wings, or other appetizers. Yes, it's called an Irish pub, but the three beers on tap are American. 2201 Estero Blvd.; 239/463-8881.

2,000 Flavors Yogurt and Ice Cream: Doggies who are watching their weight will be glad to know that nonfat, sugar-free desserts are offered. Tie your pal to the fence and take one of the few tables outside. 1000 Fifth St.; 239/765-1131.

PLACES TO STAY

Anchor Inn Cottages: With two dogs of her own, the woman in charge said she can't very well turn visiting pooches away from her fully equipped, one- to three-bedroom poolside cottages overlooking a canal, even though the resort's rate sheet said No Pets. Your buddy can make himself at home with space enough to stretch out; each room comes with a living room and a kitchen. Rates range $85–205 nightly, and weekly rates are available. Dog fee is $10 daily. 285 Virginia Ave., Fort Myers Beach; 239/463-2630.

Best Western Beach Resort: Dogs under 25 pounds are welcome to sleep in designated smoking rooms, then pad along the palm-shaded grounds or the 400-foot private resort beach, so long as they're leashed. All rooms face the Gulf of Mexico. Enjoy sunsets on your balcony. Rates range $119–240. Pet fee is $10 nightly. 684 Estero Blvd., Fort Myers Beach; 239/463-6000; www.bestwestern.com.

Casa Playa: Before he sold this property, proprietor Peter Lisich remarked about how canine travelers are "an incredible niche" in the lodging business. So while competitors turn pets away, Casa Playa waves them into the first two floors of this 35-unit, all-suite resort overlooking the Gulf of Mexico. Leashed dogs may saunter along the 100-foot stretch of private beach as long as they don't pass the high-water mark and plunge into the waves, which county law prohibits. Casa Playa was deemed a "superior small lodging" by an independent local panel; all suites have garden or water views, as well as screened balconies and kitchenettes or kitchens. Rates range $90–320. Pet fee is $10–15 daily. 510 Estero Blvd., Fort Myers Beach; 239/765-0510; www.casaplayaresort.com.

Hidden Harbor Inn: Deemed a "superior small lodging" by an independent local panel, this 18-unit establishment offers efficiencies and cottages, as well as a picnic area and a pool. Rates range $70–190. The pet deposit is $100, half of which will be refunded barring doggy indiscretions. 819 San Carlos Dr., Fort Myers Beach; 239/463-9382; www.hiddenharborinn.com.

Lighthouse Resort Inn and Suites: A peewee pet—under 15 pounds—may join you at this 72-unit lodging located across the street from the beach. Amenities include nightly live entertainment, a tiki bar, room service, and two pools, including one with waterfalls. Rates range $55–250. 1051 Fifth St., Fort Myers Beach; 239/463-9392 or 800/778-7748; www.lighthouseislandresort.com.

Silver Sands Villas: A pet under 30 pounds may join you at this 20-unit "superior small lodging," as named by an independent panel. Bicycles are available for guests to tool around the island. Fully equipped kitchens, a pool, and grills are among other amenities. Leashed dogs will love walking to the pet-permissible beaches to watch sunsets or help collect seashells. Rates range $130–199 in season, $80–155 other times. Add $25 per stay for the pooch. 1207 Estero Blvd., Fort Myers Beach; 239/463-2755; www.silversands-villas.com.

Sanibel/Captiva Islands

Your dog is in for a treat—literally—if Gary or Diane are working when you pull up to the tollbooth to get to these lush resort islands. The pair are known far and wide for giving dog biscuits to canines passing through (after asking permission from the dogs' companions, of course). Fittingly, Sanibel is a dog mecca. Devoted dog owners are known to travel a half hour or more to take their four-legged companions here, because, unlike most touristy Florida spots, Sanibel allows the furry set to romp on its beaches. That's enough to make you howl with delight, eh?

Make sure you park where it's legal, though. Otherwise, you may have to pay a $35 fine. See the listings below for safe places to park. And please remember to clean up after your dog! Hound-hospitable beaches are a rare find in the Sunshine State.

PARKS, BEACHES, AND RECREATION AREAS

13 Bowman's Beach

🐾🐾🐾 (See Fort Myers/Naples map on page 608)

Every Sanibel tourist winds up at the beach, and your leashed dog is welcome to join the throng in doing the "Sanibel Stoop." How it works: Try to find the best seashells to add to your collection by slowly walking along the shelly Gulf of Mexico beach, keeping your head slightly bent. Once you've found just the right shell, quickly stoop to pick it up. Sure, dogs don't care about seashells, but they'll welcome any excuse for a morning or sunset walk. (Noon is probably too hot except on the coolest of days.)

Leashed dogs may frolic along any Sanibel beach, but Bowman's Beach stands out because anyone can park at its lot for 75 cents an hour. Most other beach-access parking lots are limited to cars bearing residential permits. For anyone sleeping in nearby Captiva Island, this is the nearest public beach that gives visiting dogs the green light.

Take Sanibel-Captiva Road west toward the tip of Sanibel Island, then turn south on Bowman's Beach Road. 239/472-6477 or 239/472-1080.

14 Gulfside City Park

🐾🐾🐾 (See Fort Myers/Naples map on page 608)

Patient mainland visitors wend their way across Sanibel Island to get to this park, which squarely fronts the Gulf of Mexico and holds out the promise of beautiful sunsets. Still, if your leashed dog prods you to do what everyone else is doing at this beach, you'd better bring a bag to fill with seashells. (And, naturally, a pooper-scooper as well.)

The parking lot is on Algiers Lane. From the Sanibel Causeway, continue south, turn right at Periwinkle Way, left at Casa Ybel Road, then left at Algiers Lane. 239/472-6477 or 239/472-1080.

15 Lighthouse Beach

🐾🐾🐾 (See Fort Myers/Naples map on page 608)

Pooches who spend the week digging holes in backyards and sighing in locked apartments would love a trip to this renowned canine retreat, which is the nearest public beach for mainland doggies. It takes a special dog lover to drive a half hour or more to take his leashed buddies here—then brave the late-afternoon traffic exiting the island via the Sanibel Causeway. But it's a great way to spend a day and, heck, tourists fly in from hundreds of miles away to collect seashells and take in the pastel sky at sunset. Why not treat your dog?

The park owes some of its popularity to its parking lot, which gives the public access. Most local beach lots are limited to residents.

From the Sanibel Causeway, head south, turn left (east) at Periwinkle Way, and continue to the eastern tip of the island. 239/472-6477 or 239/472-1080.

PLACES TO STAY

Beach Road Villas: Dogs find ample room to walk around within these four canal-front 1,200-square-foot villas near the lighthouse end of the island. A hot tub, hammocks, a picnic area, and docks for boats and fishing are among the amenities of this "superior small lodging," as deemed by an independent panel. Nightly rates range $160–250. Well-behaved pets are accepted with a signed policy statement. 764 Beach Rd., Sanibel; 239/395-1314; www.beachroadvillas.com.

Caribe Beach Resort: Except in the off-season, it's hard to get into these kitchen-equipped time-shares, which are rented out on a weekly basis. Pet-friendly digs range from an efficiency to a one-bedroom unit. Deemed a "superior small lodging" by an independent panel, the establishment offers a heated pool, a hot tub, and a picnic area. Weekly rates range $540–1,620 in the off-season. Fee is $25 per stay for your pet (under 25 pounds). Ask about two-night stays; sometimes they're available. 2669 W. Gulf Dr., Sanibel; 239/472-1166 or 800/330-1593.

Castaways Resort and Marina: On the northern tip of Sanibel Island, the grounds of these blue waterside cottages with kitchens feature a marina, a pool, and a fish-cleaning area for lucky canine anglers. Rates range $125–329. Add $15 daily per dog. 6460 Sanibel-Captiva Rd., Sanibel; 239/472-1252 or 800/375-0152.

Mitchell's Sand Castles by the Sea: Your leashed dog can pad down sandy trails to cavort on the beach here, and if she loves the water, she can swim in the Gulf of Mexico. It's the favorite vacation spot of a black Lab named Angel, who every year would spend a week here with her chauffeur, Harriet Bonin, taking after-dinner walks on the beach before returning to their beachfront cabin. Deemed a "superior small lodging" by an independent panel, these 15 kitchen-equipped beachfront cottages and vacation homes have access to tennis and shuffleboard on-site. Rates range $105–285. Pet fee is $10 daily. 3951 W. Gulf Dr., Sanibel; 239/472-1282; www.mitchellssandcastles.com.

Signal Inn: Small pets may or may not be accepted here. It seems like it depends on how the desk clerk is feeling that day, but we're told that some units are hospitable to pets while others are not. The one- and two-bedroom beachside cottages and townhouses usually are rented for the week and are deemed "superior small lodgings" by an independent local panel. Weekly rates range $900–3,075. Three-night stays also are possible in the off-season. 1811 Olde Middle Gulf Dr., Sanibel; 239/472-4690 or 800/992-4690; www.signalinn.com.

Tropical Winds Motel & Cottages: Well-behaved dogs are accepted at these 10 frequently packed units in a quiet residential neighborhood. The furnished efficiencies—with cable TV, air-conditioning, heat, and barbecue grills—are set at the north end of Sanibel Island. Tennis is nearby. "We're not the Ritz, but we're clean," the humble proprietor says. Actually, these units have been deemed a "superior small lodging" by an independent panel. Rates range $120–260. 4819 Tradewinds & Jamaica Drive, Sanibel; 239/472-1765.

'Tween Waters Inn: Maggie skittered nervously across a polished-wood floor when she arrived at a cottage here many years ago on her first vacation. She seemed to consider the wee cottage her new home, and she paced uneasily for about an hour before she finally sat down. It took some getting used to, but she did. Want to paddle in the bay with your pal? You can rent a canoe here. Dogs aren't allowed on the beach on Captiva Island, though they are in nearby Sanibel. Some dog owners take the chance, we're told, but we figure you should just head across the Blind Pass Bridge to Sanibel. Rates vary seasonally, $155–460 a night. Add $25 per night per pet. Mention the pooch when you register, as pets are allowed only in certain cottages. On Highway 869, just north of Blind Pass, P.O. Box 249, Captiva; 239/472-5161 or 800/223-5865.

Waterside Inn on the Beach: Small pets may sleep in a few cottages of this beachfront "superior small lodging," as labeled by an independent panel. A heated pool, shuffleboard, and bicycles are among amenities, though shelling or watching sunsets on Sanibel's pet-permissible beaches remain favorite pastimes. Nightly rates range $138–365. Pet fee is $5 nightly. 3033 W. Gulf Dr., Sanibel; 239/472-1345; www.watersideinn.net.

Estero

PARKS, BEACHES, AND RECREATION AREAS

16 Koreshan State Historic Site

🐾🐾 (See Fort Myers/Naples map on page 608)

If your pooch has metaphysical leanings, this former settlement of the "New Jerusalem" will intrigue her—or maybe she'll appreciate the off chance of seeing otters scampering along the Estero River during a 30-minute leisurely walk on a nature trail. A century ago, Cyrus Teed hoped his commune at this green spot would grow into a city of 10 million people practicing the religion of Koreshanity. But the industrious, celibate Koreshans died out, even though Teed thought he was immortal.

Now you and your buddy can throw hot dogs onto a grill and hope to see manatees in the river while the kids head to the swings and slide.

The main grounds, which are very open and airy, feature a grid pattern of ruler-straight, largely unshaded paths where the midday sun can be unrelenting, especially in summer. Following the paths when it's not so hot as to endanger your pooch has its rewards: You'll see a patch of bamboo near the grave of Hedwig Michel, a longtime Koreshan spiritual leader. To the north of the grave is a leaf-covered, winding, sometimes narrow path that dips and rises a bit through a thankfully shadier and cooler oak-and-palm hammock on the bluffs of the Estero River. While the sound of cars can detract from the walk, the chirping cicadas help make up for it.

Dogs are forbidden inside the popular art hall or other restored settlement buildings. But staying outside isn't all bad. On our April visit, we plucked a red, juicy Surinam cherry that was ripe for the picking.

Entrance costs $4 per carload. The park is north of Naples on U.S. 41 at Corkscrew Road. From 1-75 (Exit 123), head west two miles on Corkscrew Road, cross U.S. 41, and continue on Corkscrew Road approximately 1000 yards to the entrance. 239/992-0311.

PLACES TO STAY

Koreshan State Historic Site: This highly popular campground can be hard to get into unless you reserve ahead. (They take reservations up to 11 months in advance.) And no wonder! Dogs will enjoy the shade and the proximity to lots of walking room at the former Utopian settlement next door (see above). The large picnic area features a nature trail, playground, and restrooms. Canoe rentals are available for launching at the boat ramp. The 60 wooded sites each offer electricity, water, a grill, and a table. Twelve tent-only sites overlook the Estero River. Pets are permitted if you bring current vaccination papers. Campsites cost $20 nightly. From 1-75 (Exit 123), go west a little over two miles on Corkscrew Road to the park, which is at the intersection of U.S. 41 and Corkscrew Road in Estero. 239/992-0311 or 800/326-3521; www.reserveamerica.com.

Bonita Springs/Bonita Beach

"Bone-eater Beach" is more like it. Hounds won't be happy to hear they aren't welcome to pad around at Barefoot Beach State Park, but Maggie sniffed out some places nearby where they can cavort.

PARKS, BEACHES, AND RECREATION AREAS

🐾 Dog Beach

🐾🐾🐾🐾🐕 (See Fort Myers/Naples map on page 608)

Swim, dogs! This sandbar is a tribute to what a wave of public support for dogs can accomplish. For more than 25 years, frisky pups bounded in and out of the water here between Estero Bay and the Gulf of Mexico, happy as they could be. In fact, Sergio and Silvana Cortella would bring their 10 dogs all the way here from Hollywood to swim beachside.

Then the state parks department got involved, taking over management of the park from Lee County in 1996. Officials began to vigorously enforce the leash law, handing out $75 tickets that required a court appearance, we're told. But citizens complained and a petition drive by Save Our Off-Leash Dog Area (SOODA) gathered 2,388 signatures urging the return of Dog Beach. The Lee County Parks Department in 2001 convinced the county commission to retake control of the land so dogs once again could run free.

Today, dogs swim joyously.

This beach is similar to nearby Big Hickory Pass, but more traditionally beachlike, better used, and an official Dog Beach.

You can take a trail and walk across New Pass Bridge for a breezy view of Estero Bay. Consider a picnic in Carl E. Johnson Park, just up the road. Lack of shade is a drawback there, but the widely spaced pavilions will give your pooch some privacy from neighboring picnickers.

Also called Lee County Off-Leash Dog Area, this beach permits two dogs per person. No child under age 15 is permitted. The beach is on County Road 865 between Bonita Beach and Fort Myers Beach. From U.S. 41, go west on County Road 865/Bonita Beach Road, which will turn north. About one-half mile beyond the Bonita Springs water tower, you'll cross New Pass Bridge. Dog Beach is just north of New Pass, at left. 239/461-7400.

18 Lover's Key State Park

🐾🐾 (See Fort Myers/Naples map on page 608)

Your leashed pooch might be curious to see manatees and dolphins swimming through the near-shore waters surrounding this nearly square-mile state park at the southern end of Estero Island. Hungry? Eat with your pal at the plentiful picnic tables. Unfortunately, dogs are not allowed to go to the beach, one of the bigger attractions. Other people-pleasers include volleyball, playgrounds, and rentals of bicycles, canoes, and kayaks.

Entrance is $5 per carload. The park is on County Road 865 just south of Big Carlos Pass and north of New Pass, on the barrier island between the Gulf of Mexico and Estero Bay.

From U.S. 41, go west on County Road 865/Bonita Beach Road, which turns north along the gulf coast. About one-half mile beyond the Bonita Springs water tower, you'll cross over New Pass Bridge. The park is north of New Pass. 239/463-4588.

PLACES TO EAT

Cool Runnings Island Deli and Market: This is no-frills eating in a rustic setting. Your pooch may join you at one of three small tables outside. 26105 Hickory Blvd.; 239/948-8885.

PLACES TO STAY

Americinn Hotel & Suites: After your workout in the exercise room or pool, your pet would like to work out by swimming at the Lee County Off-Leash Dog Area (a.k.a. Dog Beach). A game area and free continental breakfast are offered at this pleasant 87-room lodging. Rates range $65–145. Add $10 nightly for a pet under 25 pounds. 28600 Trails Edge Blvd., Bonita Springs; 239/495-9255; www.americinn.com.

Bonita Beach Resort Motel: Small dogs are fairly frequent guests at this small place just a few steps from the Gulf of Mexico beach but located on Estero Bay. Many rooms come with kitchens, so you and your hungry hound should never go wanting. The motel backs up to docks on Hogue Channel. Rates range seasonally $72–105. 26395 Hickory Blvd., Bonita Beach; 239/992-2137; www. bonitabeachresort.com.

StayBridge Suites by Holiday Inn: After a trip to the free breakfast buffet or evening reception, you can whip up food for your whiskered pal in one of these 106 pleasant suites with full kitchens. Rates generally range $100–240. Add a whopping $100 nonrefundable pet fee. 8900 Brighton Ln., Bonita Springs; 239/949-5913; www.staybridge.com.

North Naples

PARKS, BEACHES, AND RECREATION AREAS

19 Rover Run at Veterans Park

🐾🐾🐾🐾🐾 (See Fort Myers/Naples map on page 608)

At long last, the four-legged set can stretch those legs in (or at least near) Naples. The county has set up two dog runs here, one for large pooches and one for the small set. Still, all but the shyest little yappers usually go to the big-dog area, because "it's become very social," park staffer Sue Satow told us. Or maybe it's because of the fake fire hydrant at the big-dog park.

Both compounds of about one acre each are surrounded by chain-link fence and offer free-flowing water buckets and poop-scooping bags.

Outside Rover Run, the park includes a community center and fields for softball and baseball, as well as courts for tennis, basketball, and volleyball.

The park is at 1900 Immokalee Road. Drive east from U.S. 41/North Tamiami Trail on Immokalee Road about one mile. 239/566-2367.

20 Delnor-Wiggins Pass State Park

🐾🐾🐾 (See Fort Myers/Naples map on page 608)

Despite its ban on dogs on the beach, this place gets a fairly high rating because, dogwise, there are a ton of things to do. Wend your way along the boardwalk lined by round-leafed sea grapes, pointy cabbage palms, and shady black, red, and white mangroves. Climb the observation tower near parking lot No. 5 and picnic at the roof-covered picnic spot below—or at innumerable shady, windswept sites just landward of the beach and the jade-colored waves. (If you're looking for water for your pooch, stop at the faucet at parking lot No. 2.) Dogs are limited to the roads, parking lots, and picnic areas, the park staff says.

Maggie was quite happy here, panting in the breeze on a boardwalk deck and lying on her side as we cooked hot dogs. *"Perro!"* cried a frightened Spanish-speaking child who encountered Maggie unexpectedly. But a little girl from a different group of picnickers took to Maggie very well, declaring, with a cute malapropism, "I'm not scary."

If you would like to go into the water with your dog, exit the park. Go about a third of a mile east of the park entrance, over the bridge, and park there. Walk the dirt road that runs parallel to the bridge to the south. The road leads to a channel where some people fish from big rocks. You'll see a very small, shallow sandy area. It's not quite a "beach," but if you want to frolic in the water with your dog, you could here.

Entrance costs $5 per carload. From U.S. 41, head west on Vanderbilt Beach Road, then veer right (north) on Gulf Shore Drive and follow it to its end. 239/597-6196.

Golden Gate

PARKS, BEACHES, AND RECREATION AREAS

21 Picayune Strand State Forest

🐾🐾🐾   (See Fort Myers/Naples map on page 608)

Pooches and other Floridians are the beneficiaries here of the decades-old woes of a major Florida development company. This corner of the Everglades ecosystem was supposed to be part of the largest housing subdivision in the world, Golden Gate Estates—bigger than the city of Philadelphia. Instead, the Gulf American Corp. (later merged with General Acceptance Corp.) became embroiled in two state investigations in the 1960s and declared bankruptcy. Part of the Golden Gate Estates subdivision was built. Yet, the 65 square miles south of I-75 hold only a few hardy souls today. The state and federal governments are buying up the rest of the land to help restore the Everglades.

Some 200 miles of roads built by GAC still run through the forest of pines and palmettos, so access by car is pretty easy. Pull over almost anywhere to park and go for a long, long walk. In some places, you'll notice informal hiking trails. An official Sabal Palm Hiking Trail makes a 3.2-mile loop.

Keep your pooch leashed in this wild home of endangered Florida panthers and, in canals, alligators. Because of the panthers, it's doubly important to pick up your dog's leavings (which signal the presence of a possible

competitor to the panthers). Your pal should be fine if he sticks by you; panthers and alligators in wild areas like this are scared of people.

Bring plenty of drinking water. Early mornings are best for cooler temperatures and seeing wildlife. Caution: This wild country is rarely patrolled. Occasionally, you'll find rowdies on weekends shooting up the place with shotguns and generally carrying on.

From I-75 (Exit 101), go south 4.4 miles on Collier Boulevard/State Road 951 to Sabal Palm Road. Turn left. Go 3.2 miles to the Sabal Palm Hiking Trail trailhead on the south side. 239/348-7557.

Naples

Ritzy Naples, a favorite vacation haunt, is home to Florida's highest income per capita. But for dogs, Naples proper is nothing but Deadsville, with precious few places to romp and sleep. Though some restaurants and a notable bakery are canine-cordial, Maggie says, "Get out of town if you want to have fun."

Dog-tired about the state of canine affairs in Naples, some residents periodically try to persuade the city to open at least a portion of the beach to dogs. The last straw for one crusader, Brook Green, may have been the day she took her ailing elderly dachshund mutt, Freeway, to the beach at 5 A.M. A few people on the beach soon left—then police arrived to hand Green a written warning to keep Freeway and an arthritic male Chihuahua named Gizmo off the sand. "We knew she wouldn't have many days left to live," Green said of Freeway.

If it weren't for Freeway, Green figures that she and her husband wouldn't have evacuated their trailer, which was right in the path of Hurricane Andrew when the family lived in the Miami area in 1992. So even though Freeway has passed on to that Great Doghouse in the Sky, Green continued her nascent crusade to open the beach to dogs. Her inspiration is Freeway. After all, said Green, "She probably saved our lives."

The solitary saving grace of Naples is not in Naples proper. It's the Rover Run Park out on Immokalee Road (see North Naples heading).

PARKS, BEACHES, AND RECREATION AREAS

22 Rookery Bay National Estuarine Research Reserve

 (See Fort Myers/Naples map on page 608)

Don't tell your leashed dog the name of the shadiest trail here—Cat Claw Trail. Happily unaware, Maggie alternately chewed grass along the woodsy interpretive trail and strained at her leash as if to say, "Hurry up. Can't you see there are trails to walk?" The short, shady trail is flanked by one of North America's few pristine mangrove estuaries and such trees as the "tourist tree" (gumbo-limbo), so nicknamed because its peeling, reddish orange bark resembles a bad sunburn.

The wider shell-rock Monument Trail starts at a boat ramp where you could spread out a blanket for a make-do picnic under a nearby tree. This short trail is flanked by mangroves and leads to the Cat Claw Trailhead. A party of little girls stopped to pet Maggie here and tell us about their dogs back home.

Just driving along this remote reserve's long Shell Island Road may be enough to make your dog pace the backseat in hopes of jumping out to race into the dense xeric scrub. While hiking at the reserve, watch your pup's footing; hikers are asked to stay on trails, and the sharp-edged seashells on a waterfront bank might hurt tender feet. On our visit, the wail of an osprey caught Maggie's attention. Bobcats and red-shouldered hawks have also been seen amid the oaks and pines.

To reach the reserve, take U.S. 41 east from town (toward Miami) to the

DIVERSIONS

Ride in style with Rover: The proprietor of **Naples Horse & Carriages** sometimes brings her dogs along for a ride—and so can you. A $50 half-hour ride through Old Naples leaves from The Dock at Crayton Cove, a restaurant at 845 12th Ave. South at the city dock (in Old Naples). An hour-long ride also takes in the beach and other scenes for $75 plus tip. The carriage seats four adults. Of course, if you know your whiskered companion will bark hysterically as soon as he sets eyes on the horse, don't try it. Hour-long rides can be reserved; shorter rides are first come, first served. Reserve at 239/649-1210.

intersection with Highway 951 (you'll see a McDonald's and a Burger King). Make a right onto Highway 951 and go about five miles to Shell Island Road. Turn right and continue about 2.5 miles. 239/417-6310.

PLACES TO EAT

Restaurants tend to come and go in the Fifth Avenue South shopping area downtown. It reminds us of a miniature (and saner) version of Miami's Coconut Grove. Take a walk through the block and find a restaurant with outdoor seating. Many will accept well-mannered pooches at the outdoor tables.

Cheeburger, Cheeburger: A rottweiler created restaurant lore by wolfing down a one-pound burger "in about 20 seconds," an employee says. Indeed, the act used to be immortalized in a photo on the wall. Maybe your dog will be next? Some of the best thick burgers cooked anywhere are served at the tables outside 9853 Tamiami Trail North; 239/592-5555. Alternatively, try 4810 Davis Blvd.; 239/775-4655. For a sophisticated neighborhood, try the Olde Naples locale at 505 Fifth Ave. South; 239/435-9796.

Fantozzi's of Olde Naples: At this combination restaurant and caterer, well-behaved pooches can eat at a corner table on the sunny outside deck, surrounded by pink bougainvillea. In summer, it's a lunch-only spot for Spot (and humans). In winter, dinners are also sometimes served, depending on the catering schedule. Besides the recommended pastrami Reuben, beef brisket, and grouper sandwiches, offerings include tomato-mozzarella sandwiches, a tomato-mozzarella-and-prosciutto salad, lasagna, baked goods, wine, cheese, espresso, and cappuccino. 1148 N. Third St. South; 239/262-4808.

Fifth Avenue Coffee Company: Dogs often slurp at the pet water bowl here, then plop beneath the umbrella-shaded outdoor tables to watch their masters enjoy pastries, bagels, cookies, frozen drinks, coffees, and tea. 599 Fifth Ave. South; 239/261-5757.

McCabe's Irish Pub and Grill: Set at the Inn on Fifth, this popular spot for corned beef and cabbage dinners and turkey club sandwiches attracts dogs in the afternoon. At night, the place is more formal. The dozen tables aren't shaded from the sun, so a late lunch may be in order. 699 Fifth Ave. South; 239/403-8777.

Olde Naples Confectionery: The deli has "so many kinds of sandwiches it's unreal," we're told, so we won't try to list them all here. The burgers come highly recommended, and you should ask about the daily specials. Sit with your dog at an outdoor table and sample gourmet chocolates after a quick exercise break at the nearby vacant lot. 1305 Third St. South; 239/262-3975.

Pazzo Italian Cafe: After a menu experiment that included everything from tempura to Thai, Pazzo is back to what it does best: Italian. Italian with a twist, actually. Check out the osso bucco or the grouper prosciutto. You'll find four tables with green umbrellas in front of a pinkish-red storefront with two Romanesque columns. 853 Fifth Ave. South; 239/434-8494.

Wynn's Market: Calling this a restaurant is stretching things a bit, but the chicken Florentine in puff pastry, Swiss steak sandwiches, and made-to-order sandwiches certainly will do in a pinch for a hungry dog. Leave your pooch chained to one of the umbrella-topped metal tables outside, then go inside. Check out the bakery, the large selection of wines, fancy tinned goods such as sardines and oysters, and the small deli. Then take the treasure trove of eats outside, where your pooch will be shaded by the big oak tree. It's a great place to people-watch as you enjoy a midday meal or afternoon snack. 745 Fifth Ave. South; 239/261-0901.

PLACES TO STAY

Baymont Inn and Suites: This poolside motel, where dogs under 50 pounds are permitted in smoking rooms, offers a free breakfast buffet. Rates range $50–150. 185 Bedzel Cir., Naples; 239/352-8400; www.baymontinns.com.

Naples/Marco Island KOA Kampground: After resting in one of the 17 air-conditioned cabins, a dog might be eager to jump into a canoe rented at this largely unshaded campground, which features shuffleboard courts, a hot tub, horseshoes, and a pool. Cabbage palms—the state tree—provide a bit of shade. To commune more closely with nature, exit the secluded campground and stroll along the primarily unpaved Barefoot Williams Road, which cuts through woods of pines and palms. A boat ramp provides access to the Gulf of Mexico. Cabins and cottages range $59–180. Campsites range $37–71. Reservations are accepted. 1700 Barefoot Williams Rd., Naples; 239/774-5455; www.koakampgrounds.com.

Red Roof Inn: This poolside inn on the main drag coming into town is notable for the small, pine-shaded field to the side, where your dog might stretch her legs. Be careful, though: Traffic-clogged State Road 84 is right out front. You can avoid the traffic by ordering a takeout meal from the nearby Olive Garden restaurant. Rates range $49–140. Small dogs, please. 1925 Davis Blvd., Naples; 239/774-3117; www.redroof.com.

Residence Inn: Whip up dinner for the family—including the dog—in the full kitchen of these apartment-style studios and suites. Dogs are accepted, "as long as they don't weigh more than I do," joked a jovial staffer of this pleasant 120-unit lodging. Freebies include Wednesday night cookouts and the daily breakfast buffet. Rates range $70–260. Pet fee is a flat $75. 4075 Tamiami Trail North, Naples; 239/659-1300; www.naplesresidenceinn.com.

Ritz-Carlton Golf Resort: This top-echelon hotel offers such amenities as 36 holes of golf, several tennis courts, a spa, a pool, and a sauna. Your small dog may join you in one of the designated rooms, provided that the nonrefundable pet fee doesn't make you yelp—$125. Room rates start at $199. 2600 Tiburon Rd., Naples; 239/593-2000; www.ritzcarlton.com.

Staybridge Suites Wellesley Inn: Every dog sleeps in a suite at this 122-unit lodging, whose amenities include a pool with spa and an exercise center.

Rates range $80–225. Add a flat $75 pet fee. 4805 Tamiami Trail North, Naples; 239/643-8002; www.staybridge.com.

Wellesley Inn: An employee once told us that in all the years dogs have been driven past the five-tier flowing fountain to the porte cochere of this 105-room motel, only one canine guest has caused trouble. The dog chewed up a few spongy Velux blankets when no one was looking. The owner said, "Okay, just charge me for them," and all was well. Hence, be ready to sign a waiver saying you'll pay for any damages and won't leave your dog unattended. The well-kept grounds make this one of the better budget-priced places where your dog may stay. Rates range $69–130. 1555 Fifth Ave. South, Naples; 239/793-4646; www.wellesleyonline.com.

Marco Island

The neatly landscaped streets, well-tended homes, and roof-covered outdoor basketball court of Marco Island send a message: "We have money and we don't mind showing it." While that may be good news for dogs who like to sample culinary treats, it's bad news for dogs who want to prance around the parks. Aside from the sole park listed below, your buddy's only option is to dash out of the car for a quick squat on the scattered sandy, undeveloped lots found along the island's curvy streets.

PARKS, BEACHES, AND RECREATION AREAS

23 J. S. Trolley Bridge

(See Fort Myers/Naples map on page 608)

Maggie waded into the water at the "beach" beneath the bridge leading into Marco Island. While it's stretching it to call this a park, anglers nonetheless

show up to cast lines at these two little areas found on either side of the street on the bridge's north side.

PLACES TO EAT

Crazy Flamingo: Sometimes a breezy place to dine on a hot day, this laid-back eatery in the Town Center Mall may seem a little corny; its slogan is "If your seafood were any fresher, your clothes would get wet eating it." The roof overhang provides welcome shade for dogs resting on the brick-paved sidewalk beneath the four plastic outdoor tables. Among the fare are oysters, clams, shrimp, mussels, black beans and rice, conch fritters, potstickers, and linguine marinara. 1047 1/2 North Collier Blvd.; 239/642-9600.

Mozart's Restaurant: Arrive at dinner to enjoy cooler temperatures for your pal in the fur coat. Meanwhile, you'll enjoy a taste of old Austria at this southern Marco Island restaurant, whose owner hails from the European nation. Think schnitzel or, if you're in a more American mood, steak. Some Italian goodies such as pasta also may be served at your outside table. 150 S. Barfield Dr., in the shopping plaza with the Publix supermarket; 239/642-5220.

Pelican Bend: At lunchtime, leashed pooches can tag along with their people for outside patio dining. Basic lunch fare is available, along with such seafood items as broiled grouper sandwiches, shrimp, and scallops. 219 Capri Blvd.; 239/394-3452.

PLACES TO STAY

The Boathouse Motel: The folks at this 20-unit, family-owned motel in Old Marco once lent out pedalboats and welcomed pets aboard, but that practice was stopped when too many people got whisked out to the Gulf of Mexico and had to be rescued. Nevertheless, it's a fine place to stay—a quiet retreat with lots of places nearby to walk your dog. Our friend Gina Rigutto adored the place, as did her black Lab/Irish setter buddy, Foster. Dogs are accepted in designated units. Rates range $88–320. The pet fee is $15 per stay, plus $5 a day. 1180 Eddington Place, Marco Island; 239/642-2400 or 800/528-6345; www.theboathousemotel.com.

Goodland

This little fishing village and trailer-park haven is the scruffy answer to nearby tiny Marco Island. It's a good place for those canine companions who are into ruffing it a bit.

PLACES TO EAT

Stan's Idle Hour: Yes, outdoor tables are offered at this utterly casual home of the annual Mullet Festival. But call first to be sure outdoor service can be

DOG-EAR YOUR CALENDAR

Do the "buzzard lope" dance—or watch others do it: Thousands of people descend onto the tiny town of Goodland one weekend each January to watch the **Buzzard Lope Queen** contest, a highlight of the Mullet Festival hosted by Stan's Idle Hour Seafood Restaurant. Humans hop around, arms akimbo, pretending to be vultures pouncing on carrion to the tune of "The Buzzard Lope Song," written and sung by restaurant owner Stan Gober. He sings, in part: "Flap your wings up and down/ Take a few steps back/ Go 'round and 'round...."

Doesn't sound like much fun, we thought. But fan Pat Kenney corrected us.

"It's not fun to do, but it sure is fun to watch," says Kenney. A couple dozen dogs typically show up with their two-legged companions to join the crowds that wind through the arts-and-crafts booths and food stands. Not only is a Buzzard Lope Queen named, but a contest for children proclaims a Buzzard Lope Princess. For dates, call 239/394-3041.

offered to you and your dog. To get here from Marco Island, turn south on Highway 92A toward Goodland (don't cross the bridge to the mainland). The road veers to the right. Follow it to the eatery, at the left. 239/394-3041.

PLACES TO STAY

Mar-Good Resort: Efficiency cottages are offered at this decidedly casual waterfront fishing village, marina, convenience store, restaurant, and adults-only retirement RV park. Cottages range $50–70. Canine guests must be leashed. 321 Pear Tree Ave., Goodland; 239/394-6383.

Moran's Restaurant, Marina & Motel: Billed as "The Everything Marina in Goodland," this pink place attracts a few pooches who return from time to time to stay at the motel. Furry sailors may arrive by sea (or land). Rates range $69–150. You'll find Moran's under the Goodland Bridge on Goodland Bay, by the Marco River. If you're coming by water, it's by Marker No. 15. "No real big dogs," says the management. 3200 Highway 92, Goodland; 239/642-8212.

INDEXES

Accommodations Index

Restaurant Index

General Index

Acknowledgments

Thanks and a four-paw salute: To the dogged readers and organizations who went out of their way to tell us their favorite haunts. Florida will be all the more hound-hospitable thanks to them. To Maria Goodavage, for making this doggone book series possible. To all the friends, colleagues, and others too numerous to include here who put up with our dogged question: "Does your pooch have a favorite place to go?"

The Dog Lover's Companion Animal Partnership Program

The Dog Lover's Companion series is pleased to promote animal rescue and adoption organizations nationwide. In an effort to create an awareness of these worthy causes, we ask you to support your local nonprofit animal rescue and adoption organization, Humane Society, or SPCA, such as:

THE HUMANE SOCIETY OF BROWARD COUNTY

The Humane Society of Broward County, located in Fort Lauderdale, provides shelter and responsible adoptions to orphaned pets, and educates the community about treating all animals with respect and kindness. One of South Florida's largest animal welfare organizations, the shelter places more than 9,000 companion animals into loving homes every year.

A variety of programs and services is available, including low-cost obedience classes, behavior counseling, Match-A-Pet (for those who are looking for a specific breed), volunteer opportunities, a Pet Boutique selling supplies and gift items, pet-facilitated therapy (in which dogs visit nursing homes and hospitals), a mobile low-cost spay/neuter vehicle, and events that you and your pet can participate in, such as the annual Walk for the Animals.

Each year, representatives from the Humane Society's Education Department travel to schools throughout the community to talk to students about having compassion and respect for all animals. In addition, children are taught about the responsibilities of being a "pet parent," the importance of spaying and neutering, and what it means to make a lifelong commitment to our pets. This program reaches more than 150,000 children and adults every year, a number that continues to grow.

The Humane Society of Broward County invites the public to tour its facility, located at 2070 Griffin Road, one block west of I-95, in Fort Lauderdale. For information, please contact the Humane Society of Broward County at 954/989-3977 or on the World Wide Web at www.humanesocietyofbroward.com.

Keeping Current

Note to All Dog Lovers:

While our information is as current as possible, changes to fees, regulations, parks, roads, and trails sometimes are made after we go to press. Businesses can close, change their ownership, or change their rules. Earthquakes, fires, rainstorms, and other natural phenomena can radically change the condition of parks, hiking trails, and wilderness areas. Before you and your dog begin your travels, please be certain to call the phone numbers for each listing for updated information.

Attention Dogs of Florida:

Our readers mean everything to us. We explore Florida so that you and your people can spend true quality time together. Your input to this book is very important. In the last few years, we've heard from many wonderful dogs and their humans about new dog-friendly places, or old dog-friendly places we didn't know about. If we've missed your favorite park, beach, outdoor restaurant, hotel, or dog-friendly activity, please let us know. We'll check out the tip and if it turns out to be a good one, include it in the next edition, giving a thank-you to the dog and/or person who sent in the suggestion. Please write us—we always welcome comments and suggestions.

> *The Dog Lover's Companion to Florida*
> Avalon Travel Publishing
> 1400 65th Street, Suite 250
> Emeryville, CA 94608, USA
> email: atpfeedback@avalonpub.com

THE DOG LOVER'S COMPANION

A special breed of guidebook for travelers and residents who don't want to leave their canine pals behind.

CALIFORNIA

FLORIDA

NEW ENGLAND

PACIFIC NORTHWEST

WASHINGTON D.C. & BALTIMORE

WWW.DOGLOVERSCOMPANION.COM

BOSTON

CHICAGO

LOS ANGELES

NEW YORK CITY

PHILADELPHIA

SAN FRANCISCO BAY AREA